INTRODUCTIONS BY ROBERT ARNESON AND LADDIE JOHN DILL
COVER PORTRAITS BY MIMI JACOBS

Wayne Thiebaud

Joan Brown

Robert Hudson

THE CALIFORNIA ART REVIEW

Peter Voulkos

Ed Ruscha

Betye Saar

Mel Ramos

Robert Irwin

Mimi Jacobs

AN ILLUSTRATED SURVEY OF THE

STATE'S MUSEUMS, GALLERIES

AND LEADING ARTISTS

LES KRANTZ

AMERICAN REFERENCES, INC.
919 N. MICHIGAN AVENUE
CHICAGO, IL 60611

Editor/Publisher: **Les Krantz**

Editorial Director: **Mark Mravic**

Production Director: **Suzanne E. Hampson**

Art Director: **Ron Richter**

Museum Editor: **Jordan Wankoff**

Gallery Editors: **Dick Smith, Ilene Shapera**

Managing Editor: **Jean Lyons**

Contributing Editors: **Barbara Bowen, Alan Enzer, Mark Harris, Janis Hunt-Haney, Dennis Jenks, Gordan Mayer, Sheila Ralston**

Associate Editors: **Randy Albright, Penny Berkman, Aaron Chandler, Ann Davis, Barb Koenan, Lisa Leavitt, Karen Vaccaro, Eric Wadell**

Writers: **Peter Kime, Mandy Kwok, Debra Latourette, James K. McDermott, Jr., Ineke Murakami, Martha Schoolman, Jonathon Silber, Lisa Simeone, Phillip Smith, Petra Soessman, Alex Wolfe**

Production Assistants: **Carol J. Bast, Tina MacDonald, Mark Mosher, Oliver Steck, Liz Trask, Steve Wallem**

Marketing Services Representative: **Hillary Hammond-Merritt**

Business Manager: **Carol Green**

Administration: **Suzanne Dunn-Heuer, Mary Jo Drungil, Lyn Pusztai, Debra Swank**

American References Publishing Company
919 North Michigan Avenue
Chicago, IL 60611

The California art review: an illustrated survey of the states museums, galleries, and leading artists/ edited by Les Krantz.
    p. cm.
    ISBN 0-913765-16-3 — ISBN 0-913765-15-5 (pbk.)
    1. Art museums – California – Directories. 2. Art galleries, Commercial – California – Directories. 3. Artists – California – Biography. I.Krantz, Les.
N511.C2C33 1989
702'.5'794 – dc20
                                    89-18256
                                       CIP

. . . out of the mud grows a lotus.

— Robert Arneson

TABLE OF CONTENTS

TABLE OF CONTENTS

ROBERT ARNESON
On Northern California Art

BENICIA — A lot of people ask me what California Art is. Well, you can't look at something and say "this is typical California art." It's the most diverse place you can find. So is the art. But there are certain things that artists look for here. David Hockney is a California artist, in the sense he captures the sky, in color. That's why he's here, to paint the sky, the reflection in the pool, palm trees. Algeria doesn't do it. In Southern California, artists think of Catalina, and we in the North see our wheat-brown hills — Golden California.

In my developmental stage, there was an emphasis on the figurative. With Clyfford Still teaching here at the California School of Fine Arts in the late '40s, there was a movement toward total abstraction, but we never really went that way. There was always a sense of or an allusion to some kind of figurative content. The artists I was most interested in were those who were dealing with the content of something and not with perceiving the whole formalism thing that we might call "New York Art."

California is a place where ideas are developed early — political ideas, lifestyles, artistic ideas, etc. There's a great deal of tolerance out here for deviants — we've certainly given the country several good nuts in Washington. But by the same token, there's not a strong artistic patronage yet.

I'm a ceramic sculptor, and ceramics is especially popular in California. At every school there's a ceramics program — students take the courses, and it's fun. And clay is abundant in our hills.

When I was a student, there was a heavy interest in Japanese and early Chinese ceramics. Because of our proximity to the Far East, there is a strong Oriental influence on California art. I thought my teachers tried to emulate 9th-Century Sung Dynasty ceramics. Their ceramics were primarily worked on the pottery wheel, and that's how I started, within the traditions of potting and making forms.

In fact, there is a certain Zen spirit to ceramics: "Out of the mud grows a lotus." The reason we have clay is because there were living things to make it. We can't deal with just dry dirt and water. Clay is organic, it emits energy. All the artist has to do is try not to destroy that.

LADDIE JOHN DILL
On Southern California Art

VENICE — When I graduated from Chouinard Art Institute in Los Angeles in the late 60's, it was mandatory for artists who were serious about their career to go to New York and establish a relationship with the galleries and to engage themselves in the issues that were important at that time on the East Coast. My exposure to East Coast artists was first established when I was employed at Gemini G.E.L. in Los Angeles in 1969-70. This had a great influence on my work, because I had the opportunity to work with Jasper Johns, Robert Rauschenberg and Frank Stella. Earlier influences which still hold for me today were the light and space artists who were working in Los Angeles at the time, specifically Robert Irwin and James Turrell. The interaction of the physicality of the work of the New York artists and the ephemeral and Oriental-influenced qualities of artists such as Irwin and Turrell were issues in my studio in the early 70s.

Los Angeles at that time was relatively provincial in regard to its support system — collectors, museums, etc. It seemed as if people serious about contemporary art were being spoon-fed avant- garde dictums from dealers and critics based in New York.

The turning point for Los Angeles culturally, in my opinion, was the 1984 Summer Olympics. The Olympics helped create an increased artistic awareness regionally. There were a great number of culturally oriented activities in addition to the sports events — exhibitions, performances, theater — which were very well attended, mainly by residents of the city. The cultural consciousness in this city has been very high ever since. Artists in this area have benefited greatly from the international exposure. In the past, if an artist chose to live and work in Los Angeles, he or she would have to realize a certain sacrifice in terms of exposure. Nowadays this is not the case.

It has been noted that the creative ambiance in Los Angeles is very similar to the way it was in New York in the late 1940s. A healthy cross-over of disciplines and an interaction between various creative practices, such as painting, performance, dance and architecture, is taking place in Los Angeles today. I feel that the city's lack of history works positively for it, because it is not encumbered by its past; this enables a clear, progressive attitude.

The concerns between Northern and Southern California artists differ greatly. The Northern California artists seem more introspective and self-searching, and they work closer to a metaphysical approach. Whereas in Southern California, the art is about the world outside of the artist. An interest in light phenomena, landscape and societal conditions prevails in the work. Los Angeles has by no means begun to define itself culturally; but this lack of definition is one of the sources of its energy.

This volume attempts to capture the vibrant diversity of the California art scene, though the editors realize the difficulty of such a task. For there is not really one "scene" to be discovered, but a wide variety of styles, schools and influences, from artists working in traditional media such as painting and sculpture to those exploring newer avenues of expression in installation, video, fiber art and mixed media, to name just a few. With such a diversity, an all-inclusive selection of artists is impossible, as is a hard and fast set of rules for inclusion. In general, the editors selected artists based on the frequency, immediacy and stature of their public exhibitions, collections and awards. California residency was not required — we also sought a number of artists from outside the state who have a consistent history of exhibiting in California.

As with any reference that covers an ongoing contemporary phenomenon, particularly one as giant in scale as art in California, one could add to or subtract from our inclusions. We have have made an informed attempt to select influential and up-and-coming artists who work not only in the Los Angeles area, the Bay Area and other urban centers, but in regions throughout the state — artists whose influence may be more local but whose dedication to art is just as strong.

The biographical information found in this volume reflects what we deemed to be each artist's career highlights and is not intended to be a complete resume. Most artists included have had numerous additional exhibitions, collections and honors too extensive to enumerate here.

We hope you enjoy exploring this volume on contemporary art in California as much as we enjoyed putting it together.

Les Krantz
Editor and Publisher

APTOS

CABRILLO GALLERY
6500 Soquel Dr., Aptos, CA 95003

Phone: (408) 479-6308 *Hours:* Monday-Friday 9-4; Monday & Tuesday 7-9; Closed summer months or when school is not in session *Admission:* free

The Cabrillo Gallery was founded in 1975 as an adjunct to the work of the art teaching faculty of Cabrillo College. It is located in the Cabrillo Library with its own front facade and a full view of the Pacific Ocean. There are 1,000 square feet of floor space and twenty-foot ceilings.

During the school term the gallery offers eight one-person and group shows which change monthly. It emphasizes innovative directions in the arts and crafts and presents diverse media and artists from areas of the country not readily accessible to members of the mid-California community. Artists who have had recent one-person exhibitions include: Christo (lithographs), Patrick Oliphant (cartoons), Sam Hernandez (sculpture), Karen Kunc (woodcut prints), Jane Gregorius (monotype silkscreens), Nance O'Banion (bamboo constructions), Norman Tundin (paintings), Bob Dawson (photographs), Robin Smith (ceramic sculpture) and Richard Deustch (terrazo sculpture).

While the gallery is small, its staff strives to educate the community whenever there is a need and opportunity. Lectures and slide/movie presentations are usually attended by the artists themselves. Fiber arts, large-scale photography, wood sculpture and metalsmithing are included along with more traditional fine art media.

BAKERSFIELD

KERN COUNTY MUSEUM
3801 Chester Ave., Bakersfield, CA 93301

Phone: (805) 861-2132 *Hours:* Monday-Friday 8-5; Saturday, Sunday and Holidays 10-5 *Admission:* Adults $3; Seniors $2.50; Children 3-12 $1.50; under 3 free

The Kern County Museum, located in Bakersfield, focuses on historical Kern County. It was founded in 1941, and today it occupies a 1929 Spanish/Moroccan-style building that once served as a Bakersfield Chamber of Commerce. Within the museum are seven exhibition spaces, and outside there are fourteen acres of exhibits, including fifty-eight free-standing buildings.

The diverse permanent collection of over 250,000 objects is composed of Kern County historical matter and works by Kern County artists. The collection of paintings is small and local, and its most notable pieces are *Jewett Ranch* by Thadeus Welch (1898) and *Mary Pachico Tevis* by Gariot (thought to be a portrait of the late governor's daughter). There are 7,000 pieces of infrequently displayed textiles which date from the late 1800s to the 1930s. The museum holds 40,000 historical photographs of Kern County and there is also a large collection of yokuts (Indian basketry) notable for their fine workmanship.

The grounds include a wide variety of historic buildings depicting scenes from the past. Diverse artifacts relating to Kern County life between the 1860s and 1930s are displayed in genuine and recreated residences, businesses and civic buildings. There is a doctor's office, an 1868 log cabin, a blacksmith's shop, a one-room schoolhouse and a wooden oil derrick.

Festivals: Through the year the Kern County Museum features a number of special events. In May, the Flor Y Canto (Flower and Song) Festival celebrates Hispanic art and culture. Heritage Days, held in April, is a weekend festival focusing on Kern County's rich history and tradition.

Note: The Kern County Museum is partially accessible to the handicapped. Please call (805) 861-2132 to discuss special needs. Docent tours may be arranged with advance reservations. The Museum is closed Thanksgiving Day, Christmas Day, and New Year's Day.

BERKELEY

BERKELEY ART CENTER
1275 Walnut St., Berkeley, CA 94709

Phone: (415) 644-6893 *Hours:* Thursday-Sunday 12-5 *Admission:* free

The Berkeley Art Center is devoted to representing the cultural and ethnic diversity of Berkeley. It presents the work of local emerging artists, gives occasional exhibits of artists of regional or national stature, and stages educational and performance events. The center was designed by architect Robert Ratcliff, and it straddles a creek in Berkeley's Live Oak Park.

During its first ten years, the Berkeley Art Center was a City agency, but since Proposition 13, it has been run for the City by the Berkeley Art Center Association, a non-profit corporation whose Board of Directors is selected from the community.

Exhibitions: Each year the center presents from eight to ten group shows of all types of artists usually in the early stages of their careers. The annual juried competition is one of the most prestigious visual arts events in the Bay Area. The works of Elmer Bischoff, Raymond Sauder, Stephen Stabler, and Rupert Garcia have been seen in the Berkeley Art Center and among recent successful exhibitions have been "Paper Dimension: Sculptural Paper by 10 Bay Area Women Artists" and "Peter Selz Selects 17 Berkeley Artists," a show chosen by the Professor Emeritus at the University of California.

The Berkeley Art Center has also provided support for the Berkeley Art Center Association Youth Art Program, which brings professional art instruction to five Berkeley elementary schools in and after school sessions.

KALA INSTITUTE
1060 Heinz St., Berkeley, CA 94710

Phone: (415) 549-2977 *Hours:* Tuesday-Friday 10-5; Saturday 12-5 & by appointment *Admission:* free

The Kala Institute was founded in 1974 as a private studio. It soon expanded into a workshop for graphic and other visual artists from all over the world. In 1979, it moved to its present 8,000-square-foot premises in the old Heinz factory building in Berkeley, California. Today the Kala Institute continues to operate as a printmaking workshop on the old European model. Its main aim is to provide a center for the international exchange and cross fertilization of ideas among artists working in a variety of media.

Collections: Kala holds an archive of prints and works on paper by artists who have worked there since its inception, including Yuzo Nakano and Archana Horsting.

Exhibitions: The Kala Institute mounts exhibitions which give the artists-in-residence and the general public access to outstanding and experimental work in the field, including the best work produced within the institute. Exhibitions of this type have given rise to a lively exchange program with similar galleries in the U.S.A. and abroad.

Aside from visual arts the Kala Institute presents the annual "Seeing Time" series of interdisciplinary events. These performances with installations, live action pieces with scenic and photographic images, original music with natural and synthesized sounds, and audience interaction with trained performances have included *Fluid Sounds* by Liz Phillips; *Rachel's Brain* by Rachel Rosenthal; and *Vice Versa* by the experimental performance ensemble, MA FISH CO.

Artist-in-Residence Program: The Kala Institute facilities provide workshops which include etching and engraving, lithography, monoprinting, photography and photo-print processes, papermaking, and letterpress. The workshop is open to paying artists-in-residence twenty-four hours a day, 365 days a year.

Classes in basic and advanced techniques are scheduled at regular intervals, three times a year. In addition the institute arranges master classes by outstanding visiting artists.

LOWIE MUSEUM OF ANTHROPOLOGY

University of California at Berkeley, Bancroft Way at College Ave., Berkeley, CA 94720

Phone: (415) 642-3681 *Hours:* Monday, Tuesday, Thursday, Friday 10-4:30; Saturday & Sunday: 12-4:30 *Admission:* $1.50; Seniors $.50; Children $.25; Thursdays free

The Lowie Museum of Anthropology was founded in 1901 with initial funding provided by Phoebe Apperson Hearst. It is pre-eminent among museums of anthropology in the western United States. It contains the largest anthropological collection west of Chicago and draws from its vast inventory of over 600,000 catalogued objects to present a variety of exhibits and exhibitions each year. Recent exhibitions include a nostalgic retrospective of "The Panama Pacific International Exposition of 1915"; "The Kula: A Bronislaw Malinowski Centennial Exhibition," which examined the complex economic exchange system of eastern Papua New Guinea; and "Held in Value," which highlighted the Lowie Museum's valuable collections in a special 24-month series of rotating exhibits featuring the ancient cultures of Egypt and Peru, textiles from Kashmir, Persia and the American Southwest, and outstanding ethnographic artifacts from Africa, the Philippines, and the native peoples of North America.

Future exhibitions include "Beneath Our Feet: The Archaeology of San Francisco's First Sixty Years," which will feature recently excavated artifacts of American, European and Chinese origin. Plans are also underway to produce an exhibition titled "Native Alaskans and the Western World," which will present western Eskimo, Aleut and Russian material culture.

JUDAH L. MAGNES MUSEUM

2911 Russell St., Berkeley, CA 94705

Phone: (415) 849-2710 *Hours:* Sunday-Thursday 10-4; Closed Jewish and Federal Holidays; Western Jewish History Center *Hours:* Monday-Thursday 12-4 *Admission:* Free

Established in 1962, the Judah L. Magnes Museum takes its name and inspiration from the Bay Area-born Judah L. Magnes, founder of Hadassah, the Hebrew University in Jerusalem, the American Civil Liberties Union, and the American Jewish Committee.

The museum collects, preserves, and exhibits fine, ceremonial, and folk art, as well as historical and literary material reflecting modern and historical Jewish life and culture. It holds Jewish art from around the world including ceremonial and fine art, textiles, costumes from North Africa and Europe, and Torah binders. Its Judaica Library holds over 7,500 books, periodicals, and recordings and includes the Bloomenthal Rare Book and Manuscript Collection. Its Western Jewish History Center (established in 1967) is an archival research library concentrating on the Jewish contributions to the American West from the Gold Rush to the present. The History Center includes the Magnes Archives, Anglo-Jewish newspapers of the West since 1860, oral histories, photographs, organizational records and letters chronicling western Jewish history.

The Magnes Museum also presents changing exhibitions of contemporary artists in two galleries on its main floor. Major artists featured include Ben Shahn, Chana Orloff, Ben-Zion, Lenke Rothman, Raphael Soyer, Marriam Cramer Ring, Marc Chagall, and others. Works by Bay Area Jewish artists such as Susan Felix, Raisa Fastman, and Jacques Schnier are also often featured. Recent thematic exhibitions include "The Karaites," and "The Barnard Collection of Israeli Avant-Garde Art, Maps and Views of the Holy Land."

The museum also serves the public by conducting tours of its exhibitions, by displaying its materials in other institutions, and by loaning its displays to more distant areas.

UNIVERSITY ART MUSEUM, UNIVERSITY OF CALIFORNIA, BERKELEY

2626 Bancroft Way, Berkeley, CA 94720

Phone: (415) 642-1207 *Hours:* Wednesday-Sunday 11-5 *Admission:* $3; Seniors and Students $2

The University Art Museum, founded in 1970, is the visual arts center of the University of California at Berkeley.

The genesis for the current building came when a generous bequest and a gift of paintings by Modernist painter Hans Hofmann in 1963 inspired plans to build an art museum on the Berkeley campus. San Francisco architect Mario Ciampi, with design associates Richard Jorasch, Paul Reiter and Ronal Wagner won a national competition for the design of the new building. The Art Museum was completed and galleries opened in 1970.

Noted for its adventurous and dramatic design, the Museum building's exhibition space is dynamically arranged in overlapping terraces that enable visitors to view works of art from different vantage points. Ten galleries and a bookstore are on the upper level. The Pacific Film Archive, Theatre Gallery, Swallow Restaurant, and Sculpture Garden are on the lower level.

Collections: Beginning with the founding bequest of forty-five paintings from Hans Hofmann, the museum has developed an impressive collection of 3,000 paintings, photographs, prints and drawings, and 6,000 films which it holds in the Pacific Film Archive. The museum holds works by early 20th century masters such as Miro, Leger, Magritte and Maillol as well as important pre-20th century works by Rubens, Cezanne and Renoir. Among the notable masterpieces of contemporary art in the University Art Museum's collection are works by Alexander Calder, Joseph Cornell, Helen Frankenthaler, Scott Burton, Clyfford Still, Mark Rothko and Francis Bacon.

The Museum's outstanding Asian art collection of hanging scrolls, screens, fans and paintings is one of the finest in the United States. The Pacific Film Archive maintains a collection of film prints with areas of concentration in Soviet Film, international animation and American avant-garde cinema. The Archive collection of Japanese films is the largest holding of Japanese cinema outside Japan.

Exhibitions: The Art Museum offers a wide range of gallery exhibitions. The exhibitions are international in scope and draw from Western and Asian cultures in all periods of history. Among artists who have been exhibited are Richard Avedon, Juan Gris, Jonathan Borofsky, Francesco Clemente, Robert Frank, Terry Fox, Joan Brown, Howard Fried, Adolf Wolfli and Odilon Redon. Major thematic exhibitions have included "MADE IN THE U.S.A.: An Americanization in Modern Art"; "The '50s & '60s"; "Shadows of Mt. Huang: Chinese Painting"; "Andre, Buren, Irwin, Nordman: Space as Support"; and "J.M.W. Turner: Works on Paper from American Collections."

The MATRIX exhibition program embodies the Art Museum's commitment to presenting the new and experimental. Started in the late 1970s as a continuing survey of contemporary art, MATRIX has initiated over one hundred solo exhibitions of painting, sculpture, installation and non-traditional media. Among these are exhibitions of artists such as James Lee Byars, Willem de Kooning, Louise Bourgeois, Balthus, Elizabeth Murray, Eric Fischl, Andy Warhol, David Hockney, Julian Schnabel, Lars Lerup, Joan Brown, Elmer Bischoff, Al Souza and Richard Diebenkorn.

The University Art Museum also offers lectures, film programs or classes and research, public service media programs, and book traveling exhibitions. The museum shop sells books, magazines, crafts, posters, jewelry, art materials and reproductions.

CHERRY VALLEY

EDWARD-DEAN MUSEUM OF DECORATIVE ARTS

9401 Oak Glen Rd., Cherry Valley, CA 92223

Phone: (714) 845-2626 *Hours:* Tuesday-Friday 1-4:30; Saturday & Sunday 10-4 *Admission:* $1; under 12 free

Located on the grounds of the Riverside County Art and Cultural Center, the Edward-Dean Museum is set in a beautiful 16-acre, gardenlike enclave.

The focus of the museum is the decorative arts. Its primary collections are in furniture, paintings, tapestries and porcelains, but there is also sculpture dating from the 3rd century B.C. to the present and an important collection of Oriental objects including one of the finest groups of Far Eastern bronzes in the United States.

The eight-room museum is arranged to make visitors feel they are entering the 18th century. The Pine Room, for example, is highlighted by a sparkling Waterford crystal chandelier, Sir Peter Lely's portrait of Anne, daughter of the Earl of Rochester, and pine paneling carved by Grinling Gibbons in the 17th century. Tibetan and Chinese gilt bronze figures are dis-

played in one cabinet at the end of the room while another is filled with porcelain and pottery by Meissen, Wedgewood, and Spode. Outside the museum, on the loggia, a chair beckons visitors to enjoy a moment beside a quiet pool.

The North Gallery is reserved for temporary exhibits which change every three months. Recently, the museum presented "A Ton of Kimonos," an exhibition of the work of Los Angeles artist Betty Decter. In September of 1989, it celebrated its twenty-fifth anniversary with "Robes of China, Selections from the Edward Dean Permanent Collection."

CLAREMONT

GALLERIES OF THE CLAREMONT COLLEGES

Lang Art Gallery, Ninth at Columbia, Scripps College, Claremont, CA 91711

Montgomery Art Gallery, 333 College Way, Pomona College, Claremont, CA 91711

Phone: (714) 621-8283 *Hours:* Monday-Sunday 1-5 *Admission:* free

In 1974 the Boards of Trustees of Pamona College and Scripps College created the Galleries of the Claremont Colleges by joining the administration of the Montgomery Art Gallery of Pomona College and the Lang Art Gallery of Scripps College. As a result of the agreement, the members of the galleries' staff—appointed jointly by the two colleges—are responsible for both the exhibition programs and the preservation and maintenance of the permanent collections.

Montgomery Art Gallery, renovated in 1977, consists of one large and two smaller galleries, with two exhibition corridors. Adjacent to one of the smaller galleries is a print study room which houses the galleries' collection of prints, drawings and photographs. Lang Art Gallery, which will move to a new facility in 1992, contains one large and three smaller galleries.

Collections: The permanent collections include important American paintings by Maurice Prendergast and Gari Melchers; Renaissance paintings; the Pomerat print collection at Pomona; the Marer Ceramic Collection; a collection of Chinese paintings and costumes; and a collection of African Sculpture.

Exhibitions: The galleries exhibit art from a wide variety of media and historical periods with emphasis placed on contemporary art. Among recent exhibitions are: "Poetic Visions: Japanese Paintings from the Sanso Collection"; "Edward Weston: Color Photography"; "Courtly Splendors: Chinese Costumes from the Permanent Collection"; and "Native American Basketry, Ceramics, and Costume." Both galleries hold student shows and the Lang Gallery holds the second oldest ceramics invitational in the country.

The Galleries of the Claremont Colleges also have a small publications program. During the 1988-89 year they published *Art at Scripps: The Early Years* (accompanying an exhibition of the same name) and *Art at Pomona, 1887-1987: A Centennial Celebration.*

CUPERTINO

EUPHRAT GALLERY

De Anza College, Cupertino, CA 95014

Phone: (408) 996-4836 *Hours:* Tuesday, Wednesday, Thursday 11-4; Wednesday evening 7-9; Saturday 11-2 *Admission:* free

The Euphrat Gallery is part of De Anza College in Cupertino. It was established in 1971 with E.F. Euphrat's bequest in memory of his wife Helen. Its mission is to research, produce and present challenging exhibitions and educational material that provide a resource of visual ideas and a platform for communication.

Collections: While the emphasis of the Euphrat Gallery is on exhibitions, there are small collections which include paintings by Agnes Pelton, three-dimensional painted works by Tom Holland, and various prints by California artists.

Exhibitions: Exhibits at the Euphrat Gallery feature both nationally recognized and emerging artists showing in all media. Major artists who have been featured in recent Euphrat exhibits include Roger Brown, Judy Baca and Red Grooms ("GENRE: People Doing Everyday Things"), Jack Earl ("Clay etc. Works: On the Wall, Off the Wall"), Annie Albers ("Art of the Refugee Experience"), Faith Ringgold ("The Power of Cloth: Political Quilts 1845-1986"), Louise Nevelson, Alexander Calder, Elizabeth Cartlett, and Ben Shahn ("ART COLLECTORS In and Around Silicon Valley").

The gallery is also committed to featuring works of serious artists early to midway in their careers. Those who have shown recently include Lisa Reinhertson, Mark Leong, Scott Donahue, Juana Alicia, Donna Cehrs, Stan Wilson, Mildred Howard and Jean La-Marr.

As part of De Anza college, the Euphrat Gallery presents yearly exhibitions of works by college and high school artists.

Publications: The Euphrat Gallery has an active publications department, publishing various catalogues and art books related to its exhibitions.

The Euphrat Gallery's 35-by-40-foot exhibition space is also the site for lectures, poetry readings, performances, discussions and special community events.

DOWNEY

DOWNEY MUSEUM OF ART
10419 Rives Ave., Downey, CA 90241

Phone: (213) 861-0419 *Hours:* Wednesday-Sunday 12-5 *Admission:* free

Founded in 1957 and located in the City of Downey's Furman Park, the Downey Museum of Art is the only municipal art museum with a permanent collection in the Southeast Los Angeles area.

The museum's permanent collection consists of works obtained by purchase and endowed as donations from artists and art patrons. The collection includes works in all media produced by Southern California artists during the last three decades. Artists represented include Billy Al Bengston, Corita Kent, Don Emery, Sabato Fiorello, Lukman Glasgow, Stephen Longstreet, Anna Mahler, Shirley Pettibone, Betty Saar, Gordon Wagner, Raymond Vander Haegen and others.

Each year the Downey Museum of Art also presents six changing exhibitions in its five gallery rooms. The emphasis of these shows is on contemporary and 20th century California art in a wide variety of media. Often there is also a national or international component. Recent exhibitions include one-person shows by Mary Trudeau, Joan Salinger, Csaba Markus, and Don

Francis, as well as such thematic exhibitions as "California Landscape Motif: Plein Aire to Present"; "Soviet Emigres"; "Ceramics Now," a national showcase of the contemporary trends in ceramics; "Almost the 90's," an exploration of the return in painting to representational, imagistic, and metaphoric subjects in the 1980s; "Fire and Ice," an exhibition of works with aspects of Fire (hot) and/or Ice (cold); and the "Fiber Structure National," a series of shows promoting aspects of contemporary crafts.

The museum is a private non-profit institution and is wheelchair accessible.

FRESNO

FRESNO ART MUSEUM
2233 N. 1st St., Fresno, CA 93903

Phone: (209) 485-4810 *Hours:* Tuesday-Sunday 10-5 *Admission:* $2; Students and Seniors $1; under 16 free; weekends free

Since its founding in the late 1940s, the Fresno Art Museum has grown from a small community arts organization to a fully accredited museum. Its genesis came in 1948 with the formation of the Fresno Arts Council and its plans for a Fresno Art Center. The original Art Center shared gallery space with other organizations through the 1950s, and opened its own facility in the early 1960s. By the late 1980s the center had changed its name to the Fresno Art Museum, been accredited by the American Association of Museums, and been expanded several times. Today the museum has grown to include six galleries, two classrooms, a gift shop and rental gallery as well as the 154-seat Bonner Auditorium.

Collections: The museum collects works on paper, sculpture, and art of Mexican origin from the pre-Columbian period through the present. It places special emphasis on artists who are from or have worked in California. Among works on paper, the Fresno holds pieces by Johnnie Friedlander, a group of sixty bold serigraphs from Papua, New Guinea, and a number of woodcuts and lithographs by Mexican artist Alfredo Valce. The Museum's monumental sculpture collection includes works by Jack Zajak, David Bottini, Fletcher Benton and Roger Bolomy and features Robert Cremean's *Curia*, a seven-foot-tall, seventeen-foot-long wood sculpture of nine sectional figures. Among the museum's collection of seventy-six pre-Columbian artifacts are a stone yoke; the *Jalisco Woman*, a ceramic sculpture; a group of Veracruz ceramics; and a Remojades sculpture.

Exhibitions: The emphasis of the exhibition program is on the works of California artists. Recent and future exhibitions include "Wayne Thiebaud: Works on Paper 1947-1987"; "Rollin Pickford: Watercolor Retrospective"; "Helen Lundeberg: An American Visionary"; "Forty Years of California Assemblage"; and "Adam Mekler Collection: The Eye of a Connoisseur."

Programs: The Fresno Art Museum holds a variety of cultural and educational programs. The film program, held in the Bonner Auditorium, reflects the diverse expressions of contemporary, independent filmmakers from around the world. The Bonner Auditorium Concert Series brings a variety of concerts to Fresno. Art classes for children are held on an ongoing basis as are adult art classes given in association with Fresno City College.

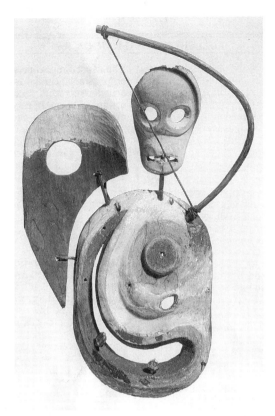

Eskimo object, Alaska, wood. Courtesy: Lowie Museum
of Anthropology, University of California at Berkeley

J. Frederick Worth Gown, circa 1890.
Courtesy: Fullerton Museum Center Collection

*Silver spice box from England 1915-1930, Jewish
ceremonial art.* Courtesy: Judah L. Magnes Museum,
Berkeley. Photograph: Tom Wachs

Note: Children under the age of sixteen must be accompanied by an adult.

FRESNO METROPOLITAN MUSEUM

1515 Van Ness Ave., Fresno, CA 93721

Phone: (209) 441-1444 *Hours:* Wednesday-Sunday 11-5 *Admission:* $2; Seniors/Students $1; Children 3-12 $.75

The genesis of the Fresno Metropolitan Museum came in 1979 when the historic *Fresno Bee* building was saved from demolition by a group of civic leaders interested in creating a cultural arts center for Central California. The Fresno Metropolitan Museum was incorporated in 1979 and a $5 million restoration began in 1982. In April of 1984, the Fresno Metropolitan Museum officially opened its doors. As renovations continue, current plans provide for the construction of history and science galleries and a youth education center in unused portions of the building.

Collections: Shortly after renovation began, the Museum acquired the nucleus of its art collection: sixty European and American still life paintings dating from the 17th through the early 20th centuries, donated by Los Angeles collectors Oscar and Maria Salzer. The Fresno also holds the Mary Alice Diener Collection of Snuff Bottles and Asian Objects dating from the 16th century and a group of 17th, 18th, and 19th century Buddhist sculptures from Thailand.

Exhibitions: The Fresno Metropolitan Museum presents a variety of traveling, self-curated, and loaned exhibitions in its several exhibition spaces. Recently it hosted "Ansel Adams: Classic Images"; "Hmong Culture," an exhibit that featured textiles, jewelry, ornaments, and paintings by Hmong artist Tou Ly; "Eleven Pre-Columbian Cultures of Ecuador: A 4,000-Year History," on loan from the Ecuadorian Government; and "Strands of Time: Yokuts Mono and Miwok Basketmakers."

Note: The museum gives tours to groups with reservations Tuesdays through Sundays 11-5.

FULLERTON

FULLERTON MUSEUM CENTER

301 N. Pomona Ave., Fullerton, CA 92362

Phone: (714) 738-6545 *Hours:* Tuesday-Sunday 11-4; Thursday & Friday 11-9 *Admission:* free

Owned by the city of Fullerton, the Fullerton Museum Center focuses on such diverse topics as history, popular culture, science and cultural arts. The museum was officially founded in 1971, and in 1974 it opened in the old Fullerton City Library, which had been built 1941 by the Works Progress Administration. In 1985, the City of Fullerton renovated the old library, bringing it up to museum standards. Today, the Fullerton Museum Center contains three galleries and over 4,000 square feet of exhibition space.

The permanent collection consists of costumes and textiles, focusing on regional ware from the 1800s, but also includes some pieces from international designers.

In its program of changing exhibitions, the Fullerton Museum Center specializes in hosting traveling exhibitions from such sources as the Smithsonian Institution, The Arizona Commission on the Arts, The Gallery Association of New York, The American Institute of Graphic Artists, and other arts organizations from around the country.

The Museum also produces its own exhibitions which emphasize cultural arts and popular culture. Individual artists are rarely featured, as exhibits are oriented toward cultural, historical, and scientific issues. Some exhibits, past and future, include "The Shakers"; "Photography: Inside/Out" (exploring contemporary photographic technique); "Document: Orange County, 1989" (an art/documentary addressing statistics through visual presentations); "The Art of Botany"; and "Four Sacred Mountains," (an exploration of contemporary native American visual arts).

MUCKENTHALER CULTURAL CENTER

1201 W. Malvern, Fullerton, CA 92633

Phone: (714) 738-6595 *Hours:* Tuesday-Sunday 12-5 *Admission:* free

The Muckenthaler Cultural Center is a community arts center designed to provide and promote visual and performing arts in a historically significant setting. The impressive Mediterranean-style home, which houses the center, and the 8.5 acres on which it stands, were granted to the city of Fullerton in 1965 by the Walter Muckenthaler family. The house, built in 1923, was once the focal point of the family's lemon and avocado ranch and is now a national historic landmark. From its vantage point overlooking the city, it continues to serve as a reminder of the cultural heritage of Southern California.

The center contains four galleries used for changing thematic exhibitions in all media. Recently the center hosted "Orange County Collects," an exhibition of works from the collections of Orange County collectors and a National Watercolor Society Juried Show. There is no permanent collection.

The center offers summer classical theater productions and a variety of educational programs including art and drama classes for students and adults. The Gift Shop and Art Rental Gallery, operated and staffed by the auxiliary organization, Center Circle, is located on the main floor of the Center.

HALF MOON BAY

COASTAL ARTS LEAGUE MUSEUM

225 S. Cabrillo Highway, Half Moon Bay, CA 94019

Phone: (415) 728-7700 *Hours:* Wednesday, Thursday, Saturday & Sunday 12-5; Friday 3-7 *Admission:* free

The Coastal Arts League Museum is a fast-growing young museum founded in 1988 by the Coastal Arts League. It presents the work of contemporary artists and those who have influenced current art trends. At present the museum is housed in temporary quarters, but in early 1990 it will move to a new prefab metal construction built on land donated by the city of Half Moon Bay. The new facility will contain gallery space for museum-quality exhibitions and an atrium with a small library where local artists will show their work.

Since the museum is so young it has not yet built any sizable, permanent collections. However, plans are being made for a sculpture garden to line the path of the Coastal Trail as it passes through Half Moon Bay.

Since the collections are small, the museum's emphasis is on monthly one-person exhibitions. Over the course of the year these rotate among artists who work in decorative, totemic and cathartic art forms. Recently the museum presented a retrospective of the works of Beaux Arts master sculptor Henri Marie-Rose, an exhibition of the work of Ruth Waters, and a group of cold hammered steel sculptures by the late San Francisco artist, Benny Bufano.

Each month the artist who is being featured gives a lecture on his or her own work.

IRVINE

SEVERIN WUNDERMAN MUSEUM

3 Mason, Irvine, CA 92718

Phone: (714) 472-1138 *Hours:* Monday-Friday 10-4
Admission: $2; Students/Seniors $1

The Severin Wunderman Museum is devoted exclusively to the study of Jean Cocteau. It houses the largest collection of his works outside of France and its purpose is "to explore and present the reciprocal relationship of the work of Jean Cocteau and his contemporaries to the concurrent social, political and cultural world."

The museum is the project of industrialist Severin Wunderman, who has had a long-standing fascination with Cocteau and who has collected an extensive array of Cocteau's visual "poetry." With the success of his companies, The Severin Group, Wunderman fulfilled a long-awaited dream and established a museum to house a permanent Cocteau collection.

Cocteau worked in every artistic medium including ballets, poems, theater, novels, films, drawings, paintings, sculpture and tapestry. The Severin Wunderman holds many of his works including the large wool tapestry *Judith et Holophernes*; the painting *Madame Favini et sa fille*; the pen and ink *Le Mystere de la mode*; the pastel *Personages classiques dans un paysage (Classical Figures in a Landscape)*; and the earthenware *Chevre-cou(Ram's Head/Moschophore)*.

Presently, the Museum exhibits a retrospective that includes pastels, drawings, paintings, ceramics, sculpture, theater masks, lithographs, tapestries, manuscripts, books and films.

The museum also houses a research center and library for Cocteau scholars.

Among the programs the Museum brings to the public are lecture tours, catalogues and festivals presenting Cocteau's work in art, theater, dance, literature and film. In 1989, the Severin Wunderman presented the "Jean Cocteau Centenary Festival," an event which included performances of Cocteau's operas *Oedipus Rex* (1952), *Le Pauvre Matelot* (1927), and *La Voix Humaine* (1929) as well as several other events.

Note: The museum goes dark four times a year when the permanent collections are rotated.

LAGUNA BEACH

LAGUNA ART MUSEUM

307 Cliff Dr., Laguna Beach, CA 92651

Phone: (714) 494-6531 *Hours:* Tuesday-Sunday 11-5
Satellite, 3333 Bristol St., Suite 1000, Costa Mesa, CA 92626

Phone: (714) 662-3366 *Hours:* Monday-Wednesday 11-6; Thursday & Friday 11-9; Saturday 10-6; Sunday 11-5 *Admission:* free

Founded in 1920, the Laguna Art Museum is one of the oldest cultural organizations in the state of California. Through the years, the museum has remained dedicated to its traditional California heritage while actively pursuing the display and collection of serious and provocative contemporary art. In the mid-1980s, it underwent an expansion almost doubling its size to 20,000 square feet of gallery and office space. Today exhibitions are housed in ten galleries at the Laguna Beach main site. Additional works are on view at their satellite gallery at South Coast Plaza in Costa Mesa.

Collections: The permanent collection of over 2,000 works emphasizes the development of art in California, with notable strengths in Southern Californian art between the World Wars, early 20th-century photography (including an extensive group of prints by avant-garde photographers Paul Outerbridge and George Hurrell), and contemporary art. Notable artists included in the collection are Charles Arnoldi, Rex Brandt, Hans Burkhardt, Maynard Dixon, Craig Kauffman, John McLaughlin, Ed Moses, Nathan Olivera, David Park, Guy Rose, Ed Ruscha, and Masami Teraoka.

Exhibitions: The museum has a six-week rotation of shows year-round. Recent exhibitions have included traveling shows organized by other institutions such as "David Park," a survey of works by the Bay Area painter organized by the Whitney, and "Granville Redmond," a retrospective organized by the Oakland Museum. The Laguna Art Museum was co-organizer of "Stephen De Staebler: The Figure," and future exhibitions will feature the works of artists Paul Kos, Illene Segalove and Jay De Feo.

Education: Educational programs at the Laguna Art Museum involve children and adults in the artworld as it relates to current exhibitions. Ongoing activities include a breakfast lecture series entitled "Good Morning Laguna," teacher workshops, children's art classes, docent tours and a self-guided-tour handout called "The Museum Game." Special events are often planned to coordinate with exhibitions.

LA JOLLA

LA JOLLA MUSEUM OF CONTEMPORARY ART

700 Prospect St., La Jolla, CA 92037

Phone: (619) 454-3541 *Hours:* Tuesday-Sunday 10-5; Wednesday 10-9 *Admission:* $3; Students/Seniors $1; 5-12 $.50

Downtown Gallery, 838 G St., 2nd Floor *Hours:* Monday-Friday 10-6; Saturday and Sunday 11-5 *Admission:* free

The La Jolla Museum of Contemporary Art exhibits and collects art created since 1945. Its focuses are on minimal, California, pop and other post-Expressionist developments in art and design. The building which houses the museum was first designed by California architect Irving Gill as a residence for Ellen Browning Scrips. In 1941, it officially became the La Jolla Art Center. In 1959, Sherwood Hall, a 500-seat auditorium, was added along with an educational wing, a sunken courtyard and the Gordon Gray Gallery. In the mid-1980s, a renovation increased the gallery space four fold, expanded shipping rooms and permanent collection storage, and improved climate control and security.

Collections: The museum holds well over 3,000 works. Its collection includes drawings, paintings, photographs, prints and sculpture as well as examples of recent European and American industrial design featuring the evolution of the modern chair. Among the major artists in the permanent collection are John Altoon, Carl Andre, Stephen Antonakos, Arman, John

Baldessari, Christo, Ron Davis, Ellsworth Kelly, Sol LeWitt, Roy Lichtenstein, Ed Moses, Claes Oldenberg, Nathan Oliveira, Robert Rauschenberg, Frank Stella and Andy Warhol.

Exhibitions: The museum presents as many as 20 shows per year including one-person, historical and thematic exhibitions of drawing, painting, graphic arts, sculpture, architecture, industrial design, photography, film and video. Artists featured in recent exhibitions include Haacke, Joan Mitchell, Judith Shea, Peter Shelton, Meyer Vaisman, Krzysztof Wodiczko, Alfredo Jarr, Richard Long and Robert Moskowitz. The museum regularly publishes scholarly catalogues to accompany its exhibitions.

The museum now also operates a satellite gallery in downtown San Diego for the purpose of exhibiting work in an urban setting and reaching new audiences.

LODI

SAN JOAQUIN COUNTY HISTORICAL MUSEUM

11793 N. Micke Grove Rd., Lodi, California 95241

Phone: (209) 368-9514 *Hours:* Wednesday-Sunday 1-5 *Admission:* free

The San Joaquin County Historical Museum documents the history of agriculture in the Stockton, California area.

The museum complex is comprised of five exhibit buildings with a total of 20,000 square feet of interior exhibit space. Collections and exhibits focus on the history of San Joaquin County with an emphasis on agriculture. The museum also holds Chinese historical artifacts, textiles, costumes, household items and decorative arts. The museum collection also includes a library of approximately 5000-pieces, an extensive collection of photographs and other archival material.

On the same grounds are trails, gardens and the sixty-nine-acre Micke Grove Park and Zoo.

LONG BEACH

LONG BEACH MUSEUM OF ART

2300 E. Ocean Blvd., Long Beach, CA 90803

Phone: (213) 439-2119 *Hours:* Wednesday-Sunday 12-5 *Admission:* free

The Long Beach Museum of Art was founded in 1954 as an art center operated by the City of Long Beach. In 1985, its operation was taken over by the Long Beach Museum of Art Foundation. The museum is housed in the 1911 California Craftsman-style mansion which sits on a bluff overlooking the Pacific Ocean. It contains 5,000 square feet of exhibition space including three galleries, a store and art rental gallery and a library for use of professional staff.

Collections: The Long Beach Museum of Art has one of the largest collections of video art on the West Coast, and has been featuring video since the late 1960s. The works of Bill Viola, Donna Matoria, and Bruce and Norman Yonemoto, and others are in its collection.

The centerpiece of the museum's more traditional collections is the Milton Wichner collection of German expressionist paintings, which includes works by Alexej Jawlensky, Vasily Kandinsky, Oscar Fischinger, Lazlo Moholy-Nagy and others. The museum also owns a group of lithographs by Marc Chagall and a large group of miscellaneous works by California artists made since WWII.

Exhibitions: The museum's yearly program of fourteen changing exhibitions features contemporary artists from Southern California and the nations of the Pacific Rim. One of the museum's three galleries is devoted to exhibitions of video works. Recently the museum presented "Icono Negro: The Black Esthetic in Video Art," guest curated by black video artist Philip Mallory Jones.

Recent static art exhibitions include a one-person exhibition of the works of Japanese-American artist Masami Teraoka; an exhibition of aboriginal and contemporary art from New Zealand; and "Raymond Saunders: Some Choices," an exhibit guest curated by black artist Raymond Saunders. Each year the museum also features the holdings of a Southern California art collector.

QUEEN MARY/SPRUCE GOOSE ENTERTAINMENT CENTER

Pier J, Long Beach, CA 90801

Phone: (213) 435-3511 *Hours:* Monday-Sunday 10-6 *Admission:* $14.95; ages 6-11 $8.95; 5 and under free; seniors $11.95

The former ocean liner Queen Mary is one of the best examples of British 1930s artwork and architecture ever constructed. In 1967, after a long seafaring career which included service during World War II, she was brought to Long Beach where she underwent three and one-half years of restoration and renovation before opening as a museum, hotel and convention center in 1971.

Because of the fifty-six types of woods used in her construction the Queen Mary is known as the Ship of Beautiful Woods. Twenty-six artists and designers contributed to her interiors, producing oils, watercolors, etched glass, plaster frieze, gesso, statuary and wood marquetry. All of the artworks on the ship are original pieces from 1936 or from the Queen Mary's post-World War II refit. British poster artist Kenneth Shoesmith produced several oil paintings and glass pieces for the ship. A three-deck-high gesso panel, *The Unicorns in Battle* by Alfred Oakley and Gilbert Baez, adorns the first class main lounge as do five of their burnished bronze relief panels. Among the other highlights are the five sculpted bronze doors to the first class private dining rooms. These glass-backed doors, completed by Walter and Donald Gilbert, were sculpted into a variety of nautical and mythical scenes.

In its archives the Queen Mary holds a large number of photographs of artists working on their pieces. Also in the archives are 2,500 photographs of the ship from its sailing days, paperwork from its wartime service, and a library where works relating to the Queen Mary, including captains' summaries, are held.

In 1988, the Disney Corporation took over management of the Queen Mary. Among its programs are the self-guided tour which brings visitors through various recreations of staterooms and passenger service areas and the Captains tour which brings visitors through the original banquet rooms where much of the art is seen.

UNIVERSITY ART MUSEUM, CALIFORNIA STATE UNIVERSITY, LONG BEACH

1250 Bellflower Blvd., Long Beach, CA 90840

Phone: (213) 985-5761 *Hours:* Tuesday-Saturday 11-5; Sunday 1-5 *Admission:* free

Hornbill Bird, Dayak peoples of Borneo, 22 x 34, painted wood. Courtesy: UCLA Fowler Museum of Cultural History. Photograph: Richard Todd

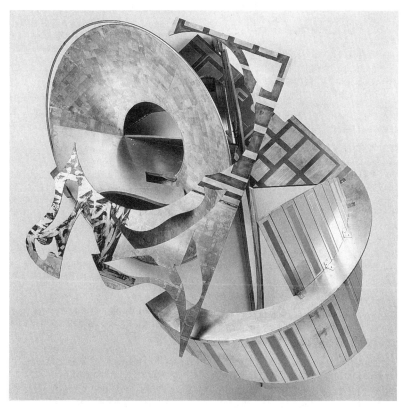

Frank Stella, *St. Michael's Counterguard,* 156 x 135 x 108, mixed media on aluminum & fiberglas honey. Courtesy: Los Angeles County Museum of Art

Founded in 1973 and located on the fifth floor of California State University at Long Beach Library, the University Art Museum provides the campus and surrounding communities with quality exhibitions in the visual arts on a year-round basis, and presents scholarly publications, guest lectures and educational outreach programs designed to reach a broad general public.

Collections: The focus of the permanent collections is on monumental sculpture and works on paper. The Monumental Sculpture Collection of eighteen pieces spread over the university's 320 acres contains pieces by Robert Irwin, Richard Turner, Terry Schoonhoven, Bryan Hunt and Woods Davy. Many of these pieces were the result of an International Sculpture Symposium held at C.S.U.L.B. in the mid-1960s. The scope of the works on paper collection is international and it includes works by Roy Lichtenstein, Lucas Samaras, Jim Dine, April Gornik and Eric Fischl. Many of these pieces were collected in documentation of exhibits. The permanent collection also includes a study collection of vintage photographs which utilize various antique processes.

Exhibitions: Though the museum does have a substantial collection, its primary focus is on bringing otherwise unavailable material to the area either through exhibitions or through traveling shows. In the cases of Laurie Anderson, Siah Armajani, Bill Viola and others, the museum caught them at seminal moments in their careers when they were just beginning to be known. Recent exhibitions have ranged from "Eric Fischl: Scenes Before the Eye" and "Robert Longo: Men in the Cities" to the traveling "Gordon Matta Clark: A Retrospective," "Ned Smyth: Three Installations," and "The Analytical Theatre: New Art From Britain."

Education: Programs which are an integral part of the museum include the Museum Studies Certificate Program, which trains students for careers in museum work; Art to the Schools; the Summer Institute for Teachers; and Get the Picture, a workshop to acquaint youth with the history and heritage of the city of Long Beach and surrounding regions.

LOS ANGELES

THE AMERICAN FILM INSTITUTE

P.O. Box 27999, 2021 N. Western Ave., Los Angeles, CA 90027

Phone: (213) 856-7600 *Hours & Admission:* vary according to program, call in advance.

The American Film Institute preserves and documents America's film and television past through conservation and collection, and nurtures America's film and television future through a variety of training programs offered at its Center for Advanced Film and Television Studies in Los Angeles.

The institute's programs are diverse and geographically divided among the Los Angeles campus, the Library of Congress (which technically holds the film collection) and the Kennedy Center in Washington, D.C. The Los Angeles campus is located on 8.65 acres in the Hollywood hills and is composed of four buildings: The Warner Communications Inc. Building, the Louis B. Mayer Library, the Sony Video Center, and the Manor House.

Education: The Center for Advanced Film and Television Studies is a two year facility for aspiring

filmmakers. The institute also offers seminars and workshops on film- and television-related topics such as acting, screenwriting, directing, producing, cinematography, editing and special events. Instructors are normally well known film and television professionals.

Louis B. Mayer Library: The library's permanent collection is composed of over 8,500 books, 160 journals, over 30,000 clippings, unpublished shooting scripts of more than 3,500 American feature films, over 2,000 scripts from television shows, seminar and oral history transcripts, and other special research materials, including personal papers and manuscript collections of leading film figures. The Jack Haley Jr. Film/Video Study Center in the Mayer Library contains a videotape collection of classic and contemporary film and television programming available by appointment.

Festivals: Each year the institute presents a variety of of film and video festivals. Its international film festival is America's largest. The AFI Video Festival is an exhibition of exemplary television and independent video from around the country and the world. "Anthropos," the International Festival of Documentary Films, is the world's largest showcase of nonfiction films, and features new, cutting-edge documentaries from all over the world.

GENE AUTRY WESTERN HERITAGE MUSEUM

4700 Zoo Dr., Los Angeles, CA 90027-1462

Phone: (213) 667-2000 *Hours:* Tuesday-Friday 10-5; Closed Christmas, New Years, and Thanksgiving *Admission:* $4.75; Seniors/Students $3.50; Children $2

The Gene Autry Western Heritage Museum is the dream child of singing cowboy Gene Autry. The museum re-creates and evokes the American West through innovative exhibitions. The recently built museum is a 140,000-square-foot, $34 million, three-level facility.

The museum's collections represent a comprehensive survey of the American West and include more than 12,000 artifacts donated or purchased by Autry and others.

Walt Disney Imagineering designed the museum's lively displays. Among the seven permanent galleries are the *Spirit of Discovery Gallery,* where displays, artifacts, and art depict the Indian's earliest occupation of the land and their interaction with Spanish and American explorers, and *The Spirit of Conquest Gallery,* where the story of western movement's conflicts are told. Other galleries are devoted to themes of opportunity, community, romance, imagination, and the cowboy.

An eighth gallery features major traveling exhibitions and special presentations. In 1989, the museum presented "Masterpieces of the American West" from the Anschutz collection and "The Beautiful Daring Western Girls . . . Women of the Wild West Shows and Rodeos."

In the Trails West courtyard, there are Disney designed tableaux of Western environments with appropriate vegetation and wildlife.

The museum also houses a large collection of both "A" and "B" Western films, the Silsby firefighting steam pumper used in Virginia City, Nevada (circa 1874), Roosevelt's ranch rifle, Cody's saddle, Wyatt Earp's revolver, and assorted historic spurs. Among the Western artists represented are Thomas Moran, Albert Bierstadt, John James Audubon, and Charles M. Russel.

Note: The museum is located in Los Angeles' Griffith Park, adjacent to the Los Angeles Zoo, near the Junction of the Golden State and Ventura Freeways.

CALIFORNIA AFRO-AMERICAN MUSEUM

600 State Dr., Exposition Park, Los Angeles, CA 90037

Phone: (213) 744-7432 *Hours:* 10-5 *Admission:* free

The California Afro-American Museum collects and preserves artifacts of the Afro-American experience. The museum was founded in 1977 and began operation in 1981. Its first home was located in the Museum of Science and Industry in Los Angeles. In 1984 it moved to a newly completed 44,000-square-foot park site containing a 13,000-square-foot sculpture court, galleries, a research library, a multi-purpose room and a 99-seat theater.

Collections: The museum holds permanent collections of artifacts, photographs, works of art, books and historical documents. The fine art collections include works in all media and feature pieces by African-American artists such as John Outterbridge, Bettye Saar, Romeo Bearden, Robert Scott Duncanson, Charles White, and Marian Hassinger

Exhibitions: As in the rest of the museum, the focus of the program of changing exhibitions is divided between historical and artistic concerns. Exhibitions like "Black Angelenos: The Afro-American in Los Angeles, 1850-1950" and "To Prove Our Worth: The Irony of the Black Military Experience 1861-1975" examine the historical conditions of Afro-Americans. Shows such as "19 Sixties: A Cultural Awakening Re-evaluated 1965-1975" examines trends in Afro-American art, while "The Portrayal of the Black Musician in American Art," examine the image of African Americans in American society.

Some art exhibitions seem to challenge the traditional lines between art and craft; "Wildlife Sculpture: A Bayou Heritage" featured the work of Louisiana decoy carvers. Other recent exhibitions include "Introspectives: Contemporary Art By Americans and Brazilians of African Descent"; "Visions Toward Tomorrow: A History of the East Bay Afro-American Community, 1852-Present"; and "Contemporary Abstractions: Prints from the Brandywine Printmaker's Workshop."

Education: The California Afro-American Museum offers an extensive program of summer workshops for children and adults. The museum's outreach program includes traveling exhibitions and lectures throughout California, the nation and abroad. Pre- and post-exhibitions programs are provided to schools.

CRAFT AND FOLK ART MUSEUM

5814 Wilshire Blvd., Los Angeles, CA 90036

Phone: (213) 937-5544 *Hours:* Tuesday-Sunday 11-5 *Admission:* $1.50, Students and Seniors $1; Under 12 $.75

Located diagonally across from the Los Angeles County Museum, the intimate Craft and Folk Art Museum had its beginnings in 1965 when Edith Wile founded "The Egg and the Eye," a gallery and restaurant specializing in folk art and contemporary crafts. In 1973, Mrs. Wile founded the museum proper.

Since the physical plant of the museum is small, without much room for the display of permanent collections, the museum directors have concentrated on community outreach and programming. In 1976, recognizing the ethnic diversity of Los Angeles, Wile created the museum's most recognizable event, The Festival of Masks. The Festival of Masks is an annual parade and two-day festival where mask makers demonstrate their craft and sell masks while masked theater groups and masked dancers perform continuously.

In 1979 the museum opened the Library and Media Resource Center, which holds extensive collections on craft and folk arts, including a slide registry and files on national crafts-people.

While the museum specializes in programming, it also has a collection of 1,800 objects, including masks from around the world, Japanese folk toys, American crafts, and Mexican, Japanese and Guatemalan folk art.

Each year, the Craft and Folk Art Museum presents six changing exhibitions on folk art, contemporary craft, design and architecture. Recent exhibitions include "Puzzles of the World," "The Vessel Studies in Form and Media" (highlighting California craftsmen), "The New Spirit in British Craft and Design," "Costumes from the Aman Folk Ensemble" (a dance group based in Los Angeles), and "Contemporary Wood Carving from New Mexico."

The museum also runs a restaurant and shop, and is currently in the process of raising money to build a new and larger tower where more space will be available for the exhibition of the permanent collection.

JOSE DRUDIS-BIADA ART GALLERY

Mount St. Mary's College, 12001 Chalon Rd., Los Angeles, CA 90049

Phone: (213) 476-2237 *Hours:* Monday-Friday 12-5 *Admission:* free

The genesis of the José Drudis-Biada Art Gallery came in 1974 when painter José Drudis-Biada agreed to donate an art department and gallery to Mount St. Mary's College on the condition that the college would house his works. Today the focus of the gallery is on presenting contemporary California artists. Drudis-Biada's works hang in the turn of the century Doheny Hall at Mount St. Mary's Santa Monica campus while changing exhibitions are held in the main gallery and smaller galleries at the main campus in Los Angeles.

Collections: The gallery's collections consist primarily of Drudis-Biada's Romantic Impressionist paintings and a group of watercolors by Sister Ignatia Cardiss, who was one of the Mount St. Mary's founders.

Exhibitions: Each year the José Drudis-Biada Art Gallery presents a variety of thematic and individual changing exhibitions. Artists who have had one-person shows include Ben Sakoguchi, Mac McCloud, Dauna Whitehead, Dorothy Churchill-Johnson, June Wayne and Peter Liashkov. Recent thematic shows include "Ex Libris: Narrative Imagery in Post-Modern Los Angeles," works by Bob Anderson, Cindy Evans and Donna Zanella, and "Clay III," works by Margaret Allen, Stephenson Burke, Philip Cornelius, Robert Glover and others.

FISHER GALLERY, UNIVERSITY OF SOUTHERN CALIFORNIA

University Park, Los Angeles, CA 90089-0292

Phone: (213) 743-2799 *Hours:* Tuesday-Friday 12-5; Saturday 12-4; closed mid-May through August *Admission:* free

The Fisher Gallery of the University of Southern California, established in 1939, is the oldest centrally located art museum in the Los Angeles area. As a university gallery it holds a permanent collection, exhibits works of contemporary artists, and conducts education programs.

Collections: The permanent collection includes 470 Dutch, Flemish, French, Italian, English and American canvases, panels, and miniatures as well as numerous small sculptures, ceramics, glass works, tapestries, silver, and works on paper.

At the collection's heart are two groups of paintings donated to the university. Armand Hammer gave the Fisher Gallery forty-eight Old Master works including *The Nativity* and *Venus Wounded by a Thorn* by Peter Paul Rubens; *Queen Tomyris with Head of Cyrus* by Giovanni Antonio Pellegrini; and *Holland Landscape* by Meindert Hobbema. Mrs. Fisher herself gave the gallery a group of seventy-two canvases including *Storm Clouds, Berkshires* by George Innes, *Mr. John Utterson of Farcham, Hampshire, England* by Benjamin West, and *Woodland Fair* by Johannes (Jan) Brueghel, The Elder.

Exhibitions: The Fisher Gallery presents approximately five shows each year, often of work by contemporary artists. Recently it featured a retrospective of Texas artist Michael Tracy's political icons and altarpieces. Other shows have included: "Sculpture da Camera," Italian chamber sculpture from the 1960s to the 1980s, and "Progressive Geometric Abstraction in America 1934-1955."

As part of the University of Southern California, the gallery also presents B.F.A. and M.F.A. shows and a show of pieces from the permanent collection curated by graduate students in museum studies.

Note: The Gallery is closed from late May through August.

FOWLER MUSEUM OF CULTURAL HISTORY

University of California Los Angeles, CA 90024

Phone: (213) 825-4361 *Hours:* Closed until completion of renovation, call in advance for hours.

When it re-opens in 1990, the Fowler Museum will be the new name of the Museum of Cultural History at U.C.L.A. At its inception in 1963, the Museum of Cultural History was to serve as a hub for the gathering of campus ethnic collections and their effective utilization. Over the years, the museum flourished and outgrew its basement quarters. In 1990 it will moved to a new facility built with funds donated by the Fowler family (former owners of the Fowler Museum in Beverly Hills), the Ahmanson Foundation, and the J. Paul Getty Trust. Designed by Arnold C. Savrann, the new 101,715-square-foot Romanesque facility will be reminiscent of the style of U.C.L.A.'s original buildings. It will contain nearly 19,000 square feet of exhibition space, a library, a central courtyard, administrative offices, a 350-seat classroom, and space for various archaeological and anthropological programs.

Collections: The Fowler Museum's permanent collections include 150,000 ethnographic objects and 600,000 archaeological specimens. Contemporary, historic and prehistoric cultures of Africa, Oceania, the Americas, Asia, the Near East and Europe are all represented. Of special note are the Sir Henry Wellcome Collection, rich in materials from Africa and Oceania, the Fowler silver collection (which has its own gallery), the George C. Frelinghuysen Collection of African and Indonesian material, and the Natalie Wood Collection of pre-Columbian art.

Programs: The "Early Man" program coordinated by community-trained volunteers brings prehistoric artifacts from the museum collection into Los Angeles area schools and provides lectures on archaeology, anthropology and paleontology.

The museum has an active publications program which produces numerous catalogs, monographs, pamphlets, study guides, slide sets and filmstrips. Student interns have the opportunity to work directly with museum objects relevant to their academic program, and the museum is included in the Arts Management internship program of the Graduate School of Management.

Also of note are the textile conservation program and the availability of consultation on such matters as conservation and identification of ethnographic objects.

HEBREW UNION COLLEGE SKIRBALL MUSEUM

3077 University Ave. (32nd and Hoover), Los Angeles, CA 90007

Phone: (213) 749-3424 *Hours:* Tuesday-Friday 11-4; Sunday 10-5 *Admission:* free

The Hebrew Union College Skirball Museum displays the art and artifacts of Jewish culture. The collection was first established in 1913 at the Cincinnati campus of Hebrew Union College. In 1972, it was moved to the Los Angeles H.U.C., and in the near future it will become the core of the soon to be built Hebrew Union College Skirball Center for American Jewish Life in Los Angeles. The planned center, through programs in the arts, a participatory museum, and lectures and conferences, will provide an innovative, educational perspective on the religious and ethnic richness of American society.

Collections: The Skirball Museum's collections date from the Chalcolithic period (*ca* 4000 BCE) to the present and include the Kirschstein collection of Jewish ceremonial art; the Dr. Nelson Glueck Memorial collection of Jewish ceremonial artifacts; the Joseph Hamburger numismatic collection; and the I. Solomon and L. Grossman collection of engravings and photo prints. In addition, there are manuscripts, paintings, sculpture, prints, textiles, drawings, Israel archaeology and graphics. The museum also has one of the finest and most representative ketubah (Jewish marriage contract) collections in the world.

In preparation for its move to the Hebrew Union College Cultural Center for American Jewish Life, the museum is expanding its Project Americana Collection of objects focusing on the culture and everyday life of Jews in America. The objects will be incorporated into interpretive, interactive exhibits.

The media resource department maintains a lending library of more than 18,000 slides related to Jewish art, history and culture.

Exhibitions: The museum presents a variety of changing and permanent exhibits on Jewish themes. Recently it presented "A Visual Testimony: Judaica from the Vatican Library"; "Danzig 1939: Treasures of a

Claes Oldenburg, Coosje & Frank O. Gehry, *The Knife/Ship, Daytime View. From "Il Corso del Coltello."*
Courtesy: Museum of Contemporary Art, Los Angeles

Asher B. Durand, *Kaaterskill Clove, 1850,* 40 x 60, oil on canvas. Courtesy: Fisher Gallery,
University of Southern California, Los Angeles

Destroyed Community"; "The Jewish Heritage in American Folk Art"; and "Earth and Spirit: Otto Natzler at 80."

Among the permanent exhibits are "Realm of Torah," exploring the Torah's significance to Judaism; "A Walk through the Past," covering Jewish biblical history; "Reflections of Triumph: Hanukkah Lamps from the Collection"; and "Celebration," ceremonial objects of the Sabbath, holidays and life-cycle events. Each exhibition is accompanied by outreach programs, lectures, family and children's programs and docent-led tours.

JUNIOR ART CENTER
4814 Hollywood Blvd., Los Angeles, CA 90027

Phone: (213) 485-4474 *Hours:* Tuesday-Sunday 12:30-5 *Admission:* free

The Junior Arts Center is a child-oriented museum which conducts integrated experiences of educational programs, hands-on workshops, school tours and museum-quality artistic exhibitions. The center was founded in 1967 and is located in Los Angeles' Barnsdall Park near Frank Lloyd Wright's Hollyhock House, the Barnsdale Art Center and the Municipal Art Gallery.

The Junior Arts Center is closely allied with the Los Angeles County School District. Each morning groups of school children are brought to the gallery where they experience museum quality exhibits. Later they participate in specially designed workshops which fit with the exhibitions' theme. For "No Strings Attached," a recent historic exhibition of puppets made during the 1930s and 1940s on Los Angeles' Olivera Street, children were allowed to make their own puppets and to share in a shadow puppet production; for "Electric Gas," an exhibition of six neon artists ranging from traditional sign makers to artists like David Swinson, who is at the cutting edge of neon art, children made sculptures from clear straws and colored telephone wire; and for Richard Godfrey's mysterious, dark, otherworldly installation, children were taught about installation as a medium and invited to make their own installations using boxes. Other exhibitions have featured California artists such as Frank Romero, Kent Twitchell, Laura Stickney, Joan de Bruin, Sandra Fene and Betye Saar.

Collections: The Junior Arts Center holds the International Child Art Collection. Administered by the Friends of the Junior Art Center, this group of 3,500 pieces from over forty countries is lent in thematic groups to local schools. The collection continues to grow, and it is the policy of the Junior Art Center to take the work of a whole class rather than discriminating between children.

In the afternoons, the Junior Arts Center is open to the public. Aside from the traditional exhibitions, it offers performance series, site specific contests, storytelling series, movie series, an annual children's festival and free family workshops each Sunday. Special artistic programs bring such visiting artists as Christo, Luiz Jiminez, Red Grooms, David Hockney and William Crutchfield to the center.

The center is closely allied with the Los Angeles Public Schools. It has programs for children with learning disabilities and offers special art-related teacher training programs.

LOS ANGELES CHILDREN'S MUSEUM
310 N. Main St., Los Angeles, CA 90012

Phone: (213) 687-8800 *Hours:* Wednesday & Thursday 2-4; Saturday & Sunday 10-5 *Admission:* $4; under 2 free; adults free on Wednesday and Thursday when school is in session.

At the Los Angeles Children's Museum, children (aged two to twelve) learn by doing. Founded in 1978, the museum first opened at its 17,000-square-foot facility in 1979. The museum operates at more than 70 percent of capacity on an annual basis and has one of the highest visitor-per-square-foot ratios of any children's museum in the country. Today the museum is planning a move to a much larger facility.

The eighteen life-size exhibits in the Los Angeles Children's Museum help demystify children's everyday experiences. They encourage children to touch, test, choose, paint, perform, experiment and explore. Among the exhibits are "City Streets," an exhibition which helps children understand highway signs, the mechanisms of traffic lights, and other street related experiences; "Ethnic L.A.," which helps children learn about the different ethnic cultures that make up Los Angeles; a television studio; a recording studio in which children create their own music and radio dramas using studio instruments and synthesizers; the "Health Education Learning Project (HELP)"; and "Zoetrope," an animator's workshop designed by Walt Disney Productions where children create their own cartoons.

Programs: Monthly programming includes a variety of art exhibits, performances, storytelling and workshops often held in the Louis B. Mayer Performance Space. Recently the museum held a birthday party for the popular movie star Godzilla, a sixty-hour reading extravaganza, and a "Weekend O'Whales," in collaboration with the Cabrillo Marine Museum. The museum also presents children's art classes held in a special art studio. These include clay workshops, wood construction, finger-painting, marble art and playdough.

Note: There are special party plans for groups of children (call for terms).

LOS ANGELES COUNTY MUSEUM OF ART
5905 Wilshire Blvd., Los Angeles, CA

Phone: (213) 857-6000 *Hours:* Tuesday-Friday 10-5; Saturday-Sunday 10-6; second Tuesday of month 12-9 *Admission:* $3; Students and Seniors $1.50; Children 5-12 $.75

The Los Angeles County Museum of Art is one of the country's major cultural institutions. Its collections range from pre-history to the present and encompass most of the world's civilizations.

History: The Los Angeles County Museum of Art was founded in 1913 as part of the Los Angeles County Museum of History, Science and Art. It first became a separate county institution in 1961. At that time, the Los Angeles County Board of Supervisors provided the museum with 5 1/2 acres of land in Hancock Park, adjacent to the famed Labrea Tar Pits, while private citizens, under the leadership of Museum Trustee Edward W. Carter, raised approximately $12 million from individuals, corporations and foundations for construction of the original buildings.

In 1981, the museum completed an ambitious building expansion and renovation plan, and today it comprises five interconnected and free-standing buildings. They include the Pavilion for Japanese Art (opened September, 1988); the recently constructed Robert O. Anderson Building, which is the main entrance and holds the museum's collection of 20th-century art; the Ahmanson Gallery; the Frances and Armand Hammer Wing; and the Leo S. Bing Center, housing the Robert Gore Rifkind Center for German Expressionism and Bing Theatre.

Collections: As a division of the Museum of History, Science and Art, the permanent collection had consisted of numerous objects spread unevenly across the history of art. Donors were many. In 1918, Mr. and Mrs. Preston Harrison began a 30-year career of giving and eventually added over 150 paintings and drawings of the American Realist, Ash Can, and Impressionist Schools. In 1939, money donated by Paul Rodman Mabury and his sisters, Bella and Carlotta, as well as a bequest from Allan C. Balch, allowed the museum to acquire European paintings from the 14th through the 19th centuries. From 1946 to 1952, William Randolph Hearst donated significant amounts of ancient, medieval, Renaissance and Baroque sculpture and decorative arts as well as more than 50 Old Master paintings. At the same time, George Gard DeSylva provided funds for additions to the Impressionist and Post-Impressionist collections. Today, the collection extends from prehistory to the present and encompasses most of the major civilizations of the world.

Indian Art: The Nasli and Alice Heeramaneck Indian, Nepalese and Tibetan collection of 345 paintings, sculptures, textiles, jades and crystals was one of the finest in America at the time of its acquisition in 1969. Augmented to fill lacunae, it is now one of the three greatest in the western world, spanning the history of Indian art from the Indus Valley civilization of the second millennium B.C. to the Mughal Courts of the 18th century.

Costumes and Textiles: The Doris Stein Costume and Textile Research and Design Center, located on the fourth floor of the Museum's Ahmanson Building is one of the most important costume centers in the western United States. The department holds approximately 40,000 items and is particularly deep in Islamic and Peruvian textiles. It holds the John Wise Collection of Peruvian textiles, which includes 100 unusually well-preserved pieces that represent almost 2,000 years of pre-Columbian weaving. Among the pieces are an embroidered alpaca fiber, the Burial Mantle, excavated from the vast gravesite at Paracas Necropolis, and a brilliantly colored Inca feather tunic from the Chimu period (1470-1530).

Also in the Stein Center are the museum's strong holdings in Renaissance and 18th-century costumes and accessories. Included in the collection are the only complete 16th-century costume in any U.S. museum; a man's red 14th-century Italian chasuble of brocaded satin; a carved wood artist's lay-figure and wardrobe, dated 1769; an 18th-century English silver and silk court dress; a worrier costume by Henri Matisse designed for Diaghilev's 1920 production of *Le Chant du Rossignol*; and a 24-piece gown collection by Mariano Fortuny (1871-1929).

Near Eastern Art: The museum's holdings of New Eastern objects were bolstered when a second Heeramaneck collection, a gift of Mrs. Joan Palevsky, came to the museum in 1973. Along with existing holdings, these 650 Islamic ceramics, metalworks, and textiles formed the basis for an exceptionally strong Near

Eastern group. In addition, five Assyrian reliefs from the 9th century B.C. palace of Ashurnasirpal II (gift of Museum Trustee Anna Bing Arnold) form a monumental group that illustrates both the decorative and political nature of Assyrian art.

Glass: The museum's collection of glass works is in large part a 1983 gift from Los Angeles collector, Hans Cohn. The Cohn collection includes over 250 outstanding examples of Ancient Greek and Roman glass dating from the 6th century B.C. to the 7th century A.D., Islamic and Near Eastern glass from the 5th through the 18th century A.D., and European glass from the late 16th to the early 20th centuries. Also, promised from Cohn are collections of Greek and Roman glass.

Pre-Columbian Art: In 1986, the museum acquired the Proctor-Stafford Pre-Columbian Collection. This group of 235 sculptures and vessels dating from 150 B.C. to A.D. 200, focuses on the fine art aspects of ancient west Mexican ceramics and is one of the most significant and representative collections of its kind. It includes works of the "Jalisco," "Chinesco," and "Colima" styles, including the Jalisco-style standing male figure, *King*, which is the largest example to have survived from ancient west Mexico, the large and elegant *Kneeling Female Figure*, whose serene enigmatic smile is one of the hallmarks of the so-called "Chinesco" sub style, and the unusual Colima-style *Dog Wearing a Human Face Mask.*

Japanese Art: Japanese art is housed in the 32,100-square-foot free-standing Pavilion for Japanese Art. Designed by the late Bruce Goff and executed by his associate, Bart Prince, the Pavilion's exterior walls are made of Kalwall, a translucent material that permits light to enter a room according to time of day, weather and season, making the movement of the sun and clouds noticeable on the works of art. In the Pavilion's East Wing, the museum exhibits scrolls, while the West Wing holds Buddhist sculptures, ceramics, lacquerware, netsuke, woodblock prints and Japanese textiles. Of note are Japanese ceramics and woodblock prints; the Shin'enkan collection of more than 300 scroll paintings and screens thoroughly representing the works of major artists of the Edo period (1615-1868); 141 Japanese netsuke (carvings) from the Bushell collection and works by contemporary Japanese artists.

Far Eastern Art: Chinese ceramics, scrolls, screens and sculpture form the core of the Far Eastern art collection. One superb example from the late Chou dynasty is a 5th century B.C. covered ting, cast in bronze and inlaid with copper. The sumptous tomb furnishings of the T'ang period, as well as the robust naturalism of the art are embodied in an early 18th century pottery *Horse* and in an exceptional *Pair of Officials*. The latter is almost four feet high and unusually large in scale. Far Eastern ceramics include a neolithic Chinese Funerary jar, a Han dynasty jar imitative of bronze, Ming dynasty porcelains, a painted jar from the earliest period of Japanese porcelain (Edo, 1615-1868), and several Korean and Thai ceramics.

Ancient European Art: Several objects of Ancient European art are worth noting. An unusually large (34 5/8") and perfect marble *Cycladic Figure, ca* 2500-2000 B.C., is the third largest such work known to exist. A finely preserved *Bust of a Young Boy* from second-century Rome melds the aristocratic idealization of the Augustan period with the withdrawn style of the era of Trajan. And a late 2nd century Roman *Biographical Sarcophagus*, one of the few remaining examples of its type, was at St. Peter's in the 15th century and served as a compositional source for Ghiberti, Mantegna and others.

European Sculpture: The museum is one of only three in the country to have a Department of European Sculpture. Founded in 1975, the collection is strongest in baroque and 19th-century sculpture. Several earlier works are also important; a late-Gothic *Virgin and Child with Bird*; a remarkable *Colossal Head*, circa 1534, by Baccio Bandinelli, the sculptor who restored the famed Hellenistic Lacoon group; and an exceptional *Allegorical Female Figure*, of the late 16th century, attributed to Dominique Florentin and one of the few large wooden statues remaining from the School of Fontainbleau. One of the most important works in the collection is a monumental, late 16th-century Neopolitan *Archangel Raphael* remarkable in the near-perfect state of preservation of its polychromed surface.

The 17th and 18th centuries are well represented with Italian, German and French sculptures. The only known cast of Giovanni Battista Foggini's *Time Ravishing Beauty*, ca. 1700, epitomizes the artist's contribution to late baroque sculpture in its unusual freedom of space. Examples of monumental Bavarian rococo religious sculpture are rare in the United States, but the museum possesses Ignaz Gunther's *Saint Scholastica*, ca. 1755, one of only a few known early works by this most important German sculptor of the 18th century. Paul Heerman's 1712 marble *Allegorical Group of an Infant Female Genius Crowning a Male Infant with a Laurel Wreath* is a rare example of the artist's work. John Deare's *The Judgment of Jupiter*, 1786-87, is perhaps the most important neoclassical relief in America, while Jean-Antoine Houdon's marble *Bust of George Washington*, ca. 1786, executed at the same time as the full-length figure now in the Virginia State Capitol, combines classical dignity with a quiet, reflective visage. The often melancholic exoticism of 19th century Romanticism is embodied in Jean Jacques Feucher's bronze *Satan*, while the apex of sculpture of that century is represented in 39 casts of work by August Rodin (gifts of the B. Gerald Cantor Art Foundation).

Though the development of a significant collection of European paintings is one of the most difficult tasks for a young museum, the Los Angeles County Museum of Art has developed a significant if not comprehensive group of Italian, Flemish, Dutch and French paintings. Of note are *The Virgin of the Annunciation*, by Bartolo di Fredi, the most important Sinnese painter of the late 14th century; a late 15th century triptych by the Master of the St. Lucy Legend; a Bartolommeo's 1498 *Holy Family*; Verone's two monumental *Allegories of Navigation*; Rubens' *Israelite Gathering Manna in the Desert*, circa 1625-1628; as well as works by Rembrandt, Hals and Gerard Ter Borch.

Prints and Drawings: The Department of Prints and Drawings holds approximately 4,500 works with particular depth in German, Dutch, Flemish and modern art. Particularly strong is its holdings of works by German graphic artist Albecht Dürer and his contemporaries, Martin Schongauer, Hans Sebald Behan, George Pencz, and Hans Sebald Grien. Among the well-known Dürer engravings are *Adam and Eve*,

1504; *Knight, Death, and the Devil*, 1513; and *Martyrdom of St. John*, 1498. German Expressionist prints and drawings of the early 20th century include works by Erich Heckel, Karl Schmidt-Rottluff, Käthe Kollwitz and the American-born Lyonel Feininger. Perhaps the finest Dutch print in the collection is Rembrandt's *Christ Presented to the People*, 1655, while Van Gogh's drawings, *The Bridge at Langlois* and *The Postman Roulin*, both 1888, are superb works from the modern era. Also included in the sizeable collection of contemporary prints are virtually every work produced between 1960 and 1970 at Los Angeles' renowned Tamarind Lithography Workshop.

American Art: American art of the 18th, 19th, and early 20th centuries is represented by a number of important works, most notably George Bellow's widely known portrayal of urban America, *Cliff Dwellers*, 1913. The influences of European art on earlier periods are evidenced in Thomas Cole's Italianate landscape, *L'Allegro*, 1845, and in its recently discovered companion piece, *Il Pensero*, 1845; in Emmanuel Leutze's *Mrs. Schuyler Burning Her Wheat Fields on the Approach of the British*, 1852; and in William Wetmore Story's *Cleopatra*, 1858. Transcendentalist interests are captured in Jasper Cropsey's *Sidney Plains*, 1874, Sanford Gifford's *October in the Catskills*, 1880, and George Inness's *October*, 1886. Winslow Homer's *Cotton Pickers*, 1876, translates French depictions of field hands into a purely American idiom. Among the outstanding portraits in the collection are John Smibert's *General Paul Mascarene*, 1729, John Singleton Copley's *Hugh Montgomery, 12th Earl of Eglinton*, 1780, Gilbert Stuart's *Richard, 4th Viscount Barrington*, ca. 1794-1803, and John Singer Sargent's *Mrs. Livingston Davis and Her Son, Edward L. Davis*, 1890.

Twentieth Century Art: The Robert O. Anderson Building (named for the Chairman of the Atlantic Richfield Company) holds the museum's collection of 20th century art. The building was designed by Hardy Holzman Pfeiffer Associates and its terracotta, glass block and Minnesota limestone facade serves as the museum's main entrance. On the third level is art from 1900 through Abstract Expressionist period, on the second is art of the past several decades, on the first, special exhibitions, and in the basement, administrative and curatorial offices.

Among the important pieces in the Anderson building are Ernst Ludwig Kirchner's important painting, *Two Midinettes*, ca.1911-1912; Kurt Schwitters' monumental painted collage, *Constructions for Noble Ladies;* Cezanne's *Still Life with Cherries and Peaches*, ca. 1883-1887; Magritte's masterpiece, *La Trahison des Images (Ceci n'est pas une Pipe)*, circa 1910-1913; Matisse's *Five Heads of Jeannette*, circa 1910-1913; Frank Stella's *Getty Tomb*, 1959; works by Monet, Mondrian, Stuart Davis, Guston, and several German Expressionists as well as David Bright's bequest of paintings by Picasso, Gris, Leger, Kupka, Modigliani, Miro, Dubuffet, Gottlieb, Rothko, Kline, Pollock, Rauschenberg, David Smith, Morris Louis, Warhol, Oldenburg, Diebenkorn, Irwin, Ruscha, Caro, Kelly, and many more.

The Robert Gore Rifkind Collection of German Expressionism (comprising 5,000 prints and drawings, and a catalogue library of over 4,000 volumes including illustrated books) is in the lower level of the Bing Center.

Auguste Rodin, *The Walking Man, 1905.* Courtesy: Franklin D. Murphy Sculpture Garden, Wight Art Gallery, UCLA. Photograph: Ernest Scott

Jonathan Borofsky, *Hammering Man,* 180 inches high, painted wood & electric motor. Courtesy: Los Angeles County Museum of Art

Hopi Kachina Doll, ca. 1920, cottonwood, feathers, horsehair. Courtesy: Southwest Museum, Los Angeles. Photograph: Doanld Meyer

Library: The Center for Education is currently under renovation. With a collection of over 65,00 books and periodicals, 25,250 auction catalogues and 79,500 exhibition catalogues, the Museum's Art Research Library is a major resource in the community.

THE MUSEUM OF CONTEMPORARY ART

250 S. Grand Ave. at California Plaza, Los Angeles, CA 90012

Phone: (213) 621-1750 *Hours:* Tuesday, Wednesday, Saturday & Sunday 11-6; Thursday & Friday 11-8 *Admission:* $4; Students with ID and Senior Citizens $2; Children under 12 free

As its name suggests, The Museum of Contemporary Art is engaged in defining the culture of the moment. It collects and exhibits post World War II art and is "characterized by a willingness to pursue the unknown and to take risks."

The museum was formally incorporated in 1979. It held an international architectural search and chose a design by celebrated Japanese Architect Arata Isozaki. In 1983, while the main building was under construction, the Contemporary opened the doors of its first facility, the Temporary Contemporary, at 152 North Central Avenue in Los Angeles. Originally a hardware store, subsequently a city warehouse and police car garage, the Temporary Contemporary was renovated by California architect Frank Gehry. The facility's accessibility, informality and lack of pretension captivated critics and the public alike.

The first public event at the Temporary Contemporary was the presentation, in September 1983, of a newly commissioned performance piece, *Available Light*. The Temporary Contemporary's first exhibition, in November of 1983, "The First Show: Painting and Sculpture from 1940-1980," comprised approximately 150 works from eight private collections in the United States and Europe. In 1986, the main building at California Plaza opened, but the Temporary Contemporary continues to operate as a satellite.

Collections: In 1984, the museum acquired Count and Countess Giuseppi Panza di Biumo's collections of 80 major works of abstract expressionism and pop art. The Panza Collections, with works by Mark Rothko, Franz Kline, Robert Rosenquist, George Segal, Jean Fautrier, and Antoni Tapies, forms the cornerstone of the museum's permanent collection. The collection was subsequently enhanced by the bequest of the Barry Lowen Collection of 64 paintings, sculptures, photographs and drawings from the 1960s, 1970s and 1980s. The Lowen collection included works by Elizabeth Murray, Susan Rothenberg, Frank Stella, Ellsworth Kelly, Joel Shapiro, David Salle, Julian Schnabel, Dan Flavin, Cy Twombly and Agnes Martin.

Concurrent with the acquisition of a permanent collection, the museum pursued its mandate as a patron for the creation of new art. Artists as diverse as Michael Asher, Jonathan Barofsky, Lee Breuer, Blondell Cummings, Jill Giegerich, Red Grooms, Michael Heizer, Maria Nordman, Anne Teresa de Keersmaeker, Rachel Rosenthal, Robert Therrien, Garry Winogrand and, more recently, Nancy Spero, Richard Deacon, Ann Hamilton and others have been commissioned or sponsored in the creation of sculptures, installation works, performance and audio pieces.

Indicative of the museum's innovative approach to the art of our time was its acquisition of Michael Heizer's *Double Negative* in 1985. This earthwork, located in the Nevada desert and donated to Museum of Contemporary Art by Virginia Dwan, is part of the museums permanent collection.

In December of 1986, the sleek, geometric Isozaki designed building at California Plaza opened with "Individuals: A Selected History of Contemporary Art 1945-1986," an exhibition of over 400 works by 77 artists, including eight commissioned works by Robert Irwin, Matt Mullican, Richard Serra, James Turrell, Richard Fleischner, Sol LeWitt, Chris Burden and Rebecca Horn. Writing in *The New York Times* (December 11, 1986), Michael Brenson echoed the nearly unanimous press appraisal: "Los Angeles now has one of the finest facilities for contemporary art in the world . . . 'Individuals' is a landmark exhibition for Los Angeles."

To celebrate the museum's continuing commitment to the media and performing arts and the opening of the Ahmanson Auditorium in its new building, the museum staged a production of "Zangezi; A Supersaga on Twenty Planes" by Russian futurist poet Velimir Khlebnikov.

Among recent exhibitions are San Francisco artist John Woodall's performance piece, *Gim Crack*, at the Temporary Contemporary; Mario Merz' series of installations at the California Plaza Building; and one-person exhibitions by Nancy Spero, Richard Artschwager, Matt Mullican, Tony Labat and others. Today the Museum of Contemporary Art looks forward to an even greater diversity of exhibitions, media and performing arts presentations and educational programs.

MUSEUM OF NEON ART

704 Traction Ave., Los Angeles, CA 90013-0184

Phone: (213) 617-1580 *Hours:* Tuesday-Saturday 11-5 *Admission:* $2.50; Students & Seniors $1; under 15 free

One of Los Angeles' newer museums, the Museum of Neon Art collects, restores and exhibits neon, kinetic and electric art. The museum was founded in 1981 by neon artist Lili Lakich, who saw and addressed Los Angeles' need of a place where new neon art could be shown and where old neon signs could be collected and restored. Since its founding, the museum has been located in an old renovated warehouse in the midst of Los Angeles' warehouse district.

Collections: In its permanent collections the museum holds over fifty commercial neon signs including an original R.C.A. Victor "His Master's Voice," as well as dancing women from Mexican restaurants and other figurative pieces. Among the contemporary neon and kinetic works are pieces by William Shipman, Eric Zimmerman, Dan Haskel and Lili Lakich. The museum continues to collect neon, kinetic and electric art.

Exhibitions: The museum presents two exhibitions concurrently. These change every three months and normally feature solo or thematic shows in the solo gallery and group shows of work by younger and/or under-represented artists in the main gallery. Many of the works on display are installations. Recent thematic shows include "Ladies of the Night," images of women in neon or kinetic art; "Cow Cow Boogie," contemporary neon and signs on bovine themes; and "The Neon Jungle," an exhibition of urban images in neon. Recent solo shows include Jan Sanchez' environmental piece, *Light Years*; a retrospective of works by Lili

Lakich; and Candice Gawne's three-dimensional neon paintings.

The Museum's educational programs range from lectures to school talks and include an eight-week course in neon design and technique which is offered to any member of the public regardless of skill level.

OTIS/PARSONS GALLERY

Otis Art Institute of Parsons School of Design, 2401 Wilshire Blvd., Los Angeles, CA 90057

Phone: (213) 251-0555 *Hours:* Tuesday-Saturday 10-5 *Admission:* free

The Otis/Parsons Gallery traces its history back to the first third of the century when it was the gallery of the Los Angeles County Art Institute. In 1954, it was formally established as part of the Otis Art Institute of Los Angeles County and in 1978 the merger which affiliated Otis with the Parsons School of Design in New York caused it to become the Otis/Parsons Gallery.

The gallery has two exhibition spaces which total 3,300 square feet. Exhibits are normally spread through both galleries though two one-person shows are sometimes offered simultaneously.

Over the years the emphasis has been on presenting the work of Los Angeles artists both emerging and under-represented. During the 1970s eccentric and conceptual artists were often featured. In the early 1980s sculpture in nearby MacArthur Park became important. Today, the gallery often reflects community interests but also seems to be branching out toward more global concerns. Recent shows include "Grand Tour: Geo-Romanticism"; "Los Angeles Sculpture"; "Visual Poetry," an exhibition of language directed art; "Czechoslovakian Art"; and the anual M.F.A. show.

There are no permanent collections and the gallery is currently engaged in a capital campaign toward the construction of a new building.

PLAZA DE LA RAZA CULTURAL CENTER FOR THE ARTS AND EDUCATION

3540 N. Mission Rd., Los Angeles, CA 90031

Phone: (213) 223-2475 *Hours:* during exhibitions Monday-Friday 12-5 *Admission:* $2 donation suggested

The Plaza de la Raza Cultural Center for the Arts and Education is a community center which educates the community and presents Latino culture and art in a wide spectrum of disciplines, including theater, dance, music and visual arts.

The Plaza de la Raza is located on lake front property in Los Angeles' Lincoln Park. In 1970, it was founded by a group of concerned citizens who wanted to save an abandoned boathouse from being turned into a parking lot for the nearby U.S.C. Medical Center. An ambitious building program headed by Margo and Eddie Albert was begun in 1979 and completed in 1981. Today the Plaza de la Raza (Place of the People) encompasses a six building complex including a theater, a dance studio, visual arts, administration and multipurpose buildings and the original boathouse where art exhibitions are held.

The permanent collections are small and the Plaza de la Raza emphasizes education and changing exhibitions. Each week its School of Visual and Performing Arts holds extensive after-school art, music and dance programs for 700 children ages five to adult.

Throughout the year the Plaza also presents the annual "Nuevo L.A. Chicano Arts Series." The first element of this series, an exhibition of painting, sculpture and jewelry by local Chicano artists, was held in 1988 and hailed as an affirmation of the Chicano/Mexican tradition. The Plaza de la Raza also plans a one-act play contest and a Chicano music series.

Changing exhibitions include one-person shows by artists such as Frieda Kahlo, Raul Anguiano and David Alfaro Siqueiros, and thematic exhibitions such as the photographic "Thirty Years of Mexican Folk Dance in California."

The Plaza de la Raza has a small collection of costumes and wares of the Mexican peoples as well as works by local artists. It is home to three local dance companies: the Rudy Perez Dance Ensemble (modern); the Francisco Martinez Ballet; and the Floricanto Dance Theatre (Mexican Folk Dance).

SOUTHWEST MUSEUM

234 Museum Dr., Los Angeles, CA 90065

Phone: (213) 221-2163 *Hours:* Tuesday-Sunday 11-5 *Admission:* $3; Seniors & Students $1.50; 7-18 $1; under 6 free

The oldest museum in Los Angeles, the Southwest Museum was founded in 1907 by Charles Fletcher Lummis and members of the Southwest Society, a branch of the Archaeological Institute of America. The museum was located in downtown Los Angeles until 1914 when the doors of the present building opened. Between 1981 and 1985, the museum underwent a major renovation. Current planning calls for physical expansion in order to increase the museum's ability to show and use its Latino and Western collections.

Collections: The museum's collections represent Native American cultures from Alaska to South America and include artifacts and art works from pre-historic, historic and contemporary times. The western North American holdings are strongest, particularly those from the Southwest and California, and include one of the largest basketry collections (11,000 pieces) in the United States. Other important holdings include over 7,000 pottery vessels from the Southwest; 6,600 Latin American colonial paintings, textiles, religious icons and other examples of decorative and folk arts; and many examples of Western Americana painting and sculpture.

The fine arts collections include a particularly strong representation of documentary art regarding the California missions. Many of these collections were formed by professional anthropologists and archaeologists and have excellent historical information associated with them.

The entire catalog record of the museum can be searched, and over 100,000 objects can be viewed from a computer-accessed laser disc.

Exhibitions: The exhibition program includes permanent, temporary and traveling exhibits. The museum presents exhibitions on the native cultures of the Great Plains, the Northwest Coast, the Southwest and California in its four permanent halls. The temporary gallery features four or five exhibits per year, representing Native American, Latino and Western Americana subjects.

The Casa de Adobe, located several blocks from the museum on Figueroa Street, houses the Spanish Colonial collections. Its eight reconstructed historic period rooms, built around a central patio, are filled with furnishings, tools and religious articles. Examples of historic and contemporary Latino art are exhibited in a changing gallery.

Braun Research Library: Housed in an adjacent three-story building, the Braun Research library contains collections of books, manuscripts, photographs and sound recordings acquired by the museum since its founding. Rare books include examples of Mexican incunabula (pre-1700); the 1787 Spanish edition of Father Francisco Palóu's *Life of Junípero Serra*; and the 1554 edition of Francisco López de Gómara's *Historia de la Conquista de México*.

The library's Photographic Archive contains approximately 120,000 photographs documenting Native American cultures in the late 19th and early 20th centuries. Its Sound Archive contains approximately 900 recorded works including 700 historic wax cylinder recordings of Mexican-American and Native American songs made between 1899 and 1912.

WIGHT ART GALLERY, UCLA
405 Hilgard Ave., Los Angeles, CA 90024

Phone: (213) 825-1461 *Hours:* Tuesday 11-8; Wednesday-Friday 11-5; Weekends 1-5 *Admission:* free

Located on the UCLA campus, the Frederick S. Wight Art Gallery emphasizes art scholarship as well as the development and nurture of new talent.

Collections: The gallery houses its permanent collections at the Grunwald Center for the Graphic Arts and in the Franklin D. Murphy Sculpture Garden.

The print collection in the Grunwald Center comprises approximately 36,000 works on paper, from the Renaissance to the 20th century. Included are master-works by Rembrandt, Hogarth, Hiroshige, Cuikshank, Matisse and Jasper Johns. The Murphy Sculpture Garden, set in a park, has over 70 sculptures from the late 19th to the 20th century. Holdings include works by such major artists as Matisse, Noguchi, Hepworth, Zuniga, Anna Mahler and David Smith.

Exhibitions: The Wight Art Gallery presents approximately eight temporary exhibitions per academic year. Normally thematic, these changing shows reflect a diversity of media and style and are often presented in concert with lectures, slide shows and guided tours. Recent and future exhibitions include "Forty Years of California Assemblage"; "The World in Miniature: Engravings of the German Little Masters, 1500-1550"; "12 Artists from the German Democratic Republic"; and "Pictures of a Poet/Stories of a Painter: Recent Monotypes by Eric Fischl."

As part of the University of California at Los Angeles, the Wight Art Gallery also holds a M.A./M.F.A. Thesis Exhibition each spring.

Note: The Grunwald Center for the Graphic Arts offers prints for study by appointment. There is a $3 daily parking charge.

THE WOMAN'S BUILDING
1727 N. Spring St., Los Angeles, CA 90012

Phone: (213) 221-6161 *Hours:* Wednesday-Friday 12-6; Saturday 10-4 *Admission:* free

The Woman's Building was founded in 1973 by artist Judy Chicago, graphic designer Sheila Levrant de Bretteville and art historian Arlene Raven. It addresses issues not typically dealt with by other arts organizations and is the first independent institution to dedicate itself to women's creative development.

Collections: In its permanent collections, the Woman's Building houses the United States' largest group of slides of work by women artists.

Exhibitions: The Woman's Building presents six thematic changing exhibitions each year. In 1989 it presented "Crossing Cultural Boundaries," works by Asian artists who immigrated to the United States; "Sounding Patterns," installations by three artists who work with sound; and "Holiday Tea Party," a group of tea pots.

Occasionally exhibitions deal with important social issues. In 1989 the building presented "Until That Last Breath: Women with AIDS," photos by Ann Meredith, and altars by various community groups. Along with this socially conscious exhibition, the building presented a symposium on the problem of women with AIDS.

Programs: Among other programs, The Woman's Building presents seminars, hosts artists-in-residence (in cooperation with the California Arts Council), and gives performances, literary readings, video screenings, lectures and classes. Recently it hosted a seminar on the politics of literary voice entitled "In Whose Voice; Culture and Representation." Other recent seminars include "Three Generations of Black Women Writers" and "Public Art and City Policies."

Each year The Woman's Building also sponsors a commissions project and an awards banquet, the Vesta Awards, honoring women who have made significant contributions to the arts in Southern California.

The Woman's Building also houses a graphic studio which is a community access facility for letterpress printing and the book arts. Often the press is used for community learning projects such as "The Postcard Project: Celebrating our Heroins."

LOS GATOS

LOS GATOS MUSEUM ASSOCIATION
4 Tait Ave. & 75 Church St., Los Gatos, CA 95030

Phone: (408) 354-6820 *Hours:* Tuesday-Sunday 10-4 *Admission:* free

Founded by concerned citizens in 1965, the Los Gatos Museum Association opened its first facility in 1966. The museum's emphasis is local in character and it is run jointly by the town of Los Gatos and the all volunteer Los Gatos Museum Association. There are two buildings. The main facility at Four Tait Avenue houses the Visual Arts and Natural History Departments while the extension in the historic mill building at 75 Church Street houses a town History Department.

The relatively small art department emphasizes local community services such as lectures, films and panel discussions. The permanent art collection is local in character with emphasis on costumes and decorative arts. The museum also offers eight or nine changing exhibitions (both thematic and one-person) of work by living, mostly local, artists. Among artists who have had recent one-person shows have been wood sculptor Andre Parker, photographer Sharon Connell, and drawer and painter Jane James.

MALIBU

J. PAUL GETTY MUSEUM
17985 Pacific Coast Highway, Malibu, CA 90265

Phone: (213) 458-2003 *Hours:* Tuesday-Sunday 10-5 *Admission:* free

The genesis of the J. Paul Getty Museum came in 1953 when millionaire oilman J. Paul Getty, a shrewd and massive art collector, authorized the creation of a "museum, gallery of art and a library."

The original museum, which opened in 1953, was a Malibu ranch house just to the northeast of the present museum. It contained five galleries and averaged 250 visitors per week on a reservation-only basis. The collections grew, and by the 1970s it became evident that the museum could no longer accommodate Getty's vast holdings. Plans began to build an entirely new facility in a classical style which would provide the proper backdrop for the collection of Greek and Roman antiquities.

The new building was a recreation of the Villa dei Papiri, a luxurious 1st century Roman house that stood on the slopes of Mount Vesuvius overlooking the Bay of Naples. The original villa had been buried when Mt. Vesuvius erupted in A.D. 79. In 1750, attempts were made at excavation. Eventually the project was abandoned but a floorplan and notes made during the excavations provided the basis for the Getty museum buildings.

When Getty died in 1976, he bequeathed a vast legacy to the museum. The bequest allowed the museum to go beyond its original collections of antiquities, French furniture, decorative arts, and European paintings and to begin departments of Sculpture and other European Works of Art, Drawings, Illuminated Manuscripts, and Photography. In order to accommodate these new collections it was necessary to rearrange the galleries extensively.

It soon became plain, however, that a new building was needed. The collections had outstripped the floorspace and the rapidly expanding activities of the Getty Trust were cramped. The new museum site, scheduled to open in the 1990s, will be a 24-acre facility located on 110-acres of a spur of the Santa Monica Mountains in west Los Angeles. Designed by architect Richard Meier, it will contain more than twice the exhibition space of the villa. After the new Museum opens, the present building will be refashioned to serve as America's only museum devoted entirely to Greek and Roman art.

Collections: The museum has seven curatorial departments devoted mainly to European art from before 1900: Antiquities, Paintings, and Decorative Arts, all of which were established during Mr. Getty's lifetime; and Drawings, Manuscripts, Photographs, and Sculpture and Works of Art, which have been added in recent years.

Antiquities: Located on the main level, the collection of Greek and Roman antiquities spans the period from 2500 B.C. to A.D. 300. In 1939, Getty began the collection by buying a terracotta sculpture purchased at Sotheby's. Today, sculpture in marble, bronze and terracotta remains at its heart. Areas of particular strength are 4th century B.C. Greek stelai (funerary monuments), Greek and Roman portraits, and Greek vases. Among the works of major significance are the Archaic Greek *Kouros*, or standing nude youth, circa 530 B.C., and the *Victorious Athlete* from the late 4th or early 3rd century B.C. Two very recent and exceptionally important additions have been a Cycladic marble harpist of the Aegean Bronze age and a statue of a standing youth of the Archaic period. Other works include sculptures, mosaics, vases, and objects in other media.

European Painting: The European Paintings collection, located on the upper level, ranges from the early 14th to the late 19th century. Getty began collecting paintings in the 1930s. By World War II he already held Gainsborough's *Portrait of James Christie* and Rembrandt's *Portrait of Marten Looten*. Before his death he succeeded in gathering a representative group of Italian Renaissance and Baroque paintings, plus a few Dutch figurative works of importance.

In recent years, these collections have been expanded. The French and Dutch Schools have been much strengthened, and later French pictures by the Impressionists have been added. Highlights now include Masaccio's *Saint Andrew* (1426), Terbrugghen's *Bacchante with a Monke* (1627), Rembrandt's *Saint Bartholomew* (1661) and Poussin's *The Holy Family* as well as works by Bouts, David, Mantegna, Millet and Munch.

Decorative Arts: Always Getty's favorite, the Decorative Arts collection, located on the upper level, features furniture, carpets, tapestries, clocks, chandeliers and small decorative items made for the French royal household, nobility and wealthy bourgeoisie. The pieces constitute a representative collection of French decorative arts from the early years of Louis XIV's reign (1643-1715) through the Empire period (early 1800s). Among the highlights are two tapestries, *The Arrival of Sancho on the Island of Barataria* and *Char de Triomphe*, made by the Gobelins manufactory, decorative screens, camodes, vases, baskets, cabinets, clocks and paneled period rooms.

Drawings: In 1981, the museum began its drawing collection (located on the upper level) with the purchase of Rembrandt's red chalk drawing of a nude woman posing Cleopatra. Since then, the museum has acquired almost two hundred drawings from the 15th to the 19th century. This group includes works by Raphael, Dürer, Bernini, Rubens, Watteau, Ingres, Goya, Millet, Cezanne and van Gogh. Although the primary emphasis has been placed on the acquisition of drawings by major artists, the Museum has also endeavored to purchase by lesser-known masters such as Savery, Bloemaert, Dolci and Gros.

Illuminated Manuscripts: The illuminated manuscripts collection, located on the upper level, was begun in 1983 with the purchase of the Ludwig collection, a distinguished group of 144 manuscripts, constituting a nearly comprehensive history of European manuscript illumination from the 8th to the 16th century. With additional acquisitions, the manuscript collections now includes examples from Italy, France, Germany, Flanders, England, Poland, Byzantium and Armenia. The variety of books in the Museum's collection includes liturgical and devotional texts, histories, romances, fables, and legal and scientific writing. Among these treasures are the *Dyson Perrins Apocalypse*, the *Hedwig Codex*, the *Spinola Hours*, and the *Model Book of Calligraphy* illuminated by Georg Hoefnagel for Emporer Rudolf II.

Photography: The photography collection, located on the upper level, was begun in 1984 with the purchase of several distinguished private collections. The gathering of these collections along with other block acquisitions made at the same time has made the Getty's collection the most comprehensive corpus of photographs on the West Coast. The strength of the collection lies in European and American examples dating from the early 1840s to the 1950s. Included are works by early practitioners such as William Henry Fox Talbot, Louis-Jacques-Mande Daguerre, David Octavius Hill and Robert Adamson, Cameron, and Nadar, as well as by later artists such as Kertesz, Weston, Sander, Evans, and Man Ray. For conservation reasons, photographs, like manuscripts and drawings, cannot be kept on permanent display.

Sculpture and Works of Art: Established in 1984, the Sculpture and Works of Art collection (upper level) features European sculpture from the Middle Ages until the end of the 19th century and European decorative arts from the medieval, Renaissance, and Baroque periods. The collections include Italian Renaissance maiolica; Venetian, Spanish, and Northern glass from the 15th to the 17th century; sculptures of the late 16th and 17th century by Giambologna, Hendrick de Keyser, and Rombout Verhulst; a small group of 18th century bronzes and portrait busts; and fine examples of Italian furniture from the 16th, 17th, and 18th centuries. The department holds works by Cellini, de Vries, Tacca, Foggini, Houdon, Clodion, Barye, and Carpeaux, many of which are shown on a rotating basis in the galleries that exhibit European paintings.

Gardens: The serene and impressive museum gardens include trees, flowers, shrubs and herbs that might have been growing 2000 years ago at the Villa dei Papiri. The Romans' fascination with geometric designs is reflected in the landscaping, pathways, and resting areas. Boxwood, used extensively in Roman Gardens, is featured in the museum's Main Peristyle Garden—over one mile of it.

The bronze statues in the gardens are modern castings of ones unearthed during the 18th century excavations of the villa; the originals are on display in the Naples Museum. Like those of Roman villas, the museum's herb garden reflects the same manicured, geometric landscaping as the formal pleasure gardens.

Exhibitions: The Museum's changing exhibitions normally come from the huge permanent collection, only a fraction of which can be on display at any one time. Recently the Museum presented "Experimental Photography," a year-long series of five consecutive exhibitions which trace the evolution of photography decade by decade over the century and a half of its history; "The International Gothic Style," an exhibition of eighteen illuminated manuscripts and three panel paintings representing the flowering of European court art in France, Bohemia, Italy, Austria, Germany, Flanders and England; "Dutch and Flemish Drawings"; and the thematic "Vie a mon desir: Illuminated Manuscripts and Their Patrons."

The J. Paul Getty Museum also presents continuing series of educational programs. Each Thursday evening it hosts lectures by leading art historians and conservators whose research addresses issues relevant to work in the Museum's collections. There are free adult education courses given by senior museum staff and a scholars in residence program brings several leading national and international art historians to the Getty.

The Getty Center for the History of Art and the Humanities: The Center is an advanced-research institute intended to foster the exchange of knowledge and ideas in art history and related humanities. It includes a Visiting Scholars and Conference Program, a library, the Photo Archive and the Archives of the History of Art.

Underscoring its interdisciplinary approach, the Getty Center library holds 500,000 volumes on history of science, philosophy and religion; social and economic history; anthropology and ethnography, as well as the history of art and architecture.

The Center also houses the Photo Archive, a study collection now containing over one million photographs but expected to grow by several million more. These photographs provide visual references for scholars studying works of art. The Archive presently has core collections in Greek and Roman antiquities, medieval art and architecture, Western European paintings and drawings, and European decorative arts that will expand into new areas as needed.

The Archives of the History of Art, the third of the Center's major resource departments, collects primary documents that illuminate the development of art history as a discipline and the course of critical and creative thinking about art. The Archives gathers unpublished studies; research files and correspondence among historians, critics, artists and dealers; archives of auction houses, dealers, and collectors of art; annotated books and photographs; significant bodies of papers of European artists, architects, craftsmen, and designers; and documents relating to historical views of the ancient world and its cultural tradition. The materials in the Center's collection, many of which were previously dispersed and difficult to consult, are available to qualified scholars.

The Getty Conservation Institute: The Getty Conservation Institute was established to further scientific knowledge and professional practice in the conservation of cultural properties—movable and immovable—including fine art collections, historical buildings and sites, and archaeological and ethnographic materials. Its activities include the Scientific Research Program which conducts studies in the museum environment, conservation material and techniques, applications of new or improved analytical techniques, architectural conservation, and in situ archaeological conservation; the Training Program which comprises a variety of activities, form short professional seminars at the GCI facility in Marina del Rey to multiyear courses and fieldwork in various countries; and the Documentation Program which helps gather and distribute technical information.

Note: Admission is free, but advance parking reservations are required. Call (213) 458-2003, 9:00 a.m. to 5:00 p.m. daily for information and reservations. Walk-in traffic is not permitted, but visitors without reservations may be dropped off at front guardhouse, or arrive by bicycle, motorcycle, taxi or RTD bus #434 (request Museum pass from driver).

Transportation: The museum is located on Pacific Coast Highway, one mile north of Sunset Boulevard and 4/5 mile south of Topanga Canyon Boulevard. The Santa Monica Freeway (West) merges into the Pacific Coast Highway.

MONTEREY

MONTEREY PENINSULA MUSEUM OF ART
559 Pacific St., Monterey, CA 93940

Phone: (408) 372-5477 *Hours:* Tuesday-Saturday 10-4; Sunday 1-4 *Admission:* free

The Monterey Peninsula Museum of Art was founded by a group of local artists in 1959 with the purpose of exhibiting art from outside the area. Today its collections include American art, with an emphasis on regional and California art; Asian and Pacific Rim art; international folk, ethnic, and tribal arts; graphics; and photography.

The regional collection consists mostly of works by artists from the Monterey area and California in general. These include paintings by William Keith, William Mitchell, and Euphemia Charleton Fortune, and paintings and etchings by Californian Armin Hansen.

The collection of Asian and Pacific Rim art includes netsuke (ivory figures), a Tong Dynasty funerary horse, and bronze Ku and Ting Dynasty libation vessels.

The photography collection contains 40 works by Edward Weston, a large number of Edward Curtis prints—all of them reproduced from the original glass negatives—and photographs by Ansel Adams, Wynn Bullock and Steve Crouch.

The majority of the space is used for rotating permanent collections but two galleries are used for temporary exhibitions. In these, the Museum explores a variety of concerns related to its permanent collections. The museum has presented one-person exhibitions by painters Wayne Thiebaud, Robert Arneson, David Gilhooly, Jim Dine and Mel Ramos, miniature tapestries by fiber artist D.R. Wagner, group exhibitions by contemporary artists from Spain, and thematic exhibitions on artists exploring the tropical environment. Each year the museum also holds a photographic juried exhibition of works by Central and Northern California photographers.

Other exhibitions have included a comprehensive display of handmade textiles from Guatemalan villages; photographs of Guatemalan views; the annual display of miniature works by regional artists in conjunction with the Monterey Peninsula Museum of Art's Festival of Trees gala; and the recent "A Brush with Shakespeare: The Bard in Painting," a private collection of 18th and 19th-century European paintings illustrating scenes from William Shakespeare's plays.

Included in museum programs are Museum on Wheels, a traveling exhibition of folk art, art education, and extensive education programs of accredited classes, lecture series, and outreach art appreciation series given in schools.

MORAGA

HEARST ART GALLERY

St. Mary's College, P.O. Box 510, Moraga, CA 94575

Phone: (415) 631-4379 *Hours:* Wednesday-Sunday 11-4; Thursday 11-8; Late hours during school year only, closed between exhibitions *Admission:* free

There has been an art gallery at Saint Mary's College since the early 1930s when Brother Cornelius Braeg began collecting the works of turn-of-the-century California landscape painter William Keith. Over the years, the gallery has had many names, and from the late 1950s until 1977 there was a William Keith Gallery on campus. In 1977, Saint Mary's College constructed the Hearst Art Gallery with the help of a grant from the William Randolph Hearst Foundation.

The gallery's 2,000-square-foot exhibition space includes the William Keith room, where the gallery's collection of 135 William Keith paintings are displayed on a rotating basis. Other collections include twenty-one works on paper by Moris Graves; graphic works on the themes of wine and Don Quixote; medieval sculpture; East European icons; and ancient ceramics of Cyprus, Mexico, Costa Rica and the American Southwest.

The gallery often presents changing exhibitions in its other rooms. Recently it hosted "Vestments East and West: Japanese Kesa and European Chasuble," an exhibition of works by contemporary Bay Area artist Rupert Garcia and 19th-century Mexican printmaker, Jose Pasada; "The Subject Is Objects: Contemporary Bay Area Still Life Paintings"; and "The Color Woodcut in America, 1895-1945." The Hearst Art Gallery is accredited by the American Association of Museums.

NEVADA CITY

MUSEUM OF ANCIENT AND MODERN ART

408 Broad St., Nevada City, CA 95959

Phone: (916) 265-9783 *Hours:* 11-5 Monday-Sunday *Admission:* free

Founded in 1979, the Museum of Ancient and Modern Art occupies three historic landmarks in Nevada City, CA and offers ongoing exhibits which range from the presentation of ancient artifacts all the way to one-person exhibitions by contemporary artists.

Collections: The Museum of Ancient and Modern Art holds one of the strongest collections of ancient jewelry in the United States, including Hollywood costume designer Theadora Van Ronkle's collection of Sumerian jewelry and the Oxford Collection from 18th Dynasty Amarna (in Egypt).

From the Middle Ages onward the emphasis of the collection is on works on paper. Medieval manuscripts are abundant. Dutch Masters are well represented, as well as Impressionists, the Italian school, English and American 20th century artists such as Johns and Lichtenstein, and the School of Paris—Matisse, Miro and Picasso.

Exhibitions: The museum's ancient exhibits reflect a Western Asiatic specialization. Many of the more modern exhibits reflect the continuity of artistic developments and connections with the past. A list of recent shows would include "Matisse: Pasiphae"; "Dutch Masters in Perspective"; "Henry Moore: Works on Paper"; "Abbeys and Monasteries in Ruins"; "Picasso: El Torrero"; "7000 Years of Technique"; and "Pectorals and Pictograms."

The museum also offers a wide variety of non-gallery services. It holds children's art classes on Saturday mornings, as well as art education classes with special presentations for collectors. The museum has the Academy of Ancient Dance, which performs throughout the area, and its reconstruction personnel produce jewelry based on ancient Western Asiatic designs for the Gift Shop. An ongoing docent program offers tours to student groups and others.

NEWPORT

NEWPORT HARBOR ART MUSEUM

850 San Clemente Dr., Newport Beach, CA 92660

Phone: (714) 759-1122 *Hours:* Tuesday-Sunday 10-5 *Admission:* $3; Students, Seniors, and Military with current ID $2; Children 6-17 $1; Tuesday free

Founded in 1962 by a group of volunteers, the Newport Harbor Art Museum is a private, non-profit institut#n dedicated to the collection, preservation and interpretation of modern and contemporary art.

Collections: The museum's permanent collection focuses on post-1945 California art and includes work by Ruscha, Diebenkorn, Goode, Baldessari, Bengston and Celmins. The Newport also has an uncommon collection of installations including Chris Burden's *A Tale of Two Cities*, a room size replica of two imaginary cities made from toy soldiers, robots, tanks and missiles; Charles Ray's *Ink Box*, a huge, gently undulating, uncovered-clear box filled with printers' ink; and Bill Viola's *The Theater of Memory*, a room sized piece involving projection and an actual tree.

The museum's changing exhibitions and educational programs feature regionally, nationally and internationally known artists in one-person and thematically-organized group exhibitions. Recent shows have included "L.A. Pop in the Sixties"; "The Figurative Fifties"; and "The Interpretive Link," a show documenting the flow of abstract surrealism into abstract expressionism. The museum also has an ongoing series of "New California Artist" exhibitions in which it features young, emerging California artists such as Tim Ebner and Marc Pally.

In the winter of 1990 the Newport Harbor Art Museum will present "OBJECTives: The New Sculpture." This show will mark the first time such neo-geo sculptors as Jeff Koons, Annette Lemieux and HaimUUteibach are looked at as a group.

The museum has been in three facilities since its inception. The building in which it currently resides is small and must go dark between shows since it cannot accommodate both permanent collections and changing exhibitions at the same time. To remedy this situation, the directors are currently raising money for a new building, to be completed in 1992. Designed by Renzo Piano (who also designed the Pompidou Center in Paris and the Menil Collection in Houston) the new 75,000-square-foot facility will have three times the exhibition space of the current museum.

Note: Since the museum goes dark between shows, visitors are advised to call in advance.

OAKLAND

MILLS COLLEGE ART GALLERY
5000 MacArthur Blvd., Oakland, CA 94613

Phone: (415) 430-2164 *Hours:* During the School Year Tuesday-Sunday 10-4 *Admission:* Free

The Mills College Art Gallery along with its sister gallery, the Antonio Prieto Gallery (also on the campus of Mills College), houses a large study collection and presents a continuing series of exhibitions. Built in 1925 by architect Walter Ratcliff, the gallery itself is a 40-by-120-foot, fully sky-lighted room which originally served double duty as a ballroom. Its sylvan campus setting and architectural details, including ornate ceilings, wrought-iron gates, and Spanish-tiled steps, make the building aesthetically interesting.

Collections: The rarely displayed study collection is available only to authorized scholars, Mills faculty and students. Among the holdings are works on paper from the 16th to the 20th centuries including pieces by Dürer; Goya; Rembrandt; German Expressionists such as Max Beckman; the Shojiru Nomura Fukusa Collection of textiles; the Antonio Prieto Memorial Ceramic Collection including works by Peter Volkos, Ron Nagle, and Antonio Prieto; a large collection of works by Bay Area artists such as Xavier Martinez, Guiseppe Gadenasso, Ann Bremer, Wally Dedrick, Dorothy Reid and Ann Carter; and a great variety of objects from around the world.

Exhibitions: Each year the Mills College Art Gallery presents ten changing exhibitions. Three of these are student degree exhibitions. Of the other seven the majority feature works by Bay Area Artists. The Gallery specializes in elaborate, room-sized installation exhibitions such as "New Interiors," an exhibition of furniture and environments by seven Bay Area designers, or "Ars Longa Vita Brevis," a large installation by Bay Area Artist Michael C. MacMillan.

Note: Since the gallery is only open during the school year visitors are advised to call in advance.

THE OAKLAND MUSEUM
1000 Oak St., Oakland, CA 94607-4892

Phone: (415) 273-3401 *Hours:* Wednesday-Saturday: 10- 5; Sunday: 12-7 *Admission:* free (with a modest charge for major exhibitions)

As the municipal museum of Oakland, the Oakland Museum brings together the energies and disciplines of three earlier Oakland Museums: the Oakland Art Gallery (founded 1916); the Snow Museum of Natural History (founded 1922); and The Oakland Public Museum (founded 1910), which was dedicated primarily to American Indian, ethnological and American historical displays. With these resources the museum endeavors to tell the story of California through activities in four areas: art, history, natural sciences and community affairs.

The museum itself was designed by Kevin Roche and John Dinkeloo of Roche, Dinkeloo and Associates. It opened on its 7.7-acre site in 1969, and it features three permanent collection halls: one presenting a chronological survey of the art of California from the voyages of exploration to the present, the second presenting the chronological history of the state from pre-Spanish Indian period to the present, and the third presenting the ecology of California in the form of a walk across the state. The building also includes a Great Hall, changing exhibitions spaces, two theaters, a print room and a multi-media room. In addition to the on-site sculpture terraces, Estuary Park, a 22-acre sculpture garden near the museum, was recently developed for large scale sculpture.

The Art Department was originally founded in 1916 as the Oakland Art Gallery. It acquires works of art and presents national exhibitions and exhibitions organized by the museum's curators.

Collections: The museum's guidelines state that an artist must have been born, raised, studied in, moved to, or worked in the state of California to be considered for the Oakland Museum's collections. Among the more than 1,000 California artists represented in the permanent collection are Albert Bierstadt, Thomas Hill, William Keith, George Inness, Xavier Martinez, Arthur Mathews, Maynard Dixon, the Society of Six, Stanton MacDonald Wright, Clyfford Still, Richard Diebenkorn, Sam Francis, Wayne Thiebaud, Larry Bell, Ron Davis, Mark Di Suvero, Peter Voulkos,

David Park, Elmer Bischoff, Nathan Oliveira, Joan Brown, Manuel Neri, Mel Ramos, Raymond Saunders, William Wiley and Bruce Conner.

Photography is also an area of strength. In addition to rare daguerreotypes, the collection features a range of significant work by Dorothea Lange, Edward Weston, Ansel Adams, C.E. Watkins, Anne Brigman, Oscar Maurer, Peter Stackpole, Alma Lavenson and others.

The museum has an active and continuous schedule of temporary exhibitions. Along with major traveling exhibitions the Oakland Museum has in the past featured the work of Calder, Diebenkorn, Christo, Mathews, Francis, Neri, Park, Bischoff, Lange, Adams and others.

OXNARD

CARNEGIE ART MUSEUM
424 South C. St., Oxnard, CA 93030

Phone: (805) 984-4649 *Hours:* Tuesday-Friday 10-5; Saturday & Sunday 12-5 *Admission:* Free

The Carnegie Art Museum, founded in 1980, is the City of Oxnard's municipal art center. It holds Oxnard's municipal collection and exhibits the works of local and national artists.

Collections: The collection of 170 works by California artists began in the early 1920s when the Arts Club of Oxnard began administering a bequest from Mary Bevans. The first piece they acquired was Cathryn Leighton's California plein air painting, *Desert Bloom.* In the 1930s the Arts Club added many others including Colin Campbell Cooper's *Malines, Belgium* and a work by Millard Sheets. The most important acquisition of the 1950s was Arthur E. Beamont's *The Wharf.*

Until 1980, the pieces hung in various city offices. At that time, the city renovated an old Carnegie Library for use as a community art center.

Exhibitions: Today the Carnegie Art Museum presents approximately thirteen exhibitions a year. These are divided almost equally between art historical exhibitions and one-person or group shows by local artists. The Oxnard Art Club often rents the space for their own exhibitions.

Recent shows have included "Black Photographers 1840-1940" (on loan from the Schomburg Center for Research in Black Culture, New York Public Library); "Candid and Studied: the Mexican Photography of George Hurrell"; "Macduff Everton," and "Madeliene Rouart, Post Impressionist 1896-1986."

PALM SPRINGS

PALM SPRINGS DESERT MUSEUM
101 Museum Dr., Palm Springs, CA 92262

Phone: (619) 325-0189 *Hours:* Tuesday-Friday 10-4; Saturday & Sunday 10-5 *Admission:* $4; 6-17 $2

Founded in 1937 and located at the base of Mount San Jacinto, The Palm Springs Desert Museum is a multidisciplinary institution which offers exhibitions in art, natural science and the performing arts.

The museum's first home was a storefront in a Palm Springs shopping center. In 1939, it moved to two rooms in the Welwood Murray Library where it stayed until the new facility was built in 1975. Designed by E. Stewart Williams, the 15-year-old, 75,000-square-foot museum has a volcanic rock facade which helps it blend in with Mt. San Jacinto at whose base it sits.

The museum specializes in contemporary American painting and sculpture and emphasizes art from California and the western United States as well as classic western American art of the 19th and early 20th centuries. The permanent collection is also strong in native American art, emphasizing basketry and other objects made by the Cahuilla Indians, the tribe indigenous to the Palm Springs area.

Highlights of the collection include large-scale works by California artists such as Lita Albuquerque, Robert Arneson, Tony Berlant, Ronald Davis, Robert Hudson, Helen Lundeberg, Manuel Neri, Edward Ruscha and William T. Wiley. In the three outdoor sculpture gardens (Sinatra Court, The Marcuse, and The Elrod) are works by Max Bill, Mark Di Suvero, Jacques Lipchitz, Marino Marini, Henry Moore and Jack Szjac.

A large graphic art collection includes suites of lithographs by Yaacov Agam, Karel Appel, Jose Luis Cuevas, and Jean Dubuffet, as well as individual graphics by Edgar Degas, Sam Francis, Roy Lichtenstein, Pablo Picasso, Auguste Rodin, George Segal, and Andy Warhol. Photogravures by Edward S. Curtis and contemporary photographers as well as drawings by Raoul Dufy, Willem de Kooning, and Lionel Feininger are also part of the collection.

The classic western American art collection includes works by masters of the genre. They include Edward Borein, Thomas Hill, Grace Carpenter Hudson, William Keith, Frederic Remington, Charles Russel and others. This collection is augmented by classic western paintings on long term loan from Philip Anschutz.

Exhibitions: Throughout the Museum season (September through July) the Palm Springs Desert Museum regularly hosts major fine art exhibitions. In past years it exhibited the world famous Armand Hammer Collection; The Phillips Collection, Washington, D.C.; and "Mouton Rothschild: Paintings for the Labels."

The Museum's Annenberg Theatre is one of the most beautiful environments of its type in America. There, the museum offers nationally and internationally famed artists from the concert stage as well as ethnic dance and music, exhibition dance from classical ballet, choral activities, chamber music and more. Movies and films as well as lecture series are offered on a weekly basis.

The thrust of the Natural Science exhibitions is the interpretation of the desert environment through such fields as physiography, biology, botany, anthropology, and geology as well as artistic rendering of the environment in painting, sculpture and photography.

PALO ALTO

PALO ALTO CULTURAL CENTER
1313 Newell Rd., Palo Alto, CA 94303

Phone: (415) 329-2366 *Hours:* Tuesday-Thursday 10-5, 7-10; Friday & Saturday 10-5; Sunday 1-5

Located near the campus of Stanford University, The Palo Alto Cultural Center is the visual-arts facility of the City of Palo Alto. It contains classrooms, studios and three exhibition spaces: the East Gallery, used for group exhibitions and thematic shows; the smaller West Gallery, used for smaller works; and the Sculpture Garden which is used for large scale outdoor work.

Exhibitions: Since the the City of Palo Alto has a small permanent collection (120 pieces which are mostly displayed in city offices), the Cultural Center concentrates on exhibiting works on loan from artists, galleries, museums and private collections. Recent and future thematic exhibitions include "Shaker Furniture and Crafts"; "Bay Area Sculpture"; "Large-Scale Ceramic Vessels"; "Contemporary Realism in Painting"; "Ceramic Traditions: The Figure"; and "The Art Book." One-person and group exhibitions have featured Mark Adams, Jay DeFeo, Manuel Neri, Frank Lobdell, Hassel Smith, William T. Wiley, Robert Arneson and Paul Wonner, as well as lesser known artists of the Bay Area.

Education: In its studio art program the museum offers classes in painting, drawing, ceramics, papermaking and printmaking taught by Bay Area and visiting artists. The studio art program also includes workshops, lectures and seminars that dovetail with the Cultural Center's exhibition.

The art education program also includes "Project LOOK!," a popular art exploration experience for children; the "Creation Location," a participatory learning gallery; and ongoing lecture series. Elementary school children tour the exhibitions with "Project LOOK!" and participate in a hands-on workshop. "Project LOOK!," "The Creation Location," and the lecture series are all planned to complement exhibitions held in the galleries.

STANFORD UNIVERSITY MUSEUM OF ART

Museum Way & Lomita Dr., Palo Alto, CA 94305

Phone: (415) 723-4177 *Hours:* Tuesday-Friday 10-5; Saturday & Sunday 1-5 *Admission:* free

In 1894, the Stanford University Museum of Art was first opened to the public. In 1906, the San Francisco Earthquake destroyed approximately three-quarters of the building. Only the central portion was left standing, the first such structure on the West Coast built of poured concrete reinforced with twisted iron bars. In the years following, the central portion of the building was cleared and opened on a very limited basis. Funds were short, and little work was done on the building itself or on the decimated collection. It was not until 1954, when a group of Bay Area citizens banded together to form The Committee for Art at Stanford, a committee dedicated to the rehabilitation of the museum and the rebuilding of its collections, that rebuilding work was begun in earnest. In 1963, the university was able to contribute a much-needed operating budget and the nucleus of a professional and technical staff. Slowly the galleries were restored, and funds raised by the Committee for Art and from some individual gifts and bequests were used to strengthen and expand the collections. Since 1981, all the exhibition spaces have been fully installed with works of art, including a two-story rotunda given over to the sculpture of Rodin. The adjacent B. Gerald Cantor Rodin Sculpture Garden was installed in 1985.

Collections: Today the museum's collections are general and range from antiquity to the present. The breadth and quality of its ancient, Oriental, and modern galleries, in particular, reflect the development of the museum at two important moments-the time of its founding from 1880 to 1905, and of its revitalization from 1963 to the present.

When Governor and Mrs. Leland Stanford funded the museum, they looked to the archaeological interests of their deceased son, Leland Stanford, Jr., in whose memory they made their gift. Consequently, the antiquities galleries are richly stocked with selections from the thousands of objects purchased by the Stanfords from the Metropolitan Museum in 1884 as "duplicates" of the Cesnola Collection of classical antiquities unearthed on the island of Cyprus by the Metropolitan's first director. Egyptian art is also well represented through purchases made by Mrs. Stanford from the Egyptian Exploration Fund.

The museum's collection of Asian art, which now comprises some 7,000 objects, also began with lavish purchases made by Mrs. Stanford in memory of her son. In 1904, the Baron Ikeda Collection came to Stanford through her intervention, and to this collection many subsequent gifts of Far Eastern art have been added, so that nearly every area of Asian art is represented. Unfortunately, the early phase of the collection's development came to a dramatic halt with the earthquake of 1906.

Resurrected in the 1960s by a new administration, the collection has since been developed with emphasis on art since the Renaissance. At present, its special strengths in modern art reside in three specific areas 18th and 19th-century painting including works by Francesco Guardi, Arthur Devis, Francis Cotes, Joseph Wright of Derby, Sir Joshua Reynolds, Thomas Gainsborough, Phillipe de Loutherbourg, Thomas Staddard, Henry Fuseli, Benjamin West, Gericault, Gerome Meissonier, Bonnat, Blanche and Whistler; Master drawings from the 16th century to the present including works by Carracci, Guernico, Boucher, Hubert Robert, Tiepolo, Blake, Flaxman, Cozens, Turner, Delacroix, Vuillard and Klimt; and more than 100 sculptures by Auguste Rodin, the gift of the B. Gerald Cantor Art Foundation.

Exhibitions: The Stanford Museum also has a vigorous schedule of temporary exhibitions which are shown in the Miedel Room and at the nearby Thomas Welton Stanford Art Gallery. Exhibitions in the past have included one-person exhibitions on the work of Whistler, Klee, Imogen Cunningham, Ansel Adams, Christo, Jose Vermeersch and Margaret Bourke-White, as well as such thematic exhibitions as "The Age of Revolution in the Works of Art from the Stanford Museum" and "Blue and White Ceramics of the Far East."

PASADENA

NORTON SIMON MUSEUM OF ART

Colorado and Orange Grove Blvd., Pasadena, CA 91105

Phone: (818) 449-6840 *Hours:* Thursday-Sunday 12-6

It would be difficult to name a museum put together with more reverence for its contents than the Norton Simon Museum of Art. The former Pasadena Art Museum was acquired by the Norton Simon group in 1974 and remodeled and reopened in 1975. Today, it is a publicly supported charitable and educational institution that houses one of the great collections of paintings, tapestries, prints and sculpture.

The museum's contemporary architecture acts as a foil for its collections. Its simple decor, polished wood and careful use of glass show each piece of art to its advantage. The flow from space to space is well designed and allows for freedom of movement and comfortable viewing.

Tsuruya Kokei, *Danjuro XII as Soga no Goro in Uirouri*, Kabuki Actor Print Series, 15 x 10, woodblock print. Courtesy: Pacific Asia Museum, Pasadena

Most of the works are from the private collection of Norton Simon which, before finding a permanent home in Pasadena, was on loan to many well-known institutions across the world, including the National Gallery of Art in Washington, D.C. and the National Gallery in London.

Collections: The collection is exceptionally solid from the point of view of scholarship. Well installed, meticulously maintained, and thoughtfully interrelated, it is a group of works possessing a unity and a high level of formal quality.

Paintings: The museum is particularly strong in European works from the Renaissance to the mid-20th century. The Italian collection of paintings begins with fine examples of the 14th and 15th centuries and features the works of Guariento, Lorenzetti, Filippino Lippi, Giovanni Bellini, and Giovanni de Paolo's *Branchini Madonna.* From the 16th century, the museum holds *Madonna and Child with Book* by Raphael and the *Flight into Egypt* by Jacopo Bassano. Masterpieces of the 18th century include *Triumph of Virtue and Honor over Ignorance* by Tiepolo and works by Canaletto, Pannini, and Guardi.

The Dutch and Flemish exhibition includes Dieric Bout's *The Resurrection*, Memling's *Christ Blessing*, and *Coronation of the Virgin* by Gerard David. These are shown in concert with the fine 15th and 16th century Flemish and French tapestries. Fairly extensive 17th century representation includes three Rembrandt paintings. They are *Self Portrait, The Bearded Man in a Wide Brimmed Hat*, and the tender portrait of his son, *Titus.* Other 17th century masterpieces include works of Rubens and Frans Hals as well as landscapes, interiors and still lifes that are fine examples of the era.

Exemplifying the art of Spain are important works by Murillo, El Greco, Goya, and Zurbaran, including the latter's well-known work, *Still Life with Lemons, Oranges, and a Rose.*

The French collections feature 17th and 18th century works by Rigaud, Poussin, Claude Lorrain, Chardin, Watteau, and Boucher. The next two centuries of French art are well illustrated with a wide range of works. Among the most impressive are Corot's *Young Woman in a Red Bodice*; Renoir's *Les Point des Arts, Paris*; Manet's *The Ragpicker*; Cezanne's *Tulips in a Vase*; Van Gogh's *Portrait of a Peasant*; Picasso's *Point de la Cite*; Braque's *Still Life with Pipe*; Matisses *Odalisque with Tambourine*; and Rouault's *The Sirens.* These are displayed along with works of Seurat, Monet, Toulouse-Lautrec, Gauguin, Degas, Modigliani and Gris.

The Degas Gallery on the lower level of the museum features nearly 100 examples of that master's works, including the extensive "modele" set of his bronzes.

Also from the 20th century are the works of the Blue Four German Expressionists—Feininger, Jawlensky, Kadinsky, and Klee—part of the famous Galka Scheyer Collection.

An extensive collection of graphics includes a number of Picasso's final proofs marked with the artist's personal approval, "bon a tirer," and signed, as well as a group of Rembrandt etchings and a collection of prints by Goya.

Sculpture: The sculpture collection covers the period from the 1830s to 1973 but focuses on French and English works of Art. In the serene sculpture garden, monumental pieces by Maillol share space with a scenic reflecting pool. Other works on view are Lehmbruck's *Standing Woman*; Jacques Lipchitz's *The Figure*; Matisse's *The Backs*; Brancusi's *Bird in Space*; Picasso's *Head of a Woman*; and Giacometti's *Tall Figure, 1.* The Norton Simon also holds the works of some of the pioneers of modern sculpture. These include Rodin's *The Burghers of Calais*; Aristide Maillol's *The River*; and Henry Moore's *King and Queen.*

Asian and Indian Art: An Asian and Indian collection includes numerous stone and bronze figures from India, Nepal, Cambodia and Thailand. The earliest sculptures in the collection are two Indian pillars dating from 100 B.C. The prolific Chola Period of India is highlighted in a group of 10th century bronzes. One of the most precious treasures of the museum is included in this grouping. It is the *Shivapuram Nataraja*, an early Chola bronze on loan from the the Indian Government.

The Museum shop has a wide array of books on Oriental art and general art history scholarly publications. It also has a section on architecture and catalogs from other museums. Visitors may choose from an excellent collections of prints, etchings, engravings, posters and greeting cards with reproductions from the collection.

PACIFIC ASIA MUSEUM

46 N. Los Robles Ave., Pasadena, CA 91101

Phone: (818) 449-2742 *Hours:* Wednesday-Sunday 12-5 *Admission:* $3; Students & Seniors $1.50

The Pacific Asia Museum is the only museum in Southern California dedicated to understanding the peoples of Asia and the Pacific. As an educational and intercultural center, the museum encourages the enjoyment and appreciation of the objects and materials it presents, and acts as a resource for the study of the aesthetics, philosophy, and values of Pacific Asia cultures and civilization.

The museum is housed in the historic Grace Nicholson Building which was designed by Marston, Van Pelt, and Maybury in the early 1920s. It has authentic Chinese architectural and decorative detail and its authentic Chinese courtyard garden is a quiet haven and backdrop for performances, receptions and other functions. The building has been designated as a Pasadena Cultural Heritage Landmark and listed in the National Register of Historic Places.

Exhibitions: Each exhibition is chosen to provide insight into the culture or civilization it represents as well as to show its importance as art. Recently the museum presented an exhibition of sixty Kabuki Actor Woodblock prints by Tsuruya Kokei (official artist of the Grand Kabuki Theatre); works from the Harari Collection of Japanese paintings from the Edo and Meiji periods (part of the permanent collection); Malaysian gold objects from the 8th through the 18th centuries; and Southeast Asian ceramics from the collection of Mr. and Mrs. Hans A. Ries.

Programs: The museum's education programs include classes in Chinese brushpainting, Tai Chi, and Ikebana (Japanese flower arranging). Its special events include the annual Taste of Asia Food Festival as well as theater, concerts and dance performances. These programs are enhanced by the Docent Training Course, the Children's Gallery, a Culinary Arts Council and a significant reference library.

The museum's shops offer a variety of Pacific and Asian fine and folk art objects, antiques, handicrafts and other items. A bookstore offers Pacific and Asian art-related books, posters, postcards and note paper.

PASADENA HISTORICAL SOCIETY AND MUSEUM

470 W. Walnut, Pasadena, CA 91103

Phone: (818) 577-1660 *Hours:* 1st, 2nd, & last Sunday of the Month 1-4; Tuesdays & Thursdays 1-4 *Admission:* $4; Students & Seniors $3

The Pasadena Historical Museum is housed in Fenyes Mansion, a beaux-arts structure which was formerly the Finnish Consulate and home of Mr. and Mrs. Y.A. Paloheimo. The mansion was built in 1905 by Mrs. Eva Scott Muse Feynes. Through the years she and her family furnished it with American Renaissance pieces, European antiques, art objects of the 15th and 16th centuries, oriental rugs and paintings by American artists. In 1970, the mansion became the headquarters of the Pasadena Historical Society. It now houses not only the original furnishings, paintings and antiques of the Feynes-Paloheimo family, but an extensive collection of photographs, newspaper clippings and artifacts of early Pasadena.

The museum's permanent collection includes works by William Keith and Benjamin Brown, both California landscape painters from the early 1900s. The work of Finnish artist Carl Oscar Borg, noted for his California landscapes and seascapes painted between 1930 and 1955, is also featured.

The Pasadena Historical Society and Museum also provides an array of services to the Pasadena community and to its visitors. Among them are museum tours available for groups and individuals, a research library of rare photographs, books, and memorabilia, frequent speakers, and slide presentations on Pasadena History.

Finnish Folk Art Museum: Also of note is the Finnish Folk Art Museum situated in the Finlandia Gardens of the Historical Museum. The exhibition is housed in a Finnish sauna house and features antique farmhouse furnishings from various Finnish provinces, textiles, carvings and folk art. It is the only exhibit of its kind outside Finland.

RANCHO PALOS VERDES

PALOS VERDES ART CENTER

5504 W. Crestridge Rd. at Crenshaw Blvd., Rancho Palos Verdes, CA 90274

Phone: (213) 541-2479 *Hours:* Monday-Friday 9-4; Saturday 1-4 *Admission:* free

Organized in 1931 as the Palos Verdes Community Arts Association, the Palos Verdes Art Center provides a varied program of art enrichment in the South Bay Los Angeles area. Construction of the present center began in 1972 and an expansion was undertaken in 1980. Today the Palos Verdes Arts Center encompasses a three-building complex including three exhibition galleries and an education center.

Exhibitions: The center has an active changing exhibition program of over twenty member-curated, self-curated and traveling shows each year. The small Members Gallery contains works by artists who belong to the center. The Norris Film Gallery is devoted to photographic exhibitions and is the site of the center's classic film series. The larger, museum-quality shows take place in the Beckstrand Gallery, where the focus is on the works of Southern Californian artists. Recent

shows include "Nathan Oliveira: Raptors and Related Images"; "The Fiber Vessel," fiber works based on containers by artists from around the country; and "Martha Alf/Helen Lundeberg".

Annually, the center also presents a Multicultural Exhibition, which includes six weeks of related programs, lectures, craft classes, performances and library story hours.

Education: As a community art center the Palos Verdes Arts Center presents a variety of educational programs. The art education facilities include a darkroom, a studio for life drawing and a print studio with two presses. There is a full schedule of changing art classes which coincide with school semesters. The center also has a variety of outreach programs in schools and in-service experiences for teachers.

Note: The Beckstrand Gallery is open 1-4 Mondays through Saturdays.

REDDING

REDDING MUSEUM AND ART CENTER

56 Quartz Hill Rd., Redding, CA 96099

Phone: (916) 225-4155 *Hours:* Tuesday-Friday and Sunday 12-5; Saturday 10-5

The Redding Museum and Art Center was organized in 1963 by members of the Redding community interested in the fields of archaeology, history and the fine arts. The museum's first home was the former Carter residence, which the city had made available to the museum. In 1976, the museum erected its present 14,000-square-foot facility which includes three galleries, storage space and offices.

Collections: It is the policy of the Redding Museum to acquire contemporary art in all media by local and Northern Californian artists. The museum holds works by Robert Arneson, Roy De Forest, Michael Beck, Sylvia Seventy, Mike Lapena and others. In addition, there is a permanent history and ethnology collection on display at all times.

Exhibitions: The Redding Museum presents approximately ten changing exhibitions each year in its two art galleries. Most are self-curated. Recent shows include a twenty-five year retrospective of the work of Southern California hard edge painter Carl Benjamin (in conjunction with Shasta College); "The Candy Store," paintings, prints and sculpture by ten artists represented by the the Gallery in Folson, known as the home of California Funk; and "Shreaded Reconstructions," photo collage by Micheal Monahan and miniature constructions by Helen Cohen.

The Redding Museum also holds an annual art competition open to artists from Northern California and Southern Oregon.

The Shasta Historical Society is housed in the same building. It operates an archive and research library of historical articles and documents (open by appointment) and presents occasional exhibits.

REDLANDS

SAN BERNARDINO COUNTY MUSEUM

2024 Orange Tree Ln., Redlands, CA 92374

Phone: (714) 825-4823 *Hours:* Tuesday-Saturday 9-5; Sundays 1-5 *Admission:* free

The San Bernardino County Museum is the general museum of San Bernardino and its surroundings. It was founded privately in 1957, and it became a county facility in 1961. In 1974, it moved to its present 47,000-square-foot domed facility standing along Highway 10, which leads from Los Angeles to Palm Springs.

Exhibitions: The domed museum holds monthly exhibitions in each of the two adjoining 2000-square-foot galleries. Of these twenty-four exhibitions, eight or nine are held in conjunction with the Fine Arts Institute, a local group which mounts juried shows, makes purchase awards and often presents work to the museum. The museum also presents Black, Hispanic and native American shows. It hosts children's art shows, watercolor shows and shows by faculty of local colleges and universities. Of the other shows, most are two- or three-person shows by artists from all over the country who submit proposals to the museum's exhibitions committee.

The curatorial focuses of the permanent collections are natural sciences, biological sciences and local history. The fine arts collection of 300 to 400 pieces is predominately regional, both in subject matter and contributing artists. Perhaps one hundred of the pieces are by artists such as B. Walsh, Carol Hamilton and Donal Jolley, who are well known in the San Bernardino area. Several others are by slightly better known artists such as Phillip Van Dyke and the native American artist Cross.

Plans are now underway for an addition which will double the gallery space by the early 1990s. For the foreseeable future the curatorial emphasis will continue to be on wildlife art.

Note: The exhibit auditoriums are multi-use rooms for many activities. To avoid disappointment, call ahead to be sure the rooms are open.

RICHMOND

RICHMOND ART CENTER
Civic Center Plaza, Richmond, CA 94804

Phone: (415) 620-6772 *Hours:* Tuesday-Friday 10-4:30; Saturday & Sunday 12-4:30 *Admission:* free

Since its inception in 1936, the Richmond Art Center has both fostered an awareness, appreciation and expression of the visual arts and crafts in Richmond and maintained an active and vital exhibition program that has focused on contemporary art in the Bay Area and Northern California.

In 1951, the Art Center moved to its current Civic Center location. With almost 4,000 square feet of gallery space, including an outdoor sculpture courtyard, the Art Center provides a professional setting for the emerging and mid-career artists it exhibits. Its lively exhibitions feature work in all media, including painting, sculpture, drawing, photography, installations, video and performance art. Many younger artists who showed at the center have gone on to national and international recognition. A partial list of these includes Robert Arneson, Larry Bell, Elmer Bischoff, Bruce Conner, Roy De Forest, Richard Diebenkorn, Lloyd Hamrol, Tom Holland, Robert Hudson, Jasper Johns, Nathan Oliveira, Dennis Oppenheim, David Park, Wayne Thiebaud, Peter Voulkos and William T. Wiley.

The list of young artists who have shown at the Richmond Art Center is quite extensive and continually changing. In the last few years alone, the Art Center has featured paintings by Pegan Brooke, Christopher Brown, and Squeak Carnwath; drawings by Eva Gar-

cia, Leslie Lerner, and Larry Thomas; prints by Enrique Chagoya and Diego Marcial Rios; sculpture by Peter Rodriguez and Leslie Van Scoyoc; and mixed media work by Patricia Roth O'Connor and Robert Dix.

The Richmond Art Center also provides on-site art education for children and adults as well as a Children's Outreach Program which places artists in the public schools and in community settings. The Art Center also has a rental/sales gallery.

THE RICHMOND MUSEUM
400 Nevin Ave., P.O. Box 1267, Richmond, CA 94802

Phone: (415) 235-7387 *Hours:* Thursday and Sunday 1-4 *Admission:* free

Founded in 1952 and incorporated in 1954, The Richmond Museum is a community history facility. During its first years, it was located in the basement of the town library. Today, it is housed in a beautiful 1910 Carnegie Library and administered by the Richmond Museum Association. It contains two galleries: one of interpretive displays of photographic material and everyday objects of local origin and another of changing exhibitions of local interest, both historical and contemporary.

The museum holds 20,000 photographs, vehicles and objects in its permanent collections including the first four cars that came off the Richmond Ford assembly line in 1931.

The museum sometimes has exhibitions of a contemporary nature in the Seaver Room Gallery, but generally it attempts to retain a regional emphasis. Recently, the museum held an exhibition of quilts made locally by living artists from extremely varied backgrounds and ethnic groups. This exhibition represented the rich diversity of traditions that make up the Richmond community. Other recent exhibitions include the traveling "Ethnic Images in the Comics" and "Fisherman by Trade," a look at the fishing industry through one family's history.

Aside from exhibitions, The Richmond Museum holds a number of other events. It has an annual Museum Day each May. There are also performing arts series, field trips and classes in genealogy and antique conservation.

Note: The museum may extend its hours during exhibitions. Scholars may also make appointments to study the archives during non-museum hours.

RIDGECREST

MATURANGO MUSEUM OF THE INDIAN WELLS VALLEY
100 E. Las Flores, Ridgecrest CA 93555

Phone: (619) 375-6900 *Hours:* Tuesday-Sunday 10-5 *Admission:* $1; Children 6-17 $.50

Founded in 1962 and originally located on the grounds of the China Lake Naval Weapons Center, The Maturango Museum of the Indian Wells Valley has as its purpose the preservation and interpretation of the cultural and natural history of the Upper Mojave Desert.

The current 4,000-square-foot facility was built with privately raised funds in 1986. Designed by local architect Pat Rogers and located on 15 acres of Kern County park lands, its split-face block facade blends with the desert environment. Inside are two exhibit rooms (The Sylvia Winslow Exhibit Gallery for changing fine art exhibitions and another room for natural historical exhibitions), a children's corner, and a gift shop.

Collections: The museum's permanent collection is small but growing. It includes paintings by Silvia Winslow and Francielu Hansen and cast paper works by Paul Bouchard.

Exhibitions: Each December the Museum holds an annual open fine arts show. During the other eleven months of the year it presents one-person exhibitions by local artists and artists from other Southwestern or Californian areas. Artists who work in all types of media have been featured and frequent topics are Native American petroglyphs, desert scenes or desert wildlife. Among recent exhibitors are Helen Bellinger, Al Naso, Al Davis, Paula Gill and Gunnel Lyn, Bojarzuk, Linda Joseph, Ed Hogan, Arthur Miller, John Komisar, and Hamil Ma.

Programming: Each weekend museum guides lead tours through the nearby centuries-old petroglyphs (native American rock art) located at the China Lake Naval Weapons Center. The museum press has published several books.

RIVERSIDE

CALIFORNIA MUSEUM OF PHOTOGRAPHY

University of California, Riverside, CA 92521

Phone: (714) 787-4787 *Hours:* closed pending move to new facility in late 1989 *Hours:* Monday-Friday 8-5

Founded at the University of California, Riverside in 1973, the California Museum of Photography is devoted to photography as an art form and a social document. It has collections, exhibitions, research and educational programs.

From 1978 to 1989, the museum was located in Watkins House on Canyon Crest Drive. With the growth of the collections, however, the need for a new facility became apparent. In the fall of 1989 the museum moved to a renovated, art-deco, Kress-variety store in downtown Riverside. The two-story, 23,000-square-foot structure increased gallery space fivefold. Special areas in the new museum include a walk-in camera obscura and other interactive displays where children and adults can experience "hands-on" the art and science of photography.

Collections: The permanent collection includes over 400,000 prints, negatives and photograhic objects. Its acquisition has come through a number of gifts. In 1973 Dr. Robert Bingham donated his collection of 2,500 cameras and photographic apparatus. In 1977, the Mast family of Davenport, Iowa, donated the Keystone-Mast Collection of 350,000 stereographic negatives and prints to the museum. This represented the entire surviving archive of the Keystone View Company and is the largest such collection in the world. In 1978 the museum received the Setzer-Alexander Friends of Photography collection of 600 prints including work by major California photographers. In 1985, Sacramento lumber company executive Meak Kibbey donated his comprehensive Zeiss camera collection. The museum also holds The University Print Collection of over 10,000 images from daguerreotypes to contemporary photographs.

Exhibitions: The museum presents as many as a dozen changing exhibitions each year. Among these are works from the permanent collection including pieces by Ansel Adams, Albert Renger-Patzsch and Edward Weston, and other traveling exhibitions such as the Margaret Bourke-White retrospective from the International Center of Photography; and pieces by contemporary artists such as Barbara Norfleet, Jean Verberg, Ruth Thorne-Thomsen, Luis Carlos Bernal, and others. The first exhibition in the new facility will be "Biennial I," a state-wide survey of current trends in photography including works by more than two dozen contemporary California artists.

Education: As part of the University of California at Irvine, the California Museum of Photography provides scholars with the opportunity to bring together photographic, social historical and technical resources. The museum also offers a number of interactive school-related programs including "Discover Photography" kits which help students understand the history and theories of photography. Discover Photography kits allow children to handle daguerreotypes and tintypes and enable them to see the products of the photographic medium as more than artifacts.

Since 1982 the California Museum of Photography has published the award winning *CMP Bulletin,* a magazine of scholarly and other articles dealing with the technical aspects of photography, photographic history, and the work of contemporary photographers.

THE RIVERSIDE ART MUSEUM

3425 7th St., Riverside, CA 92501

Phone: (714) 684-7111 *Hours:* Monday-Friday 10-5; Saturday 10-4 *Admission:* free

The Riverside Art Museum collects works by California artists, exhibits contemporary art and runs art education programs for community members. The museum was first organized in 1910 as the Spanish Arts Society. In 1921, it was renamed the Riverside Art Association, and in 1985, it became the Riveside Art Museum.

The Mission Revival-style structure which presently houses the museum was originally designed as a YWCA by the famous California architect Julia Morgan (who designed Hearst Castle). It is located on historic Seventh Street in downtown Riverside and in 1982 was placed on the National Register of Historic Places. Today, the Museum is engaged in a $3 million capital campaign and renovation which will result in increased gallery and storage space.

The permanent collection is modest and includes works by local and regional artists.

The exhibition schedule consists primarily of group shows of contemporary art based upon a specific iconographic or stylistic themes, one-person exhibitions of California artists and selections from private collections both corporate and individual. Recently the museum held a retrospective of the works of François Gilot; presented the thematic shows "An Illustrated Guide to God: Religious Imagery in Contemporary Painting" and "The Metaphoric Chair"; and held one-person shows by California artists such as Sandy Walker, Martin Facey and Chris Kidde.

The Riverside Art Museum's education programs are quite extensive and include studio art classes at levels ranging from beginning toddler to advanced adult. Classes are given over four terms and up to four hundred students participate each year.

Other services include lectures, field trips, workshops, a docent program, a restaurant and a sales and rental gallery.

UNIVERSITY ART GALLERY, UNIVERSITY OF CALIFORNIA RIVERSIDE

University of California, Riverside, CA 92521

Phone: (714) 787-3755 *Hours:* Tuesday-Friday 12-5; Saturday & Sunday 12-4; Closed mid-June through August *Admission:* free

The University Art Gallery at the University of California at Riverside was founded in 1963, and is currently located in the University's Humanities Building. In early 1990, the gallery will move to "Watkins House" at the edge of the Riverside campus, a facility given by Gordon Watkins, the University's first provost. The move will expand exhibition space from 1200 to 1900 square feet, provide a home for the beginnings of a permanent collection (at present there is no permanent collection) and allow the gallery to hold two separate exhibitions at once.

Exhibitions: In its program of changing exhibitions the University Art Gallery displays works in all media and from all periods. Exhibitions are often coordinated with the University's Art History Department and once every eighteen months, a show is curated by Art History students in graduate seminars. Each spring there are two student exhibitions.

Some of the gallery's catalogued exhibitions include "England to Egypt: The Photographic Views of Francis Frith"; "European Pewter in Everyday Life: 1600-1900"; "Diversity & Presence: Women Faculty Artists of the University of California"; "Painters, Printers and Publishers: Printmaking in France & Germany, 1900-1914"; "The International Style in Southern California"; and "Roger Herman & Italo Scanga."

Note: After its move to Watkins House in early 1990, the gallery changes its summer hours. Call in advance for further information.

ROHNERT PARK

UNIVERSITY ART GALLERY, SONOMA STATE UNIVERSITY

1801 E. Cotati Ave., Rohnert Park, CA 94928

Phone: (707) 664-2295 *Hours:* Tuesday-Friday 10-4; closed June through August and all school holidays *Admission:* free

The University Art Gallery at Sonoma State University was founded and built in 1977 in conjunction with the building of a new Art Department complex. The gallery contains 2,800 square feet of exhibition space which is divided into the Main and North Galleries. Today the Sonoma State University is the second most active gallery in California's State University system.

Collections: The gallery's collections are small and consist primarily of works on paper by national, international, and California artists. The collections are rarely displayed in the gallery; rather they can be found in the University's offices and buildings. Among the works the gallery holds are pieces by Roy de Forest, Harold Paris, Robert Indiana and Andy Warhol.

Exhibitions: The University Art Gallery presents approximately seven one-person or thematic exhibitions each school year. Those featured in one-person shows include Joan Snyder, Robert McCauley, Susan Rothenberg, Chuck Close, Terry Winters, Judy Pfaff and Terry Allen.

Often the gallery curates thematic shows which travel to other galleries and museums. Lectures and workshops are often held to help explain the work on view. Recent thematic shows include "British Figurative Painting"; "Works in Bronze," pieces by thirty-five artists including Rodin and Moore; "Brazil Ten," works by ten Brazilian artists; and "Sculptors Drawing."

As part of Sonoma State University, the gallery holds an annual M.F.A. show each May and is partly staffed by students taking an arts management minor.

SACRAMENTO

CROCKER ART MUSEUM

216 O St., Sacramento, CA 95814

Phone: (916) 449-5423 *Hours:* Tuesday 1-9; Wednesday-Sunday 10-5 *Admission:* $2.50; 7-17 $1, 65 and older $1.50; under 7 free

Named for its founder, Judge Edwin Bryant Crocker, the Crocker Art Museum is the oldest public art museum in the West. The building, an Italianate structure designed by Sacramento architect Seth Babson, began construction in 1869 and finished in 1873. Judge Crocker himself went to Europe between 1870 and 1872 and amassed the original collection which contained hundreds of paintings, almost one thousand master drawings, as well as commissioned work from California artists Charles C. Nahl, Thomas Hill, William Keith, William Hahn and Norton Bush.

The museum grew, and in 1969 the R.A. Herold Wing was built to accommodate the expanding collection and to provide new exhibition and storage space. In the early 1980s the museum went through an elaborate restoration which revived the richly carved woods, twin curving staircases in the entrance, ornately tiled and inlaid floors, as well as the exquisite decorative paintings of walls and ceilings in the foyer, ballroom, and library. The Museum now plans a new building which will include a large contemporary gallery space, a discovery room, and a historical setting for original family furnishings.

Collections: The Crocker's collection has been notably augmented since 1873 when it was first displayed for the public. Today its scope ranges from rare Babylonian tablets of the first millennium B.C. to contemporary California arts in all media. All periods of the classic, modern, and contemporary art movements are represented to some degree. Among the older European works are examples from the circles of Jan Brueghel and of Titian. Included in the contemporary collection are paintings by Rockwell Kent, Georgia O'-Keeffe, Wayne Thiebaud, Roy de Forest, Robert Arneson and Ruth Rippon. In recognition of the importance of photography, the Crocker Art Museum has developed the Margaret Crocker Forum Photography Gallery.

One area of special interest has been the addition of decorative arts and artifacts. One of the earliest collections of Korean ceramics was a gift to the museum from Mrs. J. Sloat Fassett, one of Crocker's daughters. The Oriental collection also includes outstanding examples of carved jade, painted scrolls, Chinese porcelain, Japanese sculpture and wood-block prints. Of particular interest is the rare medieval Samurai armour and accouterments.

Exhibitions: Each year the Museum hosts the Crocker-Kingsley Exhibition. Sponsored by the Kingsley Art Club, it offers an opportunity to see a cross-selection of current work by artists in the Sacramento area. Other recent exhibitions include the art historical—

Figurine Group, Tlaquepaque, Jalisco, ca. 1940, ceramic. Courtesy: San Diego Museum of Man

Groom Figure, half of wedding pair, 20th Century, Mahdya Pradesh, India, paper. Courtesy: Mingei International Museum of World Folk Art, San Diego

The workbench of Bay Area Violin maker David Gusset. Courtesy: San Francisco Folk Art Museum

"The Thinking Hand" (works on paper from the mid-1400s to the mid-1800s) and "17th-Century Dutch Painting," the ethnographic "Recent Japanese Prints" and "Elements of Design: Navaho Weaving"—and the contemporary—"Robert Brady Survey" and "Roger Hankins, Recent Works."

Trained docents provide informative tours for school children, special groups and the visiting public. A specially trained docent group brings "slide tours" out of the museum and into the classroom. Docents are also trained to accommodate visitors with special needs and interests such as senior citizens, the physically and mentally handicapped, the hearing impaired and the visually impaired.

SAN DIEGO

MINGEI INTERNATIONAL MUSEUM OF WORLD FOLK ART

4405 La Jolla Village Dr., Bldg. I-7, San Diego, CA 92112

Phone: (619) 453-5300 *Hours:* Tuesday-Saturday 11-5:30; Sunday 2-5; Friday 11-9 *Admission:* free

Through exhibitions and educational programs, the Mingei International Museum of World Folk Art furthers the understanding of the essential arts of people who share a direct simplicity and joy in making, by hand, articles both useful and satisfying to the human spirit. The Mingei's function is to locate, collect and document historical and contemporary world folk art through specialized exhibitions of broad universal and timely interest.

The museum was founded by potter and professor Martha Longenecker. In the 1950s, Longenecker had been impressed by the ideas of Dr. Soetsu Yanagi of Japan. Yanagi wanted to preserve the Japanese folk tradition and to prevent the atrophy that had happened to Western folk arts during the industrial revolution. In 1974, Longenecker founded the Mingei International Museum (Mingei is a combination of two Japanese words, "min" or all people and "gei" or art). Since 1978, the Mingei has been located in San Diego's University Towne Centre, a mall where developer Ernest Hahn donated space.

In its permanent collection, the Mingei International holds over 4,000 pieces of folk art. Among these are African masks, Ethiopian folk arts, clay pieces by Japanese ceramist Shoji Hamada, Chinese robes and burial garments, Korean Furniture, American rocking chairs, coverlets, and weathervanes, as well as Mexican and South American folk arts.

The three major exhibitions each year are supplemented with catalogs, postcards and posters as well as illustrated lectures, films and demonstrations. Some of the exhibitions that Mingei International has organized and presented include "Folk Toys of the World"; "The Folk Arts of Brazil"; "Wearable Folk Art"; "Rites of Passage"; "Mingei of Japan Known and Unknown"; "Early American Quilts and Weathervanes"; "The Eye of the Tiger," folk art of Korea; "Vivian Los Artesanos!," Mexican folk art from the collection of Fred and Barbara Meiers; "Village Ritual Arts of India"; and a Rumanian folk art exhibition.

MUSEUM OF PHOTOGRAPHIC ARTS

1649 El Prado, Balboa Park, San Diego, CA 92101

Phone: (619) 239-5262 *Hours:* Tuesday-Sunday 10-5; Thursday 10-9 *Admission:* $2.50; under 12 free; first Tuesday of each month free

Opened in 1983, the Museum of Photographic Arts collects and exhibits photography, film and video art. David Singer designed its 8,000 square feet of space (located within the Casa De Balboa, in Balboa Park), and its flexible walls and grid lighting systems allow the museum to break galleries into smaller spaces or open them up to accommodate major exhibitions.

Collections: As the museum is young, its collections are still small. It holds approximately 1,600 films, videos, daguerreotypes, and contemporary mixed-media works. Among those represented are Ansel Adams and Joel Meyerowitz.

Exhibitions: The museum presents eight or more thematic and one-person exhibitions each year. Recent shows include selections of works by Jacques-Henri Lartigue and Henri Cartier-Bresson; "Odyssey, The Art of Photography At National Geographic"; "Haiti: Revolution in Progress" and "That Was Then . . . This Is Now," a celebration of the 150th birthday of photography including the work of Jack Fulton and Misha Gordin and selections of Daguerreotypes and ambrotypes from the permanent collection. The museum is also deeply committed to video and schedules video installations on a regular basis.

Education: The museum has ongoing programs of docent tours, photo history classes, workshops, outreach to service organizations and schools, collaboration with local colleges and universities (providing internships and special tours for classes), and scholarly slide/lecture presentations by visiting photographers, curators, historians, critics and scientists.

SAN DIEGO MUSEUM OF MAN

1350 El Prado, Balboa Park, San Diego, CA 92101

Phone: (619) 239-2001 *Hours:* Monday-Sunday 10-4:30 *Admission:* $3; children 6-12 $.25

The San Diego Museum of Man presents exhibits which highlight the development of human culture from ancient to modern times and focus on the culture, arts and crafts of the Western Hemisphere, particularly those of California, the Southwest and Latin America.

The Museum traces its beginnings to San Diego's 1915 Panama-California Exhibition. At that time the Smithsonian Institution sent scientists around the world to collect artifacts and folklore for exhibits tracing the origins and cultures of man. The collection stayed in California and today the San Diego Museum of Man is located in Balboa Park's historic California Tower Building, the symbol of San Diego.

Collections: The focus of the permanent collections is on the folk arts of North, Central and South America. Particularly strong are the collections of Mexican and Indian clothing, especially pieces made in Oaxaca, Mexico. Other pieces include pottery, tonala pieces, trees of life and Talevera ceramics from the state of Pueblo.

Exhibitions: There is no permanent collection of fine arts but works of major award winning artists are frequently featured. Recent exhibitions include "Images of the Americas," by Everett G. Jackson, author and illustrator of fine books; "Jane Goodall's Chimpanzees of Gombe Stream," photographs taken by Hugo Van Lawick of the National Geographic Society; and "Treasure of Earth, Sea & Sky," a thematic exhibition of Southwest Indian jewelry by such noted artists as Harvey Begay, Joe and Rosey Cate, Christina Eustace and Victor Gabriel. In May of 1989, the museum presented "Paths Beyond Tradition: Contemporary American Indian Art," an exhibition featuring ten Indian artists including Richard Glazer-Danay, Robert Freeman and Virginia Stroud. Other exhibitions include papier-mâché sculpture by the Linares family of Mexico and the Rockefeller Collection of Mexican Folk Art. Upcoming exhibits include "Traditional Crafts of Saudi Arabia" and Russian lacquer boxes.

The Museum of Man also features works by young, emerging artists. Recently the Museum of Man mounted a show of oils, watercolors, paintings and bronze sculptures by Austin Deuel and Pat Waters depicting life in the rugged mountains of Baja, California.

Lectures and films are offered several times each month, with an ongoing educational program of classes in traditional arts and crafts.

SAN DIEGO HISTORICAL SOCIETY
Casa de Balboa, 1649 El Prado, Balboa Park, San Diego, CA 92101

Phone: (619) 232-6203 *Hours:* Wednesday-Sunday 10-4:30

The San Diego Historical Society was founded in 1928 to develop museums and research collections relating to the history of San Diego County. Today the Historical Society operates three museums: the Junipero Serra Museum; the Villa Montezuma Museum; and the Museum of San Diego History. A fourth, the George White and Anna Gunn Marston House Museum, will open in 1990 or 1991. The collections include over one million photographic images of the San Diego vicinity, constituting one of the largest local photographic resources in the country.

The Society's art collection contains over 700 pieces which cover the artistic development of San Diego from 1850 to the present, and help to interpret San Diego's role as an art center in the 1920s and 1930s. It holds paintings by Maurice Braun and Alfred Mitchell (the award winning *Cold Water Canyon*); two major bronze sculptures by Arthur Putnam; and several W.P.A. murals by Belle, Baranceanu, and Charles Reifle. In addition to paintings, sculpture, and graphic arts, the collection also contains archival material relating to the early artists of San Diego as well as examples of their tools, equipment, working drawings and models. The Society also publishes a quarterly journal which often includes articles on local art history.

Exhibitions: Aside from the permanent exhibit galleries, changing exhibits from the Society's reserve collections as well as nationally traveling shows are scheduled on a regular basis. Recent art exhibitions have included shows of work by the San Diego Watercolor Society (Serra Museum and Villa Montezuma), the Black Artists & Writers group (Villa Montezuma) and a retrospective with catalogue of Alfred R. Mitchell (1888-1972), the first artist of note to begin his career in San Diego (Museum of San Diego History). Exhibits scheduled for the future include a major international juried quilt exhibition, an exhibit of work by early San Diego sculptors and a retrospective of painter Charles Reiffel (1862- 1942).

SAN DIEGO MUSEUM OF ART
Balboa Park, P.O. Box 2107, San Diego, CA 92112

Phone: (619) 232-7931 *Hours:* Tuesday-Sunday 10-4:30 *Admission:* $5; seniors $4; military & students $3; children 6-12 $2; children under 5 free

The San Diego Museum of Art opened in 1926 and stands in the center of San Diego's Balboa Park. It occupies the largest building on the former site of the 1915-1916 Panama California Exposition. Its facade, designed by architects William Templeton Johnson and Robert W. Snyder is in the 16th century Plateresque style with intricate ornamentation resembling the lavish Renaissance and Moorish motifs found in Spanish silverwork.

Collections: The museum's holdings include renowned collections of Italian Renaissance art, work by Dutch and Spanish Baroque Old Masters, as well as comprehensive examples of American art, 20th-century painting and sculpture, 19th-century European painting and Asian art.

European paintings include a core of Spanish works by Cotan, El Greco, Goya and Zurbaran. Italian painting is represented by Signorelli's lunette for the Filippini Altarpiece, an early panel by Carlo Crivelli, the only undisputed Giorgione in America, and four vedutes by Canaletto, Bellotto and Guardi. Oil sketches by Rubens and Frans Hals and two flower pieces by Ruysch and Seghers highlight Dutch and Flemish collections. Nineteenth and 20th-century European art includes works by Ingres, Signac, Bouguereau, Daumier, Monet, Dufy, Vuillard, Toulouse-Lautrec, Matisse and Dubuffet. German expressionism is represented by fifteen works by Beckmann, Nolde, Mark and others.

American paintings include two pendant portraits by Ami Phillips, works by Durand, Innes, Bierstadt, and Cassatt, as well as pieces by Johnson, Eakins, Chase and Raphaele Peale. Twentieth-century paintings include works by Henry Sloan, Bellows, Dove, Davis, Benton, Frank Stella and O'Keeffe. The museum also holds a small group of Latin American works by Rivera, Tamayo and Zuniga.

Works on paper include more than 100 Toulouse-Lautrec graphics and watercolors by Nolde, Franz Marc, Klee, Grosz, Burchfield, Marin, Demuth, Sheeler, Homer and Cassatt.

The Marcy Sculpture Garden contains modern sculpture by Henry Moore, Barbara Hepworth, Joan Miro, Alexander Calder, Marino Marini and David Smith.

The Asian collections are among the most important and beautiful possessed by the museum and are comprehensive in their explication of Chinese, Japanese, Indian, Korean and southeast Asian decorative arts and sculpture. Chinese objects include earthenware vessels from the neolithic Yang Shao culture and Shang Dynasty; Sung dynasty stoneware and pottery figurines; archaic jade, pottery and bronze objects; fine decorative lacquerware, cloissone, ivory and rhinocerous horn objects; and porcelain vessels and figurines. Japanese objects include painted scrolls, a pair of early 16th-century wooden sculptures of Shinto guardian deities, and several examples of finely crafted ceremonial swords and swordguards. Also especially notable is the collection of 1,200 Indian, Persian, and Turkish miniatures, circa 1300-1650.

Exhibitions: The museum presents continuing series of one-person and thematic exhibitions. Recent shows include "The Latin American Spirit: Art and Artists in The United States, 1920-1970"; "Li Huai: An Artist in

Two Cultures"; and "Joaquin Sorolla: Painter of Light."

Education: Education programs include art and craft classes for children and adults, the Balboa Lectures, adult travel programs and gallery tours.

TIMKEN ART GALLERY
Balboa Park, San Diego, CA 92101

Phone: (619) 239-5548 *Hours:* Tuesday-Saturday 10-4:30; Sunday 1:30-4:30 Closed September, July 4, Christmas, New Year's Day *Admission:* free

The gallery prides itself on being a "Jewel Box" of fine paintings and the large and rare collection of Russian icons in its collection is reputed to be the finest in the United States. The icons on exhibition date from the 15th through the 19th centuries and attract connoisseurs from all over the world.

The remainder of the gallery is devoted to the paintings of Old European Masters from the 13th through the 19th centuries and consists of works by Rembrandt, Rubens, Corot, Pieter Brueghel the Elder, Boucher, David Murillo, Hals, Carlevaris, Salvaldo and many others.

An American Room houses works by American artists of the 18th and 19th centuries and counts among its artists Fitz Hugh Lane, Eastman Johnson, Cropsey and Copley.

The construction of the gallery allows all the fine works of art to be shown with natural light without deterioration of the paintings; the generous use of Travertine marble and bronze in the architecture, both inside and out, lends an atmosphere of calm and serenity for peaceful viewing of the masterpieces on display.

There are no scheduled special shows or exhibitions.

UNIVERSITY ART GALLERY, SAN DIEGO STATE UNIVERSITY
San Diego, CA 92182-0214

Phone: (619) 594-5171 *Hours:* Monday, Thursday, Saturday 12-4; Tuesday, Wednesday 10-4 *Admission:* free

The University Art Gallery of San Diego State University is located in the Department of Art and housed in a building with over 2,700 square feet of exhibition space.

The emphasis of the program is on exhibitions of works by national and international artists. Six exhibitions are presented each academic year (September through May). Recently the gallery presented "Matt Mullican: Untitled 1986/87";"Josef Mueller-Brockmann: Posters 1948-1981"; "Noriyuki Haraguchi: Present Moments"; and "The Sculptural Stage: John Frame and Jim Lawrence."

Catalogues and brochures often accompany exhibitions as do lectures, symposia and curator walk-throughs.

There is a small study collection of pre-Columbian art.

SAN FRANCISCO

ASIAN ART MUSEUM OF SAN FRANCISCO, THE AVERY BRUNDAGE COLLECTION
Golden Gate Park, San Francisco, CA 94118

Phone: (415) 668-8921 *Hours:* Wednesday-Sunday 10-5; first Wednesday of each month 10-8:45 *Admission:* $4; 12-17 and over 65 $2; under 12 free; first Wednesday and Saturday morning of each month free

The genesis of the Asian Art Museum came in 1959 when Chicago millionaire Avery Brundage donated his vast collection of Asian Art to the City of San Francisco on the condition that the City build a museum to house it. Voters overwhelmingly passed a bond issue for that purpose in the early 1960s and The Asian Art Museum, Avery Brundage Collection officially opened its doors in June of 1966.

The museum is run by a 27-member Asian Art Commission whose stated intent is to make the Asian Art Museum the "major center for the study of Asian art and culture in the Western world." Today the Asian Art Museum is an independent institution with its own staff and budget.

Collections: Although the collections have been bolstered by gifts and energetic acquisitions, Brundage's gift still represents over eighty percent of the museum's holdings. Brundage amassed his collection for nearly forty years and the pieces in it are characterized by diversity and quality. As one specialist put it, "Acquisition of the collection gave San Francisco at one stroke international distinction in the museum world and a rich, varied source for research, study, and appreciation of Oriental civilizations."

The museum holds almost 12,000 sculptures, paintings, bronzes, ceramics, jades, architectural elements and decorative objects spanning 6,000 years of history and forty countries on the continent of Asia. It maintains departments of Chinese Art, Indian and Himalayan Art, Southeast Asian Art, and Japanese Art. Its Chinese jades are among the best in the world and it holds the oldest known dated Chinese Buddha image (A.D. 338); the largest collection of Gandharan sculpture in North America; and the largest museum collection of Japanese netsuke and inro in the U.S.

Exhibitions: The exhibits are arranged chronologically and grouped in a manner which emphasizes stylistic evolution as well as sociopolitical characteristics. Nearly half of the museum's collection consists of objects of Chinese origin, and this is reflected in the general permanent layout of its displays. The first floor is devoted to China; the second floor is divided among the arts of India, Tibet, and the Himalayas, Korea, Japan, and Southeast Asia. Also of particular interest is the Leventritt Collection of Chinese blue-and-white porcelains.

Due to space limitations, only about fifteen percent of the museum's collections are on display at any one time, though the Jewett Gallery is devoted to a rotating exhibition of objects from the permanent collection, based on a theme.

Once or twice each year, the museum presents exhibitions of outstanding works of art from other museums or private collections. The museum also frequently organizes exhibitions from its own collections to travel throughout the United States and to other parts of the world.

Research: The museum maintains fully equipped conservation and photography laboratories and a 12,000-volume library whose holdings, besides books and periodicals, include collections of photographs, microfilms, and slides.

Maps and charts supplement individual labels, and numerous books and brochures dealing with various aspects of the Avery Brundage Collection are available at the Museum Shop which adjoins the Museum.

Education: The Asian Art Museum also fosters increasing public awareness of the museum's resources as an important cultural bridge between the East and West through lectures, demonstrations, school tours, film and concert series, free docent tours of the galleries, and other civic activities.

CALIFORNIA ACADEMY OF SCIENCES
Golden Gate Park, San Francisco, CA 94118

Phone: (415) 221-5100 *Hours:* 10-5 every day of the year *Admission:* \$4; 12-17 \$2; children 6-11 \$1; 5 and under free

Founded in the middle of the last century with the purpose of cataloging California's living heritage, the California Academy of Sciences is now one of the leading natural history museums worldwide.

Collections: The academy holds over 13.9 million specimens almost all of which are scientific. Its well stocked departments include Anthropology, Aquatic Biology, Botany, Entomology, Herpetology, Ichthyology, Invertebrate Zoology and Geology, and Ornithology and Mammalogy.

Exhibitions: The majority of exhibitions are permanent halls of science. The academy is completely renovating and updating its seventy-year-old North American Hall to reflect current scientific information. It is installing state-of-the-art display techniques and electronics as means of conveying the beauty of nature and messages of science. In early 1990 Life Through Time, another great hall, will open its display of fossil history. Other display halls include: the Hohfeld Earth and Space Hall (with the "Safequake," a feet-on experience) and the upgraded African Waterhole, where visitors listen to the sounds of day and night in the African Veld.

Art exhibitions are normally wildlife-related. In 1989 the academy presented wildlife illustrations by dioramist Pedro Gonzalez and photographs of vanishing California wildlife by Susan Middleton.

Steinhart Aquarium: The Steinhart Aquarium's Living Coral Reef exhibit successfully integrates most of the coral reef community. Living corals, sharks, butterfly fishes, dolphins, and numerous invertebrates live together in a captive environment.

Morrison Planetarium: The planetarium's 65-foot dome accommodates over 176,000 visitors a year. Shows such as "Mars!," "Cosmic Limits," "Stars Over San Francisco," and "Beyond the Milky Way" bring visitors closer to the skies.

The academy also presents a series of biennial scientific symposia on topics of importance and publishes the periodical *Pacific Discovery.*

CALIFORNIA HISTORICAL SOCIETY
2090 Jackson St., San Francisco, CA 94109

Phone: (415) 567-1848 *Hours:* temporarily closed at press time; call for hours

Organized in 1871, the California Historical Society collects, preserves, interprets, and disseminates information about the history of California. Until sudden financial problems hit the Society in 1989, its historic properties, library, manuscript, and photograph collections, as well as fine arts and decorative arts collections were an asset to the community. Today the collections are temporarily closed and options such as the sale of the Whittier Mansion (the main facility) are being considered as financial solutions.

Collections: The Whittier Mansion's fine arts collections include oil paintings, watercolors, drawings, prints, and letter sheets depicting California topics or executed by California artists. The focus of the collections is on the late 19th and early 20th centuries. Among 19th century painters represented are Bierstadt, Thomas Hill, William Keyes, Samuel Marsden Brooks, and Virgil Williams. The collection of rare 19th century lithographs includes historical and fine arts works by Currier and Ives, Boske, Jump, and Crucial and Ray. The permanent collections also include watercolors by McIntree, Lampsen and James Madison Alden and paintings from the 1920s by Theodore Wores, Thadeus Welch and James Walker.

Among other holdings are extensive photography collections which, though in the majority documentary, do include work by Watkins, Ansel Adams and Minor White; a decorative arts collection including costumes, silver, china and other three-dimensional artifacts from historical California; and a library collection which ranges chronologically from 1576 to the present and covers all fifty-eight counties of California. The materials in the library collection include 40,000 volumes on California history and a rich variety of rare books, manuscripts, photographs, newspapers, posters and ephemera.

Before the financial crisis the California Historical Society's exhibition program was quite extensive. The emphasis was on historical subjects such as the recent "Historical American Building Survey."

The society also operates a historic site in San Marino, as well as a history center on Wilshire Boulevard in Los Angeles.

CALIFORNIA PALACE OF THE LEGION OF HONOR
Lincoln Park, San Francisco, CA 94121

Phone: (415) 750-3614 *Hours:* Wednesday-Sunday 10-5 *Admission:* \$4; Seniors & Students 12-17 \$2; under 12 free

The California Palace of the Legion of Honor is San Francisco's museum of European Art. The Palace was originally presented to the City and County of San Francisco by Mr. and Mrs. Adolph B. Spreckels as a museum of painting and sculpture dedicated to the memory of California soldiers who died in World War I. It is located on a hilltop in Lincoln Park and overlooks the Golden Gate bridge to the north and the city to the east. Architecturally, the building is based on the Palace of the Legion of Honor in Paris, built in 1786 by Pierre Rousseau. The style is French Classical of the Louis XVI period.

In 1972 the administrations of the California Palace of the Legion of Honor and the M.H. de Young Memorial Museum were officially joined to form The Fine Arts Museums of San Francisco. The Museums are governed by a self-perpetuating Board of Trustees and operated as a department of the City and County of San Francisco. Both buildings are administered by a single staff, a situation that is very unusual in the United States.

Collections: The California Palace of the Legion of Honor was originally San Francisco's all French museum, but in the late 1980s it and its sister institution the M.H. de Young Memorial Museum underwent extensive reorganization and renovation. Today the California Palace of the Legion of Honor features paintings, sculpture, and decorative arts which illustrate the chronological development of European art from the medieval period through the beginning of the 20th century. The integration of paintings with decorative art and sculpture, and the juxtaposition of national schools within certain historical frameworks creates a contextural progression through which visitors can appreciate the interrelationships of European cultures and art forms.

Medieval Art: Monumental religious sculpture from the medieval period as well as liturgical objects and stained glass are displayed together with a rotating selection of rare and important tapestries. Works from several different countries are included, mostly of Gothic and late Gothic origins, showing the continuities of style that united the various national traditions and art forms.

The Renaissance in Germany and the Low Countries: A rich presentation of German and Dutch panel paintings, stained glass, and limewood sculpture show the enduring Gothicism of art in northern Europe, infused with new humanism and heightened realism. Several panels actually executed in Spain—two commissioned by Ferdinand and Isabella—are exhibited in this context, as they are indebted stylistically to the art of the Netherlands. Particularly notable is *Virgin and Child* by Dieric Bouts. The intense linear energy of such works is equally apparent in contemporaneous sculptures including the limewood *Lamentation* by a follower of Tilman Riemenschneider and the two large Franconian saints in the style of Hans Backhoffen.

Italian Art of the 14th and 15th Centuries: The museum's collection of early Italian goldground paintings is quite notable, and most are in exceptional condition. Examples from the 14th and 15th centuries, including works by Ugolino da Siena and Fra Angelico, illustrate the development toward increasing naturalism characteristic of Italian art in the major artistic centers during these two centuries. The smallest of these paintings are exhibited as precious objects in free-standing vitrines, while the large panels are displayed in conjunction with a 15th-century sculpture from the workshop of Verrocchio.

The Renaissance in France: Two sets of stained glass window panels, Limoges enamels, and an imposing Saint Porchaire standing saltcellar illustrate the continuing dependence of the School of Fontainebleau on Italian sources during the reigns of Louis XII, Francois I, Henri II, and Henri IV. Bergundian furniture of the period shows the elegant style that remained purely French. The cold, refined sensuousness of Fontainebleau painting is also well represented through two beautiful and rare examples. Tapestries woven in Flanders but expressive of international mannerist tendencies and French influence are also exhibited on a rotating basis.

Italian and Spanish Art of the 16th Century: Florentine and Milanese paintings as well as Venetian paintings by Titian and Tintoretto, juxtaposed with bronzes by Giambologna and his north Italian contemporaries, offer a cross section of High Renaissance and mannerist art as it was interpreted in the artistic centers of Italy. A marble bust of Cosimo I by Benvenuto Cellini and his workshop serves as the focus of this gallery, together with large altarpieces by Raffaillino del Garbo and Cesare da Sesto. Two superb paintings by El Greco show a direct linkage between 16th century Venetian painting and El Greco's unique mannerist style.

17th Century Art in Italy and France: Included in this collection are extraordinary works by such artists as Mattia Preti, Guercino, Baciccio, Giovanni Battista Tiepolo, de La Tour, and Le Nain. This collection illustrates the multifaceted interests of Italian and French artists during the Counter-Reformation and the 18th century. The newly acquired and newly restored Salvator Rosa, a fine example of the pictorial drama inherent in the art of this period, is included. Models for monumental sculpture, such as a rare large wax for an equestrian monument of Charles III by Solari and a terracotta by Angelo de Rossi for his tomb of Alexander VIII in St. Peter's, are featured. A marble portrait of Maffeo Barberini by Lorenzo Ottoni exemplifies the exuberant style of late baroque Rome. The large *Hercules and Atlas* by Anguier shows the impact of Italian baroque sculpture in France.

17th Century Dutch and Flemish Art: One of the most outstanding areas within the collection is Dutch and Flemish painting of the 17th century. Large-scale works by such masters as Jordaens, Stomer, and Rubens illustrate the northern interpretation of baroque tendencies originating in Italy. Small cabinet-size paintings demonstrate the talent and wide interests of such masters as Ter Borch, de Hooch, and Steen. Works by Rembrandt and his school, Hals, Salomon van Ruysdael and others emphasize the strength and depth of holdings in the field. Decorative arts by northern artists of the period include several sculptures and a selection of German Silver.

French Art of the 18th Century: This collection takes up four galleries. The intimate size of Gallery 7 sets off important small-scale cabinet pictures, including three works by Fragonard and Watteau's *The Foursome* and *The Fortune Teller*. A selection of French furniture by the most noted makers of the period is exhibited in conjunction with ormolu-mounted oriental porcelain and an important garniture of Sevres vases, illustrating the unique integration of the decorative style into the arts. A group of intimate paintings by Boucher, Vallayer-Coster and others round out the presentation.

Gallery 7a contains a French salon from the Hotel d'Humieres, Paris. This period room, dating from circa 1770-80, consists of white and gold boiserie, and exhibits furniture and decorative arts in the Louis XVI style. Featured are a bust of Voltaire by Houdon, a commode by Martin Carlin, and important furniture made by Foliot and Jacob for Versailles.

A cross-section of Louis XV and Louis XVI furniture illustrates the variety of forms and styles of marquetry developed during this rich and innovative period. Also displayed are a selection of French 18th century silver and a group of French tapestries, including three from a series made at Beauvais.

In the collection of large scale French paintings of the 18th century are portraits by Nattier, still lifes by Oudry and Huet, and Boucher's large tapestry design of *Vertumnus and Pomona*. These are seen with a large, recently cleaned limestone sculpture by Dupont, all exhibiting a confidence of scale and expressive esprit typical of the period.

Neoclassical Art: The classical simplicity and austerity of the objects in this collection contrast markedly with the curvilinear and more flowing forms seen in 18th century art. French paintings by David, Greuze, and Gerard are presented with late sculptures by Houdon and Canova, and with an important collection of Napoleonic silver by Auguste and Biennais. The dissemination of the classical spirit through Europe is also represented by a secretary safe by Moschini made for Marie Louise in Parma and a late 19th century table by Faberge.

Rodin: The famous Spreckels collection of bronze, marble, and plaster sculpture features prominently in the collection. In the grand spaces of Gallery 10, monumental works such as the *Age of Bronze* and *St. John the Baptist Preaching* are shown along with a huge bronze vase by Gustave Dore. Works of Rodin continue a formal axis begun outside with the *Three Shades* and *The Thinker.*

19th Century European Art: The museum's strong collection of 19th-century art includes many artists of different nationalities and stylistic directions. Academic realist, impressionist, and post-impressionist trends are all represented. Well-known works by Corot, Courbet, Bouguereau, Manet, Monet, Renoir, Degas, Seurat, and Cezanne, among others, suggest to the viewer the complex and rich evolution of 19th century French painting. To these are added major works by non-French artists, such as Segantini's *Springtime in the Alps,* giving a continental orientation to the display.

Exhibitions: The California Palace of the Legion of Honor also has an active schedule of special exhibitions. Among those scheduled for 1989 were an exhibition of watercolors by the 19th-century French artist Francois-Marius Granet: "Holy Space: Icons and Frescoes from Greece" and "Rage, Power, and Fulfillment: The Male Journey in Japanese Prints."

M. H. DE YOUNG MEMORIAL MUSEUM
Golden Gate Park, San Francisco, CA 94118

Phone: (415) 750-3600 *Hours:* Wednesday-Sunday 10-5 *Admission:* $4; Seniors and 12-17 free; under 12 free; first Wednesday of each month and first Saturday morning of each month from 10-12 free

Located in San Francisco's Golden Gate Park, the M. H. de Young Museum is San Francisco's museum of American art.

History: The de Young had its origin in the California Midwinter International Exposition of 1894. At the end of the exposition, the Fine Arts Building, along with surplus funds, was turned over to M. H. de Young, a newspaper publisher who had served as Director-General of the Exposition, for the purpose of establishing a permanent museum. Some of the fair's exhibits were acquired as a nucleus of a collection. Other donations followed, particularly from Mr. de Young himself, who also provided a temporary income to be used for acquisitions. Additional buildings were erected with funds given by Mr. de Young and other citizens. In 1921, upon completion of these buildings, the original name "Memorial Museum," which commemorated the Midwinter Exposition, was changed to the present name in honor of the Museum's benefactor.

In 1972 the administration of the de Young and the California Palace of the Legion of Honor were officially joined to form the Fine Arts Museums of San Francisco. The museums are governed by a self-perpetuating Board of Trustees and operated as a department of the City and County of San Francisco.

In 1988 and 1989 both museums underwent the first phase of extensive renovation. Under the design of Edmund Dickenson, the de Young unveiled 15 new galleries featuring one of the country's finest collections of American art—from colonial times into the 20th century. Subsequent phases of collection reorganization will include further expansion of the American art galleries and new presentations of the de Young's other significant holdings in textiles, ancient art, British art from the 16th through 19th centuries, and the arts of Africa Oceania, and the Americas.

Collections and Exhibitions: Painting, sculpture and decorative arts are combined in each of the galleries to provide visitors with an integrated view of the artistic achievements of the times. The quality and scope of the works in the American collection offers visitors a comprehensive overview of the country's visual cultural heritage.

The Hearst Court, which first welcomes visitors as they enter the de Young, features a special display of decorative and narrative paintings from Bay Area collections including the special loan of Maxfield Parrish's *The Pied Piper.* The hall cases surrounding Hearst Court display a survey of American silver including presentation pieces such as the gilt and jeweled sword presented to General Funston, and American glass—from early free-blown objects to iridescent works by Louis Comfort Tiffany, and later works by Frederick Carder for Steuben.

The first gallery contains American 17th and 18th century painting and decorative arts. *The Mason Children* of 1670, attributed to the Freake-Gibbs Painter, is the oldest American painting in the collection. Portraits from 18th century Boston and Philadelphia—including major examples by John Smibert, Robert Feke, John Singleton Cople, Charles Wilson Peale, William Benbridge, and Joseph Wright—trace the development of American art from its beginning to the years just after the War of Independence. Decorative arts of the period, including significant objects not previously on display—a Pennsylvania "kas" and a Chippendale chest-on-chest—reveal high points of American craft practices while tracing chronological development and revealing regional styles.

Recent acquisitions of Maryland furniture from the collection of Mr. and Mrs. H. McCoy Jones now augment the display of Federal period material. Drawn in many instances from the family collection of the 18th-century statesman and diplomat William Pinkney, these elegant and handsome objects form a major addition to the decorative arts collection. During the Federal period portraiture remained the staple of American paintings—attested to with examples by Gilbert Stuart and Washington Allston—but the early 19th century brought a variety of new styles. Historic paintings by William Birch and Thomas Doughty, seascapes by Robert Salmon, and a still life by James Peale, testify to this greater diversity. The museum's collection of furniture and silver of the period possesses light profiles and classically derived ornaments.

The de Young's collection of mid-19th century American marble sculpture includes works by many of the period's most notable names: Powers, Story, Randolph Rogers, Franklin Simmons, and James Henry Haseltine, artists who trained and, in many cases, spent their active lives in Rome. The new installation provides the first opportunity to see the collections gathered together within the permanent collections.

The deliberately simple and plain works of the Shakers—elegant syntheses of form and function—stand as polar opposites to the cosmopolitanism of the Roman marbles. The museum's Shaker objects are shown with some of the finest folk paintings, many of them donated by William and Bernice Chrysler Garbish.

The de Young has a wide collection of mid-19th century landscape paintings. Within one gallery is a full overview of the artists' exploration of this country and their journeys to the tropics, the arctic and Europe. Beginning the museum's survey are works by Thomas Cole, Jasper F. Cropsey, Sanford Gifford, and John Kensett. A highlight of the collection is Frederic Church's monumental *Rainy Season in the Tropics*. One key painter in this history, Albert Bierstadt, is richly represented, with examples spanning his full career. Decorative arts in the same gallery demonstrates the remarkable design and technological achievement of John Henry Belter, as well as the ornate rosewood furniture of Belter's New York rival, Joseph Meeks and Sons.

The bronze sculptors of the later 19th century—Augustus Saint Gaudens, Frederick MacMonnies, and others—trained or active in France are exhibited together for the first time. The Museum also possesses an extensive collection of works by the gifted animalier Arthur Putnam.

Perhaps the greatest strength of the museum's American painting collection is an extraordinary group of trompe l'oeil and still-life works from the turn of the century, including the masterworks of William M. Harnett, John F. Peto and Alexander Pope, and excellent examples by their colleagues. For the the first time since the American galleries opened in 1977, these magical paintings have space to work their individual spells, blurring the boundaries of illusion and reality. Juxtaposed with these well known examples are still lifes by George Lambdin and Martin J. Heade, and California artists Edward Deakin, Samuel Marsden Brookes and Thomas Hill.

In another gallery genre paintings such as George Caleb Bingham's *Boatmen on the Missouri*, and *The Country Politicians*, simultaneously glory in the life of the people and comment on the serious issues of the artist's time. Works by Thomas Eakins and his student Thomas Anshutz reveal the somber character that dominated much art at the end of the 19th century. Anshutz's *The Ironworkers' Noontime* is a masterpiece and an icon of American art. Paintings by William Page, John Quidor, Albert Pinkham Ryder and Elihu Vedder suggest the darker, more romantic aspiration of these narrative painters.

A survey of the museum's collection of 20th-century art begins with works by The Eight—among them Robert Henri, William Glackens, Everett Shinn, and Maurice Pendergast—and others who often portrayed their urban and suburban subjects with a loose and free brushstroke. Edwin Dickinson's masterful *The Cello Player* reflects his assimilation of modern European trends while regionalist masterpieces by Thomas Hart Benton and Grant Wood clearly reject avant-garde tendencies. A strong group of later surrealist paintings by Yves Tanguy, Kay Sage, and Charles Howard are displayed for the first time in many years. Also included are even more recent works by Wayne Thiebaud, Fairfield Porter, and others. Works by Herbert Haseltine, Gaston Lachaise, Boris Lovet-Lorski, and Isamu Noguchi provide a complementary survey of 20th-century sculpture.

Another gallery serves as the temporary home of works by the American expatriates Mary Cassatt, John Singer Sargent and James McNeill Whistler, whose magnificently quirky *The Gold Scab* stands out in the collection. These works join paintings by the American impressionists and tonalists Willard Metcalf, Childe Hassam, John Twachtman and Thomas Wilmer Dewing, objects designed by Frank Lloyd Wright, Gustave Stickley and Harvey Ellis, and the pattern-oriented paintings of Arthur Mathews and Herman Dudley Murphey.

Among other collections there is a strong showing of traditional arts of Africa, Oceania, and the Americas, and a fine selection of British art of the 16th through 19th centuries. The collection of tribal rugs from Central Asia is one of the most comprehensive in America, and there is a fine display of ancient arts of Egypt, Greece, and Rome.

Among recent changing exhibitions are "New Look to Now: French Haute Couture 1947-1987" and "American Paintings from the Manoogian Collection."

THE EXPLORATORIUM
3601 Lyon St., San Francisco, CA 94123

Phone: (415) 561-0360 *Hours:* Wednesday 1-9:30; Thursday & Friday 1-5; Weekends 10-5 *Admission:* $5; Seniors $2.50; Children 6-17 $1; under 6 free; first Wednesday of each month and every Wednesday after 6 free

The Exploratorium is a museum of science, art and human perception. It employs the work of both artists and scientists, because both in their way describe nature and culture.

On the museum floor art works are interspersed with more didactic exhibits. The art works that are shown are pieces that make subtle connections between art and science and which generally involve natural phenomena in some way.

In addition, the Performing Artists-in-Residence Program provides a place where artists can receive technical assistance and reinforcement for their ideas. The Exploratorium is interested in helping to develop the work of both younger and more established artists. In general, those who share common interests with The Exploratorium are encouraged to submit proposals. Past artists-in-residence have included Doug Hollis, Brian Eno, video artist Ed Tannenbaum and pneumatic artist Chico MacMurtrie.

In the temporary gallery at the rear of the facility, The Exploratorium presents a variety of changing exhibits. Recent exhibitions have included the cartoons of Sidney Harris, the fiber-optic-like sculpture of Milton Komisar, and a large photographic exhibition, "Capturing Light," which also involved interactive scientific exhibits.

Education: The Exploratorium runs a number of programs designed to teach teachers more interactive ways of teaching science.

THE FINE ARTS MUSEUMS OF SAN FRANCISCO
(See California Palace of the Legion of Honor and de Young Memorial Museum)

THE FRIENDS OF PHOTOGRAPHY
250 Fourth St., San Francisco, CA 94103

Phone: (415) 495-7000 *Hours & Admission:* Not available at press time

In 1967, a group of Carmel-area photographers, including Ansel Adams, formed The Friends of Photography, a collection, gallery, and artist member

Thomas P. Anshutz, *The Ironworker's Noontime, 1881,* 17 x 24, oil on canvas. Courtesy: Fine Arts Museums of San Francisco

Sir Thomas Lawrence, *Pinkie (Sarah Barrett Moulton), 1794,* oil on canvas. Courtesy: Huntington Art Collections, San Marino

Facial Marriage Tatoos, India. Courtesy: Tattoo Art Museum, San Francisco

organization. In 1987, The Friends closed its gallery and began searching for a new home in San Francisco. At the same time it continued an active program of publications and member service. It was not until September of 1989 that the gallery reopened on the first floor of a renovated building in San Francisco's South of Market area. The new facility contains five galleries with an education center, offices, a library, and an auditorium to follow as other floors become available.

Of the five galleries, one is devoted to rotating exhibitions of The Friends' collection of Ansel Adams photographs. Another is devoted to exhibitions of photographs by Bay Area photographers, and the final three are devoted to traveling shows and more major exhibitions.

Recent and future exhibitions include "Nature and Culture: Conflict and Reconciliation in Recent Photography"; "The Legacy of of Ansel Adams"; and "Tracings of Light: Sir John Herschel and the Camera Lucida."

The Friends of Photography presents workshops covering general interests in photography as well as related specialized fields such as history, criticism, and the teaching of photography. These workshops are structured to provide nontraditional, educational forums to students desiring short-term, high-level instruction.

Note: Museum hours and admission fees were not set at press time. Call in advance for information.

THE MEXICAN MUSEUM
Fort Mason Center, Bldg. D, San Francisco, CA 94123

Phone: (415) 441-0404 *Hours:* Wednesday-Sunday 12-5 *Admission:* $2; Seniors, Students, and Children over 10 $1; Under 10 free; first Wednesday free

Founded in 1975, The Mexican Museum collects, conserves, exhibits and interprets works of art created by Mexican peoples from antiquity to the present.

The museum occupies 20,000 square feet in San Francisco's Fort Mason Center. Its brightly lit gallery space has fourteen-foot ceilings and track lighting.

The museum's collections include over 10,000 objects, many of which were gifts of Mexican folk art from the collection of Nelson Rockefeller.

The Exhibition program consists of five rotating exhibitions from the permanent collections, and changing exhibitions of works either from the permanent collections or pieces on loan from artists. The rotating exhibitions include pre-Hispanic, colonial, folk, and Mexican fine arts and Mexican-American fine arts.

A primary goal of the exhibition program is to maintain an informal balance between contemporary and historic areas of emphasis. Recent changing exhibitions have included "Colonial and Popular Religious Art of Mexico," an exhibition of votive paintings, religious statuary, furniture, and decorative artifacts from the museum's permanent collections; "Cajas: Containers of Remembrance and Belief," works by Cristina Emmanuel, Frank Lopez-Motnyk, and Patricia Rodriguez; and one-person exhibitions by painter and printmaker Carmen Lomas Garza. The museum also seeks to promote and involve contemporary living artists in all levels of museum programs and activities.

The Mexican Museum's programming likewise aims at "fostering an awareness and appreciation of the artistic and cultural heritage of the Mexican people." Educational activities form an important part of its work, both at the building itself and through various outreach programs available to schools and community groups. Each year the museum presents cultural and historic events such as "El Dia de los Muertos," "Cacimientos," and "Cinco de Mayo."

MUSEO ITALOAMERICANO
Fort Mason Center, San Francisco, CA 94123

Phone: (415) 673-2200 *Hours:* Wednesday-Sunday 12-5 *Admission:* free

The Museo ItaloAmericano presents Italian cultural programming and is devoted to the research, preservation and display of works of by Italian-American artists.

The first of its kind in the United States, the museum is located in a new facility at San Francisco's non-profit development, Fort Mason Center. It has 5,000 square feet of space and holds two galleries, a library and a gift shop.

In the Museo ItaloAmericano's collection are important examples of painting and sculpture by such well-known Italian Americans as Mark Di Suvero, Arnaldo Pomodoro, Emilio Vedova, Tom Marioni, Emilio Tadini, Rico Lebrun, Giuseppe Cadenasso, Beniamino Bufano, Nino Longobardi, David Bottini, Amintore Fanfani, and Oliver Gagliani.

Exhibitions are not restricted to showing painting and sculpture, but are intended to bring to public attention worthy works of architecture, photography, and fashion and industrial design. Recently the museum has presented one-person exhibitions by the late artist, Lucio Fontana; painter Francesco Clemente; painter on sculpted surface Charles Arnoldi; and photographer Oliver Gagliani. In addition the Museo Italo-Americano encourages contemporary work by emerging artists. In its yearly emerging artist exhibition it has brought to attention several young artists of Italian background including Mary Parisi, Bruce Hasson, Frank Damiano, Jan Gaglione, Michael Pedroni, and Tony Ligamari.

Programming: The Museo ItaloAmericano has an active schedule of programming emphasizing Italian culture. It offers several levels of Italian language classes and there is an ongoing lecture series on Italian culture and history. An ongoing *conversazione* allows members to discuss in Italian and a program called "Food as Culture" brings interested museum members to watch the chefs at local Italian restaurants.

MUSEUM OF MODERN MYTHOLOGY
693 Mission St., Suite 900, San Francisco, CA 94105

Phone: (415) 546-0202 *Hours:* Wednesday-Sunday 12-5 *Admission:* $2; students and seniors $1.50; children 6-12; under 6 free

The Museum of Modern Mythology, founded in 1982, is the world's only museum dedicated to the collection, preservation, documentation and interpretation of American advertising characters and other mass media phenomena of the 20th century.

The museum's founders, Ellen Havre Weiss, Mathew Cohen and Jeffrey Erick, believe that advertising icons and campaigns are the modern equivalents of ancient gods and myths, and that advertising icons will enter the modern subconscious in the same way ancient myths entered the minds of ancient peoples.

The museum's collection includes over 3,000 artifacts and icons, both national and regional. The Poppin' Fresh Doughboy, Charlie the Tuna, "Bibendum," the Michelin Tire man, Aunt Jemima, an eight-foot Jolly Green Giant, a ten-foot Doggie Diner head, and Chicken Boy, a 22-foot high representation of a chicken-headed youth, are all there, as are collections of cloth and vinyl dolls, print ads, point-of-purchase displays and other promotional artifacts.

Recent exhibitions include "100% Polyester: Shirts of Art from the Palette of Science," more than 200 polyester shirts of the 1970s from the collection of Jeff Erick.

Each month resident oral historian Bertram Minkin is featured in two performance series, *The Polyester Man* and the *Myth of the Month Club: Holiday Happenings*.

In the summer of 1989, the museum moved from a four room suite on the ninth floor of a building at 3rd and Mission to a much larger 2,000-square-foot space on the ground floor of the same downtown facility. With the new location the museum plans to install a video theatre, expand its gift shop, institute innovative special programs and events, and to display many large works that have been in storage.

SAN FRANCISCO ART INSTITUTE

800 Chestnut St., San Francisco, CA 94133

Phone: (415) 771-7020 *Hours:* Tuesday-Saturday 10-5 *Admission:* free

Established in 1871, the San Francisco Art Institute is the oldest center for the visual arts in the western United States. It is a privately supported fine arts college that also provides educational and cultural programs for the San Francisco public and its visitors.

Throughout its development, the San Francisco Art Institute has kept pace with contemporary interests in art. It was a center for the Bay Area figurative movement in the late 1940s. In the 1950s, its photography department was founded by Ansel Adams and Minor White. Also, in the 1950s and 1960s, its distinct film program evolved from the California funk movement. And in the 1970s, it created the nation's first performance video department. Today, it remains at the forefront of artistic trends.

The Institute has inhabited its present Chestnut Street location since 1926. In 1969, a new wing was added, with the Emanuel Walter Gallery on the lower floors and the Atholl McBean Gallery on the upper.

Collections: The institute's permanent collections are small but include Diego Rivera's *The Making of a Fresco Showing the Building of a City* which the artist painted on a gallery space wall in 1931. Other pieces in the collection have come through a variety of bequests and gifts.

Exhibitions: For over a century, professional artists from the community have been involved with the institute, the development of its programs and the achievement of its goals. Currently, a group of thirty-six Bay Area artists form the Artists Committee and serve to advise the Art Institute on the needs and interests of the art community as well as the development of its exhibitions program. The institute has two galleries where it presents continuing series of changing exhibitions.

The Diego Rivera Gallery is student run and holds exhibitions of student works. The Walter/McBean Gallery exhibits the contemporary fine arts with an emphasis on experimental work and art in non-traditional media. The exhibitions program is both international and regional in scope. With rare exceptions, exhibitions are conceived and organized by the Art Institute itself. Exhibited work is often made on-site or presented on-site by performance artists. Among recent exhibitions were "Robin Winters: A Month in San Francisco" (performance art and street works); "Nancy Buchanan–50s/80s: Return of Style/Return of Content" (an exhibition of installations and drawings); "John Malpede/L.A.P.D."; "David Ireland–Gallery as Place"; "Linda Montano–7 Years of Living Art"; "Vertigo: The Politics of Dislocation"; and "The Open Image: German Concrete Painting."

SAN FRANCISCO CAMERAWORK

70 12th St., San Francisco, CA 94103

Phone: (415) 621-1001 *Hours:* Tuesday-Saturday 12-5 *Admission:* free

Founded in 1974, San Francisco Camerawork presents exhibitions, publications, lectures and other community services in a diverse community-based dialogue about contemporary photography and related visual arts.

Since the facility is small and there are no permanent collections, the emphasis is on exhibitions. Exhibitions are held in Camerawork's two rooms and curated by members of the board of directors who are all working artists, designers, writers or educators in the arts. The focus is on emerging and contemporary artists who are featured in thematic or group shows. Recent exhibitions have included "Spectacular Photographs: Unforgettable Faces, Facts, and Feats," documentary photographs on fantastic "Ripley's Believe it or Not" themes; "Cross Country Crosscurrents," an exchange between Camerawork and the Photographic Resource Center in Boston; and group shows including works by Nic Nicosia, Tina Barney, Joachim Schmid, Karen Keister, Jay Boersman and Richard Bolton. Besides these more professional exhibits, Camerawork also sponsors exhibitions of student works and programs at local colleges.

Four times a year Camerawork publishes *San Francisco Camerawork Quarterly*, a magazine of writing that reflects events in photography and other media. Other publications include occasional exhibition catalogues. San Francisco Camerwork's library holds nine-hundred titles and over fifty periodicals. Camerawork's bookstore is eclectic and there is a slide copy service that lets artists shoot their own work. The slide copy service reflects Camerawork's unique interaction with the San Francisco photographic community.

Each year Camerawork also holds workshops and lecture series. These are often given by famous photographers such as Robert Mapplethorpe, Mary Ellen Mark, Duane Michals and Gary Winogrand.

SAN FRANCISCO CRAFT & FOLK ART MUSEUM

Landmark Building A, Fort Mason, San Francisco, CA 94123-1382

Phone: (415) 775-0990 *Hours:* Tuesday-Sunday 12-5; Saturday 10-5 *Admissions:* $1 Saturdays 10-12 free

Founded in 1982, the San Francisco Craft and Folk Art Museum acts as a forum for contemporary crafts and traditional folk arts and fosters an appreciation of folk arts as fine art. When the museum opened, it was housed in a renovated residence on Balboa Street in

San Francisco. In 1987, it moved to a new home in San Francisco's Fort Mason Center for non-profit organizations.

Collections: The museum's collections are growing rapidly. In 1989, it acquired the Gregory Collection of 500 ethnographic dolls, the Robert Luken Collection of tribal art from Pacific Islands, collections of Indonesian textiles and Balinese masks. These works are housed in its new storage space in Fort Mason Center. The museum library holds 1,500 volumes including numerous periodicals on all aspects of craft and folk arts and a collection of 4,500 original slides.

Exhibitions: Each year the museum presents six exhibitions of contemporary crafts, folk art representative of traditional communities, and works by untrained artists who express their idiosyncratic vision outside historic trends. Recent exhibitions have included "Enduring Traditions: Tibetan Folk Art," "Minority Costumes and Textiles of Guizhou Province, The People's Republic of China"; "Innerskins/Outerskins: Gut and Fishskin"; and "Not So Naive: Bay Area Artists and Outsider Art."

In addition to its regular exhibitions, the Museum offers educational programs such as "Folk Art in the Schools" and the Docent program where trained volunteers give guided tours of exhibitions.

SAN FRANCISCO MUSEUM OF MODERN ART
Van Ness Ave. at McAllister St., San Francisco, CA 94102

Phone: (415) 863-8800 *Hours:* Tuesday, Wednesday, Friday 10-5; Thursday 10-9; Saturday & Sunday 11-5

The San Francisco Museum of Modern Art traces its origins to the 1890s when the San Francisco Art Association, a coalition of Bay Area artists, was given the Mark Hopkins mansion on Nob Hill. Exhibitions were hung in the grand ballroom which was converted into galleries with rich oriental rugs on the floor.

The 1905 earthquake and fire consumed these quarters, forcing the museum to close until 1916. That year, it was given space in the Palace of Fine Arts, which had been built as an art center for the Panama Pacific International Exposition in 1915. In 1921, the museum was established as a nonprofit organization independent of the Art Association and for a time it served as the only general art museum in the city. When the Palace building was no longer considered practical, the museum closed temporarily in expectation of quarters in the elegant new Civic Center War Memorial complex designed by architect Arthur Brown, Jr. On January 18, 1935, the San Francisco Museum of Art reopened on the fourth floor of the Veterans Building.

Renamed the San Francisco Museum of Modern Art, the museum currently occupies the War Memorial Building's third and fourth floors. In addition to galleries where the permanent collection and special shows are presented, the museum operates an award-winning first-floor bookstore and cafe on the fourth floor. Additionally, there is a library, a conservation laboratory which is now the major resource for institutions and private collections throughout Northern California, and modest space for lectures, films, chamber concerts and classes.

Plans are presently underway for the construction of a major new museum building to be located across from San Francisco's proposed Yerba Buena Gardens Cul-

tural Center. The distinguished Swiss architect Mario Botta has been selected to design the building, which, when it opens as proposed in 1993, will double the San Francisco Museum of Modern Art's current exhibition space.

Collections: The museum's collection is drawn almost entirely from the 20th century and includes pieces from almost every period and movement. Two great works by pivotal masters, the 1895-98 Picasso, *Street Scene, Paris,* and the 1898 Matisse, *Corsican Landscape,* begin the chronological development. Fauvism is represented by Matisse's *The Girl with Green Eyes,* Derain's *Landscape* of 1905-6, and by a number of other important works. Cubism, a central area of influence for 20th century work, may be studied through the paintings and sculpture of Braque, Picasso, Leger, Lipchitz, Metzinger, and Ozenfant. Surrealism, German Expressionism, the School of Paris, the American School, and the Abstract Expressionists are documented and a collection of work from Latin America is also included.

The museum has also been collecting photography for the past fifty years. The collections contain works by the greats of Western photography in the 20th century, including Ansel Adams, Wynn Bullock, Imogen Cunningham and Edward Weston, and spans the photographic medium, from the work of 19th century European and American pioneers to the artists working along the frontiers of photography today. The collection has depth as well as breadth, reflecting the nuances and the history of photography. Among the other photographers represented are Atget, Lartigue, Brassai, Stieglitz, Strand, Siskind, Lange, White and Arbus.

The museum's departments of Architecture and Design (1983) and Media Arts (1988) have distinguished themselves through active exhibition schedules and new acquisitions to the permanent collections. Primarily featuring works by prominent West Coast designers and architects, the Architecture and Design department has acquired notable pieces by Gail Fredell Smith, John Dickinson, Charles and Ray Eames, and Peter Shire, and drawings by William Wilson Wurster and Willis Polk.

The Department of Media Arts, one of fewer than six such departments in the country, addresses the increasingly important forms of media and time-based arts. Works acquired to enrich this department include Peter Fischli and David Weiss' single channel videotape *Der Lauf der Dinge* (The Way Things Go) and Doug Hall's three channel video, sound and mechanical installation, *The Terrible Uncertainty of the Thing Described.* Other names included in the museum's collection of more than 300 major artists are Gorky, Kandinsky, Marin, Feininger, O'Keeffe, Avery, Still, Pollock, de Kooning, Diebenkorn, Thiebaud, Albers, Frankenthaler, Rothko, Rivera, Orozco, Moore, Noguchi, Frank Stella, David Smith, Calder, Voulkos, Anselm Kiefer, Julian Schnabel and Sigmar Polke.

The museum has originated important exhibitions and collaborated with other institutions in sharing traveling exhibitions. It has maintained an important liaison with The Museum of Modern Art, New York, and arrangements have been made with other leading institutions. The emphasis on temporary exhibitions has, of course, been strengthened by the museum's ability to supply interpretative and background resources from its own strong collection of 20th century art.

The museum serves an ever-increasing and sophisticated public. To better serve their needs it presents lectures special events, tours and educational programs.

TATTOO ART MUSEUM
30 7th St., San Francisco, CA 94103

Phone: (415) 775-4991 *Hours:* Monday-Sunday 12-6
Admission: $1 donation requested

The Tattoo Art Museum was founded in 1974 by world-renowned tattoo artist Lyle Tuttle. Its objective is to collect, research, preserve and display the history and uses of body decoration and sacrifice. The museum is housed alongside Mr. Tuttle's tattoo studio, where visitors can observe demonstrations of the art.

Collections: In its collection the museum holds the world's largest assemblage of facts, information, artifacts and memorabilia associated with tattooing. Pieces from Mr. Tuttle's large private collection and items donated and acquired from various tattoo artists around the world serve to illustrate tattooing's unique and exotic nature.

The largest and most complete collection of any one tattoo artist held by the museum is the George Burchett Collection. Burchett gained distinction as the King of Tattoo Artists after tattooing the King of Denmark and many other members of European royalty. Other representative pieces are a circa-1800 scrimshawed walrus tusk, depicting a tattooed Marquesas islander, and a pre-Columbian clay piece identified as a tattoo pattern stamp dated A.D. 400.

Exhibitions: In its exhibitions the museum traces the anthropological history of tattooing and other body-decorating techniques from the late Pleistocene period to the present. The museum retains a tattoo machine collection that tells the story of the evolution from manual devices, used for thousands of years, through spring-powered to electrical and now transistor-operated equipment. It also contains the personal histories of many tattoo artists, some dating beyond the turn of the century. Other displays include thousands of hand-drawn tattoo designs which once served as tattooer's sales aids.

SAN JOSE

AMERICAN MUSEUM OF QUILTS AND TEXTILES
766 S. 2nd St., San Jose, CA 95112

Phone: (408) 971-0323 *Hours:* Tuesday-Saturday 10-4
Admission: free

The American Museum of Quilts and Textiles was founded in 1977 by the Santa Clara Valley Quilt Association. Its mission is to promote an understanding of the roles quilts and textiles played in the lives of their makers and to display their value as historical documents. The building itself is a 1920s Spanish Revival-style house well suited to the display of textiles.

The emphasis of the museum's permanent collections is on 20th-century quilts including contemporary works. There are also fine examples of quilts and coverlets from the 19th century.

Regularly changing exhibits feature quilts and other textiles from around the world as well as from the Museum's own collections. Recent exhibitions include

"The Great American Quilt Prize Winner Show," fifty-one Liberty Quilts from the Great American Quilt Festival in New York City; "Connections: Contemporary Quilts and their Traditional Influences"; "Star of Wonder, Star of Light," antique star quilts; "Viya Maya," textiles from Southern Mexico and Guatemala; and "Humor in Patchwork—Reinterpreting Tradition." The museum also hosts occasional juried shows.

Educational programs include docent-conducted tours of the exhibits, outreach programs to schools and adult centers, and workshops and lectures on selected topics by experts in their fields. The museum also brings quilts to United States History classes in the San Jose School system.

Note: The Museum is located one block south of 280 Freeway, between Margaret and Virginia Streets.

ROSICRUCIAN EGYPTIAN MUSEUM AND PLANETARIUM
Rosicrucian Park, San Jose, CA 95191

Phone: (408) 287-9171 *Hours:* Tuesday-Sunday 9-5
Admission: $3; 12-17 $1; Seniors $2.50; Under 12 free

Founded in 1929 under the auspices of the Rosicrucian Order, AMORC (a worldwide, nonprofit, nonsectarian, fraternal organization of men and women), the Rosicrucian Egyptian Museum has grown into the largest Egyptian museum in the Western United States. The museum itself is a large sandstone building patterned after the ancient temple in Karnak. The doors are bronze but appear golden, and the entryway is a culinated court with Egyptian columns. The galleries on the first floor are connected by an underground replica of a nobleman's tomb complete with rough hewn rock and a painted sarcophagus. On the upstairs galleries are other Egyptian galleries and a space for exhibiting contemporary art.

Collections: The Rosicrucian Museum holds over 4,000 Egyptian artifacts dating from 4,000 B.C. to just before the birth of Christ. Of note is the collection of nine adult mummies and one child mummy. The oldest of these mummies is pre-dynastic, and all are accompanied by ritual objects, jars that held the mummy's organs, and several animal mummies including a realistic baboon and the head of a bull. Other works displayed in the five galleries include jewelry, cosmetics, ancient scrolls, amulets, toys and statuary. The museum also holds some Babylonian, Assyrian and Oriental artifacts.

Exhibitions: The Rosicrucian's contemporary art gallery features work in a wide range of media including painting, sculpture and photography. The exhibitions are eclectic and include touring shows as well as one-person and group exhibitions by both emerging and established artists. The subjects of recent exhibitions include Alan Osborne; airbrush artist Wolfgang Gersch; Chinese artist Ya Min Yang; monumental panel painter Don Nix; and several exhibitions of Visionary and New Age Art.

Next door to the museum is the Rosicrucian Planetarium, the "Theater of the Sky."

SAN JOSE HISTORICAL MUSEUM
635 Phelan Ave., San Jose, CA 95112

Phone: (408) 287-2290 *Hours:* Monday-Friday 10-4:30; Saturday & Sunday 12-4:30 *Admission:* $2; seniors $1.50; children 6-17 $.50; under 6 free

Founded in 1949, the San Jose Historical Museum is a reproduction of turn-of-the century San Jose, an old time city plaza located in the southern portion of modern San Jose's Kelly Parks. Each of its buildings, whether restored or reconstructed, is placed as nearly as possible in its original relation to other structures in the plaza.

An introductory exhibit depicting the history of the Santa Clara Valley is on display in the Pacific Hotel. Other restored and reconstructed buildings include the Umbarger House, the Dashaway Stables, a doctor's office, an electric light tower, the Coyote Post Office, Chiechi House, Steven's Ranch Fruit Drying Shed, Zanker House, a 1927 Associated Oil Company Gas Station, the Empire Firehouse, the Bank of Italy, the Pacific Hotel, a print shop, a bandstand and the San Jose Trolley Barn.

A research library containing archival and photographic collections relating to the Santa Clara Valley is available to visitors with an appointment (call in advance).

Other features are the Museum Gift Shop, O'Brien's Ice Cream and Candy Store, the Pacific Hotel Meeting Room and the Firehouse Meeting Room. The San Jose Historical Museum is also the sight of the Trolley Restoration Barn.

SAN JOSE INSTITUTE OF CONTEMPORARY ART
451 S. 1st St., San Jose, CA 95113

Phone: (408) 998-4310 *Hours:* Tuesday-Saturday 12-5; Thursday 12-8 *Admission:* free

The San Jose Institute of Contemporary Art was established in 1979 as a vehicle for exhibiting alternatives to more traditional visual arts, and for building a significant arts community in San Jose. For ten years the institute was located at 377 South First Street. The building of a new convention center, however, caused prices to go up and financial considerations forced the institute in late 1989 to move to 4,000 square feet of raw space blocks away at 451 South First St.

The exhibitions program features deserving local as well as nationally known innovators in the visual arts. It is directed toward a wide range of contemporary issues and media, including painting, sculpture, printmaking and photography as well as site-specific installations, performance and video. Recent and future exhibitions include "Text/Context," works by Terry Allen, Margaret Bailey Doogan and Lita Albuquerque; "Richard Putz: Recent Sculpture"; and "Overt/Covert: Socially Informed Work," pieces by Enrique Chagoya, Michael Cook and Connie Jenkins.

There is no permanent collection.

SAN JOSE MUSEUM OF ART
110 S. Market St., San Jose, CA 95113

Phone: (408) 294-2787 *Hours:* Tuesday-Friday 10-6; Saturday 10-4; Sunday 12-4 *Admission:* free

When Micheal Danoff came to the San Jose Museum of Art in 1988 he changed its focus from that of a regional art museum to one dedicated to the presentation of contemporary art from around the world.

The museum is housed in a historic former post office built in the late 1800s. It contains two large galleries used for changing exhibitions and a multi-purpose room used for educational and exhibition purposes. In 1988, ground was broken for the construction of a 43,000-square-foot addition. When the new wing opens it will virtually double the capacity of the museum and include a large sky-light gallery, smaller galleries, space for art preparation and storage facilities.

Collections: Given the museum's change in direction, the collections, a hodge-podge of local art and oddities typical of a regional art museums, have become irrelevant and are now in storage.

Exhibitions: The San Jose Museum of Art presents both self-curated and traveling exhibitions which change approximately every six weeks. Recently the museum presented "Peter Shelton: Waxworks," an exhibition of contemporary sculpture; "Mike Glier: Recent Drawings"; "Gerhard Richter: Serigraphs"; "Forty Years of California Assemblage"; "The Appropriate Object"; and "Fresh Views–Bay Area Artists."

Education: The San Jose Museum of Art School gives studio art classes to all age groups. Children's art classes are offered and a series of adult education programs has also been proposed. The museum often presents lecture series in conjunction with major exhibitions.

SAN MARCOS

BOEHM GALLERY
Palomar Community College, 1140 W. Mission Rd., San Marcos, CA 92069

Phone: (619) 744-1150 x2304 *Hours:* Tuesday 10-4; Wednesday-Thursday 10-7; Friday 10-2; Saturday 12-4 *Admission:* free

Established in 1964, the Boehm Gallery of Palomar Community College shows a broad array of contemporary art by nationally acclaimed artists and artisans.

The emphasis of the program is on the six exhibitions offered each year. Most are one-person, although group shows are not uncommon. Recently the gallery mounted shows featuring the works of Gillian Theobald, Marjorie Wodelman, Amanda Farber, Mathew Gregoire, and contemporary Mexican artists Janet Codling and Raul Guerrero. Shows in the past have featured Andy Warhol, John Baldessari, Judy Chicago, and Italo Scanga, as well as an exhibit featuring a number of African and New Guinean sculptures. Craft exhibitions feature jewelry, furniture, glass and ceramics.

The gallery also hosts traveling exhibitions from the Smithsonian and the Western Association of Art Museums (WAAM).

SAN MARINO

HUNTINGTON LIBRARY, ART COLLECTIONS AND BOTANICAL GARDENS
1151 Oxford Rd., San Marino, CA 91108

Phone: (818) 405-2100 *Hours:* Tuesday-Sunday 1-4:30 *Admission:* free; Tickets required on Sunday (write to Huntington Library)

The Huntington Library, Art Collections and Botanical Gardens is a research institution and educational cultural center serving scholars and the general public. It was founded in 1919 by railroad land developer Henry E. Huntington and continues to be privately endowed and supported.

Collections: The gallery, originally the Huntington home, contains one of America's most comprehensive and coherent collections of British and European 18th century art.

Among the Huntington's holdings of 18th and early 19th century British art are: Gainsborough's *Blue Boy*, Lawrence's *Pinkie*, as well as major works by Reynolds, Romney, Turner, and Constable. The gallery also contains British drawings, sculpture, ceramics, furniture, silver, miniatures ceramics, and glass of the same period.

Most of the leading painters of pre-revolution France are represented in the Adele S. Browning Collection, a group of forty-two British and European paintings, principally of the 18th century, which were bequeathed to the library in 1979. This collection is on permanent display and includes works by most of the leading painters of France during the decades prior to the revolution. Watteau, Nattier, Boucher, Greuze, Fragonard, and David are all represented as are important 17th century works by Rembrandt, Van Dyck, and Claude.

American art is displayed in the Virginia Steele Scott Gallery for American Art. Opened in 1984, the Scott Gallery contains a representative collection of approximately sixty American paintings which date from the 1740s to the 1930s, including examples by Copley, West, Stuart, Bingham, Church, Kensett, Eakins, Cassatt and Hopper.

In addition, the Huntington has one of the most important collections in the country of French 18th-century sculpture, tapestries, furniture, porcelain and decorative objects.

Library: The Huntington is one of the great research libraries of the world. The collections, containing 2 1/2 million manuscripts, 352,000 rare books, and 308,000 reference books, are concentrated in the fields of British and American literature and history from the 11th century to the present. It also has important collections of 15th-century printed books, medieval manuscripts made in England, the history and philosophy of early science and technology and the history and art of the book.

The Library Exhibition Hall displays two hundred outstanding rare books and manuscripts in its main rotating exhibition. Among its finest treasures are the beautifully illuminated Ellesmere manuscript of Chaucer's *Canterbury Tales* (ca. 1410); a Bible printed by Gutenberg (1450-55); an unexcelled collection of the early editions of Shakespeare; and Benjamin Franklin's *Autobiography* written in his own hand. Also on display are first editions and manuscripts by such authors as Blake, Wordsworth, Shelley, Byron, Stevens, Thoreau, Clemens and London. In addition, the library has special changing exhibitions.

Botanical Gardens: One-hundred-fifty of the Huntington's 207-acre grounds are devoted to public botanical gardens. The gardens include shrubs, trees and other plants from every continent. The grounds are meticulously kept, and all plants are labeled. The collections include over 1,500 cultivars of camellias and a rose garden with nearly 2,000 cultivars arranged historically. The twelve-acre Desert Garden contains a large grouping of mature cacti and other succulents. The Japanese Garden has traditional Japanese plants, stone ornaments, a moon bridge, a Japanese house, a walled Zen Garden and a Bonsai Court. Among other important botanical attractions are the Herb, Shakespeare, Jungle, Australian, Subtropical and Palm Gardens.

Programs: Free public programs are offered at least once each month. Short informal dance, drama, or musical programs related to the Huntington collections are presented outdoors at 1:30 and 2:30 p.m. Mini-talks (twenty minutes) are presented by Huntington docents or staff members each month.

SAN RAFAEL

FALKIRK CULTURAL CENTER
1408 Mission Ave., San Rafael, CA 94901

Phone: (415) 485-3328 *Hours:* Tuesday, Wednesday & Friday 11-4; Thursday 11-9; Saturday & Sunday 10-1:30 *Admission:* free

Built in 1888, the Falkirk Cultural Center was the family home of industrialist Robert Dollar until 1974 when it was purchased by the citizens of San Rafael to be preserved as a historic and cultural center for the community.

Collections: The permanent collections of the Falkirk Cultural Center are the home and possessions of the Dollar estate. The seventeen-room Victorian mansion is typical of the elaborate Queen Anne style. The entrance hall to the home is enhanced by a massive fireplace. The main floor is a showcase for 19th-century and early 20th-century art and furnishing. The staircase winds past magnificent stained-glass windows and on the second floor are three galleries which feature a rotating schedule of contemporary art exhibits. The cultural center is surrounded by public sculptures, eleven acres of formal grounds, and natural wooded hillsides. The 1927 Wing houses the staff offices and the classroom facilities.

Exhibitions: Each year the Falkirk stages six contemporary fine art exhibitions by emerging Bay Area artists as well as giving concerts, lectures, and art classes. Recent exhibitions include "The Home Show," works by twelve artists whose images come from the home; "Public Sculpture in Marin," a spiritual installation by Bruce Brodie; and "Domestic Character of the Victorian Woman," an installation by Judy Moran. In December of 1989 the Falkirk will begin "The Living Nutcracker," an annual exhibition of scenes from within the ballet.

Also housed in the Falkirk Cultural Center are the home offices of the Marin Poetry Center and the not-for-profit Public Art Works, a company which produces public sculpture throughout Marin County.

SANTA ANA

CHARLES W. BOWERS MUSEUM
2002 N. Main St., Santa Ana, CA 92706

Phone: (714) 972-1900 *Hours:* Exhibition spaces closed until completion of renovation; call for hours of museum shop and educational center *Admission:* free

Founded in 1936, the Bowers Museum is a cultural arts institution specializing in the art of the Americas, Africa, and the Pacific Rim.

The museum is housed in an authentic Spanish-style stucco building with heavy wooden accents, a red tile roof and pergolas. The interior, with rough plaster walls and quarry-tile floors, is enhanced by handsome frescoed and carved ceilings. Many of the doors are of oak, hand painted in the tradition of Indian and early Spanish decor. The first floor is used for exhibition galleries and a museum shop. Offices, with wrought-iron balconies and an impressive veranda overlooking the courtyard, occupy the second story.

Currently the museum is undergoing a $12 million expansion and renovation to be completed in 1991. Larger galleries, state-of-the-art collections and a new 48,000-square-foot building will be added.

Collections: The Bowers Museum holds more than 85,000 artifacts including Pacific Rim pieces from the 19th and early 20th century; ethnic arts from the Americas, India, and Africa; American decorative arts; and California history. Some of these artifacts are featured in ongoing permanent exhibitions while others are displayed in the museum's eight to twelve featured exhibitions each year.

Exhibitions: Recent exhibitions include: "Columbia Before Columbus: 3000 Years of Ceramic Art in Prehistoric America," "First Voices: Indigenous Music of Southern California," and "Ban Chiang: Archaeological Treasures of Prehistoric Thailand." The museum also features traveling exhibitions of international scope.

A separate building houses the membership and educational center offices, and classrooms. The museum features a comprehensive educational program for adults as well as children. Other programs include guided tours, lectures, films, seminars, studio workshops, and community festivals.

ORANGE COUNTY CENTER FOR CONTEMPORARY ART
3621 W. MacArthur Blvd., Santa Ana, CA 92711

Phone: (714) 549-4989 *Hours:* Wednesday-Sunday 11-4 *Admission:* free

The Orange County Center for Contemporary Art is a non-profit artists organization which works to increase the exposure and support of contemporary art forms in Orange County.

The center was founded in September of 1980 by five California State University, Fullerton graduate students who wanted to "be as creative and innovative as possible." Over the years, the center has rejected vigorously the commercialism of the art world and remained an all-volunteer artist member organization governed by its exhibiting members. Today, the center continues to be a showplace for emerging artists and a training center where artists learn about self promotion and resume writing.

The main facility of the Orange County Center for Contemporary Art holds three galleries. One or two of the galleries normally hold member shows while the remaining one(s) contains thematic or one-person shows by visiting artists. Shows are in a variety of media including painting, sculpture and installation and exhibitions change every five weeks. Featured artists at the O.C.C.A have included Ann Page, James Strobotne, John DeHaras, Roberta Eisenberg, Tom Dowling, Donald Karwelis and William Wiley. There is no permanent collection.

Recently the center opened a satellite gallery in Hutton Centre in Downtown Santa Ana and there are plans for a completely new downtown facility to be built on grounds donated by the City of Santa Ana.

Along with exhibitions the center presents continuing series of lectures and panel discussions.

SANTA BARBARA

SANTA BARBARA CONTEMPORARY ARTS FORUM
7 W. De La Guerra, Santa Barbara, CA 93101

Phone: (805) 966-5373 *Hours:* Tuesday-Saturday 12-5 *Admission:* free

The Santa Barbara Contemporary Arts Forum, founded in 1976, is an artists organization and exhibition space that presents provocative art in every media by emerging and established artists.

Exhibitions: The Contemporary Arts Forum originates eight or nine exhibitions each year in its main 1,200-square-foot gallery. It has organized solo and theme exhibitions by artists as diverse as Nancy Reddin and Ed Keinholz, Cy Twombly, Terry Allen, William Wiley, Nancy Graves, Michael Singer, Carl Cheng, Maren Hassinger, Mineko Grimmer, Ann Hamilton and Wayne Thiebaud. Recently, it brought five eminent photographers to Santa Barbara for a special "Focus/Santa Barbara" exhibition.

Many of the Contemporaray Arts Forum's most successful exhibitions, such as "Real Surfboards" (surfboards as sculpture), and Cheryl Bowers' environmental installation "Sea Full of Clouds What Can I Do?," are indigenous to the Santa Barbara community.

In its satellite, OuterSpace gallery the Santa Barbara Contemporary Arts Forum sponsors changing exhibitions by artists living in the Tri-counties. Its WindowSpace provides opportunities for artists to make site-specific installations which have high public visibility.

Programming: The Contemporary Arts Forum sponsors a wide range of performances, readings, film, video, new music and dance, often bringing to Santa Barbara innovative performance artists such as Laurie Anderson and Spalding Grey. Because of lack of space within the gallery these events often take place at theatres, clubs, auditoriums, churches, the armory and the streets of Santa Barbara.

The forum also sponsors lectures by distinguished art world members. Among those who have spoken at Contemporary Arts Forum events are critic Kenneth Baker, curator Graham Beal, choreographer Trisha Brown, photographer Douglas Curran, and artists Judy Pfaff, Carolee Schneeman, Michael Singer and David Ireland.

SANTA BARBARA MUSEUM OF ART
1130 State St., Santa Barbara, CA 93101

Phone: (805) 963-4364 *Hours:* Tuesday-Saturday 11-5; Sunday 12-5 *Admission:* free

The Santa Barbara Museum of Art is a general art museum with a collection that ranges from antiquities (2,000 B.C.) to contemporary works of art. The museum was founded in 1941 by a group of citizens who persuaded the Santa Barbara City government to donate an abandoned post office for the purpose of a private art museum. Over the years the facility has been expanded many times. In 1985, the the total floor space was expanded to 56,000 square feet; new galleries were added, state of the art climate and light controls were installed, and a new library (which holds 30,000 books and 30,000 slides) and art education facilities were built.

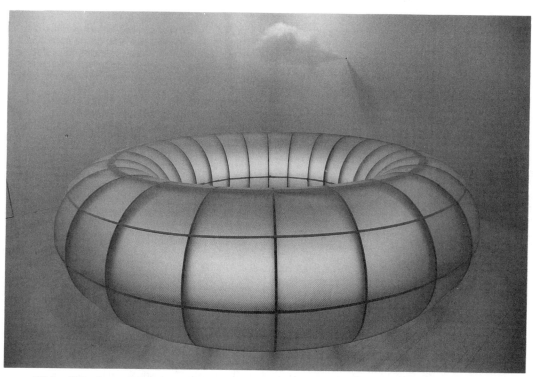

Michael Hardesty, *Polar Event,* installation. Courtesy: Santa Barbara Contemporary Arts Forum

Pablo Picasso, *Young Woman Inspired by Cranach.*
Courtesy: Santa Barbara Museum of Art

Collections: The museum's permanent collections contain over 14,000 objects and are strong in several areas.

The Donald Bear Memorial Collection was started in 1955 and, reflecting the interests of its namesake, consists primarily of modern American Paintings. Notable are *Mary, Mother of Christ* by Morris Broderson; *The Table* by John Paul Jones; *No. 3* by Bradley Walker Tomlin; and works by Rico Lebrun, John Marin, Walt Kuhn, and Henry Moore.

The European Drawing Collection was initiated in 1941 by Wright Ludington with the gift of two Dalis, three Degas, two Matisses, a Wyndham Lewis, and a Derain. Today the prints and drawings collection contains approximately 200 drawings, and over 4,000 19th-century French lithographs, many by Daumier.

The Preston Morton Collection, one of the most noted and complete collections owned by the museum, is composed of American paintings of the late 18th, 19th and 20th centuries. The core of this collection was given by Preston Morton in memory of her husband. This group of paintings includes works by most of the best-known American painters of those periods, including Peals, Sully, Cole, Bierstadt, Homer, Eakins, Sargent, Remington, Glackens, Sloan, Hopper, Burchfield and others.

The Ala Story Collection was established by Mrs. Story at her retirement as director in 1957. The collection now contains more than 90 works and consists of several groups of pictures. The largest group is of German Expressionist prints and drawings. The second portion consists of prints and drawings by contemporary American and European artists and the final group of oils and watercolors is by contemporary artists such as Stella, Diebenkorn, Marsden Hartley and David Hockney.

The Ludington collection of Greek and Roman antiquities, exhibited in Ludington court, has been on loan to the museum since 1941, though much of it has since been given to the museum.

Among other collections are 19th-century French art by Monet, Latour, Degas and others; the largest collection of Kobayashi Kiyochika prints outside Japan; pieces from the Sung Dynasty (11th and 12th centuries) in China; and photographs by Harry Callahan, Minor White, Yousuf Karsh and Ansel Adams.

Exhibitions: The Santa Barbara Museum of Art also presents a continuing series of exhibitions. Recently it organized "Regionalism: the California View," an exhibition of fifty large watercolors by California regionalists of the 1930s and 1940s. In 1991, it will mount "Standing in the Tempest," an exhibition of avant garde Hungarian art from 1908 to 1931. This exhibit will be the first time many of these paintings will be shown in the United States.

The museum's education programs include outreach programs to schools, senior centers and convalescent homes.

SANTA BARBARA MUSEUM OF NATURAL HISTORY

2559 Puesta del Sol Rd., Santa Barbara, CA 93105

Phone: (805) 682-4711 *Hours:* Monday-Sunday 9-5 *Admission:* $3; youths 13-17 & Senior citizens $2; children under 12 $1

Founded in 1916, the Santa Barbara Museum of Natural History exhibits fine art in its Main and Maximus Galleries.

The Main Gallery specializes in art exhibits that have a natural history, natural science or anthropological theme. Its gallery committee selects museum quality art exhibitions that are not, and in some instances cannot, be done in other kinds of art galleries. For example the 1984 show, "Art From Artifacts," combined contemporary watercolors of native American artifacts with actual artifacts from the Museum's collection.

The Maximus Gallery specializes in showing antique prints and books with a natural history theme. For example the museum may combine pieces from Mrs. Maximus' private collection or some of the first edition Audobon prints she has donated to the museum with specimens of birds from the Bird Taxonomy Hall, or it may combine the works of frontier artists and chroniclers Bodmer and Caitlan with artifacts from plains Indians.

Whenever possible, the museum prefers to exhibit works by artists who live in the Santa Barbara area. Recent exhibitions by Southern California artists include "Portraits of Africa," photorealistic pencil drawings of the African scene; "Stewards of the Earth: A Return to the Garden," an exhibition of photographs of world farming practices by Michael Ableman; and "Chumash Rock Painting," an exhibition of twenty-four acrylic reproductions of Chumash Indian cave paintings by Campbell Grant.

Other upcoming exhibitions include "Coyote: A Myth in the Making," paintings, lithographs and sculptures of Maidu artist Harry Fonseca; "Pat Jacquemain—Woodcuts"; "Ray Strong: Art of the Diorama"; and The Guild of Natural Science Illustration juried show.

As a natural history museum, the Santa Barbara Museum of Natural History also holds large collections dealing with the natural history and prehistoric life of the Pacific Coast.

UNIVERSITY ART MUSEUM, SANTA BARBARA

University of California, Santa Barbara, CA 93106

Phone: (805) 961-2951 *Hours:* Tuesday-Saturday 10-4; Sunday 1-5 *Admission:* free

The University Art Museum of the University of California at Santa Barbara is a generalized art museum with a collection of over 6,500 works of art. It was founded in 1959 as the gallery of the university and converted into museum space in the early 1960s.

Collections: In the early 1960s, the museum began its permanent collection with a group of Dutch and Flemish paintings from the 1400s given by Francis and Alice Sedgwick. Later in the 1960s, it acquired the Morgenroth Collection of Renaissance medals and plaquettes, one of the best of its kind in the world. At the same time Ala Story, the former director of the Santa Barbara Museum, gave a collection of Old Master graphic arts and 16th century German prints that became the nucleus of a graphic arts collection that now includes 2,000 works of 16th and 17th century art.

More recently the museum has concentrated on pre-Columbian, African and contemporary American art. The gifts of the Helm and Goodspeed collections of pre-Columbian objects have brought the museum's holdings in that area close to 1,000 pieces. In contemporary art the emphasis has been on regional California artists including works by Larry Bell, Joseph Beuys, George Herms and John McCracken. The museum also houses the Southern California Architectural Archives in the Architectural Drawing Collection Room.

Exhibitions: The Museum presents a broad range of historical, contemporary and academic exhibitions in the Main, South and West Galleries. Not limited to painting, these include sculpture, drawing, printmaking, environments and installations, ceramics, photography, indigenous art and architecture. Among recent exhibitions are "Matisse: Prints and Bronzes from the Cone Collection"; "Models for Santa Barbara Sites," urban models for Santa Barbara; "A Responsive Vision," an exhibition of Dutch and Flemish art of the 16th and 17th centuries; "Richard Ross: Museology," large scale color photos; and M.F.A. and B.A. exhibitions.

Along with the exhibitions program are over two-hundred corresponding catalogues and monographs available from the museum press. Guided docent tours are available to the public.

SANTA CLARA

DE SAISSET MUSEUM
Santa Clara University, Santa Clara, CA 95053

Phone: (408) 554-4528 *Hours:* Tuesday-Sunday: 11-4 *Admission:* free

The de Saisset Museum was built on the campus of the University of Santa Clara in 1955 through the bequest of Isabel de Saisset, who founded the museum primarily to house the paintings of her deceased brother Ernest. The museum has two floors and four major exhibition spaces.

Collections: The de Saisset's permanent collections now include paintings, sculpture, works on paper and decorative arts from America, Europe, Africa, and the Orient. Noteworthy are the Sheehan collection of Asian artifacts, the Kolb collection of prints, and the d'Berger collection of 18th century French decorative arts.

Exhibitions: Gallery IV features contemporary artists of the San Francisco Bay Area while other exhibition spaces include the works of contemporary artists as well those of historical interest. Outstanding recent exhibitions include the works of Henrietta Shore; the 120-foot mural *Grand Canyon* by Joseph DiGiorgio; photographs by Ruffin Cooper; and paintings and sculpture by Jud Fine.

In the California Mission Galleries the museum presents the story of early Santa Clara with historically important objects from the Indian period through the founding of the Mission and the College.

Films, lectures, concerts, and receptions are held in the museum auditorium.

TRITON MUSEUM OF ART
1505 Warburton Ave., Santa Clara, CA 95050

Phone: (408) 247-3754 *Hours:* Monday-Friday 10-5; Saturday & Sunday 12-5 *Admission:* free

Located in the heart of Silicon Valley, the Triton Museum of Art is the first major cultural institution to serve that rapidly expanding area.

The Triton Museum of Art was founded in San Jose in 1965 by Mr. and Mrs. W. Robert Morgan. In 1967, the museum moved to a complex of buildings in the Santa Clara Civic Center where it stayed for twenty years. Dissatisfied with these facilities and needing more space to serve the community, the museum began an ambitious construction project in the early 1980s. In 1987, it completed the project's first phase, a graceful new 22,000-square-foot facility. Designed by Barcelon and Jung of San Francisco and located in the same seven-acre parcel of land as the earlier museum, its pyramidal skylights create a soft, natural light. The rear wall of curving glass allows indoor viewing of the outdoor sculpture gardens. The historic Jamison Brown House is situated to the rear of the museum grounds and often serves as a reception hall and meeting place for local civic groups.

The permanent collection of the Triton Museum of Art is primarily composed of works by late 19th and early 20th-century artists, including Marc Chagall, Frank Duveneck, Thomas Moran and Robert Motherwell. An outstanding and sizable group of paintings by California artist Theodore Wores is featured, as are works by William Merit Chase, Jim Dine, Jerome Witkin and Milton Avery. Works of 20th-century regional sculptors can be viewed in the sculpture gardens, located throughout the seven-acre grounds. Most recently the focus of acquisitions has been on contemporary American works on paper.

Because space is limited and audience development is a primary goal, the emphasis at the Triton has been on changing exhibitions. Each year the museum presents up to twenty shows in its two gallery spaces. Among recent shows are the annual "Printmaking and Drawing Competition"; "Painting With Words: the Calligraphy of Donald Jackson"; "Drawings by Utagawa Kuniyoshi"; "Paintings by Taiji Harada"; and "Naturalism," a national realistic landscape exhibit.

The Triton also has an extensive school-age education program. In response to the elimination of school art programs in California's Proposition 13 it created "Art Reach," a program which brings thirty artist/teachers in contact with 8,000 children both at schools and in the museum itself.

SANTA CRUZ

THE ART MUSEUM OF SANTA CRUZ COUNTY
P.O. Box 8407, Santa Cruz, CA 95060

Phone: (408) 429-3420 *Hours:* Tuesday-Sunday 12-5; Thursday 6:30-8:30 *Admission:* $1; Thursday & Sunday free

Founded by a group of local citizens in 1981, The Art Museum of Santa Cruz County exhibits the works of major California artists, works in California collections, traveling exhibitions and special exhibitions relative to the Monterey Bay Area. The museum has been located in a commercial building but it is now restoring a former courthouse annex which it plans to share with the Santa Cruz organization "Historical Trust."

Collections: Though contemporary art in all its facets is the museum's focus, budget constraints have limited the collections to works of California artists from the last half of the the 20th century and made exhibitions rather than collections the primary emphasis. Of the 300 pieces the museum owns, seventy percent are prints or works on paper.

Exhibitions: Each year, the Art Museum of Santa Cruz County presents between five or six exhibitions of contemporary and historical art. It recently mounted "Mano a Mano," an exhibition of sixteen Latin American painters from the San Francisco Bay Area; "California Prison Project," works by inmates in the arts in prison program; "A Tradition of British Figurative Painting"; and "Japanese Woodblock Prints from the Late 19th Century." Upcoming exhibitions include a show of four-color woodblock prints by women printmakers of the 1920s and 1930s.

Programs: The museum gives spring and fall lecture series, sponsors a children's workshop series taught by artists from the Santa Cruz area, and leads guided trips to major museums, galleries and selected artists' studios in Los Angeles, Sacramento and San Francisco.

SANTA MONICA

ELI BROAD FAMILY FOUNDATION
3355 Barnard Way, Santa Monica, CA 90405

Phone: (213) 399-4004 *Hours:* by appointment only Monday-Friday 10-4; open to museum professionals, qualified museum groups, scholars, students and art writers.

Established in 1984 by art collector and patron Eli Broad, the Eli Broad Family Foundation serves the very real need of making contemporary art accessible to museums, art professionals, scholars, writers and the general public. It is an educational and lending resource with ongoing lending programs as well as a permanent facility which allows the art community to view and study a broad cross-section of contemporary art.

During its first four years of operation, the foundation loaned more than 155 works to approximately 100 museums in the Americas, Europe, Africa and Asia. In December 1988, it opened a research and loan facility in Santa Monica. The building, a former telephone switching station renovated by Frederick Fisher Architects, contains administrative offices, an art library, photo and documentary archives, art storage, and five levels of exhibition galleries. Selected works from the collection are installed in the exhibition space. The installations include thematic presentations of works in the collection as well as in-depth presentations of the works of individual artists.

Collections: The foundation collection encompasses both concentrated holdings of the work of important artists as well as a representative survey of major works of new and emerging artists. It includes over 300 works in all media by over 100 artists. Those represented in depth include Leon Golub, Keith Haring, Anselm Kiefer, Robert Longo, Italo Scanga, Julian Schnabel, John Baldessari, Ashley Bickerton and Cindy Sherman.

The foundation also features many large-scale works and installations that might prove difficult for a single museum or private individual to acquire and circulate, such as *Under a Rock* by Jenny Holzer and *Die Latiner* by Imi Knoebel.

SANTA MONICA MUSEUM OF ART
2437 Main St., Santa Monica, CA 90405

Phone: (213) 399-0433 *Hours:* call in advance *Admission:* free

Incorporated in 1985, the Santa Monica Museum of Art is devoted to showcasing the work of living, lesser known artists and to fostering an appreciation for contemporary art and ideas. Along with a group of offices, restaurants and shops, the museum is housed in an 8,300-square-foot warehouse space within the former Edgemar Farms egg processing plant. It contains approximately 6,000 square feet of exhibition space in-

cluding smaller and larger galleries/performance spaces as well as space for administrative offices, meeting rooms, a slide library, workshops and storage areas.

The museum has no permanent collection. Instead the emphasis is on the production, presentation and documentation of new artistic activity and the process of art-making. In that vein, the museum's programs consists of exhibitions and installations along with presentations of performance art, new music, film and video.

Recent and upcoming exhibitions include "Bon Angeles," previously completed and commissioned work made by several West German artists during a six-week residency at the Santa Monica; "Alexis Smith and Amy Gerstler: A Collaboration"; and "Art Tartar," an eclectic series of events including a Jean Cocteau retrospective organized by the Severin Wunderman Foundation; "Lunch," a new dance piece by Heidi Duckler; and "Rapture Stations in the Virtual Funhouse," a multi-media installation and performance piece by John Goss, Alan Pulner and Richard Zvoner.

SARATOGA

MONTALVO CENTER FOR THE ARTS
Montalvo Rd., Saratoga, CA 95070 or P.O. Box 158, Saratoga, CA 95071

Phone: (408) 741-3421 *Hours:* Wednesday-Sunday 1-4 *Admission:* free

The Montalvo Center for the Arts is located in Villa Montalvo, the former summer home of the late U.S. Senator and San Francisco Mayor James D. Phelan. It stands in the foothills of the Santa Cruz Mountains above Saratoga, at an elevation of 800 feet. The entrance gates are about one-half mile from the center of Saratoga and the Villa itself is a nineteen-room Mediterranean-type structure set in the midst of an estate of 175 acres, a large part of which is beautifully landscaped with formal gardens and dramatic trails to lookout points on the hillside.

In accordance with Senator Phelan's will, Montalvo has been converted into a center for creative activities in the arts, conducted on a non-profit basis under the trusteeship of the Montalvo Association. Monthly exhibitions by artists are shown in the three galleries of the main floor of the Villa. Concerts, plays and lectures are given in the Carriage House Theatre and the outdoor amphitheater.

The Villa takes its name from a novel written in the early 16th century by the Spanish author, Garcia Ordonez de Montalvo. In the book, *Las Sergas de Luy Esforzado Caballero Esplandian*, de Montalvo describes a tribe of Amazons living on an island fabulously rich with gold and jewels. The island was called California and was "at the right hand of the Indies . . . very close to that part of the Terrestrial Paradise." His Amazon queen was described as riding on a gryphon (also spelled griffin or griffon), a mythological creature with a beak and wings of an eagle, and the body, four legs, and tail of lion. Senator Phelan put carved gryphons on top of several entrance gates and used them elsewhere in the Villa's decor. Their use is doubly appropriate because, in mythology, gryphons are guardians of all types of treasure, and Senator Phelan considered Montalvo his favorite possession.

The grounds of Montalvo are maintained as an arboretum by the Santa Clara County Parks and Recreation Department and have been planted with many rare trees and shrubs. Montalvo is also an official bird sanctuary; as many as forty-one species have been observed in a single day and probably sixty-five or seventy species can be seen during the year.

STOCKTON

THE HAGGIN MUSEUM

Victory Park, 1201 N. Pershing Ave., Stockton, CA 95203

Phone: (209) 462-4116 *Hours:* Tuesday-Sunday 1:30-5 *Admission:* free

The Haggin Museum, like many regional centers, combines art and historical collections with continuing series of changing exhibitions.

Collections: Several galleries are devoted to the exhibition of the permanent fine-art collection. The bulk of the art collections are in 19th-century American and European paintings. The Rotunda contains Albert Bierstadt's *Sunset in Yosemite Valley* (1868) and *Looking up the Yosemite Valley* (1863), while the Haggin Room contains Bouguereau's *Nymphs Bathing* (1878), Rosa Bonheur's *Gathering for the Hunt* (1856), and Jean Leon Gerome's *The Artist and His Model*. Other art galleries contain collections of crystal, jade, ivory and American decorative arts.

There are also several galleries of historical California artifacts arranged in interpretive displays. Over the last several years these displays have become increasingly focused on historical Stockton. One gallery contains artifacts of the Stockton Fire Department, including "Old Betsy," the second-oldest steam fire engine on display in the United States. Another gallery concentrates on the mechanization of agriculture and recreates the shop of Stocktonian Benjamin Holt, who invented the Caterpillar tractor. In 1981, an American Indian gallery opened, and other subjects addressed included the combine harvester and Stockton's Chinatown.

Exhibitions: The Haggin Museum presents from six to ten changing exhibitions each year. These include the annual "Distinguished Artist Series," which honors artists who were born in the San Joaquin Valley; the annual "Robert Title McKee Children's Art Contest"; the Stockton National print and drawing contest; and the Stockton Art League Show (the latter two both semi-annual). Occasionally, the Haggin Museum also presents traveling exhibitions.

Education: The museum's docents give talks to school groups and other organizations.

THOUSAND OAKS

CONEJO VALLEY ART MUSEUM

191 W. Wilbur Rd., Thousand Oaks, CA 91360

Phone: (805) 373-0054 *Hours:* Wednesday-Sunday 12-5 *Admission:* free

In 1976 the Conejo Valley Art Museum was founded with the purpose of bringing art to the community. The museum made its first home in donated space in the Janss Mall of Thousand Oaks. By the early 1980s commercial pressures had forced it to move from the mall, and it now resides in the main room of the former Thousand Oaks Library. Today the facility is run completely by volunteers offering contemporary and historical art exhibits, lectures, films, concerts, workshops, tours and other events.

There are no permanent collections so the focus of the program is on exhibitions. Most, such as "The African Show," the "Japanese Exhibition," and "Etchings of the Old West" are traveling though some are drawn from the holdings of local collectors. Both the Thousand Oaks Art Association and the Westlake Art Guild are associated with the museum and each presents a yearly members show.

The museum also maintains a gift shop which offers a collection of handmade folk art from around the world and an art sales and rental gallery. The Wilbur Gallery, a satellite facility, is also owned by the museum.

Education: The Board of Trustees is working on a program to supplement art education in the elementary schools and is developing an art registry which will contain confidential information on local art collections.

UKIAH

HELD POAGE RESEARCH LIBRARY

603 W. Perkins St., Ukiah, CA 95482

Phone: (707) 462-6969 *Hours:* Tuesday, Thursday & Saturday 2-4 *Admission:* free

The Held Poage Research Library is an archival facility owned by the Mendocino County Historical Society.

The library's collections include a group of watercolors from the late 19th and early 20th centuries by Mendocino artist Bertha Emery; over 15,000 photographic negatives and bound prints dealing with historical Mendocino; and 5,000 monographs on Mendocino history, anthropology and wildlife. The library also holds the research materials for several scholarly works including Edith Van Allen Murphy's *Indian Muses of Native Plants*.

Each December the library mounts a showing of paintings by local artists.

Note: Researchers may make appointments to work during non-museum hours.

UPLAND

MUSEUM OF HISTORY AND ART, ON-TARIO

225 S. Euclid Ave., Upland, CA 91761

Phone: (714) 983-3198 *Hours:* Thursday-Sunday 12-4 *Admission:* free

The Museum of History and Art is the city museum of Upland, California. Its programs are divided equally between art exhibitions and city history. The building itself is the former city hall, a U-shaped 1937 mediterranean-style structure with a red-tile roof, corinthian columns and a historical fountain dating from the town's beginnings in the late 1890s.

The art program, located in the north wing of the building, is administered by the Chaffey Community Art Association. Founded in 1941, the Chaffey Community Art Association built the museum's permanent collection of over one hundred pieces through a series of juried shows it held in the 1940s. These works come from all over the country but the majority are regional California pieces. Among these oils, watercolors and sculptures are works by Louis Bosa, Phil Paradise, Emil Kosa, Jr., Millard Sheets, Milford Zornes and Phil Dike.

The galleries are used to display the permanent collection at least once a year for six weeks. Prints, sculpture, oil and watercolor artists are featured for six-week intervals throughout the remainder of the year. The art gallery has student art exhibitions annually, and the work of emerging artists are interspersed with that of prominent professionals. The shows are normally one-person or group exhibitions chosen by museum staff or members of the art association. Painters Orozco, Millard Sheets, and Milford Zornes and sculptors Betty Ford and John Svenson have all been featured in one-person shows.

The south wing of the building is devoted to exhibitions of local history. These include an exhibit on the history of local flight; a history of the local G.E. Hotpoint Plant including every iron that was ever produced there; a history of the Graber Olive Company; and an exhibition on the local citrus industry.

WALNUT CREEK

CIVIC ARTS GALLERY
1632 Locust St., Walnut Creek, CA 94596

Phone: (415) 943-5864 *Hours:* Monday-Saturday 12-5 *Admission:* free

The Civic Arts Gallery shows the work of Bay Area and ethnic artists. It is the public arts facility of the town of Walnut Creek and was, for its first twenty years, located in an old walnut warehouse along with several other arts organizations. In 1987 the warehouse was torn down to make room for a new regional center for the arts. The gallery moved to its present interim home in a former health food store where it will stay until it it moves to the new regional center.

Walnut Creek's collection is small and is displayed primarily in municipal offices. The emphasis of the program therefore is on exhibitions. Recently the gallery presented shows featuring the Emoryville studio community, the Benicia studio community, Roy de

Forest and Mark Bulwinkle. It also mounted the exhibition "Bay Area Bronze."

The gallery's extensive education programs include monthly visual arts slide talks, tours for school children with "hands-on" art projects, slide lectures, symposia and trips related to current exhibitions, and "Art on the Road," a program which brings docent talks to schools and community centers.

WILMINGTON

THE GENERAL PHINEAS BANNING RESIDENCE MUSEUM
401 E.'M' St., Wilmington, CA 90748

Phone: (213) 548-7777 *Hours:* Tuesday-Thursday and Weekends tours are given at 12:30, 1:30, 2:30, 3:30; tours available by appointment *Admission:* $2 donation requested

The Banning Residence Museum explains Southern California life from 1850-1900 through a period restoration of the former home of General Phineas Banning and his descendants.

The Bannings' Wilmington house was built in 1864 near the conclusion of the Civil War and is the finest example of 19th-century Greek Revival architecture extant in Southern California.

Since 1974, the twenty-three-room house has been painstakingly restored to its former Victorian elegance. Although the Banning family papers were lost in a 1946 fire, making it difficult to know exactly how each room was decorated, thirty-two pieces of furniture, original to the house, were donated by the Banning family. Rooms retain decorative aspects added during the period of family residence to demonstrate the eclectic nature of a home lived in by several generations. The collection is mostly period furniture.

ALBANY

[1] ADAME CERAMICS CRAFT GALLERY

1251 Solono Ave., Albany, CA 94706 (415) 526-9558

Mon-Sat: 10-5 *Owner/Dir:* Susan Adame

Susan Adame opened the gallery in 1981 in a renovated supermarket divided into studio space where she created "architectural ceramics" such as production basins and shower fixtures and gallery space where she sold her own work. She later turned to pottery and abstract wall hangings, distinctive for their soft pastel shades and primitive images, and rented out some of the studio space to San Francisco Bay-area sculptors and potters.

She now represents approximately twenty-five artists who create jewelry, handblown glass, copperwork, masks, sculpture and ceramic wall-hangings. Bay-area artists who rent studio space include Barbara Bobes, Nancy Jenses, James Sleeper and Cheryl Williams. Others include Thomas Knight, a Chico, California artist who creates copper-red pots by combining slender classical forms with ancient glaze techniques; Ohio copper enamel artist Barbara Culp; and Santa Fe ceramist Mei Ming.

The gallery also specializes in the smoke-fired pottery of the Jemez Pueblo, sells work of the Hopi, Zia, Laguna and Acoma tribes and imports pieces of African sculpture.

AUBURN

[2] ART CETERA

175 Almond St., Auburn, CA 95603 (916) 885-5670

Mon, Wed, Fri: 10-5; Tues, Thurs, Sat: 10-2:30 *Dir:* L. Lewis Ortiz

This nonprofit gallery is located in an old library building. It sponsors eleven exhibitions a year, concentrating on solo, two-person and group showings by local artists. Among those, Judy Keane's small petit point textiles, stitched paintings and portraits; Larry Ortiz's ceramics, pots and vessels shaped like tulips and lotus blossoms; Terry Moller's American Indian clay figures, ceramics, masks and paintings; Ursula Borbach's religious icons and portraits; and Juan Peña's rugged seascapes of the Monterey and Carmel peninsula. Other artists include fabric artist Penny Rodrick, Gene Scott, Esteban Villa and Stan Patilla. Past exhibits have also featured works of photography, raku pottery and bamboo furniture.

BAKERSFIELD

[3] CUNNINGHAM ART GALLERY

1930 R St., Bakersfield, CA 93301 (805) 323-7219

Tues-Sat: 10-4; Sun: 12-4 *Owner:* City of Bakersfield
Dir: Judith Sealy

Established in 1956, the gallery was founded in memory of California artist Marion Cunningham. It is a nonprofit organization that seeks primarily to showcase regional California art, and provide a venue for emerging local artists. Its permanent collection includes the work of Marion Cunningham, the desert landscapes of regionalist Paul Lauritz and a number of paintings by California watercolorist Phil Paradise.

In addition, it sponsors eight shows a year with an emphasis on California artists. A recent exhibit was an Ansel Adams retrospective, covering masterworks from 1930-1970. Another California artist featured by the gallery is Rico Lebrun. An important influence for generations of California artists, he is known for his unerring draftsmanship and monumental human themes. Many of his works deal with man's humanity and inhumanity. His classical subjects received a slightly surrealistic treatment, though they are always grounded in the realistic and never completely abstract.

Three contemporary black artists from Los Angeles, Matthew Thomas, Sandra Rowe and Joe Grant, were the subjects of another recent exhibit. Rowe's large and viscerally immediate paintings dwell on the uncertainty of life. Another work, a triptych, has zigzagging two- and three-dimensional aspects. Suggesting a small personal altar, it stresses a deliberate crudeness, verging on the vulgar. Grant is a mixed-media artist known for his sculptures and installation works. Thomas's very textured and patterned pieces make references to his African heritage. They are large abstractions that are given similarly abstract names such as *Cosmic* or *Transcendental.* Some incorporate unusual materials, for example, ashes from a fireplace. A joint show featured artists Mark Adams and Beth van Hoesen. They work in a variety of print techniques: lithographs, linocuts, woodblocks, serigraphs, aquatint, as well as watercolor and drawings. Other shows have focused on 19th century photographs and the works of Hispanic California artists.

BELLFLOWER

[4] DE RU'S FINE ARTS

9100 E. Artesia Blvd., Bellflower, CA 90706
(213) 920- 1312

Tues-Fri: 10-5; Sat: 10-2 *Owner/Dir:* Dewitt C. McCall

De Ru's Fine Arts, in the same location for twenty years, specializes in 19th and early 20th century American art. The gallery has an emphasis on early California Impressionists. It also provides restoration services and sells art books relating to the period.

The gallery handles paintings by: Francis McComas, one of the three California artists included in the 1913 Armory Show; E. Charlton Fortune, a leader among the California Impressionists after she had studied in Europe; and Joseph Raphael, who also spent time in Europe and introduced Post-Impressionist styles to northern California. Other Post-Impressionists represented are Anne Bremer and Gottardo Piazzoni.

The gallery also carries paintings by Dana Bartlett, Franz Bischoff, Carl Oscar Borg, George K. Brandriff, Maurice Braun, Henry Joseph Breuer, Benjamin Chambers Brown, Giuseppe Cadenasso, Emil Carlsen, Frank Tolles Chamberlin, Alson Skinner Clark, Colin Campbell Cooper, Frank Cuprien, Paul Dougherty, J. Bond Francisco, Charles A. Fries, John M. Gamble, Percy Gray, William A. Griffith, Armin Hansen, Sam Hyde Harris, Anna A. Hills, Clarence Hinkle, Clark Hobart, Thomas L. Hunt, Joseph Kleitsch, Paul Lauritz, Jean Mannheim, Xavier Martinez, Arthur Mathews, Lucia K. Mathews, Thomas McGlynn, Alfred Mitchell, Mary DeNeale Morgan, Bruce Nelson, Eugen Neuhaus, John O'Shea, Jules Pages, Edgar A. Payne, Charles Rollo Peters, Hanson Puthuff, Granville Redmond, Charles Reiffel, William Ritschel, Guy Rose, Donna Schuster, Jack Wilkinson Smith, Gardner Symins, Elmer Wachtel, Marion Kavanagh Wachtel, William Wendt and Theodore Wores.

BERKELEY

[5] ARTS AND CRAFTS COOPERATIVE, INC. (ACCI)
1652 Shattuck, Berkeley, CA 94709 (415) 843-2527

Mon-Sat: 10:30-5:30 *Owner:* Arts and Crafts Cooperative *Dir:* Pat McGraw

The oldest operating arts cooperative in the United States, the Arts and Crafts Cooperative, Inc., founded in 1959, is owned and operated by 1,500 member artists. It is a member-run arts organization which embraces both fine contemporary crafts and fine art. Located in a large, handsome, brick building in north Berkeley, the ACCI Gallery houses a wide range of artworks, including pottery, jewelry, glass, textiles, wood, sculpture, paintings, prints and photography. Over 200 Bay Area artists are exhibited at any given time in the sunlit ACCI Gallery.

Among the California artists shown are internationally known wood turner Bob Stocksdale, printmaker Elizabeth Kavaler and ceramic artists Bill Creitz and Ben Spangler.

Artists are accepted for membership in the cooperative by jury selection, monthly for the fine arts, yearly for crafts.

[6] THE AMES GALLERY OF AMERICAN FOLK ART
2661 Cedar St., Berkeley CA 94708 (415) 845-4949

Wed-Sat: 2-6 or by appt. *Dir:* Bonnie Grossman

The Ames Gallery of American Folk Art is comfortably located in the home of its director in the hills north of the Berkeley campus. The gallery's focus as well as its name have changed to reflect a specialization in exceptional eighteenth-through twentieth-century handmade objects and paintings.

Established in 1970, the gallery has become known for theme shows of antique utilitarian items alternating with contemporary folk paintings and sculpture. These include: "On the Mend," an exhibition of early artful repaired objects; "Hearth and Home," decorative kitchen utensils and quilts; "Twice Upon a Time," early pieces recycled for other uses; "Memories and Visions," contemporary folk painters contemplating their pasts or futures; "Broad Brush, Fine Line," four black folk artists; and "Guided Hands, Devoted Hearts," a show of religious images.

The main gallery has a rotating series of shows, each usually lasting close to six weeks. A continuous exhibit is displayed in the gallery's second room which encompasses a sampling of other items from the gallery's inventory. Items shown here include tramp art, memory jars, cigarette paper art, canes, whirligigs, carved creek-rocks, articulated dolls, paintings and drawings.

[7] TZIN TZUN TZAN WAREHOUSE
1042 Murray St., Berkeley, CA 94710 (415) 644-1090

Fri, Sat & Sun: 10-5 *Owners:* Henry Wangeman and Rosa Bloom

This is a gallery devoted to Mexican craftsmen who work in a traditional vein, and craftsmen whose work falls on the line between craft and art. These three-dimensional works celebrate both traditional and personal themes. For example, in October 1989, the work of weaver Zacarias Ruiz will be shown. The exhibition will trace the history of weaving design of his home town in Mexico, these influences being reflected in his creations. Certain of his pieces will explore personal themes.

In November the gallery will show the work of Aaron Bevelazco, a tinsmith who makes traditional tinware such as boxes, candlesticks and lanterns as well as personal art objects having less focus on utilitarian uses. Beginning as a wholesaler of varied items for galleries and museums, Tzin Tzun Tzan has evolved into a retail gallery. It recently had its first showing of two-dimensional art, which featured Francisco Onate, a painter of folkloric images of Michoacan. The gallery occupies 2,000 square feet and offers the largest selection of Mexican Folk Art in Northern California.

BEVERLY HILLS

[8] GALERIE MICHAEL
430 N. Rodeo Dr., Beverly Hills, CA 90210
(213) 273- 3377

Mon-Tues: 10-7; Wed: 10-9; Thurs: 10-10; Fri-Sat 10-11; Sun: 12-6 *Owner/Dir:* Michael Schwartz

The gallery specializes in fine nineteenth-century paintings, prints and drawings, as well as the work of early twentieth- century masters. There is an emphasis on French art from the turn of the century.

Featured by Galerie Michael are *belle-époque* posters by artists such as Toulouse-Lautrec, Jules Chéret, Alphonse Mucha, Theophile Steinlen. Each year there is a French turn-of-the-century poster show. The gallery carries watercolors and pastels by Paulemile Pissaro; and paintings, drawings and etchings by Manuel Robbe. Graphics and sculpture by Auguste Renoir are also available. Frequently the gallery has shows of particular schools, such as the French Barbizon painters Breton, Dupre, Lhermitte, Harpignies and Jacques.

Earlier works are also available, especially Rembrandt etchings, and each year there is a Master Graphics show with works ranging from Albrecht Durer to the twentieth century.

Also carried are works by Mary Cassatt, Marc Chagall, Henri Matisse, Pablo Picasso and others.

[9] LOUIS NEWMAN GALLERIES
322 N. Beverly Dr., Beverly Hills CA 90210
(213) 278-6311

Tues-Sat: 10-9:30; Sun-Mon: 10-6:30 *Owner:* Louis Newman

The gallery specializes in modern and contemporary paintings, sculpture, ceramics and prints. Artists exhibited include: Armando Amaya, Garo Antreasian, David Aronson, Paul Cadmus, Chuang Che, Kris Cox, Enrico Donati, Martin Green, Doug Hyde, Matsumi Kanemitsu, Katherine Liu, Bob Longhurst, Reginald Marsh, Harrison McIntosh, Peter Milton, Elie Nadelman, Otto Natzler, Lowell Nesbitt, Auguste Rodin, Paul Soldner, Linda Stevens and William Zorach.

[10] PETERSEN GALLERIES
332 N. Rodeo Drive, Beverly Hills, CA 90210
(213) 274-6705

Tues-Fri: 10-6; Sat: 11-5 or by appt. *Dir:* Mr. Jean Stern

The gallery exhibits works from the American Impressionists (1880-1930), California Impressionists (1900-1930) and Western masters (prior to 1930). Artists featured include Frederic Remington, Charles M. Russell, Thomas Moran, Childe Hassam, E.W. Redfield, Edgar A. Payne, William Wendt, Franz A. Bischoff, Alson C. Clark and others. The gallery has published monographs on important California impressionists.

CALISTOGA

[11] DONLEE GALLERY

1316 Lincoln Ave., Calistoga, CA 94515
(707) 942-0585

Daily: 10-5; Sun: 10-3 *Owner:* Lee Love

The gallery specializes in art of the West, particularly of the Southwest, showing work in sculpture, watercolor, oil, acrylic, woodcarving and a limited amount of fabric art. Styles include contemporary realism and impressionism. Artists include: Ralph Love, an oil painter who concentrates on landscapes of the Southwest, especially the Grand Canyon, deserts and seascapes; K.M. Hendricks, oil painter of Western Still-lifes; James Coleman, versatile oil painter of landscapes, deserts, Indian Mesas of the Southwest and other regions; Daniel Damiani, impressionist painter of floral subjects; and Tava, a sculptor who is a native of Arizona and who works in alabaster. In October of 1989, the works of David Whitlock, unique, realistic pieces in controlled watercolor, will be featured.

CAMBRIA

[12] THE SEEKERS COLLECTION AND GALLERY

4090 Burton Dr., Cambria, CA 93428
(805) 927-4352

Sun-Sat: 10-10 *Owner:* Lynda and Michael Adelson
Dir: Barbara Morningstar

Established in 1981, the gallery has amassed a strong collection of contemporary glass art, one of the finest in the U.S. It is devoted exclusively to contemporary glass art, and has works by over a hundred leading glass artists. Several are featured on an ongoing basis. Of these, many are internationally acclaimed artists of the American studio glass movement. Among them is Richard Marquis, known for his nonfunctional *murrini* teapots, jewelry, eggs and bottles. Murrini is a glassware technique used by the Eygptians and Romans. Also represented is Steven Maslach, preeminent designer and maker of handblown stemware. Many of his sculptural glass pieces use dichroic glass to create kinetic visual statements that challenge the viewer's perception of color and form. R. Strong works prolifically, creating pieces that range from stemware, paperweights and vases to massive abstract sculptures. He is widely recognized for his bold designs and distinctive color formulations, particularly cobalt blue. Michael Nourot produces cased glass blown in multiple layers, with colorful patterns are encased between layers of clear glass. A variety of colored enamels is used to decorate the pieces, similar to the crushed glass powders used in cloisonne. Michael Cohn and Molly Stone collaborate on sculptural pieces and vases. Cohn is renown for his works *Space Cup* and *Roll Over Mondrian and Tell Brancusi the News.* John Nygren's glassworks are characterized by radiant colors, impeccable, jewel-like detail and whimsical subjects. Josh Simpson's versatility is displayed in works ranging from simple, bold pieces in clear crystal to meteorite-like, abstract sculptures with an iridescence reminiscent of Tiffany's *favrile* glass.

CAPITOLA

[13] WALTER/WHITE GALLERY

107 Capitola Ave., Capitola, CA 95010
(415) 845-4949

Wed-Sat: 2-6
see entry for Carmel

CARMEL

[14] FIRST IMPRESSIONS/BARBARA LINHARD GALLERY

Delores & 6th St. (P.O. Box 3628), Carmel, CA 93921 (408) 625- 5626

Owner/Dir: Barbara Linhard

First Impressions/Barbara Linhard Gallery is a small, well-lit, contemporary looking gallery in the midst of Carmel's gallery row. In 1979 it began operations as First Impressions but will change its name to Barbara Linhard Gallery. The gallery's original focus was originally on prints. Today owner and director Barbara Linhard also deals in watercolors, mixed-media pieces and drawings.

The gallery exhibits one person or group shows monthly. A large percentage of its artists are from California but the gallery also features several from the East Coast and Europe. Among the artists represented are: Gordon Mortonson, who makes reduction woodcuts; Beth Van Hoesen, a watercolorist and printmaker; Mark Adams, who prints and paints watercolors on floral subjects; Alexander Beselein, a German printmaker in the current school of Munich; and Daniel Destlan, a French collage and mixed-media artist living in New York.

Owner Linhard also performs art consulting and is seeking to represent exceptional artists whose primary medium is printmaking.

[15] WALTER/WHITE FINE ARTS GALLERIES

7th at San Carlos and San Carlos at 5th, P.O. Box 4834, Carmel, CA 93921 (408) 624-4390

Daily: 10-6 *Owner:* Brendan Walter

The gallery is devoted to the works of contemporary wood designers, ceramists, paper artists, printmakers and jewelers. Many of the artists represented are internationally-known and have work in permanent museum collections around the world in such places as Musee des Arts, Decoratifs-Palais du Louvre-France, Smithsonian-Washington, D.C., Corning-New York, Victoria & Albert-London and The Museum of Modern Art-New York. The featured glass artists include: Dale Chihuly, William Morris, Gary Beecham, John Lewis and Richard Marquis. Ceramists represented by the gallery include: Matthew Leeds and Nancy Meeker. Robert Erickson and Philip Moulthrop are wood artists. Jewelry craftspeople shown at the gallery include Paul Morelli, Linda Threadgill and Barbara Heinrich. The gallery represents a collective of 300 or more artists whose unique style and high level of craftsmanship puts them on the cutting edge of contemporary fine art today.

[16] WESTON GALLERY, INC.

P.O. Box 655, 6th Ave., Carmel, CA 93921
(408) 624-4453

Tues-Sun: 1-5 *Owner:* Maggi Weston and Russ Anderson *Dir:* Russ Anderson

The gallery specializes in fine 19th and 20th century photographs, photographic portfolios and books, with emphasis on works by masters of the photographic medium. The 19th century collection includes works by Talbot, Hill & Adamson, Cameron, Fenton, Le Gray, Bisson, Emerson, Watkins and Muybridge. The 20th century collection includes works by Stieglitz, Strand, Weston, Adams, Man Ray, Steichen, Brandt and Frank. In addition to contemporary artists Olivia Parker, Paul Caponigro, Harry Callahan, Jerry Uelsmann and others, the gallery also represents emerging artists from California and other states. The gallery also shows dada and surrealist paintings and prints by Christopher James and Beth Weismann.

CHICO

[17] CALIFORNIA STATE UNIVERSITY-CHICO ART GALLERY

California State University-Chico, Chico, CA 95929
(916) 895-5750

Mon-Fri: 9-4:30; Sun 11-4; closed July, Aug *Dir:* Michael Bishop

The gallery's objective is to showcase a wide variety of contemporary art for its students and community. Seven exhibits a year feature artists whose followings are national and international in scope. Past exhibitions include a show of Rebecca Gozion's paintings, in conjunction with the Michael Himovitz Gallery; Italo Scanga's mixed media wall pieces, assemblage, paintings and sculptures; a Rodin exhibition from the Stanford University collection; and an exhibit from the L.A. Center for Photographic Studies entitled "Ethnic Documentation," which features the photography of five ethnic photographers. Other exhibitions include Richard Shaw's ceramics, Paul Kos' conceptual art and Emmanuel Neri's figurative sculptures.

In addition, an annual show is devoted to the art of its faculty. Lynn Criswell's sculptures, mixed-media works and paintings on paper reflect travels in Turkey and the Middle East. They utilize Muslim and Christian Byzantine imagery, and have a folk-art quality. James Kieper's large scale abstract paintings make references to aerial photography. Lisa Rienertson works with large ceramic sculptures and portraiture. One of her commemorative public sculptures is a commission of Martin Luther King, done in bronze. Michael Bishop creates narrative sculpture in mixed media. A typical piece is *An Eye For An Eye Is All Well Above.* It depicts a drawing in bronze of a 747 jet; below that is a picture of a howling dog, flanked by a picture of Matisse's *Dancers.* His works generally make reference to topical events; this particular piece alludes to the sabotage of the Pan Am airliner that exploded over Scotland.

CLAREMONT

[18] CLAREMONT GRADUATE SCHOOL EAST AND WEST GALLERIES

251 E. 10th St., Claremont, CA 91711
(714) 621-8071

Mon-Fri: 10-5 *Dir:* Connie Zehr

In addition to numerous student project exhibitions, the two galleries host eight to ten professional exhibitions a year. Its focus is contemporary southern California art. Many shows are installations; a number are exchange shows. A recent exchange show displayed works by inmates and instructors from a California correctional facility.

Millard Sheets, among the founding artists of the California school of watercolor, headed the art department at Scripps College, part of the Claremont Colleges. An exhibit featuring his last and most current works is planned for the upcoming year. Exhibits of other major artists include Lawrence Gipe's oily depictions of locomotive engines, as well as Jim Morphesis's paintings and Ruth Weissberg's prints. A group show featured proposals for site-specific works by such artists as Leta Albuquerque and Peter Shelton. An intriguing exhibit by Michael Brewster featured acoustical sculptures. The sculpture used standing waves and sound waves to define and shape the space between sculptural buttresses, so that sound itself is the sculpture. Other artists who have exhibited include sculptor John Frame and painter Janet Tholen.

COSTA MESA

[19] SUSAN SPIRITUS GALLERY

3333 Bear St., Suite 330, Costa Mesa, CA 92626
(714) 549-7520

Mon-Fri: 10-9; Sat: 10-6; Sun: 12-5 *Owner/Dir:* Susan Spiritus

The Susan Spiritus Gallery is one of South Coast galleries devoted exclusively to contemporary fine art photography. The gallery is newly located in the Crystal Court Mall in the South Coast Plaza. At Susan Spiritus, the work of many fine, well-known photographers can be seen, such as Ansel Adams, Jerry Uelsmann, Emmet Gowin, Eikoh Hosoe, George Tice and Marsha Burns.

The gallery also shows work by emerging artists across the U.S., Europe and Japan. Among the artists shown on a regular basis are Clinton Smith, Jeffrey Becomz, Robert Doisneau, Henry Gilpin, John Sexton, Andre Kertesz and others. Three portfolios have been published by the gallery: *WESTCOASTNOW,* containing the work of 12 contemporary photographers; *CIRCUS,* gelatin silver prints from the Barnum and Bailey Circus by Jacqueline Thurston and another by Thurston, *DIORAMAS,* published in 1985. The gallery also represents hand-made sterling silver jewelry by Carolina Cale from Chicago, and hand-turned wooden vessels by Michael Foster from Tennessee.

FREMONT

[20] OLIVE HYDE ART GALLERY

123 Washington Blvd., P.O. Box 5006, Fremont, CA 94537 (415) 791-4320

Wed-Sun: 12:30-5; Thurs: 6-8:30 *Owner:* City of Fremont, Leisure Services Department *Dir:* Cynthia Raap

A noncommercial, nonprofit gallery, the Olive Hyde Gallery's mission includes educating the public, and the promotion and support of local northern Californian artists. The gallery generally exhibits paintings, sculptures, ceramics, crafts and textiles. The gallery exhibits occasional historic retrospectives, and sponsors one or two touring shows a year. Recent touring shows include a Smithsonian exhibit on Italian photography, and an exhibit showcasing artists from Leningrad.

A sampling of past exhibitions include Wynn Bullock's photography, an exhibit of 16th century Russian

Barry Entner, *Dreamscape,* glass.
Courtesy: Seekers Collection & Gallery, Cambria

Kerry Feldman, *Modern Man,* glass.
Courtesy: Seekers Collection & Gallery, Cambria

religious icons; Martha Mans' watercolors; Keith Ward's impressionist paintings; Michele Wambaugh's photography; and Nora Vest's sculptures. Other artists featured include Pat Hickman and Lillian Elliot, who create basket constructions. Set on pedestals, they are notable for their use of unsual materials such as wood and stretched gut. Another artist who works with baskets is Susan Taber, whose bright baskets are built from large wads of thread, machine stitched over and over again. These baskets are emblazoned with geometric patterns, concentric and overlapping circles. Zoe Adorno, a Bay Area sculptor, makes free-standing glass sculptures from fused dichroic glass. The glass fuses with odd bits of unusual metals to create opalescent and translucent streaks. Dan Peterson, northern Californian watercolorist, paints photo-realistic landscapes. These bright jewel-toned paintings are studies of water.

FRESNO

[21] ALLARD'S GALLERY
2225 W. Shaw Ave., Fresno, CA 93711
(209) 225-7000

Mon-Fri: 10-6; Sat: 10-5 *Owner:* Bill and Gladia Sethre
Dir: Gladia Sethre

The gallery specializes in paintings and original graphics by contemporary artists, especially Valley Artists. Among those, Tony Bennett, Carey Alvar, Theo Tobiasse, R.C. Gorman and William Papas are offered. It features as well, limited edition prints by McCartney Terpning, Gene Harvey and Beth Doolittle. Many center around early Americana or western wildlife; typical are themes from the turn of the century or the early aviation period.

William Papas, an internationally known artist, is represented by his watercolors and hand-colored, plated colored etchings. A syndicated cartoonist from London, he relinquished a comfortable security for three years of travel in small-town America with his wife. As she collected oral narratives, he sketched its inhabitants. Fifty of his etchings are collected in *Papas' America Book and Suite*, along with commentary gathered by his wife. He also has a series of twenty plate colored etchings based on written portraits of the people of Old Jerusalem and collected in *Papas' Jerusalem Suite*. Another internationally acclaimed artist is R.C. Gorman. He is known for his works drawing on his Navaho Indian heritage, and particularly for his graceful portraits of Navaho women. A number of lithographs and several paintings are featured.

A particular emphasis is placed on local area, Fresno artists. Among these, Jane Guyer, Suzanne Baker and Lida Bell Wylie are notable. Also represented are bronzes by Lester Harry and the works of Larry De-Witt.

GLENDALE

[22] BRAND LIBRARY ART GALLERIES
1601 W. Mountain St., Glendale, CA 91201

Tues & Thurs: 12:30-9; Wed, Fri, Sat: 12:30-6 Openings: 2nd Sun of every month *Owner:* City of Glendale
Dir: Joe Fuchs and Cindy Carr

Affiliated with Brand Art and Music Library, the galleries have often been called the most beautiful spaces for the showing of contemporary art today. There is 300 feet of display space split into two sections, both sections being well-designed and aesthetically appealing. Emphasis is placed on contemporary art from California and the Southwest. There are eleven exhibitions per year, consisting of both group and solo shows, covering a broad spectrum of work from conservative to cutting-edge.

Past shows have featured the floral prints of Henry Evans; the paintings of Peter Plagens; the prints, paintings and drawings of Joe Mugnaini; brass sculptures by cartoonist Paul Conrad; and watercolors by past presidents of the National Watercolor Society. Recent showings have included glass sculpture by John Luebtow and photographs by Norman Mauskops. Recently shown was an exhibition of Haitian art. Art work is accepted through personal appointment with the gallery directors.

HAYWARD

[23] ADOBE ART CENTER
20395 San Miguel Ave, Hayward, CA 94546
(415) 881-6735

Mon-Fri: 10-4 *Owner:* Hayward Area Recreational and Park District *Dir:* Joy Glading

The Adobe Art Center offers art classes and exhibitions to the Hayward community. The center was established in 1960 and is housed in an adobe brick building designed by San Francisco architect Mario Corbett and built by the Works Progress Administration in 1938. Its timbers were hand hewn from discarded telephone poles and inside is a large copper mural designed by Clay Spone and executed by Alanzo Chard. Over the center's large fireplace is a mosaic mural depicting a bullfight and the completion of the transcontinental railroad. Also on the center's grounds is a ceramics studio and the Red Wood Studio, a 3,360 square foot facility which includes painting, jewelry and sculpture studios as well as a lounge and restaurant.

Each year the center presents approximately ten group and solo shows. All of its artists come from the surrounding Bay Area and recent one-person shows featured: Raku artist Donna Smith; basket maker Elaine Hill; ceramic collage maker Carol Molly Prier; woodcut artist Paul Zunino; and quilt maker Nora Stoffel. The center is owned and staffed by the Hayward Area Recreational and Park District.

[24] CALIFORNIA STATE-HAYWARD UNIVERSITY ART GALLERY
California State University-Hayward, Hayward, CA 94542 (415) 881-3299

Sept-June Sun: 1-4; Mon-Wed: 11-4; Thurs: 11-7 *Dir:* Lou Carson

The gallery mounts six shows during the academic year, the first of which features works by art department faculty, and the last by students in the graduate program. The remaining four exhibitions are decided by faculty committee, and reflect a broad array of interests. Among them, exhibits on the book as an art form, a show on photo-montage, on pre-Columbian pottery, as well as site-specific installations. The gallery aims to expose its public to a wide variety of different and unusual media. Several have featured pieces with such unusual media as fish skins stretched over primitive pottery and works of fish guts and wire.

[25] CHABOT COLLEGE ART GALLERY
25555 Hesperian Blvd., Hayward, CA 94545
(415) 786-6829

Mon-Thurs: 8am-10pm Fri: 8-5; closed July, Aug *Dir:* John Komisar

The core of this gallery's exhibits are the works of beginning and emerging artists. One or two shows a year feature works by the college's students, and on alternate years a show features works by high school students from south Alameda County. The gallery's additional seven or eight yearly shows are, for the most part, solo or two-person shows. Recent exhibitions include Sheila Perry's large abstract oils, Harry Wilson's black-and-white photographs, Anthony Santolla's photographs that resembled Polaroid distortions, Risa Teitelbaum and Max Benjamin's large abstracts, Robert Horning's figurative drawings in pastel, Bill Broder's large figurative oils, Paul Bouchard's large abstracts and Barry Kramme's shamanistic wall hangings. Upcoming exhibits will feature Helene Rice and Kin Hsieh's Chinese brushpaintings, Terry Baranouskas's color montage, Susie Elkind's black-and-white photography and Juana Alicia's muralistic political paintings.

HUNTINGTON BEACH

[26] JOHN AND LYNNE BOLEN FINE ARTS

P.O. Box 5654, Huntington Beach, CA 92615
(714) 968-0806

By appointment *Owner/Dir:* John Bolen

This gallery deals privately in American art, specializing in the decades between 1920 and 1940. Its collection is comprised of paintings and sculptures from the regionalist, social realist and modernist movements, which sprang up in the interim between the wars. Its collection also includes drawings and prints produced before 1950.

Among the gallery's offerings are important pieces by seminal midwestern regionalists Thomas Hart Benton, Grant Wood and John Steuart Curry, as well as Paul Sample. A recent acquisition is Charles Sheeler's *Worker Open Hearth Building*, a 1928 painting from the River Rouge Industrial Plant series. This piece is among those that marked a shift in Sheeler's works from an abstract, cubist representation to a more cubist-realism style. Significant Californian regionalists are represented in paintings by Emil Kosa, Jr. and in the rare watercolors of James Patrick. Social realists include Joe Jones, Arnold Blanch and Harry Sternberg. A number of modernist pieces are presented, including those of Karl Knaths and William H. K. Yarrow. An important though underrated modernist is David Burljuk. He, along with Kandinsky and brother Vladimir, founded the futurist movement in Moscow, as well as the Blauer Reiter. Several of his faux naive style paintings are represented.

[27] CHARLES WHITCHURCH FINE ARTS

16172 Brent Circle, Huntington Beach, CA 92647
(714) 846-8859

Mon-Fri: 10-4 (by appt. only); *Owner/Dir:* Charles Whitchurch

The gallery, located within a private residence, is brimming with works of modern and contemporary art. In addition to works of modern masters such as Marc Chagall, Friedensreich Hundertwasser, Henri Matisse, Joan Miro, Pablo Picasso and Rufino Tamayo, the gallery offers works by contemporary California artists such as Peter Alexander, Carlos Almarz and Eric Orr. A recent display featured original prints by Richard Diebenkorn, Jim Dine, David Hockney, Jasper Johns, Roy Lichtenstein, Robert Motherwell, Frank Stella, Wayne Thiebaud and Tom Wesselmann. The gallery often offers unique works by established artists, such as monoprints by Charles Arnoldi, vapor drawings by Larry Bell, solar burn works by Jay McCafferty, mixed-media collages by Jim Morphesis, epoxy-and-resin paintings by Helen Pashgian, mineral-leaf-on-glass pieces by Judy Stabile and oil on canvas-with-grommet paintings by Bert Yarborough.

The gallery is the west coast distributor for watercolorists Nell Anderson and Darrell Ebert, and also carries a wide variety of original prints, paintings and drawings by Dan Allison, assisting in mounting exhibitions for Allison's work in Calgary, Chicago, Los Angeles, New York, San Francisco, Tokyo, Vienna and other cities.

Owner/director Charles Whitchurch, a professor of humanities active in the international art scene, takes pleasure in acting as a resource for visitors and clients. A member of the Board of Directors for the Art Dealers Association of California, Whitchurch lectures in the United States and Japan on topics ranging from proper authentication of art to the future of the contemporary art market. He provides art to collectors and galleries in Canada, Mexico, Europe and Japan. Recently he curated a master print exhibition for Golden West College, and curated the largest museum show of Tamayo paintings ever held on the west coast. His articles on aesthetics ("Rufino Tamayo: Transformation and Metaphor") and investment ("Investing in Original Prints") have been published here and overseas. Whitchurch frequently advises clients on art conservation and appreciation, and particularly enjoys explaining new art forms to clients and "helping them expand their vision."

IRVINE

[28] UNIVERSITY OF CALIFORNIA-IRVINE FINE ARTS GALLERY

University of California-Irvine, Irvine, CA 92715

Tues-Sun: 12-5 *Dir:* Melinda Wortz

Its focus is primarily, though not exclusively, contemporary art by established national and international artists. It was founded in 1965 by former director and photographer John Copeland, who was also the founder of *ArtForum Magazine*. The painting, sculpture, photography and installation exhibits are generally accompanied by lectures from the artists.

The gallery's shows are strong on installation works. Jennifer Bartlett's installation, entitled *Rhap Sody*, displayed a thousand pieces of baked enamel panels. These white panels featured imagery in a range of styles, from abstract to pointillistic. Alice Aycock's installation resembled a giant loom, and commented on late industrial culture. Dennis Oppenheim creates mixed-media installations of wood, metal and glass. Other exhibits include Jonathan Borofsky's multimedia works and Larry Bell's coated paintings and sculptures. In addition, there have been exhibits of works by David Hockney, Roy Lichtenstein and conceptual artist David Ireland.

LAGUNA BEACH

[29] COLLECTOR'S CHOICE

20352 Laguna Canyon Rd., Laguna Beach, CA 92651 (714) 494- 4515

Sat-Sun: 10-7; weekdays by appt. *Owner/Dir:* Beverly Inskeep

The gallery specializes in folk and "tramp" art. There is a special emphasis on animated sculptures such as whirligigs, or the type of moving stage scenes made by nomadic theater groups. Collector's Choice does not carry antiques but, rather, contemporary created works, including those created by new and emerging talent.

Twice a year the gallery features theme shows with over 100 artists participating. The recent "Art and Technology" show included a Tesla Coil sculpture, a wall of "folk neon" works and a giant ball-and-chain with a set of keys attached. The gallery insists that the work be entertaining and use materials in an interesting way.

A few of the many artists exhibited are Larry Gill, Len Glasser, Pat Klotz, Tom Kress, June Richardson, Pat Sparkuhl and Joan Swanson.

[30] ENGMAN LIMITED

1492 S. Coast Highway, Laguna Beach, CA 92651
Second Location: 26 Glenneyrie St., Laguna Beach, CA 92651 (714) 497-7135

Mon-Fri: 9-6 Weekends: 11-6 *Owner/Dir:* Glenn Engman

For the past ten years Engman Limited has been the worldwide agent and publisher of Columbian painter Orlando A.B. (Agudelo-Botero). The gallery handles his exhibition arrangements, sells his work to dealers from around the world and publishes his books. The gallery presents from one to three exhibitions each year and has two Laguna Beach locations: a 1600 square foot space on South Coast Highway and a twenty-four foot high, 3000 square foot space on Glenneyrie Street. In addition to Orlando A.B., Engman Limited represents the metal sculptors Michi Rafael (from New York) and David Segal. Both Rafael and Segal create works in a variety of sizes from small to monumental.

[31] RICHARD YEAKEL ANTIQUES

1099 S. Coast Hwy., Laguna Beach, CA 92651
(714) 494-5526

Tues-Sat: 9-5 *Owner:* Richard Yeakel *Dir:* Robert Yeakel

Furniture and decorative arts are the main stock in trade of this gallery, surrounded by a community of art galleries and artists in a region of Southern California noted for its artistic history. The gallery carries Laguna Beach artists of the early 20th century plein air school. Owner Richard Yeakel is the son of the gallery's founder, who began the business 50 years ago. They specialize in 18th century furniture from all over the world. There's also a second store near the main space, where the gallery exhibits 16th century furniture and old paintings, such as Rembrandt etchings and master prints. Although most of the stock is furniture, the gallery also focuses on other decorative arts and painting.

One special piece in the gallery is a 14th century gothic carving from the cathedral of Cologne. A rare triptych showing six male and six female saints, it was brought from Germany in 1944 by a collector to New York, from whom the gallery acquired it. The gallery offers tours with the Ritz-Carlton hotel.

LA JOLLA

[32] THOMAS BABEOR GALLERY

470 Girard Avenue, La Jolla, CA 92037
(619) 454-0345

Tues-Sat: 10-5, by appointment only *Owner/Dir:* Thomas Babeor

Located in the coastal resort town of La Jolla, this gallery specializes in contemporary American and European art by well-known artists whose works appear in museums and private collections world-wide.

The gallery's collection ranges in style from the colorful, buoyant constructions of Frank Stella to the earthy, hermetic creations of Joseph Beuys. The gallery also carries the lyrical calligraphic drawings of Cy Twombly and the simple shaped-canvas paintings of Ellsworth Kelly. The art represented here is consistent in its high-level collectablity. The work of such California notables as word-imagist Ed Ruscha and painter Billy Al Bengston share company with the work of such major European artists as painter Gerhard Richter and sculptor Mario Merz. Also featured is the work of Jasper Johns, Mimo Paladino and Woods Davy.

The gallery is committed to several outstanding local artists as well, including Jay Johnson, Robin Bright, Barbara Weldon and Ann Thornycroft.

[33] GALLERY EIGHT

7464 Girard Ave., La Jolla, CA 92037 (619) 454-9781

Mon-Sat: 10-5 *Owner:* Florence Cohen, Ruth Newmark, Barbara Saltman, Sheryl Stougaard *Dir:* Ruth Newmark

Dedicated to providing a forum for the best in contemporary crafts, the gallery represents American and international artists whose innovative design and fine craftsmanship cover the spectrum from functional to decorative art. Continuous, ever-changing exhibits feature work in clay, glass, wood, metal, fiber and jewelry. Initially located in the International Center on the campus of the University of California at San Diego, Gallery Eight moved to its present location in 1978, and in 1986 more than doubled its floor space.

The gallery has exhibited works by such artists as ceramists Anne Hirondelle, Yoshiro Ikeda, Gail Kendall, Thomas Kerrigan and Warren McKenzie; glass designers Steven Correia, Robert Levin, Lisa Schwartz and Kurt Swanson (Pinkerton Glass); jewelry makers Carolyn Bach, Ross Coppelman and Thomas Mann; master wood artisans Philip Moulthrop, David Ellsworth and Robert Stocksdale; basket weavers John Garrett and Fran and Neil Kraynek-Prince; and furniture-maker Wendy Maruyama.

In addition, the gallery always features the work of young, emerging craftspeople. Recently displayed work includes ceramic sculptures by Dina Angel-Wilson, jewelry by Steven Brixner, glass ladies by Robert Sullivan and screens by Catherine Sicango.

[34] GWYDION GALLERY

7825 Fay Ave., La Jolla, CA 92037 (619) 456-3737

Mon-Sat: 10-5 *Owner/Dir:* Rebecca Cabo

The gallery, which occupies a large space in the heart of La Jolla, specializes in contemporary paintings, sculptures and works on paper. Figurative and abstract styles by emerging artists predominate. Some of the California artists represented are Holly Crawford, N'ina Leveton, Stuart Lehrman, Stuart Fineman and

Diana Folsom. Harly Gaber, internationally-known photographer, collagist and painter, is also featured.

[35] THE JONES GALLERY
1264 Prospect St., La Jolla, CA 92037 (619) 459-1370

Mon-Sat: 10-5 & by appt *Owner/Dir:* Doug Jones

Since 1965, the Jones Gallery has featured American realist painters and sculptors.

Several of the artists represented by the Jones Gallery work with bright colors or watercolors. Dan McCaw paints California beach scenes; he and Claire Ruby, a Wisconsite, use impressionist techniques. Stan Davis is a realistic Western painter; Jack Lestrade, French-born, paints watercolors of Europe; June Maxion, the gallery's only local artist, is a watercolor painter, who prefers to paint *plein air* rather than in the studio. She is one of the gallery's non-realistic artists. Tom Nicholas is a member of the National Academy; Larry Riley and Robert Gray are the gallery's younger artists. Richard Schiele, a Chicagoan, paints scenes from Mexico and Central America. Howard Rogers is both a sculptor and painter; his western-influenced canvases reveal his Montana upbringing. Other sculptors displayed by the gallery are Stanley Bleifeld; James Bottoms; Chapel; Western sculptor Edward Fraughton; Robert B. Krantz; James McCain, who works with wood and bronze; J. Chester Armstrong, who works in wood; and National Academy Fellow Kent Ullberg.

[36] KNOWLES GALLERY
7422 Girard Ave., La Jolla, CA 92037 (619) 454-0106

Mon-Sat: 10-5; Sun: 1-5 *Owner:* William & Mary Knowles *Dir:* Mary Knowles

The emphasis of this long-established gallery is on presenting the works of some of San Diego's most noted artists. A large selection of regional art by sixty artists can be found in diverse styles and media in 4,000 square feet of exhibition space.

Artworks presented include Esther Davis' and Beth King's bold abstracts; Robert Goldman's impressionist oils; brother Ken Goldman's veiled watercolors and pastels; photo-realism by Daniel Hole; rich collage paintings by Frances Crowell and Helen Dowd; and the orientally-inspired watercolors of Kwan Jung, A.W.S.

Among the many California watercolorists featured are Virginia Bendixen and Beverly Franklin, painting with an impressionist style; Georgeanna Lipe, Joan McKasson and Eleanor Lane, bold colors in the garden and landscape; Sharon Hinckley and John Applegate, crisp detail; and understated realism by Nancy Wostrel; Linda Doll, A.W.S, creates figures defined by light and shadow; and Nancy Livesay, A.W.S., makes strata land and sea scapes.

Classically painting the nude are Glen Maxion and Odile Crick; Chrissa O'Brien catches her "ladies" with a touch of humor. Also showing are the neo-surrealist gouaches of Thierry Chatelain; the delicate airbrush horizon paintings of Jim Saw and the color field canvases of Don de Llamas and Vera Felts.

Sculptors presented include Teresa Cherny and Robert Holley, each creating flowing figures, he in bronze, she in bronze and stone; Malcolm Jones, illusionary acrylic; Shirley Lichtman, abstractions in stone; and Barry Bunker, polished wood.

[37] MANDEVILLE GALLERY
University of California-San Diego, B-027, La Jolla, CA 92093 (619) 534-2864

Tues-Sun: 12-5; closed July, Aug *Dir:* Gerry Macalester

The gallery focuses on contemporary art. In addition to painting, drawing, photography and sculpture, the gallery also exhibits video and installation works. There are six exhibitions per year during the academic year. Past exhibits have included "Gifts of the Sea," large scale studies of the ocean's waters by major expressionist painter Richard Bosman; and "Chile From Within," documentary photographs from fifteen photographers that give a Chilean perspective on the events surrounding the overthrow of Chilean president Allende. Other exhibitions include a joint show by Russian dissidents Komar and Melanid, world renowned for their conceptual art; Los Angeles artist James Trivers; and a major architectural exhibit.

[38] RICHARD L. NELSON GALLERY & FINE ARTS COLLECTION
University of California, San Diego, B-027, La Jolla, CA 95616 (916) 752-8500

Mon-Fri: 12-5; Sun: 12-5 *Dir:* L. Price Amerson, Jr.

The gallery's focus is contemporary northern California art, especially by artists who have taught, studied or been involved with the University of California-Davis fine arts program. Named for the first chair of the art department at Davis, the gallery's collection comprises over 2500 objects from various cultures and periods. There is a strong collection of ceramics, from rare Chinese to contemporary, and a large paper collection that ranges from early prints to works on vellum. The gallery also maintains a growing inventory of outdoor sculpture.

The gallery exhibits mainly painting and sculpture. Particularly notable is the collection of art from the funk movement of the 1970s. These include paintings by internationally-renowned artist Wayne Thiebaud, William T. Wiley, Robert Arneson, Roy de Forest and Manual Neri. Among sculptors of this school are David Gilhooly, Steve Kaltendach and David Walburg. Artists connected with its highly regarded graduate program include photographer Judith Golden, painter Chris Brown, sculptors Bruce Naunan, Deborah Butterfield and John Buck.

[39] RIGGS GALLERIES
875 Prospect St., Ste. 115, La Jolla CA 92037 (619) 454-3070

Mon-Fri: 9-5; Sat: 11-5 *Owner/Dir:* Mary Kathryn Riggs

Since 1980, the gallery has shown an international selection of paintings and graphics, from turn-of-the-century works from Europe and America to contemporary works. Photography and small-scale sculpture also are featured.

Among the two-dimensional works are the nudes of Jan De Ruth, the impressionistic paintings of Nancy Bowen and the representational oil paintings of Melinda Miles, whose style recalls Edward Hopper.

Notable among the gallery's collections are the works of French painter François Gilot, now a California resident, who presents large-scale works with strong imagery. The gallery exclusively represents this artist.

The gallery's graphics and sculpture are diverse in style and media. There are the monotypes and prints of Martin Green; the non-representational works of Thai artist Wattana Wattanapun and the sculptures of Ernestine Voss, Robert Holmes, bronze sculptor I.

Ben Shalom, Naomi Saran and German artist Cornellia Megenhausen.

[40] TASENDE GALLERY

820 Prospect, La Jolla, CA 92037 (619) 454-3691

Tues-Sat: 10-6 *Owner/Dir:* José Tasende

Tasende Gallery opened in La Jolla in 1979. The gallery building was designed by La Jolla architect Robert Mosher, with assistance from gallery director José Tasende.

The ample exhibition space, part of which is in the open air, is particularly well-suited for the exhibitions of sculpture by international artists that the gallery has been presenting. These have included an exhibition of sculpture and drawings by British sculptor Henry Moore, with monumental pieces installed in various locations in La Jolla.

Among the other sculptors featured are Lynn Chadwick, a younger contemporary of Moore whose work, though abstract, carries strong figurative suggestions; Basque artist Eduardo Chillida, whose abstract work in forged iron, wood and stone expresses the raw mass and strength of his materials and the historic vision of his heritage; and Italian artists Marino Marini and Giacomo Manzu. Both are recognized masters of the human figure, which in Manzu's work is charged with classical poise, and in Marini's work reveals the primitive forces that mold human gestures.

Paintings and drawings by Chilean surrealist Roberto Matta and Mexican artist José Luis Cuevas have been presented as well.

LONG BEACH

[41] WILLIAMSLAMB GALLERY

102 W. Third St., Long Beach, CA 90802
(213) 432-2291

Tues-Sat: 12-7; Sun: 12-5 *Owner/Dir:* Marcia Lamb, Marylea Williams Ross

WilliamsLamb Gallery emphasizes figurative work by west coast artists. Painter Sol Aquino is known for his colorful parodies of American culture, which focus on consumerism and the art world. Karen Fuson, an assemblage artist, transforms female beauty products into hilarious glitter and gilt shrines to culture-inflicted torture. Sculptor Neal Taylor also uses assemblage to playfully transform common objects such as chairs and garden tools into surprising metaphors. Jean Towgood paints expressive, energy-filled canvases that capture the unconscious associations we have with natural phenomena such as ocean waves and fires. Other major artists represented by the gallery include Juan Alonso, Guillermo Bert, Les Biller, Mary Bonic, Ann Chernenko, Lee Chesney, Diane Gamboa, Hal Honigsberg, Daniel Kelly, Leo Limon, Paul Sierra and Linda Vallejo.

WilliamsLamb Gallery also features works by Alex Alferov, Gregg Bayne, Diane Best, Robin Ghelerter, Jason Graves, Audrey Lancaster, Nick Lawrence, Sandra McCarthy, David Nicols, Nancy Nye, Robert Royhl, Robin Ryan, Daniel Salazar, Mark Sparks, Lani Tanaka, Karen Taylor, J. Michael Walker and Jack Zoltak.

The gallery has a corporate sales and leasing department and provides complete client support services, including consulting, interior and exterior installation.

[42] THE WORKS GALLERY

106 W. Third St., Long Beach, CA 90802
(213) 495-2787

Sun-Mon: 12-5; Tues-Sat: 11-7 *Owner/Dir:* Mark Moore

The Works Gallery specializes in contemporary California painting and sculpture. Many of the artists represented are associated with the Light and Space movement.

Major established artists include Lita Albuquerque, whose sand installations and pigment works evoke the poetry of the unconscious; Peter Alexander, whose canvases resemble lights in the night sky; Craig Antrim, a colorist who explores spiritual themes; Mary Corse, who paints surfaces with light-reflecting glass beads; Woods Davy, who constructs zen related sculptures of steel and rock; and George Geyer, whose glass sculptures are beautiful and untouchable. The gallery represents many other established artists: Larry Bell, Billy Al Bengston, Michael Davis, Tony DeLap, Laddie John Dill, Peter Erskine, John Paul Jones, Craig Kauffman, Jay McCafferty, Jim Morphesis, Eric Orr, Helen Pashgian, Bruce Richards and Stephanie Weber. By and large, the work of these artists tends to depict simple abstract forms.

The Works Gallery also represents emerging artists Deanne Belinoff, Poupee Boccaccio, Hilary Brace, Judith Davies, Frank Dixon, Tom Dowling, Candice Gawne, Michael Hayden, Jim Kenny, Franz Rudolf Knubel, Hoon Kwak, Clinton MacKenzie, Gary Martin, Betty Rodger, Judy Stabile, Berbara Sternberger, Craig Cree Stone, Craig Syverson, Ann Thornycroft, Patricia Turnier and Clark Walding.

LOS ANGELES

[43] ACE CONTEMPORARY EXHIBITIONS

5514 Wilshire Blvd., 2nd Floor, Los Angeles, CA 90036 (213) 935- 4411

Tues-Sat: 10-6 *Owner/Dir:* Douglas Christmas

Ace has perhaps the largest exhibition space of any gallery in the city, taking up the entire second floor of a former department store in a notable 1920s Art Deco building on the miracle mile. The space has small rooms for one person painting shows and large open areas to display sculpture. During any one month Ace will have several concurrent artists on exhibition, each represented by a body of work.

The artists represented include many major figures and promising new talent. These include James Hayward, known for his painterly monochrome paintings; Roger Herman, who shows his large expressionistic canvases and, lately, concrete sculptures of animal parts; Timothy Hawkinson, whose works are in the assemblage tradition but with a fool-the-eye conceptual twist; minimalist sculptor Richard Nonas, who shows his steel ingots; and sculptor Roland Reiss, whose new work consists of heroically scaled human icons.

Many other major figures are exhibited, including Carl Andre, Dan Flavin, Michael Heizer, Donald Judd, Bruce Nauman, Maria Nordman, Robert Rauschenberg, Richard Serra, Robert Smithson and James Turrell.

Mark Lere, *Shadow #1 (424c),* 1989, 59 x 39, lithograph, ed. 35.
Courtesy: Cirrus Gallery, Los Angeles

[44] ANKRUM GALLERY
657 N. La Cienega Blvd., Los Angeles, CA 90069
(213) 657-1549

Tues-Sat: 10-5:30 *Owner/Dir:* Joan Ankrum

Joan Ankrum represents a diverse group of California painters and sculptors many of whom work in a realistic manner.

The gallery has 4,500 square feet of exhibition space and presents new group and solo shows every four weeks. Recently shown works ranged from the detailed watercolors and figures of Morris Broderson to the expressionistic watercolor figures and landscapes of Keith Crown to the body-casts of Richard Bower.

On July 30, 1989, the Ankrum Gallery closed permanently. Its last exhibition was a solo show by painter Morris Broderson, the owner's nephew and the artist whose work was shown at the gallery's opening in 1960. Joan Ankrum, the gallery's owner will continue to deal privately.

[45] L.A. ARTCORE
652 Mateo St., Los Angeles, CA 90021
(213) 617-3274

11-4 *Dir:* Lydia Takeshita

The gallery concentrates on contemporary art of southern California. It places strong emphasis on the support of emerging artists. Part of its mission is to provide an open and encouraging venue for area artists. In so doing, it hopes to allow young artists to produce without the pressure of the art market, and without compromising the integrity of their approach. In addition to showing paintings, drawings and sculptures of all media, it is involved in the area art scene through a broad variety of activities. It is the sponsor of *Visions, Art Quarterly Magazine* which focuses on American West Coast artists.

There is a three week rotation of shows throughout the year. Among works exhibited are John Outterbridge's sculptures of metal and found objects, and Charles Dixon's sculptural pieces incorporating wood, polyethylene foam and found objects. A number of major artists have had solo shows. They include Joseph Piasentin and David Moen, whose relief collages and tableaux depict imagery ranging from the objective to the non-representational. His works incorporate a variety of unusual media, including bones, jewelry, metal screens, fields of color, rubble and bows. A recent joint show featured Katherine Liu's acrylic, tar and oil pastel canvases and Paul Carmichael's abstract wall constructions of metal screening, wire, wood and acrylic. An exchange exhibition entitled "Pacific Rim Exhibition" provided exposure for artists from the Pacific Rim area. Artworks shown include Junko Chodos's oil paintings, Daniel Wheeler's large sculptures and Minora Ohira's wall hangings that utilize organic materials intricately and dramatically combined. In addition, Korean artists Kim Jai Kwan and Bai Dong-Hwan have been invited to show their works.

[46] ASHER/FAURE
612 N. Almont Dr., Los Angeles, CA 90069
(213) 271-3665

Tues-Sat: 11-5 *Dir:* Patricia Faure

In addition to showing the work of young artists, the gallery has held exhibitions of painting and sculpture by celebrated contemporary American artists such as early abstract painter Arthur Dove, abstract expressionists Franz Kline and Philip Guston and Morris Louis, a poineer in the movement beyond abstract expressionism. Other exhibitions have included Sam Francis' paintings of the 1950s; sculpture and paintings by Richard Artschwager and drawings and sculptures by Joel Shapiro.

The gallery's German artists include: Walter Dahn, Jiri Georg Dokoupil and Hubert Kiecol.

Among the California artists presented are Craig Kauffman, Llyn Foulkes, Maxwell Hendler, John Okulick, Gwynn Murrill, Viola Frey, Margaret Nielsen, Laura Lasworth and Bruce Cohen. Also featured are painter and sculptor John Buck and sculptor Deborah Butterfield.

From New York, the gallery has had installations of paintings by David Reed, Ron Janowich, Jack Goldstein, Robert Yarber and Richard Bosman.

[47] TAMARA BANE GALLERY
8025 Melrose Ave., Los Angeles, CA 90046
(213) 651-1400

Tues-Sat: 11-7 *Owner:* Robert and Tamara Bane *Dir:* Tamara Bane

The gallery offers original contemporary art by many important artists in all media: oils, acrylics, watercolors, gouache, drawings, sculpture and limited editions. The gallery emphasizes the work of "young postmodern artists."

A number of artists represented by the gallery grew prominent in New York's East Village scene during the early 1980s. Among these are Ronnie Cutrone, known for his paintings of cartoon characters including Felix the Cat; Crash, whose paintings contain an explosion of pop and cartoon imagery; Mark Kostabi, whose paintings of faceless figures satirize corporate and contemporary life; and Keith Haring, who paints in a graffiti style. The gallery also carries work by the well established pop artist Mel Ramos; neo-expressionistic paintings by Anca Ionescu; and the realistic erotic paintings and drawings of Olivia.

The Tamara Bane Gallery also represents Eyvind Earle, Walter Girotto, Aldo Luongo, Anton Sipos, Genevieve Blons and Siquing Zhou.

[48] BAUM GALLERY
170 S. La Brea Ave., Los Angeles, CA 90036
(213) 932-0170

Tues-Sat: 10-5:30 *Owner:* Jan Baum *Dir:* Daniel Stearns

International contemporary art as well as African and Indonesian primitive art are the focus of this gallery. Many of the artists represented by the gallery exhibit widely throughout the United States, Europe and the Orient.

Abstract paintings, both gestural and geometric, by well-known artists Peter Plagens, Linda Burnam, Trevor Norris are balanced by expressive figurative work by Robert Gil de Montes, Mel Rubin, Milano Kazanjian, Joe Fay, Ernest Silva, Laurie Pincus and Takako Yamaguchi.

Alison Saar's small and life-size sculptures are both iconic and primitive; while the works of Steve Heino, Jim DeFrance and Steve Grossman reflect the gallery's interest in constructivism.

Berlin artists Stephanus Heidecker and Rainer Fetting demonstrate the range of German painting from expressionist to classical; while Barcelona artist Tom

Carr, known throughout Europe, showed his metaphoric wood sculpture for the first time in the United States at the Jan Baum Gallery.

[49] BURNETT/MILLER
964 North La Brea Ave., Los Angeles, CA 90038
(213) 874-4757
Tues-Sat: 10-5:30 *Owner/Dir:* Brian D. Butler

The gallery presents a range in contemporary American and European art works. Some pieces contain elements arising from traditional influences; others rest on the ground-breaking edge of new conceptual territory. Post-minimalist sculptor Serge Spitzer's creations break from formalist boundaries; Nancy Spero and Leon Golub work in the figurative tradition and deal with political themes. Other important artists represented are Ulay and Marina Abramovic, Kate Ericson and Mel Ziegler, Fred Fehlau, Ulrich Horndash, Wolfgang Laib, Denzel Hurley, Gregory Mahoney, Charles Ray, Ettore Spalletti and Gunther Umberg. Special exhibitions include the work of Richard Long, Bruce Nauman, Giovanni Anselmo, Serge Spitzer and Anthony Gormally. Well-known in Europe and emerging in the U.S. are Fred Sandbach and Franz Erhard Walther.

[50] CIRRUS GALLERY
542 S. Alameda St., Los Angeles CA 90028
(213) 680-3473
Tues-Sat: 11-5 *Owner/Dir:* Jean R. Millant

The unusual combination of an art gallery, a print workshop and a publisher of fine graphics makes Cirrus gallery stand out. Since 1970 Cirrus has shown and published the work of leading contemporary California artists.

Presently featured are painters Damian Andrus, Kyoko Asano, Richard Baker, Charles Hill, William Hemmerdinger, Ted Kerzie, Jay McCafferty

Jay, G# 50 and Gillian Theobald; and sculptors Michael Farber, Jim Lawrence, Jay Willis and Judith Vogt.

Cirrus is a major publisher of print editions. Jean Millant, Tamarind Master Printer, is known for producing fine quality limited editions with special sensitivity to the artist's work. Ed Ruscha's lithographs and food prints, the silk tissue lithography of Ed Moses, and the torn and sewn prints of Joe Goode and Charles C. Hill are examples. In Cirrus's extensive inventory one will also find works by Lita Albuquerque, Peter Alexander, Billy Al Bengston, Vija Celmins, Ron Cooper, Tony Delap, Laddie John Dill, Craig Kauffman, Mark Lere, Bruce Nauman, Kenneth Price and William Wiley.

[51] COUTURIER GALLERY
166 N. La Brea Ave., Los Angeles, CA 90036
(213) 933-5557
Tues-Sat: 11-5; and by appointment *Owner/Dir:* Darrel Couturier

The Couturier Gallery specializes in fine works of the American Arts and Crafts movement. In addition, eight to ten exhibits a year are devoted to paintings, sculpture, ceramics and furniture by master and emerging artists. Such exhibits include the modernist paintings of Jens Jensen, a renowned Rookwood ceramist. His paintings, cubist portraitures and still lifes in saturated primary colors, are provoked by his response to modern art of the 20th century. They quote from but do not copy the works of major 20th century artists. Yu Wu-Lin's approach reflects a meld-ing of Chinese and Western artistic traditions. Traditional Chinese subjects are given heavy colors and a saturated impasto treatment. The resulting textures appear to have been applied with a palette knife. His art is cerebral, and as with Chinese landscapes, is meant to be studied rather than viewed; meaning comes from more than the sum of visual parts. Echeveste's male figure sculptures are, in bronze and neon, a revisionist interpretation of the Greek ideal. Jay Stanger's wood and metal furniture makes satiric comments on societal foibles. In his functional contemporary furniture, wit is combined with superb craftsmanship. A number of sculptural ceramists have been featured. Notably, Australian Jeffrey Mincham, whose large scale raku pieces draw on native Aboriginal designs; Greg Daly, in various sophisticated vessels and urns of enamel and 22-kt gold; and Paul Chaleff, a ceramist working out of the Japanese ceramic tradition. His ceramics are angular, rough-textured pieces of muted colors and resemble ancient artifacts. Other sculptural ceramists represented are Jenny Orchard and Liz Williams.

The gallery also sponsors regular displays of craftwork. A recent exhibition featured works of furniture craftsmen. Among them are Daniel Mack's twig furniture, which makes references to Adirondack furniture, and John MacAlevey's finely crafted mahogany and cherry furniture which refers to early American colonial furniture.

[52] WILLIAM & VICTORIA DAILEY
8216 Melrose Ave., Los Angeles, CA 90046 (213) 658-8515; 2nd location: 7220 Beverly Blvd., Los Angeles, CA 90036 (213) 931-1185
Tues-Fri: 10-6; Sat 11-5 *Owner/Dir:* William and Victoria Dailey

This combination gallery and rare book shop offers a wide selection of graphics as well as art and rare books of all periods. In addition, the owners have recently put together another branch, the Turner-Dailey gallery with Steve Turner, which stocks posters and decorative art objects from 1910 to 1940.

In the field of graphics, nineteenth-century French artists are a specialty, with works by Manet, Delacroix, Gericault, Tissot, Lepere, Meryon, Daumier and Daubigny are among those offered. English and American artists are also available, including works by Whistler, Haden, Turner, Hassam, Bellows and Sloan. *Catalogues raisonnés* and monographs on the works are available. Complementing the graphic offerings are rare books in the areas of science, literature, the history of printing, decoration and bibliography.

[53] DEVILLE GALLERIES
8751 Melrose, Los Angeles, CA 90069 (213) 652-0525
Tues-Fri: 9-5; Sat: 11-3 *Owner:* Christian Title *Dir:* Lyn Lincoln

The gallery shows nineteenth and twentieth century American impressionist painting. Works by American masters William Merritt Chase, Robert Reid, Jane Peterson, Louis Reitman and Childe Hassam are available. Included in the gallery's collection are contemporary impressionist works by John Powell, Henri Plisson, Don Hatfield and Christian Title.

[54] ANDREW DIERKEN FINE ARTS
8563 1/2 Cashio, Los Angeles, CA 90035
(213) 652-2190
by appt. only *Owner/Dir:* Andrew Dierken

This is a private dealer of contemporary established and emerging artists, both American and European, who acquires chiefly through museums. The collection is heavily weighted toward contemporary and avant-garde art.

Major artists represented are Richard Diebenkorn, Jim Dine, Sam Francis, David Hockney, Jasper Johns, Roy Lichtenstein, Robert Motherwell, Frank Stella, Wayne Thiebaud, Andy Warhol and Tom Wesselmann. Other artists include Christian Boltanski, Calum Colvin, Tony Cragg, Rebecca Horn, Juan Munoz, Gerhard Richter, Jose Maria Sicilia, Donald Sultan and Terry Winters.

[55] GEORGE J. DOIZAKI GALLERY

Japanese-American Cultural & Community Center, 244 S. San Pedro St., Los Angeles, CA 90012
(213) 628-2725

Tues-Fri: 12-5; Sat-Sun: 11-4 *Owner:* JACCC *Dir:* Robert Hori

The gallery's emphasis is traditional and contemporary Japanese art, though it attempts to show from a broad spectrum of art. An integral part of its cultural center, the gallery holds exhibitions whose purposes are multiple. Its interests are not only aesthetic; often the gallery exhibits highlight social and cultural history, or political concerns. A recent exhibition was "Images for Survival," a collection of peace posters by American and Japanese graphic artists. Originating in Hiroshima as part memorial and part anti-nuclear protest, the ultimate goal of the show's organizers is an exhibit in every country. Similar shows have since been organized in the Soviet Union, Sweden, France, Germany, Australia and Finland.

Ikko Tanaka, Japan's leading graphic designer, has exhibited his paintings and graphic designs at the gallery. Other exhibits include contemporary Japanese-American painter Matsumi Kanemitsu's bold, sweeping black-and-white abstracts that are reminiscent of calligraphy; Echiko Ohira's oddly shaped mixed-media works of metal, wire, paper and wood; Minoru Ohira's exploratory wall pieces of woven wood; as well as painters Homare Ikeda, Duetryuichi Okabayashi and Mayumi Oda.

The gallery often showcases Japanese craftworks such as 16th century Japanese tea ceremony utensils. Another exhibit, entitled "The Art of Netsuke, Ojime, Sagemono," focused on 18th and 19th century Japanese ornaments. Netsuke are heavy beads of ivory, wood or porcelain, typically miniature carvings of people, crabs or other figures; ojime are pouches suspended from the sashes worn by samurai and wealthy merchants; and sagemono are fastening beads. With a cord strung through them, sagemono served as counterweights for the ojime, which were used to carry medicine, money or tobacco. Each year, it hosts a Nisei Week Exhibit, featuring traditional Japanese arts: flower arrangements, bonsai, bankei, stencil-dyeing, ceramics and calligraphy.

[56] JOSE DRUDIS-BIADA ART GALLERY

12001 Chalon Road, Los Angeles, CA 90049
(213) 746-0450

Mon-Fri: 12-5 *Dir:* Olga Seem

The gallery focuses on the work of contemporary California artists, whether established, mid-career or emerging. Its 2200-square-foot space is appropriate for concurrent solo efforts, as well as large group shows.

A recent installation by "political artist" Ben Sakoguchi, in collaboration with his wife Jan, is a two year effort at an extraordinary memorial entitled *Remember Me*. Installed as a mock cemetery, it is a meticulous collection of grave-markers, mementos, artifacts and devotional replicas. This installation speaks of hundreds of incidents that occurred between the start of WWII to the recent past, marking the series of tragic events, and is eloquent testimony to the lives lost. Other exhibits have been solo shows by sculptor Eugene Sturman, painter Peter Liashkov, painter Mac McCloud, photographer Dauna Whitehead, and a show featuring the drawings of Dorothy Churchill-Johnson. A group show entitled "Narrative Imagery in Post-Modern Los Angeles" featured works by Bob Anderson, Walter Askin, JoAnne Berke, Wes Christensen, Leonard Esbensen, Cindy Evans, Deborah F. Lawrence, John August Swanson, J. Michael Walker and Donna Zanella.

[57] DUBINS GALLERY

11948 San Vincente Blvd., Los Angeles, CA 90049
(213) 820-1409

Tues-Sat: 10-5 *Owner/Dir:* Lisa Dubins

The gallery's original purpose when it opened in 1977, was to serve corporate collections, architects and designers. It now serves private clients as well. Larger pieces on canvas and original works on paper are predominant. Shows represent well-known painters and sculptors from the U.S., their styles ranging from lyrical abstractionism through abstract expressionism, minimalism and photo-realism. There are monthly shows of these artists' work, and with its expansion over four years, the gallery now exhibits the work of younger artists in rotation.

[58] FRANCINE ELLMAN GALLERY

671 N. La Cienega Blvd., Los Angeles, CA 90069
(213) 652-7879

Tues-Sat: 10-5 *Owner:* Francine Ellman *Dir:* Michael Conway

The gallery is best known for exhibiting American contemporary paintings, drawings and sculpture by artists with established records of accomplishment, but director owner Francine Ellman constantly seeks out provocative works from emerging artists to expose to the ever-expanding Los Angeles art community. Ms. Ellman sees the gallery's mission as not so much to address trends in the art market of today as to present artists whose work will stand the test of time as a result of their innovation and creative importance.

Set back from La Cienega Boulevard in a shady courtyard, the gallery stands out in a neighborhood known for its fine art galleries. The gallery space occupies a renovated former "artist's loft," with exposed architectural detailing, such an the open-beamed ceiling whose over 20-foot height allows for the comfortable exhibit of works of various dimensions and scale.

Artists represented by the gallery include Meg Freeman, a contemporary realist painter whose witty compositions juxtapose people in unlikely interior spaces, to create a commentary on the underlying insanity in life; Jim Sajovic, whose focus is women and societal perceptions of them; and Ken Matsumoto, whose sculptures of steel, glass and concrete poetically recreate natural harmonic forms. Other artists ex-

Dennis Elliott, *Logform Series #2,* 10 inches high, 11-21 inches in diameter, woodturning.
Courtesy: del Mano Gallery, Los Angeles

Carolyn Cardenas, *Temperance,* 4 x 4, egg tempera and oil on panel.
Courtesy: Koplin Gallery, Los Angeles

hibited at the gallery include Kevin Beer, Erik Budd, Kim Cheselka, Tom Christopher, Rebecca Crowell, Eileen Dailey, Cecilia Davidson, Anthony Emerton, Cindy Kane, Michael Ledet, Jeff Long, Leif Olson, Alex O'Neal, Mary Swanson, Jacqueline Warren and Dana Zed.

Typically, exhibitions change continuously, with a one-month duration for each show.

[59] FAHEY/KLEIN GALLERY

148 N. La Brea Ave., Los Angeles, CA 90036
(213) 934-2250

Tues-Sat: 10-6 *Owner/Dir:* David Fahey, Randee Klein

The gallery shows contemporary painting, sculpture, photography and vintage photography.

Fahey/Klein's "Main Room" is devoted primarily to exhibitions of more established artists. Shows have included Nick Taggart's satirical paintings about the art world; and Ted Rosenthal's assemblages from aerospace parts that evoke a humorous interplay between U.S. government paranoia and UFOs. The gallery's emphasis on photography is represented by Lance Carlson's Polaroids of mundane objects; the platinum fashion, portrait and nude photographs of Horst; and vintage works by such photographers as Henri Cartier-Bresson and Andre Kertsz. Exhibitions in the "Main Room" have also included Sylvia Martins, Herb Ritts, Rhonda Zwillinger, Joel-Peter Witkin and Nicholas Africano.

The gallery's "New Room" is a space devoted primarily to exhibitions by young or upcoming artists. Shows have included Robert Strini, Christopher Tanner, Blue McRight, Holly Roberts, Stephen Arnold and others.

[60] FEINGARTEN GALLERIES

8380 Melrose Ave., Los Angeles, CA 90013
(213) 655-4840

Tues-Sat: 11-6; Sat: 12-5 *Owner/Dir:* Gail Feingarten

For over 25 years the gallery has been dedicated primarily to exhibiting fine sculpture by 20th century masters. They also show contemporary sculptors and painters.

Bronzes and marbles by Henry Moore, Alexander Archipenko, Jean Arp and Auguste Rodin are available, as are the works of Barbara Hepworth, Auguste Renoir, Emile-Antoine Bourdelle, Joseph Csaky and Chana Orloff. Tengenenge sculpture from Zimbabwe is a recent addition to the gallery's sculpture collection. Other sculptors include Howard Newman, Jim Ritchie and Sandra Sloane.

The gallery also exhibits such paintings as the Art Deco-period work of Csaky, Charley Brown and the Zhou brothers. The gallery also stocks master drawings and watercolors.

[61] ROSAMUND FELSEN GALLERY

669 N. La Cienga Blvd., Los Angeles, CA 90069
(213) 936-2486

Tues-Sat: 11-5 *Owner/Dir:* Rosamund Felsen

The gallery specializes in contemporary works by southern California artists. In particular, it provides a venue for those who live and work in Los Angeles. The gallery exhibits paintings, sculpture, drawings and photographs.

In general, the gallery represents artists whose works are conceptual, whose art is concerned with the play of ideas. Among those featured are John Boskovich, Chris Burden, Karen Carson, Roy Dowell, Jeff Gam-

bill, Richard Jackson, Mike Kelley, Paul McCarthy, Grant Mudford, Maria Nordman, Marc Pally, Renee Petropoulos, Lari Pittman, Steve Rogers, Erika Rothenberg and Jeffrey Vallance.

[62] GALLERY WEST

107 S. Robertson Blvd., Los Angeles CA 90048
(213) 271-1145

Tues-Sat: 10:30-5 *Owner/Dir:* Roberta Feuerstein

The gallery carries contemporary paintings, drawings, sculpture and graphics of the East and West Coasts, by both established and emerging artists.

Abstract painters featured by the gallery are Tom Gathman, Ed Haddaway, Cathy Halstead, David McCullough, James Mitchell, Helen Bershad, Stuart Williams and Roger Weik. Realist painters include Paul Kane, Alberto Magnani and Lawrence Taugher. Of the sculptors at the gallery, Vasa works in laminated acrylic, Dorothy Gillespie makes painted metal sculpture; and Franco Assetto uses surrealist/pop imagery in his sculpture and painting. The gallery also features the transformable metal sculpture of Yaacov Agam.

One may also see ceramic works by Fred Stodder, wall constructions by Ken Anderson and Daniel Winchester and the constructions and handmade paper works of Kamol Tassananchalee.

[63] GARTH CLARK GALLERY

170 S. La Brea Ave., Los Angeles, CA 90036
(213) 939-2189

Tues-Sat: 11-5 *Owner:* Garth Clark *Dir:* Wayne Kuwada

The Garth Clark Gallery specializes in modern and contemporary ceramic art. The artists represented by the gallery are among the leaders in the medium, and have contributed to the increased recognition of ceramics as a fine art.

Lidya Buzio makes burnished earthenware pieces that integrate the images and forms of architecture with traditional vessels. Philip Cornelius's pieces combine the forms of two separate kinds of vessels, the porcelain teapot and the ship, to create complex metaphors. Adrian Saxe, inspired by Eighteenth Century Sevres porcelain, makes humorously precious teapots and jars with exotic shapes and exquisite surfaces. Akio Takamori's large vessel forms embody figures intertwined in erotic ways.

The Garth Clark Gallery also represents Ralph Bacerra, Carmen Collell, Kenneth Ferguson, Keiko Fukazawa, Anne Kraus, Judith Salomon, Hitoshi Sasaki, Anna Silver and Beatrice Wood.

[64] GEMINI G.E.L.

8365 Melrose Ave., Los Angeles, CA 90069
(213) 651-0513

Mon-Fri: 9-5:30 Sat: 11-5 *Dir:* Sidney B. Felsen and Stanley Grinstein

Gemini G.E.L. (Graphics Editions Limited) is an internationally known print publisher housed in a building designed by Los Angeles architect Frank Gehry. The gallery displays graphics by American artists, all of which are produced in Gemini's workshop. The work is created and closely supervised by the artists, who are present in the workshop itself during the entire proofing session. Most of the exhibits center around lithography and etchings by artists, including Jonathan Borofsky, Sam Francis, David Hockney, Jasper Johns, Ellsworth Kelly, Roy Lichtenstein, Malcolm Morley,

Robert Rauschenberg, Susan Rothenberg, Ed Ruscha and Richard Serra. The gallery also shows limited edition sculpture by Isamu Noguchi, Richard Serra, Robert Rauschenberg, Claes Oldenburg and Coosje Bruggen among others.

[65] GOLDFIELD GALLERIES, LTD.
8400 Melrose Ave., Los Angeles CA 90069
(213) 651-1122
Mon-Sat: 11-4 *Owner:* Edward Goldfield *Dir:* Pam Ludwig

Goldfield Galleries specializes in American Impressionists, Ash Can School, California Impressionists, Western artists and other important painters of the late nineteenth and twentieth century.

The gallery features American Impressionists Childe Haasam, Edmund Greacen, Edward Potthast, J. Alden Weir Lawton Parker, Edmund Tarbell, Wm. Merritt Chase, Richard E. Miller, Cecilia Beaux, Guy Wiggins, Charles Hawthorne, Gari Melchers, J. J. Enneking, Hovsep Pushman, Walter L. Palmer and others. The Ash Can School of social realists is represented by Robert Henri, George Luks, John Sloan, Everett Shinn and Arthur P. Davies. Also represented are artists associated with the Ash Can School Reginald Marsh, Guy Pene du Bois and Jerome Myers.

California Impressionists include Edgar Payne, Maurice Braun, Donna Schuster, John Gamble, James Swinnerton, Gardner Symons, Francis McComas and Paul Lauritz.

Landscape painters of the nineteenth century include Thomas Hill, John Ross Key, Raymond Yelland, William Hart, Albert Bierstadt and Benjamin Champney.

The gallery also includes in its collection Stanton MacDonald Wright and Morgan Russell, two of the first abstract painters; and American regionalist Thomas Hart Benton.

[66] G. RAY HAWKINS GALLERY
7224 Melrose Ave., Los Angeles, CA 90046
(213) 550-1504
Tues-Sat: 12-5 *Owner:* G. Ray Hawkins

This is Los Angeles' oldest gallery devoted exclusively to photography. The gallery opened a new space in 1980 with murals and Polaroids by Ansel Adams. Since opening the new space, exhibitions have included the work of Robert Frank, Walker Evans, George Hurrell, Max Yavno, Garry Winogrand, Arthur Tress, Helmut Newton, Henri Cartier-Bresson, Robert Doisneau and Andre Kertesz. Representing approximately 100 vintage, modern and contemporary masters, the gallery has produced portfolios by Max Yavno, Umbo, Alice Steinhardt and Helmut Newton. The gallery also sponsors public information programs, symposia and workshops.

[67] DONNA GROSSMAN GALLERY FOR ARCHITECTURE
964 N. La Brea Ave., Los Angeles, CA 90030
(213) 876-7012
Tues-Sat: 11-5 *Owner/Dir:* Donna Grossman

Donna Grossman Gallery exhibits fine artworks by architects. Project drawings are shown as well as drawings, prints and silkscreens that architects design aside from architecture.

Los Angeles' iconoclastic architect Frank Gehry is represented, as well as local postmodern experimenters

Charles Moore and *Morphosis* (Thom Mayne and Michael Rotundi). Japanese Architect Arata Isozaki, who designed the Los Angeles Museum of Contemporary Art, exhibits silk screens; and Richard Meier, who recently established a local office while he designs the new Getty Center, has exhibited collages.

Chicago architect Stanley Tigerman, whose work is characterized by playful metaphors, exhibits drawings. The other architects represented by the gallery also have established international reputations: Michael Graves, Hans Hollein, Antoine Predock and Aldo Rossi.

[68] HERITAGE GALLERY
718 La Cienega Blvd., Los Angeles, CA 90069
(213) 652-7738
Tues-Sat: 11-5; *Owner/Dir:* Benjamin Horowitz

The gallery, established in 1960, stresses figurative painting as well as rare prints by international artists.

Social realists Raphael Soyer and William Gropper are among the artists whose work is shown. Soyer's style is looser and more impressionistic than that of Gropper, who works in a linear, satirical manner akin to the caricatures of 19th century painter Honore Daumier. Other artists exhibited include Robert Russin, Milton Hebald and Sherman. Recent exhibits have featured Louis Eilshemus, the paintings of Ruben Kocharian, paintings and bronzes by Andre de Toth, and a group exhibit, entitled "American Visions," featuring collage by Romare Beardon, constructions by C. Ian White and the work of Charles White.

The gallery also carries prints by Pablo Picasso, Joan Miro, 19th century French genre painter James Tissot, Ashcan School painter John Sloan and many others.

[69] KIYO HIGASHI GALLERY
8332 Melrose Ave., Los Angeles, CA 90069
(213) 655-2482
Tues-Sat: 11-6 *Owner/Dir:* Kiyo Higashi

The gallery specializes in contemporary abstract work with an emphasis on minimalism. The gallery space was designed by Larry Bell, a principal figure in Los Angeles's celebrated light and space movement. The interior environment of leaning and tapered walls, rounded corners and unique windows, provides an excellent showcase for all of Bell's work, from his early glass cubes and sculptures to his "Vapor Drawings" and his newer works on canvas, the "Mirage" paintings. These mixed-media collages have three-dimensional flat surfaces that capture light through a layering of painterly brushstrokes and surfaces colored by the vapor drawing process found in his earlier works.

The gallery also features the work of prominent constructivist Guy Williams. Williams' recent works are large-scale formal abstractions combining the geometry of hard edges and forms with lively gestural marks.

Kiyo Higashi Gallery also features work of other established and emerging artists: abstract oil paintings by Penelope Krebs, wire sculptures by William Dwyer, paintings and drawings by Lies Kraal, paintings and mixed-media constructions by Madeline O'Connor, paintings by Perry Araeipour, drawings by R. Doen Tobey and wood sculptures by Roy Thurston.

[70] HOLOGRAPHIC VISIONS
300 S. Grand Ave., Los Angeles, CA 90071
(213) 687-7171

Wed-Sun: 11-5 *Owner:* Los Angeles Museum of Holography *Dir:* William Hilliard

The gallery exhibits holograms by artists and craftsmen from around the world. It has the largest permanent display of holograms on the west coast. Changing exhibits feature both solo and group shows; and consist of holograms of many styles and applications, including industrial, commercial and fine art.

Holographic Visions exhibits work by a variety of leaders in the field. John Kaufman is well known for his multi-color reflection holograms, which are unique since most holograms are monochrome. Kaufman layers monochromatic holograms to produce his colorful limited editions on glass plates. Australian holographer Alexander has expanded the size of the medium to produce large-scale works, and also produces holographic films.

Greg Cherry, of Cherryoptical Co., makes commercial holograms on glass. Hilliard makes a variety of types of holograms, and the gallery has copies of a commission he made for the King of Bhutan. Hungarian artist Katalin Sallai incorporates holograms with other media such as fabric and prints. Nancy Gorglione creates one-of-a-kind holograms of flowers.

The gallery also carries work by holographers Sascha Brastoff, Lon Moore, Lloyd Cross, Sharon McCormick and others.

[71] HUNSAKER-SCHLESINGER GALLERY
812 N. Lacienaga Blvd., Los Angeles 90069
(213) 657-2557

Tues-Sat: 9-5 *Owner/Dir:* Joyce Hunsaker & Laura Schlesinger

Hunsaker-Schlesinger is an eclectic art consultant and gallery that supports the work of up-and-coming artists. Although the majority of the gallery's specialty is art consultation, where it helps build private collections and cement deals for large-scale hotel and public art space projects, the gallery also represents collage artist Raymond Saunders, fiber artist Neda Al-Hilali and the estate of California painter Donald Sorenson.

Hunsaker-Schlesinger has been in its present gallery row location for the past thirteen years. Its 1400-square foot building contains two exhibition spaces and an office. Each year, Hunsaker-Schlesinger presents between four and six formal shows. At other times varied prints and paintings hang at the gallery. Subjects of recent exhibitions have included: the tromp l'oeil frescoes of Gary Willoughby; the figurative ceramics of Elain Carhartt; the realistic watercolors of Bruce Richards; and the work of Peter Lodato, whose cerebral paintings and environments deal with distortion of perspective. The gallery actively seeks emerging artists.

[72] IVEY KAUFMAN GALLERY
154 N. La Brea Ave., Los Angeles, CA 90036
(213) 937-9299

Tues-Sat: 11-6 *Owner:* Mark and Susan Kaufman *Dir:* Rebecca Bubenas

The Ivey/Kaufman Gallery specializes in contemporary California painters and sculptors, in particular expressionist artists who work with the figure.

The small gallery consists of two rooms; in the main room, the gallery features one-person shows, such as Ann Chernenko's vivid characters depicted in paintings, ceramics and fiberglass sculptures. Recent shows have also included Trevor Southey's classically inspired oil paintings, bronzes and etchings; Robin Ryan's works on paper in which a subtle figure emerges beneath an abstract grid; and Wayne Forte's monumental models and acrobats who struggle to break free of the picture plane. Other featured painters include Helen Flint with her photo-inspired views of Los Angeles street life; abstractionists Robert Inman and Diana Hobson; and German expressionist Herman Lederle.

The smaller rear room is a continually changing group show in which the Ivey/Kaufman gallery highlights its newest emerging artists, as in Arnold Schulenberg's whimsical masks; Mark Beam's surf-pop sculpture; and Diana Feld's oil pastel abstracts based on the Santa Monica pier. In addition, the gallery promotes digital painting (computer generated graphics) by various artists.

[73] JAN KESNER GALLERY
164 N. La Brea Ave., Los Angeles, CA 90036
(213) 938-6834

Tues-Sat: 11-5 *Owner/Dir:* Jan Kesner

The gallery specializes in 19th and 20th century photography and contemporary art. Photographers represented range throughout the modern period, and the quality of the work is consistently high, such as Henri Cartier-Bresson's photographs of French life in the early years of this century, and Garry Winogrand's candid depiction of transforming American life from the late 1950s to the 1970s. The gallery also has group shows that focus on specific periods, such as Bauhaus photography; or themes, such as the way photographers have depicted dogs.

Current photographers include JoAnn Callis, who models small scenes specifically to be photographed; Nancy Burson, whose work is computer-generated; and David Levinthal, whose polaroids of toy cowboys and horses examine the child-like quality of the myth of the West.

Jan Kesner Gallery also represents Berenice Abbott, David Bunn, Robert Doisneau, Robert Frank, O. Winston Link, Richard Misrach, Jim Morris, Josef Sudek, Jan Saudek, Lou Stoumen and Ruth Thorne Thomsen.

[74] MICHAEL KOHN GALLERY
313 N. Robertson Blvd., Los Angeles, CA 90048
(213) 271-8505

Tues-Sat: 10-6 *Owner/Dir:* Michael Kohn

The gallery carries modern and contemporary art from Europe, New York and Los Angeles. A large spectrum of art is shown by both established and emerging artists, with a tendency toward recognizable, rather than abstract, imagery.

Mark Innerst executes representational academic drawings, and the Italian artist Carlo Maria Mariani also paints and draws figurative works in a style of postmodern mannerism. Keith Harring and Kenny Scharf work in a quick and lively style that grew out of the East Village graffiti movement.

Susanna Dadd works in landscape painting. Young Los Angeles artist Cindy Bernard pushes representation in a different direction, by photographing the patterns used to prevent reading through envelopes, and enlarging them to create abstract images.

The gallery also represents Jamey Bair, Barbara Ess, Kevin Larmon, Joan Nelson, Aimee Rankin and Alexis Rockman. The Kohn gallery is also involved in resale

Rev. Howard Finster, *Elvis.* Courtesy: La Luz, Los Angeles

and there is always a selection of works by important 20th century artists such as Picasso, Leger and Warhol.

[75] KOPLIN GALLERY

8225 1/2 Santa Monica Blvd., Los Angeles, CA 90046
(213) 656-3378

Tues-Sat: 11-5 *Owner:* Marti Koplin *Dir:* Marshall Battani

Situated in west Hollywood, the gallery was established in 1982 as an outgrowth of Marti and Allen Koplin's burgeoning collection of art. Their interest in contemporary art is reflected in the paintings, drawings and sculptures of the gallery's collection. Many of the gallery's artists are established artists of national stature, as well as emerging regional artists. Among the artists represented are Philip Ayers, Malinda Beeman, Peter Charles, Jung Yong Chaing, Robert Colescott, Peter Dean, James Doolin, Giselle Freund, Mineko Grimmer, Gaylen Hansen, Connie Jenkins, Steve Jones, Michael Kessler, David Ligare, Kerry Marshall, Barrie Mottishaw, John Mottishaw, Patrick Nagatani and Andree Tracey, John Nava, Orleonok Pitkin, Stephen Rubin, Sandra Sallin, David Settino Scott, Julie Scott, Tony Scherman, Terry Schoonhoven, Richard Sigmund, Robert Stackhouse, Janet Tholen, John Wehrle, Mark Wethli, Robert Yasuda, Elyn Zimmerman and Christopher Warner.

[76] KOSLOW GALLERY

2507 W. Seventh St., Los Angeles, CA 90057
(213) 487-7610

Tues-Sat: 12-5; Thur: 12-7 *Owner/Dir:* David S. Koslow

The gallery sells contemporary art, with emphases on figurative narrative work in all media, and on photography. Works in various media are represented, including kinetic sculpture, ceramic sculpture, paintings, drawings, collage paintings and prints.

Among the artists represented is Suzanne Bothwell, who paints expressionistic scenes suffused with an eerie light. Robert Dowd, well-known in the 1960s as a "pop" artist, currently paints common objects enclosed in a highly activated space.

Other painters with the gallery, such as Paul Carpenter and Andy Yoder, also keep the tradition of pop imagery alive, with a frequent humorous edge. Sculpture in the gallery can be in any medium, from the ceramic pieces of Anne Scott Plummer, to the humorous kinetic works of Jim Jenkins. The gallery represents the photographers Jonathan Reff, Steven Josefsberg, Regina DeLuise and Ani Gonzalez-Rivera.

In addition, Koslow gallery represents Jerry Brainin, Chris Daubert, Joel Feldman, James Geigle, Deborah F. Lawrence, Joel Leivick, Willy Lenski, Elaine Towns and Tom Wolf.

[77] KURLAND/SUMMERS GALLERY

8742 A Melrose Ave., Los Angeles, CA 90069
(213) 659-7098

Tues-Sat: 11-6 *Owner/Dir:* Ruth T. Summers

The gallery exhibits primarily three-dimensional glass works, created through various techniques including blown glass, slumped glass, fused glass, flat glass and plate-glass sculpture. Steve Linn, for example, shows large-scale sculptures cast in bronze, carved wood and sandblasted glass. The sculptures are free-standing and meant to be viewed from three sides. The stories lie within the realm of narrative realism. Linn is concerned with ideas about human quality and a way of life. The gallery's versatile artists come from the U.S., Canada and Europe. The list includes: Rick Bernstein, Dan Dailey, Dale Chihuly, Flora Mace, Joey Kirpatrick, Christopher Lee, John Luebtow, Colin Reid, Ann Warff, David Huchthausen, Giani Toso and Bertil Vallien.

[78] LA LUZ DE JESUS GALLERY

7400 Melrose Ave. (upstairs), Los Angeles, CA 90046 (213) 651-4875

Mon-Thurs: 11-9; Fri-Sat: 11-Midnight; Sun: 12-8 *Owner:* Bill Shire *Dir:* Robert Lopez

The gallery is wide ranging and constantly changing and surprising. La Luz de Jesus Gallery carries folk art, pop art, psychedelic art, furniture; everything from turn-of-the-century crucifixions to art about Elvis Presley. Adjacent to the gallery is a store that specializes in folk art from around the world.

The gallery has shown Gary Panter, creator of the punk comic book *Jimbo*; the neo-pop artist Robert Williams; furniture maker Jon Bok; Hollywood primitive painter Mr. Stark; Polish monumental bronze sculptor of the 1930s Stanislaus Szukalski; East Los Angeles printmaker Richard Duardo; pop ceramist Byron Warner; paintings by "Devo" singer Mark Mothersbaugh; folk artist Howard Finster; New York East Village performance artist Joe Coleman; and skull ceramics by Suzi Ketchum.

As La Luz de Jesus does not represent a regular "stable" of artists, and since its schedule is so eclectic, it is no doubt the most unpredictable gallery in Los Angeles.

[79] RICHARD IRI GALLERY

8172 Melrose Ave., Los Angeles, CA 90046
(213) 852-4737

Tues-Fri: 10-6; Sat: 10-4 *Owner:* Richard Iri *Dir:* Wendy L. Posner

The gallery specializes in 20th century master prints and contemporary art. The gallery also has a Corporate Art Division, which provides quality art for the business community. The gallery represents both regional and international artists.

Exhibits of master prints include the work of such artists as Ivor Abraham, Gregory Amenoff, Richard Bosman, John Cage, Chuck Close, Richard Diebenkorn, Jim Dine, Carlos Almarez, Sam Francis, David Hockney, Alex Katz, Robert Longo, Robert Rauschenberg, Italo Scanga, Francesco Scavullo, Julian Schnabel, Wayne Thiebaud, David True and Andy Warhol.

In addition, the gallery features the works of emerging artists. For example, a recent exhibit focused on emerging California artist Susan Shlaskey, whose mixed-media (oil, latex, paint stick and charcoal)-on-paper works depict the juxtaposition of concrete and expressionistic forms, symbolized by such objects as pipes, satellite dishes and solar windmills. Other emerging artists exhibited at the gallery have included Shoichi Ida, Janet Jenkins, Carl Hayano, Stanley DeSantis, Sergio Fingerman, Michael Gallagher, Sam Ow and Susan Wilder. The gallery was formerly the Lasorda/Iri Gallery.

[80] MARGO LEAVIN GALLERY

812 N. Robertson Blvd., & 817 N. Hilldale Ave., Los Angeles CA 90069 (213) 273-0603

Tues-Sat: 11-5 *Dir:* Lynn Sharpless

Bruce Everett, *Thicket,* 64 x 96, oil on canvas Courtesy: Jan Turner Gallery, Los Angeles

The Margo Leavin Gallery exhibits contemporary American and European sculpture, paintings and drawings by the following artists: John Baldessari, Alan Belcher, Lynda Benglis, Jennifer Bolande, John Chamberlain, Sarah Charlesworth, Clegg & Guttmann, Dan Flavin, Jill Giegerich, Donald Judd, Mel Kendrick, Joseph Kosuth, Jannis Kounellis, Liz Larner, Mark Lere, David Lloyd, Andrew Lord, Richard Milani, Robert Morris, Peter Nagy, Claes Oldenburg, Joel Otterson, Martin Puryear, Alexis Smith, Haim Steinbach, Gary Stephan, John Torreano and Not Vital.

[81] GRACE LOZANO GALLERY
8205 Melrose Ave., Los Angeles 90046
(213) 653-4971

Mon-Sat: 11-6:30 *Owner:* Grace Lozano *Dir:* Benny Tessler

The brand new Grace Lozano Gallery shows modern work that is often abstract, large and expressionistic, indicating deep feelings and emotions on the part of the artist. According to director Benny Tessler the gallery is "trying to do something that is more avant-garde" and is "looking for people who love serious content and serious form."

The gallery has 2,000 square feet of exhibition space and is located near the Los Angeles County Museum. Every other month, the gallery presents group shows in its two exhibition rooms. It is still recruiting artists and at present has a roster of twenty, most of whom are from Los Angeles, San Francisco and San Diego. Among the artists it represents are: Erica Daborn whose figurative paintings are an ironic comment on California life; Charlene Knowlton, an abstractionist who mixes a German expressionist flavor and primitive African imagery; Kiki Sammarcelli who paints colorful abstractions in bold yellows, reds and blacks; Bret Price whose highly polished twisted metal sculpture resembles high-tech; and Joseph Piasentin who deals with Christian subjects in an abstract way and often works in diptychs and triptychs.

[82] EARL MCGRATH GALLERY
454 N. Robertson Blvd., Los Angeles, CA 90048
(213) 652-9850

Tues-Sat: 11-5 *Owner/Dir:* Earl McGrath

The gallery carries 20th century modern and contemporary art, including painting, sculpture and prints. In its two intimate galleries and garden, the McGrath Gallery shows the work of contemporary artists from Los Angeles, New York and abroad.

Los Angeles sculptor Doug Edge makes free-standing pieces and wall-reliefs whose surfaces are covered in intricate geometric patterns. Patrick Morrison's canvases depict painterly rendered figures set in a variety of urban situations. Shows of emerging artists, like the realist painter Sandow Birk, are also offered by the gallery. Some painters represented, such as Ryo Okabayashi and William Paiden, have extensive printmaking backgrounds; and the gallery has a strong focus on graphic works. The gallery features prints by Bruce Nauman, Bryce Marden, Andy Warhol, Jasper Johns and Larry Rivers.

The gallery also carries work by Dianne Blell, Gregory Botts, Carl Dern, Willard Dixon, Marina Karella, Basil Langton, Francine Matarazzo, Alexander Mihaylovich, Richard Mock and Ann Honig Nadel.

[83] MEKLER GALLERY, INC.
651 N. La Cienega Blvd., Los Angeles, CA 90069
(213) 659-0583 Tues-Sat: 11-5 or by appt. *Owner/Dir:* Adam Mekler

The gallery shows primarily 20th century sculpture, painting, collage and graphics. Regular exhibitions feature sculpture by George Baker, Sorel Etrog and Paul Suttman. Painting and graphics are shown by artists Ynez Johnston, Susana Lago, Ulfert Wilke and Corda Eby. Paintings by Fred Reichman and Elen Feinberg can be seen; paintings and prints by Alan Magee; and pastels by Joan Carter. Works from the estate of Rico Lebrun, designer of stained glass, and muralist who portrayed the human figure in a semi-abstract style, can also be seen. Special exhibitions have featured works on paper by Alberto Giacometti, Pablo Picasso and Henri Matisse. Works by Pierre Bonnard, Vuillard, Camille Pissarro, Reuben Nakian and Henry Moore have been featured in other exhibitions.

[84] MIXOGRAFIA GALLERY
1419 E. Adams Blvd., Los Angeles, CA 90011
(213) 232-1158

Mon-Fri: 9-5; Sat & evenings by appt. *Owner:* Luis and Lea Remba *Dir:* Lea Remba

Previously headquartered in Mexico City, the Mixografia Gallery was opened in Los Angeles in order to participate in the emerging status of Los Angeles as an international and cultural center. The gallery serves as both a workshop and an exhibition space for works created using the Mixografia process. The process was invented in 1973 by Luis Remba. This three-dimensional artistic printing process incorporates the basic qualities of etching, wood-cutting and lithography within one printing plate. An artist can now use any solid surface such as canvas, wax, glass, plaster, instead of traditional etching, wood or stone. The artist creates a three-dimensional matrix on this base using materials of his or her own choosing. These materials, which can be collaged, incised or carved, may be those used in traditional printmaking, or can include others, such as sand, wood, charcoal, clay or plaster. A negative copper plate is then produced from the artist's master plate. This plate is used to print limited editions, monotypes and multiples on hand-made paper and metal.

The gallery/workshop was designed to allow the participating artists maximum use of the flexibility allowed by the Mixografia process. The 30,000-square-foot workshop houses a paper mill, a press with a 20-by-7-foot bed (the largest in the world), a 6-by-9-foot lithographic stone (also the largest in the world), the equipment to produce copper sculptures up to 10 by 8 by 14 feet in a single unit, an experimental photographic laboratory, a fine arts precious metal workshop and an additional 5,000 square feet of exhibition space.

The gallery displays and houses the work of the various artists who have worked with Luis Remba in the creation of Mixografias. The flexibility of the Mixografia process has attracted artists of international stature, and the collaborations which have followed have enriched the medium with succeeding innovations. Artists represented by the gallery include British artist Henry Moore, Dutch artist Karel Appel, Peruvian artist Fernando de Szyszlo, Mexican artists Carlos Merida, Rufino Tamayo and Francisco Zuniga, and American artists Stanley Boxer, Laddie John Dill,

Helen Frankenthaler, Robert Graham, Kenneth Noland and Larry Rivers.

Other artists exhibited in the gallery include Alberto Burri, Luis Fernando Camino, Vladimir Cora, Teodulo Romulo, Costas Tsoclis and Francisco Toledo.

[85] TOBEY C. MOSS GALLERY
7321 Beverly Blvd., Los Angeles CA 90036
(213) 933-5523

Tues-Sat: 11-4 *Owner/Dir:* Tobey C. Moss

The gallery offers four centuries of prints and drawings plus paintings and sculpture of the 1920s through the 1960s, encompassing modernism through hard-edge and social realism.

Tobey C. Moss Gallery features the work of Helen Lundeberg and Lorser Feitelson, who co-founded post-surrealism in 1934, and went on to become leaders of California hard-edge painting in the 1950s; along with John McLaughlin, Frederick Hammersley and Karl Benjamin.

Other artists whose works are offered in the gallery include California modernist painter and sculptor Peter Krasnow; Bauhaus-trained Werner Drewes, who was a founding member of the American Abstract Artists Group in New York, 1936; June Wayne, a paper and printmaker who founded the Tamarind Lithography Workshop in 1960; abstract film pioneer Oskar Fischinger; regionalist Palmer Schoppe who captured the rhythm and jazz of Harlem, New Orleans and Los Angeles; Clinton Adams; and Jean Charlot, painter, printmaker and muralist in the Mexican tradition.

[86] NEWSPACE
5241 Melrose Ave., Los Angeles, CA 90038
(213) 469-9353

Tues-Sat: 11-4 *Owner/Dir:* Joni Gordon

Newspace gallery specializes in Los Angeles painting and sculpture. The work varies from representational to abstract, and many of the artists are among the city's well-established figures.

Martha Alf paints and draws still lifes, exquisitely rendered and bathed in pastel-colored light, of pears and other objects found around the home. Edith Baumann-Hudson, on the other hand, paints organic abstract canvases in the tradition of purist minimalism. Sculptor Peter Zecher works with simple, geometric forms repeated and stacked into complex columns. Photographer Judy Fiskin examines single objects with her camera in several series that document the exteriors and interiors of our urban environment.

Other works by the gallery's stable of artists include Alan Wayne; paintings of the native Southwest by Lisa Ferrante; conceptual painting, drawing and video by Paul Knotter; landscape and interior paintings, murals and installations by Patricia Patterson; organic abstract paintings, sculpture, prints and drawings by Jeff Price; painting in three dimensions by James Trivers; assemblage sculpture by Danial Wheeler; conceptual figurative and landscape painting by Peter Zokoski; and organic abstract painting by Ken Hurbert.

Newspace gallery also represents Lisa Adams, Sidney Gordin and Anne Marie Karlsen.

The gallery also specializes in American modernist painting and sculpture, with an emphasis on the period 1919-1960s. Newspace presents master works by European and American painters and sculptors, in-cluding those of Willem de Kooning, Fernand Leger, John McLaughlin, Joan Mitchell, Claude Monet, Henry Moore, Georgia O'Keeffe and Mark Rothko. Recently, the gallery has begun to focus on the works of pop painters, such as Andy Warhol and Roy Lichtenstein.

[87] NFA ANTIQUITIES
10100 Santa Monica Blvd., Ste. 600, Los Angeles, CA 90067 (213) 282-7588

Mon-Fri: 10-5; by appt. *Owner:* Bruce P. McNall *Dir:* Katya L. Shirokow

NFA Antiquities exhibits Egyptian, Greek, Etruscan and Roman Antiquities. Ancient art works exhibited include sculpture in marble, bronze, terra-cotta, silver and gold; vases, mosaics, frescoes and wearable ancient jewelry.

The gallery's large exhibition space, located on the sixth floor of a Century City office tower, is the site of a continuing series of shows focusing in different forms of art from the ancient classical world.

The gallery's artists, many of whom, in the case of vase painting, have been identified, represent some of the high points of artistic achievement in the classical world. Among these, the greatest was Euphronios, a vase painter living in the late sixth century B.C. Fewer than ten vases of Euphronios are known to exist in the world, of these NFA has handled two.

NFA Antiquities and its sister company, Numismatic Fine Arts, have handled the sale and purchase of ancient art works and coins for 40 years. The galleries clients include most major American Museums that collect antiquities, as well as private collectors. NFA Antiquities supported the L.A. County Museum of Art's exhibition of ancient bronze sculpture entitled "The Gods' Delight."

[88] OVSEY GALLERY
126 N. La Brea Ave., Los Angeles, CA 90036
(213) 935-1883

Tues-Sat: 11-5 *Owner/Dir:* Alice & Neil Ovsey

Ovsey Gallery specializes in contemporary American painting, sculpture and drawing. The artists represented are at various stages of development, but are aligned by the gallery's emphasis on recognizable imagery and figuration.

F. Scott Hess paints colorful genre scenes of American family life that are filled with both humor and despair. Nancy Pierson paintings re-interpret old ID photographs, and transform them into dignified and complex human characterizations. Ron Rizk's oil-on-panel paintings are pristine, trompe l'oeil depictions of crafted objects such as lures and decoys. The visually intense paintings of Bobby Ross juxtapose real and imagined, sublime and horrific imagery in a meticulously rendered technique. The gallery also represents a few abstract painters such as Mary Jones, whose lyrical canvases develop a personal language of symbolism.

The gallery also represents Roger Boyce, Susan Hall, Tom Leeson, Ron Linden, Ed Nunnery, Judith Simonian, Chris Unterseher, Ed Valentine and Nancy Youdelman.

[89] PAIDEIA GALLERY
765 N. La Cienaga Blvd., Los Angeles CA 90069
(213) 652-8224

Tues-Sat: 11-4:30 *Owner/Dir:* Stevan Kissel

The Paideia Gallery has a varied inventory which includes seventeenth- to early twentieth-century works, Renaissance drawings, Russian and European bronzes, California impressionists and European and American paintings by noted artists.

Paideia is especially interested in American artists of the nineteenth- and early twentieth-centuries. Among the oil paintings at the gallery are works by Bruce Crane, Maurice Braun, Albert Bierstadt, Maynard Dixon, Edgar Payne, Robert Philipp, Granville Redmond, Guy Rose and others working usually in an impressionistic idiom.

[90] HERBERT PALMER GALLERY
802 N. La Cienega Blvd., Los Angeles, CA 90069
(213) 854-0096

Tues-Fri: 10-6; Sat: 11-5 *Owner:* Herbert Palmer *Dir:* Meredith Palmer

The Herbert Palmer Gallery is the oldest gallery in southern California that handles painting and sculpture of the 20th century. Established in 1963, the gallery has shown works of Master European, American modern, and contemporary artists. The gallery has also introduced leading contemporary artists from around the world to the Los Angeles community.

The gallery represents contemporary artists Karel Appel, Joseph Beuys, Christo, Sam Francis, Helen Frankenthaler, Adolph Gottlieb, Red Grooms, David Hockney, Shoichi Ida, Morris Louis, Man Ray, Claes Oldenburg, Robert Rauschenberg, Italo Scanga and Frank Stella. It also represents American modernist artists Oscar Bluemner, John Marin, Kay Sage, Joseph Stella; and European Modernists Pierre Boddard, Marcel Duchamp, M. Luce, Joan Miro and Pablo Picasso.

In addition, the gallery features the work of the Dynaton painters Wolfgang Paalen, Gordon Onslow-Ford and Lee Mullican. This important movement, from 1948 to 1958, paralleled and, according to some critics, preceded abstract expressionism.

[91] MARILYN PINK FINE ARTS, LTD.
P.O. Box 491446, Los Angeles CA 90049
(213) 395-1465

Mon-Fri: 10-5 *Owner/Dir:* Marilyn Pink

The gallery houses an extraordinary collection of art on paper, drawings and prints from the fifteenth-through the mid-twentieth century. Major artists and schools of both Europe and America are represented.

One is likely to find first edition Audubon prints, Currier and Ives popular lithography, as well as work by well-known American artists of the nineteenth- and twentieth-century: American Impressionists Mary Cassatt and James Abbott MacNeill Whistler; Regionalists Thomas Hart Benton, and John Steuart Curry; John Sloan, Paul Landacre and Rockwell Kent. Here you may also find American Modernists such as Arthur Dove, Louis Lozowick, Louis Schanker, Marsden Hartley and Max Weber.

The gallery is noted for drawings of the Old Masters and contemporary European masters. Drawings by the French Intimists Pierre Bonnard and Edouard Vuillard are a mainstay of the gallery, as are watercolors and drawings by impressionists, post-impressionists and other nineteenth- and early twentieth-century French artists.

German artists represented are: social realist Kathe Kollwitz; expressionists Max Pechstein, Erik Heckel,

Franz Marc and Viennese artist Oscar Kokoschka; and German impressionists such as Lovis Corinth and Max Liebermann.

Contemporary artists include Ynez Johnston, who works in a semi-abstract style; Ralph Gilbert, a new figurative artist working in large color monotypes; abstract artist Paul Kelpe; and Roy Lichtenstein.

[92] RICHARD/BENNETT GALLERY
830 N. La Brea Ave., Los Angeles, CA 90038
(213) 962-8006

Tues-Sat: 11-5 *Owner/Dir:* Richard Heller, Bennett Roberts

The gallery shows modern and contemporary painting and sculpture. Norton Wisdom paints the simple shape of the square, with endlessly shifting variations of perspective. Cameron Shaw makes sculpture in the assemblage tradition, filling roughly-made boxes with beetles, coins, and other evocative objects. The gallery also represents Anselm Kiefer, Lance Letscher, Yolande McKay and Craig Roper. Though much of the work exhibited reveals a strong interest in ideas, the gallery shows an equally strong emphasis on materials, especially common ones such as lead.

Richard/Bennett also shows work by internationally known artists such as the French photo-conceptual artist Christian Boltanski, California pop-conceptualist Ed Ruscha and the late New York photographer Robert Mapplethorpe. The directors have received acclaim for several "curated" shows on such themes as "Art as Religion," and "Aesthetics." They have also curated shows outside of their own gallery space.

[93] MARC RICHARDS GALLERY
4847 W. Jefferson Blvd., Los Angeles, CA 90016
(213) 732-9408

Tues-Sat: 12-5 *Owner/Dir:* Marc Richards *Mgr:* Isabelle Baertschi

The gallery specializes in contemporary American and European painting, drawing and sculpture, with a strong emphasis on abstract painting.

In a new location beginning in 1989, a large space in an industrial neighborhood, the Marc Richards Gallery has shifted its exhibition focus from one-person shows to large, well-organized group shows addressing specific themes. Such themes as simple, monochrome painting; or current Los Angeles abstract painting, have brought together artists like Mary Corse, Jeremy Gilbert-Rolfe, James Hayward, Bill Komoski, Robert Mangold and Robert Therrien.

The gallery also has works available by Ross Bleckner, John C.,Cracken, John McLaughlin, Ed Ruscha and Jonathan Borofsky.

[94] JACK RUTBERG FINE ARTS, INC.
357 N. La Brea Ave., Los Angeles CA 90036
(213) 938-5222

Tues-Fri: 11-6; Sat: 11-5 *Owner/Dir:* Jack Rutberg

Jack Rutberg Fine Arts Specializes in American and European modern & contemporary paintings, drawings, prints and sculpture.

One of the premiere exhibition spaces in Los Angeles, Jack Rutberg Fine Arts is housed in an Art Deco building dating back to the 1930s. The gallery's two grand spaces, combined with its more intimate rooms, offer an ideal setting for viewing the work of such master artists as Picasso, Chagall, Matisse, Kollwitz, Calder, DeKooning, Gorky, Man Ray, Hockney,

Max DeMoss, *Equus V,* 1989, 48 inches wide, bronze.
Courtesy: Wenger Gallery, Los Angeles

Stamos, Hundertwasser, Appel, Wesselmann, Warhol and Lichtenstein.

Additionally, the gallery represents such artists as the much-awarded Irish expressionist Patrick Graham; Hannelore Baron, subject of a major 1989 Guggenheim exhibition; Los Angeles artists Ruth Weisberg and Edward Glauder; the pioneering sculptor Claire Falkenstein; and abstract-expressionist painter Hans Burkhardt whose historic impact and formidable reputation are causing him to receive renewed attention for his unique role in American painting.

[95] SAXON-LEE GALLERY
7525 Beverly Blvd., Los Angeles, CA 90036
(213) 933-5282

Tues-Sat: 10-5:30 *Owner/Dir:* Daniel Saxon & Candace Lee

Supporting both emerging and established artists, the gallery's exhibitions rotate on a monthly basis. Contemporary paintings, sculpture, drawings, ceramics and art furniture are shown. East Coast artists featured include: Red Grooms, Judy Rifka and Michelle Stuart. Hispanic artists Gronk, Rupert Garcia, John Valadez and Raul Guerrero have exhibited their works in the gallery's exhibitions. Upcoming exhibitions will feature sculptors Margaret Honda, Michael Speaker, Jay Johnson and Elizabeth Gutierrez. Younger painters Luis Serrano, Nancy Riegelman, Ilene Segalove, Anna Bialobroda and Rose-Lynn Fisher have exhibited representational and abstract work.

[96] SOUTHERN CALIFORNIA CONTEMPORARY ART GALLERY
825 La Cienaga Blvd., Los Angeles, CA 90069
(213) 652-8272

Tues-Fri: 12-5; Sat: 12-4; Sun 2-4 *Dir:* Christine Dailey

The Southern California Contemporary Art Gallery is the exhibition arm of the Los Angeles Art Association, a nonprofit California Corporation organized in 1925 which exhibits works of professional Southern California artists from San Diego to Santa Barbara. Many gifted young artists first introduced by the gallery have gone on to receive wide recognition. One-person shows have been organized for older artists as well, such as Anders Aldrin, Stanton MacDonald Wright, Lorser Feitelson, Nick Brigante, Ron Blumberg and Mabel Alvarez.

In its 55-year history, the gallery has been instrumental in giving artists a place to show their work, and in bringing the works of lesser known European artists to Southern California. The gallery carries on monthly exhibits in a wide variety of media and styles. Exhibiting members must be accepted by the Art Committee.

[97] SPACE LOS ANGELES
6015 Santa Monica Blvd., Los Angeles, CA 90038
(213) 461-8166

Tues-Sat: 11-5 and by appt. *Owner/Dir:* E.D. Lau

Residing in the same extensive space since 1975, the gallery features primarily contemporary sculpture and works with great dimensionality. Rotating exhibitions are presented in addition to the work of other gallery artists. Internationally-known artists Norman Lundin and Pepo Pichler have shown at the gallery. Others artists include Ann Page, Tom Stanton, Kazuo Kadonaga, Judith Foosaner, Doug Young, Masami Teraoka, Seiji Kunishima, Bob Alderette, Norman Schwab, Robert Anderson, Minoru Ohira and Roberta Eisenberg. Most of the artists represented by Space are at mid-career, although some emerging California artists are also shown.

[98] DAVID STUART GALLERIES
748 1/2 N. La Cienega Blvd. (Penthouse), Los Angeles, CA 90069 (213) 652-7422

Tues-Sat: 1-5 *Owner:* Jacqueline Stuart *Dir:* Kerry Burt

The "penthouse" gallery prides itself on providing a feeling of discovery by juxtaposing one of California's finest collections of Pre-Columbian and Primitive art with contemporary works and California art from the 1950s and 1960s. Works by such artists as Laurence Drieband, Mineo Mizuno, Mel Ramos, Llyn Foulkes, Peter Voulkos, David Furman and June Harwood are shown.

The gallery also features the furniture of Frank Gehry and the works of John Altoon, Robert Doud, Hassell Smith and William Brice.

Exhibitions held by the gallery have included: Gil Elvgren's calendar art; Erte's designs and a collection of erotic art.

[99] STUDIO 1617
1617 Silver Lake Blvd., Los Angeles, CA 90026
(213) 660-7991

Mon-Wed: 9:30-12:30; Tues, Thurs, Fri: 9:30-4:30; and by appt. *Owner:* Bill Wheeler *Dir:* Marty Gattuso

Studio 1617 considers itself the neighborhood gallery of the Silver Lake area of Los Angeles. It specializes in limited edition graphics, works on paper and paintings and tends to show the work of professional California artists who are not well known in the main stream.

The gallery which opened to the public in 1976 is the former studio and workshop of artists Bill Wheeler and Drusilla Sumner. It represents approximately 20 artists who are featured in rotating one-person and group shows. Work shown recently ranges from Ilee Kaplan's large, multi-color figurative woodcuts to Ruth Kaspin's jewelry and mystical watercolor landscapes to Bill Wheeler's abstract hand-colored viscosity collographs and paintings on masonite to Drusilla Sumner's dimensional paper pieces.

[100] THINKING EYE
1318 S. Figueroa St., Los Angeles, CA 90015
(213) 748-3411

Wed-Sat: 11-4 *Owner/Dir:* Bill Lasarow, Beate Bermann-Enn

Thinking Eye gallery shows contemporary art in all media. There is no consistent style to the works shown, which range from highly realistic to abstract, but rather a commitment to the aesthetic integrity of each of its artists.

The realistic interest of the gallery is represented by Phyllis Davidson, whose portraits are given a surrealistic twist through depicting incongruous situations; and Kent Twitchell, whose large murals of his fellow artists decorate many Los Angeles buildings and freeways. Thinking Eye carries Twitchell's preparatory drawings and arranges commissioned murals. Abstract artists include Patrick Alt, whose painterly canvases depict geometric forms that often symbolize women; and gallery co-owner Bill Lasarow, whose paintings convey galaxies of circles and, more recently, imagery based on automatic drawing. Several of the artists at the gal-

Frank Damiano, *Point, 1988* 72 x 60, oil on canvas.
Courtesy: Site 311, Pacific Grove. Photograph: M. Lee Fatherree

lery have an interest in works that convey a sense of spiritual or cosmic connection. Ron Pippin transforms old nautical maps, with colors and diagrams, into "paradise maps." Margi Scharff makes minimalist sculptures and environments that often contain natural elements such as tumbleweeds, and glow with subtle neon lights.

The gallery also represents Joan Carl, Pat Cox, Nick Gadbois, Eva and Paul Kolosvary, David Quick and Richard Shelton.

[101] JAN TURNER GALLERY

8000 Melrose Ave., Los Angeles, CA 90046
(213) 658-6084

Tues-Fri: 10-5:30; Sat: 11-5:30 *Owner:* Jan Turner, *Dir:* Craig Krull

The gallery handles painting, sculpture and photography by contemporary artists from California, the East Coast and Europe. Artists represented are John Alexander, Carlos Almaraz, David Bierk, Christophe Boutin, Tim Bradley, Laurie Brown, David Bungay, Sigrid Burton, Emanuele Cacciatore, Elaine Lustig Cohen, Larry Cohen, Jay Defeo, Tony Delap, Laurence Dreiband, Bruce Everett, Ole Fischer, John Frame, Gary Hall, John Hull, Keith Jacobshagen, Randall Lavender, Peter Liashkov, Michael Maglich, Paul Manes, Michael Mazur, Astrid Preston, David Shapiro, Steven Sorman, Fulvio Testa, Donald Roller-Wilson and Isaac Witkin.

[102] RAGNARS VEILANDS ARTS

560 S. Main St., Los Angeles, CA 90013
(213) 624-7464

by appt. *Owner/Dir:* Ragnars Veilands

A private studio and gallery, Veilands exhibits works in neo-primitive passionism, subjective narrativism, naif narrative & socio-political symbolism. Photography and computer-generated pixelgraphs are also exhibited here.

Artists represented by the gallery include: Jim Clausnitzer, Thomas Dougherty, Jay Koepke, Erich Santner, Werner T. Pavlovich, James Wittkopf, Leonard Marcel and Victor Acevedo as well as Ragnars Veilands himself.

[103] WADE GALLERY

750 N. La Cienega Blvd., Los Angeles, CA 90069
(213) 652-1733

Tues-Sat: 10-5 *Owners:* John Long, Ron Kram, Denise Wakeman *Dir:* Marlene Bauer

The Wade Gallery shows contemporary American and Canadian painting and sculpture. The work carried by the gallery tends toward abstraction, though often with some landscape, figurative or still-life reference.

Maryann Harman's abstract canvases, stained with washes of color, then re-worked with expressionistic drawing, respond to the locales around Vermont and Virginia where she resides. Claribel Cone also paints with thin veils of paint, mostly in primary colors, to explore landscapes that are more inner than worldly. Gayle J. Novak's paintings, built up with layers of impasto paint which are then scraped away, only vaguely hint at the Arizona landscape where she lives. Pat Service paints simple shapes with broad expanses of color, landscape-based but primarily concerned with light and form. Leslie Poole paints stilllifes, filled with bold color and gestural brushwork.

The Wade Gallery also represents Peter Aspell, Norman Badion, Tom Berg, Dorothy Fratt, Lilly Fenichel, Maryon Kantaroff, Clinton MacKenzie, Ramon Munoz, Maurianna Nolan, Seka Owen, Daniel Phill, Michael Richters and Arthur Yanoff.

[104] DANIEL WEINBERG GALLERY

619 & 625 N. Almont Dr., Los Angeles, CA 90069
(213) 271-7101

Tues-Sat: 11-5 *Owner/Dir:* Daniel Weinberg

Daniel Weinberg Gallery represents contemporary American painters and sculptors.

Artists shown include painters Robert Ryman, Robert Mangold, Terry Winters, Carroll Dunham, Richard Artschwager, Ralph Humphrey, Elizabeth Murray and sculptors Scott Burton, Bruce Nauman, Sol LeWitt and Barry Le Va.

Younger artists are also exhibited at the gallery including Jeff Koons, Meyer Vaisman, Kenji Fujita, Ashley Bickerton, Peter Halley, Saint Clair Cemin, Bob Gober, Annette Lemieux and Christopher Wool.

Also represented by the gallery are Richard Prince and Laurie Simmons.

[105] WENGER GALLERY

828 N. La Brea Ave., Los Angeles, CA 90038
(213) 464-4431

Tues-Sat: 11-5 *Owner/Dir:* Muriel and Sigmund Wegner

The Wenger Gallery specializes in contemporary painting and sculpture by respected artists from the United States and around the world.

Among the artists exhibited are the pop-assemblage artist Arman; Tom Bacher, who shows his phosphorescent paintings inspired by the L.A. cityscape; Max DeMoss, who exhibits life-sized rough bronze figurative sculpture; Guy Dill, whose steel sculpture of arcs and lines express forces in tension; Malcolm O'Leary, who makes expressive abstract sculpture out of wood and steel; David Provan, who creates dynamic constructivist sculpture; and Philemona Williamson, a New York figurative painter of social themes.

The Wenger Gallery also represents Tom Aprile, Robert Bassler, Ellen Brooks, Klaus Fussmann, Alfred Jensen, Joan Miro, Alfonse Pagano, A.R. Penck, Jean-Pierre Raynaud, Gerhard Richter, Kenneth Snelson, Antoni Tapies, Mark Tobey, Jan Vanriet, Bernar Venet, Kay WalkingStick and Emerson Woelffer.

[106] ZERO ONE GALLERY

7025 Melrose Ave., Los Angeles, CA 90038
(213) 965-9459

Tues-Sat: 11-6 *Owner/Dir:* John Pochna

Located at an intersection where the fine art galleries along La Brea Avenue meet the younger gallery scene on Melrose, the Zero One Gallery combines both worlds. The look of much of the art shown is similar to that produced in New York's East Village in the early 1980s, and Zero One has held group shows of East Village artists, as well as group and one-person shows of contemporary artists from Los Angeles, Europe and the Soviet Union.

Zero One carries the paintings of Brian Routh, better known as a member of the notorious performance team "The Kipper Kids." Painter Mark Gash's lively canvases are filled with cartoon-like humor and deep feeling; Tomata du Plenty, also, paints in an expressionistic cartoon style. Curtis Gutierrez's paintings convey a raw, tribal power. Mike Parker, on the other hand, paints in a wry style he calls "Surf Realism." Joni Mabe filled the gallery with her fantastically baroque installation *The Elvis Museum.*

The gallery also represents Anthony Ausgang, Charles Bojorquez, Walter Robinson, Richard Hambleton, Christof Kohlhofer, Raymond Pettibon, Hudson Marquez, Luis Frangella, Carol Lay, Marcy Watton, Michael Petry, Max Couper, Antonio Gomez Bueno, May Zone, Ed "Big Daddy" Roth, Keiko Bonk, Robert Williams, plus original drawings from *The Umbrellas* by Christo.

MANHATTAN BEACH

[107] SHAHIN REQUICHA GALLERY

3301 Crest Dr., Manhattan Beach, CA 90266 (213) 545-8549

By appointment *Owner/Dir:* Shahin Requicha

The gallery carries many works by New York Expressionists, as well as a number of European sculptors. Relocating from Rochester, New York, the gallery will reopen October 1, 1990.

Many of the artists whom the gallery represents were students of Hans Hoffman. Among them are Peter Dean, Jay Milder, Bill Berrell and Nicholas Sperakis. Another is Mary Lou Dooley, whose large lyrical abstract canvases make resplendent use of color. The gallery also represents a number of sculptors who work abstractly. Armanda Balduzzi is an artist now showing in New York City whose first showing of painted wood pieces was at Shahin Requicha. Other exhibits featured Gigi Guadagnuci's marble sculptures, James Marshall's carved wood pieces, James Thomas' abstractly lyrical Plexiglas and light sculptures and Arch Miller's stone and bronze pieces.

MILL VALLEY

[108] SUSAN CUMMINS GALLERY

32B Miller, Mill Valley, CA 94941 (415) 383-1512

Mon-Sat: 11-6; Sun: 12-5 *Owner/Dir:* Susan Cummins

Founded in 1984, the Susan Cummins Gallery exhibits contemporary clay, ceramic and mixed-media sculpture, contemporary paintings and fine art jewelry. It is noted as an exceptional gallery in Marin County that shows an international collection of one-of-a-kind pieces.

The gallery features the porcelain figures of Margaret Keelan, the ceramic sculpture of Bennett Beane, Mike Moran and Poe Dismuke and the figurative paintings of Gail Chase-Bien.

The Susan Cummins Gallery also presents works on paper by Illinois collage artists John Fraser, California charcoal draughtsperson Tobin Keller and the mixed media sculpture of David Best.

All of the jewelers presented at the Susan Cummins Gallery work with precious and semiprecious stones as well as gems and fine metals. Among them are Carolyn Morris Bach, Thomas Mann, and Joyce Clements. The gallery has three rooms: a back room with permanent and monthly-rotating collections of jewelry, a middle room with a permanent collection of painting and sculpture and a space for monthly painting and sculpture exhibits.

MONTECITO

[109] MAUREEN MURPHY FINE ARTS

1187 Coast Village Rd., Suite 3, Montecito, CA 93108 (805) 969-9215

Tues-Sat: 12-5 *Owner/Dir:* Maureen A. Murphy

The gallery specializes in American art of the early 20th century, with a focus on the California impressionist and post-impressionist period.

Works available frequently include impressionist portraits, nudes and landscapes by Michca Askenazy; post-impressionist portraits by Louis Ritman; portraits by Lawton Parker; landscapes by Jean Mannheim; and city street scenes by Alson Skinner Clark.

Maureen Murphy Fine Arts also displays works by other painters of the period such as Jules Pages, Paul Lauritiz, Emil Kosa, Jack Wilkinson Smith and Edgar Payne.

NORTHRIDGE

[110] CALIFORNIA STATE UNIVERSITY-NORTHRIDGE ART GALLERIES

Fine Arts Building, 18111 Nordhoff St., Northridge, CA 91344 (818) 885-2156

Mon: 12-4; Tues-Fri: 10-4 *Dir:* Louise Lewis

Connected with California State University (Northridge), CSUN is mainly devoted to international art and design of the 20th century, though historical and ethnic shows are also featured annually. The gallery's primary objective is to showcase work of an experimental nature which explores the boundries of what is considered art. Artists recently featured include Cultural Odyssey, a performance group; Beverly Naidus, a mixed-media artist who explores social issues; contemporary video artists and art of the Australian Aborigines. Of special importance to the gallery is art of the Pacific Rim nations from such artists as the Chicana Artists, the Molas of Central America and landscape work from China.

OAKLAND

[111] CREATIVE GROWTH GALLERY

355 24th St., Oakland, CA 94612 (415) 836-2340

The Creative Growth Gallery is a professional exhibition space for art works produced at the Creative Growth Art Center, a not-for-profit organization which provides creative art programs, educational and independent living training, counseling and vocational opportunities for adults who are physically, mentally or emotionally disabled. Creative Growth also serves as an advocate for the disabled and provides services to teachers, caretakers, families, therapists and other persons who work and do research in the fields of art and disabilities. The goals of the organization include: artistic development; creative self-expression on the visual arts; integration of the personality through creative experience in the visual arts; enhancement of self-image and self-esteem; mainstreaming and normalization; prevention of institutionalization; appreciation by the public of the creativity of disabled artists; research on creativity of disabled artists; and advocacy for the arts and people with disabilities.

The Center's professional art studio has been developed for clients who are especially gifted and have the potential for becoming partially or fully self-supporting through their art. Drawing, painting, printmaking, graphic arts and ceramic sculpture are included in a program designed to suit the talents and needs of individual clients. The program is further enriched by field trips to museums, art galleries and artists' studios. Whenever possible, clients are taken "on site" for drawing and painting experiences, reflecting the varied environmental visual stimulation available in the Bay Area. Clients develop exhibition portfolios and produce marketable items for sale in the gallery, gift shop and rental gallery. Earned income opportunities are provided for each client through sales of their work. The Center also sponsors a rug/tapestry project, in which training is provided in the design and production of rug/tapestries. Clients have the opportunity to earn hourly stipends while participating in this craft workshop which provides rug/tapestries for sale to the general public. Clients in this program continue their involvement in the general art studio program. In addition to the independence clients can achieve through such income, the opportunity to view their own work and the work of other artists in the Creative Growth Gallery enhances their self-image, while participation in the creative process allows them to grow and develop through the richness of the creative environment.

The Center also provides training in independent living. Individual and group instruction in self-care, physical and emotional growth, socialization, communication, counseling, academics, movement, community safety and integration skills and culinary arts are fully integrated into the program and tailored to the needs of individual clients.

The Gallery professionally exhibits not only the work of Creative Growth clients, but also that of emerging and well known artists. Exhibits of Creative Growth art in community spaces and corporate lobbies can be arranged. A gift shop featuring the work of Creative Growth artists and outside craftspeople is a unique example of mainstreaming in the arts. The Rental/Sales Gallery provides Creative Growth art for home or office at modest prices. Exhibition in the gallery and outside shows demonstrates to the public the creative potential of disabled artists.

The Creative Growth Art Center and Gallery are staffed by credentialed teachers, artists and professionals in the creative arts, social welfare, psychology and related fields. Instruction is supplemented by lectures by visiting artists and professionals in the art world which are open to the public. The most recent series of lectures featured Judy Hiramoto, Ron Nagle, Michael Stevens, Beverly Mayeri, Mary Chomenko and Alan Winkler.

Funding for the Center and Gallery is provided by fees for services (usually paid by various forms of donations), grants, gifts, private and public contributions, memberships and fundraising events. In addition, the Creative Growth project is supported in part by an Oakland Arts Council grant funded by the City of Oakland.

[112] VICTOR FISCHER GALLERY
1333 Broadway, Ste. 100, Oakland CA 94612
(415) 444-2424
see San Francisco listing

PACIFIC GROVE

[113] SITE 311
311 Forest Ave., Pacific Grove, CA 93950

Tues-Sat: 9-5 *Owner/Dir:* Chris Grimes

The gallery exhibits the work of established and emerging artists from California. Most of the younger artists featured are recognized by museums, media and corporate collections. Evidenced by their shows, Site 311 continues to stay abreast of the newest directions taken by San Francisco and Los Angeles artists. Past shows have included Southern California artists: Laddie John Dill, whose unique cement and glass constructions inspire the geometric form and saturated color in his other media; plus John Baldessari, whose photo-etchings challenge assumptions about contemporary culture. Bay area artist George Miyasake exhibited collaged canvases combining geometric construction and classical composition. Future shows will feature nine Los Angeles artists, including Dill and Baldessari, plus books and works on paper by Robert Motherwell and others. Additional pieces available in the gallery are canvases and works on paper by Eva Bovenzi, Robert Brokl and Frank Damiano. There are sculptural assemblages by Robert Dix; canvases and linotypes by Carol Doyle; kinetic sculpture by Matt Gil; paintings and monotypes by Matt Glavin; paintings and works on paper by Stuart Fineman, Inez Storer and Audrey Welch; steel and bronze sculpture by Clay Jensen; ceramic sculpture by Rovert Kvenild; photography by Dar Spain; paintings by Mark Johnson and Steven Pon; mixed-media sculpture by Ken Matsumoto; paintings and monotypes by Patrick Surgalski and works on paper by Tobin Keller and L.G. Williams.

[114] TROTTER GALLERIES
309 Forest Ave., Pacific Grove, CA 93950
(408) 373-7166

Mon-Sat: 10-5:30 *Owner/Dir:* Terry & Paula Trotter

Trotter Galleries specializes in California painting of the 19th and early 20th centuries but also deals in American and European art of the same period. The gallery holds no contemporary art but does sell some early graphics.

The Gallery which opened in 1980, is located in a freestanding building on the main street of Pacific Grove, near Pebble Beach and Carmel. It has one large exhibition space and at any one time has 75 to 80 paintings hanging on its walls. Artists whose work the Trotter Galleries represents include: Thomas Hill, a 19th century California painter of the Rocky Mountain School; California landscape painter William Keith; Southern California impressionists Edgar Payne, Marion Wachtel, Maurice Bruan and Franz A. Bischoff; and Northern California impressionists William Ritschel, Arman Hansen and Percy Gray.

Trotter Galleries also exhibits at California's major antique and art shows. It maintains a collectors list and is always soliciting to buy. Recently the gallery loaned a piece by Guy Rose to the Laguna Art Museum for an exhibition.

PACIFIC PALISADES

[115] DEANNA MILLER FINE ARTS
951 Kagawa St., Pacific Palisades, CA 90272
(213) 454-6241

Owner: Deanna Miller

The gallery's main focus is on contemporary artists, both established and emerging. A broad range of styles are represented. Deanna Miller is an experienced art

James Dallas Parks, *Riverman on the Mississippi,* 44 x 32, oil on canvas.
Courtesy: Atelier Dore, Inc., San Francisco

consultant. She has worked in Los Angeles, San Francisco, New York City, and has established contacts with major art institutions across the U.S. The gallery provides art services to major corporations, professional offices, business industry and private collectors; from placement of a single work, to development of an entire private or corporate collection. Services include art consultation, selection and acquisition, quality matting and framing, design and space planning for installations and crating and shipping. Art selections range from original art, paintings, drawings, sculpture, photographs, wall hangings and ceramics.

PALM DESERT

[116] ADAGIO GALLERIES
73-130 El Paseo, Palm Desert, CA 92260
(619) 346-8816
Owner/Dir: Dusty Maurer
see entry for Palm Springs

[117] VALERIE MILLER FINE ART
72-785 Highway 111, Palm Desert, CA 92260
(619) 773-4483
Owner/Dir: Valerie Miller

The gallery specializes in contemporary paintings, sculpture, and graphics by established American artists. The artists represented include Peter Alexander, whose large canvases capture an interplay of dark and light across the urban sky; Michael Davis who makes large geometric steel sculpture; Woods Davy, another sculptor, whose pieces are a subtle dialogue between open steel forms and rocks. George Geyer is a sculptor who works with stacked sheets of glass; Betty Gold, whose sculptures are complex designs of flat steel shapes; Karla Klarin, who paints cityscapes in which outlines extend out into space to form low reliefs. Eric Orr makes sculptures that enhance our awareness of natural elements, especially water.

Valerie Miller also represents Rita Deanin Abbey, Sheila Elias, Nancy Kay, Michael McCall, Jim Morphesis, Ed Ruscha, Sylvia Shap and John White.

PALM SPRINGS

[118] ADAGIO GALLERIES
193 S. Palm Canyon Dr., Palm Springs CA 92262
(619) 320-2230
Daily: 10-5; Closed Tues *Owner/Dir:* Ralph Lewin

Adagio Galleries concentrates on art of the Southwest, and has one of the most extensive collections of Southwestern art on the West Coast. Among the artists featured are R.C. Gorman, Amado Pena, Bert Seabourn, Katalina Ehling and Bob Garcia.

R.C. Gorman is a Navaho artist who paints with classic grace, and his works are internationally known. Amado Pena, one of the foremost painters of the Southwest, combines Spanish and Indian cultures in his art.

The gallery also features work by Robert Rivera, an award-winning gourd artist whose works are also displayed at the Smithsonian Institute. Robert Parkinson works in watercolor and has just produced his first diptych silkscreen. He is a master who uses light and shadow in his pastel pueblos and creates both monumental sized works as well as small-scaled pieces.

[119] ELAINE HORWITCH GALLERIES
1090 N. Palm Canyon Dr., Palm Springs, CA 92262
(619) 325-3490

Mon-Sat: 9:30-5:30; Sun 12-5; closed July and Aug
Owner: Elaine Horwitch *Dir:* Sidney Williams

Located in the garage of the landmark El Mirador Hotel, Elaine Horwitch Galleries specializes in contemporary art, particularly works from the American Southwest. The gallery focuses primarily on painting, sculpture and graphics, but it also represents over twenty ceramic artists and jewelers. Established more than twenty-five years ago, the gallery moved to its present location in 1986, and underwent extensive renovation. The renovation project was headed by architect Michael Kiner and Heard Museum exhibit designer Patrick Neary.

Many renowned artists have exhibited their works at Elaine Horwitch gallery. Among them are Larry Rivers, Frank Stella, Red Grooms, Tom Wesselmann and James Havard. Well known Southwest artists include Joe Baker, Anne Coe, George Judson, David Kraisler, Masoud Yasami, Merrill Mahaffey, Frank Duchamp, Robert Brubaker, Bob Wade, John Fincher and Dick Mason. In addition, ceramists Karen Koblitz, John Donoghue, Nicholas Bernard and Rico Piper have exhibited at the gallery.

[120] B. LEWIN GALLERIES
210 S. Palm Canyon Dr., Palm Springs, CA 92262
(619) 322-2525

Daily: 10-1, 2-5; closed Tues; closed July and August.
Owner: Bernard Lewin *Dir:* Bernard & Edith Lewin

The gallery specializes in art of contemporary Mexican masters. The gallery's 10,000 square feet of floorspace allows ample space for exhibitions of very large graphics and paintings, and life-sized sculptures. Rufino Tamayo, lauded as the greatest living artist of contemporary Mexican art, is represented. Included as well are sculptor Felipe Castaneda, Federico Cantu, Jean Charlot, Rafael Coronel, Jose Luis Cuevas, Ricardo Martinez, Carlos Merida, Roberto Montenegro, Gustavo Montoya, Chavez Morado, Felipe Orlando, José Clemente Orozco, Chu Chu Reyes, David Alfaro Siqueiros, Sarah Tarrab and Francisco Zuniga.

Rapidly achieving recognition for his brilliant colorations and unusual interpretations is Vladimir Cora, a protege of Tamayo. The youngest and most innovative artist under this gallery's sponsorship, he was discovered by B. Lewin in 1984, and has since been represented by the gallery exclusively.

PALO ALTO

[121] SMITH ANDERSON GALLERY
200 Homer, Palo Alto, CA 94301 (415) 327-7762
Tues-Sat: 10-4 *Owner/Dir:* Paula Kirkeby

The gallery concentrates on 20th century artists, primarily in works on paper, with a special emphasis on monotypes.

Monotypes are unique works executed with printing media. This simple technique, used extensively by Edgar Degas, consists of painting directly on lithographic stone or metal plate and printing the image by laying paper directly on the inked surface. Susceptible to infinite variations, monotypes have recently become an important medium for many contemporary artists.

The gallery exhibits works by Sam Francis, Tom Holland, Ed Moses, Bruce Connor, Matt Phillips, David

Gilhooly, Gustavo Rivera, Stanley Boxer, Steve Sorman and others.

PASADENA

[122] DEL MANO GALLERY

33 Colorado Blvd., Pasadena, CA 91105
(818) 793-6648

Tues-Thur, Sat: 10-6; Fri: 10-10; Sun: 12-5 *Owner:* Jan Peters & Ray Leier *Dir:* Pam Laswell

The gallery specializes in contemporary American crafts with an emphasis on signed and/or numbered editions of crafts. Crafts shown include: glass, metals, woods and wearables.

Del Mano gallery features a consistent group of artists, including standing shows with ceramists David Zweifel and Cheryl Williams; glassmaker Sissy McKay; fiber artist Martha Chatelain; wood artist Dennis Elliot; jewelers Anne Quisty and Yves Kamioner; metal artist Bernie Wyer; woodworker Don Kent; and glass artist Dean Memell.

The gallery has exhibited special shows for William & Mary Anne Yunter who create wood and ceramic jewelry, and a display of the leather masks of John Flemming.

[123] IZARDI/HARP GALLERY

290 West Colorado Blvd., Pasadena, CA 91105
(818) 792-8336

Tues-Sat: 11-5:30 *Owner/Dir:* Grady Harp, Armando Lizardi

The gallery specializes in contemporary art in all media. There is an emphasis on Southern California artists although artists from across the United States and Europe are also represented. The spacious gallery has three large exhibition rooms, enabling the hanging of large, monthly, one person shows along with a concurrent sampling of all the gallery artists.

The gallery's emphasis is on representational art. Miguel Condé unites the tradition of European draughtsmanship with 20th century surrealism; DeLoss McGraw draws his themes from literature; Sylvia Glass explores cave pictography; Walter Askin explores human foibles. Simie Maryles and Kendahl Jan Jubb paint from nature with an appreciation for exotic color and light. LaMonte Westmoreland's collages contrast autobiographical imagery with black stereotypes to explore the black experience with disturbing wit; similarly, John Valadez examines the cultural stereotypes of Chicano life in his masterful representational paintings.

The gallery also represents other well established American artists while continuing to introduce new artists in its "Summer Introduction" show.

PETALUMA

[124] MADISON STREET GALLERY

414 A Madison St., Petaluma, CA 94952
(707) 778-7568

Tues-Fri: 9-5; Sat: 10-4 *Owner/Dir:* Steven Richards

Early Californian art of the 19th and 20th centuries, and post-World War II art (1940s, 1950s and 1960s) are the gallery's focus. Particular emphasis is placed on Bay Region and Bay Area Figurative painters. These include artists from the San Francisco Art Association and from the East Bay Art Association. Post WW II artists include: Horst Trave and Jean Halpert-Ryden.

Objets d'art are increasingly a part of the gallery's three dimensional representation. The assemblage of artist Robert McChesney is on display.

SACRAMENTO

[125] ARTISTS CONTEMPORARY GALLERY

542 Downtown Plaza, Sacramento CA 95814 (916) 446-3694

Mon-Sat: 10-6; Sun: 12-5 *Dir:* Betty D. Mast

The gallery prides itself on its attempts to represent and display exciting ideas in contemporary painting, sculpture, print, drawing and ceramic media by local and regional fine artists. The gallery is knows for its lively and varied year-round exhibition schedule: its group shows and one-person shows include both two-dimensional abstract and representational art work by established artists and new local talent.

Programming within a two year cycle includes one-person shows by painters Fred Dalkey, Boyd Gavin, Miles Hermann, Greg Kondos, Pat Mahony, Jerald Silva, Michael Tompkins, monoprint artist Jian Wang and Larry Welden. Sculptors Linda Carpenter and Ruth Rippon are also represented.

Other exhibitions offered by the gallery include group shows of a thematic nature such as "The Self Portrait." A regional and city-wide exhibit titled "Introductions" is also part of the gallery's scheduled events.

[126] DJUROVICH GALLERY

727 1/2 2nd Floor, J St., Sacramento, CA 95814 (916) 446-3806

Mon-Fri: 11-5 *Owner/Dir:* Karlo Djurovich

The Djurovich Gallery sells work in all media including painting, glass, prints, sculpture and tapestry. Karlo Djurovich, the gallery's owner and director began operations in 1985. His huge 6,000-square-foot gallery is situated in a balconied building in the middle of Sacramento's rapidly growing financial district. The gallery contains a smaller 2,000-square-foot space and a 4,500 foot room which permits unobstructed views of art from as far away as 100 feet.

Djurovich is a Professor of Art History with a degree from the University of Zagreb, Yugoslavia and an intimate knowledge of art from around the world. His gallery represents artists from places as diverse as Yugoslavia, Israel, Mexico and Europe, though many are from California and the East Coast. Among the approximately thirty-five artists whose works are shown at the Djurovich Gallery are: sculptor David Gilhooly; California watercolorist James Estey; painter Rod Kunston; and Karlo Djurovich himself who is an internationally known tapestry artist.

[127] FIDO GALLERY

1730 27th St., Sacramento CA 95816 (916) 422-3816

By appt. only *Owner:* Brian Gorman *Dir:* Gary Dinnen

The Fido gallery specializes in ceramic sculpture and figurative expressionistic paintings. Some the the gallery's artists do site-specific installations. The gallery features steel and aluminum sculptures by Urban-O; etchings, drawings and paintings by Gary Dinnen; ceramic sculpture by Robert Charland and Glenn Takai; site-specific installations by Michael Pribich; wood sculpture by Jim Adan; and paintings by Paul Richards.

[128] MICHAEL HIMOVITZ GALLERY

1020 10th St., Sacramento, CA 95814 (916) 448-8723

Tues-Sat: 11-4:30 *Owner/Dir:* Michael Himovitz

The Michael Himovitz Gallery deals in the figurative works Northern California painters, sculptors and photographers. The gallery began operations in 1980 and today represents between 35 and 40 artists, 70% of whom are women. Its 3,500 square feet of exhibition space are broken up into four exhibition areas where the gallery holds concurrent one person shows on a regular basis. Work shown recently includes: Susan Adan's tightly stroked Chicago imagist paintings; Mike Stevens' wood sculpture; Fred Babb's humorous ceramics; and Stephanie Skalisky's naive style paintings and wood reliefs. Also shown often are the works of Clayton Pinkerton and northern California painter M. Louise Stanley.

[129] JENNIFER PAULS GALLERY

1825 Q St., Sacramento, CA 95814 (916) 448-4039

Tues-Sat: 10-5 *Owner/Dir:* Beth Jones, Dean Moni

Founded by Maria Alquilar, the gallery is committed to a belief in the distinctive narrativism of northern California art. This is typified by the figurative clay sculpture often shown. Much of it relates to the "Funk" school that characterizes works by Robert Arneson and David Gilhooly.

The main exhibit room is a large high-ceilinged space featuring architectural industrial forms from the 1950s. There, artists drawing from a cross-cultural perspective are featured, such as Carlos Villa, George Longfish, Maria Alquilar, Jimmy Suzuki and Joe Mariscal. In addition, Mary Warner's large narrative paintings, and Ken Little's sculpture have also been exhibited.

The gallery has a strong relationship with the artists from the area's fine arts graduate programs, both at the University of California-Davis and at California State University-Sacramento. Many of the best young artists of California have shown there. These include Urban-O, known for monumental mixed-media sculptures of steel and stone; Gary Viriano, known for his enigmatic mixed-media drawings; Glenn Takai, known for expressionistic figurative clay works; and Younhee Paik, a graduate of the San Francisco Art Institute, known for large, visionary canvases.

ST. ANSELM

[130] PASCAL DE SARTH GALLERY

P.O. Box 1610, St. Anselm, CA 94960 (415) 453-2983

Tues-Sat: 10-5 *Owner/Dir:* Pascal de Sarthe

The gallery carries both blue-chip and emerging artists. The works displayed at the gallery range from impressionists to modern masters and include Americans and Europeans of the 1950s and 1960s as well. Pascal de Sarth Gallery has been in San Francisco for eight years, since the owner came from Paris, where he also ran a gallery.

The gallery's main goal is to "promote young international artists." They represent five, from Chicago to Tokyo to Arizona, all of whom have shown extensively. One recent show was Dennis Oppenheim's "Project for Seoul Korea."

Pierre Buraglio works with pieces of glass framed or partially-framed by the wooden armatures of windows or doors. He has shown work at the Centre Georges Pompidou in Paris. Other artists include Toshikatsu Endo, employing motifs of essential materials such as fire, water and earth; Rik Ritchey; Rotraut; and

Thomas Skomski, a Chicago sculptor whose work pursues the theme of relationships between opposites.

SAN DIEGO

[131] THE ART COLLECTOR

4151 Taylor St., San Diego, CA 92110

(619) 299-3232

Mon-Sat: 10-5:30 *Owner/Dir:* Janet Disraeli

Established in 1971, the gallery concentrates on contemporary works in a variety of media. These include paintings, sculptures, photography, ceramics, textiles and mixed-media works. The Gallery also houses an art consulting service whose clients include corporations, hospitals and hotels, as well as major private collectors.

Its 4800-square-foot building is divided into an exhibition room, a showroom and a presentation room. The gallery represents nationally established artists such as James Byrd, Madeline De Joly, Daniel Goldstein, Sherry Andrens, Michael Gustavson, Jennifer Luce, Wayne Forte, Robert Parkison, Greg Ochocki, Ken Harbaugh, Martha Chatelain and George Geyer. Among them, DeWain Valentine is a renowned glass sculptor, and Laddie John Dill is known for his mixed-media collages of glass and cement. It also exhibits works by sculptors Frank Riggs, Arthur Silverman, Jim Huntington, Robert Mansfield, Dennis Sohocki, Michael Anderson, Gil Watrous, Essie Pinsker, Jack Zajac and Jesus Morales.

[132] ARTRAGEOUS!

Main location: 5350-A Eastgate Mall, San Diego, CA 92121 (619) 452-7280

Tues-Fri: 10-6; Sat: 10-5 *Dir:* Barbara Markoff.

Second location: 3545 Del Mar Heights Rd., Suite H, San Diego, CA 92131

Mon-Thur, Sat: 10-6; Fri: 10-7; Sun: 12-5 *Owner:* Rob and Barbara Markoff *Dir:* Susan Mayer

A contemporary gallery specializing in works on paper, three-dimensional paper art and ceramic art, Artrageous! has catered mainly to corporate clients and served as an information center to the public by providing lectures, demonstrations and workshops. However, this image may be altered a bit with their new, high-tech retail space opened in March of 1989. The new space, which is 1000 square feet, or half of the size of the old location, will feature exhibitions at least four times per year whereas the older space exhibits only semi-annually.

The gallery represents approximately eighty artists including California natives Justin Coopersmith, Pat Pfeffer, Chick Hayashi, Penny King, Victoria Ryan and Sherry Schrut, who frequently execute customized commission work for corporate and residential clients. Others include Tennessee artists William Buffett, Gary Oglander and Maura Reed, Massachusetts artist Christine Vaillancourt, Doug Danz of Seattle and Merri Pattinian of Texas.

[133] CIRCLE GALLERY

2501 San Diego Ave., San Diego, CA 92110

(619) 296-2596

Sun-Tues: 10-6; Wed-Sat: 10-8 *Owner:* Circle Fine Art Corp. *Dir:* Barbara Cox

The gallery concentrates on established American and European artists, with an emphasis on contemporary

Orlando A.B. *Dusk,* 31 x 23, oil and acrylic on d'Arches paper.
Courtesy: Engman Limited Fine Arts

Robert Arneson, *California Artist,* 60 inches high, glazed ceramic.
Courtesy: San Francisco Museum of Modern Art

Lisa Adams, *Splash,* 60 x 90, oil, acrylic, linoleum on canvas. Courtesy: Newspace

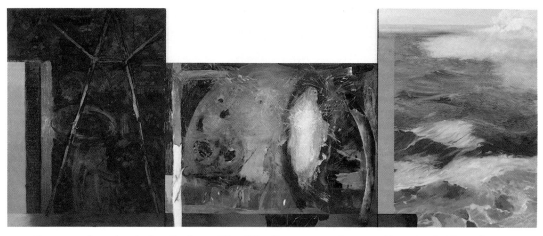

Bergman, *Invective Against Darkness,* 78 x 198, oil on canvas. Courtesy: Dorothy Goldeen Gallery

George Douglas Brewerton, *Firing on Ft. Sumter,* 18 x 35, mixed media.
Courtesy: Atelier Dore, Inc., San Francisco, CA

Roy De Forest, *Cookout of Mr. Fred Moon,* 75 x 86, polymer and alkyd on canvas.
Courtesy: Fuller Goldeen Gallery

Todd Garner, *Mist Sentinel,* 67 x 17 x 13, ceramic and
mixed media Courtesy: Orlando Gallery

Robert Goldman, *Low Tide–La Jolla,* 36 x 30, oil on canvas.
Courtesy: Tarbox Gallery

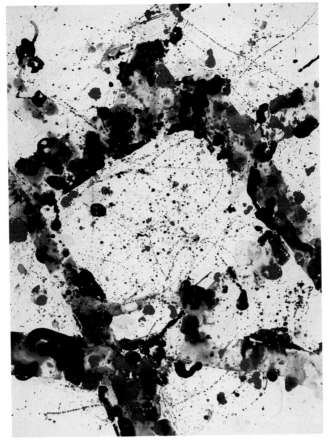

Sam Francis, *untitled,* 48 x 63, acrylic on paper.
Courtesy: Smith-Anderson Gallery.

Simone Gad, *Les Misfits avec Barbie et Self Portrait,* 36 x 40 x 10, mixed media,
collage/assemblage. Courtesy: B-1 Gallery.

Steve Grossman, *Noumenon Nine,* 70 x 80 x 7, acrylic and wood construction on canvas and panel. Collection of M. Herzstein. Courtesy: Jan Baum Gallery, Los Angeles

Jessie Homer, *Tending the Graves,* 36 x 36, oil. Courtesy: Ankrum Gallery

Daniel Kilpatrick, *Interior,* 48 x 54, 1989, acrylic on canvas.
Courtesy: Breckenridge Gallery, San Francisco

Nancy Kittredge, *The Dove and the Dog,* 54 x 42, oil on canvas.
Courtesy: J.J.Brookings Gallery, San Jose, CA

Shilla Lamb, *Mac Kerricher Park Series #2,* 64 x 67, oil on canvas.
Courtesy: De Vorzon Gallery

Randall Lavender, *Silent Voices,* 43 x 48, oil on panel.
Courtesy: Tortue Gallery Inc., Los Angeles

Les Lawrence, *Fern Guessed Wrong on the Radio Secret Sound Contest,* 32 x 18 x 8,
oxidation stoneware glaze, underglaze, colored slip, sandblast. Courtesy: Alexander Gallery

Jan Lassetter, *Tug for Two,* 44 x 66, oil on canvas. Courtesy: Modernism

Michael Lawrence, *Italian Landscape,* 67 x 126, acrylic on canvas.
Courtesy: Wenger Gallery, Los Angeles, CA

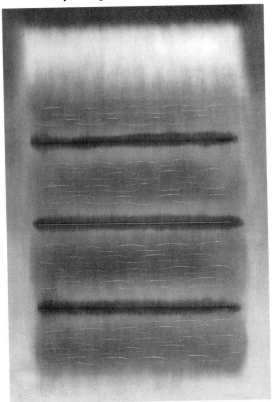

Hiroki Morinoue, *Ocean,* 38 x 26, watercolor.
Courtesy: Joanne Chappell Gallery

John A. Montgomery, *Women's Liberation,* 40 x 32, pencil.
Courtesy: Mill Creek Gallery

Keith Monaghan, *Homage 5-85,* 40 x 44, acrylic on canvas. Courtesy: William Sawyer Gallery

Bob Nugent, *Amazon Study II,* 40 x 30, oil on paper.
Courtesy: Roy Boyd Gallery

Minoru Ohira, *Kappa #4,* 90 x 264 x 42, wood, twine, varnish. Courtesy: Space Gallery

Brad Pettigrew, *Malibu,* 48 x 48, acrylic on canvas. Courtesy: John Thomas Gallery

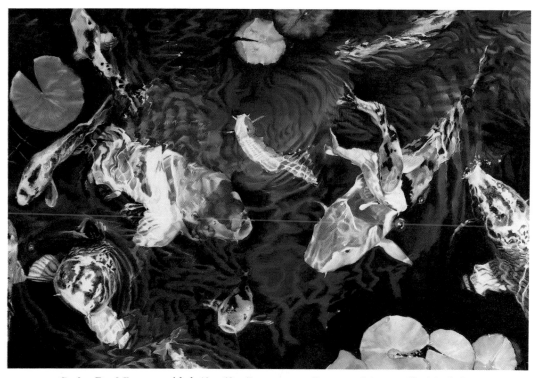

Carlos Raul Perez, *untitled,* 40 x 60, oil on canvas. Courtesy: Schwartz Cierlak Gallery

Jack Reilly, *Implications of Ideology,* 85 x 106, acrylic, oil and mixed media on shaped canvases.
Courtesy: Merging One Gallery, Santa Monica

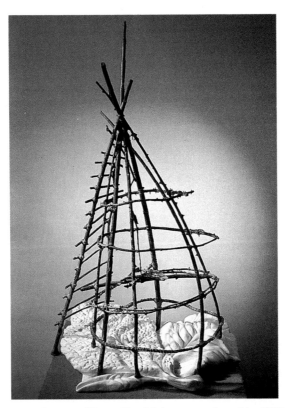

Lynne Streeter, *Home,* 30 x 36, bronze and marble, 1984.
Courtesy: Udinotti Gallery, San Francisco, CA

Blessing Semler, *Harlem,* 26 x 50, acrylic, collage painting. Courtesy: Ruth Bachofner Gallery

Micheal Todd, *Tantric Circle I,* 42 x 38 x 10, bronze.
Courtesy: Tortue Gallery, Santa Monica, CA

Brook Temple, *untitled,* 30 x 40, oil on paper. Courtesy: Boritzer/Gray Gallery, Santa Monica

Bill Wheeler, *For Soldiers Who Died for Forgotten Kings,* 83 x 105, acrylic on masonite.
Courtesy: Studio Sixteen-Seventeen, Los Angeles

works. The gallery focuses primarily on paintings, graphics and sculpture.

Circle gallery is divided into two exhibition spaces. One room is devoted to a four week rotation of shows featuring such artists as Agam, Erte, Rene Gruau, Victor Vasarely, Lebadang, Hofmann, Will Barnet, Jamie Wyeth and the soft paintings of Calman Shemi. An adjacent room offers a continuous exhibition of artists whom the gallery represents. Among those exhibited here are Judith Bledsoe, Markespel, sculptor Frank Gallo and painter Joan Balet.

A sampling of recent exhibitions includes "Driven to Abstraction," paintings showcasing a variety of abstract styles and techniques, and the "Art of Walt Disney." A permanent exhibition is devoted to animation art. Each of the major studios are represented: Disney, Hanna-Barbara and Warner Brothers. In addition, the gallery houses an Art-to-Wear Salon that features jewelry.

[134] INTERNATIONAL GALLERY
643 G St., San Diego, CA 92101 (619) 235-8255

Mon-Fri: 10-6; Sun: 11:30-4:30 *Owner/Dir:* Stephen Ross

The gallery specializes in contemporary American craft and folk art. It also has an extensive collection of primitive art from Africa and Oceania. These works are housed in a restored building that was constructed in 1898.

The gallery's exhibitions have earned it regional acclaim. Here Robert Tolone exhibited his chainsaw-carved polychrome wood pieces. This show marked a shift in his work from animal forms to human figures. Other craft artists such as Kate Jacobson, Will Jacobson and Don Sprague have shown contemporary ceramics, and Peggy Barkley has exhibited her polychrome wood figures. Po Shun Leong, an architect by trade, has shown his three-dimensional sculpted boxes. Ellen Zahorec has exhibited fabric constructions, many of them paper and canvas wall hangings. The gallery also offers a selection of jewelry pieces and hand-woven textiles from North Africa and Asia.

[135] DIETRICH JENNY GALLERY
660 Ninth Ave., San Diego, CA 92101 (619) 239-8592

Wed-Sat: 11-5 and by appointment *Owner:* Dietrich Jenny *Dir:* Dietrich Jenny, Jill D'Angelo

The gallery features the work of emerging American artists, with an emphasis on painting, sculpture and installation art. Jean Lowe, whose paintings on canvas and furniture are concerned with ecological issues, is a nationally-renowned artist represented, as is Mathieu Gregoire, whose elegant minimalist sculptures have been exhibited in several museums and at Art Park. The gallery also represents Steven Criqui, who paints the neighborhoods of the 1950s and 1960s adding new-found excitement; Greg Reser, whose unusually shaped canvases explore a range of art issues; Keneth Johnston, whose complex sculptures constructed from cardboard and painted wood suggest historical references; painters Wick Alexander, Steve Ilott, Alexia Markarian; and sculptor David Wilson.

The gallery also features the work of many other artists. Recent shows include sculptures by Amanda Farber paintings by Manny Farber, paintings and installations by Ernest Silva and paintings by Patricia Patterson.

[136] ORR'S GALLERY
2222 4th Ave., San Diego, CA 92101 (619) 234-4765

Mon-Fri: 10-5; Sat by appt. *Owner/Dir:* Dan Jacobs

Concentration is on important nineteenth- and twentieth-century works, including prints and sculpture.

Works are available by California Impressionists circa 1890-1950, including Alfred A. Mitchell, Maurice Braun, J. Christopher Smith, Charles Reiffel and many others. The gallery collection features a large selection of late nineteenth- to early twentieth-century English watercolors by such noted artists as Sir William Russell Flint as well as etchings by Augustus John, James McBey, Sir Frank Short and others. Contemporary works include paintings, prints and sculpture by Fritz Scholder, and a collection of contemporary American crafts.

[137] TARBOX GALLERY
1202 Kettner Blvd., San Diego, CA 92101
(619) 234-5020

Tues-Fri: 11-9; Sat: 5-10 *Owner:* Ruth Tarbox

The gallery, located in an historic, renovated building, spotlights the work of emerging artists in contemporary, impressionist, realist and primitive styles. The work of internationally-known artists such as Arthur Secunda (collage), William Hayter (original prints) and Edward Evans (airbrush painting) is also represented. Californian artists Geer Morton and Robert Goldman paint in a popular impressionist style. A variety of sculptures in various media can also be seen at the gallery; original copper work by Alan Kravitz; limited edition bronzes by Teresa Cherny and natural wood sculptures by Steve Kuntz, to name a few. The gallery holds bi-monthly shows and periodic demonstrations of painting techniques and printmaking, as well as lecture discussions.

SAN FRANCISCO

[138] ALLPORT GALLERY
210 Post St., San Francisco, CA 94108
(415) 398-2787

Tues-Sat: 10:30-5:30 *Owner/Dir:* Ardys Allport

Contemporary painters make up the bulk of work shown in this gallery. A number of West Coast artists' work also figures in the gallery's roster, especially in the area of contemporary prints. Sam Richardson, Peter Volkas, Raymond Saunders, Katherine Porter and Frank Lobdell are all involved in the contemporary printmaking renaissance. These printmakers work abstractly and with collage for the most part, and strive to stay on the edge of what's occurring in printmaking. Other artists include Marilyn Baum, who employs paperwork collage in abstract forms; Paul Harcharik, whose landscapes are surrealistic contemporary ruins; DeWitt Hardy, Seiji Kunishima, Norman Lundin — an interior still-life artist — realist Allan Magee and Don Williams, a pastel realist. Although noted for realism and pastels, the gallery has now cultivated an interest in abstract art as well. The gallery shows eleven exhibitions a year.

[139] ALLRICH GALLERY
251 Post St., San Francisco, CA 94108 (415) 398-8896

Tues-Sat: 11-5 *Owner:* Louise Allrich *Dir:* Michelle Bello

Established in 1971 as the premiere gallery for contemporary tapestries, the Allrich Gallery has dramatically broadened its range over the past eighteen years to include contemporary painting, sculpture, works on paper, ceramics, glass work and other fine museum-quality crafts. One of the larger galleries in San Francisco, the Allrich features a wide variety of artists, from recently emerging artists to well-established masters.

As one of the founders of the fiber movement, owner Louise Allrich continues to feature the work of some of most renowned contemporary tapestry artists in the world. Among them are Olga de Amaral from Bogota, Colombia, who creates tapestries with 24-karat gold leaf. Joining her is Lia Cook, a leading American tapestry artist.

The Allrich Gallery also features the varied works of Nance O'Banion in mixed media, including handmade paper and bamboo constructions. Richard Deutsch's contemporary marble and terrazzo sculptures are also presented, as are Jerry Concha's large contemporary abstract paintings. The Allrich also represents Stephen Fleming, known for large figurative paintings and floating sculptures. The gallery also represents the San Francisco-based Korean painter Younhee Paik, whose canvases capture unusual contemporary representational dreamscapes.

The Allrich Gallery is also noted as a major presenter of large-scale public works and site-specific contemporary sculptures, such as those by sculptor Larry Kirkland.

[140] AMERICAN INDIAN CONTEMPORARY ARTS

685 Market St., Ste. 250, San Francisco, CA 94105
(415) 495-7600

Mon-Sat: 10-5:30 *Dir:* Janeen Antoine

Founded in 1983, and operated by American Indians, the gallery is the only independent non-profit gallery exhibiting the work of contemporary emerging and renowned Indian artists. The gallery shows artworks in a variety of media and represents more than 85 Native American artists. These include: Harry Fonseca, Linda Lomahaftewa, Emmi Whitehorse, Conrad Hovse, Jean Lamarr and Frank La Pena.

The gallery publishes a bimonthly journal, *Native Vision*, which highlights American Indian artists and exhibitions.

AICA also offers ongoing classes in traditional arts, lectures, demonstrations and performances.

[141] GALLERY PAULE ANGLIM

14 Geary St., San Francisco, CA 94108
(415) 433-2710

Tues-Fri: 11-5:30; Sat: 11-5 *Owner:* Paule Anglim *Dir:* Kevin Ford & Paula Sasso

Located two blocks from Union Square in downtown San Francisco, Gallery Paule Anglim specializes in contemporary American Art. The gallery represents nationally and internationally known Bay Area and West Coast artists in addition to exhibiting work from New York City. Exhibitions change monthly in both the main gallery and Gallery II.

Exhibitions in collaboration with New York galleries include one-person shows by painters Alice Neel, Leon Golub, Jess, Sue Coe and Charles Garabedian and sculptors Louise Bourgeois, William Tucker and William King. The gallery also undertakes historical shows such as "Solid Concept," a group exhibition of work by conceptual artists such as sculptor Terry Fox, and

David Ireland, Paul Kos, Tony Labat and Tom Marioni.

Among the artists represented by the gallery are painters Milton Avery, William Allan, Terry Allen, Christopher Brown, Jay DeFeo and conceptual artist Howard Fried. Sculptors Deborah Butterfield, Barbara Penn and John Zurier are among the artists who are also shown by the gallery.

Paule Anglim, who has been involved in the art arena for thirty years, opened the gallery in 1976. Previously she was a corporate art consultant.

The gallery provides a warm and relaxed atmosphere in which to view the work of familiar and not-so-familiar artists of the twentieth century.

[142] ARION PRESS

460 Bryant St., San Francisco, CA 94107
(415) 777-9651

Mon-Fri: 8:30-5 *Dir:* Andrew Hoyem

Strictly speaking not a gallery but a printing house, art books are the product of Arion Press. The books include James Joyce's Ulysses, illustrated by Robert Motherwell, and Jim Dine's version of the Apocalypse from St. John the Divine. John Baltessari illustrated Tristram Shandy. Another upcoming work is a story by Poe, with Baudelaire's translations into French, which Terry Winters will illustrate.

The gallery recently bought a foundry for the setting of type, allowing them to carry out the entire book-making process in-house, with the exception of most binding. Only about half a dozen houses set monotype prints in the country, according to the gallery. Generally, they seek artists to illustrate planned books. Although basically book-oriented, they have recently emphasized more prints than in the past.

[143] SAN FRANCISCO ARTSPACE & ANNEX

1286 Folsom St., San Francisco, CA 94103
(415) 626-9100

Tues-Sat: 11-5; *Dir:* Anne MacDonald

A non-profit exhibition space, Artspace is devoted mainly to painting and sculpture, but also shows work in various other media by such artists as Jennie Holzer, David Mach, Marcus Lupertz, Robert Mapplethorp and Michael Tracy.

The space is funded by two grants per year. Outside activities are sponsored by Artspace such as a recent showing of Jennie Holzer's work at Candlestick Park during the Giants vs. Mets game. The Annex, which contains a video library, is devoted primarily to to video and performance art. Artists represented in the Annex include Tony Labat, Paul Kos, Tom Marioni and Matias Jaramillo .

[144] ATELIER DORE, INC.

771 Bush St., San Francisco, CA 94108
(415) 391-2423

Tues-Sat: 11-5 *Owner:* Chester Helms *Dir:* Chester & John Helms

Founded with the proceeds from the sale of two huge canvases by French wood engraver Gustave Dore, the gallery specializes in American paintings of the late 19th and early 20th century. It also houses an eclectic collection of European paintings from the same period.

The gallery carries paintings by artists of the Hudson River School, Academic Realism, American Impressionism, Precisionism and various schools of American scene painting, such as social realism and regionalism. Represented as well are WPA artists and artists from a variety of Federal Arts Projects. Included are works by Seldon Connon Gile, Grafton Tyler Brown, George Winger, Joseph Henry Sharp, Lillian Genth, Thomas Hill, Robert S. Duncanson, Joshua Johnston, Theresa Bertstein, Henry J. Breuer, Nils Gren, William Posey Silva, Jules Tavernier, Grant Wood, Thomas Hart Benton and Carl Hoeckner. Historical paintings of the American frontier, especially those of California, Taos and Santa Fe, and the pioneer movement are also featured.

[145] HANK BAUM GALLERY & GRAPHICS GALLERY

P.O. Box 26689, San Francisco, CA 94126
(415) 543-1908

Mon-Fri: 12-5, By appt. *Owner/Dir:* Hank Baum

The gallery specializes in paintings and original works on paper by contemporary West Coast artists. The owner Hank Baum was formerly associate director of the Tamarind Lithography Workshop in Los Angeles, executive director of the Atelier Mourlot (New York) and Collector's Press in San Francisco. Some of the artists shown shown are James Bolton, Georg Heimdal, David King, Robert McGill, John Ploeger, Mel Ramos, Emerson Woelffer, Rolando Castellon and Bruce Kortebein. There is an extensive collection of works on paper in all media in the Graphics Gallery. Works are available by the following well-known artists: Ay-O, Richard Anuskiewicz, José Luis Cuevas, Richard Diebenkorn, Robert Indiana, Masuo Ikeda, Nicholas Krushenick, Robert Motherwell, Arnaldo Pomodoro, Frank Stella, Claes Oldenburg and Emerson Woelffer. Other artists include: Ann Burke, Eleanor Coppola, Mary Glenn, Harold Gregor, John P. Jones, Joel Oas, Steve Poleskie, Barbara Romney, Jill Rosoff, Seymour Rosofsky, David Simpson, Sheila Benow, Mimi LaPlant and Cynthia Stan.

[146] GEORGE BELCHER GALLERY

340 Townsend St., San Francisco, CA 94107
(415) 543-1908

by appt. *Owner/Dir:* George Belcher

George Belcher specializes in Mexican and Latin American paintings. The gallery buys and sells work by 19th and 20th century Mexican and Latin American painters, including the work of Dr. Atl. Fernando Botero, Jean Charlot, Gunther Gerzso, Frida Kahlo, Wilfredo Lam, Ricardo Martinez, Carlos Merida, Jose Clemente Orozco, Emilio Pettoruti, Diego Rivera, David Alfaro Siqueiros, Rufino Tamayo, Francisco Toledo and Jose Maria Velasco.

The gallery also includes in its inventory works by Mexican sculptor Francisco Zuniga.

[147] JOHN BERGGRUEN GALLERIES

228 Grant Ave., San Francisco, CA 94108
(415) 781-4629

Mon-Fri: 9:30-5:15; Sat: 10:30-5

2nd Location: Monadnock Bldg. 685 Market St., San Francisco, CA 94105 (415) 495-6850

Tues-Sat: 10:30-5:30

The John Berggruen Galleries specialize in twentieth-century paintings, drawings, sculpture and prints.

Exhibitions of historical interest have included works by Pablo Picasso, Henri Matisse, Georgia O'Keefe,

Marsden Hartley and Arthur Dove. The galleries' range of exhibitions also encompasses important sculpture by Henry Moore, Alexander Calder, George Rickey, H.C. Westermann, Mark di Suvero and Beverly Pepper.

Works are available by major New York artists, including Robert Motherwell, Helen Frankenthaler, Frank Stella, Robert Rauschenberg, Hans Hofmann, Jasper Johns, Ellsworth Kelly, Friedel Dzubas, Roy Lichtenstein and Franz Kline.

West coast artists Wayne Thiebaud, Richard Diebenkorn, Ron Davis, Joseph Raphael, Fletcher Benton, Nathan Oliviera, Tom Holland, Sam Francis, Manuel Neri, Paul Wonner, Elmer Bischoff and Mark Adams are also featured.

[148] FRANK BORN ARTS

866 Capp St., San Francisco, CA 94110
(415) 647-6118

By appt. only *Owner/Dir:* Frank Born

An eclectic private art broker, Frank Born presents a diverse inventory of nineteenth- and twentieth-century American and European paintings and drawings, along with some Mexican masters.

Modern masters handled by Frank Born Arts have included Marcel Duchamp, Henri Matisse, Fernand Leger, Morgan Russell, José Guerrero, Joseph Henry Sharp, Richard Diebenkorn and Sam Francis. Born currently specializes in the early works of Victor Vasarely and is handling a Bay Area collection of works dating from 1965 to 1980, including paintings by Fletcher Benton, Harold Paris, Nathan Olivera and Stephen DeStabler.

An art historian who has operated as a private dealer in the Bay Area for about three years, Frank Born appraises and represents individual works and collections from private individuals and estates, as well as counseling collectors and performing searches for particular artists.

[149] BRAUNSTEIN/QUAY GALLERY

250 Sutter St., San Francisco, CA 94108
(415) 392-5532

Tues-Fri: 10:30-5:30; Sat: 11-5; Aug 23-30 closed
Owner/Dir: Ruth Braunstein

This adventuresome gallery has moved several times since it first began showing contemporary painting and sculpture in Tiburon in 1961. Known for its willingness to take risks on behalf of unknown artists, the gallery shows the work of both new and established artists from the Bay Area and from around the world. In response to the growing number of emerging contemporary artists, the gallery recently inaugurated a special program called ACCESS, a small space within the gallery where each month an unaffiliated or emerging artist is featured along with regular exhibits.

John Altoon, Jeremy Anderson, Ursula Schneider, Nell Sinton, Mary Snowden, sculptor Peter Voulkos and assemblage artist Richard Shaw are among the established artists who have been with the gallery for over 15 years. New to the group are sculptors David Anderson Robert Brady, Karen Breschi, Dominic DiMare, David Jones and Michael Stevens, as well as painters Michael Alfe, Patricia Tobacco Forrester, Ben Gordon, Arthur Okamura and Paul Pratchenko.

[150] BRECKENRIDGE GALLERY

545 Sutter St., San Francisco, CA 94102
(415) 397-7090

Wed-Sat: 11-4; by appt. *Owner/Dir:* Charlotte Breckenridge

The gallery specializes in contemporary California art and provides a showcase for emerging artists of special promise. The gallery also highlights mature artists whose work deserves wider recognition. Abstract, figurative, assemblage, collage and small sculpture works are shown.

The figurative works of Howard Hack, a nationally-renowned painter and master of silver point drawing were featured at the gallery in 1988. Kay Omata and Farrar Wilson, mature artists working in abstract expressionism are represented by the gallery. Also represented is Michael Tang, a younger artist who works in a figurative style using mythological themes. Tang exhibited an installation work at the De Saisset Museum in Santa Clara. Steve Kursh, who works in three-dimensional assemblage, is another gallery artist.

Norbert Schlaus, a German artist who has lived and worked in Oakland for twenty-five years, is a distinguished member of the gallery's roster. The gallery provides space to an artist-in-residence. Daniel Kilpatrick, an emerging artist who paints in an abstract style reflecting landscapes, cityscapes and interiors now works in the gallery.

[151] CHARLES CAMPBELL GALLERY
647 Chestnut St., San Francisco, CA 94133
(415) 441-8680

Tues-Fri: 11-5:30; Sat: 12-4 *Owner/Dir:* Charles Campbell

A famous "back room", where regulars of the art scene gather distinguishes this gallery. Campbell, involved in art since just after World War Two, founded it in the early 1970s, but before opening his gallery he ran a frame shop in the Bay Area. Campbell has plans to expand the gallery in upcoming years.

Featured artwork in the gallery ranges from works by Lundy Siegrist, a California plein air painter, to contemporary artists such as Mary Robertson, who paints California's Russian River valley and includes realist Stan Washburn. Gordon Cook produces subdued landscapes and still-lifes, Charles Eckart paints slightly abstracted figurative works and landscapes, Peter Allegaert, sophisticated naive painting. All of the artists hail from the Bay Area, and most are from San Francisco. Others include Dennis Hare, who does painterly, bright Southern California landscapes, Charles Griffin Farr, whose mature realism and "American modern primitivism" resembles Grant Wood, and sculptor Alan Osborne. The gallery also shows Frank Lobdell's drawings from the 1960s and 1970s. They mount eight exhibits a year, usually including one group show, and On alternate years the gallery's shows feature items such as Mexican masks, Indian blankets or pre-Columbian art.

[152] CARLSON GALLERY
257 Grant Ave., San Francisco, CA 94108
(415) 982-2882

Mon-Sat: 11-6 *Owner/Dir:* David & Jeanne Carlson

Founded in the mid-1980s, the Carlson Gallery exhibits the works of American and European masters dating from 1860 to 1960 and ranging from European realism to American abstract painting, with an emphasis on the works of California artists.

In the Carlson Gallery collection are the works of California *plein air* painters of the 1920s and 1930s,

William Ritschelitschel, William, G# 152 and Armin Hansen. The gallery also shows the late nineteenth-century paintings of California realist Samuel Marsden Brookes and of marine painter William Coulter, whose nineteenth-century works on marine themes are difficult to find.

Among the contemporary artists exhibited at the gallery are the California abstract painter Roy de Forest and the New York-based Jack Brusca, known for his large-scale abstract works. The Carlson Gallery also represents contemporary California expressionist painter Walter Kuhlman.

[153] JOANNE CHAPPELL GALLERY/EDITIONS LIMITED WEST
620 Second St., Ste. 400, San Francisco, CA 94107
(415) 777-5711

Mon-Fri: 9-5 *Owner:* Joanne Chappell *Dir:* Andrew Korniej

The gallery exhibits the work of emerging and established contemporary artists from California and across the U.S., and strongly emphasizes the diversity of media found on the West Coast.

The gallery has a 3,000-square-foot exhibition space located in an old warehouse building which lends itself to showing monumental works as well as intimate pieces. The gallery is particularly strong in works on and of paper such as the large, vibrant, semi-referential watercolors of Peter Kitchell and Hiroki Morinoue; the delicately-wrought chine collé etchings of Gloria Fischer or the lively paper constructions of Carole Rae. The gallery also shows large-scale works such as the powerful yet contemplative paintings of Brook Temple and Marcia Myers; Robert Minuzzo's highly-textural layered paintings and the stone sculpture of Ralph O'Neill.

The gallery is an active publisher of original graphic work including the atmospheric landscape imagery of Christy Carleton and the etchings of Bruce Weinberg. Aside from its regular stable of artists, the gallery displays a willingness to reviewing and showing the work of artists who are new to the gallery. Recently, the gallery has introduced glasswork by John Anderson, ceramic reliefs by Barbara Sebastian, photography by Barry Brukoff and a series of screens in different media by Arlene Elizabeth.

[154] JOSEPH CHOWNING GALLERY
1717 17th St., San Francisco, CA 94103
(415) 626-7496

Tues-Fri: 10:30-5:30; Sat 12-4 *Owner/Dir:* Joseph Chowning

Although the art at this gallery falls into many different categories, is both abstract and figurative, and generally runs the gamut of art forms, it is distinguished by a unique vision. "It's not ordinary or conservative," the gallery says. The artists are mainly Californian, and most are modern or contemporary. The gallery handles the estate of Stanton Macdonald-Wright, who developed the Synchromist school in 1912. The gallery also shows David Gilhooly, an artist who specializes in plexiglas sculptures and colorful shirts. One such shirt design is called *Foodfight*, and juxtaposes the images of sushi and ice cream cones. Bill Martin produces landscapes; Clayton Bailey creates robots; Eduardo Carrillo, a mural painter, works alongside several latino artists. John Battenberg, Richard Berger, Ken Waterstreet and William Snyder also show their work

Joanne Chappell Gallery Limited *Works by Charles Wolters, Christy Carleton, Joyce Clark-Binen*

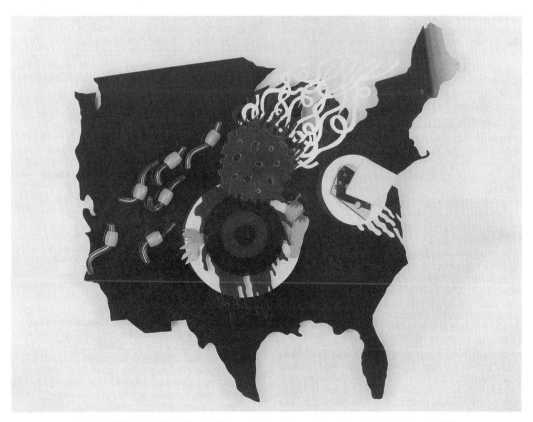

David Gilhooly, *The Meatball from Outer Space,* 40 x 32 x 5.5, plexiglas, 1986.
Courtesy: Joseph Chowning Gallery, San Francisco

at the gallery. Other emerging artists at the gallery include Kristin Peterson, Beth Foley and Elizabeth Eve.

Exhibitions change ten times a year, each hanging for approximately five weeks. Mostly exhibitions feature new pieces by gallery artists, but once a year, the gallery organizes a Holiday Show of less-expensive work. The Holiday Show is included in the gallery's Introductions show, for new Bay Area artists.

[155] CIRCLE GALLERY UNION SQUARE
140 Maiden Lane, San Francisco, CA 94108
(415) 989-2100

Mon-Sat: 10-6; Thurs: 10-7; Sun: 11-4 *Owner:* CFA Corporation, Carolyn Solomon, President *Dir:* Karen Anderson

The gallery represents contemporary American and international artists, working in a variety of media, including painting, cast paper, sculpture, soft painting, lithography, serigraphy and jewelry.

The building housing the gallery was designed by Frank Lloyd Wright as a prototype of the Guggenheim Museum, making a perfect location for the artists Circle represents. Those artists include Hungarian artist Victor Vasarely, known as the "father" of optical art; German artist Jan Balet, whose "sophisticated primitive" art conveys his peculiar humor through detailed and stylized images; Israeli artist Calman Shemi, whose unique soft paintings in vivid colors reflect the strong colors of his country; Italian artist Rene Gruau, a well-known master of art and design in the world of fashion and art; Carol Jablonsky, master of the imaginary and mythical; and Clarence Measelle, an illusionist/realist painter. Other artists represented by the gallery have included Yaacov Agam, Erte, Frank Gallo and Douglas Hoffman.

Of special interest is the gallery's Art-to-Wear Jewelry collection, with limited edition jewelry crafted by Erte, Yaacov Agam, Lebedang, Calman Shemi, Victor Vasarely, Braque and Montesinos.

[156] CONTEMPORARY REALIST GALLERY
506 Hayes St., San Francisco, CA 94102
(415) 863-6550

Tues-Fri: 10:30-5:30; Sat: 12-5 or by appt. *Owner:* Michael R. Hackett & Tracey Freeman *Dir:* Michael R. Hackett

Established in 1986, the Contemporary Realist Gallery specializes in contemporary American representational painting, drawing and sculpture. The gallery focuses on figurative work, ranging from loose, gestural works to neoclassical pieces.

The gallery represents both established and emerging artists from around the country, with special emphasis on New York and Bay Area painters. It has hosted solo exhibitions of paintings by Gabriel Laderman, Bruno Civitico and Richard Savini, as well as a rare exhibition of Gretna Campbell's last landscape paintings completed prior to her death in 1987.

Many of the younger artists represented at the gallery have studied with major figures in American realism, such as Gabriel Laderman, Lennart Anderson, William Bailey, Wayne Thiebaud and Elmer Bischoff. Recent exhibitions of young artists include: Anthony Martino, figure paintings; Peter Nye, Bay Area landscapes; Paul Braucher, narrative figure paintings; Brian Jermusyk, still-life paintings; David Vereano, landscapes; Elen Feinberg, New Mexico landscapes;

Constance LaPalombara, landscapes and still-lifes; Lynn Kotula, still-lifes; Mel Adamson figures; and April Funke, still-lifes.

Other solo exhibits have included the paintings of Steven Bigler, Diana Horowitz, Cynthia Charters, Richard Piccolo and Christopher Terry.

The gallery also hosts an annual Architecture Invitational featuring the drawings and designs of numerous Bay Area artists.

[157] CROWN POINT PRESS
871 Folsom St., San Francisco, CA 94107
(415) 974-6273

Tues-Sat: 10-5 *Owner:* Kathan Brown *Dir:* Stephanie Bleecher

A West Coast-based gallery with a New York branch, Crown Point publishes contemporary etchings and color woodblock prints. The prints are made in San Francisco, although they are now also shown in the New York space. The gallery was founded 25 years ago.

The gallery attempts to produce works of "artists who influence other artists," in a broad range of traditions. Many of the artists are among today's better-known. Among the artists represented are: John Cage, Francisco Clemente, Richard Diebenkorn, Helen Frankenthaler, Hans Haacke and Steve Reich. Two of these artists, Reich and Cage are established composers. They illustrate the scores to their well-known works. Edwardo Ruscha, Italo Scanga, Sol Lewitt and Vito Acconci are other artists published by Crown Point Press. Another program established by the gallery sends artists to China. Tom Marioni, Robert Bechtle and Pat Steir were the first artists to travel to China on the program, which was designed to provide an opportunity to make prints and study Asian techniques. The press publishes Japanese woodblocks, and since 1982, has sent artists to Kyoto, Japan as well.

[158] MICHAEL DUNEV GALLERY
77 Geary St., San Francisco, CA 94108
(415) 398-7300

Tues-Fri: 10-6; Sat 11-5 *Owner/Dir:* Michael Dunev

Founded in 1983, the Michael Dunev Gallery exhibits American and European modern and contemporary masters in painting, sculpture and graphics. Bringing together an international group of artists (both well established and emerging), the gallery is guided by a consistent aesthetic direction, which is nonobjective and reductive in nature.

The Michael Dunev Gallery exhibits the paintings, etchings and lithographs of contemporary California-based painter and printmaker Sam Francis, the paintings and prints of contemporary American master Robert Motherwell (presently of Provincetown, Rhode Island) and the paintings of the contemporary Spanish painter Anthony Tapies.

The gallery also shows the works of the emerging West German painter Hans Sieverding and of West German ceramic sculptor Sinen Thalheimer. Among the gallery's other contemporary painters are Philadelphia artist Frank Hyder and Margaret Rinkovsky of Santa Cruz. The gallery also shows the expressionist paintings of the Russian artist Alek Rapoport, who has made his home in San Francisco for thirteen years.

[159] 871 FINE ARTS
871 Folsom St., San Francisco, CA 94107
(415) 543-5155

Tues-Sat: 10-5 *Owner/Dir:* Adrienne Fish

The gallery shows mainly contemporary art, with some emphasis on post-World War II American work. Every six weeks, gallery exhibitions change. Every show has a title, and once or twice a year, major thematic shows are organized. Some recent examples are "Women Abstract Expressionists of the 1950s" and Basy Area Figurative Art. The latter show featured gallery artists from San Francisco and Los Angeles, such as Howard Margolis, June Felter and Adelie Landes, as well as artists like David Park and Elmer Bischoff. The Abstract Expressionism show featured Lee Krasner, Joan Mitchell and Elaine DeKooning, who passed away at the time of this exhibition. The gallery put up a show of work by DeKooning and works lent by other artists such as Richard Diebenkorn. They also operate a bookstore, which specializes in rare, out of print, difficult to find modern art books. It is located on the first floor of a warehouse around the corner from the planned location of San Francisco's Modern Art museum.

[160] VICTOR FISCHER GALLERIES

30 Grant Ave., San Francisco CA 94108
(415) 433-4414

Tues-Fri: 10:30-5:30; Sat 11-5 *Owner:* Victor & Linda Fischer *Dir:* Dana De Kalb

Along with contemporary paintings, the Victor Fischer Galleries exhibit more sculpture than other galleries on the West Coast. In addition to the indoor spaces at both Oakland and San Francisco, the galleries also display between thirty and forty sculptures in the lobbies, plazas and lawns of the six square blocks within Oakland City Center. The galleries specialize in sculpture for both indoor and outdoor public and corporate settings, as well as presenting a wide range of sculpture for collector's gardens and estates.

The galleries feature work by noted Bay Area painters Patrick Humble and Robert Loberg as well as other talented American abstract painters Sonia Hahn, George Lloyd, Matthew Thomas and Glenn Watson.

Other featured artists are *plein air* painter Terry St. John; color field painter Richard Wilson; painter and aerial photographer Robert Hartman; British abstractionist Stuart Jennings and German expressionist Wilhelm Holderied.

Figurative artists include Carol Levy, Joan Savo and watercolorist Karen Frey.

Among the sculptors working primarily with painted, weathering or stainless steel, aluminum or bronze are Kati Casida, Dan Dykes, Richard Mayer, Arthur Silverman, Obie Simonis, William Wareham and Michael Weinstein.

Other sculptors include Bill Bell and Christian Schiess, kinetic light sculptors; Peter Boiger and Norman Hines, stone and bronze; Phillip Levine, figurative; William Wainwright, kinetic; Philip Dow, cast acylic; and noted Swiss sculptor Joseph Staub.

[161] FRAENKEL GALLERY

55 Grant Ave., San Francisco, CA 94108
(415) 981-2661

Tues-Fri: 10:30-5:30; Sat: 11-5 *Owner/Dir:* Jeffrey Fraenkel and Frish Brandt

The gallery deals exclusively in photography. Exhibitions have covered the history of the medium, with shows spanning from the work of 19th century masters such as William Henry Fox Talbot, Edouard

Baldus and Carleton Watkins to that of contemporary practitioners, including Joel-Peter Witkin, Robert Mapplethorpe and Nicholas Nixon. Other important exhibitions have included vintage, unpublished photographs by Diane Arbus and the first West Coast retrospectives of work by Garry Winogrand and Lee Friedlander. The gallery has also exhibited photographs by artists who work outside the standard photographic tradition, such as David Hockney, Andy Warhol, Chuck Close, Bruce Connor and William Wegman.

In addition, the gallery handles the photographs of Walker Evans, Robert Frank, Helen Levitt, O. Winston Link, and Bay Area artists John Gutmann, Richard Misrach, Henry Wessel and Catherine Wagner.

[162] FULLER GROSS GALLERY

228 Grant Ave., San Francisco, CA 94108
(415) 982-6177

Tues-Fri: 10-5:30; Sat: 10:30-5 *Owner/Dir:* Diana Fuller & Brian Gross

The gallery deals in contemporary art and presents a strong group of artists working in abstract, figurative and conceptual traditions. Both established and younger artists from the Bay Area and from around the United States are represented.

Among the artists featured are Doug Hall, known for his vivid video installations and drawings, and Matt Mullican, who has shown his neo-iconic drawings and paintings throughout the United States and abroad. Artists working in the Bay Area conceptual tradition include James Melchert, Doug Hollis, Tom Marioni, Tony Labat and John Roloff. Bay Area artists with a national following include Robert Arneson, William T. Wiley, Roy De Forest and Robert Hudson. Internationally-recognized painters Charles Arnoldi, Laddie John Dill, Janis Provisor and Pat Steir are also represented at the gallery, as are Mary Campbell, Roger Hankins and Yoshitomo Saito, artists who launched their careers at Fuller Gross.

[163] GALIMAGO

619 Post St., San Francisco, CA 94109 (415) 775-0707

Tues-Sat: 11-7 *Owner/Dir:* Will Stone

Originating on Sutter Street in 1978 as the Will Stone Gallery, Gallery Imago, in its new location since 1983, now features new works by established and emerging artists from North and South America, Africa and Europe. The result is an eclectic mixture of all genres of contemporary art complimented by artifacts from primitive Africa.

In 1986 Stone established A.R.T.S. Resource, which now operates Gallery Imago, as a management agency to help emerging fine artists artists to learn marketing and publicity skills. The gallery consists of a two-floor, 2,000-foot exhibition space in the heart of downtown and features eight month-long shows of individual artists and two two month-long group shows.

The gallery represents more than thirty artists from all over the world including oil painters Arthur Bell, E. Dale Erickson and John Wotipka, sculptors Elio Benvuento, Lee Madison and Horace Washington, mezzotint artist Yu Aekee, printmaker Don Dolan and watercolor artist Marcela Ottonello.

[164] GRAYSTONE

250 Sutter St., San Francisco, CA 94108
(415) 956-7693

Tues-Sun: 11-5:30 *Owner/Dir:* Edmond Russell

The gallery shows works on paper, including drawings paintings and prints, of major American artists. Some of the artists featured at the gallery are David Gorn, Jasper Johns, Wayne Thiebaud, Roy Lichtenstein, Robert Motherwell and Ed Rauschenberg. Sam Francis' and Richard Diebenkorn's works are also seen at the gallery. Recently the gallery has branched into monotypes. Pieces by Francis, Thiebaud and Diebenkorn, are among those shown in addition to works in the artists' primary media. The gallery's exhibitions, which they organize three times a year, are survey shows. Recent examples have been "Diebenkorn: Ocean Park Prints, 1969-1988" and "Universal Limited Art Edition Prints, 1980-1985."

[165] GUMPS GALLERY

250 Post St., 3rd Floor, San Francisco, CA 94108
(415) 982-1616

Mon-Sat: 9:30-5:30 *Owner:* Gumps Art Gallery *Dir:* Helen Heninger

The oldest gallery in northern California, the Gumps Gallery was founded in 1861 as an integral part of one of the three great specialty stores in the world. Located on the third floor of the exquisite, landmark Gumps retail store, the Gumps Gallery specializes in contemporary American paintings, sculpture and fine graphics.

Among the artists presented are sculptors Melvin Schuler and Ron Tatro and painters Carol Fremlin, Robert Harvey, Forrest Moses and Bird Robinson. The Gumps Gallery also shows fine graphics by Robert Motherwell. In addition, the gallery exhibits the glasswork of contemporary Washington artist William Morris and the turned wooden bowls of Ed Moulthrop.

In addition to its changing monthly exhibitions, the Gumps Gallery presents large storewide shows each October. Shown in October 1989 is "Art of the Americas," featuring paintings and sculptures by Hispanic and Latino artists from the U.S., Mexico, Cuba, Colombia, Chile and elsewhere in Latin America.

[166] JAN HOLLOWAY GALLERY

414 Francisco, San Francisco, CA (415) 398-2055

Tues-Sat: 11-5 *Owner/Dir:* Jan Holloway

The gallery centers around the work of Northern California painters and sculptors with special focus on urban realism of the 1920s and 1930s. In addition to urban realism, the gallery offers a wide variety of California landscapes, featuring mountains, deserts and shores of the past and present. Early western painters and sculptors featured at the gallery include John Langley Howard, Ralph Stack Pale, Otis Oldfield, Victor Arnautoff, Gerald Green, John Haley and G. Fletcher.

[167] HARCOURTS GALLERY, INC.

535 Powell St., San Francisco, CA 94108
(415) 421-3428

Mon-Sat: 9-6 *Owner:* Fred Banks *Dir:* James P. Healey

Harcourts Gallery carries rare and historic works by nineteenth- and twentieth-century European, American and Latin American painters, sculptors and printmakers.

The inventory of the gallery contains works by French Impressionist Pierre-Auguste Renoir; Post-Impressionist Georges Rouault; twentieth-century European masters Joan Miro, Pablo Picasso, Marc Chagall, Georges Braque and Henri Matisse; twentieth-century sculptors Alexander Calder and Henry Moore; and German painter and graphic artist Friedensreich Hundertwasser. Latin American artists include Mexican muralist David Alfaro Siquieros, painter Rufino Tamayo, painter and draftsman Jose Luis Cuevas, sculptor Francisco Zuniga, painters Francisco Toledo and Carlos Merida.

[168] HOLOS GALLERY

1792 Haight St., San Francisco, CA 94117
(415) 668-4656

Mon-Sat: 11-6; Sun: 12-6 *Dir:* Gary Zellerbach

Established in 1979, Holos Gallery is Northern California's first gallery devoted to holography. Holographer John Kaufman's well-known work continues to be featured at the gallery. His recent pieces involve a laborious multi-color technique used to produce holograms of rocks, leaves and found objects in vibrant, pastel shades. Rotating exhibits feature works by other of the world's top holographic artists. Recently, a local group called the Laser Arts Society for Education and Research presented new holograms, holographic collages and a multimedia installation combining holograms with bronze sculpture. In addition to their displays of work with dual emphasis on art and technology, Holos deals in custom-made and commercial holograms for small businesses and large corporations. They offer wholesale and mail-order distribution, traveling hologram exhibitions and educational services.

[169] IMAGES OF THE NORTH

1782 Union St., San Francisco, CA 94123
(415) 673-1273

Mon-Sat: 11-5:30; Sun 12-4 *Owners:* Helene F. Sobol and Lesley Leonhardt *Dir:* Helene F. Sobol

Established in 1979, Images of the North has gained a reputation for the scope and quality of its Native North American Art collection. The comprehensive selection of Eskimo art from Alaska and Canada includes sculpture by today's leading Eskimo artists, such as Cape Dorset artists Pauta, Etungat, Tukiki Manomie and Tootooya Ikkidluak, and Baker Lake artists George Arluk, Barnabas and Matthew Akeah. The gallery's Eskimo print collection includes Cape Dorset stonecuts, which have become know for their striking, colorful and imaginative images. The gallery also features contemporary masks by Gerard Tsonakwa (Abenaki), Lillian Pitt (Yakima) and Larry Ahvakana (Inupiat), as well as a collection of Zuni fetishes and jewelry from the Southwest.

Exhibitions are presented on a regular basis, highlighting individual artists, themes or tribes and communities. Recent exhibitions have included sculpture by Tukiki Manomie, masks by Lillian Pitt, wearable sculpture by Denise Wallace, and theme shows such as "Stone in Motion: NANUK, the Magnificent Polar Bear" and "Life of the People: The Inuit at Work and Play."

[170] IVORY/KIMPTON GALLERY

55 Grant Ave., San Francisco, CA 94108
(415) 956-6661

Tues-Fri: 10:30-5:30; Sat: 12-5:30 *Owner:* Jane Ivory and Kay Kimpton

Caiman Shemi, *Brazil,* 63 x 98, soft painting. Courtesy: Circle Gallery, San Francisco

Robert Misrach, *untitled* 15 x 15, 1976, toned gelatin-silver print.
Courtesy: Grapestake Gallery, San Francisco

The gallery, located in San Francisco's Gallery Row, features primarily emerging painters and sculptors with museum exposure. Styles range from formal abstraction to highly articulated realism. Also seen at Ivory/Kimpton, are exhibitions of modern masters such as Robert Rauschenberg, whose intriguing pieces are a combination of offset, newsprint and screen print transfer on semi-transparent fabric. Other masters include Roy Lichtenstein, Donald Sultan and Eric Fischl. The list of emerging artists includes Don Grant, Tom McKinley, Susan Marie Dopp, Holly Lane, Donald Bradford, Robert McCauley, Joe Amrhein, Linda K. Smith, Bruce Rod, Jerome Witkin, Larry Brown and Susan Crile.

[171] ROBERT KOCH GALLERY

210 Post St., San Francisco, CA 94108 (415) 421-0122

Tues-Sat: 11-5:30 *Owner/Dir:* Robert Koch

Founded in 1985, the Robert Koch Gallery exhibits masters in nineteenth- and twentieth-century European and American photography, specializing in nineteenth-century European masterpieces and photographic works from the avant-garde movements of the 1920s and 1930s.

The Robert Koch Gallery exhibits the photographic works of such nineteenth-century European masters as Julia Margaret Cameron, P. H. Emerson, Gustave Le Gray, Charles Marville and Edouard-Denis Valdus.

Among the master photographers of the twentieth century exhibited at the gallery are Ansel Adams, Lois Connor, Imogene Cunningham, Andre Kertesz, Josef Koudelka, Laszlo Maholy-Nagy, Irving Penn, Man Ray, Alexander Rodchenko, Jan Saudek, Josef Sudek and Edward Weston.

The Robert Koch hosts one of the most extensive inventories of distinguished photographic works in San Francisco.

[172] LIMESTONE PRESS GALLERY

357 Tehama St., San Francisco, CA 94103
(415) 777-2214

Mon-Fri: 10-5 *Dir:* Charles Henri Hine

The Limestone Gallery is the exhibition space of Limestone Press, the printers and publishers of hand-pulled editions in etching, lithography and woodblock. The press also designs and publishes artist books and books about the arts.

Founded in 1975, Limestone Press' exhibition space shows the work of artists whom the gallery represents, as well as the works of artists who have been printed by Limestone Press.

Artists shown at the gallery include: Raymond Saunders, Gustavo Rivera, Kate Delos, Leslie Lerner and Irene Pijoan.

[173] MAXWELL GALLERIES LTD.

551 Sutter St., San Francisco, CA 94102
(415) 421-5193

Mon-Fri: 9:30-5:15; Sat: 11-5 *Owner/Dir:* Mark Hoffman and Colleen Hoffman

Established in 1940 by Fred Maxwell and acquired in 1973 by Mark and Colleen Hoffman, the Maxwell Galleries present selected American and European nineteenth and twentieth century painting and sculpture, paying particular attention to early American landscape and genre scenes and to impressionist and post-impressionist paintings from both the American and European schools. In addition, the gallery has an extensive collection of early California landscape, *plein air*, and Western paintings. The Maxwell Galleries also feature works by select contemporary painters and sculptors.

Among the many international masters exhibited at the Maxwell are Eugene Boudin, Edouard Cortes, Jean Dufy, Raoul Dufy, Eugene Fromentin, Kate Greenaway, Stanislas Lepine, Bernard Lamotte, Henri Martin, Diego Rivera, Auguste Rodin, Adolf Schreyer, Rufino Tamayo, Maurice de Vlaminck and Edouard Vuillard. The Maxwell Galleries also feature American artists Albert Bierstadt, Mary Cassatt, William Merritt Chase, Colin Campbell Cooper, George Luks, Maxfield Parrish, Frederic Remington, John Singer Sargent, N. C. Wyeth and dozens of other American masters. California artists exhibited include Beniamino Bufano, Alice Chittenden, William Coulter, Edwin Deakin, Maynard Dixon, Percy Gray, Armin Hansen, William Ritschel, Will Sparks, Taddeus Welch and Theodore Wores.

California artist Raimonds Staprans is represented in San Francisco exclusively by Maxwell Galleries, Ltd. The Maxwell is the sole agent for the paintings from the estate of Karl Baumann (1911-1984) and is the exclusive representative of American sculptor Robert Russin.

[174] ERIKA MEYEROVICH GALLERY

231 Grant Ave., San Francisco CA 94117
(415) 421-9997

Mon-Fri: 9:30-6:30; Sat: 10-6 *Owner:* Erika & Alexander Meyerovich *Dir:* Erika Meyerovich

Located in the center of the blue-chip gallery row off Union Square in San Francisco, the gallery specializes in Modern and Contemporary art by European and American Masters. The focus is on limited edition fine art graphics, and the gallery has an impressive collection of unique paintings, sculptures, drawings and ceramics.

Pablo Picasso leads the gallery's modern artists with a collection that includes etchings, aquatints, lithographs and linoleum cuts, as well as his ceramic works. Also included are graphics and drawings by Henri Matisse; paintings and graphics by Marc Chagall; graphics by Joan Miro; paintings by Raoul Dufy; and works by Auguste Renoir. David Hockney and Andy Warhol highlight the gallery's comprehensive collection of contemporary artists. Also featured are paintings and graphics by Alex Katz; sculpture by Lynn Chadwick; and significant works by Frank Stella, Mimmo Paladino and Helen Frankenthaler.

The gallery's *New Faces* exhibitions are designed to showcase a select number of innovative and emerging artists from the San Francisco Bay Area and beyond.

[175] MILLER/BROWN GALLERY

355 Hayes St., San Francisco, CA 94102
(415) 861-2028

Tues-Sat: 11-5 or by appt. *Owner:* Edward Brown & Michael Miller *Dir:* Signe Mayfield

In 1984 Michael Miller joined forces with Edward Brown as co-director of a new expansive space near the Louise M. Davies Symphony Hall. The gallery specializes in contemporary works in fiber, painting, prints and sculpture. Artists represented include Ed Rossbach, an important pioneer in recent fiber art; Long Nguyen, a collagist and painter who fled Vietnam during the collapse of Saigon in 1975, explores

Lillian Pitt, *Wapashush Woman,* 18 x 9 x 3, anagama fired clay, leather, beads and shells. Courtesy: Images of the North, San Francisco

Jonathan Barbieri, *Una Noche Mexicana,* 29 x 23, oil pastel on paper.
Courtesy: Miller/Brown Gallery, San Francisco

with a sense of mystery the relationships between men and women, the individual and the universe, oil and canvas, subjects and ground; Trevor Southey, native of Africa, and mixed-media artist working with bronze, etching and paint, captures condradictory forces in nature which seem to be held in suspension. His elegant images convey humanitarian concern. Other contemporary painters exhibited are Jonathan Barbieri, Claudia Bernardi, Franta, Margeauz Klein and Philip Michelson. Other fiber artists include Gerhardt Knodel, Cynthia Schira, Warren Seelig, Kay Sekimachi and Lillian Elliot. Exhibitions at the gallery change monthly.

[176] MINCHER/WILCOX GALLERY

228 Grant Ave., San Francisco, CA 94108
(415) 433-4660

Tues-Fri: 10:30-5:30; Sat: 10:30-5 *Owner/Dir:* Michele Mincher & Tessa Wilcox

Formerly the Khiva Gallery founded by Michele Mincher in 1984, the gallery became the Mincher/Wilcox when Mincher and Wilcox joined forces in 1987. The gallery features contemporary American and European painting, sculpture and photography.

Among the artists presented are the Bay area abstract, minimalist painters George Lawson and John Meyer. The gallery also exhibits the sculptures of contemporary German artists Sabine Funke and James Reineking. The Mincher/Wilcox Gallery also features the work of California sculptor Shauna Peck. Also shown are the works of mixed-media conceptual artist Nayland Blake.

[177] MODERNISM

685 Market St., Suite 290, San Francisco, CA 94105
(415) 541-0461

Tues-Sat: 10-5:30 *Owner:* Martin Muller *Dir:* Katya Slavenska

Founded in 1979, Modernism hosts a wide international range of modern and contemporary art in abstract and figurative modes. The gallery features unique pieces and major works in oil and on paper, ranging from historical early twentieth-century European and Russian, Russian avant garde (1910-1930s), German Expressionist, and International Constructivism, to modern (1940-1960s) and contemporary American painting and sculpture.

Among the Russian avant garde artists presented are Kasimer Malavich, L. Lissitzski, Alexandra Exter, Natalia Goncharova, Kirill Zdanevich, Ivan Kliyn, Alexander Rodchenko and Alexander Bogomazov.

Moderism also represents the postmodern sculpture and furniture of Los Angeles artist Peter Shire, who, along with Peter Graves, is one of two American members of the Italian Memphis group. Among Modernism's contemporary American painters are the Malibu-based figurative painter John Register, well-known for his paintings of rooms with empty chairs and empty seats, and Mark Stock the Los Angeles-based realist of subtle macabre imagery. Stock is best known for his "Butler's in Love" series which portrays a liveried butler pining for unattainable love.

Among the gallery's abstract painters are James Hayward of Santa Barbara, known for his monochromatic large-scale paintings, and Frederick Hammersley, one of the four major abstract classicists of the Los Angeles art scene in the 1960s known for their hard-edged geometric abstractions.

Housed in the historical Monadnock building in downtown San Francisco, the pre-earthquake home of several galleries, Modernism hosts a wide range of on-going, rotating special exhibitions. Recently featured have been the paintings of Viennese and Austrian dark "performance" painter Hermann Nitsch and German-American photo-realist painter Gustav Heinz.

[178] SAN FRANCISCO MUSEUM OF MODERN ART RENTAL GALLERY

Building A, Fort Mason, San Francisco, CA 94123
(415) 441-4777

Tues-Sat: 11:30-5:30 *Dir:* Marian Parmenter

A non-profit branch of the San Francisco Museum of Modern Art, the Art Rental gallery rents and sells the work of 750 Bay Area artists. The gallery features sculptures, paintings, prints and photographs by emerging, mid-career as well as established artists. All contemporary styles are included in the gallery's inventory.

The gallery also has an exhibitions program in which all media forms are featured , including mixed-media events and installations. These works are often avant-garde in nature, offering a view of the most recent developments in West Coast visions. Artists represented by the gallery include Michael Almaguer, Michael Ashcraft, Carl Dern, Keith Ferris, Judith Foosaner Carrie Lederer, Dan McCarthy, Julius Hatofsky, Tony Ligamari, Inez Storer and many more. The Rental Gallery is located near the bay at the Golden Gate Recreation Area.

[179] MONTGOMERY GALLERY

250 Sutter St., San Francisco, CA 94108
(415) 788-8300

Mon-Sat: 10:30-5:30 *Dir:* Peter Fairbanks

Montgomery Gallery features important American and European paintings and sculpture spanning the period from 1860-1920.

Changing exhibitions present impressionist, nineteenth-century European, modern, luminist and Western works of art. The gallery is located several blocks from Union Square in the heart of San Francisco's gallery district.

[180] MOSS GALLERY

55 Grant St., San Francisco, CA 94108
(415) 433-7224

Tues-Sat: 10-6 *Owner/Dir:* Marvin Moss

The gallery represents international artists, specifically those from South America, Central America and Mexico. It is a major dealer in Latin American and Mexican paintings, selling to collectors and many museums, including the modern art museums of Caracas, New York, Mexico and Bogota. Moss Gallery exhibits works by their own artists approximately six times a year, generally in one-man shows. Currently on the gallery's roster are abstract painters Fernando Szyszlo and Felix Angel, the well-known Peruvian painter; Argentinian Hugo Sbernini, Victor Chab and Ines Vega, a sculptor. In the category of "up and coming" artists, the gallery displays artists such as Armando Londoño and Francisco Rocco, representational painters, as well as Santiago Cardenas, and Jim Amaral.

[181] EDUARD NAKHAMKIN FINE ARTS, INC.

377 Geary St., San Francisco, CA 94102
(415) 362-7665

Daily: 9am-11pm *Owner:* Eduard Nakhamkin *Dir:* Klimenty Granovsky

This San Francisco gallery, established in 1986, is one of seven Nakhamkin galleries (the others in New York, Beverly Hills and Japan) originally founded in 1976. Eduard Nakhamkin Fine Arts, Inc. specializes in internationally acclaimed Russian/Soviet and emigre art.

In March 1989, Eduard Nakhamkin Fine Arts entered into a groundbreaking joint venture with the Soviet Ministry of Culture and the Soviet Artists' Union whereby the galleries will serve as the center for thousands of Soviet artists as a primary exhibitor and clearinghouse for American and European dealers. The first exhibition to grow from this agreement was a show of 25 to 30 artists currently living in Riga, Latvia. The Nakhamkin also will feature an exhibit of twenty years of Socialist Realism, as well as a show of the enamel and painting work of Georgian mosaic artist Zurab Tseretely. The gallery also plans to present a comparative show entitled "10 Plus 10," which will feature ten American and ten Soviet artists.

Among the master Soviet emigre artists presented at the gallery are contemporary sculptor Ernst Neizvestny, Oleg Tselkov and Vladimir Yankilevsky. The gallery also features the works of contemporary Muscovites Viatchelav Kalinin and Leonid Purygin.

[182] NEW LANGTON ARTS

1246 Folsom St., San Francisco, CA 94103
(415) 626-5416

Tues-Sat: 11-5 *Owner:* New Langton Arts *Dir:* Renny Pritikin

A nonprofit arts organization founded in 1975, New Langton Arts was formed by Bay Area artists, gallery owners and art supporters to provide support and exhibition and performance space for emerging, undersupported, non-traditional Bay Area artists working in experimental areas and/or with new technologies.

The gallery is funded by the National Endowment for the Arts, the California Arts Council, the San Francisco Hotel Tax Fund and numerous other agencies both public and private and housed in a multi-use structure in San Francisco's SoMa (South of Market) district. New Langton Arts supports five programs: exhibitions, video installations, performance art (in a 100-seat theatre downstairs), literature (readings) and music (under the direction of Music Curator Paul Dresher).

Featuring ten one- to three-person shows yearly, New Langton has exhibited the photographic installations of Louise Lawler and Connie Hatch, altar installations of Amalia Mesa-Bains, video installations of Tony Labat, sculpture and painting of Allan McCollum, interactive video/Djerrassic technology of David Wilson and the work of Texas Latino artist Celia Munoz.

[183] THE NORTH POINT GALLERY

872 North Point St., San Francisco, CA 94109
(415) 885-0657

Tues-Sat: 10-6 *Owner/Dir:* Alfred C. Harrison, Jr.

Originally founded in 1972, the North Point Gallery was acquired in November 1985 by art historian and researcher Alfred C. Harrison, who applied his many years as a collector to assembling for his gallery a dis-

tinguished collection of nineteenth century American and early California paintings. Located on an old San Francisco cobblestone courtyard in a classic turn-of-the-century wooden building (part of which was a nineteenth century houseboat), the North Point Gallery specializes in Hudson River School landscape paintings, still-life paintings and genre paintings dating from the second half of the nineteenth century.

The North Point Gallery presents well established American artists whose works predate the California Impressionist movement and whose reputations have steadily grown in the last century. Among the nineteenth century California landscape artists presented are Thomas Hill, and William Keith. (Owner Harrison authored a monograph on the latter published last year by St. Mary's College in Moraga, California.) The North Point also presents the paintings of John R. Key, who came to California from Washington, D. C. and Baltimore to devote himself to California landscapes in the 1870s and 1880s. The gallery also presents the works of well-known watercolorists L. P. Lattimer and Percy Gray; while the paintings of these two artists date from the early twentieth century, their styles vividly reflect the virtues of the slightly earlier Hudson River School style.

The North Point Gallery also houses an extensive archive of nineteenth century California art reviews, products of the significant historical research of the gallery's owner.

[184] OWL GALLERY

465 Powell St., San Francisco, CA 94102
(415) 781-5464

Wed-Sat: 10-10; Sun-Tues: 10-5 *Owner:* Circle Fine Arts *Dir:* Pierre Reynolds

One of the 32 galleries around the U. S. operated by Circle Fine Arts, founded in 1964, the Owl Gallery in San Francisco features the work of contemporary, international graphic and animation artists, sculptors and jewelers.

Among the European masters of the graphic arts presented by the Owl Gallery are Victor Vasarely, the father of the Op Art movement known for his bold colors and geometric designs that create the illusion of movement. Presented along with Vasarely are the works of fellow Parisian Labadang, whose "art of topography" melds images and technics where east meets west. The third Parisian master presented by the Owl is Rene Gruau, internationally acclaimed fashion illustrator (for such designers as Christian Dior and Yves St. Laurent), whose illustrations have been in the public eye for over forty years.

Among the animation arts shown at the Owl are original paintings by Walt Disney, Chuck Jones, Friz Freleng and Hanna-Barbera.

[185] PASQUALE IANNETTI ART GALLERIES, INC.

522 Sutter St., San Francisco, CA 94102
(415) 433-2771

Mon-Sat: 10-6 *Owner/Dir:* Pasquale Iannetti

Pasquale Iannetti deals in original prints and drawings, as well as paintings and sculpture, from the 16th through the 20th century, and offers a full range of professional services.

Included in the gallery's collection are old masters such as Dürer and Rembrandt, master etcher Jacques Callot and English satirical etcher and painter William

Hogarth. Late 19th century French artists are well represented with works by Honore Daumier, Fantin-Latour, Toulouse-Lautrec, Edouard Manet, Auguste Renoir, Camille Pissarro, Paul Gaugin, Paul Signac and Odilon Redon. The gallery has turn-of-the-century, art nouveau and Art Deco posters by artists such as Alphonse Mucha. The 20th century is represented by such artists as Fernand Leger, Georges Rouault, Emil Nolde, Wassily Kandinsky, Lionel Feininger, Paul Klee, Georges Braque, Kathe Kollwitz, Joan Miro, Pablo Picasso, Salvador Dali and Marc Chagall. Contemporary artists include French painter Pierre Alechinsky, Swiss graphic artist Jean-Michel Folon, Costa Rican sculptor Francisco Zuniga and Mexican sculptor Armando Amaya. Also included in the collection are ceramics by Picasso and Cocteau.

[186] PAUL-LUSTER GALLERY
336 Hayes St., San Francisco, CA 94102
(415) 431-8511

Tues-Sat: 11-6; Sun: 12-5 *Owner/Dir:* Barbara Paul

Recently changed from the Elaine Potter Gallery after Potter retired, the new owner plans to maintain similar aesthetics at the center for contemporary craft arts. All media, from fiber and woodwork to jewelry and glasswork, are featured at the gallery. They also show craft art from Europe and the Far East. The gallery represents up to 200 artists at one time.

Artists include jewelers Ann Gundler; Thomas Mann, whose work consists of what he calls techno-romantic collages, mixing hearts and photos for example; and Eun Mee Chung; furniture maker Edward Gottesman; fiber artists Randall Darwall and Dominique Caron, a leatherworker known for her masks. Ceramists David Paul Bachrach and Dina Angel-Wing also show their work with the gallery, as do Laurie Phal and glassworker Jessie Gregg.

[187] PENCE GALLERY
750 Post St., San Francisco, CA 94109 (415) 441-1138
Mon-Sat: 10-5, or by appt. *Owner/Dir:* John Pence

The gallery resides in a luxurious old garage space, renovated by local artisans and gallery artists. The focus is on living American realists. Also featured are the American Masters from 1850-1950. Works by artists regularly displayed include: Michael Bergt's evocative egg tempera paintings; Donald Jurney's oil landscapes of New England; Robert Maione's old-master style landscapes from around the world; Michael Lynch's superb American West impressionist paintings; Randall Lake's fauvist still lifes and florals; Will Wilson's white-lead media; Douglas Fenn Wilson's impressionistic watercolors and pastels; plus George Wingate's miniature oil paintings. Sculptors Donald Davis, Tom Morandi and Kirk St. Maur carve marble and cast bronze. John Pence stages an annual competition for new artists and presents the winners in two yearly group shows. The gallery also sponsors at least one yearly traveling exhibitions, usually consisting of older American works.

[188] WILLIAM SAWYER GALLERY
3045 Clay St., San Francisco, CA 94115
(415) 921-1600

Tues-Sat: 11-6 *Owner/Dir:* Dr. William Sawyer

Founded in 1962 by its present owner and director, the William Sawyer Gallery presents contemporary painting, sculpture and works on paper by American artists from both the west and east coasts. One of the longest

established and most respected galleries in San Francisco, Sawyer has introduced more new artists than most galleries in California. Owner William Sawyer is publisher of the *San Francisco Gallery Guide* and a founder of the San Francisco Art Dealers Association. He is committed to showing and supporting American artists who are newly-emerging to mid-career. Housed in what was once a ballroom dancing school for the children of Pacific Heights, the William Sawyer Gallery is tucked away in a quiet residential neighborhood.

Among the artists presented by the gallery are Brian Isobe, the contemporary Japanese-American cross-cultural painter known for Japanese motifs and sensibilities presented in the Western media of acrylic and pastels. Painter Willard Dixon has been featured by the Sawyer for fifteen years and is well known for his interpretive contemporary landscapes, mostly of California.

The William Sawyer Gallery also features the paintings of Christopher Gerlach, best known for several series of landscapes capturing the light of specific regions, such as the south of France, Venice, the California vineyards, New Mexico, in the style of the old Impressionists. The gallery also shows the colorful semi-abstract oils and pastels of California artist Frances McCormack and the sculptures of Barbara Spring, which combine different animal and human forms in many different kinds of wood.

[189] WOLF SCHULZ GALLERY
383 Geary Street, San Francisco, CA 94102
(415) 397-5335

Mon-Wed: 9:30-6:30; Thurs-Sat: 9:30am-11:30pm; Sun: 10-6 *Owner/Dir:* Wolf Schulz

Founded in 1981, the Wolf Schulz Gallery exhibits an international range of original works and graphics. The gallery specializes in early twentieth-century European masters.

Among the European masterworks shown at the gallery are paintings by Pablo Picasso, Joan Miro, Marc Chagall and Andre Masson.

The Wolf Schulz Gallery also presents the work of temporary French painters of the *Figuration Libre* movement Francois Boisrond, Remi Blanchard, Combas and the Dirosa brothers, as well as the prints of contemporary American lithographer Harold Altman.

Also featured at the gallery are paintings by Tamayo Rufino and works by sculptor Francisco Zuniga.

[190] DON SOKER GALLERY
871 Folsom St., San Francisco, CA 94107
(415) 974-6489

Tues-Sat: 11-5 *Owner/Dir:* Don Soker

Specializing in works on paper, the gallery does less retail work than brokering. They show 3 or 4 exhibitions a year. One such show recently featured four major Hungarian artists, one of the first big shows from that country to be mounted in the United States. Sculptor Jaza Samu and Imre Bukta, a painter, both included in the show, work with Hungarian agricultural art. Both appeared in the Venice Biennale. Others at the gallery include Japanese artists Shoichi Ida, Yutaka Yoshinaga, who works in Japanese pigments on handmade paper, Tetsuya Noda, Kenji Manao, an abstract painter, Persian Touradj Ebrahimi and Theodora Varnay Jones, who makes drawings, paintings and monotypes. Most of the work at the gallery is minimal or abstract.

[191] SOUTHERN EXPOSURE GALLERY

401 Alabama St., San Francisco, CA 94110
(415) 863-2141

Wed-Sun: 2-6 *Owner:* Southern Exposure Gallery
Dir: Jon Winet

Founded approximately a decade ago and housed in San Francisco's south of Market Project Artaud complex, Southern Exposure Gallery is a nonprofit, artist-run arts organization that exhibits primarily the work of San Francisco and Bay Area emerging and experimental artists.

The main floor gallery features a 28-foot ceiling, over 2000 square feet of linear wall space, and over 2400 square feet of floor space; it can accommodate large-scale work, large bodies of work, and group exhibitions. A 16-by-25-foot mezzanine gallery with 16-foot ceilings provides a more intimate space for small works, as well as contained installations. Southern Exposure also presents non-static events, including performance, music, literature, symposia and artists' talks.

Exhibited arts include painting installation by Jean Lowe, large-scale photographic installation by Mark Durant, sculpture by Rene de Guzman, painting by Rudy Lemcke, sculptural installation by Susan Mc-Whinney and temporal sculptural installation by Reiko Goto.

Artists are selected for exhibition on the basis of artistic excellence and adventurousness; commercial potential is not a factor. Applications are reviewed by a committee of working artists; all media are considered.

[192] ST. ALBUS FINE ARTS

225 Scott St., San Francisco, CA 94117
(415) 861-4458

By appt. only *Owner/Dir:* Lynn St. Albus

An art dealer for seventeen years, Lynn St. Albus began her private art dealership in San Francisco in 1984. She specializes in nineteenth- and early twentieth-century American artists working up to approximately 1940. She focuses primarily on painting, but also specializes in bronzes, sculpture and prints. She handles artists from the American Impressionists and California and Hudson River Schools, including Plein Air painters and early American moderns. Artists she has handled include William Merritt Chase, George Inness and John Henry Twachtman to Preston Dickenson. An art historian, St. Albus's interests range from major to lesser known American artists.

[193] JEREMY STONE GALLERY

23 Grant Ave., San Francisco, CA 94108
(415) 398-6535

Tues-Fri: 10:30-5:30; Sat: 12-5 *Owner/Dir:* Jeremy Stone

Founded in 1982, the Jeremy Stone Gallery features contemporary American paintings, works on paper and constructions.

The artists presented by the Jeremy Stone Gallery are Robert Bairbeau, John Barnes, Richard Brewer, Madeleine Carolan, Donna Cehrs, Kyung Sun Cho, Dennis Clive, Marshall Crossman, Guy Dieghl, Barry Eagle, Stanley Goldstein, James Havard, Richard Hickam, Kathleen Jesse, Cindy Kane, Sylvia Lark, Joanne Leonard, Grace Munakata, Susan Parker, Barbara Pierce, Laura Raboff, Richard Sheehan, Albert Smith, Pia Stern, Inez Storer and Roger Van Ouystel.

[194] RICHARD THOMPSON GALLERY

80 Maiden Lane, San Francisco, CA 94108
(415) 956-2114

Mon-Fri: 10-5; *Dir:* Richard Thompson

The gallery centers around original oil paintings by modern masters of American Impressionism. The gallery features work by artist Richard Thompson. There is a link to the French Expressionist School palpable in his work, though the evolution in color has provided Thompson with even greater variations of light and color. The artist has perfected this use of color to such a degree that the paintings vary from high brilliance to subtle mood scenes to pleasant, tranquil settings. Another celebrated artist represented by the gallery is Henry Casselli, whose watercolors are being recognized as some of the finest in the country. He was the recipient of a Gold Medal from the American Watercolor Society and Silver Medal Award in 1986 for a mother/child composition. Other artists include James Cecko, whose impressionistic landscapes communicate the tranquil scenes of his native state of Minnesota and Claire Ruby, whose impressionist works take on a skillful blend with realism. Ruby began her studies as a child in her native Hungary. The gallery represents other contemporary Impressionists, including Mary Helen Hurlimann Armstrong. Published by the gallery, is a comprehensive line of limited edition reproduction prints, posters and open edition reproductions of Richard Earl Thompson and Claire Ruby.

[195] TRIANGLE GALLERY

445 Bush St., San Francisco, CA 94108
(415) 392-1686

Tues-Sat: 11-5 *Owner/Dir:* Jack Van Hiele

One of the oldest art galleries in San Francisco, it was established in 1961. Its seven-room layout accommodates group shows so as to seem to be several mini-solo shows. Rooms with 16-foot ceilings are amply suited for large-scaled installations; there are smaller rooms as well which provide thoughtful settings for sculptures and works on paper.

Triangle Gallery represents a range of local and international artists, some of whom have a 25-year history with the gallery. Ronald Chase reveals a new direction in recent work, three-dimensional abstract relief paintings in Renaissance colors. These are architecturally geometric, with an edginess that is modulated by restraint. Louis Siegriest, surviving member of the Society of Six, a group of *plein air* painters who gathered together in the 1920s outside Oakland, produces abstract desert landscapes. In the recent book, *The Society of Six: California Colorists,* Siegrist is hailed as one of the greatest of contemporary landscape painters. Soichiro Tomioka is famous in Japan on the basis of his 30-year series of abstract paintings, "Snow Country." Sculptors connected with the gallery are Kek Tee Lim, who uses carved acrylic to create abstract symbolistic sculptures that become restless meditations on water; Joseph Romano, whose somewhat primitive, tenuously elongated sculptures, made from paper pulp, have echoes of Giacometti; and James Prestini, known for ultra-tech constructivist pieces of nickel-plated steel and aluminum. Recent additions to the gallery are abstract expressionist painters Susan Wexler and Susan Keizer.

New talent is represented by the twig sculptures of Randy Beckelheimer, the abstract minimalist paintings of David Tangney as well as works by Kathleen Edwards and Jeremy Morgan.

[196] VISION GALLERY

1155 Mission, San Francisco, CA 94103
(415) 621-2107

Mon-Sat: 9-6 *Owner:* Joseph G. Folberg *Dir:* Nancy B. Cross

Established in 1979, Vision Gallery is now one of the largest photography galleries on the West Coast. Collections include black and white, color, as well as other work created by alternative processes. Major photographers represented include Ansel Adams, Brett Weston, Van Deren Coke and others. There is a large selection of work by contemporary, emerging artists such as Garry Gay. Every six weeks the gallery presents a new major show. An intriguing selection of posters, postcards, magazines and books is available for purchase.

[197] DOROTHY WEISS GALLERY

256 Sutter St., San Francisco, CA 94108
(415) 397-3611

Tues-Sat: 11-5; *Owner/Dir:* Dorothy Weiss

The gallery's specialization is American contemporary ceramics and glass sculpture created by both established and mid-career artists.

Among the first category are such sculptors as Ruth Duckworth, Rudy Autio, Jun Kaneko and Tony Hepburn. Philip Cornelius, another established craft artist, shows his teapot forms here. Mid-career artists the gallery exhibits include Yoshio Taylor, whose works are inspired by his native Japan, Oakland artist Stan Welsh and Jamie Walker. The gallery's emphasis is on clay, but two of their twelve or so shows every year feature glass. Hank Murta Adams, Jay Musler and Richard Marquis all exhibit their glasswork here. The owner also plans an expansion, which will add space to exhibit more drawings and paintings.

[198] WIRTZ GALLERY

345 Sutter St., San Francisco, CA 94108
(415) 433-6879

Tues-Sat: 10:30-5:30 *Owner/Dir:* Connie and Stephen Wirtz

The works of such artists as Man Ray and Antoni Tapies can be seen amongst the contemporary European and American sculptors, painters and photographers exhibited in this expansive, multi-level space. The gallery supports emerging artists in addition to lesser-known and well-known artists. There is a wide variety of media and styles represented. The gallery has exposed the West Coast to such masters of fine art photography as Ralph Steiner, Willard Van Dyke and Gyorgy Kepes. It also has a special program including the work of Richard Avedon, Michael Kenna and Sandy Skoglund. Wirtz has collaborated with other galleries to bring to the Bay Area such artists as Gregory Amenoff, Gianfranco Pardi and Jedd Garet.

[199] WYLIE WONG ASIAN ART AND ANTIQUITIES

1055 Washington St., San Francisco, CA 94108
(415) 433-7389

By appt *Owner/Dir:* Wylie Wong

Located on San Francisco's Nob Hill, the gallery specializes in Asian scrolls, fans, album leaves, painting and calligraphy from the 17th to the 20th century.

Subject matter from the extensive inventory includes calligraphy, landscape, bird and flower painting, portraits, figures and other subjects. The gallery features woodblock prints of the Ch'ing dynasty and the late Meiji period of Japan. Major artists in the gallery's collection include: Chang Ta-Chien (1899-1983), Chi Pai-Hsih (1863-1957), Chien Tu (1783-1844), Fu Pao-shih (1904-1965), Huang I (1744-1802), Jen Po-nien (1840-1896), Yoshitoshi Tsukioka (1839-1892) and C.C. Wang (1907-).

Artworks are exhibited in changing monthly exhibitions, in austere chambers reminiscent of traditional Chinese scholars' studies. Visitors interested in specific artists or works are encouraged to request a private showing.

SAN JOSE

[200] SAN JOSE ART LEAGUE DOWNTOWN GALLERY

66 N. Market St., San Jose, CA 95113 (408) 287-8435

Tues-Fri: 1-4 *Dir:* Anthony Torres

The San Jose Art League Downtown Gallery hosts exhibitions of contemporary art by Bay Area artists. Other programs and activities include: international exchange shows; juried two- and three-dimensional competitions; an art lecture series; art classes and a Collector's Choice Art Auction. The gallery also sponsors outreach programs in convalescent hospitals and correctional institutions.

An Artist-in Residence program is sponsored at the gallery by the California Arts Council. The National Endowment for the Arts also sponsors free art classes to seniors and the public at the gallery.

SAN MARCOS

[201] BOEHM GALLERY

Palomar Community College 1140 W. Mission Rd., San Marcos, CA 92069 (714) 744-1150 X2304

Tues 10-4; Wed-Thurs 10-7; Fri 10-2; Sat noon-4 *Owner:* Palomar Community College *Dir:* Louise Kirtland

Established in 1964 to provide its community with exposure to fine art in a broad array of styles, approaches and media, the Boehm Gallery shows contemporary art by nationally acclaimed artists.

Six exhibitions a year are provided for the students, faculty and community. Recent exhibitions have included the works of Gillian Theobald, Marjorie Wodelman, Amanda Farber, Mathew Gregoire, as well as contemporary Mexican artists Janet Codling and Raul Guerrero. Shows in the past have featured Andy Warhol, John Baldessari, Judy Chicago and Italo Scanga. It has also held exhibits featuring African and New Guinean sculptures.

Most exhibitions are one-person, although group shows are not uncommon. Craft exhibitions feature jewelry, furniture, glass and ceramics. The gallery also hosts traveling exhibitions from the Smithsonian and the Western Association of Art Museums (WAAM).

SAN MATEO

[202] GALLERY 30
30 E. 3rd Ave., San Mateo, CA 94401 (415) 342-3271

Tues-Sat: 11-5:30 *Owner/Dir:* Ronnie Goldfield

Founded in 1982, Gallery 30 specializes in selling contemporary paintings, sculpture and graphics made by well known California and international artists. The gallery is located in a Victorian building in a downtown San Mateo neighborhood which has the flavor of the upper west side of New York City. With 3,200 square feet of exhibition space, it is the largest gallery on the San Francisco Peninsula. It contains three exhibition rooms on two levels with a second floor space for changing exhibitions and one space on either floor devoted to rotating exhibitions of works by artists represented by the gallery. Exhibitions change every six weeks. Recently seen at Gallery 30 were: Duane Wakeham's oil and pastel California landscapes; Joe Price's realistic serigraphs; Jack Cooper's figurative oil paintings; and Rosslyn Mazzilli's large, colorful, site-specific sculptures in steel.

SANTA BARBARA

[203] DELPHINE GALLERY
1324 D. State St., Santa Barbara, CA 93101
(805) 962-6625

Mon-Fri: 10-5:30; Sat: 10-3 *Owner/Dir:* Caroletta Rossbach

The Delphine Gallery began its operations in 1979 and moved twice before arriving at its current location, a small, 600-foot room beside a frame shop in a shopping center. After many years of featuring only specific gallery artists, the gallery recently changed its artistic emphasis and began to specialize in contemporary, often non-objective California landscape paintings of the Santa Barbara area. Today the artists the Delphine Gallery represents are mostly painters (though there are some sculptors). Among its artists are Richard Schloss, a California landscape painter whose subject is the Santa Barbara; and Sara Vedder a local pastel artist with similar concerns.

The Gallery is known for its friendly but serious mood, its personalized service and its excellent framing. Owner Caroletta Rossbach often gives personal consultations in customer's homes.

[204] ELIZABETH FORTNER GALLERY
1114 State St., Studio 9, Santa Barbara, CA 93101
(805) 966-2613

Mon-Sat: 10:30-5:30; Sun: 1-4 *Owner/Dir:* Elizabeth Fortner

The gallery carries fine contemporary crafts by many nationally known artists. Every month to six weeks, the Fortner Gallery changes its shows to feature the work of artists from all over the country who work in a particular medium such as ceramic, wood, glass, fiber or jewelry.

Among the artists shown are Suellen Fowler, whose miniature glass vials are noted for their unique coloring technique; Polly Frizzell, who makes whimsical ceramics such as salt and pepper shakers consisting of cats in chairs; David Gilhooley who makes funny, ceramic pieces, frequently of frogs, with satirical content; Coille Hooven who makes tiny porcelain cups and baskets; Rick and Janet Nicholson, known for their large contemporary hand blown glass vases and bowls; Eileen Richardson, Santa Barbara resident with a national reputation, whose hand painted plates and bowls are created in thematic series; and David Settino Scott, who crafts wooden tables and shelves in the form of animals.

Many other well-known artists are included in the gallery's stable, although, because of their changing schedule of shows, not all of the gallery's collection is on display at any one time.

SANTA CRUZ

[205] GILTWOOD STUDIOS, FINE ART
Santa Cruz Art Center, 1001 Center St., Santa Cruz, CA 95060 (408) 423-1298

Tues-Wed: 10-6; Thurs-Sat: 10-8 *Owner/Dir:* Carol Sweetzer Elsworthy

The gallery specializes in 19th and 20th century English oils and watercolors. Giltwood also offers a selection of American and early California art, and limited edition prints.

The gallery's exhibition space is divided into two rooms. The first is a constantly changing exhibit of 19th and 20th century English art. These works are typified by the traditional oils and watercolors of James Orrock and Copley Fielding. Other Artists featured in the gallery include Percy Telford, English oil painter who has documented English landscapes and also scenes from Chicago, where he moved in 1926 and Jeanie Sellers, whose impressionistic floral still-lifes have be exhibited at the Glasgow Institute of Arts. An adjacent room is set aside for the display of works by local artists. Young, emerging craftspeople are particularly highlighted here. An upcoming exhibition will highlight Peggy Borgman, a contemporary abstract painter working with oils and acrylics. In April of 1990 the gallery will host an exhibition of wildlife paintings. Among the wildlife artists featured is June Payne Hart, whose wildlife prints are available in original and limited edition.

The gallery is involved in restoration work, as well as gold-leaf gilded framing.

[206] TED MILLS FINE ART
Santa Cruz Art Center, 1001 Center St., Santa Cruz, CA 95060 (408) 459-8018

Tues-Wed: 10-6 Thurs-Sat: 10-8 *Owner:* Ted Mills
Dir: Carol Sweetzer Elsworthy

The gallery specializes in early California and American art, primarily oil and watercolor paintings. It is located in an art cooperative, a building that houses many galleries and shops devoted to arts and crafts.

Ted Mills has exhibited works by James Patrick and Millard Sheets, as well as William Keith. Other artists to have been featured include Walter Bailey, Claude Buck, Granville Redmond, Pauline Polk and Keith Manheim. There is a monthly exhibit of local artists, primarily from the Monterey Bay and San Francisco area.

SANTA MONICA

[207] ANGELES GALLERY
2230 Main St., Santa Monica, CA 90405
(213) 396-5019

Tues-Sat: 11-5:30 *Owner/Dir:* David McAuliffe

The gallery specializes in contemporary American and European painting and sculpture. Its focus is abstraction and conceptually based works.

Characteristic of the gallery is the work of Los Angeles sculptor Greg Colson. Colson's wall reliefs are constructed from common objects such as weathered mail boxes, toilet seats and inner tubes The artist superimposes a chart of "meaning," such as a seating plan, a map or a clothes pattern, over the design. The juxtapositions are humorous and conceptual. Another sculptor, Jeff Colson, shows laminated and sanded pieces with simple, ovoid forms. The gallery shows works by the well-known minimalist Donald Judd, and the British sculptor Richard Long.

The Angles Gallery also carries works by Sam Francis, George Ketterl, Lienhard von Monkiewitsch, Jean St. Pierre, Rudolph Serra and Reinhard Voigt.

[208] B-1 GALLERY
2730 Main St., Santa Monica, CA 90405
(213) 450-4014
Tues-Sat: 10-6 *Owner/Dir:* Robert Berman

B-1 Gallery specializes in contemporary mid-career artists. The gallery's major artists include Frank Romero, well-known for his expressive paintings and murals; Daniel J. Martinez, whose installations, video-generated works on steel and site-specific works are on the cutting edge of art; and German artist and master printmaker Zara Kriegstein, whose large, sweeping canvases reflect such disparate influences as German expressionism and the Mexican muralists. The Gallery also represents Sol Aquino, whose brightly colored acrylics parody contemporary culture; and Brad Howe, who constructs abstract metal wall sculptures and mobiles.

Other artists regularly featured in the gallery are Margaret Garcia, whose oils and prints evoke the feel of the Southwest; Michelle Roberts, whose works expose the development of symbolic imagery and refer to primitive and contemporary common icons; Leo Limon, whose passionate pastels portray recurrent hispanic imagery; Craig French, who juxtaposes steel, glass, stone and neon to form wall sculptures which evoke emotional response; and George Yepes, a former muralist with L.A. Streetscapers, who creates intensely powerful images that are clearly rooted in the hispanic tradition.

[209] BACHOFNER GALLERY
926 Colorado Ave., Santa Monica, CA 90401
(213) 458-8007
Mon-Fri: 9-5:30; Sat: 10-5:30 *Owner/Dir:* Ruth Bachofner

The Ruth Bachofner Gallery specializes in contemporary art with emphasis on paintings, sculpture and wall constructions. The gallery focuses primarily on emerging talent concentrated in the Los Angeles area. However, several well-established artists and New York artists are also represented.

The gallery's large exhibition space presents an active schedule of one and two-person shows that change every four to five weeks. One-person shows have included: Craig Antrim, whose paintings employ color and spiritual imagery to investigate visual manifestations of the unconscious; Mary Chomenko's narrative bronze sculptures, which combine animals, words and architectural fragments to explore the conflict between heart and mind; Michel Alexis who combines painting

and relief to create abstract fields relating to an imaginary space and time; and Thomas Schulte, whose wall sculptures merge elements from religious icons with secular scientific instruments.

The Bachofner Gallery also represents Karl Benjamin, Nick Boskovich, Stanley Boxer, Michael Brangoccio, Richard Bunkall, Connor Everts, Faiya Fredman, Stephen Greene, Eva Holmstrom, Stephen Kafer, Brock Klein, Reuben Ramot, Carl Reed, Leo Robinson, Joshua Rose, Joan Thorne, Selina Trieff and Margi Weir.

[210] BLUMHELMAN LOS ANGELES INC.
916 Colorado Ave., Santa Monica, CA 90401
(213) 451-0955
Tues-Fri: 10-6; Sat: 11-6 *Dir:* Deborah McLeod

The BlumHelman gallery, in conjunction with its two locations in uptown and downtown New York City, shows 20th century and contemporary American and European painting and sculpture. The artists represented by the gallery are frequently exhibited in major museums of contemporary art.

Donald Sultan uses materials such as linoleum and tar to make his paintings of plants, fruit or urban scenes; he also shows his small sculpture and drawings at the gallery. Robert Lobe's aluminum sculptures capture large natural forms such as trees and rocks. The artist creates this effect by hammering large sheets of the metal around the objects to create a cast. Richard Tuttle's sculptures are made from traditional painting materials, canvas and wood boards, but stand freely like tents or costumed beasts. Michael Young's paintings echo the look of familiar signs, with circles and crosses, but read as abstract icons. David True's paintings are figurative and narrative but the imagery is dream-like and mysterious.

The BlumHelman gallery carries many other fine artists, such as Carl Andre, Mark di Suvero, John Duff, Donald Judd, Win Knowlton and Robert Moskowitz.

[211] BORNSTEIN GALLERY
1658 1/2 10th St., Santa Monica, CA 90404
(213) 450-1129
Tues-Fri: 10:30-5:30; Sat: 11-5 *Owner:* Karl Bornstein
Dir: Pamela Tapp

The gallery represents the most promising artists in the Los Angeles area. An eclectic body of work is shown here, including abstract and figurative styles of both painting and sculpture. Subjects range from the politically-charged enamel paintings of Tom Jenkins to the urban sculpture of Michael Davis, to the dramatic factory paintings by Lawrence Gipe. The gallery believes it is of benefit to the community to exhibit the work of internationally-known artists as well. Distinguished German artists Gunther Forg, Gerhard Merz, Isa Genzken, Helmut Dorner and Georg Herold were recently featured in a survey of New German Abstract Painting and Sculpture. Other featured artist include surrealist-inspired painter Leonard Koscianski, landscape painter Larry Gray and German abstract painter and sculptor Eberhard Bosslet.

[212] MARILYN BUTLER GALLERY
910 Colorado Ave., Santa Monica, CA 90401
(213) 394-5155
Tues-Sat: 10-6 *Owner\Dir:* Marilyn Butler

The gallery maintains an eclectic niche, showing contemporary art of high quality in a variety of media. Major artists include Fritz Scholder, widely known for

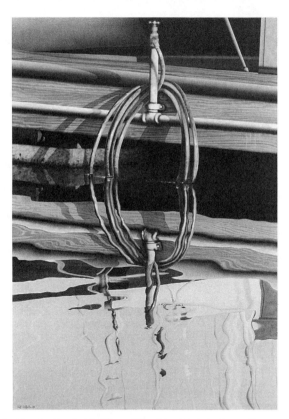

Jeff Griffeath, *Dockside Hose,* 36 x 24, airbrushed acrylic on canvas.
Courtesy: William Sawyer Gallery, San Francisco

Cheryl Gross, *Daily News,* 40 x 34, oil and crayon on canvas.
Courtesy: B-1 Gallery

his brightly colored, expressive canvases that depict figures and landscapes, frequently focusing on the American southwest; James Brown, who paints in an expressionistic style inspired by tribal art from around the world. Wayne Thiebaud is also represented by the gallery. He has sometimes been associated with the pop artists for his subject matter, rows of common objects such as food items, depicted in a confident, painterly style. The British Boyle Family reproduce small, randomly selected sites down to the most exact detail. Important sculptors represented by the gallery include Catherine Lee, and Louis Jimenez, whose life-sized tableaux portray rural scenes along the border.

The Marilyn Butler Gallery features young and emerging artists Laura Russell, Susan Venable, Mark Mc-Dowell, Leslie Werner, Ned Evans and Diane Hall and Lucian Burg.

[213] JAMES CORCORAN GALLERY

1327 5th St., Santa Monica, CA 90401 (213) 451-4666

Tues-Fri: 10-6; Sat: 11-5 *Owner:* James Corcoran *Dir:* Sandra Starr

The James Corcoran Gallery specializes in contemporary paintings and sculpture, as well as modern 20th century art. The artists represented by the gallery have substantial international reputations. Many of the gallery's artists were major contributors to the recognition of Los Angeles as an important art scene during the 1960s and 1970s, and continue to be important forces.

The James Corcoran Gallery represents Peter Alexander, Gregory Amenoff, Charles Arnoldi, Don Bachardy, Billy Al Bengston, Laddie John Dill, Steve Galloway, Joe Goode, Tom Holland, Allen Jones, David Lynch, Tomoharu Murakami, Manuel Neri, Eric Orr, Beverly Pepper, Kenneth Price, Allen Ruppersberg, Edward Ruscha and Frank Stella.

[214] DOROTHY GOLDEEN GALLERY

1547 Ninth Street, Santa Monica, CA 90401 (213) 395-0222

Tues-Sat: 10:30-5:30 *Owner/Dir:* Dorothy Goldeen

The gallery exhibits contemporary painting, sculpture and works on paper. Although the art works are both figurative and abstract, there is a strong humanistic perspective. Color is emphasized. The majority of the artists represented are in the mature stages of their careers. Many have exhibited internationally and are represented in major institutional and private collections.

The front room of the gallery is used mainly to exhibit paintings. A recent show of paintings by Squeak Carnwath explored the spiritual similarities between bee behavior and human life. The rear room of the gallery is used for sculpture exhibitions. Italo Scanga's painted sculpture addresses the theme of human suffering in both the Christian passion and in world politics. Behind the gallery is an outdoor sculpture garden, currently displaying a large, abstract, rusted steel piece by Fletcher Benton.

Many of the artists represented reside in the San Francisco Bay area, but others are from southern California, Chicago and New York. The gallery also represents Robert Arneson, Ciel Bergman (Cheryl Bowers), Roy DeForest, Charles Ginnever, Robert Hudson, Terence La Noue, Dennis Leon, Donald Lipski, Nathan Oliveira, Nam June Paik, Ed Paschke, Janis Provisor, Zizi Raymond and John White.

[215] FRED HOFFMAN GALLERY

912 Colorado Ave., Santa Monica, CA 90401 (213) 394-4199

Tues-Fri: 9:30-5:30; Sat: 10-5 *Owner/Dir:* Fred Hoffman

The Fred Hoffman Gallery shows work in all media by leading contemporary artists. Some of the gallery's artists produce conceptually-oriented works, such as French photographer Sophie Calle, who follows and documents people without their knowledge. Several of the artists work with texts, such as Jenny Holzer, who shows her elaborately programmed electronic signs; Barbara Kruger, whose graphic works combine text and images to question American ideals; and Tim Rollins & K.O.S., who produce images inspired by well-known novels. The gallery has several artists who work in the minimalist tradition, such as German artist Imi Knoebel, who combines large wooden panels into austere geometric configurations; John McCracken, whose new work consists of free standing stainless steel pieces with highly reflective surfaces; and Richard Serra, whose monumental steel arcs take advantage of the Hoffman Gallery's large exhibition space. Well-established painters are also carried by the gallery, like A. R. Penck and David Salle.

The Fred Hoffman Gallery also shows the work of John M. Armleder, Ross Bleckner, Vernon Fisher, Glenn Goldberg, Michael Heizer, Ilya Kabakov, Gerald Kamitaki, John M. Miller, Harvey Quaytman, Ulrich Ruckriem, Peter Schuyff, Sean Scully, Doug Wheeler and Michele Zalopany.

[216] KRYGIER/LANDAU CONTEMPORARY ART

2114 Broadway, Santa Monica, CA 90404 (213) 453-0086

Tues-Sat: 10-5 *Owners:* Irit Krygier, Susan Landau

The gallery began in 1984 and emphasized works by the new generation of Los Angeles painters. In 1989, Krygier/Landau moved to a new 5000-square-foot. space, also expanding its artistic concentration, and today specializes in avant-garde painting, sculpture and photography by Los Angeles and New York artists.

The gallery represents the painters Manny Farber, John Mandel, Dan McCleary, Richard Sedivy, and has recently added David Humphrey, Robin Palanker and Nancy Reese. McCleary's work is representational and painterly, while Humphrey twists the psychoanalytically-inspired conventions of surrealism.

Krygier/Landau has begun to show sculpture and photography, and represents Stephen Berens, Diane Buckler, Barbara Kasten and Masayki Oda.

The gallery as also begun to represent a group of recent M.F.A. graduates from Art Center School and California Institute of the Arts, Lynn Aldrich, Rachel Lachowicz, Kirk Miller and Peter Seidler. These artists have added a conceptual edge to the gallery. Aldrich's works, for example, re-create fragments of well-known paintings and then change them into strange, upholstered objects.

Krygier/Landau also represents the artists Kai Bob Cheng and Joe Clower. The gallery features prints by many major contemporary American artists, and is active in the secondary (resale) market.

[217] RICHARD KUHLENSCHMIDT GALLERY

1634 17th St., Santa Monica, CA 90404
(213) 450-2010

Tues-Sat: 11-5:30 *Owner/Dir:* Richard Kuhlenschmidt

The Kuhlenschmidt Gallery deals in conceptual and post-conceptualist works. Several of the artists represented are much discussed by writers of art theory, and are frequently included in major exhibitions of post-conceptual art such as "A Forest of Signs" at the Museum of Contemporary Art in Los Angeles.

A wide variety of media are used by the artists. Mitchell Syrop, for example, combines texts and photography in works that resemble, but question, advertising; while Allan McCollum makes sculptures of simple, reduced and repeated forms that complicate the boundary between creativity and commodity.

Jim Ebner's highly finished paintings also resemble commercial factory products. Jim Isermann paints colorful, playful tributes to 1960s Pop and Op art. Barbara Bloom makes installations, such as *Esprit de l'Escalier*, that question the reliability of our perceptions of objects.

The gallery also represents Nayland Blake, James Casebere, Douglas Huebler, Louise Lawler, Thomas Lawson, Matt Mullican and James Welling.

[218] MERGING ONE GALLERY

1547 Sixth Street, Santa Monica, CA 90401
(213) 395-0033

Owner: Diana Wong *Dir:* Diana Wong, Meibao Nee

Specializing in painting, sculpture, photography and prints, Merging One Gallery concentrates on the work of emerging artists. Among the variety of art work represented by the gallery is a wide range of contemporary abstract art by such painters as Kay Omata, Stephanie Weber and Diana Wong. Sculptors include Jeffrey Laudenslager, whose metal works form precariously balanced illusions, Karlin Wong working in wood and stone, and Enrico Bonizzato, who makes spheres and pyramids out of bronze. Fine art photographers Jerry Burchfield, Joyce Neimanas and Sheila Pinkel push the limits of their medium, all creating work without the means of a camera. Burchfield and Neimanas make color and black-and-white photograms respectively, and Pinkel makes composites of xeroradiographs. Other artists include painter and assemblage artist Shannon Landis, mixed-media painters Joe Grant and Linda Vallejo, Judith Spiegel and Junko Chodos.

[219] MEYERS/BLOOM GALLERY

2112 Broadway, Santa Monica, CA 90404
(213) 829-0062

Tues-Sat: 10-5 *Owners:* Jeanne Meyers, Ruth Bloom
Dir: Mary Artino

The Meyers/Bloom Gallery's attempts "to show work that challenges both the intellect and the eye, and extends the boundaries of convention." The gallery exhibits work by contemporary artists in all media, several of whom have produced elaborate installation pieces inside the gallery. The gallery seeks out artists who present a particular world view in a challenging representation.

Rod Baer's realistic, but rusted, installations of steel sculpture playfully address the interplay of meaning and time. Gretchen Bender creates large scale multimedia works that deal with aesthetic and political issues. Nancy Dwyer reconstitutes words into paintings and sculptures. Karl Matson's sculptural groupings of small objects complicate the distinction between toys and weapons. Jack Ox's paintings translate classical musical scores onto canvas. Large installations have been produced by Craig Stecyk, who converted the gallery temporarily into a duck preserve; and George Stone, who takes abstract and disturbing themes such as violence and death and makes them intensely personal.

The artists represented come from Los Angeles, New York and many foreign countries. In addition to those mentioned above, they include Troy Brauntuch, Steven Dobbin, Gilbert & George, Jerry Kearns, Bertrand Lavier, Leonel Moura, Susan Rankaitis and Boyd Webb.

[220] NATOLI-ROSS GALLERY

2110 Broadway, Santa Monica, CA 90404
(213) 453-6662

Tues-Sat: 10-6 *Owner/Dir:* Andrea Ross, Richard Natoli

The gallery handles in contemporary fine art, specializing in sculpture and paintings by emerging and some mid-career artists. The gallery represents Ron Cooper's unique bronze "portrait vases." Rafe Affleck creates large-scale site-specific steel and water sculptures. Betty Gold, also a sculptor, is internationally known for her large scale abstract steel pieces. Painter James G. Davis shows strong painterly and emotional figurative works on canvas. Jerald Silva, a master of the watercolor technique, works in large figurative and landscape imagery.

The Natoli-Ross Gallery also represents Deborah Baca, Bob Haozous, Howard Hersh, Carlos Quinto Kemm, John Massee, C.A. Michel, Brian O'Connor, Jan Isak Saether, Bill Schenck, Charles Villiers, R. Lee White, Steve Lapin, Richard Beckman, Carl Johansen and Michael Hart.

[221] PENCE GALLERY

908 Colorado Ave., Santa Monica, CA 90401
(213) 393-0069

Tues-Fri: 10-6; Sat: 11-5 *Owner:* Putter Pence *Dir:* Christopher Ford

Pence Gallery specializes in contemporary art from new and emerging as well as mid-career artists. The gallery shows painting, photography and sculpture in all media.

Cam Slocum's paintings are derived from photographs, then mediated through various processes and layers of varnish to evoke the blurring selectivity of history. The layered mediation of familiar photographs also characterizes the work of Paul Laster, who covers the images with veils of collaged texts. David Levinthal makes very large polaroid photographs of small toys, such as cowboys, creating images that are, paradoxically, filled with both cynicism and wonder.

Creighton Michael makes delicate, abstract, sculpture out of wood and cloth; while Shauna Peck makes sculpture that is no less delicate, but out of bronze. Ann Preston's large sculptures and wall reliefs are filled with subtle and sensual references to the female body.

Other artists featured by Pence Gallery include Phoebe Adams, Cliff Benjamin, Tom Butter, Tom Knechtel, John Monti and Sabina Ott.

[222] ROY BOYD GALLERY

1547 10th St., Santa Monica, CA 90401
(213) 394-1210

Tues-Sat: 10-5:30 *Owner:* Roy Boyd *Dir:* Richard Telles

The Gallery specializes in contemporary art with an emphasis on emerging American artists. Work in all media is represented, from photography, to painting, to installation.

Photographer Eileen Cowin depicts simple, staged scenes that have complex references to art history, films and inter-personal psychology. Connie Hatch uses photography to combine conceptual and feminist approaches. The geometric, abstract paintings of David French portray the patterns of Universal Price Codes; while Eric Magnuson silkscreens imagery derived from sign painting. David Bunn creates site-specific installations around the theme of controlled viewing, drawing on his background in photography. Buzz Spector shows objects made from altered books that evoke the interplay of personal and social history.

[223] SCHWARTZ CIERLAK GALLERY

3015 Main St., Santa Monica, CA 90405
(213) 396-3814

Wed-Sun: 11-6 *Owners:* Yvonne Schwartz, Clark Cierlak *Dir:* Clark Cierlak

The gallery specializes in emerging California painters and sculptors who work in a narrative or whimsical manner. The gallery's bright, open space is a showcase for several upbeat west coast artists known for their eclectic mix of contemporary iconoclastic pop. The pop-cartoon paintings of ZOX; the cerebral color patterns of Linda Smith and Ann Chernenko; the striking multi-dimensional hard-edge paintings and sculpture of Todd Gray; and the viewer interactive totem sculptures of Mark Bryan are among the works displayed at the gallery. The gallery also features many realist painters including the visually dramatic paintings of Carlos Perez; the photo-realist airbrush work of James Gucwa; and the exceptional detailed brush work of Wade Reynolds.

Known for its strong print department, the Schwartz Cierlak Gallery stocks a selection of contemporary and modern prints. Robert Rauschenberg, James Rosenquist, Matta and Marino Marini prints are continually featured in the Schwartz Cierlak Gallery, which also includes two print exhibitions in its yearly schedule of shows.

[224] SHOSHANA WAYNE GALLERY

1454 Fifth St., Santa Monica, CA 90401
(213) 451-3733

Tues-Fri: 10-6; Sat 11-5 *Owner:* Shoshana Blank *Dir:* David Pagel

The gallery specializes in contemporary paintings, sculpture and mixed-media work, with emphasis on works by emerging artists from California, New York and Europe.

The art shown is quite eclectic in style. Tom Savage's large, dark canvases resemble abstract painting, but reveal layers of microscopic, quasi-biological forms. Fay Jones, on the other hand, paints and collages colorful, childlike scenes that evoke a daydream filled with mystery. New York painter Joseph Nechvatal captures the overlapping, computer-generated visual information of the media age.

Sculptors with the gallery range from German artist Michael Schulze, whose poetic work is inspired by the California assemblage tradition; to Peter Millett, whose geometric wood sculptures are monochromatic and elegant. Mia Westerlund Roosen sculpts large, organic abstract pieces with sensual, active surfaces.

The gallery also represents Mari Andrews, Robert Bourdon, Jacqueline Dreager, Donald Fels, Colin Gray, Bogdan Perzynski, Deborah Remington and Jim Waid.

[225] SITE 311

1662 12th St., Santa Monica, CA 90404
(213) 450-5962

Mon-Fri: 9-5

see listing under Pacific Grove

[226] LEE SPIRO ASSOCIATES

840 18th St., No. 5, Santa Monica, CA 90403
(213) 828-2581

By appt. *Owner/Dir:* Lee Spiro

In general, the gallery shows works that are highly conceptual and expressionist in nature. Many of its exhibits feature sculptural works. These pieces represent a synthesis of surface and form and as such, relate to concerns at the mainstream of contemporary art. Among artists represented by the gallery are Jack Barl, Victor Spinski, Bennett Bean, Peter Van De Berg, Alex Segal, Robert Sperry and Patti Warashina.

The gallery is the exclusive agent for Magdalena and Michael Frimkess, whose works are represented in major public collections, including the Smithsonian Institute, the National Museum of Modern Art in Kyoto and the Oakland Museum. Their works are classic vessel forms characterized by a cultural hybridization that meld Chinese, Greek and native American influences. Its classic form is juxtaposed with the iconographic imagery of its surface, which depicts appropriated cartoon icons and other pop imagery. Ultimately, these works represent an effort to take classical form and redefine it in a post-modernist sense.

[227] TATISTCHEFF GALLERY, INC.

1547 10th Street, Santa Monica, CA 90401
(213) 395-8807

Owner: Terrence Rogers and Tatistcheff NYC *Dir:* Terrence Rogers

Tatistcheff shares its lobby with another reputable fine art gallery amidst a cluster of newly arrived galleries in Santa Monica. Both the Santa Monica gallery and Tatistcheff's New York gallery specialize in contemporary American representational painting and works on paper.

An emphasis is placed upon work that illuminates the unique nature of the 20th century American experience. For example, in Simeon Lagodich's landscape paintings the pastoral views of Southern California's mountains and valleys also reveal the urban sprawl to be found there. Another landscape painter, John Griswold, makes paintings of what at first appear to be ruins of Roman villas, but are in fact still lifes of hardware and other objects painted in faux finishes and set up outdoors against grassy hills and rocks to resemble an Italian scene.

Major gallery artists working with the figure include Lincoln Perry, Tina Barney and Kent Bellows. Other

Karl Benjamin, *#1, 1987,* 63 x 45, oil on canvas.
Courtesy: Ruth Bachofner Gallery, Santa Monica, CA

Eileen Cowin, *untitled*, 1988, 5 x 4 , silver gelatin print. Courtesy: Roy Boyd Gallery, Santa Monica

landscape painters represented are Richard Crozier, William Clutz and Hank Pitcher. Other artists represented include Stephanie Sanchez, Adam Schnitzer, Harold Reddcliffe, Philip Geiger and George Harkins.

[228] TORTUE GALLERY
2917 Santa Monica Blvd., Santa Monica, CA 90404
(213) 828-8878

Tues-Sat: 11-5:30 *Owner/Dir:* Mallory Freeman

Tortue Gallery was established in 1969. The gallery specializes in contemporary painting, sculpture and works on paper, with an emphasis on Los Angeles artists. The artists represented include many long established figures and several younger emerging artists.

A wide stylistic range is represented. Joyce Treiman paints figurative, narrative canvases; as do Jon Swihart, Mark Stock and John Rose. The paintings of Jim Morphesis depict themes from Christian and Greek myth in an expressive style that verges on abstraction. Purely abstract work is represented by the paintings of Patrick Hogan, Allen Harrison and 1960s painter John Altoon; as well as the sculpture of Woods Davy and Michael Todd. The gallery also features works by realists such as Shirley Pettibone, James Murray, Arsen Roje and Daniel Douke.

Tortue Gallery also carries works by John De Andrea, Edie Ellis, Martin Facey, Robbert Flick, David Furman, Tom Lieber, Robert Natkin, Peter Saari and Tino Zago.

SARATOGA

[229] YOUNG GALLERY
14440 Big Basin Way, Saratoga, CA 95070
(408) 741-1900

Tues-Fri: 10-4; by appt. *Owner:* Farley Young *Dir:* Edna Young

The Young Gallery is located in the Village of Saratoga, near the foothills of the Santa Cruz mountains. Exhibitions feature both local and nationally-recognized artists.

The focus of the Young Gallery is neither abstract nor representational, but rather a presentation of consistently high-quality work.

The gallery features four to six shows per year, interspersing one-person exhibitions with thematic group shows and installations.

Recent exhibitions have included intaglio and lithographic prints, small sculpture, paintings, artists toys and raku-fired ceramics.

SAUSLITO

[230] DJ'S, THE ARTS AND CRAFTS SHOP
1417 Bridgeway, Sausalito, CA 94965 (415) 331-2552

Tues-Sat: 9:30-5:30 or by appt. *Owner/Dir:* D.J. Puffert

This gallery represents American arts and crafts from the early 1900s Arts and Crafts Movement. Primary focus is on furniture, lamps and pottery. Also on display are paintings, Navaho rugs and other textiles. All pieces are authentic. Furniture designs by Greene and Greene are featured. Also featured are Tiffany lamps, copper objects (lamps, mica shades, etc.) by Dirk van Erp , and items by Gustav Stickley , L. & J.G. Stickley, and Stickley Brothers. Pieces by Roy Croft and by Limbert are featured as well. Every October the gallery sells period furniture, pottery, metal crafts, light-

ing, painting, textiles and photography at an auction at the Ebel Club, Los Angeles. Quality period items are accepted on consignment. Auction catalogs and videos on the history of the Arts and Crafts Movement are sold. This gallery tries to offer the most well-rounded selection of arts and crafts material in America.

SHERMAN OAKS

[231] ORLANDO GALLERY
14553 Ventura Blvd., Sherman Oaks, CA 91403
(213) 789-6012

Tues-Sat: 10-4 *Owner:* Orlando *Dir:* Robert Gino

The gallery has supported experimental forms such as mail art, sound art, xerography, video, microfiche, performance art and process art since its opening in 1958. Distinguished exhibitions include such artists as José Clemente Orozco a primary force in Mexican mural art; and Ben Shahn, a social realist who is most noted for his gouache series on the trial of Sacco and Vanzetti. Artists presently exhibiting at Orlando gallery work in various styles of figurative paintings, watercolors, drawings and pastels. Realists include: Don Lagerberg, Susan Clover, Ruth Bavetta, Ester Reeves, Stuart Caswell and Walt Impert. Impressionists include: Dona Windbiel, Jesse Bunch, Vicki Livingston, Michael Hickman, Susan Santiago, Michael Lloyd, Stanley Wilson and John Carter. Surrealists include: Pan Mower Conner and Ernest Velardi. Artists working in mixed media, paint, collage, construction and book work) include Edie Danieli Ellis, Philip Orlando, Len Poteshman, Lynne Westmore and Vida Hackmen. Abstract painters working in various subjects are: Enzo Paligyi, Chris Mooridian and Michael Moon. Metal sculpture by Robert Gino is featured. Nancy Quinn and James Budde work in ceramic sculpture. Figurative sculpture by Richard Bauer is also shown. Also on view is a permanent collection of art from West Africa.

STINSON BEACH

[232] CLAUDIA CHAPLINE GALLERY
3445 Shoreline Hwy., P. O. Box 946, Stinson Beach, CA 94970 (415) 868-2308

Fri-Sun: 12-5 and by appt. , *G# 231Owner/Dir:* Claudia Chapline

Founded in March 1987, the Claudia Chapline Gallery features contemporary painting, sculpture and drawing, focusing on the works of northern California artists.

The gallery presents the art of photo-surrealist painter Jim Alford, the watercolors of mystical poet/painter John Brandi, the watercolor landscapes of Whitson Cox, and the ceramic sculpture or "archetypal ancestral figures" of Gillian Hodge. Claudia Chapline also features the paintings of photorealist James Warren Perry and the suburban cartoon paintings of his alter-ego "Sal." The gallery also exhibits the paintings of symbolist painter Billy Rose and the scroll paintings and pastel works of Harold Schwarm, a fusion painter who combines eastern and western influences. The gallery also shows the contemporary, expressionist, figurative sculpture of Peter Schifrin and the impressionist drawings and prints of Gary Smith, whose takes as his subject matter primarily the landscapes of west Marin County. Also shown are the neo-primitive, folk-art-influenced paintings and sculpture of Gary Stephens.

The Claudia Chapline Gallery is located on the Shoreline Highway just below Mt. Tamalpais and offers four exhibit areas, lit with skylights, and an outdoor sculpture gallery.

VENICE

[233] L.A. LOUVER GALLERY

55 N. Venice Blvd., & 77 Market St., Venice, CA 90291 (213) 822-4955

Tues-Sat: 11-5 (55 N. Venice); 12-5 (77 Market) *Owner/Dir:* Peter Goulds, Kimberly Davis

L.A. Louver gallery, founded in 1976, is in the heart of a neighborhood that has been an artist's community for four decades. The gallery shows contemporary art by well-established artists from Los Angeles, New York, Chicago and other parts of the country, as well as many artists from London, Paris, Rome, Berlin and other European cities. Through solo and group shows, the gallery emphasizes the international perspective of the art.

Los Angeles artists are well represented by leading abstract painter Ed Moses, veteran figurative painter Charles Garabedian, and rising sculptor Peter Shelton, whose bronze pieces are humorous visual puns on the human body. The gallery has organized survey shows on the Dada artists, for example, to give historical context to gallery artists in the Dada and assemblage tradition. These artists include George Herms, Ed and Nancy Reddin Kienholz, Wallace Berman and William Wiley. In a similar manner, British painting surveys have given context to gallery artists David Hockney, Leon Kossoff and John Walker; and an show of artists from Rome gave context to painter Domenico Bianchi.

In addition to the above, L.A. Louver represents Terry Allen, Tony Berlant, Eduardo Carrillo, Michael Goldberg, Robert Helm, Lee Jaffe, Robert Janz, Wesley Kimler, Bernd Koberling, Judith Linhares, Sandra Mendelsohn-Rubin, David Nash, Richard Shaffer, Rich Stich, Don Suggs, James Surls and Tom Wudl.

WEST HOLLYWOOD

[234] CAZ GALLERY

8715 Melrose Ave., West Hollywood, CA 90069 (213) 623-6724

Tues-Fri: 11-7; Sat: 11-5 *Owner:* Carol Lopes *Dir:* Neva Jakich

The gallery specializes in Australian Aboriginal art. Traditional sand paintings are executed in the more permanent materials of acrylic on canvas, but retain the familiar Western Desert "dot" style. Natural ochres are used to color stringbark paintings and wood carvings. The paintings and carvings depict the symbolic landscape and figures of the "dreaming" that is depicted not only by the art but by the society's songs and rituals. The artists do not stand out from the rest of the culture as "stars," so the gallery tends to show the work in group exhibitions.

Many artists are shown, including Clifford Possum Japaljarri, Michael Nelson Jakamarra, Billy Stockman, Turkey Tolson Jupurrula and Alison Anderson Nampijinpa.

The large, 5,500-square-foot gallery is occasionally divided in half; the back gallery features works by non-Aboriginal artists such as the painter Damian Elwes.

WESTLAKE VILLAGE

[235] MAURICE-HEYMAN FINE ARTS

813 Rimcrest Dr., Westlake Village, CA 91361 (805) 495-8601

Mon-Fri: 9-5 *Owner/Dir:* Joanie Heyman

Maurice-Heyman Fine Arts deals in original, fine quality contemporary art as well as native American contemporary art. Owner/director Joanie Heyman is not a conventional dealer but a corporate art consultant who "line[s] up the artist with the company product, the image the company wants and the budget the company has." For instance, she placed works of a fabric sculptor with a furniture manufacturer and brought people in the music industry together with a painter whose expressionistic works are a physical representation of the feelings he experienced while listening to rock-and-roll-music.

Heyman is currently writing *Message from Turtle Island as found in the Art of the People*, a book on contemporary native American artists. She plans to donate the book's profits to the Museum of the Institute of American Indian Arts in New Mexico. These activities have given her access to some of the finest contemporary native American Art in the United States.

A.B., ORLANDO (Painter)
c/o Engman Ltd., 1492 Cost Hwy., Laguna Beach.,
CA 92651

Born: 1946 *Collections:* Gannett Publishing,
Washington D.C.; Penn Central Corporation *Exhibitions:* Engman Limited Fine Arts, Laguna Beach; Jacqueline Westbrook Gallery, La Jolla *Dealer:* Engman
Ltd., Laguna Beach

With no further training than his own creative instincts, this Columbian born artist developed a rich
artistic vocabulary and a distinctive style. His themes
explore inner growth, and aspects of the human condition. Applauded by critics for bringing a sense of
humanism to the contemporary format, his images
radiate the emotional, spiritual and intellectual characteristics of the artist himself. Dynamic brush strokes
and vivid palette choices reveal his enjoyment of the
process. He combines various media with an effortless
understanding of what each piece requires. Some
works have employed unexpected pieces of Tarlatan,
birch bark or sheet music for definition. The spontaneous feel of his abstract backgrounds balances his
stylized human figures.

ABBEY, RITA DEANIN (Painter, Sculptor)
5850 N. Park St., Las Vegas, NV 89129

Born: 1930 *Awards:* Governor's Art Award for the
State of Nevada *Collections:* Palm Springs Desert
Museum; Nevada Museum of Art, Reno, NV *Exhibitions:* Palm Springs Desert Museum; U. of Nevada,
Las Vegas *Education:* U. of New Mexico; Hans Hofmann School of Fine Arts

Her strong affinity for the American Southwest is apparent in the light, color, space, form and texture of
her brightly colored abstractions. As a youth, she
studied realistic painting and sculpture. In college, she
developed an interest in abstract expressionism. By the
early 1950s, when she studied with Hans Hofmann,
she had enhanced her awareness of color and form. In
addition to figurative and abstract paintings in oil and
acrylic, she has investigated and produced large bodies
of work in drawing, printmaking, sculpture, plexiglas,
fiberglass, polyester resin and, most recently, porcelain
enamel fired on steel panels and hammered relief
shapes.

ABEL, W. (Painter, Mixed Media Artist)
P.O. Box 134, Berry Creek, CA 95916

Born: 1949 *Awards:* Honorable Mention, California
Expo *Exhibitions:* Herb Shop, Nevada City; C & R'S
Dragonfly, Brownsville *Dealer:* C & R's Dragonfly,
Brownsville

A self-taught artist, he has explored a variety of disciplines and media. His own surrealist style has
developed from interests in Max Ernst and Salvador
Dali. His paintings feature recognizable, often highly
commercial, figures in unusual combinations. As an
effort to portray his dreams, these groupings of images
incorporate pointillism, abstraction and realism,
through the use of a vivid palette of pencil, watercolor,
pens and ink.

ABELES, KIM VICTORIA (Sculptor)
2401 Santa Fe, #100, Los Angeles, CA 90058

Born: 1952 *Awards:* Purchase Award, American
Academy and Institute of Arts & Letters *Collections:*
California State U. Art Museum, Long Beach;
Fashion Institute of Design and Merchandising, Los
Angeles *Exhibitions:* Karl Bornstein Gallery, Los Angeles; A.I.R. Gallery, NYC *Education:* UC-Irvine;
Ohio U. *Dealer:* Karl Bornstein Gallery, Los Angeles;
Anuska Gallery, San Diego

Employing acrylic, enamel, wood, photography, metal,
X-rays and found objects, her work is a combination
of painting, mixed media sculpture, photography and
narrative. Early sculptures consisted of kimonos that
were suspended from the ceiling as personas housing
visual narratives on the "human condition." Later
works incorporate the human form in what become
biographical portraits balancing fact and fiction, historical remembrance, created images and truth. Her
installation *The Image of St. Bernadette* explores the
intrusion into and exploitation of the life of Bernadette
Soubirous, a mid-19th century French saint. The
various mixed media pieces, including knick-knacks,
souvenirs, busts of the saint, paintings and odd contraptions create a shrine imbued with reverence while
at the same time mocking and condemning the inevitable cheapening and destruction of the spiritual
beauty of saintliness which Bernadette embodied. In
other works as well, history and historical personae
play an important role. She often removes objects
from their original contexts, placing them, for instance,
in glass cases and boxes. "I juxtapose the artificial with
the real, the 'artificial' becoming its own reality," she
says.

ABRISHAMI, HESAM (Painter)
18801 Kefurick, Redesa, CA 91335

Born: 1951 *Collections:* Brea Civic Cultural Center
Exhibitions: San Bernardino Museum; UCLA

By the late 1970s, he had developed the expressionist,
figurative style that characterizes his work. He paints
in primary colors, using acrylics on paper. His imagery
is drawn from his Middle Eastern heritage and
numerous trips to Europe.

ACCONCIA, CARMINE (Painter)
1518 9th Ave., San Francisco, CA 94122

Born: 1955 *Exhibitions:* Brazilian Consulate of San
Francisco; Artists Society International Gallery, San
Francisco *Education:* U. of San Paulo

The composition of his earlier works reflects his formal
training in mathematics. Surrealist forms gave way to
visionary landscapes after his move to California in
1982. Influenced by mid-19th century American artists
Thomas Cole, Elihu Vedder and William Rimmer, the
scenery in these paintings is always obstructed by an
intrusive, man-made object, reflecting our tendency to
upset the balance of nature by imposing artificial elements. He has continued to explore this idea since his
switch from watercolor and pastel on paper to oil on
canvas. Recent studies of the deforestation of his native Brazil mix recognizable details with abstractions to
produce a subconscious effect. Earthtones and red
oranges are often used, wide lines and warm colors
give a strong sense of organic pattern. Massive realistic
figures are attracted towards a golden triangle, in
which images become more abstract. His original
brush technique is largely informed by the work of
artists Frederic E. Church and Joseph M. William
Turner.

ACCURSO, JOHN (Printmaker)
8 Wanflete Ct., Orinda, CA 94563

Born: 1963 *Exhibitions:* Worth Ryder Gallery,
Berkeley *Education:* UC-Berkeley

Bill Anderson, *Thundering Herd,* 24 x 48, oil. Courtesy: Lodi Art Gallery, Pasadena

Rita Deanin Abbey, *Cascades, A-44,* 69 x 45, porcelain enamel fired on steel

Maria Alquilar, *Dressing for the Exhibit,* various works in clay with mixed media. Courtesy: John Pence Gallery, San Francisco

His career began with etching, which form, in turn, influenced his drawing; he continues to develop both his printmaking and drawing skills. Recently, he has been working on large charcoal drawings and colored pastels. These are landscape based: some are desert scenes, some feature a spaceship and the planet Saturn. Most are black and white or monochromatic. Many of the drawings are rendered one atop another, with parts of the layers sanded away. The images lie somewhere between super-realism and surrealism. He cites Christopher Brown and Larry Thomas as influences.

ACE, KATHERINE (Painter, Printmaker)
50 Claremont Ave., Orinda, CA 94563

Born: 1953 *Awards:* NEA Congressional Presentation; Grumbacher Gold Medallion Award, Batavia Annual National Exhibition *Collections:* Oakland Children's Hospital; AT&T, New Jersey *Exhibitions:* Rockford International Biennial; Spiritual Art Annual *Education:* Knox College

A portraitist, she has studied the techniques of Rembrandt, Da Vinci and Sargent. She was commissioned by a large publishing company to paint a series of famous composers, in her unique "classical" style. Her philosophical series, "Face to Face," began with studies in ink, gesso, watercolor and pastel, and were developed into powerful oil paintings. "Face to Face" combines Christian and Jewish myths, to depict a civilized humanity that must confront error before attaining transcendence. Her current series of strong, simple drawings on the Book of Job are reminiscent both of William Blake and Greek pottery painting.

ADAMS, FREDI, S.W.A. (Painter, Mixed Media Artist)
31 McAllister Ave., Kentfield, CA 94904

Born: 1919 *Awards:* Artist of the Year Trophy and Signature Award, Society of Western Artists *Exhibitions:* Retrospective Exhibit, Civic Center, San Rafael; Gallery on Main, St. Helena *Education:* Pratt Institute

She is best known for her most recent series, recreations of Paleolithic cave paintings on a two- to three-inch-thick marble impression material of her own creation. These pieces feature stylized, representational prehistoric animals in a combination of cool hues and earth tones. She wants these pieces to be felt as well as seen. She also makes watercolor and acrylic paintings, which display the spontaneity and sensitivity epitomized by the Impressionists. These works often take the form of office or home murals. She prepares for them by carefully studying the room's light source before rendering the subject matter. She incorporates calligraphy to integrate the pattern for a pleasing effect.

ADAMS, LISA (Painter)
2040 Glencoe Way, Los Angeles, CA 90068

Born: 1955 *Awards:* Millard Sheets Art Scholarship *Exhibitions:* Newspace Gallery, Los Angeles; SoHo Center for Visual Artists, NYC *Education:* Claremont Graduate School *Dealer:* Joni Gordon, Newspace Gallery, Los Angeles

Her early biomorphic abstractions, influenced by Tom Wudl, were painted with a thin, almost poster-like look in acrylic. In 1981, she moved from Venice Beach to SoHo and began experimenting with acrylic landscapes on carpet. The canvases that followed were recognizable, almost surreal combinations of landscape and still life. Now living in Los Angeles, she is working on a more sophisticated version of her earlier biomorphic abstractions. These pieces have an animated imagery that bring to mind a kind of landscape/still life feel, none of which is intentionally recognizable. With large mudding knives, she applies a combination of acrylic paint and modeling paste to stretched canvas. She follows this with thin layers of oil applied with a palette knife and then with cut-outs of linoleum affixed with caulking.

ADAMS, LOREN (Painter)
P.O. Box 5688, Carmel, CA 93921

Collections: Leggett & Platt, Inc.; Sammy and Betsy Hagar *Exhibitions:* Lahaina Galleries, Maui; Connoisseurs Gallery

In his formative years, the artist was influenced by the Old Masters, and later by the Hudson River school—particularly the sense of grandeur in the latter's paintings. Early works were accomplished marine and seascapes. Later, he developed a love for the surrealism of Magritte, Escher and Dali, and began working in a new style of "classic surrealism." These later works, part of the "Accelerated Evolution" series, are painted with extreme technical virtuosity and reflect a historical, intellectual and mathematical perspective. The artist normally creates a smaller oil study on silk in preparation for the major work, in addition to Cibachrome prints. The works embody symbols of antiquity based on spiritual ideals and are inspired by a fascination with archaeology, ancient sacred symbols, mystery schools and evidence of lost cultures and civilizations, for instance, the theories discussed in the writings of Col. James Churchward on the lost continent of "Mu" or "Lemuria." In the later works, the sea becomes a backdrop; the fascination with grandeur also remains.

ADAMS, MARSHA RED (Photographer)
P.O. Box 1042, San Rafael, CA 94915

Born: 1948 *Collections:* Security Pacific; Sonoma State University *Exhibitions:* Oakland Center for the Visual Arts; San Francisco Camerawork *Education:* UC-Irvine

Following formal training in sculpture, her work began to take the form of installation, which then led into art performance. The need to document performances begat an interest in photography, and she has concentrated her work within that medium since the mid-1970s. Her first photographic work took the form of large, hand-colored photo-collages and later, multiple prints that often incorporated language. Of late, the work is a balance between art performance, installation and the photographic image. Exhibits often include all three media as aesthetically interrelated. *At Odd,* a photographic installation, features twenty-two black-and-white photographs of solid white silhouettes of men and women in natural landscapes. At the center of the installation is a group of life-size silhouettes with rocks and dead plants brought in from the desert. The various scenes have feminist overtones, but these are not strident—more important are issues of the relationships of human beings to the landscape, language to photography, and figure to field.

ADAMS, NANCY (Ceramist)
10 Creamery Rd., San Geronimo, CA 94963

Born: 1948 *Awards:* Finalist, Art Quest *Exhibitions:* American Ceramics Now, Crocker Art Museum; Del

Loren Adams, *The Magic Spell of Sun Lady(detail),* 12 x 12, lithograph.
Courtesy: Mr. & Mrs. Sammy Hagar

Loren Adams, *The Magic Spell of Sun Lady,* 12 x 12, lithograph.
Courtesy: Mr. & Mrs. Sammy Hagar

Mano Gallery, Los Angeles *Education:* City College of San Francisco *Dealer:* Clay Pot, Brooklyn, NY; Del Mano Gallery, Los Angeles

In the early 1970s, she made high-fire porcelain pieces in the tradition of Sung Dynasty ceramics. She then studied the work of Adelaide Robineau and Maria Martinez, gradually becoming more aware of the American sense of ceramics. By 1982, she switched to a white earthenware medium and a low-firing temperature. She combined the vessel form with animal and vegetable motifs and developed an innovative technique for using the air-brush to apply underglazes. She now uses the airbrush to apply multiple layers of glaze and underglaze. This has allowed her to develop a wide palette of colors and textures. She now combines the vessel form with motifs of corn, grapes, leaves, cactuses and animals.

ADAN, SUZANNE (Painter)
3977 Rosemary Circle, Sacramento, CA 95821

Born: 1946 *Awards:* Purchase Award, Crocker Museum *Collections:* Continental Bank, Houston; Crocker Museum, Sacramento *Exhibitions:* Whitney Museum, NYC; Betsy Rosenfield Gallery, Chicago *Education:* California State U., Sacramento *Dealer:* John Berggruen Gallery, San Francisco

The most obvious influences on her work are the Native American folk tradition and the school of Chicago artists who create art out of fantastic images. During her early period, she tended to paint either fantastic images or pure abstracts, but as she progressed, she turned to mixing the two styles within the same paintings. Against abstract patchwork friezes, she placed small, fantastic images that seemed to float over the background. At first producing small paintings in this style, she moved toward the panoramic, creating long paintings that can be "read" as easily from right to left as they can be from left to right. Her paintings are filled with strange creatures emanating from her own imagination; they resemble bestiaries as they might have been imagined in a medieval monastery filled with particularly superstitious monks. She uses small brushstrokes to create a rich texture reminiscent of a quilt or a tapestry.

ADCOCK, CHRISTINA and MICHAEL (Mixed Media Artists)
P.O. Box 31109, Santa Barbara, CA 93130

Born: 1949 *Exhibitions:* Elizabeth Fortner Gallery, Santa Barbara; Del Mano Gallery, Pasadena *Education:* (Michael) UC-Santa Cruz

He worked for several years as a functional potter, while she studied various weaving and basketry techniques in the Los Padros National Forest, and in Arizona with the Papago Indians. In the early 1980s, they joined their talents to create a unique collaboration of sagger-fired stoneware vessels and natural fibers. Over the years, they have developed many techniques for combining the primitive, earthy effects of sagger/smoke finish stoneware with a wide variety of indigenous natural fibers. These are often dyed several times, then woven, coiled and lashed with raw silks. Pine needles, date palm fruit stalks, sea grass, birch bark, river willow, cottonwood and other fibers are used. The primitive materials, synthesized with the subtle colors and sophisticated designs, help to reveal and emphasize the natural beauty of the materials.

ADELE, SISTER (Photographer)
1520 Grand Ave., San Rafael, CA

Born: 1915 *Awards:* Design International *Collections:* Bibliotheque Nationale, Paris; San Francisco Museum of Modern Art *Exhibitions:* Pittsburgh Plan for Art; Honolulu Academy of Art *Education:* UC-Berkeley

An English professor at California State University for ten years, she entered the Dominican Convent of San Rafael in 1950. In 1974, she was named Artist-In-Residence at Dominican College. She is fascinated with the difference between photography as a craft and photography as an art. She uses photomontage to transform original images into new realities. Subtitling all of her series "Counterpoint Imagery," she works with harmony and opposition—juxtaposing differing components within a single image. Summer and winter are combined, as are man-made and organic forms. Throughout her work, man and nature are common themes: man being represented by subjective devices, and nature by textural ones.

ADELL, CARRIE (Fine Jeweler, Sculptor)
53 Canyon Rd., San Anselmo, CA 94960

Born: 1931 *Awards:* Design, Diamonds Today Competition *Collections:* Berndt Munsteiner Collection; Archdiocese of Missouri *Exhibitions:* Smithsonian Institute; E. Potter Gallery *Education:* Hunter College; Art Students League *Dealer:* Elaine Potter

Formally trained in painting and art history, she moved from two-dimensional media to pottery and then to metalsmithing. Organic images from nature and nature's underlying geometric structure appear in her jewelry. Through casting, she has explored modular designs and forged mobile, flexible and interactive riveted forms for the metallic body of the jewelry. Preservation of the planet is the underlying theme of her recent work. The hollow-formed, "marriage-of-metals" touchstones emphasize the wearer's connection to the Earth. She uses elaborately patterned jewels with inlaid, overlaid and laminated surfaces of patinaed metals, recalling her earlier explorations of painterly spontaneity. The wearable sculptures employ a wide variety of materials ranging from pebbles to precious stones. Palladium, shakudo and gold are patterned, seamed and married together in a recent series that includes strands of pearls intended to be fingered as worry beads. Among her major works is *A Greenhouse Winter*, based on NASA satellite photography of the ocean surrounding Antarctica. The collar is studded with sapphires representing expanses of sea water surrounded by ice. One edge of the collar duplicates the contours of the Antarctic continent.

ADLER, JOCELYN (Painter, Draughtsperson)
378 E. Strawberry Dr., Mill Valley, CA 94941

Born: 1930 *Exhibitions:* Artisans Gallery, Mill Valley; Society of Western Artists, San Francisco

The subjects of her expressionist paintings and drawings include figures, abstractions and seascapes. Many of her works feature figures set in indistinct, ambiguous surroundings. Working in both oils and acrylics, she varies her palette according to what she determines is required by the subject. Travel to Italy and teaching have proved to be the most important influences on her style and artistic approach. Her current work expresses a spiritual quality, more quiet and somber than her earlier works.

Loren Adams, *Stabile–The Crystal Cave with The Jeweled Head of the Four Cosmic Forces (foreground), The Augmented Sea, Garden of Eden, The Motherland (background),* 36 x 48, wood carving, mixed media, oil on jeweled head, oil on canvas

Ruby Aranguiz L., *Staircase,* 16 x 19, enamel on copper

ADORNO, ZOE (Sculptor)
10599 Johansen Dr., Cupertino, CA 95014

Born: 1930 *Awards:* 1st Award, Vincent and Mary Price Gallery, Los Angeles; Special Award and 1st Award, Palo Alto Art Club *Exhibitions:* Olive Hyde Gallery, Fremont; San Jose Art League, Downtown Gallery

She began working with glass in the early 1950s. In 1978, while attending the Pilchuk School near Seattle, she discovered the material that has been her trademark for the last decade: dichroic glass. In a vacuum chamber, clear sheets of glass are treated with heat-evaporated metals, such as beryllium, chromium, selenium, silicon, titanium and yttrium. She then cuts the resulting thin, fragile, multicolored glass sheets according to a pre-planned design and fuses up to twenty of them in her home kiln. Because of the interaction of the metals, the available light and the laws of refraction and reflection, the glass appears to change color when viewed from different angles. In the past, her works have been large, circular plates decorated with strong, colorful designs. She is currently working on a series of rather large, freestanding animal figures.

AFFOLTER, JOHN (Painter)
359 Bowery 4, New York, NY 10003

Born: 1946 *Awards:* City College Research Grant, NYC *Collections:* Security Pacific Bank, Los Angeles *Exhibitions:* 112 Green St. Gallery, NYC *Education:* City College of New York; Cornish Institute, Seattle *Dealer:* Deson-Saunders Gallery, Chicago; Foster/White Gallery, Seattle

Working with abstracted landscapes, he pits the traditional content associated with landscape against the pure form of the canvas. Utilizing cut-up photographic elements containing landscape images, he creates a dialogue over the referent and its indiscriminate displacement in order to challenge the viewer's perception. Most of his images are derived from the schema found on the dipylon vases of the 8th-Century Greek geometric style, which became a focus of his interest during five years he spent in Greece. Aesthetic essays by the Russian literary critic Victor Schlovsky influenced the development of his philosophical theory based on deconstructivism; his landscapes examine the many aspects of place as a signifier and then deconstruct their meaning.

AINSLIE, HELEN KATHLEEN (Painter)
1076 Pebble Hills B., Suite 279, El Paso, TX 79935

Born: 1922 *Exhibitions:* National Watercolor Society Regional, Los Angeles; Society of Western Watercolor Artists, San Diego *Education:* U. of Florida; Park College, Kansas City, MO

She received training in oil painting as a child, and she first discovered abstraction at age sixteen. She began her mature career while pursuing an art education in Kansas City and taking a variety of art courses during a child-raising period from 1947 to 1962. Today, her rendering is an expressionist combination of fantasy and reality. She has a "Wildflower" series, an "Open Road" series, a "Cactus" series and groups of night paintings and non-objective paintings. Her works are always related to people she knows and most are symbolic in some way. Her colors range from the very bright to the very dark, and her media now include acrylics and transparent watercolors.

AISAWA, ROBERT (Painter)
9179 La Luna Ave., Fountain Valley, CA 92708

Born: 1953 *Exhibitions:* Rizzoli International Bookstore and Gallery, Costa Mesa; Print Works Gallery, Long Beach *Education:* Cal. State U. *Dealer:* L.A. Artcore, Los Angeles

His influences include a diverse group of artists—Duchamps, Rivers, Rauschenberg, Warhol—as well as elements of Japanese, folk and medieval art. These influences manifest themselves in his sense of color and composition. His energetic, primitive style is characterized by block-like, aggressive human forms rendered in surrealist colors. He often paints faces since their variety holds his interest. He prefers a canvas or masonite surface and works in latex, acrylics, gel, white ink, oil pastels, charcoal and colored pencils.

ALAIMO, TERRY M. (Painter, Draughtsperson)
P.O. Box 1142, Laguna Beach, CA 92652

Born: 1942 *Awards:* Chautauqua Art Institute Award for American Painting *Exhibitions:* Memorial Art Gallery, Rochester, NY; Laguna Beach Museum of Art *Education:* Rochester Institute of Technology *Dealer:* Terry M. Alaimo Studio, Laguna Beach

She began her professional career at the age of eight. Her first works were pastel still lifes and watercolor fashion designs. These led to landscapes, figurative paintings and a period of cartoons and satire. With the influences of Dali, DaVinci, Winslow Homer and Van Eyck, she explored the interaction of light and line that occurs when two colors are juxtaposed. This brought her art to a detailed, realistic style. She has become known as a strong realist and surrealist painter. Her paintings are statements about the times, the state of contemporary society, and what the future may hold. She paints with oils on gessoed masonite and builds up color through many thin layers. Her work today is best described as trompe l'oeil.

ALBA, BENNY (Painter)
6610 Heather Ridge Way, Oakland, CA 94611

Born: 1949 *Awards:* Merit Award, San Francisco Women Artists Gallery *Exhibitions:* Berkeley Art Center; Shared Visions, Berkeley *Education:* U. of Michigan

She began her career as an abstract colorist in the 1970s. Her oil paintings have since evolved and during the 1980s she made brilliantly colored, graphically strong commentaries involving the symbols she had developed during her study of prehistoric images. In a recent series she wittily juxtaposed ancient Mycenean figurines with kachinas, Navajo sand paintings, and roads that form trapezoids. Her recent works are large oil paintings and occasionally ink drawings. She has also researched and developed a method of permanently applying gold leaf to canvas.

ALBANESE, ROBERT (Painter, Sculptor)
P.O. Box 1104, Pebble Beach, CA 93953

Born: 1934 *Collections:* U. of Hawaii *Exhibitions:* Hawaii Library

He was influenced early in his career by the Abstract Expressionists; he now attempts to bring to light the phantasms of the mind. At first, his works suggested a visual remoteness in time through a sculptural and painterly combination of canvas, house paint, potting soil, sand, wood, metals and ceramic. Today, he con-

Robert Aisawa, *Barking Dogs,* 30 x 40,
mixed media collage on canvas

A.B., Orlando *Portrait of a Noble Woman,* 31 x 23, oil, acrylic
and resin on d'Arches paper. Courtesy: Engman Limited Fine Arts

tinues to sculpt in unconventional and non-objective ways. His recent work shows a concern with surface texture and represents a search for identity and expression. "The true beauty of the non-objective aspect is apprehended in the reflection of ideas beyond reason itself," he says.

ALBERTANO, LINDA J. (Performance Artist)
11 Wavecrest, Venice, CA 90291

Born: 1952 *Exhibitions:* John Anson Ford Theatre; Schoenberg Hall, UUCLA *Education:* UCLA *Dealer:* Cactus, Los Angeles

She studied filmmaking, but turned to jazz singing when she realized how difficult it would be to finance films with her earnings as a waitress. Club dates became performance art, when she amplified the meaning and context of her songs with light and slide displays, video projections, and other elements of movement and physical imagery. She considers herself "a contemporary troubador who puts these elements to use in documenting a cultural landscape pockmarked with skirmishes between the sexes or races." Unlike the work of other performance artists, her songs and performances concentrate more on the emotional, personal, and social sides of life than the state of contemporary art practice.

ALBRIDES, JOSEPH (Paper Weaver)
739 Seminole Way, Palo Alto, CA

Born: 1948 *Collections:* Balazs Analytical Laboratories, Inc., Mountain View; Burnside & Burnside, Palo Alto *Exhibitions:* Palo Alto Medical Foundation; Seipp Gallery, Palo Alto *Education:* Foothill College *Dealer:* Beth Christensen Fine Art, Tiburon; Suzanne Frazer Fine Art, Saratoga; Carol Dabb, Art Consultant, Mountain View

The son of Mexican immigrants, he is a self-taught artist, who, in 1982, created a form called weaving in paper. His works are brilliantly colored and often involve paint, fabric dye and previously colored materials. He begins the work by weaving together a variety of materials, including cotton, wool yarns, paper strips and paper inlays. He then adds paper pulp made from an assortment of rag papers. Finally he presses and dries the assemblage. He has studied art at Foothill College and has acquired skills and inspirations during his extensive travels throughout Central and South America and Europe. His work has been featured in *Fiber Arts Magazine.*

ALBUQUERQUE, LITA (Painter, Sculptor)
1670 Sawtelle Blvd., Los Angeles, CA 90025

Born: 1946 *Collections:* Los Angeles County Museum of Art; Newport Harbor Art Museum *Exhibitions:* Museum of Modern Art, NYC; San Francisco Museum of Modern Art *Education:* UCLA; Otis Art Institute *Dealer:* Janus Gallery, Los Angeles

Influenced by the Light and Space movement begun in California, she uses color, light and shadow to create a sense of mystery in color photographs, paintings and sculptures, employing natural elements such as metals, sand and stones. *The horizon is the place that maintains the memory,* for example, is a large copper circle mounted on a base made of pigment and stone; the circle casts refracted shadows on the wall, creating an enigmatic iconic structure.

ALCANTARA, JOHN G. (Painter)
513 N. Sycamore Ave., #6, Los Angeles, CA 90036

Born: 1940 *Exhibitions:* Tortue Gallery, Santa Monica; Summer Olympics, Seoul, Korea *Education:* California Art Institute; Laguna Beach Art School

Like many others, he claims Picasso as a major influence; but he finds that the simplicity and ideal serenity of oriental philosophy has made an even greater contribution to his art. Blending the influence of Sueo Serisawia, his mentor at Laguna Beach Art School, with his Latin upbringing has brought him to explore the color, dynamism and painterly techniques identified with to Latin expression. Working with oil and acrylics, as well as with graphite, he continues to search for order in the abstract. In light of oriental thought, he feels he achieves aesthetic meaning only when he reveals his understanding of nature by recreation and altering all that it is. To do this, he works to develop a space which draws the viewer to interact with the painting. Recent work is semi-figurative, featuring distorted figures and crucifixions, as symbols of the struggle on earth between good and evil.

ALDANA, CARL (Painter)
386 Ultimo, Long Beach, CA 90814

Born: 1938 *Awards:* Gold Medal & Award of Merit, Society of Illustrators, NYC *Exhibitions:* Municipal Art Gallery, LA; Roberts Gallery, Santa Monica *Education:* Santa Monica College; Cal. State-Long Beach

Though he has worked as an illustrator for such motion pictures as *Ferris Bueller's Day Off* and *Robocop,* his own paintings led him to create more austere landscapes. This is evident in his "City Scapes of L.A.," which depict neither windows nor signs of life, just the bare atmosphere of the landscape. Early paintings are *plein air* watercolors, in which the values are kept close and the colors limited in capturing the local landscape. Still attracted to the same colorless locales, he now paints works which include passages of bright colors juxtaposed to neutralize each other and applied with harsh gestures to display minimal "airscapes."

ALEXANDER (Video Artist)
1323 14th St. Suite L, Los Angeles, CA 90404

Born: 1927 *Awards:* Australia Council Fellowship *Collections:* Powere House Museum, Sydney *Exhibitions:* Sao Paulo Bienale; Stella Polaris Gallery, Los Angeles *Education:* St. Martins School of Art

Until the 1980s, he sculpted in the English tradition, combining geometric elements with organic ones. As he became more successful, he received commissions for public monumental works, the most famous of which is *The Great Tower* in Rutland Water, England, a piece that was and is still possibly the largest bronze sculpture in modern times. In the early 1980s, he developed what he called "four-dimensional sculpture." This in turn led him to light-sculptures that he makes with the holographic process. In 1989, he was invited to have a major retrospective exhibition at the Museum of Contemporary Art in Sao Paulo. The installations he created for this exhibition seem to defy the traditional classifications of "figurative" and "abstract."

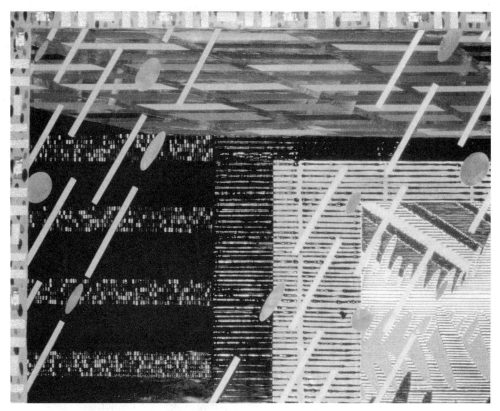

John Affolter, *Map #1-NW,* 36 x 45, mixed media and acrylic on paper.
Courtesy: Mr. and Mrs. Larry Youngblood

Lois Anderson, *Venus de Milo,* 72 x 36 x 36, assemblage. Photograph: Jon Easton

Robert Albanese, *Larvatus Prodeo,* 48 x 36 x 6, canvas, polyurthane and resin

ALEXANDER, DALE (Painter)
324 N. Niagara St., Burbank, CA 91505

Born: 1939 *Collections:* Alan Goldman Collection, Phoenix *Exhibitions:* Brand Library Art Gallery, Glendale; Alexander Gallery, Los Angeles

With a background in visual arts, including signage, he began to formulate painted planes of color and to break down words and letters into pure, oriental-influenced characters. Spurred by a desire to capture personally meaningful places before they were destroyed, he used a similar technique to produce his "Intersections" series. The subjects of these "mind Polaroids" were personally meaningful Los Angeles traffic intersections. In "Intersection," he "spelled out" the place with carefully composed abstract letters and forms and used colors to evoke feeling and ambience. His media are oil, enamel and watercolor. He has long been a Disney employee, and his work was used on the set of the film "Big Business."

ALEXANDER, EVERETT C. (Stained Glass Artist)
4400 Brunswick Ave., Los Angeles, CA 90039

Born: 1947 *Awards:* 1st Prize, Stained Glass, Pioneer Days *Exhibitions:* Membership Show, Fine Arts Federation of Burbank; Los Angeles Fringe Festival

His early work was characterized by conventional shapes with fixed borders. Following his apprenticeship with Narcissus Quagalida, he felt able to explore more unconventional, imaginative, and fluid forms. His colorful images of unicorns, dragons and castles are constructed from pieces of German glass, blown glass, metal foils and strips, gems, precious stones and neon. He has recently completed a series of twelve pieces, each an example of a specific technical style.

ALEXANDER, JOHN (Painter)
825 Rivera St., San Francisco, CA 94116

Born: 1953 *Exhibitions:* Miller/Brown Gallery, San Francisco; Current Directions, San Francisco *Education:* San Francisco State U. *Dealer:* Miller/Brown Gallery, San Francisco

Studying at San Francisco State University led to his exposure to Bay Area painters Nathan Oliveira, Manual Neri, Joan Brown, Raymond Saunders and William Wiley. His own work at the time was figurative, emphasizing what he calls the "accident of a scene," or the psychological in addition to the physical aspects. Currently, his work is evolving towards a more narrative style. While maintaining the figurative emphasis, he is allowing a personal mythology to surface. The paintings deal with a psychological metamorphosis of a particular place and idea. The recent series "Coriolis Effect" is a reflection of the way the world spins. On one side is a man who wears above his head the saying, "you are what you are," the other side is an empty raft. His intention is that we stop and take notice of physical and natural laws and the mysterious effect they have on us.

ALEXANDER, KENT (Painter)
1700 Golden Gate Ave., #10, San Francisco, CA 94115

Born: 1955 *Exhibitions:* The Mark Reuben Gallery, Sausalito; Desert West Juried Art Show, Lancaster *Education:* UCLA; Alliance of Figurative Artists, NYC *Dealer:* Jan Holloway Gallery, San Francisco

As a student he developed an expressionist style, influenced by Max Beckmann. In the late 1970s and early 1980s, he explored his experiences in New York City, by painting large mythological figure compositions in oils. Since 1982, changes in his spiritual outlook have lead him to work in a style that celebrates the spirit's contact with nature. Light has become increasingly important in his oil landscapes and seascapes. Now influenced by Bellows, Cassatt, the Impressionists and Kokoschka, he pushes toward ever richer combinations of alla prima, scumbling, glazing and color techniques to capture the beauty he sees around him.

ALEXANDER, PETER (Painter)
9 1/2 Wavecrest, Venice, CA 90291

Born: 1939 *Awards:* NEA Fellowship *Collections:* Museum of Modern Art, NYC; Los Angeles County Museum of Art *Exhibitions:* Museum of Modern Art, NYC; Whitney Museum *Education:* UCLA *Dealer:* Charles Cowles Gallery, NYC; James Corcoran Gallery, Santa Monica

He became known first for his cast polyester resin works while associated with the California "Light and Space" movement during the early 1960s, and later for his series of sunset paintings, black velvet paintings, moonscapes and jungle and animal paintings. He uses the play of light over water and clouds as a primary subject. Paintings and drawings depict underwater fantasies, shimmering seascapes and dark clouds glowing with sunlight or lightning. His seemingly obvious use of prosaic subject matter and medium is in fact not deliberate, but a coincidence in that these elements contain the same sensibilities: luminosity, fascination with natural phenomena, seductiveness, mystery, emotion, romance. Within a sumptuous yet ordered world of fantasy, colors are often exaggerated, and fluorescent paints, metallic pigments and glitter are sometimes applied in thick clots and thin ribbons to create shining, alluring surfaces. These help add new sensations to common images that are often overexposed or dulled.

ALEXANDER, TIM (Sculptor)
7646 1/2 Kester Ave., Van Nuys, CA 91326

Born: 1960 *Awards:* Honorable Mention, Long Beach Art Association *Exhibitions:* Irvine Fine Arts Center; Overact Gallery, Long Beach *Education:* UC-Irvine; Claremont Graduate School

He has been known for his large, complex, geometrical sculptures which incorporate wood, wire, ball-bearings and other media into organically inspired forms. His interests in the structural integrity of living cells and crystalline formations have been filtered through the diverse influences of abstract expressionism, minimalism, surrealism and constructivism. His intention has not been to force his materials to achieve organic results, but to work with the materials' indigenous organic qualities. *Rising,* for example, is a tall, honey-combed pagoda-shaped sculpture, constructed from over 240,000 BBs glued into compact, cellular forms. In recent pieces, he explores the relationship between organic and mechanical forms. Using modeling clay, mixed media and found objects, he fills these three-dimensional collages with a reckless joy, and, simultaneously, a realization of the world's agonies.

Kent Alexander, *Stormy Coast,* 30 x 24, oil on canvas

Katherine Ace, *Jester's Quartet (Face to Face Series),* 20 x 24, ink

ALEXANDER, WICK (Painter)
3327 Nile St., San Diego, CA 92104

Born: 1955 *Awards:* Silver Certificate of Excellence, Los Angeles International Art Competition *Exhibitions:* La Jolla Museum of Contemporary Art; Dietrich Jenny Gallery, San Diego *Education:* UC-San Diego; San Diego State U. *Dealer:* Dietrich Jenny Gallery, San Diego

While traveling in Mexico, he began a series of small watercolor still lifes. He explored different compositions and developed narratives by arranging masks, folk-art objects and postcards of landscapes. As the work progressed, he began using bright and unexpected color combinations similar to those popular in Mexico. Later he focused on landscape and used a bird's eye perspective to create abstract patterns. Recently, he began to expand the work's size and subject. He now makes large, specific, critical narratives about the grim relationship between Mexico and the U.S. in the border region around San Diego.

ALFEROV, ALEX (Painter, Video Artist)
5653 Fountain Ave., Los Angeles, CA 90028

Born: 1946 *Awards:* Honorable Mention, Artists Liaison Competition, Venice *Collections:* Belgrade National Gallery; Transamerican Corp., Los Angeles *Exhibitions:* Los Angeles Municipal Gallery *Education:* Cal. State-Northridge *Dealer:* 18th St. Gallery, Santa Monica

His figurative paintings refer to people's preconceived self images. In some works, the subjects seem to see themselves as icons; in others, they see themselves as masks. He is a physical painter whose paintings involve heavy layering. He works against walls, or horizontally, on work tables, applying paint with brushes, felt pens or squeeze bottles. At times, he uses razors to scrape and expose underlayers. Once he cuts the skin of the painting, he reshapes it like a plastic surgeon, creating expressionistic abstractions of the human form. He has been influenced by the energy of Van Gogh and Pollock, the beauty of Degas and the flatness of Toulouse-Lautrec.

ALLAN, WILLIAM (Painter)
Art Dept., Cal. State-Sacramento, 6000 Junior St., Sacramento, CA 95819

Born: 1936 *Collections:* San Francisco Museum of Modern Art; Museum of Modern Art, NYC *Exhibitions:* San Francisco Museum of Modern Art; Whitney Museum of American Art, NYC *Education:* San Francisco Art Institute *Dealer:* Hansen-Fuller Gallery, San Francisco

He paints in both acrylic and watercolor, and his works often investigate nature and man's relationship to it. For instance, in a recent interview, he said of his work, "I got studio crazy, making art about art. What did I know about? Fish." This revelation led to series of watercolor studies of trout and salmon—delicate and finely detailed works, contemplative rather than analytical, that probe not only natural forms but their effects on the artist, and vice versa. These works, critic Ellen Schlesinger has said, "like Monet's water lilies, go far beyond mere description, rendering every nuance and changing condition of the subject. Allan's watercolors offer both an intellectual and sensuous experience: while the eyes feast upon the translucent, evanescent properties of the paint, the mind races with thoughts of paradoxes of existence." His acrylic work treats similar themes. The large-scale (7-by-10-foot) *Shadow Repair for the Western Man* depicts a snow-covered mountainscape foregrounded by a standing but empty pair of blue jeans. The painting is a wry comment on and challenge to man's place in nature.

ALLEN, BOYD (Painter)
1711 Arlington Blvd., El Cerrito, CA 94530

Born: 1931 *Awards:* James Phelan Traveling Fellowship in Art; 1st Prize, San Francisco Museum of Art *Collections:* Newark Museum; San Francisco Art Commission *Exhibitions:* San Francisco Museum of Art; Phoenix Gallery, San Francisco *Education:* UC-Berkeley

He worked as an abstract expressionist until the mid-1960s, when he developed a style distinguished by broadly painted images of mysterious architecture and landscapes. Since the 1970s, his work has featured radiantly colored, highly simplified, mystical landscapes with ranges of mountain peaks. He often interchanges foreground and background, challenging the viewer's perceptions of depth and perspective. He makes each element of the work conceptual rather than natural; this imparts to the painting a sense of discovery. His present medium is watercolor on paper, but he also uses gouache and acrylic. He is a member of the art faculty at Berkeley.

ALLEN, EFFIE (Printmaker)
3236 Sterne St., San Diego, CA 92106

Born: 1940 *Awards:* 4th Prize, Printmaking, Del Mar Fair *Exhibitions:* Cabrillo Art Center; San Diego Art Institute *Education:* Bowling Green State U.; U. of Iowa

Inspired by a life-long interest in fibers and textiles, and a personal interpretation of nature, she has been a printmaker for many years. Her work is figurative, yet abstract, with an emphasis on the balance between negative space and the image. She has recently become acquainted with the monoprinting process, which has opened new artistic possibilities. Her ideas are generated from personal experiences: reflected upon, redrawn and refined. Her extensive travels in South America, Mexico, Spain and Portugal have provided her with a rich understanding of color, texture and mood.

ALLEN, JAMES P. (Painter)
P.O. Box 731, San Pedro, CA 90733

Born: 1950 *Awards:* Bank of America Art and Humanities Grant *Exhibitions:* Brand Library; P.U.C.A.A. *Education:* Otis Art Institute

He has always been influenced by art that draws upon primitive and subconscious roots, including Kandinsky, Gross and Klee. He has combined their approach, use of materials and content with his own study of Mayan, Aztec and Chumash pictography sites. Embedding found objects into the painting process—which includes paper and glass as basic surfaces—he seeks an understanding of the role art plays in documenting the experience of culture. In assemblage formats, the textural, three dimensional feel of the work counterpoints refracted and translucent backlighting. Interior and psychological profiles explore the separation of emotional and rational life, with a larger view toward urban anthropology.

Raul Anguiano, *Sorrow,* 26 x 20, lithograph

Boyd Allen, *Ice Wall Castle,* 19 x 24, watercolor and gouache.
Courtesy: David Ruml

ALLEN, TERRY (Multimedia Artist)
c/o Wanda Hansen, 615 Main St., Sausalito, CA

Born: 1943 *Awards:* NEA Fellowship; Guggenheim Fellowship *Collections:* Museum of Modern Art, NYC; Fort Worth Art Museum *Exhibitions:* Santa Barbara Contemporary Art Forum; L.A. Louver Gallery, Santa Monica *Education:* Chouinard Art Institute, Los Angeles *Dealer:* L.A. Louver Gallery; Gallery Paule Anglim, San Francisco; John Weber Gallery, NYC

A writer, composer, performer, and visual artist, he makes art a total experience involving the mind with all the senses. He conveys the physical activities and psychological states of his fantasy characters in many forms simultaneously, using whatever media he feels are appropriate. Works are episodes in circular scenarios of life. Themes are basic, and his subjects are the cliches of life. Recent work includes *Anterabbit/Bleeder (a Biography)*, an installation including a related theater piece, and *The Nelson 1980*, an installation at the Nelson Atkins Museum which included recorded music by three Nelsons—Willie, Tracey and Rickey.

ALLISON, CHARLOTTE (Painter)
44 Ralston Ave., Mill Valley, CA 94941

Born: 1934 *Awards:* Museum Purchase, Marin Society of Artists *Collections:* El Paso Museum of Art; Pacific Gas and Electric Company *Exhibitions:* Marin County Fine Art Galleries; Richmond Art Center

After working in watercolor and oil, she started working in acrylic paint in the 1970s. Influenced by the line qualities of Oriental art, she first put down an underpainting of complementary color, over which she combined calligraphy with palette knife technique. Scenes from the Sierra Nevada Mountains make up the subjects for most of these paintings. In 1981, she began to develop a new technique. By heavily priming and sealing the canvas, and painting on a flat surface, she found that it was possible to apply multiple transparent washes of acrylic paint, while utilizing the white of the surface, as in watercolors. Influenced by Joseph Rafael's brilliant color and Dong Kingman's wet washes, she has translated these qualities into her process. The first of these paintings were of water—tide pools, lily and fish ponds. She is fascinated with the combination of architectural and plant forms, which leads her to greenhouses and flower conservatories to find her subjects.

ALLISON, CHERYL A. (Commercial Illustrator, Painter)
P.O. Box 3400, Anaheim, CA 92803

Born: 1946 *Awards:* Best in Show, Laguna Expo; Cultural Arts Center Symposium, Santa Barbara *Collections:* The Police Gazette, Anaheim *Exhibitions:* Santa Barbara Art Expo; Mt. Carmel Art Fair *Education:* Orange Coast College; Nicholas Pasko Art Institute *Dealer:* Media Research Inc., Anaheim

She was one of five students selected for individual study with Nicholas Pasko. Her early training included extensive study both in the relationship between light and color, and in the effects of light and color on three-dimensional objects and textured surfaces. In the manner of the Old Masters, she used this training as the foundation for her own style and technique. She paints "original copies" in a wide variety of styles. Oils, water color and pen and ink are her media. Best known are her original impressionistic works on primed canvas. She uses a combination of pallet knives and brushes to blend and soften her bold impasto style. Her works are color-intense, with sharp definition and an emphasis on mechanical construction. Her modern pieces exhibit bold pen and ink delineation with exceptional balance between objects and primary focus.

ALLRED, DAVID L. (Sculptor)
16509 Power Line Rd., Redding, CA 96002

Born: 1939 *Exhibitions:* Redding Museum and Art Center; International Sportsmans' Exhibition, San Francisco *Education:* U. of Utah

A former art teacher, he aims his torch at brass, copper, steel and wood to sculpt realistic, life-size fish, birds, fly hooks and figures in action. Always working on commission, he makes pieces that are humorous, utilitarian, realistic or abstract. He plans to market a line of lightweight concrete reproducible sculpture for beautifying home and commercial properties. He is currently making a 14-by-9-foot interior wall sculpture for a large bank. His work is sold in Boston and in fine stores along the West Coast.

ALMARAZ, CARLOS (Painter, Printmaker)
P.O. Box 94236, Pasadena, CA 91109

Born: 1941 *Awards:* Kay Nielsen Award for Printmaking, Los Angeles County Museum of Art *Collections:* Corcoran Gallery, Washington D.C.; Jack Nicholson, Los Angeles; *Exhibitions:* Hirshorn Museum of Art, Washington, D.C. *Education:* Otis/Parsons School of Design *Dealer:* Jan Turner, Los Angeles

Influenced by both Mexican Muralists and French Impressionists, his work is typified by bold chromatic colors. His figures lie in a mythical and unreal Jungian landscape. His intense city scenes move, his night scenes glow with a velvety luminescence, and his fierce car crashes are uncompromising. He begins his large-scale paintings with studies drawn with pastels on velvety black paper. Then he transfers his ideas to the canvas, using a palette knife to apply layers of shiny thick oil paint over oil paint. He has recently begun painting in watercolor and working on an 8-by-40-foot oil on canvas mural on the history of Los Angeles.

ALMY, MAX (Video Artist)
3454 Standish Rd., Encino, CA 91436

Born: 1948 *Awards:* NEA Fellowship; U.S. Film and Video Festival Award *Collections:* Museum of Modern Art, NYC; Stedelijk Museum *Exhibitions:* Long Beach Museum of Art; Museum of Contemporary Art *Education:* U. of Nebraska; California College of Arts and Crafts *Dealer:* Electronic Arts Intermix, NYC; Video Data Bank, Chicago

Utilizing video as an installation, performance, and broadcast medium, she explores new possibilities for the formal presentation of narrative content that is emotionally and psychologically compelling. The works often incorporate digital effects and are characterized by a highly-polished appearance matching the post-production standards of commercial television. Such recent video tapes as *Modern Times*, *Leaving the 20th Century*, *The Perfect Leader* and *Lost in the Pictures* have become increasingly concerned with social commentary and political statement, while maintaining a slick, fast-paced format that is both humorous and non-didactic.

Lorraine Almeida, *Microcosm-Macrocosm,* 19 x 25, charcoal

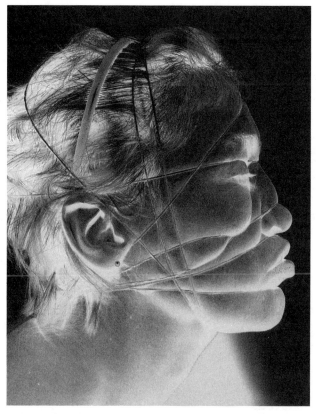

Linda J. Albertano, *Joan of Compton, Joan of Arcadia,*
performance, L.A. Theater Center. Photograph: Frank Lutz

ALPERT, GEORGE (Photographer, Painter)
5849 N. Casa Blanca Rd. Paradise Valley, AZ 85253

Born: 1922 *Awards:* Alfred Stieghty Award *Exhibitions:* Light Gallery, NYC; Udinotti Gallery, San Francisco & Venice

He has exhibited extensively in photography for twenty years and has published three books of photo essays, including *The Queens, Second Chance to Live,* and *The Suicide Syndrome and Taos Pueblo.* He turned to painting, using bright acrylics to express the emotions surrounding an image or mood. In his piece *Empire Tit Building,* a humorous canvas shows stylized female breasts incorporated into architecture. His work focuses on male-female relationships and their peculiarities. He achieves this through his use of luminous colors that give the paintings a glossy, candied appearance.

ALQUILAR, MARIA (Multimedia Artist)
703 Darwin St., Santa Cruz, CA 95062

Born: 1938 *Awards:* Art In Architecture Award, General Service Administration, U.S. Government *Collections:* National Museum, Washington, DC; Chase Manhattan Bank, NYC and Phoenix, AZ *Exhibitions:* Smithsonian Institute, Washington, DC; Triton Museum, Santa Clara

The style of her early work is anthropomorphic, mythical, primitive and classical, and her current work retains those stylistic features. Paintings during the early period depict idealized visions of paradise, with landscapes inhabited by anthropomorphic animals. The works tell a tale of a man, woman and child riding a yellow horse through tropical jungles and villages that resembling Mexico. These early works are chiefly in acrylic with painted wooden frames, and in acrylic on reverse glass with painted wood, papier maché, or ceramic frames. At that time she also worked heavily in ceramic, including sculpted plates and other sculpture, and in bas relief with reversed glass. Motifs included animals, especially cats, and people. Her more recent work is in a variety of media, including blinking neon light. She uses found objects such as broken glass, shells, bones, fish hooks and small dolls or pieces of dolls, which she often burns or melts. Public art includes the installation of 18 pavement works, entitled *Arkeology,* for a light rail station in Sacramento, and a life-sized mythical altar of clay, steel, and brass for the U.S. Port of Entry in San Luis, Arizona.

ALTER, WALTER (Sculptor, Installation Artist)
959 Valencia St., San Francisco, CA 94110

Born: 1943 *Collections:* ArtSpace, San Francisco *Exhibitions:* San Francisco Art Commission Gallery; Squiggle Gallery, San Francisco *Education:* UC-Berkeley; San Francisco City College *Dealer:* Hatley-Martin, San Francisco

Ten years ago, he began to study ways of fusing his artistic vision with electronic technology. Influenced by Marshall McLuhan, he developed an artistic approach that establishes video as a multi-screen medium intrinsically suited to display information in breadth. He creates large-scale, site-specific sculpture installations constructed from a variety of industrial found objects. Reaching nearly three stories in height, these architectural installations, made of electrical conduit, pipe, hose, scaffolding and other objects, are assembled in free-form fashion with strong rubber strips to hold objects together. Up to fifty video monitors, some of them damaged, are installed in the sculpture. The monitors present prepared video material and live interactive performances. These sculptures have formed the backgrounds or stage sets for well over fifty music and performance pieces in San Francisco over the past few years. He has recently been experimenting with electronic music as an additional installation element.

ALTMAN, BOBBIE (Ceramist)
2024 Eighth St., Berkeley, CA 94710

Born: 1946 *Awards:* California Arts Council Artist- in-Residence Grant; Artist-in-Residence Grant, South Carolina Arts Commission *Collections:* BioQuest Inc., San Francisco *Exhibitions:* Crocker Art Museum; California State Fair *Education:* U. of Iowa; School of the Art Institute of Chicago

After formal training with Michael Tyzack, Joseph Patrick, and S. Carl Fracassini, she came under the influence of Paul Jenkins' color abstractions and began creating large canvases of luminescent color washes and smaller watercolor pieces. These are done with liquid Luma colors using a unique monoprint method. She then studied pottery-making in Japan and began working in porcelain, creating wheel-thrown and altered sculptural pieces evocative of the Japanese aesthetic. She has recently combined her interest in clay, color, spirituality and Far East travels in a series of mixed-media drawings on paper and porcelain. Using layers of vibrant color over xerox transfers of photographic images, she builds up light-infused architectural environments to create spaces of mythology and mystery.

AMDUR, JUDY (Painter)
560 Main St., Studio 11E, Los Angeles, CA 90013

Born: 1948 *Awards:* 2nd Place, Long Beach Art Association; 1st Place, La Mirada Festival of the Arts *Collections:* City of La Mirada; Hyatt Regency Hotel, Kansas City, MO *Exhibitions:* Riverside Art Museum; California State Polytechnic U., Pomona *Education:* Boston U.; Minneapolis College of Art and Design *Dealer:* Shoshanna Wayne Gallery, Santa Monica

She initially painted landscapes, figures and interiors in a direct manner. Study with James Weeks and Philip Guston influenced her sense of color and perspective. From 1978 until her move from Massachusetts in 1983, she focused on allegorical still lifes with a variety of pattern, and landscapes referring specifically to human presence. The California quality of light was later a dramatic influence, and larger, warmer and more open canvases resulted. A painting of a single cactus has developed into a series of more abstract works in green and deep blue oils. These atmospheric studies of light and form render new form and composition with each turn of the model. Most recent versions concentrate on small details in large scale, so that the subject appears sculptural and mountainous in nature.

AMENOPHIS, KERMIT (Painter)
604 1/2 Haight St., San Francisco, CA 94117

Born: 1957 *Awards:* Leroy and Martha Norwood Mickeens Foundation; 2nd Place, Art in the Park *Exhibitions:* Colorbox Gallery, San Francisco; Sargent Johnson Gallery, San Francisco *Education:* California College of Arts and Crafts; Center for Creative Studies *Dealer:* Roy Monceaux, Seattle

He was originally influenced by Dali's eccentric and surreal paintings, and his source of archetypal imagery

George Alpert, *10 Bronze El Ropo Cigars,* life size, bronze and wood.
Courtesy: O'Brien Art Emporuim, Scottsdale, AZ

Lisa Adams, *Evidence,* 50 x 41, oil, acrylic, linoleum on canvas.
Courtesy: NEWSPACE, Los Angeles, CA

is rooted in African and ancient Egyptian mysticism. He works principally in oils, and his figurative works range from subtly distorted realism with a Renaissance-like clarity to a style characterized by extreme elongation and contortion of bodily features, often with an erotic edge. This latter style incorporates sculptural forms that appear to be dimensional, and atmosphere and negative space are exaggerated to suggest a heightened spiritual vision. A recent series, "Egypto-Makonde," is a synthesis of the Armana court art of the 18th dynasty in Egypt and the modern Makonde wood carving of East Africa.

AMMIRATI, JOHN (Sculptor, Painter)
1127 Bowdion St., San Francisco, CA 94134

Born: 1944 *Awards:* Critics' Circle Award *Collections:* Museum of Modern Art *Exhibitions:* Dana Reich Gallery, San Francisco; Gregory Ghent Gallery, San Francisco *Education:* New York U. School of the Arts; UC-Davis

He began his career as a scene designer in the theatre. To extend his knowledge of art, he built constructions and collages that resembled small stage settings, and, influenced by Kurt Schwitters and the Dadaists, participated with other artists to stage "happening"-type art events. In the theatre, he experimented with urethane foam and resin, and under the influence of Claes Oldenburg, whose power of metaphoric expression he greatly admired, he explored the possibility these new materials afforded for the creation of art independent of its theatrical utility. His more recent works in resin and paper are called "metaphoric landscapes," which suggest the rugged California terrain—both its beauty and its deterioration. These he constructs by crumpling and sculpting heavy paper that is then coated with a fiberglass resin and painted, often so as to achieve a pewter or leaden effect. An early example of this work is *King of Beers,* a realistic and detailed depiction of a crumpled beer can. His painted wall sculptures, although admirable as pure abstractions, admit of other interpretations, and the titles he selects for them encourage this.

AMOY, SUSAN (Ceramicist)
240 Powers St., Brooklyn, NY 11211

Born: 1957 *Awards:* Honorable Mention, "Dimensions '86," Lenexa, Kansas *Collections:* State of Hawaii; Urasenke Foundation, Japan *Exhibitions:* 1987 Scripps 43rd Annual Ceramics Exhibition; Bronx Museum, NY *Education:* U. of Hawaii

Her clay sculptures reflect the immediacy and directness of the material and its responsiveness to physical and chemical change. An affinity for geological and biological forms and a fascination with creation and destruction as life forces are reflected in the solid and expressionistic forms, which are created with casual disregard for "proper" technique. She previously imposed fragments of mechanistic systems on the rough work, but her more recent pieces allude to forms that predate civilization. In addition to ceramics, the artist also works with found wood objects, which she binds to paper with acrylics in an organic and slightly figurative manner.

ANCONA, PATRICIA (Sculptor)
132 Woodland Ave., San Rafael, CA 94901

Born: 1939 *Awards:* NEA Fellowship *Exhibitions:* Atrium Gallery, San Francisco; Los Angeles Institute

of Comparative Art *Education:* San Francisco Art Institute; San Francisco State University

Having explored both sculpture and painting in her training, she calls upon a number of skills and influences to create both sculpture and design work. Her sculpture, once in clay then wood, then clay again, is architectural in form. Her "Structures" are house forms with no openings. The clay, fired at low temperature, is broken in places and glued back onto the form; the surface treated with thin layers of oil-based colored waxes. In some pieces, a wooden frame is placed around the clay form. In either case, the pieces have the presence of ancient structures. Her design work, most influenced by her hard-edge painting and geometric drawings, includes original designs for Kohler Company's Artists Edition sinks. She also creates original designs for rugs that are later made in India. Her rug designs are also geometric with an architectural feel.

ANDERSON, CATHERINE H. (Painter)
1779 Tanglewood Dr., San Luis Obispo, CA 93401

Born: 1926 *Collections:* Sheldon Jackson College, Sitka, AK *Exhibitions:* Brooking Fine Art Club, SD; Alaska Fur Rendezvous, Anchorage *Education:* State Teacher's College, Mankato, MN

Her paternal grandmother was a professional portrait painter and she herself has been painting since the age of twelve. Her landscapes are in a stylized realism, while her portraits tend towards impressionism. She paints wet on wet and uses india ink for accent with watercolor. When she paints wet on dry, she tends to let the fresh white paper show through. Among her influences are Durer, Da Vinci, Rembrandt, Raphael and Gainsborough. Since graduating college, she has taught art to native Americans in high school and junior college. She teaches adult education classes in acrylic and watercolor methods of painting landscapes, florals, portraits and still lifes.

ANDERSEN, CYNTHIA L. (Painter)
10037 Commerce Ave., Tujunga, CA 91042

Born: 1951 *Collections:* Grand Hyatt, Hong Kong; Aston-Tate, Four Seasons, Austin *Exhibitions:* Visual Environments, Newport Beach; John Thomas Gallery, Fullerton *Education:* Art Center College of Design *Dealer:* Jim Schwartz, Los Angeles

Though she takes influence from her study of advertising and illustration at the Art Center College of Design, she credits her real education to nine years of billboard painting for the record industry. Within those experiences, she points to the inspired work of Gustav Klimt: his mix of romanticism and realism; the expressive and adventurous elements are a constant reference for her work. Her own painting is an eclectic exploration, in pastels on paper and oil on canvas, ranging from abstract to photo-realistic, traditional landscapes, to her own "translation" of Paleolithic cave art. Typically, she uses a full, vibrant palette. She pays close attention to surface quality creating magical patinas and visual textures.

ANDERSON, GAYLE (Painter, Printmaker)
P.O. Box 1134, Kailua-Kona, HI 96745

Born: 1919 *Awards:* Purchase Award, Hawaii Foundation of Culture and Arts; Hawaii Watercolor Society *Collections:* Colorado Museum of Art *Exhibitions:* Pioneer Square, Seattle; Hawaii Watercolor Society *Dealer:* Penelope Culberton, Kailua-Kona A retired

C.H. Anderson, *Checking Strays,* 14 x 18, acrylic on canvas

F.N. Ashley, *Streets of Santa Cruz,* 32 x 40, oil

college and university instructor, she is a watermedia experimentalist who expresses landscape and environmental concerns with a variety of media. With tempera and transparent watercolors, she paints very simple larger landscapes. With prepared watercolor papers, handmade paper and the textures and fibers of Hawaii, she creates dynamic contrasted paper and paint collages of the volcano. Finally with her own hand-stained, handmade paper and rusted cast-off metal pieces, she creates environmental collages that are statements about the pollution of the earth. She has been influenced by Rothko, Klimt, Toulouse-Lautrec, Reuben Tan and Helen Frankenthaler.

ANDERSON, GLENNA (Painter)
1526 Cherrywood Dr., Modesto, CA 95350

Born: 1926 *Awards:* Best of Show, Central California Art League *Collections:* City of Modesto *Exhibitions:* Central Savings, Modesto; Central California Art League, Modesto *Education:* U. of Nebraska

Her early work shows the influence of her traditional training in representational art. She learned the drawing styles of the Old Masters and developed an interest in the abstract work of Marsden Hartely's oils and John Marin's watercolors. Her style incorporates a strong color statement and dramatic composition with a realistic representation of the subject matter. She taught art to youth and adults formally and in workshops, as she advanced her own education: opaque acrylics and ceramics in Great Britain; oils, with Foster Caddell in Connecticut; and with watercolorists Shapior, Milford Zornes and George Post. These studies led her to an impressionistic treatment of subject matter and a strong interest in using light to design and enhance a painting. In the last several years, she has concentrated on commissioned portraits, though she continues to explore many subjects and techniques in her non-commissioned pieces.

ANDERSON, KURT (Painter)
6603 Whitney St., Oakland, CA 94609

Born: 1954 *Collections:* Baker-Bunker Collection, San Francisco *Exhibitions:* Twin Palms Gallery; Gallery 44, Oakland

His study with sculptor Leif Brush and his formal training in figure and landscape painting influenced the artist to focus on form. He developed a style of non-stenciled airbrush painting by which he portrays subject matter (images of women, for instance) with pre-Raphaelite undertones. The style, complemented by stark 20th-century advertising technique, is a complex blend of images. Using masonite as canvas, the artist incorporates interplay of flatness and depth into the works. He has also produced a body of smaller (12-inch-square) works of abstraction in which the depth and spatial concerns of his early works are explored freely. The confines of the smaller medium counter the expansiveness of the artist's abstract, emotional interpretation of water and sky.

ANDERSON, LOIS (Sculptor, Multimedia Artist)
50 Catalpa, Mill Valley, CA 94941

Born: 1927 *Awards:* NEA Fellowship *Collections:* The Oakland Museum *Exhibitions:* Vorpal Gallery, San Francisco; Judah H. Magnes Museum, Berkeley *Education:* Wisconsin State College, Milwaukee; UC-Berkeley

A car she saw in Marin County in 1971 bedecked with statues, dolls and jewels inspired her to begin "gluing" and led to her first large piece, *Buddha Lamp.* Her work is heavily influenced by the art of the Orient and by Mexican church art and incorporates religious figures and cultural artifacts; objects such as jewelry, icons, shells, beads, glass and tiles create an effect of ornateness and opulence. An old dresser she purchased at a flea market became *The Dresser,* a mosaic work of beads, eucalyptus pods, Indian figurines and candles assembled to create a kind of altar. The 8 x 7 x 4 work entitled *Altar* consists of sculptures, reliefs and icons along materials such as as jewelry, tile, glass and plastic. Her newer pieces are more humorous, whimsical, and sometimes sardonic.

ANDERSON, RUTH A. (Sculptor)
454 Seaton, #5, Los Angeles, CA 90013

Born: 1944 *Awards:* Interdisciplinary Residency, Yellowsprings Institute, PA *Exhibitions:* Long Beach City College; Los Angeles City College *Education:* Cal. State- Long Beach

Early work was influenced by George Segal, Ed Kienholz and Magdalena Abakanowica. She combines classical skills with a spiritual interest in neo-pagan religions. Her abaca paper sculpture has the appearance of weighty stone. In these "Menhirs"—a Celtic word meaning man and stone—she juxtaposes figurative shapes against earth shapes. Faces, body parts and whole figures appear in what, at first, seem to be rocks. Her work serves as a spiritual dialogue, which addresses the necessity for the integration of our environment with everyday living. As such, she creates environments for her sculptures by surrounding them with sand, stones, dried leaves, concrete and black slate. She also works in bronze, clay and body casts of mailing tape and/or plaster.

ANDERSON, SARA A. (Painter)
122 Los Gatos Blvd., Los Gatos, CA 95032

Born: 1934 *Awards:* 1st in Watercolor, Fremont *Exhibitions:* Keystone Co., Los Gatos; Varian Assoc., Santa Clara *Education:* Mills College; Cal. State- Northridge *Dealer:* Jade Garner, Los Gatos

She has developed an individual watercolor style and her paintings exude energy and color. Although she works from living subjects, her imagery is a synthesis of what she sees and what she feels. Whether her subject is a scene from life or a portrait, the viewer becomes involved in the representation of a fleeting moment. She began her art career at Mills College and later studied with art historian Alfred Newmeyer and painter Robert Gaw. In the 1960s she studied painting at California State University in Northridge. More recently, she spent several years as a "protege du Roi" at the Academie Royale des Beaux Arts in Brussels, where she studied expressionism.

ANDERSON, WILLIAM T. (Painter)
Humboldt State Univ. Art Department, Arcata, CA 95521

Born: 1936 *Exhibitions:* Whitney Museum of Art, NYC; San Francisco Museum of Modern Art *Education:* Cal. State- Los Angeles

His images, done in monotype combined with painting, are inspired by the solitude and expanse of the American West. The works explore distorted perspective and non-Euclidean spatial relationships. The landscapes' realistically rendered figuration plays a

Patricia Ancona, *Structure Four,* 18 x 13 x 18, clay with wax patina and wood

Cynthia Andersen, *Floral untitled,* 24 x 24, oil on canvas

tense counterpoint to the unrealistic spaces and the objectified, symbolic representations of mountains, clouds, flowers and sky. The use of these images juxtaposed with a conventional horizon, or with a sky that reveals a second or even a third perspective plane, creates a hyper-reality. This effect is strengthened by a surrealistic sense of color and a brilliance of surfaces achieved through the use of acrylic lacquers.

ANDREAS, BRIAN (Sculptor)
6141 Afton Pl., #311, Los Angeles, CA 90028

Born: 1956 *Collections:* The Betsey Nelson Group, NYC *Exhibitions:* Danica Gallery, Beverly Hills; Los Angeles Invisible Gallery *Education:* Luther College

In the late 1970s, he progressed from his earlier multimedia work and to explore the plastic possibilities of sculpture. Influenced by Calder and Klee, he used wires leaping into free space to fashion recurring motifs of myth and sacred dance. These small pieces gave way to larger works in cast and handmade paper and lead. With an alchemical flair, he transformed the weight and mass of lead into ghost-like forms that rose effortlessly into space. His translucent papers hid faces and forms as they surrounded and enclosed subdued volumes of space. His recent work continues to explore his anthropomorphic view of the living universe.

ANGEL-WILSON, DINA (Ceramist, Mixed Media Artist)
1054 Cragmont Ave., Berkeley, CA 94708

Born: 1944 *Awards:* Purchase Award, California Clay '84; Merit Award, ArtQuest '88 *Collections:* Antonio Prieto Collection, Mills College *Exhibitions:* Alan Short Gallery, Stockton; Mendocino Art Center, Mendocino *Education:* Haifa U., Israel

She had been well-known for her functional raku pieces with cracked glazes when an invitation to an art show opened a new venue of artistic expression. "Make anything you want," the curator had said. Remembering a small silver box that was too small for storage, she used it as the basis for her first "dream box." Inspired by the Japanese art of "furoshiki," or wrapped gifts, and modeled after the form of Japanese lanterns, these "dream boxes" are constructed from handmade cast papers with touches of metal paint and/or calligraphic characters, clay vessels, paint, black bamboo sticks, thread, ribbon, and other material that seems appropriate. Each piece displays a serene balance of color and texture. More recent work in cast paper is increasingly abstract and gestural and seems less contained by other materials. They feature primary shapes in black and gray.

ANGUIANO, RAUL (Muralist)
17831 San Leandro Ln., Huntington Beach, CA 92647

Born: 1915 *Awards:* 1st Prize, Salon Panamericano, Brazil; Decorated "Commendatore," Italian Government *Collections:* Museum of Modern Art, NYC; San Francisco Museum of Modern Art *Exhibitions:* Scott Alan Fine Arts Gallery, NYC; Carnegie Cultural Center, Oxnard *Dealer:* Lodi Art Gallery, Pasadena

Often compared to fellow countrymen Rivera, Siqueiros, Orozco and Tamayo, he is one of the important Mexican muralists of this century. Influenced by Goya and by the Mexican painters of his time, in the 1930s he worked as muralist and a printmaker. While studying in New York City on a scholarship, he came under the influence of Picasso, which left an impres-

sion on the development during the 1940s of a style he termed "poetic realism." In this later stage, he turned his eye upon Mexican culture, especially the life of the Native American people. His figures are simply painted in muted colors, with many of them, such as *The Creation of Mayan Man,* drawing upon Native folklore.

ANSELL, JILL (Painter)
13858 Moonshine Rd., Camptonville, CA 95922

Born: 1944 *Awards:* Art In Public Places Grant, Calif. Arts Council; Commemorative Plate, International Year of the Child, UNICEF *Collections:* Brackenridge Hospital, Austin TX; Pima County Jail, Tucson, AZ *Exhibitions:* Crocker Museum, Sacramento; The Edge Gallery, Fullerton *Education:* School for Visual Arts

Her work has evolved from detailed geometric mandalas to pieces that involve a more personal exploration of the feminine psyche. The imagery she employs concerns death and transformation, and her settings are taken directly from nature. She works primarily in acrylics, often using both found and constructed small objects such as feathers and hand-painted wooden eggs. Figures in her works include animals, winged skeletons and snakes. Each of her painting recalls a personal "myth" in combination with an archetypal theme; for example, one work explores the death of her father and the archetype of Cerberus, the dog that guards the entrance to Hades in Greek and Roman mythology. Colors range from bright reds and blues to soft lavenders, greens and browns.

ANTHONY, DAVID B. (Sculptor)
1420 45th St., #25E, Emeryville, CA 94608

Born: 1961 *Awards:* Fellowship Academy of Art College, San Francisco *Collections:* The Berkeley Art Exchange; Gruen, Gruen and Associates, San Francisco *Exhibitions:* Richmond Art Center; Emeryville Redevelopment Show *Education:* Academy of Art College, San Francisco

Early work involved plaster over rusted steel structures. For a two year period, he fought the rust as it stained the surface red-orange, after which time, he began to encourage the rust by guiding it with various solutions and sun light. His is a primitive language, deeply rooted in his study of the figure. The pieces are often linear, rising from the ground in a vertical space. The work is whimsical and full of recognizable objects. Each piece stands between five feet ten inches and six feet, with an average width of twenty inches. The work of this period shares an affinity with the steel work of Gonzales and Picasso. Recently, he has expanded his repertoire of materials, putting together found pieces of wood, steel, plaster and everyday objects to create abstract figurative constructions. Both wall and floor pieces are in this group of work. The underlying material in each piece is wood: wood with plaster, wood with steel or a picture frame, wood with a broom or a ball of copper. White paint, used sparingly over these surfaces to unify them, has given way to color. His greatest influences during this period were David Smith and Frank Stella.

ANTIKAJIAN, SARKIS (Painter)
P.O. Box 247 Cheshire, OR 97419

Born: 1933 *Awards:* 2nd Place, Watercolor Society of Oregon *Collections:* Eugene Water and Electric Board *Exhibitions:* Pastel Society of America, NYC; Oregon Art Institute, Portland

Ariel, *Grifon,* 7 x 9, ink and paint on paper

Sarkis Antikajian, *Sailing at Richardson Park,* 29 x 36, pastel

He loves to work outdoors and paint directly from life. Although he has had no formal art education, he began painting impressionist and post-impressionist oils as a child growing up in the Middle East. He received a degree in pharmacy and followed that career for many years. In 1983, he became a full-time painter. His oils and watercolors reflected a love of color. He had shows in Oregon and California and studied under Sergei Bongart, and he has recently begun working with pastels. His current style is "representational but not realistic." He continues to work with landscape and natural subjects.

ANTIN, ELEANOR (Performance Artist, Installation Artist)
P.O. Box 1147, Del Mar, CA 92014

Born: 1935 *Awards:* NEA Grant *Collections:* San Francisco Museum of Modern Art; Museum of Modern Art, NYC *Exhibitions:* Museum of Modern Art, NYC; Whitney Museum *Education:* City College of New York; Tamara Daykarhanova School for the Stage, NYC *Dealer:* Ronald Feldman, NYC

In the mid 1960s, she created conceptual pieces influenced by the women's movement, exploring the possibilities of personal autobiography using a variety of media that includes performance, photography, video, drawing, sculpture, text and installation. Eventually she developed an allegorical psychology in which she distributed elements of her own personality among three personas: the ballerina, the king and the nurse. Recently she has mounted full-scale theatrical presentations and created elaborate filmic installations, while still working in video. The subject of all her work is the continuing career of her three personas.

ANTON, DON G. (Photographer)
1236 S St., Eureka, CA 95501

Born: 1956 *Awards:* Rauschenberg Support Grant; Lorser Feitelson-Helen Lundberg Grant *Collections:* Bibliotheque Nationale, Paris; San Francisco Museum of Modern Art *Exhibitions:* Humboldt State U., Arcata; Los Angeles Photography Center *Education:* San Francisco State U. *Dealer:* Weston Gallery, Carmel

He grew up in the barrio of East Los Angeles. Without access to formal art education, he found his creative medium in photography. His photographs, often produced by using the sandwich negative technique, speak of his cultural heritage and religious upbringing. Death is a recurrent theme, and he has used images of cadavers and exhumed mummies, juxtaposed with organic material, to express his appreciation for life and the proximity of death. He works consistently in black and white and has developed a lush, emotional style, with stark lighting contrasts and symmetrical compositions. He is now using multiple printing techniques with cadavers, petroglyphs and fire to produce haunting, meaningful images.

ANTONAKOS, STEPHEN (Sculptor)
435 W. Broadway, New York, NY 10012

Born: 1926 *Awards:* NEA Grant; New York State Creative Artists Public Service Program Grant *Collections:* Museum of Modern Art, NYC; La Jolla Museum of Art *Exhibitions:* Whitney Museum, NYC; San Francisco Museum of Modern Art *Dealer:* Helene Trosky, Purchase, NY; Works of Art for Public Spaces, NYC

In the 1960s, he used neon non-figuratively in order to create "the shock of the unexpected" with "silent streams of color"; one such work, of programmed neon and metal, was *Orange Vertical Floor Neon*. Applying the logic of minimalism to a formalist vocabulary during the next decade, he installed neon-edged panels and boxes on the outside and inside of buildings, suggestive of architectural forms or sculpture. These works and other recent installations reorganize space, with subtle blends or glaring oppositions of light and color.

AONA, GRETCHEN M. (Painter, Photographer)
45-453 B Mokulele Dr., Kaneohe, HI 46744

Born: 1933 *Awards:* Purchase Awards, Hawaii State Foundation of Culture and Art *Collections:* Watumull Foundation; Hawaii State Foundation of Culture and Art *Exhibitions:* Hawaii Watercolor Society Annual; Amfac Plaza Exhibition Room *Education:* San Jose State U. *Dealer:* Koolau Gallery, Kaneohe; Arts of Paradise, Waikiki

She is a painter and photographer whose concerns are with composition and light. She studied under Robert Wood, and her earlier vibrantly colored, abstract watercolors showed the influence of the California school. She has since moved toward a more realistic rendering and is now exploring an integrated transparency of forms through a softer, more lightly colored palette. In her early photographs, she, like Edward Weston, sought images that were meaningful in themselves. While teaching at a community college in Honolulu, she discovered black-and-white infrared photography. She exploited infrared's dreamlike qualities at first in landscape and presently in portraiture.

ARANDA, GUILLERMO (Painter, Printmaker)
160 San Benito, Watsonville, CA 95076

Born: 1944 *Awards:* 1st Place, Printmaking, All Indian Spring Market, San Juan Bautista *Exhibitions:* White Gallery, UC-Los Angeles; Sonoma State U. *Dealer:* Reynas Galleries, San Juan Bautista

He was born into a family of musicians and craftspeople, and has spent his artistic life developing themes and motifs from his Mexican and Native American background. While in school, he became familiar with the tenets of contemporary mural painting and the works of Siguicros, Rivera, and Orozco. One of his major works from this period is a mural in San Diego's Balbo Park. *The Duality* features a whirl of figures including pyramids, winged creatures and feathered serpents to express positive and negative aspects of life as well as the balance between our earthly existence and our spiritual place in the universe. In the late 1970s, he became interested in intaglio printmaking and is currently studying multicolored etching and monoprinting. He has also taught art classes and participated in many mural projects at the Correctional Training Facility in Soledad, California.

ARANGUIZ, RUBY L. (Painter)
238 Seville Way, San Mateo, CA 94402

Born: 1932 *Awards:* Scholarship, Rockefeller Foundation, NY *Collections:* Museo de Arte Figurativo, Cuenca, Spain *Exhibitions:* Coyote Point Museum, Burlingame; Providencia Museum, Santiago, Chile *Education:* U. of Chile; Art Students League

She has studied and exhibited her paintings here and abroad, including New York, Hawaii, Mexico, Madrid, Santiago and Vancouver. After her European back-

Gretchen Aona, *Liliuokalani Gardens Bridge,* infrared photo.

Eleen Auvil, *The Other Man,* 70 x 30 x 16, mixed media

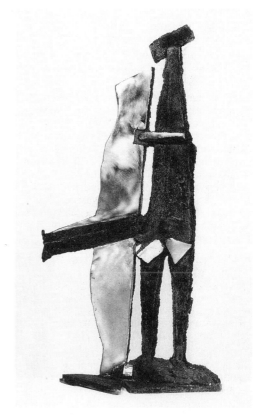

Kathryn Armstrong, *Embrace of the Other Side,* 22 x 10 x 3, cast bronze

ground and many years of residence in the Continent, her style was strongly influenced by the French and Spanish masters, including Van Gogh, Matisse and Goya. Her distinct idiom is characterized by her command of colors, her rendition of light, her attraction for decorative patterns and her powerful interpretation of the human figure. Working in oil, pastel and silkscreen, she paints landscapes, seascapes, still lifes, portraits and other subjects. The MacMillan Publishing Company has recently chosen one of her paintings for the cover of a book for the Stanford University Department of Foreign Languages.

ARBOGAST, VICTOR (Sculptor)
1543 Plymouth St., Mt. View, CA 94043

Born: 1953 *Collections:* The Museum of Art, Huntington, WV *Exhibitions:* The Renco Building, Mt. View; The Palo Alto Cultural Center

In the 1970s, his works were both expressionist and surrealist in nature. The pieces were almost always dark and heavily textured. Constructed from bronze, steel and Corten steel, forms were torch-cut and welded into dreamlike organic shapes. His underwater diving experiences and his emotional state were clearly reflected in his work. In the 1980s, he has gravitated toward a minimalist approach. Forms are clearly expressed in large scale, characterized by simple, precise cuts and the use of color to define both form and space. Sculptures are extroverted, communicating without complexity. He has recently been working on a series of large-scale ribbon sculptures made from rolled flat strips of stainless steel and bronze.

ARCHER, DAVE (Painter, Glazier)
P.O. Box 1229, San Rafael, CA 94915

Born: 1941 *Collections:* Wernher Von Braun; Frank Herbert *Exhibitions:* DeYoung Museum; Swanson Art Galleries, San Francisco

He achieves his remarkable special-effect, spacescape paintings by "painting" with a nine foot, free-swinging electrode connected to a seven foot high Telsa coil which generates over a million volts of electricity. His "brush" emits sizzling bolts of magenta lightning which stream over triple strength sheets of glass supported on a ceramic insulating frame. Sometimes he adds methyl alcohol inducing the paint to burst into flames and vaporize. The results are the swirling gaseous clouds and filmy nebulae which have become the hallmark of his work. His present influences are the mythological writings of Joseph Campbell.

ARCHULETA, JUAN (Painter)
1645 Clayton Way, Concord, CA 94520

Born: 1948 *Awards:* Best in Show, International Fine Arts Commemoration, Reno, NV *Collections:* Lesher Communications, Inc., Walnut Creek; California Insurance Co., Monterey *Exhibitions:* Americana, Carmel; Ruth Carlson, Mendocino *Dealer:* Addi Gallery, Bally's Grand Hotel, Reno, NV

Impressed by the simplicity of oriental painting and the brushwork of the impressionists, he paints forestscapes, seascapes and mountain scenery. He works in acrylic, on masonite or untempered press board, and uses earth tones, umber, yellow, blue, red and white. He has recently been working on a commission for the Yosemite Foundation, depicting winter on El Capitan.

ARIEL (Painter, Designer)
1001 Cragmont, Berkeley, CA 94708

Born: 1926 *Awards:* American Film Festival; Bay Area Theatre Critics Circle Award for Set and Costume Design *Collections:* Library and Museum of the Performing Arts at Lincoln Center, NYC; Cooper-Hewitt Museum of the Smithsonian Institution, Washington, D.C. *Exhibitions:* San Francisco Museum of Modern Art; Oakland Museum *Education:* Scripps College; U. of California *Dealer:* Vorpal, San Francisco

She works as a painter (in oil and watercolor) and as a designer of theatre sets and costumes. Her paintings reflect the formative influences of abstract expressionism, and mythological themes and paradigms. Each piece is figurative—intensely rendered against a field, from which the figure seems to emerge. Her brushwork is essentially abstract expressionist, and she sometimes builds up a painting surface with an underpainting of acrylic gesso. The overall quality of her work is visionary in the tradition of William Blake and Odilon Redon. Sculpture for theater is constructed from wire, papier mache, plastic, paint and cloth. Costumes, sets and paintings show a commitment to classic form, and a transcendental, dramatic vision of reality.

ARMAJANI, SIAH (Public Artist)
c/o Max Protech Gallery, 37 W. 57th St., New York, NY 10017

Born: 1939 *Collections:* Reading House for 1980 Olympics at Lake Placid; Reading Garden at SUNY *Exhibitions:* Institute of Contemporary Art, Philadelphia *Education:* Macalester College *Dealer:* Max Protech Gallery, NYC

Sculptures and structures make use of the vocabulary of architectural forms, particularly that of historical American structures. Describing himself as a midwestern populist, he creates works that are intended to be "read"; architectural borrowings point to the ways in which social concerns and ideals are expressed architecturally. The works also incorporate literary elements in the form of quotes from such American writers as Emerson and Dewey. He describes his on-site works as "structured locations," whose forms evolve out of the dialectic between the built object, its site and its intended use. Not content with providing merely an aesthetic experience, he provides an opportunity for the viewer to learn through an active engagement with the work.

ARMISTEAD, EUGENE (Painter)
1400 Edgehill Rd., #3, San Bernardino, CA 92405

Born: 1950 *Awards:* Best of Show, Texas Fine Arts Association *Collections:* Union Bank, Las Vegas; Clarion Hotel, Anchorage *Exhibitions:* Spectrum Gallery, Palm Desert; Desert Center, El Centno *Education:* U. of Texas, Austin *Dealer:* Vallerie Miller, Los Angeles

He paints in a highly developed figurative style, which emphasizes composition and a fully integrated surface. His current work consists of rather small-scale pieces, in which he combines acrylic, chalk and enamels on primed canvas. He lays canvases on the floor and uses paint right from the tube. Color acts as a design element, connecting earth-hued forms. Citing de Kooning, Pollock and Rod Bayer as major influences, he considers his style abstract expressionist, with undertones of figuration.

Dave Archer, *Earth Dream,* 24 x 32, lacquer and acrylics on reverse glass

Karen Atkinson, *Era After Era,* installation

ARMSTRONG, DUANE (Painter)
500 W. Park Ave., Boulder Creek, CA 95006

Born: 1938 *Collections:* Hewlett/Packard; Transamerica Corp., San Francisco *Exhibitions:* I. Magnin; Haakman Gallery, Ventura *Dealer:* Bridgeway Gallery, Sausalito

He was first recognized for a series of paintings of rural scenes, known as "Fields of Grass." Tiny houses and children lie far in the background of his broad, tranquil canvases. He evokes nostalgia and his paintings awaken the urban dweller's longing for peaceful contemplation. Combining smooth pastel tones with metallic inks that shimmer and blend, he creates broad areas of intense light in cloudless, open skies. His work has been reproduced and distributed by Heritage Publications, Windsor Art Company, Turner Art Company and Art Market International. Reproductions of his work can be purchased in nearly every department store in the nation.

ARMSTRONG, KATHRYN (Sculptor)
P.O. Box 79, Bodega, CA 94922

Born: 1933 *Exhibitions:* Museum of Modern Art; California Museum of Art *Education:* California College of Arts and Crafts; UC-Berkeley

While a student of Volkas at UC-Berkeley she developed a deep affinity for the process by which Stephen De Stabler came to his clay forms. The physical experience of creating and destroying and then recreating has been more important to her work than the theories in fashion over the decades. Aside from several years' interest in animal forms, her primary interest in both bronze and clay has been the metaphor of the human form. She currently juxtaposes unforgiving, harsh, mechanistic shapes with the soft impromptu forms of the figure, reflecting the life she sees in the media and in the fast changing world.

ARNESON, ROBERT (Ceramic Sculptor, Printmaker)
110 East E. St., Benicia, CA 94510

Born: 1930 *Collections:* Oakland Art Museum; San Francisco Museum of Modern Art *Exhibitions:* Whitney Museum, NYC; Museum of Modern Art, NYC *Education:* California College of Arts and Crafts; Mills College *Dealer:* Allan Frumkin Gallery, NYC; Fuller-Goldeen Gallery, San Francisco

For the last twenty years, he has created ceramic sculpture as well as prints and drawings. A cartoonist as a youth, he later became interested in the glazed, multipart clay forms of Peter Voulkos. The quality of rich color in his sculpture carries over to drawings and prints—his color prints employ from three to seven different hues. In recent years, a good deal of his work has centered on the subject of the self-portrait and on oversized ceramic busts glazed in bright colors. Other major concerns focus on the questions of identity and artistic persona that come naturally to the subject of the self portrait. The work pushes explicitness to an absurd extreme, a state that is the core of his characteristic wit.

ARNITZ, RICK (Painter)
345 Sutter St., San Francisco, CA 94108

Born: 1949 *Awards:* Roslyn Schneider Eisner Award, Univ. of California, Berkeley *Exhibitions:* Stephen Wirtz Gallery, San Francisco; Nexus Gallery, San Francisco *Education:* UC-Berkeley *Dealer:* Stephen Wirtz Gallery, San Francisco

He often paints illusionistic frames around the edges of his canvases, imparting to the pieces a pictorial, illusionistic feel that frames and sets at a distance abstract images of standing wave patterns, dots and bands of color. One critic compared the artist's unpretentious non-figurative paintings to "memories of bad TV reception." He works his surfaces with layers of oils and oil enamels, often using uncommon tools such as paint rollers. His earlier works were abstracted landscapes filled with odd boulders that resembled gum drops. His work has been compared to that of Frank Stella and Ralph Humphrey.

ARNOLDI, CHARLES ARTHUR (Painter, Sculptor)
721 Hampton Dr., Venice, CA 90291

Born: 1946 *Awards:* Guggenheim Fellowship; NEA Fellowship *Collections:* Los Angeles County Museum of Art; San Francisco Museum of Modern Art *Exhibitions:* Whitney Museum, NYC; Fuller-Goldeen Gallery, San Francisco *Education:* Chouinard Art Institute *Dealer:* James Corcoran Gallery, Los Angeles

Originally intent on becoming a commercial illustrator, he quickly turned to painting. He is known for large-scale works made of two panels, one resembling an intricate mesh of painted twig shapes and the other consisting of actual twigs affixed to the canvas and painted, as in *Plummet* and *Volcano—Log Jam*. These wood-and-oil pieces are boldly colored and full of explosive energy. Recently he has begun working in sculpture on its own. "I have become interested in wood as an alternative to painting," he says. "I especially like tree branches, which have a very distinct line quality. They feel hand-drawn, they have a certain gestural quality, a naturalness. . . . It provides a solution to my desire for subject matter." The pieces are in wood and bronze.

ARO, PHILIP G. (Painter)
179 11th St., San Francisco, CA 94103

Born: 1959 *Exhibitions:* Emmanuel Walter Gallery, San Francisco; Cafe Pastoral, Berkeley *Education:* San Francisco Art Institute *Dealer:* San Francisco Museum of Modern Art Rental Gallery, San Francisco

After an initial exploration of classical surrealism, he became interested in non-referential formal schemes and worked to develop the abstract so that it would reflect on the artist's personal experiences more directly than in most non- representational art. His earliest works were executed as etchings or with pencil on paper. In Los Angeles, he began experimenting with color painting and dabbling in multimedia forms of artistic expression, but after moving to San Francisco, he settled on acrylic on canvas as his medium of choice. His method of working has been compared to a cartographer's: he begins with a series of sketches and a set of notes and from there creates the painting, careful to let the painting grow organically beyond the ideas expressed in his preliminary designs.

ARSON, DIANE (Sculptor, Glazier)
360 N. Whipple St., Fort Bragg, CA 95437

Born: 1942 *Exhibitions:* Northcoast Artist's Cooperative Gallery, Fort Bragg; Winona Gallery of Mendocino *Education:* UC-Berkeley

Influenced by Nolde, Gauguin, Cezanne and Parks, her paintings of figurative forms and landscapes during the 1960s and 1970s reflected her interest in the inherent qualities of color, light and line. Since the begin-

Fredi Adams, S.W.A, *Winter's Eiderdown,* 36 x 42, acrylic.
Courtesy: "The" Gallery, Burlingame, CA

E. Armistead, *Pinch-Bowl,* 9 x 6 x 5, stoneware

ning of 1980s, she has been experimenting with different media, adding sculptural considerations to images of dancers and figures of myth and legend. She shapes and assembles hand-made paper in collage fashion, creating wall reliefs. She carves and texturally treats sand-etched glass panels, exploring the control of shifting light. With the pure pigments of pastel, she describes dancers and landscapes, exploring the interplay of color and reflecting the influence of Degas.

ASH, LUCY (Photographer)
149 Highlands Dr., Carmel, CA 93923

Born: 1929 *Exhibitions:* Focus Gallery, San Francisco; American River College, Sacramento *Education:* UC-Berkeley; San Francisco State College *Dealer:* Josephus Daniels Gallery, Carmel

What she calls "straight" black and white photography led to "Photo Constructions," or photographs that were combined in a three-dimensional manner. The most important of these early pieces could be rotated and manipulated by the viewer to obtain sixty-four different face composites. Next she developed "Photo Synthesis," a technique which maps fact and fantasy onto one another. In these works, black-and-white images on positive film are placed over a variety of materials, such as hand colored photographs, water colors, cyanotypes, children's drawings and collages. The result is multimedia photographs. There is a whimsical, humorous quality to these pieces. In *Models and Mannequin*, a refectory-type table has been transformed into a swimming pool of water supplying refreshment for a model in the pool's center. In "Sky High Series," a man relaxes in a chair, oblivious to a hang glider enmeshed in a tree overhead. Of late, she has returned to realism. Using cibachrome color photography, she is interested in capturing that moment when natural light transforms the ordinary, familiar object into the extraordinary.

ASHLEY, FRANK N. (Painter)
Box 4951, Carmel CA 93921

Born: 1920 *Awards:* Grand Prize, Art U.S.A. New York; Alma Spreckels Award, 4th Invitational, San Francisco Oak Lawn Jockey Club, Hot Springs, AR; California Jockey Club, San Mateo, CA *Exhibitions:* Oehlschlager Gallery, Chicago; Palace of the Legion of Honor *Dealer:* Zantman Gallery, Carmel, CA; Red Fox Fine Arts, Middleburg, VA

Following his receipt of two Distinguished Flying Crosses in World War II, he worked as Reginald Marsh's assistant in New York. Marsh's work influenced his slightly Old-Master-styled renderings of figures. The dynamics of his pieces are powerful, in both his tense, active use of composition and his subtly expressionistic use of color. He is best known for his studies of horse training, point to point racing and other equestrian events and has painted at Newmarket and Chantilly. While his work with horses continues, a recent painting centers on the murder of civil rights workers in Philadelphia, Mississippi. Influenced by the etchings of Goya and the moody, emotional works of Picasso, the darker tones of this piece are a brutal contrast to his typical use of strong brights and rich pastel tones. His "Jazz Series" combines emotional momentum in his figures with a compressed, intensified sense of place to confront the viewer with a bold representation of life at its most fully lived moments. The images are based on his memories and experiences with the jazz played in New York, Chicago and New Orleans. The Italian

Renaissance artists' inspiration and enthusiasm for form is the cornerstone of all his work.

ASKEW, R. ANTHONY (Painter)
1759 Glen Oaks Dr., Santa Barbara, CA

Born: 1939 *Awards:* Artist Liaison, Laguna Art Museum *Collections:* Ashton Tate Corp., Los Angeles; Pacific Mutual Realty, Newport *Exhibitions:* Delphine Gallery, Santa Barbara; Kirvan/Bartosewitz Gallery, Palm Springs *Education:* Cal. State-Los Angeles; UC-Santa Barbara

Influenced by abstract expressionism, he searches for an austere broadness, in which geometry is simplified and set in floating space, creating an experience of scale, color and light. He is concerned with atmospheric colorations and geometric shapes as he strives for "a mood of quiet resignation with symphonic contrasts." His colorful work reminiscent of clouds is inspired by nature, reflecting a personal buoyancy and optimism. He is currently painting large, non-objective geometric watercolors, often as triptychs. He is also a children's illustrator, a printmaker, a designer and associate professor of art at Westmont College.

ASMAR, ALICE (Painter, Printmaker)
1125 N. Screenland Dr., Burbank, CA 91505

Awards: Harriett Hale Wooley Grant; Distinguished Alumni Award, Lewis and Clark College *Collections:* Franklin Mint; Smithsonian Institution *Exhibitions:* Southwest Museum, Los Angeles; Museum of Science and Industry, Los Angeles *Education:* U. of Washington, Seattle *Dealer:* Dr. Julian Feingold, Senior Eye Gallery, Long Beach

During her early years, she drew seascapes and old Victorian buildings. She painted a moody abstract series of works, culminating in the innovative visual opera *Pelleas and Melisande*. For this unique presentation, she developed a secular polyptych, placing Pablo Neruda's poems on wood panels that surrounded oil paintings. Her imagery and dark, moody colors captured the symbolist moods of Debussy's opera of the same title. During the late 1950s, she studied in Paris. There she created another secular polyptych, using Schoenberg's music as the basis of semi-abstract Parisian mood paintings. She moved to California in the early 1960s, where she began making European- influenced mural-like drawings and mixed-media compositions. California buildings and scenes and flora and fauna began to appear in her work. A visit to New Mexico brought desert colors and Indian imagery to her works. Her recent work combines unusual color harmonies, a love for flowers, and unusual compositions in a very contemporary mood.

ASTON, MIRIAM (Mixed Media Artist)
P. O. Box 241, Claremont, CA 91711

Awards: Award of Distinction, Scarab Club, Detroit; Gold Medal for Sculpture, Scarab Club *Collections:* U.N. Conference for Women, Nairobi *Exhibitions:* Chrysallis Gallery, Claremont; Museum of Science and Industry, Los Angeles *Education:* Center of Creative Arts, Detroit; Wayne St. U.; U. of Michigan; USC

Her formal art training began when she was very young. First a painter, she was highly influenced by abstract expressionism and impressionism. She later turned to sculpture, using modern materials, such as stainless steel, aluminum, wood and fabric, combined with the traditional materials of hard wood, bronze and aluminum casting, to explore the symbolism of

Loren Adams, *La Mia Prerogitiva,* 18 x 60, oil on canvas. Photographer: Duncan McDougall, F.R.P.S.

Alice Asmar, *Moonlight & One Indian Vase,* 24 x 36, casein on Haruki.
Courtesy: Senior Eye Gallery, Long Beach

light and color in ancient art forms. A continuing concern with light and color brought her back to painting. Working on large surfaces with mixed media, movement, time and light are the primary subjects as she seeks to express spiritual values. Most recent works are experiments with the human figure fractured into optical imagery, expressions of the elusive and ethereal presence of light.

ATKINS, BILL (Painter, Illustrator)
31568 First Ave., South Laguna, CA 92677

Born: 1947 *Exhibitions:* Laguna Beach Festival of the Arts; Sawdust Festival of Laguna Beach

Watercolor illustrations show the influences of classic illustrators Norman Rockwell and Maxfield Parrish. His specialty is idealized landscape, rendered predominantly in purples, reds, greens and lush earth tones. Since moving to California, he has been more interested in advertising and commercial art. He has designed and painted many logos, menus and brochures for southern California businesses.

ATKINSON, KAREN (Sculptor)
3348 W. 9th, #9, Los Angeles, CA 90006

Born: 1956 *Exhibitions:* New Langton Arts, San Francisco; California Institute of the Arts *Education:* California Institute of the Arts

Her sculptural installations increasingly center on non-permanent public sites, heightening the immediate impact of her social imagery. For instance, in a recent installation, she collaborated with filmmakers and performance artists, projecting slides in storefront windows from dusk to midnight. The common objects she uses in her installation—books checked out of a local library, overhead projection transparencies, photography, playing cards— are accessible to all audiences. In her work, she strives to engage and interact with the viewer. She also contends with the relation of subject to object and with social issues. *Playing for Time* directly addresses the AIDS crisis. She combines the image of a microscope with an altered deck of cards at the center of a blue pedestal. The cards contain images, words, photos, and drawings and are meant to be handled by the viewer. Numbers on the cards correspond to pins on back panel maps shaped like of human figures—representing national populations. A symbolic microscope hovers above, examining the scene below.

ATTIE, SHIMON (Photographer, Assemblage Artist)
100 Hermann St. #1, San Francisco, CA 94102

Born: 1957 *Awards:* Top 100 New Photographers of the United States *Collections:* Lee & Lee's Contemporary Art Gallery, San Francisco *Exhibitions:* ProArts Juried Annual, Oakland; San Francisco State U. Gallery; *Education:* UC- Berkeley; Antioch U.

After training in formalist urban landscape photography, influenced by Jack Welpott, Catherine Wagner and Don Worth, he developed his own style devoted to the assemblage of objects and environments which he photographed in his studio. While still formal in nature, his more recent work has become more conceptual and psychological. In the series entitled "Photo-soma- topographies, 1988," he has used maps as a ground onto which diagrams, objects and drawings of various parts of the body are arranged and then photographed with a 4 x 5 camera to produce large-scale Ektacolor prints. Deceptively simple images are enhanced by a textual component that seeks to transform commonplace assumptions about the meaning of form as well as the meaning of language. In the series called "DSM-III, 1989," various psychological character types are represented by individuals posing in richly colored environments filled with floating body parts and organs. These images express connections between personality type, representation of the body, color and gender. The major influences on his work are conceptual art, psychoanalysis, medicine, semiotics and deconstruction and his own work as a psychotherapist and body therapist.

AUFHAUSER, GRETA (Painter, Printmaker)
33018 Pacific Coast Hwy., Malibu, CA 90265

Awards: Scholarship, Rijks Academy of Fine Arts, Amsterdam; Cash Award, Los Angeles All City Art Festival *Exhibitions:* San Francisco City Hall; Los Angeles Natural History Museum *Education:* USC; Ecole des Beaux Arts, Paris

The single most profound influence of her life was the Nazi occupation of her homeland, Holland. This experience, together with the unceasing hunger, the unremitting degradation of the individual and the senseless executions made her even more aware of the indispensability of freedom and led her to regard social and racial injustice as a total aberration. Her style and approach have been influenced by the works of Kollwitz and Van Gogh. She has completed several commissions for stained glass windows.

AUSGANG, ANTHONY (Painter)
1013 Madison Ave., Hollywood, CA 90029

Born: 1959 *Exhibitions:* Los Angeles County Museum of Art; San Diego Art Institute *Education:* Otis/Parsons School of Design; U. of Texas

A childhood passion for Charles Addams, Billy Bunter and *Krazy Kat* comics is probably his greatest influence, though exposure to ethnic and fine art through travel has also contributed to his singular way of regarding American culture. Inspired by all forms of mass communication, he began to study cartoon art and the practice of animation. This led to a realism that dealt with the concept of the critical moment, in which situations change suddenly. He began to paint in acrylics when introduced to animation cells. Combining the distortion of cartoons with the scale and posture of fine art, he has achieved a hybrid in which fantastic environments and their inhabitants are rendered with a refined technique. Displaying human endeavor in animal form provides a humorous and disarming method by which to inform the viewer of more pressing issues. In one mural, a workman digs a grave for three dead mice beside a cat, whose tail wags like a dinner bell. It is an invasion of Saturday morning cartoons into the gallery, or onto the walls of Los Angeles.

AUSTIN, ANTHONY (Mixed Media Artist)
4966 Franklin Ave. #3, Los Angeles, CA 90027

Born: 1942 *Collections:* Ruth & Marvin Sackner Archive of Concrete & Visual Poetry, Miami *Exhibitions:* Stella Polaris Gallery, Los Angeles; Barnsdall Municipal Art Gallery, Los Angeles *Education:* Chouinard Art Institute; California Institute of the Arts

His fascination with the foreshortening in Michelangelo's figures and his passion for studying world atlases arose from a profound curiosity about

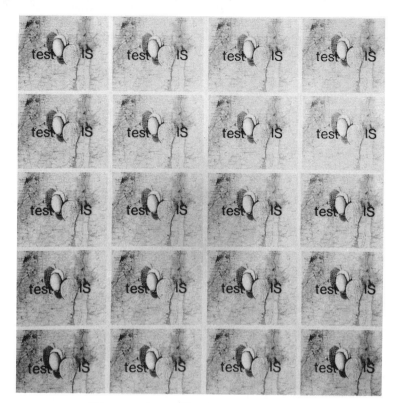

Shimon Attie, *test IS,* 40 x 40, ektacolor print

Benny Alba, *Back into Mother's Arms,* 36 x 40, oil and metallics

the nature of matter and its relationship to space. He probes this relationship through the use of 3-by-3-inch grids placed over a paper surface, reminiscent of the Cartesian coordinate system upon which mapping is based. He selects two geographic locations that are dissimilar, and by juxtaposing symbols, alters the viewer's perceptual state. The images move from opposite directions towards each other and are forced to meet, thus altering their appearance and meaning. The viewer's original perception is challenged by means of overlaying and transforming recognizable imagery, the intention being to cause aesthetic estrangement and create a moment in which the viewer accepts the unfamiliar.

AUVIL, ELEEN (Weaver, Sculptor)
278 Corral De Tierra, Salinas, CA 93908

Awards: AID International Design Award *Collections:* Detroit Institute of Art; Cranbrook Academy of Art Museum, Bloomfield, MI *Exhibitions:* Alan Short Gallery, Stockton; Carmel Art Association, Carmel *Education:* Cranbrook Academy of Art

She trained as a sculptor and weaver and for many years produced hanging woven sculptures. In 1981, she switched her primary emphasis to bronze sculpture and since then has been producing sculptures of people and birds. Often, her avian pieces have elements of human figuration used to humorous effect. The years of working with textiles leave their influence on the tactile surface, giving an impression akin to Matisse and Henry Moore. She also produces welded armatures in airy shapes that she covers with handwoven fabric, treats for permanence and paints with acrylics. The fabric is woven from wool, linen and silk, and she uses the spectrum of colors applied with both the brush and the spraygun. She is a great admirer of Brancusi and David Smith.

AVARY, BETH (Painter)
70 Sioux Way, Portola Valley, CA 94025

Born: 1941 *Exhibitions:* Collins Gallery, San Francisco; Lawrence Hall of Science, Berkeley *Education:* California College of Arts and Crafts

An interest in astronomy and physics has led this painter from work in abstract landscapes using watercolors and oils to "astrosurrealism" executed mainly in acrylics. In these three-by- four-foot paintings, deep space images—galaxies, nebulae, etc.— are juxtaposed with earthly subjects—plants, people, seashells. The seashell is of particular significance: As it lays on a beach or a rock, its small spiraled formation is echoed in the giant swirling cosmos behind it. Influenced by the pre- Raphaelites and by Victorian and Art Nouveau painters, she paints in a naturalistic manner, although she employs airbrush and wash technique, lighting the "hot" black space with bright colors.

AZEVEDO, DANILO (Painter)
1211 N. Flores St., Hollywood, CA 90069

Born: 1927 *Awards:* Museu de Americana, Brazil *Exhibitions:* UCLA; Cal. State-Northridge

He was born in northeastern Brazil and grew up under the strong influence of Covarrarubias, Rivera, Chagall, Matisse and Portinari. He studied with Rodolph Lima, Balthazar da Camara and Emilio Castellar in Brazil. Later, he went to Europe and had classes with G. Rouaux and Eduard Loeffler. He begins his work by making up to a dozen drawings. He paints abstractions with some figurative forms. In these pieces, he combines personal emotions with a witty sense of his environment.

AZZOLA, OLGA (Painter, Sculptor)
555 Pierce St., #744, Albany, CA 94706

Exhibitions: La Raza Graphics, San Francisco; Berkeley Art Center *Education:* Cal. State-Hayward

After formal training in oils and airbrush, she progressed rapidly from realism to abstract expressionism. Her masks on canvas and her primitive-style paintings were influenced by cave paintings, African art and especially by Native American rock etchings. Her work exhibits a love of texture; she often paints with her finger or with a wooden knife. Working in earth tones and blues, she attempts an honest and communicative art. Her materials include molding paste, sand, acrylic and Japanese handmade paper.

BABCOCK, JO (Photographer, Sculptor)
808 Arlington Ave., Berkeley, CA 94707

Born: 1954 *Awards:* Grant, NY State Council on the Arts; Grant, Interarts of Marin *Collections:* The Brooklyn Museum; Visual Studies Workshop, Rochester, NY *Exhibitions:* Marcuse Pfeifer Gallery, NYC; Zwinger, Berlin *Education:* San Francisco Art Institute *Dealer:* Marcuse Pfeifer, NYC

As an undergraduate, she experimented with several silver and non-silver print processes; during graduate school, she began working extensively with pinhole photography. She continued to develop sculptural pinhole work, while also building installation works. Influenced by Sue Coe, Robert Arneson and Bertolt Brecht, she has recently merged aspects of photography and sculpture with topical concerns. She constructs simple cameras out of common objects, and uses them to make photographs: suitcase cameras photograph hotels; ammunition-can cameras photograph war monuments. The buildings in her photographs are usually in a state of erection or deconstruction. Her prints are large, negative color images. Her vision is post-apocalyptic.

BACA, LORENZO (Painter, Sculptor)
P. O. Box 4353, Sonora, CA 95370

Born: 1947 *Awards:* NEA Folks Arts Grant *Collections:* Heard Museum, Phoenix *Exhibitions:* Chaw'se Indian Grinding Rock State Park, Volcano; Mother Lode Art Show, Sonora *Education:* Cal. State-Long Beach; UCLA

This painter, sculptor, printmaker and silversmith frequently recalls his Isleta Pueblo and Mescalero Apache background for subject matter and inspiration. The paintings are done mostly in acrylics on large, five-by-six-foot canvases, the images referring to Native American history and iconography. His subject matter does not, however, dwell exclusively on Native American themes. Working with hand-made paper to which he transfers computer-enhanced magazine photographs in a process similar to Rauschenberg's montages, he produces "photo-based altered image montages." He continues to sculpt and craft jewelry, and recently he has been investigating the creation of animal forms using metal cylinders.

BACHENHEIMER, BETH (Painter)
P.O. Box 66353, Los Angeles, CA 40066

Born: 1948 *Collections:* Neuro Development Center, Glendale; Judy Chicago, Fresno *Exhibitions:* Irvine Art Center; Beyond Baroque, Venice *Education:* Califor-

Greta Aufhauser, *Election Day,* 40 x 30, conte crayon

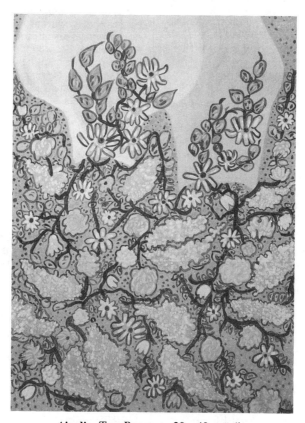

Ainslie, *Two Bouquets,* 30 x 40, acrylic.

nia Institute of the Arts; Chouinard Art Institute *Dealer:* Barbara Pascal, Los Angeles

Influenced by mentor Miriam Schapiro and the feminist art program, she decided, upon graduation, to explore painting in a more isolated environment. For some time, she explored different ways of approaching a single subject, such as closets. Landscape drawing followed, and oil paintings of dried proteas and bancias emphasizing their rare and exotic appearance. The works of de Kooning, Matisse, Manet and Janet Provisor have informed her oils and "scarfscapes" in watercolor and book form. She intends to push her imagery into greater levels of abstraction on a larger scale without losing center and focus.

BAEDER, JOHN (Painter, Author)
1025 Overton Lea Rd., Nashville, TN 37220

Born: 1938 *Collections:* Whitney Museum,; Cooper-Hewitt Museum *Exhibitions:* O.K. Harris, NYC; Modernism, San Francisco *Education:* Auburn U. *Dealer:* O.K. Harris Works of Art, NYC; Zimmerman/Saturn Gallery, Nashville

His works are characterized by a painterly, photo-realistic approach and reveal a fascination with diners as icons of American culture. His depictions of diners are done with extreme accuracy and a nearly imperceptible brushstroke. Recent works include *Moran St. Diner, North End Diner (Torrington, CT)* and *Shorty's Shortstop, Hendersonville, TN.* Interest in the subject led to his publication in 1982 of *Gas, Food, and Lodging,* inspired by postcard images of the 1920s, '30s and '40s. The publication contained anecdotes and stories gathered through visits and documented diners that have withstood the test of time. His work also reveals an ongoing interest in folk art, found objects, and artifacts—he collects Cadillac images and toys. *No Loud Cussing Please,* a recent project, deals with folk signs.

BAER, ROD (Sculptor)
3803 San Rafael Ave., Los Angeles, CA 90065

Born: 1951 *Awards:* Environmental Sculpture, Tri-City Corporate Center, San Bernardino *Exhibitions:* Security Pacific Plaza; University of Southern California *Education:* San Diego U.; Claremont Graduate School *Dealer:* Meyers Bloom Gallery, Santa Monica

Originally influenced by the plays and performances of the absurdist and existentialist writers, he engages his "audience" in a visual dialogue by implying their presence within structural tableaux of familiar objects. Furniture, sidewalks and creative tools such as easels, paint brushes and cameras provoke contemplation of ways of living and seeing on both a personal and an archetypal level. These metaphorical puzzles bring into play a surrealist preoccupation with the relationship between perception, reality and the artistic production of meaning. In earlier work, safety pins and pencil tips protrude from chrome- plated or rusted steel boxes. On the recent *In Contemplation of Missing Teeth,* located in downtown Los Angeles, full-sized chairs mounted on and scattered around a twenty-seven-foot hoop mimic the sprockets of a broken gear wheel. Connotations of the cyclic, fragmented, often grandiose nature of communication reveal the subtle humor of his work.

BAILEY, ALICIA (Photographer)
P.O. Box 613, Lake City, CO 81235

Born: 1958 *Awards:* Maria Elkin Award *Collections:* Amoco Oil *Exhibitions:* Gallery 44, Oakland; Pacific

Grove Art Center *Education:* U. of Colorado *Dealer:* Accent Art, Valencia, CA; Ginny Williams, Denver, CO

She shoots photographs in 35mm black-and-white, then enlarges the image to a print up to 30 x 40 inches. At this point, she begins to alter the image, painting with oils, acrylics and enamels. She may also add metal leaf, stitch pieces of rag paper to the photo with thread, or color with pencil, pastel and ink to create a collage that simultaneously suggests fragmentation and wholeness. Living forms are often juxtaposed with inanimate objects. She is strongly influenced in this approach by the rural way of life, in which she witnesses nature cycles—her pieces representing our fragmented glimpses of these cycles.

BAILEY, CAROLINE (Painter)
1840 Rachael Ave., National City, CA 92050

Born: 1950 *Exhibitions:* CityFest Art Show, San Diego; Art Corner, National City *Education:* Southwestern College

Her work often combines fine, hard-edged shapes with finer, geometric shapes on canvas, using black, white and one other color graduated either from dark to light or from dark to darker. The work alludes to the moody elements of design and is expressionistic in spirit. Her recently completed "Gold Leaf" series is an abstract expressionist body of work using gold, copper and aluminum leaf with variegated blues and greens applied to the canvas and gessoed. The "Patience" series is more typical of her use of blacks—fluid, free flowing forms of green and blues graduating in darkness, with bare canvas showing like veins through the forms. Her newest work is executed in pastel etchings, an old technique she has adapted for use with modern materials. She is also experimenting with the vacuum-form plastics process, developing lightweight plastic forms to be applied to the canvas as reliefs, underscoring the fine design elements.

BAIN, JENNIFER (Painter)
4701 San Leandro Blvd., Oakland, CA 94601

Born: 1955 *Awards:* Exhibition Award, Bay Arts '87, San Mateo; Honorable Mention, Los Angeles Design Center *Exhibitions:* Southern Exposure Gallery, Berkeley; San Francisco Fiberworks Gallery *Education:* San Francisco Art Institute *Dealer:* San Francisco Museum of Modern Art Rental and Sales Gallery

She finds inspiration through the lens of a microscope, and the source of her work is nature seen up close. She paints biomorphic shapes in complex landscapes, dense and geometric. These images derive not only from the physical world but from the imagination, resurrected and abstracted. To arrest viewers' attentions and to impose on them not only a visual but also a tactile relationship to her work, she applies her paint with particular concern for weight and density, thus rendering the very surface of her painting an object for contemplation. She achieves this end by adding wax to the paint, then applying it in layers with a conscious, painterly technique. Among the artists who have influenced her style and approach are Matisse, Cezanne, Bonnard, Kandinsky, and the German expressionists, the abstract expressionists and folk artists.

Anthony Austin, *Tutankhamen Meets Forest Lawn at Santa Monica Beach,* 32 x 40, mixed media

Bobbie Altman, *Lessons of Survival: Thoughts of Release,* 22 x 29, mixed media on paper

BAKARICH, MARY JANE (Sculptor, Ceramist)
604 11th St., Davis, CA 95616

Born: 1953 *Exhibitions:* P.J. Shields Library, UC-Davis; Rara Avis Gallery, Sacramento *Education:* Sacramento City Junior College; Cal. State U.

After college, she built "folded" pots out of slabs of multi-colored porcelain, sculpted wire-mesh trees and, in a Chinese style, painted goldfish and lily pads on silk, tiles and paper. Her double-spiral-constructed "tree" sculptures originated as an exploration of plant structure and need no internal supports. Later, larger "trees" resembled stumps and were made with cyclone fencing, nuts and bolts. In her current open-walled, lacy "tree" structures, she uses hand-woven wire ribbons to better communicate this double spiral theory. In these pieces, she keeps the volume of the trunk and reinstates the "tree's" top, giving the work the look of a tubular, open-roofed room.

BAKER, ANN (Painter)
72 Calle de Este, P.O. Box 335, Carmel Valley, CA 93924

Born: 1930 *Exhibitions:* Leedo Gallery, Gilroy; Gallery Americana, Carmel *Education:* California College of Art & Crafts *Dealer:* Gallery Americana, Carmel

After completing her art training, she moved to the Monterey Peninsula with her husband, artist Eugene Ames Baker. There she established a career as a realist painter under the name Ann Rugh. Several years ago, she changed her style and subjects, pursuing a desire to paint memories of American life, particularly from the turn of the century. The photographs and memories handed down from her mother and grandmother formed the basis of her new style. Now she paints not only historical scenes of life in old California, but scenes of early 20th-century life from throughout the United States. Her acrylic paintings exhibit a stylized realism and are executed in flat colors. Small, delicately rendered figures inhabit urban and rural landscapes in all seasons and weathers. Each work is characterized by exacting attention to detail in the architecture, activities, vehicles and dress. She has recently resumed painting under the name Ann Rugh and divides her time between her early and her later styles.

BAKER, JOE (Painter)
277 E. Tuckey Ln., Phoenix, AZ 85012

Born: 1946 *Awards:* Sarpe Scholar *Collections:* Metropolitan Museum of Art; Smithsonian Institution *Exhibitions:* Corcoran Biennial of American Painting; Western States Biennial *Education:* U. of Tulsa; U. of Arkansas

He lampoons the western lifestyle with a fresh and humorous approach to social satire, through animal characters such as "Chief Thunderfoot," "The Fat Bride," and an elusive cat. Although he also draws, he is known for his paint application—a sumptuous combination of a marvelously thick medium and quick and aggressive brushstrokes. His areas of figuration provide him with fields for exploring rich, sumptuous color with drips, swirls and marks. His painting *Monkey Business* is a strikingly contemporary, bright and modern view of four monkeys traveling across an abstracted plain. Evidence of the painter's hand is everywhere, yet the work is figurative and recognizable.

BAKER, SALLY (Painter)
5990 Vine Hill School Rd., Sebastopol, CA 95472

Born: 1949 *Awards:* 1986 Graphic Design Merit Award, Nekossa Papers, Inc., Santa Rosa *Collections:* DeLoach Vineyards, Santa Rosa *Exhibitions:* Arts Guild of Sonoma; Earthworks, Santa Rosa *Education:* UC-Santa Barbara *Dealer:* First Impressions, Carmel; Arts Guild of Sonoma

After formal training in drawing and painting, she studied for many years with artist Corinne Hartley in Los Angeles. She concentrated on watercolor and was encouraged to follow her own unique style of sharp-edged shapes and intense shadows. After a painting trip to Santa Fe in 1982, her subject matter changed dramatically to reflect the desert landscape she had just come to know. Although her style is quite different from O'Keeffe's, the drama of the high desert light is apparent in her work as well. In addition to depicting the play of light and shadow, she is drawn to the desert colors, rendered in soft pastels with a subtle intensity. The subjects of her paintings include adobe structures and a series of works that feature Navaho blankets as "mountain landscapes."

BAKER, TERRY (Painter)
1067 Marcheta Ln., Pebble Beach, CA 93953

Born: 1942 *Awards:* Best of Show, Annual Watercolor Competition, Pacific Grove Natural History Museum; National Watercolor Society Annual Exhibition and Traveling Show *Exhibitions:* National Watercolor Society; Redding Museum of Art *Dealer:* Cottage Gallery, Carmel

For almost twenty years, he was a draughtsman, graphic artist and illustrator. He developed his technique, studying with Tom Nicholas, Tom Hill, Christopher Schink, Millard Sheets and others. Recently, the intricate shadows cast by trees and foliage are the subjects of his historical and architectural paintings. He paid visual homage to the Monterey Peninsula's architecture and landscape in his exhibition, "Landscapes and Victorians." His works are tonally nuanced and he uses a wide range of layering techniques and subtle pigments, ranging from the palest grays to the deepest violets.

BALDESSARI, JOHN ANTHONY (Photographer, Conceptual Artist)
2001 1/2 Main St., Santa Monica, CA 90405

Born: 1931 *Awards:* NEA Grant; Guggenheim Grant *Collections:* Museum of Modern Art, NYC; Los Angeles County Museum of Art *Exhibitions:* Museum of Modern Art; Documenta 5 and 7, Kassel, West Germany *Education:* San Diego State U.; Otis Art Institute *Dealer:* Sonnabend Gallery, NYC

Originally a painter, his work of the 1960s reflected an interest in minimalism and in the formal and semantic applications of words in the manner of Magritte. *Work With Only One Property*, created in 1966, was a blank white canvas with only the title of the piece professionally lettered upon the pristine surface. As a conceptual photographer, his interests have been similar. He photographs words out of context from various pages of text, with an anonymous finger pointing to a phrase, as in *Scenario (Scripts) (1972-73)*. His film loops also repeat words, objects or actions. In photography and in films, he hypothesizes about what art can be, expanding the definition of Conceptual Art.

Bobbie Altman, *Passages: Illusions of Freedom,* 32 x 40, mixed media on paper

Kathryn Armstrong, *3 Standing Figures with Steel,*
23 x 10 x 3, ceramic and steel

Lois Anderson, *The Throne,*
78 x 48 x 36, assemblage

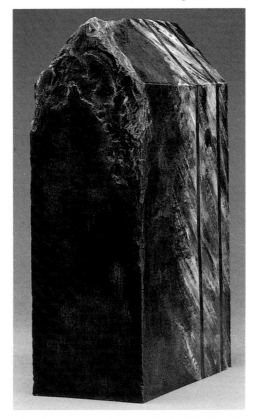

Patricia Ancona, *Structure Eight,* 18 x 5 x 17,
clay with wax patina

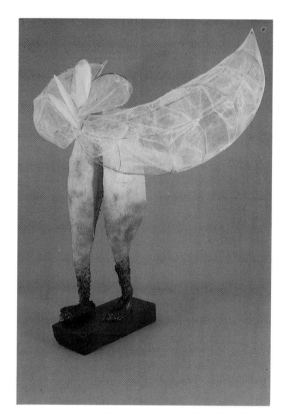

Eleen Auvil, *The Jubjub Bird,* 82 x 68 x 46,
mixed media

Dave Archer, *Aerobix,* 30 x 20, lacquer and
acrylic on reverse glass

Loren Adams, *The Crystal Cave, "Oh Great Star What Would Your Happiness be if You Had Not Those For Whom You Shine," From the Prologue of Thus spake Zarathustra by Fred Nietszche, The Last Perfect Day of Midsummer, Mu, the Motherland: The Day the Mountains were Raised, The Magic Cave of Merlin,* mixed media

Loren Adams, *The Disappearing Chalice which becomes the Face of Mozart at the site of the Coronation of the Lady of the Sun...During the Arrival of the Visitation Party from the Planet Hesperus twenty thousand years ago,* 40 x 30, oil on canvas.
Courtesy: Mr. John Paul Jones DeJoria

Boyd Allen, *Bocchear,* 21 x 29, watercolor and gouache.
Courtesy: David Ruml

Katherine Ace, *Juggler (Face to Face Series),* 24 x 20,
watercolor, pastel, charcoal

Gretchen Aona, *Rainbow-Colored Gingers,* 13 x 9, watercolor

Robert Aisawa, *War Zone,* 30 x 40, mixed media collage on canvas

Maria Alquilar, *Watching as My Soul Ascends,*
29 x 21 x 2, clay, mixed media

F.N. Ashley, *Man with Horn,* 65 x 48, oil

Rita Deanin Abbey, *Emergence,* 86 x 76, acrylic on canvas

Linda J. Albertano, *Summertime,* performance, John Anson Ford
Theater. Photograph: Basia Kenton

Anthony Austin, *Houdini Meets China Town in Lancaster at 183rd and Ave. B,* 32 x 40, mixed media

Sarkis Antikajian, *Rhodies with Green Bottle,* 30 x 30, oil

Loren Adams, *Telos- Mu/ " Many Thousand of Years Ago in the
Eastern Section of the Motherland, Lemuria, in a Land Known as Telos,
the First Trade Ships Arrived from the Planet Hesperus,* 30 x 36, oil on canvas

Loren Adams, *The Naacal Temple of the Pristine Wilderness in the Western Section
of the Motherland, Mu, in a Land Known as Hiranypura, the Legend of Creation and
the First Cosmogonic Diagram of the Eight Roads to Heaven Were Taught to the Nagamayas...Homage to
Rodin, 20 x 24, oil on canvas.* Courtesy: Mr. and Mrs. Sammy Hagar

Ariel, *Emperor's Pavement,* 34 x 36, oil on masonite

Fredi Adams, S.W.A, *Summer Mist,* 36 x 42, acrylic. Courtesy: "The" Gallery, Burlingame, CA

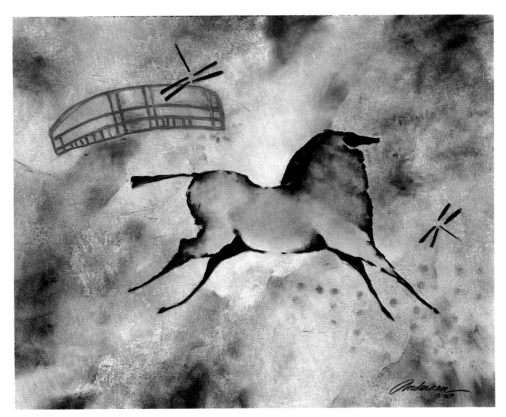

Cynthia Andersen, *Niaux,* 49 x 38, pastel, paper

Kent Alexander, *Oval Sunset: Hopes and Dreams,* 11 x 14, oil on canvas

Raul Anguiano, *Woman Resting,* 23 x 30, lithograph

E. Armistead, *Volcano,* 38 x 52, acrylic on paper

George Alpert, *The Last Supper,* 36 x 48, acrylic. Courtesy: Udinotti Gallery, San Francisco

Alice Asmar, *Sunday at Descanso,* 36 x 48, mixed media on canvas. Courtesy: Senior Eye Gallery, Long Beach

Ruby Aranguiz L. *Green Maja,* 40 x 30, oil

C.H. Anderson, *Magnolia,* 11 x 15, watercolor

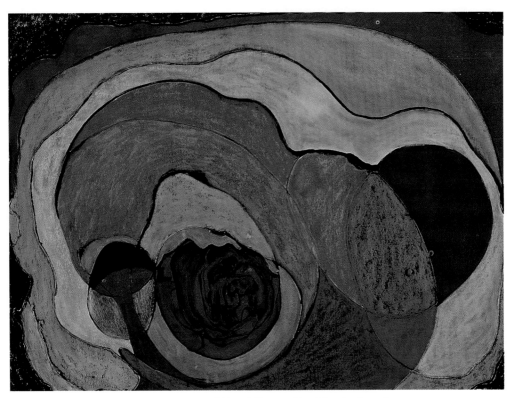

Lorraine Almeida, *Gifts of Nature,* 19 x 25, mixed media

Ainslie, *from "SUN DAY" series,* 19 x 15, acrylic.

BALL, KEN (Sculptor)
12108 W. 62nd Place, Arvada, CO 80004

Born: 1942 *Awards:* Blue Ribbon, American Film Festival *Collections:* Southland Corporation, Dallas; Harmsen Collection *Exhibitions:* Gene Autry Heritage Museum, Los Angeles; Artists of the Southwest, Tucson, AZ *Education:* U. of Colorado

The works of traditional western artists such as Russell and Catlin, as well as contemporary sculptors Fritz White and George Carlson have had an influence on his work. Shifting from watercolors and oil to sculpture in 1980, he found a greater structure to provide the missing dimension to his inspirational, lifelong study of Native Americans. He has experimented by mixing bronze and stone as composite original sculptures. Producing life-sized, figurative sculptures. His current are directed at contemporary western themes. His works are found in public, private, and corporate collections in eighteen states.

BARAJAS, CALVIN (Painter)
1316 Peralta Ave., Berkeley, CA 94702

Born: 1940 *Awards:* Phelan Awards Exhibit, Palace of the Legion of Honor, San Francisco *Collections:* Mexican Museum, San Francisco; Arizona State U. Art Museum, Tempe *Exhibitions:* Smithsonian Institution; National U. of Mexico, Mexico City *Education:* California College of Arts And Crafts

During the 1970s, he painted a long mural in Union City, California based on the ancient Mexican prayer symbols. Currently he works with Mexican and Native American symbols. His small radiant piece, *Pecho Adornado (Adorned Breast)* is a form of visual mandala based on Pre-Hispanic design motifs. Geometrically composed to reflect the ancient principle of the four cardinal points, its devotional disposition is enhanced by the three successive boarders of metal, copper and gold leaf that encase the cadmium red glazed heart glowing in the center like a precious relic. He is presently painting "Visual Prayers," images of geometric altars on landscapes painted in acrylic and metallic, gold and silver leaf.

BARBACHANO, BELISA (Painter)
11680 S.W. 92 St., Miami, FL 33176

Born: 1957 *Awards:* Best of Show, Chimerical Gregg Art Gallery, La Puente; Prix D'Excellence, Diploma D'Honor, Tonneis, France *Collections:* Dadeland Bank, Miami; Club Cozumel Caribe, Mexico *Exhibitions:* Chimerical Gregg Art Gallery, La Puente; Ariel Gallery, NYC *Education:* U. of Miami, FL *Dealer:* Salad'art, Barcelona; New Dimensions Art, Miami

During her undergraduate years, she studied with Eugene Massin and became his assistant. Her work was mostly figurative. Her love of color and space proved influential in her artistic development. She explored various media and techniques, eventually choosing acrylic on canvas. Color and abstract forms became her main expressive vehicles. After spending the early 1980s as an Art Thesis Director in Mexico, she returned to the U.S., and devoted herself to painting. In recent work, she has successfully combined her love of color and sense of composition in joyful abstract paintings. Her compositions are brightly formed and exhibit a zestful vitality. She has a forceful style, and the influence of her Mexican heritage is apparent in her work.

BARCHERS, NELDA M. (Painter, Sculptor)
7816 Eureka Ave., El Cerrito, CA 94530

Born: 1948 *Awards:* Fellow, MacDowell Colony, Peterboro, NH *Exhibitions:* Palo Alto Cultural Center; The Right Foot, San Francisco International Airport *Education:* Rhode Island School of Design *Dealer:* Lawson Gallery, San Francisco

Study in Italy during the late 1960s inspired a fascination with pattern and a love of aged, scarred and rubbed surfaces. In the 1970s, her clear and brilliant Mediterranean colors gave way to darker, Oriental-inspired works. Using combs dipped in wet paint, she made linear paintings that had the appearance of weavings or textiles. In the early 1980s, she discovered the small whimsical constructions Calder and Picasso had made using found objects. She began creating figures, torsos, heads, shoes and lingerie out of nails, wire mesh and hand sewn and twisted wire. At the same time, she started painting with crayon-like paint sticks. Her canvases have a naive, childlike feeling and a rich surface, which she achieves by building up layers of color, scrapes, wipes and sands.

BARKER, HELEN (Painter)
P.O. Box 1914, Carmel, CA 93921

Awards: Gold Medal for Watercolor, Friday Morning Club, Los Angeles; Gold Medal for Oil, Descanso Gardens, Los Angeles *Exhibitions:* Carmel Art Association; The Lindsey Gallery, Carmel

She comes from an artistic family and though she is mostly self-taught, she studied briefly with the well known portrait painter, Christian Von Schneidu. In the early 1960s she moved to Carmel where the artist Donald Teague encouraged her to develop her own style and advised her not to study with anyone. Her recent florals, still lifes, seascapes, and landscapes are traditional and impressionist. By painting realistically she feels she can convey the vibrance of her own joy in nature. Her subjects are meant to be enjoyed. Until 1987, she owned her own gallery. She has illustrated a book of poetry titled *Verse and Views.* The book, published by Angel Press, also contains some of her own poems and was written in collaboration with Peggy Peter. She works in all media.

BARKUS, MARIONA (Painter, Book Designer)
P.O. Box 34785, Los Angeles, CA 90034

Born: 1948 *Awards:* Artist-in-Residence, Women's Graphic Center *Collections:* Library of the Museum of Modern Art, NYC; California Institute of Art, Valencia *Exhibitions:* Thinking Eye Gallery, Los Angeles; U. of Illinois, Chicago *Education:* Northwestern U.

Her style has been referred to as "numinous luminous," the primary concern of her art being the emotional and spiritual content of pure colors and forms themselves. Influenced by the work of psychologist Carl Jung, she explores in her work the belief that luminous organic forms are actually tied to archetypical human experiences. Her pieces also reflect her faith in the "numen," an indwelling, guiding, spiritual light within all things. She works by slowly and carefully layering pigments until the surface shines with the sense of reflected depth. Major influences on her style are Itten, Birren and especially Kandinsky.

BARNARD, MARBO (Painter)
444 Que St., Rio Linda, CA 95673

Born: 1928 *Awards:* Best of Portrait, California Artists League; 2nd Place, National Open, Pastel Society of the West Coast *Exhibitions:* Hall of Flowers, San Francisco; Sacramento Fine Arts Center

After working extensively with oil and watercolor, she studied with master pastelist, Daniel E. Green. Excited by the medium's spontaneity and versatility, she began working in pastel during late 1970s. Although she has painted a wide variety of subjects, portraits and figures are the main focus of her work. She is a signature artist of The Pastel Society of the West Coast, the Society of Western Artists and the California Arts League. She says of her chosen medium: "Pastels provided an infinite variety of brilliant colors and reflect light like no other medium."

BARNES, CLIFFORD V. (Painter)
7341 La Vina Trail, Yucca Valley, CA 92284

Born: 1940 *Awards:* Gold Medal In Drawing, American Indian/Cowboy Artists; National Competition Winner, American Artists *Collections:* Pepsico; Arizona Bank *Exhibitions:* San Bernardino County Museum; Los Angeles County Fairgrounds *Education:* Art Center College of Design

After formal training at the Art Center, he satisfied his love for painting landscapes by traveling in Europe and working on location. In 1970, he became interested in western art. His bold use of color in his western oils, and his unusual charcoal drawing techniques raised him to the top of his craft. He gives his paintings an unusual depth and clarity, by using large brushes and a palette knife, on both linen and cotton canvas. He creates his deeply textured portraits through a variety of charcoal techniques, including wet charcoal and charcoal dust. Two of his largest Western murals (eight by ten feet) hang in the San Bernardino County Government Center.

BARNES, JOHN (Painter, Sculptor)
3023 Balboa St., San Francisco, CA 94121

Born: 1949 *Collections:* Japan Bank, San Diego; Mitsui Bank, San Francisco *Exhibitions:* Magic Theatre, San Francisco; San Francisco Art Institute *Education:* Southern Illinois U. *Dealer:* Jeremy Stone Gallery, San Francisco

He studied traditional painting and sculpture, then moved on to printmaking. When he returned to painting and sculpture, he began to experiment with new ways of applying traditional materials to canvas. In one instance, he appears to have applied the paint with a cake-decorating cone: small, peaked dollops of color sit in carefully arranged rows, small wisps of paint extending at right angles from their tops. All painted surfaces are obsessive, dense and colorful. His trademark is a compulsive mixture of painting and sculpture. He designs sculptures, made from acrylic and wood, for specific settings; pieces appear to be growing out of ceilings, floors and corners. He cites figurative painter Francis Bacon as a major influence.

BARNSLEY, AMANDA (Painter)
4618 Los Feliz Blvd., Los Angeles, CA 90027

Exhibitions: Nonantane Art Gallery, Newton, MA; Newton, Mass. Library *Education:* Boston Museum of Fine Arts; Brockton Art Center

Following her studies at Mitchell College, the Boston Museum of Fine Arts and Brockton Art Center, she began designing and creating silver and gold jewelry. Acrylic and Venetian glass tiles were then incorporated in pieces resembling abstract paintings. At the same time, she designed and executed glass-top tables and painted florals similar to those of Redon. Her current work includes flowers painted on silk and cotton clothing. In addition to her creative work, she is also a charter member of the Museum of Contemporary Art in Los Angeles and sells to clients in Massachusetts and California. She has recently been asked to demonstrate her work at Descanso Gardens and Catalina Island.

BARNY, T. (Sculptor)
4370 Pine Flat Rd., Healdsburg, CA 95448

Born: 1956 *Awards:* 1st Prize, Central California Biennial; 1st Prize in Sculpture, California Expo *Collections:* Poinsettia Ranch *Exhibitions:* Frye Museum, Seattle; Lawrence Galleries, Sonoma *Education:* Rhode Island School of Design *Dealer:* J. Noblett, Sonoma, California

He developed his fascination with sculpture through studies of architecture, physical and social sciences, and design and fine arts. Early in his career his media were diverse. He carved stone, sculpted classical clay figures, welded cast metal abstractions, and sculpted blown glass filled with gaseous neon, argon, and mercury. In the past, his works ranged from jewelry- size sculptures to monumental forty-foot fabric installations. Since the early 1980s he has sculpted in marble. He carves out the flaws of geological tension, releasing the sound, free form inherent in each block of marble. His forms evoke a sense of universal beauty through archetypal continuous curves.

BARR, PRISCILLA (Painter)
315 Fernando Ave., Palo Alto, CA 94306

Born: 1936 *Exhibitions:* Pacific Arts, Santa Clara; Great American Gallery, Palo Alto

Born and raised in the Bay area, she is best known for her pastel finger painting. People and faces are her favorite subjects. She specializes in the depiction of the costumes, mores and traditions of many foreign countries, as well as the U.S. She also spends a great deal of time on the matting and custom framing of her paintings.

BARR, ROGER T. (Sculptor)
920 McDonald Ave., Santa Rosa, CA 95404

Born: 1921 *Awards:* Catherwood Foundation; Djerassi Foundation *Exhibitions:* Victor Fischer Galleries, Oakland; Pier 39 East, San Francisco *Education:* Pomona College; Claremont Graduate School *Dealer:* Victor Fischer, Oakland and San Francisco; Nina Owens, Ltd., Chicago; Artists' Circle, Ltd., Potomac, MD

He is self-taught as a sculptor, and his current work is in stainless steel. The steel is pre-formed and cut up, and the pieces are tack-welded until a structural order develops. He submits the maquettes in slide form for commission. When funded, the work is fabricated either in his own shop or by other professionals. Many of his most noted works are presented with a mirror finish. Used to stunning effect in *Sundance,* this shiny steel ribbon appears to float gently from the sky to its resting place. Two other similar sculptures, *Arch/Flight* and *O? Oh!,* feature circles standing upright on one edge. The first circle is opened with carved metal disc placed in the center; the second circle is adorned with a cascading steel curl.

Roger Barr, *Spirit Bridge,* 384 x 432 x 96, welded stainless steel

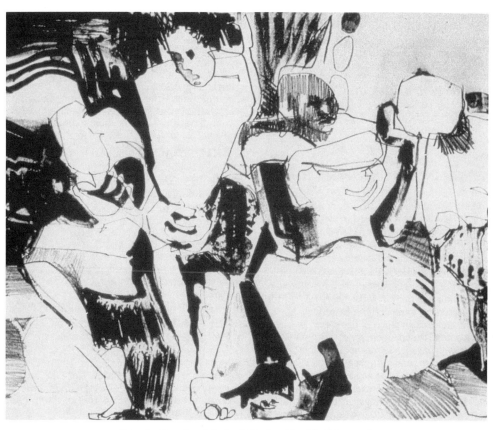

Phoebe Beasley, *Musical Chairs,* 14 x 22, lithograph

BARTCZAK, PETER W. (Commercial Illustrator)

P. O. Box 7709, Santa Cruz, CA 95061

Born: 1951 *Exhibitions:* Dancing Man Gallery, Santa Cruz; Eloise Smith Gallery, Los Angeles

Influenced by everything from the animation of Walt Disney to the homespun lyricism of Norman Rockwell, he has developed his own whimsical and realistic illustration style. Done primarily on primed panels or illustration board, his work betrays a delight in bright colors and in quaint, surreal touches, which do not so much undermine his realistic style as poke fun of it. A sense of humor pervades his work, but so does a sense of discipline. All his art bears the mark of careful preparation and meticulous workmanship. He has also been influenced by the popular art of the 1970s, particularly art tied to science fiction and fantasy. He paints with both a regular brush and an airbrush, choosing his medium from acrylics, lacquers, casein and various inks.

BARTLETT, MICHAEL, E. (Painter)

70 Barda Landing, Sausalito, CA 94965

Born: 1947 *Awards:* Theta Award, Energy Art, Golden, CO; 2nd Place Oil, California Expo *Exhibitions:* Vorpal Gallery, San Francisco; San Francisco Museum of Modern Art Rental Gallery *Education:* San Francisco Art Institute; Montana State U., Bozeman *Dealer:* Vorpal Gallery, San Francisco

Rooted in the aesthetic sensibilities of the craft movement, he did undergraduate work with jewelry and metal-smithing before turning to oil on canvas and board. The open plains of his native Montana have permanently marked his work, and he admires C.M. Russell, Thomas Moran's use of space and the light of George Inness. His visceral involvement with the Bay Area school has also been an influence, particularly through the work of Russell Chatam and earlier California plain air painters. He takes a very traditional approach to the documentation of his experiences with nature. Bright, composite images are drawn through memory to produce realistic, yet personal representations.

BARTLETT, NANCY (Painter, Printmaker)

8961 Moorcroft Ave., Canoga Park, CA 91304

Awards: Ann Steppenhagen Memorial Purchase Award, Pierce College, Woodland Hills *Exhibitions:* MacHouston Gallery, Pasadena; Diodati Gallery, Los Angeles *Education:* UC-Berkeley *Dealer:* Artifex, Newbury Park

Her style is soft realism and her subject is always nature in some form. Early work in portraiture was followed by large acrylic floral paintings in soft rose, coral and turquoise. Her recent work in serigraphy reflects her experience in poster design while in her teens. Paintings and prints contain much open space and portray a natural serenity typical of Japanese and Chinese art, revealing a strong Oriental influence. An acrylic painting entitled *Autumn Window* depicts persimmons sitting on a windowsill that looks out over a distant hill. She enjoys the challenge of extracting a strong design from a natural scene and has begun to use curving lines more as she explores the relationship between the traditional and the contemporary.

BARTLETT, SCOTT (Film/Video Artist)

440 Davis Ct., #818, San Francisco, CA 94111

Born: 1943 *Awards:* Guggenheim Fellowship; Cannes Film Festival *Collections:* Smithsonian Institute, Washington, D.C.; Museum of Modern Art, NYC *Exhibitions:* Museum of Modern Art, NYC; Whitney Museum, NYC *Education:* Illinois Institute of Technology *Dealer:* Facets Multimedia, Chicago

Originally trained in architecture, he moved into filmmaking in 1967. Because film art manipulates perceived time, it afforded him the opportunity to explore the processes of transformation and metamorphosis. He has moved from film to video, embracing the tools of electronics and computers. His work continues to render the human experience in terms of primal myths, archetypes, order and chaos. He has recently been making sample reels for a new project, Video Radio Channel, a new video channel featuring Earth Beat music and visuals mixed by veejay's in real time. His work has been displayed in over seventy museums and has garnered more than sixty international film festival awards.

BARTON, PAMELA (Fiber Artist, Handmade Paper Artist)

P.O. Box 625, Volcano, HI 96785

Born: 1929 *Awards:* Purchase Award, Hawaii State Foundation on Culture and the Arts; Craft Excellence Award, Hawaii Craftsmen *Collections:* Hawaii State Foundation on Culture and the Arts; Arts Council of Hawaii *Exhibitions:* Fiberworks, Berkeley; Honolulu Academy of Arts *Education:* U. of Hawaii, Manoa

A desire to understand clay and printmaking led her to study paper and to explore the fiber medium she now works in. With fibers, she can span the sublime and the ridiculous with a clear conscience. She works spontaneously and intuitively, allowing her materials to influence her and her own personality to emerge. "Just being alive energizes me, and I am inspired by my surroundings—the sun, the moon, the rain, trees, plants, the glitter in society, the bulk in industry, a lot by my husband, and by being me." She uses both natural and synthetic fibers.

BARTUS, NAOMI (Painter)

6057 1/4 Selma Ave., Los Angeles, CA 90028

Born: 1955 *Exhibitions:* Abstraction Gallery, Los Angeles; Mesa College, San Diego

Since moving to Los Angeles in the early 1980s, her main artistic concern has revolved around the destruction of nature. Her acrylic-on-board paintings feature images of floral landscapes and colorful, natural patterns combined with machetes, drills, hatchets and other instruments of destruction. She also paints fantasy landscapes, prompted by life in the concrete jungle. The manifestations of these desires take the form of floral landscapes and images of "paradise."

BASCOM, EARL W. (Sculptor)

15669 Stoddard Wells Rd., Victorville, CA 92392

Born: 1906 *Awards:* Canadian Rodeo Hall of Fame, 1984; Utah Sports Hall of Fame, 1985; Raymond, Alberta Sports Hall of Fame *Collections:* President Ronald Reagan; Gene Autry; *Exhibitions:* Whitney Museum; National Cowboy Hall of Fame *Education:* Brigham Young U.

This world champion rodeo cowboy, son of a deputy sheriff and grandson of an Indian fighter is a cousin of

Mary Jane Bakarich, *Inorganic Tree,* 7 feet high, aluminum screening.
Courtesy: University of California at Davis

Brice Bowman, *Companion,* 60 x 48, oil on canvas

Western artist Frederic Remington. His work reflects his own experiences as a young man growing up in the West and preserves the life of the turn-of-the-century cowboy. He is one of the few western artists to have lived the life of a true cowboy when Frederic Remington and Charles Russell were alive. His bronze sculptures capture the real elements of equestrian subjects and are instilled with a feeling of strength and movement. He is also a painter and has earned the title "Cowboy of Cowboy Artists."

BATES, BETTY (Printmaker, Collage Artist)
c/o Citadel Print Center and Gallery, 199 Martha St., San Jose, CA 95112

Born: 1951 *Awards:* Grant, California Arts Council; Residency, Masareel Center, Kasterlee, Belgium *Collections:* San Jose Museum of Art; Bibliotheque Nationale, Paris *Exhibitions:* Vorpal Gallery, San Francisco; J.M. Cupillard Galerie, Grenoble, France *Education:* UC-Santa Cruz *Dealer:* Cuisine Perel Gallery, Tiburon

Formally trained in all printmaking media, she uses eating as a humorous metaphor for our over-consumptive society. In *Our Lady of the Frigidaire*, she has used the refrigerator as a shrine, a chicken jumping out of its halo. In *Panhandlers*, a woman with eight arms throws cookware around. The gestures of her characters give a new definition to the concept of eating. Her sense of color was influenced by Seurat; her satire by Oldenburg; and her content by George Tooker and Rene Magritte. She employs a subtle use of color complements in drawings, collage, collograph and linoleum cut prints. In 1985, she composed the rock opera *Potato Polka*.

BATES, GARY (Sculptor)
9250 Amsterdam Rd., Manhattan, MT 59741

Born: 1946 *Awards:* NEA Fellowship; First Place, Sculpture, ArtQuest '87, Cal. State-Northridge *Collections:* Yellowstone Art Center, Billings, MT *Exhibitions:* Cal. State-Northridge; Art Institute of Boston *Education:* Kansas City Art Institute and School of Design

He constructs large, site-specific sculptures from welded steel and industrial scrap metal such as giant gears, the ends of tank cars, boilers, and augers. His art is influenced by the memories of childhood surroundings—the abandoned concrete foundation of a railroad tower, hulks of disused farm machinery, and the tools and of a nearby smithy. He is inspired by the land and by the industrial and agricultural machinery found on the land. One typical project is a series of kinetic steel and iron sculptures which ring the farmland of the Gallatin Valley in Montana. He has also created a performance art sculpture, an enormous roll of polyethylene seats which extends for half a mile and takes eight minutes to inflate. A recent project involves planting 7,000 living trees over a twenty acre area. The trees are planted in a serpentine sculptural form.

BATES, MARY (Sculptor)
243 Arlen, Rohnert Park CA 94928

Born: 1951 *Awards:* Fine Arts Fellowship, Sculpture, New Jersey State Council on the Arts; Ford Fellowship in the Arts, Indiana U. *Exhibitions:* University Gallery, Chemeketa Community College, Salem, OR; Zenitram Gallery, Santa Rosa *Education:* Colorado

State U.; Indiana U. *Dealer:* San Francisco Museum of Modern Art Rental Galleries

Her copper, stainless steel and aluminum sculptures convey the tension between the materials' cool reserve and clean form and the interior energy just under the surface. The images derive from landscape elements of prairies, plains and mountains, and have become more abstract and less narrative in the last few years. Some of her work, *Incendiary Totem,* for example, is playful and joyous. In others, such as *High Voltage* and *Connected Houses,* the symmetrical, self-contained images allude to internal emotional forces. More personified works— *Dutiful Daughter* and *Mistress*—also exemplify the containment/release theme.

BATRA, ROMILLA (Ceramist)
76 The Plaza Dr., Berkeley, CA 94705

Born: 1937 *Awards:* Best of Show, National Exhibition In Clay Polytechnic State U., San Luis Obispo *Collections:* Nora Eccles Harison Museum of Art, Logan, UT; Coos Museum, Coos Bay, OR *Exhibitions:* Everson Museum, Syracuse, NY; Cork, Ireland *Education:* St. Bede's College, Simla, India *Dealer:* Village Artistry, Carmel

In a series of functional and non-functional porcelain forms, she represented her personal experiences with the beaches and rock formations of California's Bay Area. Working with the same design through successive pieces, she was able to capture different natural moods: i.e., changing light or stages of an opening bud. The work is primarily hand built in press molds and inlaid with porcelain, colored with oxides. After the first firing, the pieces are finished by painting oxides on the surface, which is partially removed by a sponge. The interiors of her pots are then washed with a clear glaze. In a recent series of porcelain and bamboo wall-hung pieces, she deals with Japanese religious imagery.

BAUER, RICHARD (Sculptor)
113 Elmira St., San Francisco, CA 94124

Born: 1944 *Awards:* Panel Member, 12th Annual Sculpture Conference; Archives of American Art *Collections:* George Neubert Collection of the U. of Nebraska, Lincoln *Exhibitions:* U. of Judaism, Los Angeles; San Francisco Art Institute *Education:* San Francisco State U. *Dealer:* John Pence Gallery, San Francisco

He developed a personal method of casting sculptures—primarily figures—in a highly expressive style influenced by George Segal, Manuel Neri and Stephen de Staebler. Recently he has explored the sociological connotations of the making and exhibition of art in society and in contrast to the function of art in tribal or historically primitive societies. He begins his highly detailed sculptures with a mold made from live models, manipulating and enhancing the form; then he makes a cast of white hydrocal. The patina and finish he adds tends to give the works a feeling of movement: the transparent and subtle hues seemingly floating over the surface. Yet for all their external play, the focus in his successful works is the interior lives of his figures, into whom he urges us to look deeply.

BAUMAN-HUDSON, EDITH (Painter)
6848 West Blvd., Los Angeles, CA 90043

Born: 1948 *Collections:* Private *Exhibitions:* Newspace, Los Angeles; Art Center, Pasadena *Education:* USC *Dealer:* Newspace, Los Angeles

Baumann, *Emerald Bay Storm,* 14 x 18, oil on canvas

Craig M. Black, *Metamorphosis,* 42 x 30 x 8, cement and forged steel. Photograph: Phillip Cohen

Influenced by John McGlaughlin and by medieval Japanese screen painting, she explores space and structure through non-symbolic abstraction. During the past decade, her work has developed from paintings of juxtaposed colorful rectangles to monochromatic explorations and recently to a series of narrow vertical canvases punctuated by horizontal bands at the top and bottom. Her transparent colors give the appearance of black and white. The phenomenon of simultaneous contrast is everywhere operative, bringing out in a neutral color the complement of the neighboring hue. She is currently creating a series of double bar paintings.

BAUMANN, STEFAN W. (Painter)
85 Cerritos, San Francisco, CA 94127

Born: 1962 *Collections:* Contra Costa Times, Contra Costa; *Exhibitions:* De Young Museum School, San Francisco; Sierra Galleries, Tiburon *Education:* Stanford U. *Dealer:* Royal Swan, Saratoga

Inspired by the art of the Hudson River School artists, he has developed a style of landscape painting that emphasizes the textures and brilliance of his paint. This interest in the surface finds further expression in the fascination with optical illusion that pervades his work. These concerns allow him to explore beyond the landscape that he is depicting, to the act of landscape painting itself—the artist's attempt to explore on canvas the emotional resonances in a landscape. He is perhaps best known for his series of panoramas of America's National Parks. He also lectures frequently on landscape painting, its role in this century, and its place in the next.

BAUMGARTEN, BARBARA DEE (Painter, Quilter)
545 Farallon Dr., Morgan Hill, CA 95037

Born: 1955 *Awards:* A.A.U.W. Project Renew Grant; Award of Merit, Quilt San Diego *Exhibitions:* Paul VI Institute for the Arts, Washington, DC; Graduate Theological Union Library, Berkeley *Education:* California Lutheran U.; Pacific School of Religion

Her contemporary images rooted in the biblical tradition directly confront the values of secular culture. As a painter, she is deeply influenced by the German Expressionists. By focusing on the organic human form within interrupted systems, she depicts humanity as a living expression of the divine within a mortal environment. This theme is particularly evident in her quilting. A black-and-white checkerboard motif suggests that ethics are often presented in adversarial terms, while the fluid emotional reality is superimposed in grey contast. The quilt *Woman*, for example, illuminates the biblical text of the adultress. The faceless woman kneels in a posture that does not neatly fit into the surrounding squares, and her grey form is naked and transparent, fully exposed. This work further refers to the fact that quilting is traditionally a woman's art. Recent work shows a growing interest in the folk art of Latin America.

BEAM, MARK (Sculptor)
434 S. Plymouth Blvd., Los Angeles, CA 90020

Born: 1957 *Collections:* Vestron Pictures, Los Angeles; Spago Restaurant, Los Angeles *Exhibitions:* Patton/Duvall Gallery, Los Angeles; Taylor/Beam Gallery, Los Angeles

He makes whimsical, colorful sculptures featuring such characters as "Hollywood power cows" and enormous "fish-men." Media include surfboards, papier maché, foam, pipe cleaners and ping pong balls. His working style is strictly improvisational using whatever materials are at hand to solve special structural problems as they arise.

BEASLEY, BRUCE (Sculptor)
322 Lewis St., Oakland, CA 94607

Born: 1939 *Awards:* Purchase Prize, Paris Biennale; Purchase Prize, San Francisco Arts Festival *Collections:* Museum of Modern Art, NYC; Guggenheim Museum, NYC *Exhibitions:* San Francisco Museum of Modern Art; Middleheim Sculpture Park, Antwerp, Belgium; *Education:* UC-Berkeley

Although his early career focused on metal sculpture, for which he won the prize at the Paris Biennale, he became best known for large, transparent acrylic pieces that he began making in 1970. The monumental *Apolymon* launched California's Art in Public Buildings program, and it was followed by *Tragamon* in the entry pool of the Oakland Museum, where it uses the interplay of prismatic reflections between the water and the sculpture. Smaller pieces include *Star Gazer* and *Hemihedral Eclipse*, in which the sculptures' transparency teases the eye with ambiguity as to where the surfaces actually lie in space. Returning to metal work, he created *Artemon*, a large, stainless-steel sculpture that was exhibited at the Los Angeles Olympics. His most recent work in cast and fabricated metal is a study of the complex intersection of geometric forms and is a combination of his two previous artistic impulses. The latest of these, *Titiopolis Arch*, was exhibited at "Monumenta—19th Sculpture Biennale" in Antwerp.

BEASLEY, JOANNE HORSFALL (Painter)
125 Bryant St., Palo Alto, CA 94301

Born: 1940 *Awards:* Radcliffe Institute Fellowship *Collections:* Kane Financial Corporation, Boston; Koll Corporation, San Jose *Exhibitions:* Gallery House, Palo Alto; San Mateo County Council for the Arts *Education:* Cornell U.

While in graduate school, she spent her time experimenting with printing images incorporating plants, insects and abstract figurations. Toward the end of this time, she had developed a style of contrasts: abstraction/figuration, detail void, color/non-color, organic/geometric. This contrasting style has since evolved in two directions. In one, she has developed very dense pastel abstractions with hints of figuration influenced by patterned arts and crafts. These collaged paintings exhibit her fascination with sensuous surfaces, intense colors, organic shapes and mathematical grids. She has also been creating watercolors and oil pastels with abstract, yet recognizable, features. Painted with intense colors from a full palette, these works are multi-sheeted, often symbolic and sometimes alligorical.

BEASLEY, PHOEBE (Painter)
6110 El Canon Ave., Woodland Hills, CA 91367

Born: 1943 *Collections:* Savannah College of Art and Design, GA; American National Can Company, Greenwich, CT *Exhibitions:* Museum of African American Art, Los Angeles; UCLA *Education:* Art Center College of Design; Ohio U. *Dealer:* Gallery/Tanner, Los Angeles

In her early oil paintings, de Kooning's influence manifests itself in her concentration on the color and

Bruce Beasley, *Arristus,* 120 x 192, stainless steel. Courtesy: Coll Djerassi Foundation, Woodside, CA

Barbara Burritt, *Blood Sacrifice,* 72 x 84, oil

spatial relationships outside a central figure. Some canvases were ripped and worked from the back, in an effort to show inside or beyond the figure. This emphasis led towards increasingly less representation. Since her exposure to the works of Romare Bearden and Jacob Lawrence, however, she has expressed the need to explore subject definition through a looser style that conveys a sense of story-telling through nuance, gesture and movement. Still emphasizing bold colors, her figurative collages now combine Mingei and tissue paper, oil and gesso on canvas. Her use of translucent tissue over large gessoed areas produces a three-dimensional effect, as well as one of fragility that intensifies the emotional power of the subject. Some found objects may also be used. The cubist overtones of the fractured planes retain a modernist aesthetic. But her focus is human and implicitly accessible: members of the Black community sharing the religious experience of a gospel revival, the moment of athletic victory, waiting for a bus, dancing, preaching, nurturing their children, mourning the loss of a friend, growing old, being lonely, anything real people do and are.

BEATTIE, PAUL (Painter)
7184 Mill Creek Rd., Healdsburg, CA 95448

Born: 1924 *Collections:* San Francisco Museum of Modern Art; Oakland Museum of Art *Exhibitions:* California Museum of Art, Santa Rosa; Bruce Velick Gallery, San Francisco

He exhibited as a painter with some of the Abstract Expressionists in New York in the early 1950s; he was at that time known as a photographer, filmmaker and early experimentalist in light shows. For the past two years, astrophysics and astronomy have become the dominant themes for paintings. Painted with acrylic on masonite panels, the surface is covered with loosely-brushed, basically monochromatic fields, applied in an abstract impressionist style; it is spotted with irregular daubs and patches of darker tones or dappled, mottled, splotched, striated and fused with light or with contrasting colors. Here and there, a more sharply defined mark, or color line, appears. Some of the lines are two-dimensional, applied with a china marker; others are in relief, via little match-stick lengths of lead press, themselves splotched with paint. These works evoke a feeling of cosmological wonder—a dramatic reflection of his excursions into astronomy and astrophysics.

BEAUMONT, MONA (Painter, Graphic Collage Artist)
1087 Upper Happy Valley Rd., Lafayette, CA 94549

Born: 1927 *Awards:* Purchase Award, San Francisco Arts Festival *Collections:* Oakland Museum of Art; City of San Francisco *Exhibitions:* Honolulu Academy of Art; Palace of the Legion of Honor, San Francisco *Education:* UC-Berkeley

She was raised in Europe and received formal training under Erle Loran in Berkeley, and Hans Hoffman in New York. Her work developed along classic cubist and constructionist lines. Her acrylic paintings are brilliant, but subtle, experimentations with minimalist light and color. In drawing, she has broken with strict cubism, creating bold, linear and volumetric abstractions that are not only organic and geometric, but sensually complex. She works equally well with collages, prints and, to a lesser extent, assemblages. Her current influences include Robert Motherwell, Bruce Nauman, Cy Twombly and Sol Le Witt.

BECHTLE, ROBERT ALAN (Painter)
4250 Horton St., Apt. 14, Emeryville, CA 94608

Born: 1932 *Awards:* NEA Grant; James D. Phelan Award in Painting *Collections:* Whitney Museum of American Art, NYC; Museum of Modern Art, NYC *Exhibitions:* San Francisco Museum of Modern Art; Corcoran Gallery of Art, Washington D.C. *Education:* California College of Arts and Crafts; UC-Berkeley *Dealer:* O.K. Harris Works of Art, NYC

He was first influenced by the work of Richard Diebenkorn and Nathan Oliveira; a desire to avoid the current styles of the 1960s brought him to realism. An almost imperceptible brush stroke was employed to depict as closely as possible the actual appearance of things. His photo-realistic paintings depict scenes from the California middle-class families, houses, suburban streets, and cars so that the viewer might "find significance in the details of the commonplace."

BECKER, CHARLES (Painter)
315 E. Cotati Ave., Cotati, CA 94928

Born: 1952 *Awards:* Best of Show, Rohnert Park Art Festival; Third Place, Society of Western Artists *Exhibitions:* Peninsula Art Exchange; California State Exhibition *Dealer:* San Francisco Art Exchange

He is known for his "magic realist" style which is highly reminiscent of seventeenth-century Dutch painting, yet is distinguished by the use of brilliant color and the convincingly rendered areas of light, dark, and shadow. His technique involves several preliminary steps. He begins by applying three layers of gray-tinted gesso to linen canvas, followed by an underpainting with charcoal to insure the purity of the colors. After applying a fixative, he proceeds with oil paint and glaze, working from dark to light. Subjects include portraits, still lifes, and landscapes. Eschewing photo-realism, he strives to enhance and highlight the beauty in life for others.

BECKER, GARY (Painter)
6057 Felix Ave., Richmond, CA 94805

Born: 1947 *Collections:* Marin Headlands Art Center *Exhibitions:* Maturango Museum, Ridgecrest; George Lithograph, San Francisco *Education:* The Oakland Museum

He is a self-taught artist, though in his early years, he studied with Ben Hazard and painted non-figurative abstractions. Dissatisfied with painting, he left art and studied poetry's symbolism for several years, before beginning to draw again. When he returned to art, he found a new style. There is a strong subconscious or automatic vein in his current work. Beginning with small ink drawings, he develops brightly colored, symbolic acrylic paintings. Trees, chains, birds, skulls, dwelling places and Indian masks are often his subjects. In a recent series of drawings and paintings, he uses woman as a symbol of transformation. He has been influenced by Miro, Picasso and Hundertwasser.

BECKER, MARK (Photographer)
267 Miller Ave., Mill Valley, CA 94941

Born: 1956 *Collections:* Chevron *Exhibitions:* Mill Valley Public Gallery

His work as an architect inspired his work in photography. Using his knowledge of buildings and structures, he depicts and interprets the positive and negative qualities of spaces and physical forms. He photographs urban, industrial landscapes and uses

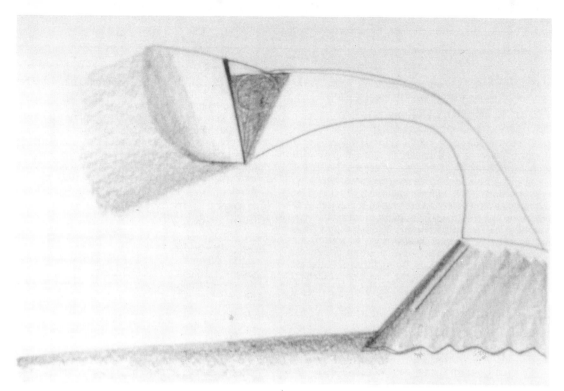

Mona Beaumont, *Countdown,* 5 x 8, graphite on paper

Helen L. Bell, *Monkeyshines,* 33 x 47 x 3, handmade paper and metal construction

large structures as elements in abstract designs. Working in available light, he shoots in the 4 x 5 format.

BEDRICK, JEFFREY K. (Painter)
15 Jessup St., San Raphael, CA 94901

Born: 1960 *Exhibitions:* Illuminarium Gallery, Corte Madera; Dyansen Gallery, NYC *Dealer:* Isis Unlimited, Beverly Hills

While still in his teens, he apprenticed with California visionary artists Bill Martin and Gage Taylor. The visionary movement is characterized by highly detailed, hyper-real images drawn from nature and mythology. Bedrick is best known for idyllic landscapes, portraits and figurative work in a classical style with romantic themes. Depicting realistic subjects, often in tropical or Mediterranean settings, he uses light as a metaphor for spirituality. He has also worked as an animator and commercial illustrator, most recently completing a project for the Trump Plaza Casino.

BEEBE, SANDRA E. (Painter)
239 Mira Mar Ave., Long Beach, CA 90803

Born: 1934 *Awards:* Foothills Art Center Award; Watercolor West Award *Exhibitions:* Brand Gallery, NYC; Brea Cultural Center *Education:* UCLA; Cal. State-Long Beach *Dealers:* B-Q Gallery, Long Beach; A Gallery, Palm Desert

A master of color and pattern design, she works primarily in series, notably watercolors of the Monterey/Carmel/Pacific Grove area. Working from life and her own reference photographs, she meticulously designs her paintings, gathering the exact materials—scarfs, beach towels, cans—that she finds beautiful. Paintings in her "Japan," "Mexico," "Match Box," "Pattern" and "Litter" series have been selected for exhibition in most major competitions in the U.S. Her painting, *My Table,* is the cover of Gerald Brommer's textbook *Exploring Painting,* which includes five other examples of her work. She is a signature member of nearly all the major watercolor societies in the U.S.

BEERE, SUSAN (Ceramist)
P.O. Box 70, Del Mar, CA 92014

Born: 1951 *Exhibitions:* Carousel Art Gallery, Encinatas; Ocean Song Gallery, Del Mar

For more than a decade, she has created brilliantly glazed tile works. She is completely self-taught, and her earliest influences were the glazed bas relief animals of the Ishtar Gate of Babylon. With daily experimentation, she developed her own bas relief style and began making smaller free-hanging tile pieces of the local scenery, wildlife and birds and of still lifes. She has now progressed to more sophisticated and difficult works. In 1987, she completed two large fountains, and she routinely does murals in living rooms and on fireplace surrounds and kitchen and bathroom walls. Her latest achievements include a line of greeting cards.

BEESON, MARY A. (Sculptor)
P.O. Box 1079, Desert Hot Springs CA 92240

Born: 1924 *Collections:* Marin County Civic Center *Exhibitions:* Frank Lloyd Wright Civic Center, San Rafael, CA; A. Albert Allen Fine Art Gallery, Palm Desert, CA *Dealer:* A. Albert Alden, Gallery, Palm Springs

She has been influenced by Barlach, Rodin, Henry Moore and Barbara Hepworth, as well as by her teachers. The human figure predominates in her sculp-ture, as it does in all her media; animals have also been a fascination, and she has completed abstracted sculptures of animals in both wood and stone. In 1986, she studied marble carving from Pasquale Martini in Milan, and since then she has split her time between stone carving and clay sculpture. Her major work, *The Brothers,* is a Vietnam and Korean War memorial commissioned by Marin County. This six-foot- tall bronze depicts a black soldier supporting his white comrade.

BEHRENS, ROBERT (Sculptor)
3304 Geary Blvd., #830, San Francisco, CA 94118

Born: 1939 *Awards:* 1st Place, Massachusetts Avenue Project, Cambridge, MA; Award of Excellence, Calif. Council of Landscape Architects *Collections:* City of Vancouver, BC; City of Cambridge, MA; Denver Art Museum *Education:* U. of Denver; Kansas City Art Institute

All of his works are site-specific and "place-rooted" in concept. The idea evolves from his perception of the site, and from its climate, orientation and history, in addition to available materials and cultural and social conditions. His approach is not to provide simply an unrelated object set into a foreign environment, but to evolve a sculptural idea based on the enviromental conditons and forms that are of interest to him at the moment. Current projects include the art masterplan of a 225-acre "smart park" for the Channel Island Business Center on the Pacific Coast Highway in Ventura County. *Connections,* comprised of three sites that frame the center, responds to the scale of the surroundings and the experience of the viewer. One site is made up of nine 80-foot steel columns treated to reflect spectral light. In 1986, he created *Centennial Grove,* a synthesis of landscape and artwork, to commemorate Stanford University's 100th anniversary.

BELDNER, LYNN (Painter, Photographer)
1920 Union St., Oakland, CA 94607

Born: 1954 *Awards:* James D. Phelan Award *Exhibitions:* ProArts Annual, Oakland; Berkeley Arts Commission *Education:* New College of San Francisco

Using a 4 x 5 camera in a studio, she makes conceptual photographs which highlight the contextual relationships among disparate objects. Her abstract paintings in tempera, oil or acrylic on gessoed paper or ragboard are subjective interpretations of landscapes, objects and her own state of being. She feels that the immediacy of painting has been a cathartic complement to the slower, more analytical process of photography. Recently she has combined these two elements in a series of collages.

BELINOFF, DEANNE (Painting)
707 Venice Blvd., Venice, CA 90291

Born: 1941 *Awards:* California Arts Council Grant *Collections:* Security Pacific *Exhibitions:* Long Beach Museum of Art; The Works Gallery, Long Beach *Education:* U. of Iowa; Cal. State-Long Beach *Dealer:* Karl Bornstein, Santa Monica

Her interests turned from traditional drawing and painting to the use of color as a metaphor for enlightenment. Luminous rays of light appear to emanate from unseen sources to form circles, arcs and squares. Her current works continue to express this theme. They are also compositional experiments, balancing the circle and square, symmetry and asymmetry. She applies spackle or acrylic modeling paste to

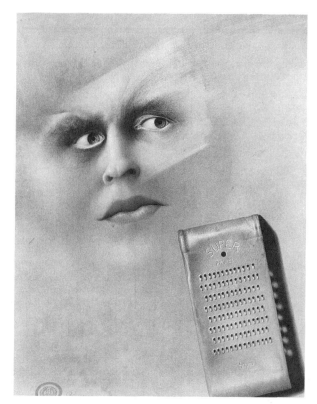

Herbert C. Bell, *Self Portrait at Greenwood,* 14 x 20, pencil

Mary A. Beeson, *Brothers,* 72 x 60, bronze. Courtesy: A. Albert Alden
Gallery, Palm Springs, CA

coated canvas or wood, creating textured images inspired by the kiva, a Native American structure devoted to spiritual pursuits.

BELL, BILL (Light Sculptor)
56 Perry St., Brookline, MA 02146

Born: 1928 *Collections:* Museum of Contemporary Art, Los Angeles; The Exploratorium, San Francisco *Exhibitions:* New Langton Arts, San Francisco; Fleet Science Center, San Diego *Education:* Princeton U. *Dealer:* Victor Fischer Gallery, San Francisco

His formal training was in physics, and for many years, he worked on the development of the computer. In the late 1970s, he left industry, and went on a two-year safari and sabbatical. When he returned, he dedicated himself to the construction of high- technology sculpture. In particular, he is fascinated with perception and the eye-brain interface, and his works concentrate on teasing and playing with this faculty. He is the inventor of the Lightstick, a computerized light-display machine which is capable of flashing a message or image, which lingers for moment in space, then fades. He accomplishes this with computer memory, integrated circuit chips, solid-state light sources, motors, electro-optic shutters and fiberoptics. The Lightstick, for which he holds the patent, has been on display in science centers, museums and retail establishments all over this country and in Japan. He derives his inspiration from the technical libraries of Harvard and MIT, and from reading science classics, such as Einstein. His wish is to create works of art that highlight the principles and achievements of scientific thought.

BELL, ELEANOR (Photographer)
2130 Archdale St., Riverside, CA 92506

Born: 1940 *Exhibitions:* Los Angeles County Museum of Art; Bowers Museum, Santa Ana *Education:* Syracuse U.

After many years of training as a painter, she switched to photography in 1980. Her photographs, large Cibachrome color abstractions, continue to show painterly influences. Work as a book designer introduced her to letter-forms as art subjects, a theme which permeates her work. Her photographs focus on the relationship of form, color and light—all emphasized by her close-up style, and by the use of colored gels over tungsten lights to shoot metallic and non-colored objects. She works with both found and created subjects, and thinks of her work as still- life abstraction.

BELL, HELEN L. (Sculptor, Painter)
5350 Argyle Way, Riverside, CA 92506

Born: Awards: Scholarship, Telefair Academy of Art & Science; Purchase Award, City of Riverside *Collections:* Sheraton Hotel, Riverside; Riverside City Hall *Exhibitions:* Riverside Art Museum; Rizzoli Gallery; *Education:* Western Maryland College *Dealer:* Laguna Museum of Art Sales Gallery, Costa Mesa; Zola Fine Art, Los Angeles

She constructs non-objective, multi-media wall sculptures and hand-made paper constructions. In her asymmetric three-dimensional designs, she incorporates machine-formed metal sheets of brass, aluminum, steel, and copper. The colors and surfaces of these metals contrast with the handmade paper, paint and etching that she also employs in each piece.

BELL, HERBERT C. (Draughtsperson)
240 N. Wilson, Pasadena, CA 91106

Born: 1940 *Collections:* Stanford Art Gallery, Palo Alto *Exhibitions:* Kingsley Exhibition, Sacramento; Orlando Gallery, Sherman Oaks *Education:* Cal. State-Chico; Washington State U., Pullman *Dealer:* Thinking Eye Gallery, Los Angeles

His finely controlled, super-real style has been influenced by Hieronymus Bosch, as well as by Renaissance and Pre-Renaissance religious painting. Fantasy remains the subject matter of his painting, but in drawing, he now explores the way photography represents shapes and edges of shapes. He makes the imperfections of modern reproduction techniques subjects for his drawings, and he takes great pains to remove evidence of his pencil. He uses a variety of colors to reproduce the way photographs give the illusion of homogeneous shade, and turns figurative forms into design elements. His recent, highly-detailed still life works can take up to four months to complete.

BELL, KRISTIN (Painter)
313 S. Central Ave., Los Angeles, CA 90013

Born: 1955 *Awards: Images and Issues* Magazine Emerging Artists Show *Exhibitions:* Riverside Museum of Art; L'Express *Education:* UC-Irvine *Dealer:* Hallway Gallery, Los Angeles

Her early experience and understanding of dance initially led her to make surreal paintings that were figurative in form, and rhythmic and musical in dynamics. Her images were frozen moments in time, with subjects in mid-gesture. Today her coloristic work follows two direction. With an extreme yet cohesive palette, she paints life size figures or empty landscapes that seem figurative in their muscular structure and fluidity. She also does 2-by-3-foot oil pastel drawings, which evolve from figurative or verbal ideas. She has been influenced by Bonnard, El Greco and Bernini, as well as by the dancing figures and the mythical and symbolic landscapes of medieval religious paintings.

BELL, LARRY STUART (Sculptor)
P.O. Box 1778, Taos, NM 87571

Born: 1939 *Awards:* NEA Fellowship; John Simon Guggenheim Memorial Foundation *Collections:* Museum of Modern Art, NYC; Whitney Museum, NYC *Exhibitions:* Museum of Modern Art, NYC; Guggenheim Museum, NYC *Education:* Chouinard Art Institute *Dealer:* New Gallery, Houston; Sena Galleries West, Santa Fe, NM

In the late 1950s, he made shaped canvases before turning to sculpture around 1961. During the next few years, media included mirrors, glass and plastics in the form of large, cubic floor pieces. He experimented with transparent, translucent and opaque surfaces in redefining space. In 1966, coated vacuum-glass boxes were placed on transparent bases so that light could be transmitted through every part of the work. Free-standing panels of coated glass explore varying degrees of opacity and reflection. In the 1970s, space technology was used to create large coated-glass screens, which were placed at right angles, combining reflection and transparency so that observers would seem to disappear and reappear as they walked around the piece. Recent works include "vapor drawings" made from paper coated in a vacuum chamber. He is exploring the same technique with modular glass panels.

Eleanor Bell, *untitled #25,* 16 x 20, cibachrome

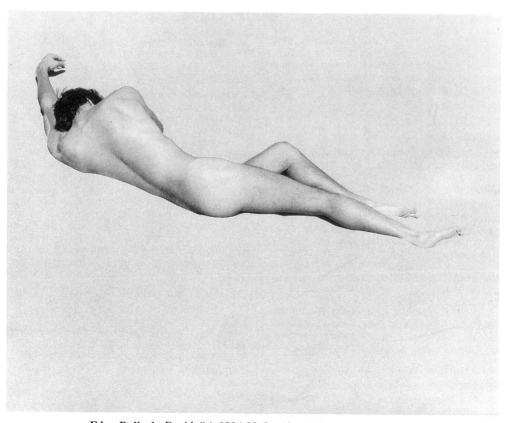

Edna Bullock, *David #4, 1984-89,* 8 x 10, gelatin silver photograph

BELL, MARY (Painter)
3257 Beaumont Woods Pl., Honolulu, HI 96822

Born: 1927 *Awards:* 1st Place, National Miniature Show, La Luz, NM *Collections:* American Red Cross; Kauai Library Museum of Art *Exhibitions:* Gallery Artique, Carmel; Shell Fisher Gallery, Carmel *Education:* Vassar College; U. of Hawaii *Dealer:* Village Gallery, Lahaina, Maui, HI

She was originally interested in a cubist rendition of natural form through multiple perspectives, which led her to treat her canvas as a design center rather than illusionistic space. Eventually, she was drawn to realism, especially landscape. Influenced by Seurat and the Impressionists, her drawings are comprised of layers of india ink dots which she likens to a "multifarious universe of atoms," analogous to life. In her paintings of landscapes and plants, a carefully planned layering technique using either oil, acrylic or watercolor enables her to travel from the immediate foreground to deep space in the piece.

BELLAVER, HELEN L. (Painter)
1462 Turriff Way, San Jose, CA 95132

Born: 1942 *Awards:* 1st Place, Society of Western Artists, Fresno; 2nd Place, Pastel Society of the West Coast *Exhibitions:* American Museum of Quilts and Textiles, San Jose; Santa Cruz Statewide Exhibition

Although her recent work combines several media, the artist is best known for her expertise in pastel. The homey subjects she favors are treated in a warm, naturalistic manner, the color laid on with confident, easy strokes that have more in common with paint than with chalk. One series of pastels juxtaposes the dusky beauty of her family's heirloom quilts against vibrantly colored irises and daffodils. Her recent mixed media efforts have concentrated primarily on the human figure. Oils, acrylic and watercolor pieces executed on primed canvass possess a looser quality than earlier work. Abstract and symbolic elements are successfully utilized to a narrative effect.

BENDA, PAMELA (Painter)
P.O. Box 4628, Carmel, CA 93921

Born: 1952 *Awards:* 1st Place, John H. and Mary Lehman Award; 1st Prize, John Sloan Competition *Exhibitions:* Salmagundi Club, NYC; Albuquerque Museum of Art *Education:* Art Students League, NYC

With a thick impasto of paint, she boldly sets loosely painted figures of bent farmworkers or enduring Native Americans against abstracted backgrounds of flat, bright color. She first developed her talent for portraiture while training with Daniel E. Greene at the Art Students League. As she strove to free herself from traditional restraints and to synthesize her political views with her paintings, her figures became less literal. She now works for a double marriage of politics with aesthetics and realism with abstract expressionism. She sees herself as a colorist, and she has been influenced by Robert Henri's "spots of color" and by Degas' and Toulouse-Lautrec's masterful use of living lines.

BENDER, JAMES (Multimedia Artist)
4220 Birkland Rd., B.I., WA, 98110

Born: 1951 *Collections:* Safeco Corp.; City of Seattle *Exhibitions:* Stonington Galleries; Bailey Nelson Gallery, Seattle *Education:* U. of Washington *Dealer:* Bailey Nelson Gallery, Seattle

He uses the primitive but highly developed techniques of the native Northwest Coast people to create contemporary jewelry. While in college, he first became interested in their art forms. After extensive study and analysis of the two and three-dimensional examples of this form that exist in museums and collections, he began working with Duane Pasco, who is the foremost practitioner of the form. He found that primitive techniques could be used in a contemporary context. His current images range from abstractions to natural figures. His materials include precious metals, types of exotic wood and acrylic and water based paints. His dramatic colors range from the bright to the muted.

BENDER, SHARON (Sculptor)
1507 Western Ave. #405, Seattle, WA 98101

Born: 1938 *Collections:* School of Visual Arts, NYC *Exhibitions:* Instituto Superior Per Le Artistiche, Italy; Gallery 209 Bellingham, WA *Education:* U. of Washington *Dealer:* Foster/White Gallery, Seattle

She began her artistic career as an abstract color-field painter in the 1960s. In the summer of 1987, she studied in Urbino, Italy with Enzo Cucchi, Eliseo Mattiachi, and Jannis Kounellis and, under the latter's encouragement, began sculpting. She cast her bronze works in the "lost wax" method, incorporating stones and pieces of glass in her work. Her sculptures tend to range from two to six feet in height. Many of her pieces, such as *January,* reveal the influence of pre-Columbian culture, especially Aztec or Mayan art. Her works symbolize life and struggle, death and eternity, hope and completion.

BENDER, STUART (Video Artist)
335 Carroll Park West, Long Beach, CA 90814

Born: 1953 *Awards:* Grant, Long Beach Museum *Collections:* Long Beach Museum of Art; Chicago Video Data Bank *Exhibitions:* Videonale, Bonn, West Germany; Museum of Modern Art, Rio De Janeiro *Education:* State U. of New York, Buffalo

After formal training in the arts, he began to explore video as a way to blend the diverse elements of his education. In his early, darkly comic works, he experimented with electronic effects and editing techniques. Thematically, they were concerned with socialization and belief systems. Recent work elaborates on the same themes and includes single channel videos, multi channel room installations and live performance. Collaborating with composer Angelo Funicelli, his absurdist and sardonic commentaries on contemporary lifestyles range from music videos to full-scale operas. Currently, he and Funicelli are producing an operatic song cycle forvideo based on ancient and contemporary prophecies. The work examines the futile human effort to grasp the ineffable: in this case, the past and future.

BENDER-KLINEFELTER, RAYE (Painter)
690 Los Angeles Ave., Suite 152, Simi Valley, CA 93065

Born: 1950 *Awards:* Grand 1st Prize, Josephine County Art Association, Grants Pass, OR *Collections:* Grants Pass Art Museum; Rogue Valley Art Gallery, Medford, OR *Exhibitions:* The Framery Gallery, Ashland, OR; Southern Oregon Historical Society, Jacksonville *Education:* U. Bois de Boulogne, Canada

Taught watercolor techniques by her friends and influenced by the works of Zoltan Szabo, she painted watercolor landscapes and still lifes early in her career.

Benny Alba, *Nuclear Secrets,* 16 x 38, oil and metallics

Robert Albanese, *Jue d'Enfant,* 72 x 84, acrylic on canvas with sand

Karen Atkinson, *Era After Era II Nevada(detail),* installation

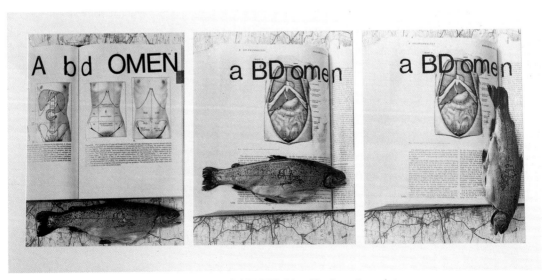

Shimon Attie, *AbdOMEN,* 24 x 60, ektacolor print

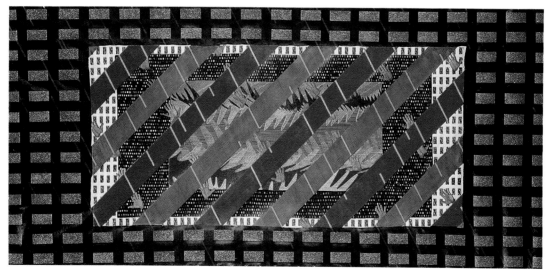

John Affolter, *It's Raining,* 84 x 168, mixed media and acrylic on canvas. Courtesy: Foster/White Gallery

Gerald F. Brommer, *Yosemite Valley/Early Spring,* 22 x 30, watercolor and collage.
Courtesy: Fireside Gallery, Carmel

Randall Bruce, *M.X. Funereal,* 20 x 7,
earthenware. Courtesy: Trapezoid Gallery

Fred L. Berensmeier, *Shield Bear Carrying Pure Water,*
17 x 29, linocut. Courtesy: Standing Bear Gallery

Roger Barr, *Skygate,* 312 x 240 x 96,
welded stainless steel

Roy Buchman, *Stepping Into Red,* 77 x 61,
oil on wood and canvas

Francis Berry, *Fusion,* 32 x 19, monotype
(etching ink on paper). Courtesy: Mr. and Mrs. Marohn
Photograph: Susan Scott

John Bruce, *Armed and Ready,* 24 x 30, oil

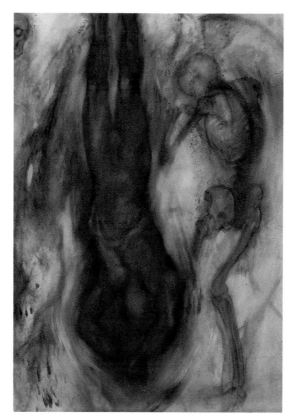

Barbara Burritt, *Tékel,* 84 x 72, oil

Sharon Bender, *April,* 12 x 36 x 7, bronze.
Photograph: Chris Webber

Mona Beaumont, *Freefall,* 18 x 12, pastel
and ink on paper

Madeline Bohanon, *Shalaka Mana,* 40 x 26, watercolor.
Courtesy: Sierra Galleries, Tahoe City, CA

Karl Benjamin, *#12, 1986,* 63 x 45, oil on canvas.
Courtesy: Ruth Bachofner Gallery, Santa Monica, CA

Barbara Biggs, *Peruvian Girl,* 16 x 20, cibachrome

Monica Bryant, *Country Blue Apron,* 22 x 29, watercolor

Ken Ball, *Iron Eyes Cody—A Portrait in Bronze,* 33 inches tall,
bronze. Courtesy: Gene Autry Western Heritage Museum, Los Angeles, CA

Craig M. Black, *Spanish,* 18 x 23 x 11, ceramic.
Photograph: Phillip Cohen

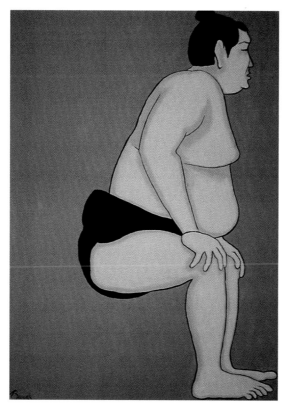

Barak, *The Sumo Man,* 36 x 48, oil on canvas

Charles Lynn Bragg, *Corporate Head,* 24 x 30, acrylic on canvas

Baumann, *Yosemite,* 62 x 42, oil on canvas.
Courtesy: Contra Costa Times Building

Veronica Brutosky, C.S.J., *Road Rising,* 16 x 20, oil on canvas.
Photograph: E.Z. Smith

Mary A. Beeson, *Elsa,* 20 x 15 x 8, pink portugal marble.
Courtesy: A. Albert Alden Gallery, Palm Springs, CA

Brice Bowman, *Companion,* 60 x 48, oil on canvas

Gary Bates, *Lunar Kecherschmitt,* 168 x 132 x 68, steel boiler-plate.
Photograph: Jens Selvig

George J. Bleich, *The Orion Concept Challenger,* 30 x 36, acrylic.
Courtesy: Bleich Gallery, Carmel

Suzanne Bloomfield, *Origin,* 48 x 60, encaustic mix

Pat Berger, *Cactiscape,* 60 x 54, acrylic

Douglas Bremner, *The Bird,* 48 x 120, welded steel

Over the years, she expanded her technical range through experimentation with rice paper, natural pigment prints and natural dyes and is today working with an imagery related to her Abenaquis Indian heritage. She uses an Indian symbolism to transform traditional landscapes into mystical views of nature and calls this style "New Age Watercolor." She is a member of the Watercolor Society of Oregon, the artist chapter of the Jacksonville Historical Society and the Rogue Valley Art Association.

BENGSTON, BILLY AL (Painter)
110 Mildred Ave., Venice CA 90291

Born: 1934 *Awards:* Guggenheim Fellowship; National Foundation for the Arts *Collections:* Museum of Modern Art, NYC; Art Institute of Chicago *Exhibitions:* Los Angeles County Museum of Art; Corcoran Gallery *Education:* Otis Art Institute; San Francisco Art Institute *Dealer:* James Corcoran Gallery, Los Angeles; Acquavella Contemporary Art, NYC

After study with Peter Voulkos, from about 1960 until the mid- 1970s his paintings and ceramics featured a central motif, either a cross, an iris or the chevrons of an army sergeant. Paintings were stapled to gallery walls, sometimes attached around corners. He often used crumpled aluminum sheets rather than canvas, and his diverse media included oil, acrylic, lacquer and epoxy. The images were two-dimensional, placed on an undefined translucent background rendered in a rich brushstroke. During this time he also made a series of motorcycle paintings. In the late 1970s central images were replaced with overlapping planes in a cubist mode. He continues a concern with the refinement of a well- crafted surface.

BENJAMIN, D. JOBE (Photographer)
1930 S. Robertson, #8, Los Angeles, CA

Born: 1956 *Exhibitions:* Summer Art Festival, Hollywood; Bizou's Cafe-Gallery, Huntington Beach

He has studied zone system photography and the technical expertise of Ansel Adams, Edward Weston and Minor White. His early, barren landscapes have gradually evolved into figure studies and portraiture. Recent work is progressing in two directions. His fine art photography consists of large format—8 x 10 and 20 x 24—textural studies, tide pools and nudes in landscape settings. Using technical information acquired through his work as a lab technician, he also produces graphics for the advertising, recording and fashion industries. The photographs are medium-format studies of light patterns projected on nude figures. These black and white prints are then toned brown or selenium, or are hand-colored with transparent permanent dyes.

BENJAMIN, KARL (Painter)
675 W. 8th St., Claremont, CA 91711

Born: 1925 *Awards:* NEA Grant for the Visual Arts *Collections:* Whitney Museum, NYC; Los Angeles County Museum of Art *Exhibitions:* Museum of Modern Art, NYC; Corcoran Gallery, Washington, D.C. *Education:* Claremont College *Dealer:* Ruth Bachofner, Santa Monica

He bases his abstract work on number systems, semi-random progressions and large conglomerates of rotating modules or units, using a hard edge and oils in his various experiments with line shape and color. The series "1985" depicts repeated patterns playing optical tricks with on the viewer. His current works—

vague cityscapes in both high-key and subdued colors—display a concern with architectural design. The formal concerns that informed his work of the 1950s and 1960s have reappeared, and these recent paintings allude to the pre-Abstract Expressionist American painting of the 1930s and 1940s.

BENNETT, MARGARET P. (Painter, Metal Artist)
5607 Sobrante Ave., El Sobrante, CA 94803

Born: 1939 *Awards:* New York International; Watercolor, Mercedes Benz Centennial Design *Collections:* Library of Congress, Washington, D.C. *Exhibitions:* Del Mano Gallery, Los Angeles; Crain-Wolov Gallery, Tulsa, OK *Education:* U. of Michigan; Sorbonne, Paris

Her extensive formal art education included studies in design with Frank Lloyd Wright. She draws her inspiration from the natural world and from the imagery, artistry and crafts of Elizabethan England. Her sculptural and decorative metalwork includes jewelry, tableware and tools, such as crochet hooks, lacemakers' bobbins, boxes and letter-openers. She uses traditional craft methods, employing casting techniques, and hand-tool work with bezel pushers, dental tools and other custom- designed instruments. She has recently been focusing on the fine arts aspect of her talent, exhibiting and competing internationally with her prints, watercolors and oils.

BENNETT, MARK (Collage Artist)
10810 Valley Spring Ln., N. Hollywood, CA 91602

Born: 1956 *Awards:* Best of Show, East Gate Art Fair *Exhibitions:* Memorial Union Gallery, U. of Arizona; By Design, Beverly Hills *Education:* New York U.

Inspired by Andy Warhol's "Campbell Soup Can" paintings, he created collages depicting American consumerism. He xeroxed photographs from 1950s *Life* magazines and finished them in bright, surreal colors. His recent work involves poster-sized enlargements of 4-by-6-inch sketches of numerical scenes—*Four Nuns in a Liquor Store* and *Three Men in a Pickup Truck* for example. The surreal influence is still apparent in the bright colors he uses to fill in the images. He believes that art can comment on society's foibles and also be humorous.

BENTON, FLETCHER (Sculptor)
250 Dore St., San Francisco, CA 94103

Born: 1931 *Awards:* President's Scholar Award, San Jose State University; Award of Honor for Outstanding Service in Sculpture, San Francisco Arts Commission *Collections:* Whitney Museum of American Art, NYC; Hirshhorn Museum and Sculpture Garden, Washington, DC *Exhibitions:* San Francisco Museum of Modern Art; Whitney Museum of American Art Annual, NYC; *Education:* Miami U. Oxford, OH *Dealer:* John Berggruen Gallery, San Francisco

His early work was similar to the painting of the Bay Area figurative painters of the 1950s. Eventually, though, his paintings became "kinetic," the figures being replaced by mechanized and ever-changing geometric color planes. He later developed this kinetic statement even further by exploring the "implied motion" in the composition of elements. Because of his strong commitment to geometry, he is often referred to as a constructivist. He allows his materials to speak for themselves, primarily using steel to distinguish time and space. *Balanced/Unbalanced, Steel Watercolors, Folded Circle* and *Folded Square* are among his major works. Dynamic in their spatial relationships, the works maintain an orderly yet at times whimsical perspective. His governed sense of composition builds upon a vocabulary of precision realized through subtle contradictions and a precarious recognition of time.

BENVENUTO, ELIO (Painter, Ceramist)
870 45th Ave., San Francisco, CA 94121

Born: 1914 *Awards:* A.I. Architect *Collections:* Oakland Museum; Richmond Art Center *Exhibitions:* Museo Italo-Americano, San Francisco; Richmond Art Center

He was born in Italy and classically trained; his early influences were the modern Italian artists Gothic Pisanos and Tino da Camaino. In the 1940s and 1950s, he sculpted expressionistically in wood and bronze. Later, he made abstract geometric pieces from stone, marble and bronze. During the 1970s, he did figurative studies and worked with drawings and ceramics. In recent years, he has traveled annually to Pietrasanta, Italy, where he carves large abstract sculptures. These monumental, but minimalist figures allude to but are not reminiscent of prehistoric cultures. He also paints large acrylic canvases, which he articulates with geometric patterns of flat but vibrant colors.

BERAN, LENORE (Multimedia Artist)
4740 Mt. Aukum Rd., Placerville, CA 95667

Born: 1925 *Collections:* U. of Evansville, IN; Hunt Wesson Co. *Exhibitions:* Glory Hole Gallery, Sonora; Lu Martin Gallery, Laguna Beach *Education:* Art League of Los Angeles

Constantly experimenting with materials and techniques over the past twenty years, she has developed proficiency in many different media. While her training stressed conventional still-life and landscape painting, she soon discovered the expressive advantages of a looser, rub-out and wash technique. Musicians and America's sub-cultures fascinated her, inspiring many early projects. An interest in collage precipitated her development of a technique wherein torn pieces of paper are applied like brushstrokes of paint. When her focus returned to the human figure she found that abstractions of the sitter's body captured the essence of her subject. Line and rhythm overrode the importance of realism in her work. This expressive fluidity also marks her recent stoneware sculptures of Native Americans. Pieces of turquoise, agate and other stones add to the earthy effect.

BERARDO, MARGARET F. (Painter, Architectural Designer)
P.O. Box 373, El Dorado, CA 95623

Born: 1914 *Awards:* Los Angeles Exposition Gallery *Collections:* El Dorado Historical Society; Placerville Art Association *Exhibitions:* Sawg, Tucson; Mother Lode Annual Show *Education:* Art Center College of Design

After leaving the Art Center in Los Angeles, she studied under Millard Sheets, Barse Miller, Jerry Becker, Edward Abey and Jason Mason Reeves. Her whimsical paintings reflect a varied life. Frequent themes are social commentary and Maori myth. She has created color models for the Walt Disney Studios, and she continues to create residential and construction blueprints. Her futuristic landscapes reflect recent scientific ideas such as positive and negative communications, fourth dimensions and "squeezed

sound." She is a member of the Southern Arizona Watercolor Guild and the Placerville Arts Association.

BERENSMEIER, FRED (Printmaker)
P.O. Box 286, Lagunitas, CA 94938

Born: 1932 *Awards:* U.S. National Park Service Print Commission; Best in Show, Marin Art and Garden Show *Collections:* Univ. of the Pacific; Standard Oil Co. *Exhibitions:* City Arts Gallery, San Francisco; Phillips/Allen Gallery, San Francisco *Education:* California College of Arts and Crafts; San Francisco State U.

He is a printmaker who manipulates the surface textures of his medium to strike at meanings beyond image and composition. An early interest in German expressionism, in particular the graphic works of Edvard Munch, led to prints that attempted to integrate the expressiveness of such influences with the abstract qualities of wood and metal print matrices. In the late 1950s and the 1960s, his works focused on 'synthetic' subject matter such as toys and slot machines, with an emphasis on flatness that reflected the pop ethos. Recent works have utilized imagery from the petrographs and pictographs of primitive cultures and have witnessed an increasing emphasis on color, achieved through the use of multiple transparent ink overlays. The artist has also been hand-coloring heavily embossed relief images. These works address the relationship between the human race and the world at large, in stylistic terms derived from the artist's global influences.

BERG, DARLENE (Painter)
2 Ardmore Rd., Larkspur, CA 94939

Born: 1939 *Awards:* San Francisco Art Commission Award of Show *Exhibitions:* Galleria, San Francisco; Design Showplace Center, San Francisco *Education:* U. of Illinois

Although her early training and work was highly representational, she now works exclusively in large, acrylic-on-canvas abstractions, sometimes moving into triptychs. Rhythmic color relationships direct viewers' attention to the perimeters of the canvas, creating a tense dynamic of movement within the non-conceptual figures and lines. Her brushwork is linear and often textured, intensifying the sense of energy evoked by densely applied pastel colors. The textured affect is often increased by the use of additives in her paints. Recent works are increasingly lighter in palette, introducing an interplay of non-directional light to the elements the pieces already address.

BERGER, PAT (Painter, Sculptor)
2648 Anchor Ave., Los Angeles, CA 90064

Awards: Brody Arts Fund Fellowship, Los Angeles; Ford Foundation Purchase Award *Collections:* Skirball Museum, Los Angeles; Long Beach Museum of Art *Exhibitions:* Palm Springs Desert Museum; Downey Museum of Art *Education:* UCLA; Art Center College of Design, Los Angeles *Dealer:* Valerie Miller Gallery, Palm Desert; Adelle Taylor, Dallas

Her early, Milton Avery-influenced oils of people in environments were characterized by simple flat shapes and a thick application of medium. She experimented for a number of years before progressing to acrylics and her current, more realistic style. Her work has since diverged into two separate series; the first are "cacti-scapes," consisting of large, detailed blow-ups of cacti whose size gives them an abstract quality; the second series details the plight of the homeless. She

Lenore Beran, *Play It Again,* 21 x 27, mixed media on paper

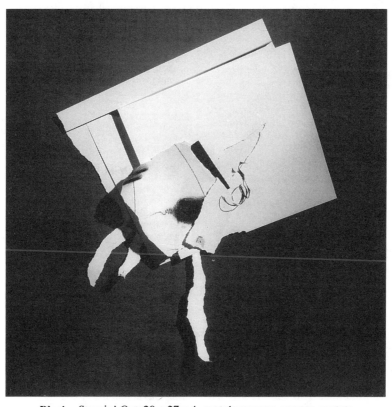

Blazin, *Steppin' Out,* 30 x 27 x 4, pastels, copper, papers, acetate

recently received a Brody Arts Fund Fellowship to continue this work. She has also been an educator for two decades and currently teaches painting and drawing for the Los Angeles Unified School District.

BERGMAN, CIEL (BOWERS, CHERYL O.) (Painter)
1710 Calle Cerro, Santa Barbara, CA 93101

Born: 1938 *Awards:* Society for the Encouragement of Creative Arts (SECA), San Francisco Museum of Modern Art; L.C. Tiffany Award, Great Neck, NY *Collections:* Metropolitan Museum of Art, NYC; San Francisco Museum of Modern Art *Exhibitions:* Whitney Biennal; San Francisco Museum of Modern Art *Dealer:* Ian Birksted, London; Dorothy Goldeen Gallery, Los Angeles

Her formal training in figure painting was influenced by Abstract Expressionism and by Duchamp and several Bay Area painters, including Nathan Olivera and William Wiley. From the middle to late '70s, she worked in acrylic on large expanses of unstretched linen. Images depicted tawny fields punctuated by brilliant ruptures of blue and violet. During this period, a metaphorical iconography consisting of bones, water holes, gates and paths began to emerge. The water hole motif has since expanded into a larger concern for water and the ocean. Large panels in oil convey a unique sense of time, portraying distinct moments simultaneously. While she still employs brilliant blues, violets and silvery grays, her palette has become much darker. Paintings include *The Red Fence*, a 20-by-8-abstract expressionist work in three panels, and *Rice Memory, Black Fan, Dead Water Buffalo, Blood Water*, a watercolor in black and gray with vivid touches of scarlet and rose. In addition to painting, she has begun to work in sculpture, installation and video.

BERK, BARBARA (Sculptor)
20358 Sun Valley Dr., Laguna Beach, CA 92651

Born: 1940 *Awards:* Fulbright Grant, Oslo, Norway; 1st Prize, California State Fair *Collections:* Chase Manhattan Bank; Statens Kunstfond (National Art Foundation), Copenhagen *Exhibitions:* A.I.R. Gallery, NYC; Orlando Gallery, Sherman Oaks *Education:* Pratt Institute; Cal. State-Fullerton

Her development has involved a movement from paintings and drawings that emphasize the flat surface, to those that give the illusion of depth, to actual three-dimensional work in sculpture. In the transition from two dimensions to three, she explored a variety of materials and techniques, but she currently works almost exclusively with wood. Recent work combines free-standing multiple sculptural forms with drawings. Using landscape references to explore real and illusory space, and the overlap between the two, she looks for forms that convey her idea of nature as something serious yet playful, spiritual, mysterious, changing, moving and full of energy. One such installation consists of a tableau of carved shapes in pale wood—a floor piece with a rippling silhouette, a pair of undulating wooden strips slung on a wooden trestle and, suspended from the ceiling, two white frames fitted with more undulating strips of wood suggestive of hilly terrain. The wall and floor are painted in a flat gray-and-white design that can be read as a shadow or as a gorge and cliff landscape.

BERLANT, TONY (Sculptor, Collage Artist)
1304 12th St., Santa Monica, CA 90401

Born: 1941 *Awards:* Annual Exhibition Award, San Francisco; Ford Foundation Purchase Award, Houston *Collections:* Los Angeles County Museum of Art; Art Institute of Chicago *Exhibitions:* Whitney Museum, NYC; John Berggruen Gallery, San Francisco *Education:* UCLA *Dealer:* L.A. Louver Gallery

He is noted for the wide range of his styles and media, from three-dimensional metalwork collages to Mexican folk art and traditional painting. Early pieces often use tin scraps and enameled metal, whose previous incarnations had been in commercial packaging material, transforming these mundane materials into personal images and pop icons, such as cubes and small houses occupied by salvaged objects. He continues to explore a diversity of media and techniques, with images and influences reminiscent now of cubism, now abstract expressionism, now folk art. In later works, he employs the techniques he used to transform the mundane into the magical in his large-scale pieces, such as the "History of L.A." series and the mural *Dancing on the Brink of the World*. These works—found metal collage on wood puncuated with steel brads—address themes of discovery, progress and place with the same energy, vitality and joie de vivre that characterize all his work.

BERNHARD, RUTH (Photographer)
2982 Clay St., San Francisco, CA 94115

Born: 1905 *Awards:* San Francisco Arts Commission *Collections:* San Francisco Museum of Modern Art; Museum of Modern Art, NYC *Exhibitions:* San Francisco Museum of Modern Art; Gallery Zur Stockeregg, Zurich *Education:* Academy of Art, Berlin *Dealer:* Photography West Gallery, Carmel, CA

She worked in commercial photography for the early part of her career, her photographs appearing in such publications as *Advertising Art* and *The New York Times Magazine*. In 1935, she met Edward Weston and for the first time realized that photography could be art. From that point on, she worked more intuitively and began to develop a technique that led to a preoccupation with light and with the black-and-white print. The female nude is a favorite subject. *In the Box* (horizontal) depicts a nude reclining in a long, narrow box, knees bent and eyes closed in an expression of repose and introspection. This image serves as the cover photograph for her 1986 book, *Ruth Bernhard: The Eternal Body*. Her subject matter is often drawn from nature, using such objects as dried magnolia leaves, seashells, skills and bones. Some of these images are included in her 1976 portfolio, *The Gift of the Commonplace*.

BERNSTEIN, AMY C. (Painter, Photographer)
P.O. Box 221233, Carmel, CA 93922

Born: 1948 *Awards:* Phi Kappa Phi Honor Society; Susan Reagan Award, Outstanding Woman Scholar *Collections:* Lazarus/Isis Illuminarium, Beverly Hills *Exhibitions:* Coast Gallery, Maui; Collins Gallery, San Francisco *Education:* UC-Davis *Dealers:* Coast Gallery, Maui; Isis Illuminarium, Beverly Hills

Working with watercolors on handmade paper and an iconography that can be traced to comparative religions and anthropology, she calls her style "celestial impressionism." Georgia O'keeffe, Monet, Van Gogh, Matisse and Gauguin have all influenced her, as have

Bergman, *Woman to Woman VI,* 44 x 30, pastel, black Arches. Courtesy: Dorothy Goldeen Gallery

her travels, both through the outer world and in the inner realms of dreams. Images of landscapes, flower angels and trees evoke mystical ecstasy. Using a slow process of building rich, vibrant colors by adding layers of light color washes blended with iridescent gold and silver inks, her work shimmers with the changing light.

BERRIE, ROBIN (Textile Artist)
3760 S. Bentley Ave., Suite 104, Los Angeles, CA

Born: 1956 *Awards:* Best of Show, Fremont Textile Exhibition *Exhibitions:* Brea Art Exhibition; Hayward Art Exhibition

She began painting in oils as a child. An interest in patterns from nature, and an early study of abstract impressionism have both carried over into her current work. She now creates beautiful mixed-media fabric paintings by overlaying repeated textile patterns on a printed, dyed or airbrushed, abstract ground. Her work continues to display a fascination with vibrant colors. She currently works under the name "Wild Berrie Textiles."

BERRY, CAROLYN (Multimedia Artist)
78 Cuesta Vista Dr., Monterey, CA 93940

Born: 1930 *Collections:* Judith Hoffberg, UCLA; Library, Museum of Modern Art, NYC *Exhibitions:* UCLA; Rutgers University, New Brunswick, NJ *Education:* U. of Missouri, Columbia; Humboldt U. *Dealer:* Artworks, Los Angeles; Viewpoint, Carmel

Her books include poetry, autobiographical writing, painting, photography and handwork. She makes one-of-a-kind altered books and multiple books as well as letterpress and commercially printed books. Her work in the 1960s concerned issues of civil rights — she would find racist and sexist remarks in literature and criticize, change and discard them or revise and compile them in books. Maps, genealogy and personal and general history have served as subjects, as have women such as Isabella Bird, Eleanor Stewart and Anna Akhmatova. She is currently working on a series of drawings and watercolors depicting the endeavors of independent women. She also works in oil, acrylic and pencil and does sculpture and assemblage using plaster, wood, resin, polyform, balsa wood and occasionally stone.

BERRY, FRANCIS (Painter)
1114 Sutter St., #12, San Francisco, CA 94109

Born: 1957 *Exhibitions:* Graystone Gallery, San Francisco; American Institute of Architects Gallery, Santa Clara; Print Biennale, Cabo Frio, Brazil

After formal training in classicism and romanticism, he was introduced to Abstract Expressionism in 1982 by California artist Richard Faralla. He produced a number of mixed media works on paper comprising colorful energy fields ranging from the bold to the lyrical. Inspired by California artists David Park, Elmer Bishoff, Nathan Olivera, Manuel Neri and Richard Diebenkorn, he returned to a representational approach. This has taken form in a group of works—chiefly composed of monotypes and acrylic paintings—that focus on biomorphic shapes placed either within romantic color fields or, more recently, amid "fragmented reality" fields punctuated with diagrammatic symbols. A series of "Hero" works brings together monotype, painting and sculpture in an exploration of classical architecture and its relationship to man.

BERRYMAN, VIRGINIA (Painter)
4707 Norwalk Dr., #J101, San Jose, CA 95129

Born: 1924 *Awards:* 1st Place & Best of Show, Heritage Showing, San Jose Library *Collections:* Stanford U., Orthopedics Department *Exhibitions:* Triton Museum, Santa Clara; First Methodist Church, Palo Alto *Education:* San Jose State U.

Her work is characterized by a free-flowing expressionism and a concern with the continuity of past and present. Her subjects include historic sites, old barns, boats, flowers, horses, landscapes, and commissioned portraits. She prefers to paint her portraits from eight by ten inch photographs. Her most well known work is a full dress painting of George Woodward, a member of the Sioux and Menominee Indian tribes. Her current mixed media work involves researching her North American heritage. She has studied illustrating and drafting at the California Institute of Technology and graphic arts at Pasadena Community College.

BESNE, FRANCES (Ceramist, Painter)
5829 Rich Hill Dr., Orangevale, CA 95662

Born: 1936 *Awards:* Best Sculpture, 1st Auburn Clay Show; Merit Award, Honorable Mention, 2nd Fresno College Invitational *Exhibitions:* Crocker Art Museum, Sacramento; Theodore Styc Gallery, Fair Oaks

Mythological figures are sculptural ceramic expressions of her interests in nature, ecology and dance. Motion, gesture, and mood are her main concerns. Early work was characterized by conventional forms fired with a combination of low and high fire glazes. These have evolved into more elongated forms colored with stains or raku. Recently she has begun to make watercolors and prints, greatly influenced by other California art styles.

BESS, JIM (Painter)
903 K St., San Diego, CA 92101

Born: 1933 *Exhibitions:* San Diego Art Institute; Brushworks Gallery, San Diego *Education:* Southern Illinois U.; Illinois State U.

Starting with a large primed canvas and no preconceived subject matter, he creates through direct interaction with the developing images. The human form is a central theme; faces are often painted masks which obscure the hidden self. He is influenced by the expressionists. Bold color contrasts and varying textures are juxtaposed to promote a dynamic tension. Emotional responses to his work may range from serenity to agitation; such diversity reflects his proclivity for change. The intensity essential to such a spontaneous process led him in 1965 to burn all of his paintings and abandon future projects. Many years later he resumed his work prolifically. The Artplex Gallery in San Diego has sponsored three solo shows since 1976, and in 1988 the San Diego Art Institute featured sixteen of his large acrylic canvases.

BEVAN, SHARON (Painter)
118 N. June St., Los Angeles, CA 90004

Born: 1932 *Collections:* Dr. Sun Yat Sen Memorial Hall, Taipei *Exhibitions:* Fine Arts Gallery, San Gabriel; Audubon Society Wildlife and Environmental Art Show, Los Angeles *Education:* UC-Los Angeles

Although she addresses many subjects, she is primarily a landscape artist. Following a brief exploration of the abstract, she returned to a more representational style.

Robin Bressoud, *Jenny in My Easter Bonnet #2,* 24 x 30, acrylic. Courtesy: Thomas P. Carrico

S. Bevan, *Balboa,* 24 x 30, oil

She captures the impact of light upon the landscape in surprising combinations of peach, light blue and green. Strong form and dependable composition underlie the subtle surface textures, which are reminiscent of the Impressionists. A poet and naturalist, she brings to the canvas a sensitivity reflecting her life-long pursuit of the innermost moods of nature.

BEVERIDGE, DWAN (Painter)
3035 Hartford Rd., Orange, CA 92669

Born: 1919 *Awards:* 1st place, Costa Mesa 9th Annual Juried Show; Orange County Art Association Award *Exhibitions:* Ankrum Gallery; Muckethaler Cultural Center, Orange County *Education:* Art Students League, NY; Chouinard *Dealer:* Southwest Passage Gallery, San Juan Capistrano

A background in commercial art and classical education provides both realism and sense of design to drawings and watercolors. Recent works incorporate small household plastics that are subjected to high heat, affixed to watercolor backgrounds with silicone, and reinterpreted in pen and ink. Subject matter is figurative and inspired by the plastic form; colors are bright, as in the two- and three-dimensional combinations of blues and oranges in *Geisha.* The works subtly imply a theme of transformation as integral to art.

BEVILLE–FISH (Painter)
300 Tolak Rd., Aptos, CA 95003

Born: 1932 *Awards:* 1st Prize, Portraits, Beaumont Art League; Baytown Parks Purchase Prize, TX *Collections:* Right Assoc., Philadelphia; Baytown Parks and Recreation, TX *Education:* Scripps College *Dealer:* R.A. Fish

As an undergraduate at Scripps College, she was impressed with the watercolors of instructor Millard Sheets, and fascinated by the design patterns of Jean Ames. Though she has been influenced by Gauguin, she uses color in her own way, creating what she calls "enhanced realism." Like many artists she has had to turn to commercial work to cover the expenses of having children. She has created stage sets, painted sailboat portraits, and designed makeup and costume fantasies for theater. She paints with gouache and continues innovating with colors in scenes of local seascapes, Victorian houses, and fantasy or news-related subjects.

BIANCHI, TOM (Multimedia Artist)
5845 W. 6th St., Los Angeles, CA

Born: 1945 *Collections:* Bank of America, Los Angeles; Laguna Beach Museum of Art *Exhibitions:* Gibbs Museum; Spoleto Festival; International Center for Photography *Education:* Northwestern U. of Law *Dealer:* Glenn/Dash Gallery, Los Angeles

Formerly Senior Counsel at Columbia Pictures, he left the motion picture industry in 1980 to pursue a career in the fine arts. His first works consisted of large, highly textured paper tapestries. His recent work has followed several directions. Using wood, plaster overlay and polychrome, he constructs public sculpture installations, as large as two stories tall. These evocative, abstract pieces are site-specific and often place old forms in new contexts. Working also in black and white photography, he creates prints of nudes, both in studio and outdoor settings, frequently having a classical awsthetic enlivened with a celebration of real life play. He also produces three-dimensional wall constructions and free-standing, geometric-abstract sculptures made from wood, plaster, metal, concrete, acrylic paint and metallic leaf.

BIBBS, CHARLES A. (Painter, Ceramist)
25796 Cartier Dr., Moreno Valley, CA 92388

Born: 1948 *Awards:* Honorable Mention, San Bernardino Inland Exhibition *Exhibitions:* Long Beach Art Gallery; San Bernardino Museum *Education:* Long Beach City College *Dealer:* Things Graphics and Fine Arts, Washington, D.C.; Wanda Wallace & Associates, Englewood

His goal is to make ethnically-rooted aesthetic statements that arouse spiritual emotions. His subjects are African herdsman and blues singers, whose movement and rhythm he renders through exaggeration and stylization. He obtains rich undertones of color and line texture by combining acrylic and ink. He also creates fantasy paintings, in which he translates the flying life forms and images of his dreams into cohesive shapes: "The Land of Little Folk." He occasionally mixes his two concepts, creating what he calls "Wind Faces." In this work, he transforms the majestically adorned faces and heads of Maasia Tribesmen into a wind-swept appearance.

BIE, ALFRED (Photographer)
527 S. Manhattan Pl., #1, Los Angeles, CA 90020

Born: 1966 *Awards:* 1st Place, Photography, Artists Awards Exhibition *Exhibitions:* North Gallery, Otis/Parsons, Los Angeles *Education:* Otis Art Institute of the Parsons School of Design

From early childhood, he has been interested in narrative and the juxtaposition of disparate images. This interest has been fueled by television, films and especially comic books. His early work focused on traditionally presented visual narrative. Recent work, guided by the teaching of Peter Reiss and Lisa Bloomfield, has been more free-flowing and psychologically oriented: spontaneous narrative, which seeks to describe the intangible. He works in the 35mm format, usually shooting black and white. He has also been experimenting with paper negatives.

BIELINSKI-WYATT, MARY (Painter)
5583 Castleglen Ave., San Jose, CA 95129

Born: 1933 *Awards:* Woman Artist, American Pen Women *Exhibitions:* San Jose Art Museum; Rosicrucian Museum, San Jose *Education:* U. of Wisconsin; Layton Art Institute

After formal training in acrylic, oil and watercolor, she began painting with watercolors. She has studied art for her entire life, drawing inspiration and influence from Robert E. Wood, Jad Zon, Zolton Szabo, Nita Engle and Bud Shackleford. She paints on 140- or 300-pound French hand-made paper, scraping, sanding, washing and stamping it until the work is done. Bright images of dry-dock boat scenes and storms, skies, and atmospheres dominate her 30-by-40-inch canvases. "I paint for the joy of painting . . . Feelings, not things are what painting is all about," she says.

BIERCE, KAREN (Painter)
P.O. Box 601, Graeagle, CA 96013

Born: 1949 *Awards:* 1st place, Emerald City Classic VI, Nepenthe Mundi Society *Exhibitions:* American Artists Professional League, NYC; Salmagundi Club, NYC *Education:* U. of Hawaii

Her paintings are in the photo-realist style, depicting tropical environments—dense green foliage and tropi-

Buskirk, *December,* 20 x 30, wool and silk

Dwan Beveridge, *The Sitter,* 15 x 22, ink and plastic

Barak, *untitled,* 48 x 60, oil on canvas

cal birds. They are in oil on linen, painted wet on wet in a series of glazes working light into dark. Her use of color has been greatly influenced by her studies under Gary Pruner in California, but her subject matter derives from time in Hawaii and travels in the Caribbean and the South Pacific, visiting galleries and museums and photographing. The work of the painter Jesse Botke has also been an important influence on her development. Her paintings are highly detailed and intensely colored, illuminated by warm tropical light. While she originally considered the objects in the paintings to be her subjects—the *Four Macaws* of one painting, for example—she now considers the light and color of the painting's environment to be the real subject.

BIGGS, BARBARA E. (Photographer)
10780 Santa Monica Blvd., #450, Los Angeles, CA 90025

Born: 1931 *Exhibitions:* Installations Gallery, Encino; Brand Library, Glendale *Education:* New York U.; UCLA

Influenced by Ansel Adams, her work throughout the 1970s focused on landscapes and the contrast between majestic, broad views and more intimate scenes featuring leaves, insects, pebbles, tiny flowers and the textures of bark and water. After studying with George Hurrell, she experimented with portraiture. Work from this period included a series of romantic portraits of pregnant women in lacy, very feminine clothes. In the 1980s, her subjects and style broadened to include a more journalistic approach. She was asked to illustrate a book of poems written by Guggenheim Fellow Colette Inez. Their collaboration resulted in the book *Double Images*. Recently, she has been exploring the figure in landscape. Her portraiture has moved away from the dramatic lighting effects of Hurrell to naturalistic studies that emphasize more personal attributes of her models.

BIGWOOD, BEVERLY (Painter)
7904 Santa Monica Blvd., Los Angeles, CA

Born: 1952 *Collections:* Palm Springs Desert Museum *Exhibitions:* Los Angeles County Museum of Art *Education:* School of the Worcester Art Museum, Worcester, MA *Dealer:* Patten/Duval Gallery, Los Angeles

Her early career was spent in New York City; during this period, her work consisted largely of figurative works in oil, acrylic or watercolors. She also worked in pastels and in mixed media, including plaster and sand. In 1980, she moved to Los Angeles, where she began to work in paper collage, creating architectural interpretations of landmark buildings in the city. Recently, she has worked on a series of acrylic paintings inspired by her first trip to Europe. This work depicts classical subjects, such as Psyche and Cupid, and Diana the Huntress, in a whimsical, cartoon-like style. She has also continued to work in collage, creating pieces in black-and-white paper with a bold, primitive style. She has also begun to move toward commercial design work.

BILLICK, DONNA (Mixed Media Artist)
Rte. 2, Box 2560A, Davis, CA 95616

Born: 1950 *Awards:* Ceramic Tile Institute Mural Artist Award *Collections:* UCD Medical Center, Sacramento; Truffini Fountain, Senior Center, Davis *Exhibitions:* Natsoulas/Novelozo Gallery, Davis; Bruce

Velick Gallery, San Francisco *Education:* UC-Davis *Dealer:* City Gallery, Sacramento

Early work consisted of large ceramic pieces painted in oil on glass. She experimented with many different media, her style and approach then influenced by Wayne Thiebaud, Roy DeForest, and Manuel Neri. Currently, she creates murals for public and private spaces using Japanese ceramic tiles and Italian marble. She works in a limitless range of colors. Imagery includes landscapes, geometrics and abstract and realistic figures. She considers herself a "20th-century cave painter," inspired by the forms in ancient cave paintings and in European public art, especially art in architectural settings.

BINDER, ERWIN (Sculptor)
4632 W. Magnolia Blvd., Burbank, CA 91505

Born: 1934 *Collections:* Smithsonian Institute, Washington, D.C.; City of Burbank *Exhibitions:* Heritage Gallery, Los Angeles; Century Towers Hotel, Los Angeles *Dealer:* Topaz Universal, Inc., Burbank

His work has passed through several periods of development. Early sculptures featured groupings of two or three figures melded into a single organic unit, displaying space, volume and movement. Now, he is best known for monumental pieces in bronze and marble. These sculptures are more abstract, expressing and evoking deep emotions. He has also created a series of large, free-standing sculptures based on enlarged photographs of human cells. A large body of his work comprises public art and commissioned memorials, awards, medals and plaques. *Requiem*, for example, a bronze, flame-shaped sculpture, is a tribute to the sacrifice and bravery of American war veterans.

BING, BERNICE (Painter)
P.O. Box 437, Philo, CA 95466

Awards: San Francisco Art Institute Alumni Award; San Francisco Art Commission Honor Award *Exhibitions:* San Francisco Museum of Modern Art; San Francisco Art Institute *Education:* San Francisco Art Institute

As an undergraduate, she studied with Richard Diebenkorn, Nathan Oliveira, Elmer Bischoff and Sabro Hasegawa. Her early paintings contained traces of her Bay Area figurative school background, but she also incorporated non-specific rural references. In graduate school, she studied with Frank Lobdell, a student of Clifford Still. She then worked in an abstract expressionist mode, often creating sensuous organic abstractions that existed on the boundary between expressionism and surrealism. In 1984, she studied Chinese calligraphy at Zhejiang Art Academy in Haugzhou, China. Her recent work is an integration of Eastern calligraphic ideographs and Western abstraction. She superimposes fluid calligraphic lines over shapes of highly contrasting colors.

BIONDO, SARAH (Sculptor, Painter)
102A Riverside, Sequim, WA 98382

Born: 1941 *Awards:* Certificate of Excellence in Sculpture, Art Horizon International Art Competition; Best in Show, Nassau Coliseum *Collections:* Russel Sage College *Exhibitions:* National Arts Exhibit, Cooperstown, NY; Juried National Exhibit, Tyler, TX *Education:* Louisiana State U.; Kansas City Art Institute

As a painter and sculptor, her concerns are with the interplay of form and space. In sculpture, her subject

Barbara Biggs, *In the Light of Hot and Cold,* 11 x 14, black and white print. Courtesy: Double Images, a book co-authored with Guggenheim Fellow, poet Colette Inez

Belisa Barbachano, *Color and Frost #15,* 30 x 36, acrylic on canvas

is the figure. At first, she sculpted in the round, but as she began to focus on negative space, she began making fragmented and segmented works that described sections of the human form. Concave and convex areas became more important than details of portraiture. Her painting career began in 1977. She achieved bold textures by mixing oils, silk-screen inks and watercolor-based pigments and is now using color relationships to explore space in a similar mixed media. Her combinations of form float and extend into each other.

BISBEE, BONNIE (Painter)
P.O. Box 627, Mariposa, CA 95338

Born: 1941 *Exhibitions:* Collins Gallery, San Francisco; Civic Arts Gallery, Walnut Creek *Education:* Ecole des Beaux Arts; San Francisco Art Institute

She considers herself within a school of art that emphasizes creation through "revelation," that is, working directly from the unconscious. She uses a full palette of bright colors and works in oil or acrylic. Her paintings are both figurative and symbolic, filled with images of the natural and the supernatural. In *Solar Angel,* a flaming angel rises from the sea and reaches out to another figure in flames, a human form in lotus position. Painted in bright colors against a dark background crowded with stars, the work exudes a primal, exotic sensibility.

BISCHOFF, ELMER (Painter)
2571 Shattuck Ave., Berkeley, CA 94704

Born: 1916 *Awards:* Ford Foundation Grant; National Institute of Arts and Letters Grant *Collections:* Metropolitan Museum of Art, NYC; Hirshorn Museum, Washington, DC *Exhibitions:* Tate Gallery, London; San Francisco Musuem of Modern Art *Education:* UC-Berkeley *Dealer:* John Berggruen Gallery, San Francisco; Hirschl & Adler, NYC

After dabbling in abstract expression in the immediate postwar years, he began the early 1950s to explore figuration, pioneering along with such artists as David Park and Richard Diebenkorn the movement that became known as the Bay Area Figurative School. His works of this period are characterized by a balance between abstraction and representation, which he achieves by the use of abstract expressionist techniques and vivid colors in representational images. The paintings progressed from figures in rough but identifiable landscapes and architectural settings to those in less well-defined backgrounds and then to specific, clearly defined settings. The former are marked by a moody range of emotions, the latter by self-absorbed figures whose relationships are ambiguous and disturbing. His recent work has shown a surprising shift back to pure abstraction and gesture. These latest compositions are vibrant collisions of color and geometric shapes, perhaps the most playful and celebratory work of his career.

BISCONTI, PATRICK (Painter, Sculptor)
600 Whiskey Hill Rd., Watsonville, CA 95076

Born: 1945 *Awards:* 1st Place, Sculpture, Venice Marina; 3rd Place, Sculpture, Santa Cruz County Art Show *Exhibitions:* The Front Porch Human Arts Gallery, Venice, CA *Dealer:* The Front Porch Human Arts Gallery, Venice, CA

His sculpture is done in metal and painting in oil, and he always has several series of works in progress. Paintings range in size up to six by seven feet and depict seascapes, stilllifes, human and animal figures, faces and dreams. Sculptures are typically of welded steel in styles ranging from the realistic to the abstract. He recently completed a "Sculpture Symphony" of functional musical instruments in welded steel that are designed to play "modern art music." These stringed, percussion and wind instruments are free-form in design and differ from traditional instruments by employing alternative scales.

BLACK, CRAIG M. (Sculptor)
1155 5th St., #404, Oakland, CA 94607

Born: 1959 *Awards:* Barclay Simpson Award; Merit Award, C.C.A.C. *Exhibitions:* San Francisco State U.; Rhodes Gallery, Contra Costa College, San Pablo *Education:* California College of Arts and Crafts, Oakland; Cal. State- Hayward *Dealer:* Himovitz, Sacramento

Influenced by the California funk school, his early mask-like ceramic abstractions were filled with puns and politics. The work involved social commentary and often referred to man's relationship to nature. He has now moved almost completely away from ceramics as a medium; his new pieces have increased in size and are somewhat figurative. He continues to experiment with structures, media and processes, including application in layers and the burning out of inside structures. His surfaces also continue to evoke feelings of organic processes and deterioration. He is currently working with making hydrocal and steel sculptures as well as large-scale charcoal-on-paper drawings and experimental monotypes.

BLACK, MARGARET (Painter, Printmaker)
6016 Broadway, #2, Oakland, CA 94618

Born: 1954 *Collections:* Kala Institute, Berkeley *Exhibitions:* University Press Books Gallery, Berkeley; Pro Arts East Bay Open Studios, Oakland *Education:* Florida State U., Tallahassee *Dealer:* 871 Fine Art, San Francisco

Fascinated by the concrete materials of her art, she has studied printing, papermaking and jewelry, as well as painting. She prefers working with more traditional techniques—egg tempera, pastel, watercolor and, most recently, encaustic. She relishes the textural, sculptural dimensions of paper and metal surfaces. As she explores the physical properties of her materials, abstraction becomes concrete. Her brilliantly colored paintings embody a visceral geography of kinesthetic balance. They are maps of biological energies that generate a physical charge for the viewer. Her recent paintings draw the eye strongly from left to right. Multipaneled works— *Seeing Darkness/Breathing Light* is 56 panels, and 102 feet, 8 inches long—challenge the viewer to sustain dynamic contact with a painted universe that extends horizontally in space.

BLACKBURN, TESIA (Painter)
5446 Geary Blvd., San Francisco, CA 94121

Born: 1954 *Awards:* Artist in Residence, Cummington Community of the Arts, Cummington, MA *Exhibitions:* Alonso/Sullivan Gallery, Seattle; San Francisco Art Commission, Fort Mason Art Center *Education:* Academy of Art *Dealer:* Gallery Six Oh One, San Francisco

During her formal training, she was influenced by Bay area figurative artists Nathan Oliveira and Joan Brown, as well as Francis Bacon and Egon Schiele. Her exploration of the figure has been transformed, as

Bonnie Bisbee, *Magical Moon,* 36 x 36, oil

Sandi Blank, *Cairo Market,* 48 x 48, acrylic

she has worked for a deeper understanding of the figure from a psychological perspective. Her imagery revolves around the archetypal female form, and the concomitant themes of life, birth, renewal, creation and nurture. The figures inhabit sparse landscapes in muted colors. She uses mixed media techniques such as painting, printmaking, graphite and embossing to build earth-like, organic textures. Recently, she has completed a series of iconographic drawings, which continues the themes of women and spirituality.

BLADEN, RONALD (Sculptor)
c/o Washburn Gallery, 8th Fl., 41 East 57th St., New York, NY 10022

Born: 1918 *Awards:* National Arts Council Grant; Guggenheim Fellowship *Exhibitions:* Washburn Gallery, NYC *Education:* Vancouver School of Arts; California School of Fine Arts *Dealer:* Washburn Gallery, NYC

He began his career as an abstract expressionist painter before turning to sculpture exclusively in the 1960s. His recent aluminum wall sculptures emphasize, and control through the logic of their construction, the way that light interacts with surfaces. His abstract wooden constructions focus on form and structure, yet retain an interest in the phenomenology of perception, especially in the dynamic large-scale geometric works of the 1960s. In the 1970s, he turned to public art, a change which involved translating his works into steel and aluminum structures.

BLAHA, MICHAEL S. (Painter, Ceramist)
P.O. Box 1391, Santa Barbara, CA 93102

Born: 1959 *Exhibitions:* Idaho Biennial Exhibition; Santa Barbara Arts Festival *Education:* U. of South Florida; Boise State U.

Influenced by expressionist figurative artists, he began his early works with spontaneous, intuitive, arbitrary gestures reminiscent of Masson's "Automatic Drawings" and Pollock's early figurative work. These were developed into semi-abstract human figures in earth tones. While still primarily concerned with the figure, he has shifted to brighter colors, and has begun including objects and animals in his work. His small fired-clay figures—"Apocalyptic Stoneware"—appear, at once, to be in organic decay and mechanical disrepair. His interest in art that intuitively strives to define primary archetypes includes primitive art, children's art and the art of the mentally retarded.

BLAISDELL, DON (Painter)
5117 Tendilla Ave., Woodland Hills, CA 91364

Born: 1942 *Exhibitions:* Art Rental Gallery, Los Angeles County Museum of Art; Heritage Gallery, Los Angeles *Education:* Cal. State-Long Beach

He is known for his lush, densely colored landscapes of Mediterranean Europe, Southern California and various locations throughout the U.S. In his art, his intention is to create a suite of paintings exploring a new concept of landscape painting, resolving the conflicts between traditional concepts of nature, and the ecological/technological views of contemporary society. He finds his inspiration in the coastline of Southern California and has spent many years painting this area. His extensive travels in the U.S., Holland, Mexico, France, Spain and Italy have afforded him opportunities to expand upon previous experiences and to further explore new landscapes. All of his current paintings demonstrate continuing concerns, involving a sense of color akin to fauve paintings of the turn of the century—differentiated, however, by the primacy of the artist's vision. He considers himself a colorist, and his recent concern is the resolution of visual sensation with the conceptual signification of color, in order to create a new dimension of meaning for our century's understanding of landscape painting. He not only paints in order to reach this idea; he is also writing a book on this subject.

BLAKE, BOB (Sculptor)
551 W. Pueblo, #4, Santa Barbara, CA 93105

Born: 1954 *Exhibitions:* Hillcrest Invitational, Whittier; U. of California, Santa Barbara

He started as a studio potter, making utilitarian pottery in high-fire clay. Later, he began slip-casting dinnerware, as well as working with the figure in special porcelain clay. Influenced by Arneson, Mason, Soldner and Otto, this work grew into plaster, concrete and steel pieces. He now works in fabricated sculpture and large scale-drawings of geometric shapes. These large-scale works are site-specific and often require many helpers and a considerable amount of time to complete.

BLAKE, BUCKEYE (Painter, Sculptor)
P.O. Box 423., Augusta, MT 59410

Born: 1946 *Awards:* Purchase Award, Mountain Oyster Club, Tucson *Collections:* Wells Fargo Corporation, Los Angeles; Cowboy Hall of Fame, Oklahoma City *Exhibitions:* C.M. Russel Museum, Great Falls, MT; Museum of the Rockies, Bozeman, MO *Dealer:* Main Trail, Scottsdale

The son of a rodeo competitor and horse breeder, he uses the Old West as the theme and source of his work. Well researched cowboys, Indians and horses predominate both oil paintings and bronze sculptures. Some pieces reflect the West of the 1930s and '40s. He apprenticed in commercial art in Los Angeles and spent years designing. In 1986 his life-size bronze of artist C.M. Russel, *Kid Russell and Monte, c. 1889* was unveiled in Great Falls, Montana. A recent bronze of Kit Carson stands in front of the Nevada Capitol in Carson City. He has also done Western book covers and artwork in magazines.

BLANCO, AMANDA (Photographer)
10551 Yarmouth Ave., Granada Hills, CA 91344

Born: 1933 *Awards:* Aurora Award, Professional Photographers of America *Collections:* Getty Museum; UCLA Special Collections *Exhibitions:* California State U., Northridge, Oviatt Library; Brooks Institute of Photography, Santa Barbara *Education:* Brooks Institute of Photography; California Institute of the Arts

Vincent Van Gogh was her favorite painter, even before she attended the Brooks Institute of Photography in Santa Barbara, California. But it wasn't until she studied at the Brooks Institute, under Boris Dobro, that she began to appreciate art and to study the work of the great masters. Today, the viewer can see the influence of Van Gogh's colors and painting style, especially in her color work. The greater portion of her images are portraits, but she is also a collage maker. When she does collage, she mixes pieces of photographs, and paints designs over and around them. She prints her photographs on papers with the highest silver content.

Don Blaisdell, *Courbet's La Source,* 72 x 72, oil on linen

Calvin Barajas, *Elotito de oro,* 16 x 16, acrylic and metallic leaf.
Photograph: Scott McCue

BLANK, LES (Film Artist)
10341 San Pablo Av., El Cerrito, CA 94530

Born: 1935 *Awards:* British Academy Award *Collections:* UC-Berkeley Art Museum, Pacific Film Archives; Los Angeles & San Francisco Public Libraries *Exhibitions:* Guggenheim Museum, NYC; Museum of Modern Art, NYC *Education:* Tulane U.; USC *Dealer:* Flower Films

His films pursue the documentation of the passion for life, particularly among unique musical traditions, yet extending to such esoteric subjects as people who eat garlic. He now working exclusively in color, and his ability to keep the camera invisible creates a sense of participation and intimacy that prompted *Time* critic Jay Cocks to define his films as "a casual, soft-spoken revelation." Among his recent projects are a three-hour series for public television documenting the history of Cuban music and narrated by Harry Belafonte, and a film on San Luis Obispo artist Gerry Gaxiola, "The Maestro." He continues to develop and explore the feeling produced by pure music and image suggested in the work of montage innovator Slavko Vorcapich.

BLAUSTEIN, ALAN (Photographer)
422 Live Oak Dr., Mill Valley, CA 94941

Born: 1958 *Collections:* Sea Cliff Photography Gallery, NY; U. of Wisconsin *Exhibitions:* Academy of Art College, San Francisco; South Park Cafe, San Francisco *Education:* Academy of Art College, San Francisco; Rochester Institute of Technology *Dealer:* Sea Cliff Photography Gallery, Sea Cliff, NY

His images explore the tension between photographic reality and pure graphic abstraction. In his creative method, the initial image is merely a working sketch that is altered to achieve a new, personal reality. Using alternative, non-silver processes— particularly gum bichromate—he can reduce detail, change contrast or apply color, in ways that range from subtle to highly expressionistic. The subjects of his images—people, animals and still lifes—remain recognizable, but as the image is altered, it becomes increasingly general and universal. Thus the viewer is invited to to experience and interpret the image according to his or her personal needs or interests.

BLAZIN (Painter)
42 Sanchez St., San Francisco, CA 94114

Born: 1947 *Awards:* Triton Art Museum *Collections:* Rod Wessel, San Francisco; Melanie Grant, Denver *Exhibitions:* San Francisco Art Commission Gallery *Education:* Henderson State U.; U.of Colorado, Boulder

The imaginary subject matter of her current series of landscapes are rocks in otherworldly environments and abstract settings. Her renderings are realistic and employ vibrant, contrasting colors that create an liveliness between light and dark colorfields. She also creates wall-sized collages that employ pastel drawing and texturing with torn, pleated or woven surfaces. Her use of materials reveals movement and an intensity of color and line in sympathy with their environment.

BLECKNER, ROSS (Painter)
c/o Mary Boone Gallery, 417 W. Broadway, New York, NY 10012

Born: 1949 *Exhibitions:* Museum of Modern Art, NYC; Mary Boone Gallery, NYC *Education:* NYU;

California Institute of the Arts *Dealer:* Mary Boone Gallery, NYC

Paintings examine and utilize the qualities of luminescence. Light emanating from his canvases often functions symbolically, while creating the space and form within the works and producing, at times, a mysterious or surrealistic atmosphere. In the past few years, he has made "stripe" paintings with long, thin, alternating bars, the darker of which refer to gates, while the other stripes suggest a shimmering of light behind them. Some recent paintings with images of vessels commemorate the deaths of AIDS victims.

BLEIBERG, GERTRUDE TIEFENBRUN
(Painter, Printmaker)
275 Southwood Dr., Palo Alto, CA 94301

Born: 1921 *Collections:* San Francisco Museum of Art; San Jose Museum of Art *Exhibitions:* Monterey Peninsula Museum of Art; San Jose Museum of Art *Education:* San Francisco Art Institute *Dealer:* Jennifer Pauls, Sacramento

After an extensive career in domestic engineering, she took up art in her fiftieth year, painting in oil and acrylic on canvas, making lithographs, and, by way of experimentation, "sculpting" objects such as a cut-out blouse and a battered handbag. Her paintings, often of familiar objects and domestic concerns, have a naive and childlike quality. Her figures have been likened to those of Edvard Munch and Willem de Kooning, her style to Van Gogh's. Early in her career, she painted kitchen sinks and dripping spigots and, showing a predilection for black and white, combined graphite and charcoal in her paintings. Since then, the subjects of her paintings have included chunky turquoise high heels showing beneath a yellow skirt hem; big, blooming flowers; a giant pair of pink and aqua thongs; and the marriages of her four daughters in a series entitled "Let Us Savor This Moment."

BLEICH, GEORGE J. (Painter)
3080 Strawberry Hill Rd., Pebble Beach, CA 93921

Born: 1936 *Collections:* Ronald Reagan; Yosemite National Park *Exhibitions:* Artists of the Rockies; Golden West Retrospective *Dealer:* Bleich Gallery, Carmel

He has more than twenty years of experience in plein air painting, and his development has followed a similar evolution as those of the early impressionist masters. He has offered his own impressionist versions of the masters' subjects: Monet's Giverny, Van Gogh's St. Remy, Renoir's South of France and Gauguin's Tahiti. An artist most inspired on location, he has painted in sub-freezing temperatures in New Hampshire and has captured such images as the sea claiming the freighter *Nefelli* off England's Cornish coast, the gentle pleasure of wildflowers in Carmel Valley and Yosemite, and the warmth of Bermuda's sun and pink sand. His background in design and scientific color theory plays an important role in his work. Recently he has been combining an understanding of the luminosity of the Old Masters with the spontaneity of the Impressionists.

BLEVISS, SHIRLEY (Photographer)
456 N. Cadden Pl., Los Angeles, CA 90004

Born: 1929 *Collections:* Palm Springs Desert Museum *Exhibitions:* Los Angeles Municipal Art Gallery; Coleman- Karger Gallery, Los Angeles *Education:* Columbia U.

Shirley Bleviss, *Out of the Shadow,* 30 x 40, photograph

Sandra E. Beebe, *Litter Series: 27 Cans,* 22 x 30, transparent watercolor

She entered the art field as a painter, but switched to photography in the early 1980s. Considering herself an artist who uses the photographic medium, rather than a photographer per se, she composes in the camera and leaves all processing and printing to others. Excepting enlargement, images are never cropped or manipulated, which builds a sense of immediacy and visual gestalt. She is best known for insightful photographs of modern buildings. These structures best lend themselves to the types of abstract images for which she searches. Referring to her art as macrospatial photography, she photographs one small detail of a larger mass, selected for its patterns of line, shape and color, and then has the image enlarged to 20-by-30-inches. She works with a Minolta XG7 and a Minolta XD11, with an 80mm to 200mm zoom lens, a 28mm wide angle lens and a 50mm normal lens. She prefers the zoom since it allows her to vary the limits of the composition until she decides on the correct proportions.

BLIZZARD, ALAN (Painter)
c/o Dept. of Art, Scripps College, 10th & Columbia, Claremont, CA 91711

Born: 1939 *Collections:* Metropolitan Museum of Art, NYC; La Jolla Museum of Art *Exhibitions:* Oxford U., England; James Ulrich Gallery, NYC *Education:* U. of Iowa; U. of Arizona

His paintings incorporate words and everyday phrases from contemporary American culture and depict abstract images. The underlying concept of interchangeable component elements adapted from American industrial production serves to further the abstract qualities. Color and shape are his greatest concerns in seeking spatial definition. The perimeter of each painting is important, with the casting of resulting shadows that shift throughout the day. The effect of these shadows is to enhance the feeling of time in the paintings. Titles are chosen from the lyrics of popular music of the early 20th century and the present.

BLOOD, LINDA M. (Painter, Sculptor)
1251 Linda Mar Blvd., Pacifica, CA 94044

Born: 1955 *Collections:* New Mexico Doll Museum *Exhibitions:* Olive Hyde Gallery, Fremont *Education:* San Mateo College *Dealer:* Victoria Impex, Concord

Growing up in a house in which both her father and grandmother were artists, she began in the arts as a child. In high school, she studied ceramics; when she was fifteen, she started painting in both acrylics and oil. For a period after college, she worked as a hair designer. It was after those experiences that she started making dolls, designing the clothes, making the original faces based on her children and using hair from her clients to complete the heads. As a dollmaker, she has the opportunity to combine her various skills in design, sewing, clay sculpture and painting.

BLOOD, PEGGY (Painter)
436 Turner Dr., Benicia, CA 94510

Born: 1947 *Awards:* Outstanding Bay Area Artist, PCTV, Oakland; 1st Prize, Alpha Kappa Alpha Sorority Regional Art Award *Exhibitions:* Geberon Gallery, Napa; BCA Art Gallery, Benicia *Education:* Union Graduate School; U. of Arkansas, Fayetteville

She paints from her personal experiences, employing brightly colored oils and acrylics on canvas. Her bold figurative style has been influenced by the works of Gauguin, Jacob Lawrence, and fellow Arkansas native John Howard. Focusing on the emotional and mysterious aspects of life, her artistic approach has also been shaped by the trends of modern Black American art. Although her recent work is more abstract, she continues to work with the themes, ideas and colors that have always interested her.

BLOOM, SHARON E. (Painter)
220A W. 2nd Ave., Chico, CA 95926

Born: 1961 *Awards:* Award of Merit, California Works; 3rd Place, Nepenthe Mundi Society *Exhibitions:* The Vagabond Rose, Gridley, CA; 1078 Gallery *Dealer:* Marilyn Souza, The Vagabond Rose, Gridley

Influenced by the bold colorists Joseph Raffael and Masami Teraoka, as well as by an early fascination with graphic design's intricate patterns and textures, she fills her watercolors with bold contrasts and bright colors. Her figurative paintings often tell a whimsical story, encouraging viewers to look beyond the image and toward the artist's message. Using either watercolor board or 140-lb. d'Arches cold press paper, she first partially sketches her subject. Then, after flooding areas with one or more colors, she lets the paint "play" on its own, adding color and pattern around the subject until the work is completed. She is fascinated by the representation of robots from the 1940s and 1950s and is currently working on a series of robot paintings.

BLOOMBERG, JOEL D. (Glass Sculptor)
600 N. Highway 101, Leucadia, CA 92024

Born: 1953 *Awards:* Finalist, Art Quest, Los Angeles and Chicago; Medal Award, Metro Art International, NYC *Exhibitions:* Eileen Kremen Gallery; Downey Museum *Education:* Chico State U.

His career in the arts derives from a varied academic background and years of experimentation with different media. He is most challenged by working in glass and bronze, and feels that this work is well supported by his past studies. His current glass sculptures are synthesized from a range of glass-working techniques, including rolling and blowing. These laminated pieces relate to modern society, both in their architectural form, and in their kinetic, light-reflecting qualities.

BLOOMFIELD, SUZANNE (Painter)
4270 E. Holmes St., Tucson, AZ 85711

Born: 1934 *Exhibitions:* U. of Portland; Penn State U. *Education:* Ohio U.; U. of Arizona

She is known for her work in encaustics, a process developed in the fifth and sixth centuries in which pigments are added to heated beeswax. The result is a glazed field of brilliant coloration, form and texture. Her works are abstract figurations, energized by vibrant colors and a sense of sweeping movement. The works, she says, express a search for the "life force"—the universal force of transformation.

BLOTNICK, ELIHU (Photographer)
723 Dwight Way, Berkeley, CA 94710

Born: 1944 *Awards:* American Institute of Graphic Arts; Federal Design Council, Washington, DC *Collections:* Library of Congress; Oakland Museum *Exhibitions:* Stedelijk Museum, Amsterdam; London Film Festival *Education:* San Francisco State U. *Dealer:* The Little Known-of Gallery, Berkeley

From his origins as a poet, he became part of the documentary movement in photography in the late 1960s. However, his interest remains tonal and internal.

Randall Bruce, *Flair,* 12 x 10, reduction fired lusterware. Courtesy: Rob Kibler

Alan Blizzard, *Girls Just Wanna Have Fun,* 22 x 23, oil and rhoplex on canvas and wood.
Courtesy: Maurice-Heyman Fine Arts

He always works to incorporate a mood, a tone and a personal element within a larger theme. "People's Park" is his first color slide series. Among his books are *Saltwater Flats* and a volume of poetry entitled *Russian Hill/Storm Year, 1982*. His use of facing pages for counterpoint and his interest in sequences led to a short animated film drawn from stills, entitled *Webfooted Friends, a Film that has Nothing to Do with Ducks*. Other projects include *The Canyon Kids*, a documentary representation of the children in the two-room schoolhouse in a redwood grove. He is currently exploring the stylization of a voice, in novels and recorded narratives, to accompany his photographs. He pursues the documentary impulse in large format and with the pre-WWII miniature rangefinder, which he values for its silence.

BLUMBERG, DONALD (Photographer)
16918 Donna Ynez Lane, Pacific Palisades, CA 90272
Born: 1935 *Education:* Cornell U.; U. of Colorado, Boulder

One of the pioneers in experimental photography, he has used collage frequently, sewn found objects onto prints, used *cliche verre* and stain photographs, and experimented with filmmaking. Among his notable works are his antiwar images made in the 1960s during the Vietnam conflict. A recent series is "Collaboration with Rachel," which depicts his relationship with his daughter. He works in black-and-white and color and has made several films with his wife, Grace.

BLUNK, J.B. (Sculptor, Ceramist)
Box 83, Inverness, CA 94937
Born: 1926 *Collections:* San Francisco Museum of Art; Oakland Museum *Exhibitions:* Artspace, Los Angeles; San Francisco Craft and Folk Art Museum *Education:* UCLA *Dealer:* Smith Andersen Gallery, Palo Alto

His art education began in Japan in 1951, when he met sculptor Isamu Noguchi and potters Rosanjim Kitaoji and Kaneshige Toyo. This experience remained the single most important influence on his work until a series of extended trips to Central and South America in the 1970s. He works on a monumental scale with California redwood and stone, and on a smaller scale with ceramics. All of the pieces reflect his love of nature and his life spent living close to the land. His redwood sculptures are primeval in form, and his renowned redwood arches are nearly overwhelming in size and appearance. He works spontaneously rather than from preliminary sketches or drawings.

BODINE, MELISSA (Painter)
201 Ocean Ave., 503B, Santa Monica, CA
Awards: Honorable Mention, California State Fair

Her figurative paintings begin with loose charcoal sketches applied directly to unprimed canvas. Working with live models, the artist intuitively selects a pose and proceeds to rough out the figure. She fleshes out the drawing with oil paints in rich, emotive hues inspired by her admiration of the work of Cezanne and Van Gogh. Her colorist instincts are given even greater freedom in her abstract paintings. Even in realistic works, the artist relies heavily on her emotional response to subject matter. Color's unique ability to dramatize and conduct mood continues to fascinate her.

BOGUE-OVERBAY, PAULA (Painter)
2574 NW Thurman St., Portland, OR 97210
Born: 1940 *Awards:* Artist-in-Residency, Belgian Government; Oregon Arts Commission *Collections:* Osaka University of Arts, Tokyo; Honolulu Academy of Art *Exhibitions:* Rubicon Gallery, Los Altos; San Francisco Museum of Art *Education:* Carnegie-Mellon, Pittsburgh, PA; Portland Museum School of Art, Portland, OR *Dealer:* Harleen and Allen, San Francisco

At the beginning of her formal career as a minimalist printmaker the grid styles of Sol Le Witt and Carl Andre influenced her intricate and subtly valued prints. These weavings of lines merge into solid, deep areas of color. Figurative color drawings supplanted the grid paintings during a two year period of transition that culminates in her recent work. The exploration of color remained an essential characteristic throughout all her work. Her paintings' imagery has opened into large, finely detailed flowers and foliage. Dense and flatly painted, she refers to them as "luminous realist." She seeks to communicate certain human tendencies through the images, such as privacy, tenacity, sustenance, fragility of spirit, the stubborn pursuit of living and the shortness of life.

BOHANON, MADELINE E. (Painter)
P. O. Box 1709, Tahoe City, CA 95730
Born: 1918 *Awards:* Teacher of the Year, Sierra Nevada College; Society of Western Artists, San Francisco, Sacramento & Fremont; *Collections:* Coldwell Banker; Placer County Libraries *Exhibitions:* Sierra Nevada Museum of Art, Reno, NV; Sierra Gallery, Tahoe City, CA *Dealers:* Sierra Gallery; Reed Gallery, Timberline, Tahoe City, CA

After formal training and private workshops, she has developed a style of watercolor painting that employs abstracted and free-flowing images involving Southwest, Northwest and Western landscapes. She draws her symbolism from the Southwestern Indian cultures and often bases her work on her interpretations of Hopi Indian Kachinas and dances. Northwest Indian cultures also serve as foundations for works. An Oriental influence is evident in her rice-paper images. In her use of color, she incorporates traditional turquoise against soft pinks and greens as well as earthy palettes, emphasizing spirituality in the abstractions and stylized interpretations. The Sierra Nevada mountains are frequently the subject of her landscape studies in both watercolor and oil. In recent works, movement is all-important, underscored through her handling of color and design. Lively, bright, transparent color unifies abstract and semi-abstract interpretations.

BOISVERT, NICK (Painter)
1572 Boulevard Way, Walnut Creek, CA 94595
Born: 1944 *Awards:* L.A. Municipal Art Gallery, Purchase Award; Long Beach Museum of Art Purchase Award *Collections:* Transamerica Occidental Life, Los Angeles; Fluor Corporation, Irvine *Exhibitions:* Pennsylvania Academy of Fine Arts, Philadelphia; Los Angeles County Museum of Art Rental Gallery *Education:* UCLA

He was formally trained at UCLA under the guidance of Llyn Foulkes and John Caruthers. His early works were hard-edged geometric abstractions in which he used bright primary hues of acrylic paint on canvas. The colored areas were three-inch wide bands in the

Nick Boisvert, *Shadows Deepening,* 25 x 42, acrylic on canvas

Wilsdon Brenner, *Tapeats Creek,* 40 x 75, acrylic on foamcore

shapes of triangles, rectangles and heraldic-type forms. After his volunteer work with Native Americans in the Southwest, he began to paint unspoiled desert landscapes and rock formations using his one-color hard-edged technique. Inspired by pointillist devices, he paints single enclosed areas of flat, ungradated pigment beside each other which vary in hue. The viewers distance from the canvasses affects his perception of the shadows and rocks in these landscapes. He attempts to achieve a sense of purity and crispness in his depictions of geological formations.

BOLTON, JANE (Painter, Mixed-Media Artist)
6108 Glen Alder, Los Angeles, CA 90068

Born: 1940 *Awards:* Honorable Mention, Oakland Art Museum *Exhibitions:* Women's Building, Los Angeles *Education:* Duke U. *Dealer:* Forecast Gallery, Santa Monica

The formal thrust of her work is in integrating painting and sculpture in mixed-media, three-dimensional, frontal work. She also plays hard, cut-out edges against painterly and patterned surfaces. She feels the most important aspect of her work is that she creates it for people's sake, not for art's sake. Most of the work has some form of audience participation—parts to be moved, tapes to be played, notes to be written. She uses sources from many eras and much of her recent work features images of pre-historic female goddesses. In "More Mother Figures," a series of works in acrylic on archival board, goddess images from the Cro-Magnon period to modern day are juxtaposed, compared, and depicted in ways spirituality of motherhood. These pieces, as well as others, are designed to help viewers reorient themselves vis a vis the cosmos. While the work is metaphysical and political in its intent, the style is often humorous and joyful.

BOLTON, SUZANNAH (Painter)
19585 Grand View Dr., Topanga, CA 90290

Born: 1948 *Awards:* Nominee, Artists Society International Exhibition, San Francisco *Exhibitions:* Maryland Pastel Society, Baltimore; Merced College; Puccinelli Gallery, San Francisco *Education:* State U. of New York, Buffalo

Influenced by Swiss concrete art and minimalist art, she began incorporating Carthaginian and Roman symbols in multimedia serigraph paintings. She lives part of the year in Carthage, Tunisia and has been influenced by Klee and Miro, who have worked in and been fascinated by that area. Her recent work has taken on a more narrative, figurative approach which is evident in her watercolor and acrylic painting. She admires watercolors for their lyrical flexibility and portable quality. What has remained consistent in her work is a recurrence of imagery and color which is a direct result of the artist's living in two disparate cultures.

BORGHEI, BADRI E. (Painter)
23656 Bessemer St., Woodland Hills, CA 94367

Born: 1941 Exhibitions; Los Angeles Art Association; Pacific Asia Museum *Dealer:* Ketab Corporation, Van Nuys

The work is an idiosyncratic combination of contemporary and primitive techniques. She has been influenced by the Persian miniature masters of the Qajar period and those of the 14th and 15th centuries. In her early small watercolors, she applied brilliant colors in a pointillist manner, using fine brushes to enhance the detail of her work. She has since progressed to larger works, and now uses gouache along with watercolor and highlights the pieces with gold and silver. Her perspectiveless subjects are fascinating, colorful and two-dimensional. She is a member of the The Los Angeles Art Association and she currently teaches at Learning Tree University.

BOTERO, FERNANDO (Painter, Sculptor)
c/o Marlborough Fine Arts, 40 W. 57th Street, New York, NY 10019

Born: 1932 *Awards:* Guggenheim International Award; Andres Bello Award, Venezuela *Collections:* Museum of Modern Art, NYC; Guggenheim Museum, NYC *Exhibitions:* Marlborough Fine Arts, NYC; Hokin Gallery, Chicago *Education:* Universidad de Antiquia, Columbia; Real Academia de Bellas Artes, Spain *Dealer:* Marlborough Fine Arts, NYC

Studying in Spain, he was influenced by Goya and Velazquez; however, the daily life, religious myths and folk art traditions of his native Columbia remain the basic subjects of his paintings and sculptures. The swollen, pneumatic figures which are his hallmark present views of the human comedy and demonstrate his affinity for plasticity of form. Since 1975, he has been concentrating on sculpture, casting figures in bronze and polyester resin. "I start as a poet, put colors down on canvas as a painter, but finish my work as a sculptor, taking delight in caressing the forms." Recent work includes a series of paintings that have as their subject "la corrida," the bullfight.

BOTHUM, J. SHIRLY (Sculptor)
1545 Critchfield Rd., Clarkston, WA 99403

Born: 1937 *Collections:* Museum of the Dog, NY; Pillsbury *Exhibitions:* Art Expo, Los Angeles; Audubon Society Convention, Bellingham, WA *Dealer:* Zantmans Art Gallery, Palm Desert

She creates realistic, small-scale sculptures of animals, both wild and domestic.

BOTHWELL, DORR (Painter, Printmaker)
HC-1, Box 1055, Joshua Tree, CA 92252

Born: 1902 *Awards:* Abraham Rosenberg Fellowship, San Francisco *Collections:* Metropolitan Museum of Art, NYC; Whitney Museum, NYC *Exhibitions:* Bay Window Gallery, Mendocino; Tobey C. Moss Gallery, Los Angeles *Dealer:* Tobey C. Moss, Los Angeles

Throughout her long career, her subject has been the evocative quality of color. At first she painted abstractly. Gradually however, she began employing recognizable forms, using them for their symbolic impact. This was most noticeable in her early serigraphs. Her work of the 1920s often swung between three- dimensional forms and the flat, naturalistic painting of the Chinese Sung-period masters. Awarded the Abraham Rosenberg Fellowship, she spent three years in France studying stained glass in an effort to resolve realism with decorative design. Since 1970, the divisions of stained glass and enamels have appeared more often in her paintings. Today she divides the canvas into defined units and mixes painting, collage and printmaking, doing whatever she feels is necessary to communicate symbolically.

BOUETT, LOUISE (Printmaker)
23450 Salt Creek Rd., Red Bluff, CA 96080

Born: 1916 *Exhibitions:* Redding Museum and Art Gallery; Los Angeles Audubon Society Wildlife and Environmental Art Show *Education:* Cal. State-Chico

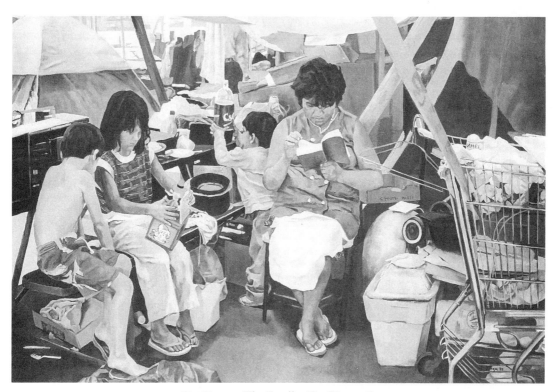

Pat Berger, *The Family,* 48 x 72, acrylic

Jane Bolton, *The Last Lunch,* 11 x 31 x 11, acrylic, archival board, plexiglas, cotton, xerox.
Courtesy: Marie Feuer, Los Angeles

Dealer: Randy Moller, Red Bluff; Miriam Perlman, Chicago

She usually works in linoleum cuts, but occasionally does wood cuts. The pieces are in both black and white and color, using watercolor, prismacolor or a combination of the two. Prints are cut by hand and are printed with a baren or spoon, using a separate block for each color or hand-coloring each print. The countryside and its wildlife inspires her work and serves as the source of her images. She often depicts pairs of animals in a natural setting, as in *Nesting Canada Geese* and *Geese By the River.* These charming black-and-white prints are suffused with the respect and admiration she feels for the natural world.

BOUSSARD, DANA (Painter, Fabric Artist)
Two Heart Creek, Rt. #1, Arlee, MT 59821

Born: 1944 *Awards:* NEA Fellowship; Western States Arts Foundation Fellowship *Exhibitions:* Munson Gallery, Santa Fe, NM; Minneapolis Art Institute *Education:* U. of Montana

Her large fiber works and the drawings accompanying them are stylized and symbolic pictographs drawn from the artist's experience with her environment, reflecting a vanishing way of living on the Montana plains. The works create images of life in transition and the relationship of humanity to the natural environment. The fiber constructions are pieced, sewn and painted, emphasizing textural variations that maintain the delicacy of her drawings. Much of the work takes the form of pictorial diaries, documenting everyday occurrences with a combination of symbolic figures and stylized geometric borders.

BOUTELL, YVONNE (Ceramist)
40 Edgecroft Rd., Kensington, CA 94707

Born: 1922 *Awards:* 2nd Prize, Cooperstown 50th National Exhibition, NY *Exhibitions:* Collectors Gallery, Oakland; Art Coop, Berkeley

Her training in traditional patterns was influenced by an exhibit of Peter Voulkos' work at the Art Institute of Chicago. Abstract expressionism, accidental and intentional design through color and texture, became the focus of her work. While visiting Sydney, Australia in 1973, she became familiar with the hand-building technique of Hireo Suen, which influenced her use of color. She builds bowls, plates, vessels and slab sculptures in white and colored clay using both the traditional potter's wheel method and the "veriege" method of wedging together colored clays. The inlays of color and overlays of color, both inside and out, express her desire to interpret the patterned textures of the environment.

BOWERS, JACK (Sculptor)
1163 Union St., San Francisco, CA 94109

Born: 1947 *Awards:* Best of Show, Redding Museum, CA; Best of Show, Conway, AZ *Collections:* State of Colorado; City of Aspen, *Exhibitions:* Dorothy Weiss Gallery, San Francisco; Redding Museum *Education:* San Francisco Art Institute *Dealer:* Dorothy Weiss Gallery

Throughout the 1970s, his ceramic sculptures were geometric and environmental. Several public pieces recreate stream beds—sand from a site was picked up, fired onto a molded surface and permanently mounted on a wall. The result is not an illusion of a riverbed, but an actual transposition of a site in nature to a public environment. The works of the 1980s are a fusion of two dimensions with three. The resulting ceramic sculptures contain highly glazed, amorphous surfaces that create illusions of depth. These illusions challenge the viewer's sense of visual reality. His work continues to inquire into how we see, and his goal is to create an object of illusory size.

BOWLES, MARY (Painter)
71 Castle St., San Francisco, CA 94133

Born: 1927 *Exhibitions:* Jan Holloway Gallery, San Francisco; John Berggruen Gallery, San Francisco *Education:* Black Mt. College; San Francisco Art Institute

Her original training under Josef Albers was in abstract relationships, as applied to color, design, drawing and painting, within a context of minimalism. Later, she was encouraged to use paint more lavishly, and to pursue a more expressive, emotional point of view. She then took a fifteen year hiatus from painting to work in sculpture. Her main interest now is in the rendition of space and perspective. Working in yellows, blues and greens, her work is influenced by Wayne Thiebaud and Richard Diebenkorn. This has resulted in a style that tempers realism with abstract principals.

BOWMAN, BRICE (Painter)
2571 Shattuck Ave., #1A, Berkeley, CA 94704

Born: 1951 *Awards:* Best of Show, Napa All California Art Exhibition *Exhibitions:* Museum Gallery, San Francisco Museum of Modern Art; Crocker Museum, Sacramento *Education:* San Francisco State U.; Cal. State-Sacramento

His work strives for the middle ground between abstraction and primitivism—between art that is divorced from human emotion and experience and the techniques of formal narrative.

BOWMAN, DANIEL (Painter, Sculptor)
140 Plymouth St., Brooklyn, NY 11201

Born: 1957 *Exhibitions:* Pacific Gallery, Venice *Education:* Hunter College, NYC; California Institute of the Arts, Valencia

After studying at California Arts with Jonathan Borofsky, John Baldessari, Doug Huebler and Jeremy Gilbert-Rolfe, he became interested in idea art. The pieces were figurative and not purely formal. More recently he has been working in a mixed media format. He now uses photography, found objects, and painted images to make make pieces that encompass social, cultural, and political concerns.

BOWMER, LILLIAN (Painter, Dollmaker)
400 N. Walton Ave., #10, Yuba City, CA 95991

Born: 1927 *Awards:* Honorable Mention, Yuba Fairgrounds *Exhibitions:* Continental Gallery, Yuba City; Monogram Gallery, Yuba City *Education:* Yuba College; Butte College

Influenced by Al Walsh Jr., she paints with watercolor, oil and acrylic in a free-flowing wet-into-wet style that concentrates on capturing light. Her brightly colored, non-realistic flowers are more like floral designs than actual plants. Likewise her landscapes, seascapes and portraits of animals and people leave much to the viewer's imagination. For animals she uses pastels on velour paper to suggest a realistic fur texture. She also makes styrofoam "dip and drape" dolls that resemble the Holly Hobbie dolls.

Raye Bender-Klinefelter, *Tourmaline,* 30 x 23, watercolor. Courtesy: Marie-Raymonde Aubin

J.B. Blunk, *Santa Cruz, 1968,* 180 x 120 x 180, redwood

BOYSEL, SHARON (Photographer, Mixed Media Artist)
16230 Matilija, Los Gatos, CA 95030

Born: 1940 *Awards:* Small Works National Award *Exhibitions:* DeSaisset Museum, U. of Santa Clara; Bank of America *Education:* U. of Michigan; San Jose State U. *Dealer:* Allrich, San Francisco

"Photographic Environments" consist of multiple hand colored photographs, combined with various other materials and three dimensional objects. She took the photographs at various archaeological sites in Italy, Greece, India, Tibet and China. Three-dimensional elements are used to clarify, extend and question our ideas about these ancient civilizations. A human, often feminine, presence is suggested by carefully placed shoes, footprints, furniture and discards. Work explores the interplay between the two- and three-dimensional, the real and the imagined and the past and the present. Many of the pieces are self-lit, and use theater gel filters for special effects.

BRACKEN, DONALD (Painter)
644 29th St., Manhattan Beach, CA 90266

Born: 1951 *Awards:* Grant, Robert S. Scull Foundation for the Arts; Best in Show, NCAA Juried Show, Winstead, CT *Exhibitions:* Attack Gallery, Los Angeles; Insection Gallery, San Francisco *Education:* UC-Berkeley *Dealer:* Stephen Haller Fine Arts, NYC

He was heavily influenced by abstract expressionism, especially the school's emphasis on freedom of expression, the process of painting and the concentration on medium integrity. Beginning in the 1980s, he has painted dreamlike, figurative images in a process called synthetic fusion. He uses calligraphic strokes to build up layers of acrylic paint on paper and canvas.

BRACKMANN, HOLLY (Weaver)
436 N. Pine, Ukiah, CA 95482

Born: 1947 *Awards:* 3rd Place, Handweavers Guild of America Exhibit *Exhibitions:* Allan Short Gallery, Stockton; Grace Hudson Museum, Ukiah *Education:* San Jose State U.; UCLA

Over the past thirteen years, her main interest in weaving has been in three-dimensional forms constructed from flat-woven pieces. Her technique entails weaving pieces flat on the loom and afterwards manipulating them as three-dimensional objects. Many of her latest pieces employing this technique use of pearl cotton and hand-dyed wood sticks in warp face repp weaves to form abstract designs. The sticks float across some areas of the weaving and are hidden in others, finally emerging at the woven edge. She now uses the computer as a design tool and is exploring repp weaves to produce multiple blocks of color and three- dimensional effects.

BRADY, STACIA DIANE (Painter)
140 E. Napa St., Sonoma, CA 95476

Born: 1948 *Exhibitions:* Artworks, Sonoma; Arts Guild of Sonoma *Education:* UC-Berkeley; Dominican College *Dealer:* Artworks, Sonoma

After exploring large sculptural vessel forms in her early ceramic work, she began painting and drawing on clay surfaces, and eventually combined the painted surface with ceramic relief. At the same time she was exploring figure and movement in a symbolist/expressionistic manner, using acrylic and latex on paper and wood. She eventually adopted oil paint sticks as her primary medium, and now paints on paper and canvas with paint sticks, graphite, crayons and charcoal. The figure is the central focus of narrative work that is concerned with psychological states and stages of growth, and often deals with women's issues.

BRADY, VERNA (Painter, Mixed Media Artist)
155 Andrea Lane, Felton, CA 95018

Born: 1925 *Collections:* Gruenwald Collection, UCLA; Bank of America, Beverly Hills *Exhibitions:* Orlando Gallery, Sherman Oaks; Eloise Pickard Smith Gallery, UC-Santa Cruz *Education:* UC-Irvine

Her early years were spent making realistic paintings in oil on canvas, with Rembrandt her greatest influence. As her ability increased, so did her desire to express more than realism, and Hans Hofmann became her mentor. His teachings were clarified by George McNeil in Paris in 1964; her work changed dramatically as a result. In 1968, she began working in acrylic on canvas, often with sand, cheesecloth, tissue paper and pieces of canvas attached to the surface for their textural and sensual significance. Her work ranged from the purely abstract to paintings in which a sense of landscape or figuration seemed to emerge from the abstract. Since the early 1970s, music and philosophy have become strong influences. Her work has begun to include lyrical and flowing abstractions based on music, a personal symbolism and a desire to express the universal life force that is the basis of all creativity. Works on paper have also become an important means of expression, first in monoprints and more recently in watercolor and acrylic. In her monoprints and watercolors, texture is often achieved by layering in a transparent manner—often using collage materials to remove or add pigment. Textural additions continue to be important to her visual statements on both paper and canvas.

BRAGG, CHARLES LYNN (CHICK) (Painter, Printmaker)
4147 Moore St., Los Angeles, CA 90066

Born: 1952 *Exhibitions:* B-1 Gallery, Santa Monica; Asylum Gallery, Beverly Hills *Education:* California Institute of the Arts *Dealer:* Hasson Publishing, Inc., Newport Beach

His studies have included drawing, painting, printmaking, photography, filmmaking and computer graphics, and his travels have taken him to Bali, Java, Europe, Mexico and the South Pacific, studying the people, culture and art of each region. The focus of his art has been on styles of realism, surrealism and impressionism and on Oriental brush techniques. He has recently been working on surreal imagery using acrylic on canvas, etchings and computer graphics. Objects, animals and people are juxtaposed in compositions that concentrate on people and their relationships to their environment. This surreal imagery includes a suite of wilderness etchings in which elephants stand next to street lights and giraffes are juxtaposed with construction cranes. In another series, a photo-realistic painting entitled *Kicking Back* depicts a man with a five-foot neck sitting in a chair that has only three legs.

BRAICO, LILLIANA (Painter)
P.O. Box 5633, Carmel, CA 93923

Born: 1925 *Exhibitions:* La Galleria, Capri, Italy; Artist Guild of America, Carmel *Dealer:* Jack Lewis, Carmel

She studied non-objective painting with Lida Giambastiani, and composition and color with Patricia Cunnin-

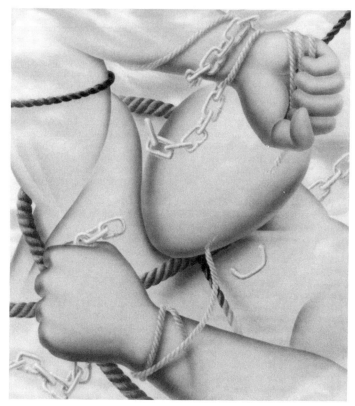

Charles Lynn Bragg, *Chain Reaction,* 36 x 42, acrylic on canvas

Bernice Bing, *Abstract Calligraphy,* 22 x 35, mixed media. Courtesy: Susan Carlsen

gham at Carmel Art Institute. A study tour of Milan and Paris—with special emphasis on Matisse, Bonnard, Dufy and Kandinsky—dramatically altered her style, approach and subject matter. She continued to develop her work at a studio on Capri, where she lived during the 1960s and 1970s, and which she still maintains. Using loose, rhythmic brushstrokes, and working in oil on canvas, she is best known as a colorist. Subjects include floral still lifes and portraiture. She often works on large canvas panels and 4-by-6-foot standing floor screens.

BRAIDEN, ROSE M. (Commercial Illustrator, Painter)
2929 Paeo Tranquillo, Santa Barbara, CA 93105

Born: 1922 *Exhibitions:* Cody Gallery, Los Olivos; Faulkner Gallery, Santa Barbara *Education:* California College of Arts and Crafts *Dealer:* Cody Gallery, Los Olivos

Primarily an art teacher, she is guided by feeling and intuition rather than by linear thought. Beginning with meticulously detailed drawings, she creates loosely figurative watercolors of floral scenes and children. In her egg tempera work, she employs an ancient Greek method of building up seventy-five to one hundred layers of transparent, traditional Greek colors. She has illustrated *Choices: A Young Woman's Journal*, and has supplied Bible illustrations for a Brazilian feminist work. Recently concentrating on color and experimentation rather than subject matter, she has introduced inks and gessoes into watercolor work, which, above all, is an attempt to render texture and feeling. She is the founder of Los Padres Water Color Society.

BRANDT, REX (Painter, Printmaker)
405 Goldenrod, Corona Del Mar, CA 92625

Born: 1914 *Awards:* 1st Prize, California Watercolor Society; Samuel F.B. Morse Medal, National Academy of Design Annual *Collections:* San Francisco Museum of Modern Art; Los Angeles County Museum of Art *Exhibitions:* California Palace of the Legion of Honor, San Francisco; National Gallery, Washington, DC *Education:* UC-Berkeley; Stanford U.

Along with Phil Dike and Millard Sheets, he is one of the artists whose paintings came to epitomize the California Watercolor style that began to achieve widespread success in the middle parts of the century. His works revel in the brilliant sunshine, blue waters and white sails of Balboa Bay in Southern California, capturing the essence of the West Coast through casual but vigorous planes of bold color. He has served as president of the influential California Watercolor Society and has written numerous books on watercolor methods and techniques.

BRANSBY, ERIC JAMES (Muralist)
9080 Highway 115, Colorado Springs, CO 80926

Born: 1916 *Awards:* Edwin Austin Abbey Foundation Fellowship in Mural Painting; U. of Missouri Veatch Award for Distinguished Research and Creative Activity *Exhibitions:* Loveland Museum, Loveland, CO; Colorado Springs Museum *Education:* Colorado College; Yale U.

His mural designs, influenced by analytical cubism and by Renaissance altarpiece design, are painted in acrylic, egg tempera, buon fresco, or silicate media on portable laminated panels. Individual murals consist of multiple panels, each existing as its own three-dimensional shape, articulating with each other and with

linear-planar design elements in the architecture. His murals include works at Brigham Young University, the Planetarium at the U.S. Air Force Academy, the University of Illinois, the University of Missouri, the St. Paul School in Chicago, Kansas State University, Colorado College, Colorado Springs Fine Arts Center and the Sedalia, Missouri, Municipal Building. He strongly believes that art has a socio-cultural function, and that the finest achievements in mural painting are those that successfully synthesize figurative elements with the mural's existing abstract design matrix.

BRANUM, PHILIPP (Painter)
P.O. Box 620, Moss Landing, CA 95039

Born: 1951 *Awards:* Nepenthe Mundi Society *Exhibitions:* San Bernardino Museum of Modern Art; San Francisco Museum of Modern Art *Education:* UC-Santa Cruz *Dealer:* Dancing Man Imagery, Santa Cruz

He was highly influenced by German Expressionist artists Klee and Hundertwasser. His figurative paintings contain mystical, religious forms, in a highly individualistic view of the "other" world. Works often resemble paleolithic cave art in their semi-completed appearance. Using everything from crayons to spray paints, he prefers to paint on a hard, unforgiving surface, such as Masonite. He often works on several paintings at once, standing over the surface, never labeling one side the top or the bottom. He continually balances the applied colors and forms until a theme image presents itself. This image is then pursued and developed. Recent works are much larger in scale.

BRAUCHER, PAUL (Painter)
42-37 155th St., Apt. 14B, Flushing, NY 11355

Born: 1954 *Exhibitions:* Contemporary Realist Gallery, San Francisco *Education:* Queens College *Dealer:* Contemporary Realist Gallery, San Francisco

He began painting under Frederick Ortner at Knox College. Much like Cezanne, he was concerned with constructing a two and three-dimensional pictorial architecture from the play of light on the subject. He worked alla prima from still life, figures and landscapes. In graduate school and afterward, he began painting figures in psychologically charged situations, which suggested but did not define a narrative. In these works, he employed unusual points of view, thematic colors and a range of attitudes toward form making. He sites Balthus, Caravaggio, Tintoretto, Pottormo and former instructor Gabriel Laderman as influences.

BRAY, ANGIE (Environmental Sculpture, Installation Artist)
496 Bluebird Canyon, Laguna Beach, CA 92651

Born: 1936 *Education:* Sarah Lawrence College; Harvard U.

Although she has always made objects, her eye has been more influenced by drawing, theater and dance than by pieces of sculpture. Even her earliest works of wire, wood, woven cord or welded steel dealt more with line, shadows and changing spatial relationships than with mass. The installations that evolved from that work evince the same concerns, but involve the viewer more directly with the human, as well as the formal, issues of perception, illusion, projections and orientation in space. The indoor installations are very spare, using elements that can be seen as common objects—ladders, swings, beds—with perspectives that shift from two to three dimensions and changing

Gary Becker, *New Mask,* 4 x 6, ink on paper

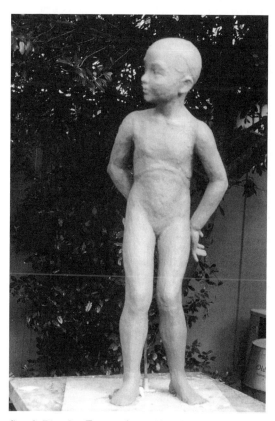

Sarah Biondo, *Expectations,* 46 x 17 x 15, plasterlene for bronze casting

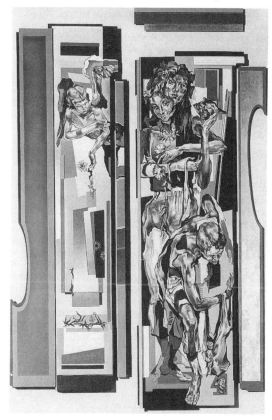

Eric James Bransby, *Primavera,* 96 x 300, acrylic. Courtesy: University of Missouri, Kansas City

horizons lines. *Swings and Shadows* features six simple white swings mysteriously suspended from a dark, high ceiling, the swings carefully illuminated from a low gently swinging light source. Because the shadows move and the swings remain stationary, the viewer experiences a startling sense of discontinuity. Her outdoor pieces also maintain a spare, linear quality that acts to define space and heighten our awareness of existing landscape elements.

BREED, JOHN (Sculptor)
613 Canada St., Ojai, CA 93023

Born: 1927 *Exhibitions:* Ojai Art Center; Santa Monica National Park *Education:* U. of Utah

Though he does not associate himself with any particular school or tradition of sculpture, nor with any particular sculptor, he does cite Monet, for the way he lived, as an influence and inspiration for work. Working with stone and steel, he aims for simplicity and starkness in both line and form. He has recently been sculpting 15-inch human figures. He prefers alabaster stone from Utah, the place of his training. The pieces are abstract and playful; they include busts and upper body torsos.

BREEN, MARTHA (Painter, Glass Artist)
30 Domingo, #4, Berkeley, CA 94705

Born: 1954 *Exhibitions:* Walter White Gallery, Carmel; Del Mano Gallery, Los Angeles *Education:* Indiana U.

She spent her childhood in India, and became familiar with local traditional folk arts, especially embroidery. This influence is still apparent in her paintings, carved glass bowls and jewelry. She fleshes out her designs in gouache and colored pencil, then uses a sandblaster to carve the multi-colored glass that she has blown specifically for her projects. The laminated glass pieces (in pinks, aquas and purples) are decorated with simple, expressive designs. Her earrings, necklaces and bracelets are characterized by the combination of traditional and non- traditional design elements. She expresses her love of pattern in all the materials with which she works.

BREGER, LEONARD (Painter, Multimedia Artist)
80 Bronte St., San Francisco, CA 94110

Exhibitions: Palace of the Legion of Honor, San Francisco; De Young Museum, San Francisco *Education:* California College of Arts and Crafts

His career in the arts has included teaching, stage design, display art, art therapy and thirty years of exhibiting fine art. His paintings since the mid-1960s have broken with the rectangular form. The images have ranged from the somber in early work to the joyous, celebratory and humorous in recent work. He creates by doing preliminary drawings on index cards. Then, using chalk, he transfers the drawings to sheet masonite. Figures are cut out, and strips of wood are applied to the back to prevent bending and warping. After applying a base coat of white paint, he uses a variety of media and collage materials, including acrylics, padded fabrics, graphite and colored pencils, to build up areas of color and texture. Finally, he sprays the piece with a protective coating.

BREMNER, DOUGLAS ALDEN (Sculptor)
P.O. Box 235, Cazadero, CA 95421

Born: 1938 *Exhibitions:* Santa Rosa City Hall; International Sculpture Conference 1982 *Education:* UC-Berkeley; California College of Arts and Crafts

A sculptor comfortable with every metal, he has done custom fireplaces, wrought-iron railings, staircases, gates and chandeliers, as well as free-standing sculpture. His experiences as an underwater welder for salvage and construction operations enhanced his training in more traditional confines to give him a particular mastery of welding and sculpture. He creates forms that speak of his long-time attraction to to the beauty of speed- -on land and in the air and water. The forms are clean and streamlined—and at times surrealist—suggesting flight and motion and appearing to defy gravity. David Smith was an early inspiration; the works of Miro and Ernst have had lasting influence.

BRENNER, LESLIE (Photographer, Draughtsperson)
375 Sackett St., Brooklyn, NY 11231

Born: 1954 *Awards:* Sponsored Project's Grant, Artist's Space, NYC *Exhibitions:* Minor Injury Gallery, Brooklyn; Bronx Museum of Art *Education:* California Institute of the Arts

Works redefine the different components of the art audience, and explore how that audience operates. Installations, writings, advertisements, discussions and photography take the form of documentation. The work deliberately becomes embedded in the production of mythical meaning with social implications. Subject and purpose determines the medium for each project. Current color photography work involves the use of famous European paintings. Subjects are staged according to scenes in paintings, which are projected into each subject's home. Specifically, the artist uses paintings which depict tableau compositions, juxtaposing these with people participating in the tableaux. This work is about art in the marketplace, its accessibility and subject participation in a theatrical production.

BRENNO, VONNIE (Painter)
2835 Colorado Ave., Santa Monica, CA 90434

Born: 1950 *Collections:* Continental National Bank, Fort Worth *Exhibitions:* Butler Institute of American Art; Dassin Gallery, Los Angeles *Education:* USC; Art Center School of Design

Her early figurative and portrait paintings reflect her formal training in the technique of the Old Masters. The works were created with a painstaking process of underpainting and repeated glazings. In 1980, she became interested in the light and color of the Impressionists. Her recent work displays technical ability in the sure, deft handling of the pigment; the application, on the other hand, is more spontaneous. Her large canvases are modern genre paintings, depicting people in familiar urban settings. Elements of photo-realism and touches of surrealism are present in these paintings, which capture ordinary moments with startling clarity and focus.

BRESLIN, MARY K. (Painter)
2671 Placer St., Santa Cruz, CA 95062

Born: 1960 *Exhibitions:* San Jose Art League; Santa Cruz County Artists Open Show *Education:* San Jose State U.

Spontaneous and design elements have balanced each other in her acrylic landscapes. Early on, she developed a highly personal approach to color and design, influenced by Richard Diebenkorn and her professors at

Sally Baker, *Navajo Snow,* 29 x 37, watercolor. Courtesy: De Loach Vineyards, Santa Rosa

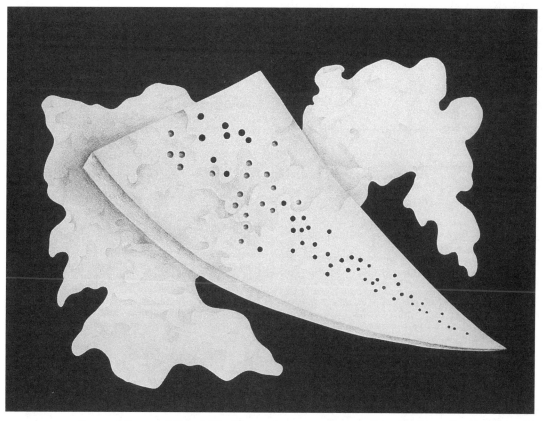

Leonard Breger, *Chlonal,* 36 x 24, cut-shape masonite, acrylic, colored pencils

San Jose State. She has continued with her landscape subject and with her personal and spontaneous application of acrylic media to paper and canvas. She uses black as a hub for all her colors. Her textures modulate through a surface that is made from other paintings and wet media. She is also a free-lance illustrator and designer, and she has produced real estate renderings, logos, cartoons, t-shirt designs and signages.

BRESSOUD, ROBIN (Painter)
295 W. Davies Ave. So., Littleton CO 80120

Born: 1954 Exhibitions: Neighbors Community Publications, Fresno

Though she is a great admirer of Georgia O'keeffe, she has developed her own style. She applies transparent layers of acrylic on canvas to create depth and life on the flat surface. Some areas are very flat; others are more rounded. Work has evolved into an individual contemporary realism. In her portraits, she informs the viewer about her subject, giving clues and creating a sense of intrigue. Recent acrylic on canvas work includes, "All Gods Children," a series of cultural portraits, painted from a female point of view.

BRICE, WILLIAM (Painter, Printmaker)
427 Beloit St., Los Angeles, CA 90049

Born: 1921 Awards: Los Angeles City Exhibition Award Collections: Los Angeles County Museum of Art; Whitney Museum, NYC Exhibitions: San Francisco Museum of Modern Art; Los Angeles Institute of Contemporary Art Education: Chouinard Art Institute; Art Students League Dealer: Robert Miller Gallery, NYC; L.A. Louver Gallery, Los Angeles

After formal art study, he worked in various media, and his concerns included diverse formal and expressive considerations. The works varied in degree of abstraction and associative reference, with nature and the human form the predominant subjects. More recent work involves a juxtaposition of differentiated elements of line, shape, form, value, color and substance in a spatial interaction that establishes a tension and equilibrium. He has become increasingly concerned with the interrelation of formal values and associative qualities. The human figure and forms in nature still predominate as a source of reference; the works tends toward a fragmented imagery. His media include painting in oil, drawing and printmaking.

BRIDGHAM, TERRE (Painter)
40 29th Place #2, Venice, CA 90291

Born: 1954 Awards: Whit Slemmons Fine Art Scholarship; Long Beach Gallery Cash Award Collections: Seven-Up Corp. Bottling Headquarters, Ft. Worth, TX Exhibitions: Riverside Art Museum; Matrix Gallery, Sacramento

Her paintings reflect her life-long interests in expressionism, primitivism and symbolism. Through the use of symbolic figures, the gestural application of paint and mixed media, and her somewhat naive style, she expresses her feelings about contemporary society. She considers herself a social artist, concentrating on depictions of the human condition and gender relations. She often integrates graffiti into her works, a reflection of her childhood in East Los Angeles. She covers the canvas, wood or metal with gestural brushstrokes in a variety of colors. Figures emerge or become more concentrated and intense as she applies more paint and other unconventional materials. Imagery revolves around ancient history and architecture, particularly Egyptian.

BRIGHTON, CAROL J. (Mixed Media Artist)
3103 Deakin St., Berkeley, CA 94705

Born: 1950 Collections: Cultural Center of the American Institute, Taipei Exhibitions: Retina Gallery, Oakland; Aptos Gallery Education: UC-Berkeley

After training in printmaking, she learned both Western and Japanese styles of papermaking. These handmade papers have since been a part of her work. Her monoprints and etchings feature realistic subjects, such as passageways and doorways, which act as metaphors for psychological states. Chinese calligraphy is often incorporated into the compositions. Frequent trips to China and Southeast Asia provide her with many images for her work. She is currently working on "Prayer Tract," a series of images that feature large, flat areas of color, especially blue, green and sienna. They are monoprints on handmade papers, often twenty by thirty inches.

BRISCOE, STEVE (Multimedia Artist)
1920 Union St., Oakland, CA 94607

Born: 1960 Awards: Sculpture Trophy, Annual Confectioners' Competition, San Francisco Fair; 3rd Place, Sculpture, Hayward Area Forum of the Arts Exhibitions: Southern Exposure Gallery, San Francisco; Berkeley Art Center Education: Santa Clara U.; San Francisco Art Institute

He began as a wood sculptor who used formal shapes—to investigate the relationships of volume and mass—as well as weapon iconography and intent. After 1985, he shifted his interests from formal properties to content, using recycled objects as armatures for sculptural shapes. While in Missouri, he was impressed by the lack of interest in urban art culture and the dependence on tools and quick-fix solutions. He was struck by the usefulness and grace of fence post construction, and has been striving to achieve this same elegance ever since. His current work combines photo-murals with sculptural installations. The photographs are iconic in style, and depict hands, tools or the fruits of labor. Many of these same objects are often displayed in the accompanying installations.

BROCKMANN, GEORGE R. III (Photographer)
131 Park St., #4, San Rafael, CA 94901

Born: 1954 Awards: Best of Show, Sonoma/Marin Fair Exhibitions: Disneyland State Fair, Los Angeles; Connoisseur's Collection, San Francisco

Inspired by the work of Ansel Adams, he began photographing landscapes. His early work was in black and white. He has since moved to color, still using the landscapes and architectural forms of Marin County as his prime subject matter. His compositions are characterized by repetitive images and shadows. This combination, echoing the main images, can be illusory and realistic.

BRODERSON, MORRIS (Painter)
657 N. La Cienega Blvd., Los Angeles, CA 90069

Born: 1928 Awards: New Talent U.S.A., Art In America; 1st Prize and Purchase Award, Los Angeles County Museum of Art Collections: Whitney Museum. NYC; Hirshhorn Museum Exhibitions: Ankrum Gallery, Los Angeles; Laguna Art Museum Education: USC Dealer: Ankrum Gallery, Los Angeles

Phoebe Beasley, *Waiting Room,* 36 x 36, collage.
Courtesy: Mr. and Mrs. Samuel Casey, Chicago

Helen L. Bellaver, *The Reading,* 24 x 36, pastel on paper

Calvin Barajas, *Pecho Adornado,* 19 x 19, acrylic and metallic leaf.
Photograph: Scott McCue

Belisa Barbachano, *Color and Frost #5,* 36 x 36, acrylic on canvas

Bruce Beasley, *Titiopoli's Arch,* 120 x 144, corten steel.
Courtesy: Middleheim Sculpture Park, Belgium

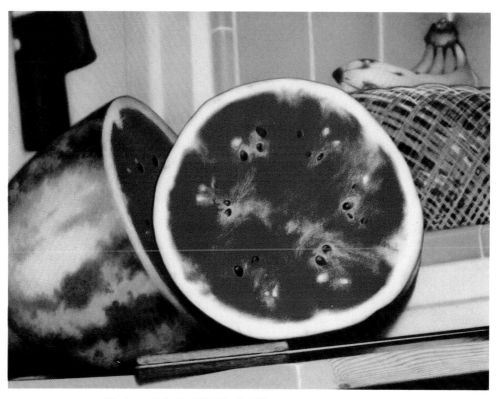

Herbert C. Bell, *Still Life C. Mills,* 30 x 40, colored pencil

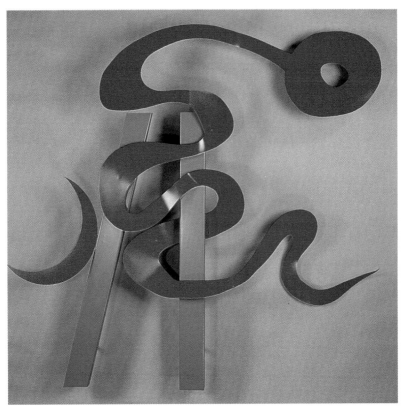

Benbow Bullock, *Omphalos '88,* 96 x 96 x 24, painted aluminum.
Commissioned by: Del Amo Financial Center, Los Angeles

Lilliana Braico, *Tulips and Silk Scarves,* 36 x 36, oil. Courtesy: Braico/Lewis Gallery

Alan Blizzard, *Sittin' at the Ritz,* 22 x 22, oil and rhoplex on canvas and wood.
Courtesy: Maurice-Heyman Fine Arts

Dwan Beveridge, *Geishas; 2D, 3D,* 18 x 22, watercolor and plastic

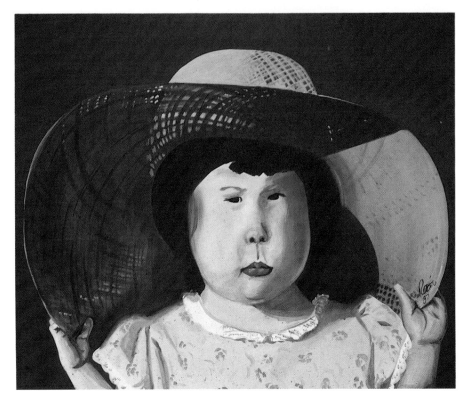

Robin Bressoud, *Jenny in My Easter Bonnet #1,* 24 x 30, acrylic. Courtesy: Thomas P. Carrico

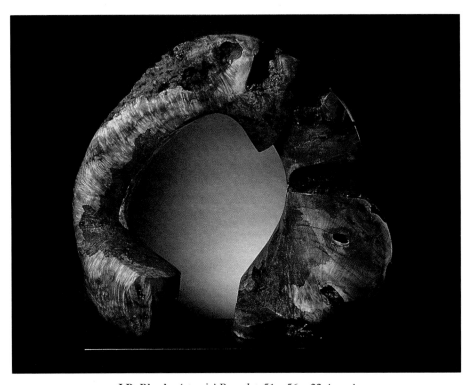

J.B. Blunk, *Artemis' Bracelet,* 51 x 56 x 23, laurel

Jane Bolton, *More Mother Figures,* 20 x 20, acrylic, archival board and wood.
Courtesy: Marie Feuer, Los Angeles

Philipp Branum, *Allah-Before Me,* 20 x 24, mixed media Courtesy: Judy Steen

Janice Rae Brown, *Rectangular Version,* 56 x 45, paint, multimedia

Sandi Blank, *Summer in Samos,* 48 x 48, acrylic Courtesy: Schiff, Harden and Waite, Sears Tower, Chicago

Eleanor Bell, *untitled #23,* 16 x 20, cibachrome. Photograph: Janice Felgar

S. Bevan, *Reflections,* 24 x 30, oil

Vonnie Brenno, *California Afternoon,* 36 x 48, oil on canvas

Don Blaisdell, *Monk's Sunlit Olive Grove,* 72 x 96, oil on linen

Bonnie Bisbee, *Sacred Dreamsmoke,* 36 x 48, oil

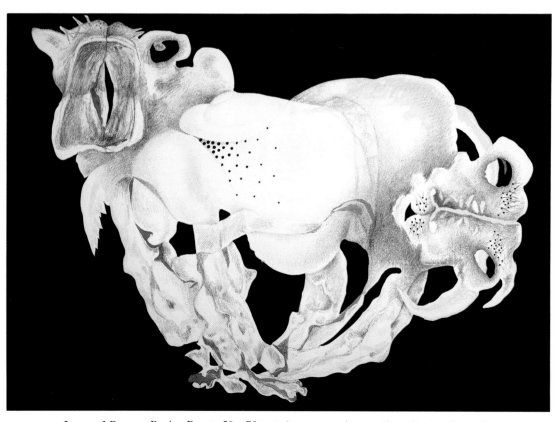

Leonard Breger, *Benign Beasts,* 50 x 78, cut-shape masonite, acrylic and colored pencils

Lore Burger, *Cottonwood,* 36 x 48 x 4, handmade paper, mixed media

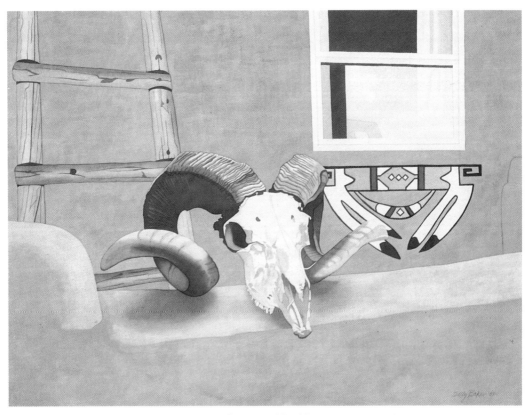

Sally Baker, *Passages,* 29 x 37, watercolor

Bernice Bing, *Circle Sutra,* 22 x 30, mixed media

Suzanne Brower, *Stardust Dream,* 18 x 24, oil

Lenore Beran, *"Ambush,"* 21 x 29, mixed media on paper

Gary Becker, *Fading Encounter,* 34 x 50, acrylic on canvas

Sandra E. Beebe, *Palette: After the Workshop,* 22 x 28, transparent watercolor

Carolyn Berry, *Laurence Hope (Adela Nicolson),* 6 x 4 x 1, mixed media (book). Photograph: Lestar Zucchini

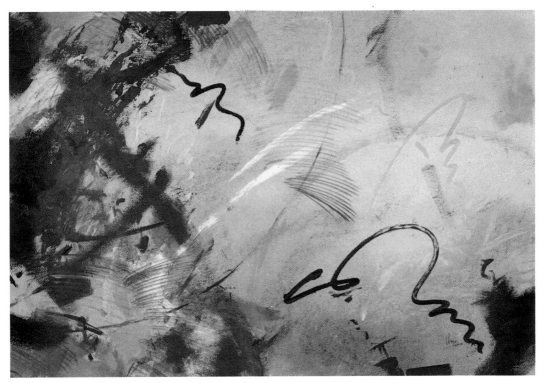

Blazin, *Chopin's Stardance,* 37 x 25, acrylics, pastels and conte on paper. Photograph: Bob Hsiang

Shirley Bleviss, *Time Out the Window,* 30 x 40, photograph

After formal, highly disciplined training in drawing and painting, he broke away from representational form and developed an intense, expressionistic figurative style, somewhat sculptural. Travels in Europe and the Far East were inspirational influences. Religious paintings and depictions of Portuguese bullfights characterized this early period. Later works comprise watercolors and pastels that are rich in color and pattern, the formal elements uniting seemingly unrelated subjects. Humanistic and passionate, these paintings reveal his concern with man's emotional response to the world around him. Recent work with embellished vases, textiles and portraiture depicts both exotic and common subjects. Images are imbued with a multitude of associations and allusions sometimes approaching fantasy. Themes include ballet, landscape, floral arrangements and occasionally the figure.

BRODIE, PAT (Fiber Artist)
384 Mira Monte Ave., Santa Barbara, CA 93108

Born: 1953 *Exhibitions:* Del Mano Gallery, Pasadena; Elizabeth Fortner Gallery, Santa Barbara

For four years, she studied landscape design, bonsai and floral art in Tokyo. When she returned to America, she began weaving in natural fibers. She studied basic basketry techniques in Santa Barbara, and went on to incorporate plant materials and hand-dyed reeds into a basket style that also involved the ideas of asymmetrical balance, taught in Japanese flower arrangement. Her current baskets show a mastery of weaving design and organic form. Each is a study of light and balance. Spiral movement, unusual, complex color combinations, special details and contrasting textures and colors characterize these earthy works.

BROMMER, GERALD F. (Painter)
11252 Valley Spring Ln., North Hollywood, CA 91602

Born: 1927 *Awards:* Purchase Awards, San Diego Watercolor Society; Alumnus of the Year, Concordia College *Collections:* Alan Hancock College; Utah State U. *Exhibitions:* American Watercolor Society, NYC; National Academy of Design, NYC; National Watercolor Society, Los Angeles *Education:* U. of Nebraska, Lincoln *Dealer:* Fireside Gallery, Carmel; Esther Wells Collection, Laguna Beach

From the coastline of Carmel to the crowded street-markets of China, the artist is never at a loss for subject matter for his watercolor landscape paintings. Inspired early in his career by Cezanne, his figures contain strong design elements, but his palette with its earthtones, is more reminiscent of the American landscape artists. Paintings can be quite large, up to 4-by-8- feet, and recent projects have employed rice paper as a collage element. He is an author of many books, and the teacher of workshops and college courses; his knowledge and involvement in art is extensive. His work can be viewed in permanent collections throughout the United States and in seven overseas countries.

BRONSON, JONATHAN (Sculptor)
855 N., 200 W., Pleasant Grove, UT 84062

Born: 1952 *Awards:* 1st Place, World's Fair; Medal, Audubon Show, AK *Collections:* White House; Prince Phillip *Exhibitions:* World Wildlife Fund Exhibit, Toronto; Gene Autry Exhibition, Palm Springs

He has spent much of his life studying, sketching, and sculpting wildlife. As a child, he cared for injured wild animals, orphaned owls, hawks and ravens. He began drawing at the age of six and sold his first sculptures at the age of ten. In countless field studies in the Rocky Mountains and Alaska, he has gradually expanded his contact with wildlife to include bears, moose, caribou, rams, eagles, wolves and other animals native to these locations. He has created a life-sized baby rhino for a public installation and a 3/4 bust of a man with a falcon on his arm. Working in the field, he sculpts wax with his fingers and later casts the piece in bronze.

BROOKE, PEGAN (Painter)
P.O. Box 857, Bolinas, CA 94924

Born: 1950 *Awards:* Louis Comfort Tiffany Painting Grant *Collections:* Guggenheim Museum, NYC; San Francisco Museum of Modern Art *Exhibitions:* Des Moines Art Center; Guggenheim Museum, NYC *Education:* Stanford U.; UC-San Diego *Dealer:* Fuller-Gross Gallery, San Francisco; Sharon Lee Gallery, Los Angeles

Her stylized, postmodern nature images are metaphors for the human condition. The works are full of wildernesses and primitive agricultural scenes, with dark clouds on the horizon. Her influences range from the American painters Arthur Dove, Marsden Hartley, Thomas Hart Benton and Grant Wood to the transcendental writings of Emerson and Thoreau and the rhythmic and spiritual qualities of natural forms. "I paint from natural phenomena to more fully understand its non-verbal logic, for in these 'simple' things the pathos and mystery of life will be found," she says. She is presently an instructor at the San Francisco Art Institute.

BROOKS, ALAN (Painter)
1216 Palm Ave., San Mateo, CA 94402

Born: 1931 *Awards:* 1st Place, California State Fair; 1st Place, San Mateo County Fair *Collections:* City of San Francisco; A.T.& T. Public Arts Program *Exhibitions:* John Bolles Gallery, San Francisco; Van Doren Gallery, San Francisco *Education:* San Jose State U. *Dealer:* Van Doren Assoc., San Francisco

His oils and watercolors are both figurative and realistic. Through a wide range of subject matter, he both evokes an emotional response to a given event and helps the viewer search for its deeper meaning. His style has been influenced by Sargent, Velazquez, Homer and Hopper. Though his technique has grown more gestural and expressive, the content of his work has remained consistent throughout his career. He has also explored the problems presented by the static nature of painting. Utilizing the motion study research of Edward Muybridge, he has attempted to extend the time of a visual experience.

BROOKS, G.I. (Painter)
4691 Ranchview Circle, Huntington Beach, CA

Born: 1928 *Awards:* Best of Show, Eastern Washington Watercolor Society; 1st Prize, Newport Salute to the Arts *Collections:* Nicola Museum, Yugoslavia *Exhibitions:* City Hall Gallery, Newport Beach; Huntington Beach City Gallery

She believes that the three major elements of a successful painting are the careful design of shapes, the judicious use of color and the overall emotional impact. After a career as a commercial and industrial artist, she now devotes herself to painting and exhibiting. She works in watercolor and acrylic, using large pumi brushes for clearly accented areas of color. Her

Western and California landscapes and floral still lifes are realistic, with special attention to meticulously depicted detail and the play of light and shadow. She concentrates on a search for the surprising, in order to challenge the viewer's established concept of how the world looks.

BROOKS, JON (Sculptor)
Artkamp, Pine Rd., New Boston, NH 03070

Born: 1944 *Collections:* American Craft Museum, NYC; Queen Victoria Museum, Launceston, Tasmania, Australia *Exhibitions:* Wita Gardiner Gallery, San Diego; American Craft Museum, NYC *Education:* Rochester Institute of Technology *Dealers:* Wita Gardiner, San Diego; Gallery of Functional Art, Santa Monica

He received formal training from Wendell Castle at the Rochester Institute of Technology, and he was also influenced by Brancusi, Gaudi and Naguchi. His early work was massive and curved. He now makes some utilitarian pieces, including his prize-winning furniture and his sculptural house/studio, but many of his works are statements about utility. In *Styx Ladderback Chairs*, he subverted the conception of a chair and made fun of utility. In his current pop and cartoon-influenced gossamer constructions, he combines wood with metal, glass, stone and other materials to produce refined, finished surfaces in which he carves brightly colored hieroglyphs.

BROOKS, TOM (Painter, Mixed Media Artist)
1432 Drake Ave., Burlingame, CA 94010

Born: 1952 *Collections:* Rorick Gallery, San Francisco *Exhibitions:* The Art Corridor, Menlo Park; 3 COM Corporation, Mountain View *Education:* San Jose State U. *Dealer:* Gallery 30, San Mateo

His formal training focused on traditional representation from life—the nude model, the still life and the landscape—in oils and pastels. Classic Renaissance artists, as well as impressionist and photo-realist painters were among the most important influences on his style and approach. From this diverse background, he has developed a unique style, which he calls contemporary romantic realism. This style is well represented by the two works reproduced here. He works primarily in this style, and has recently been developing a series of French landscapes in pastel. Since 1985, however, his sources for inspiration and stylistic influences have broadened, which, he says, "offers him a creative balance." This other work, influenced by surrealism and pop art concerns war, isolation, the "American Dream" and other social issues. For example, *Life, Liberty, and the Pursuit of Happiness*, a large painting in acrylics and watercolors on paper, features an overweight, Middle American family eating by an outdoor pool—a pointed comment on the materialism that has undermined a cherished national ideal. He has also continued to work in landscapes, recently producing a series of large, boldly patterned pieces in acrylics and mixed media. These serial paintings are typical of his working style, in which he thoroughly investigates a chosen idea or theme.

BROTHERS, LYNDA (Textile Artist)
386 Avenida de la Vereda, Ojai, CA 93023

Born: 1949 *Awards:* Best of Show, Santa Barbara Arts Festival; 1st Place, Ojai Arts Center *Exhibitions:* Gilbert Gallery, Ojai; Gallery International, Capetown, South Africa *Dealer:* Mckeon Art Consulting, Ojai

In 1975, she became interested in Casper Friedrich and A. W. Turner's blurring of boundaries as an expression of the sublime. Working with fiber, she has always been attracted to its unique color and textural qualities. Combining her vision for the sublime and a desire to capture the intensity of African landscape, she enjoys the particular challenge of translating these images in tapestries. Working on both miniature and large-scale pieces that sometimes take up to six months to complete, she continues to expand the use of soft mohairs, hand dyed wools, Gobelin and Swedish techniques, with her own modern interpretations.

BROWER, SUZANNE
205 Pirie Rd., #65, Ojai, CA 93023

Born: 1911 *Awards:* Gold Medal, Baltimore Photography Salon *Collections:* Ojai Art Center, Ojai *Exhibitions:* Ojai Valley Studio Tour; Ojai Atrium *Education:* Los Angeles City College

She was born in Austria, and as a child she attended the State Artcraft School of Vienna. In 1963 she did a series of poster- color paintings depicting childhood memories. In 1983 she entered a class at a local senior center and started painting landscapes from her own color slides. By 1985 she had changed her style and begun to express in paint the "inner visions" she had seen during meditation. These canvases of brilliant, unusual and harmoniously colored shapes, figures and faces all share a dark blue background. The artist's influences are El Greco and Vermeer. She also makes collages from wallpaper, tin foil, greeting cards and wrapping paper, on a painted background.

BROWN, CAROLE R. (Painter, Collage Artist)
19 Rio Vista Ave., Oakland, CA 94611

Born: 1941 *Awards:* Artist Liaison Award *Collections:* Elmhurst College, Elmhurst, IL *Exhibitions:* Auburn Arts Center Gallery; The Matrix Gallery, Sacramento *Education:* School of the Art Institute of Chicago

Working in a variety of media, she has always used a wide range of techniques. Her collage/assemblage work combines found and created objects of plastic, wood, metal and/or paper, attached to wooden surfaces. She uses bronze, cement, plaster or wood to construct her three-dimensional pieces. Her Chicago background is apparent in her attraction to the collage format and to the low- brow imagery placed within a surreal, fantastic setting. Although her principal medium is now acrylic painting on unprimed Arches 300 lb. deckle edge paper, she continues to work in both collage/assemblage and sculpture. In these works, she combines autobiographical symbolism with images and impressions gathered from historical and contemporary sources and actual found objects. These flat, freely associated references are then transformed into her fantasy landscapes and abstracted compositions, using such methods as incongruent juxtapositions, spatial ambiguities and non-representational colors. Even in her paintings, the collage approach is evident in the use of overlapping, two-dimensional shapes.

BROWN, FREDERICK J. (Painter)
120 Wooster St., New York, NY 10012

Born: 1945 *Awards:* Award, New York State Council on the Arts *Collections:* Metropolitan Museum of Art, NYC; Aldrich Museum of Contemporary Art *Exhibitions:* Marlborough Gallery, NYC; Aldrich Museum of Contemporary Art, Ridgefield, CT *Education:*

Tom Brooks, *Stourhead Gardens, England,* 13 x 22, pastel on paper

Evelyn Bundren, *California Quail Family,* full scale, wood and oils

Southern Illinois U. *Dealer:* Marlborough Gallery, NYC

Older works are in an abstract expressionist vein, strongly influenced by Pollock and de Kooning. Though many such works use current brush techniques, they often employ "pour and splash" techniques as well to relate perspective in the spirit of the New York school of "Action" painting. Recent works have been exclusively representational. Religious themes dominate the figurative realism painted on large-scale canvases. Perspective now takes the form of spiritual levels not easily recognizable because of their conceptual nature.

BROWN, GARY H. (Painter)
Art Studio Department, University of California, Santa Barbara, CA 93106

Born: 1941 *Awards:* Greenshields Foundation Grant for European Travel *Collections:* Yale University; Tyler Museum of Art, Tyler, TX *Exhibitions:* Art/Life Gallery, Santa Barbara; Source Gallery, San Francisco *Education:* U. of Wisconsin

A painter, designer and teacher, he considers his work in art to be autobiographical research, deriving from the complexity and variety of daily life. Training and vision guides him in his goal to explore a meaningful life in the context of the larger society. His love of drawing has led to experimentation in design, typography, papermaking and book design; he has recently been painting in oil and has become involved in glazing and varnish formulas. He teaches painting and drawing at the University of California in Santa Barbara.

BROWN, GLORIA (Painter)
2701 Larkin St. 202, San Francisco, CA 94109

Born: 1921 *Awards:* Biennial Corcoran, Washington, DC; Monterey Conference Center *Collections:* Monterey Museum of Art *Exhibitions:* Palace of the Legion of Honor, San Francisco; Monterey Museum of Art *Education:* California College of Arts and Crafts

She began as an abstractionist but in recent years has begun doing representational still lifes. She works in oil on canvas with concentrations on color, brush technique and form. Through the use of soft edges that create a slight halo, she paints figures of deliberately rich, flat color that stand off the canvas. The images are further animated by impastos and glazes. Paul Mills, former curator of the Oakland Art Museum, said of her works as a colorist, ". . . they have a subtlety of nuance, a cool, bright, bittersweet quality which is very personal and has endured through every phase of her work . . . ." Influences include Gauguin and Matisse.

BROWN, JANICE RAE (Painter)
2421 Portland St., Eugene, OR 97405

Born: 1942 *Exhibitions:* Opus 5, Eugene, OR; Scarlett O'Heifer's, Eugene, OR *Education:* U. of Oregon

After experimenting with a variety of independent pigment media, including acrylics, latex, enamels and metallics, the artist has developed a style that utilizes a combination of these to achieve a variety of effects in her paintings. Likewise, initial works on canvas have given way to experiments with painted utilitarian objects such as furniture and clothing. Primarily concentrating on color and shape, she uses a semiautomatic method to preserve surprise and spontaneity. The abstract potential of this technique is counterbalanced by representational iconography and pictorial symbolism reinforced with layered pigments and varnish to achieve a sense of depth. Influences include the Fauves, Cubists, and Abstract Expressionists, as well as the Bay Area art scene of the early 1960s.

BROWN, JOAN (Painter)
c/o Allan Frumkin Gallery, 50 W. 57th St., New York NY 10019

Born: 1938 *Exhibitions:* University Art Museum, Berkeley; Allan Frumkin Gallery, NYC *Education:* California School of Fine Arts *Dealer:* Fuller-Goldeen Gallery, San Francisco; Allan Frumkin Gallery, NYC

Her early works, influenced by the Expressionists, the Impressionists and the Old Masters, employed the impasto technique. After later studying with Elmer Bischoff, she became interested in the dynamic interactions between forms. Mysticism and Eastern thought also have affected her work. She deals with introspection, regardless of the subject matter: "The form or image varies, but the content is the same," she says. A California Bay Area artist, she travels in order to study belief systems and cultures. Impressions and images gathered from extensive travels in Europe, Egypt, South America, China and India have inspired recent works in enamel.

BROWN, JOAN INGOLDSBY (Photographer)
P.O. Box 60066, Palo Alto, CA 94306

Born: 1932 *Awards:* Packaging Award, AIGA, NYC; Merit Award, San Francisco Women Artists Gallery *Exhibitions:* Houston Center for Photography; Monterey Peninsula Museum of Art *Education:* Cooper Union Art School, NYC

After working in graphic design and commercial advertising for twenty years, she discovered photography as a fine art medium. Intrigued by the energy of light, she studied with Ruth Bernhard, Don Worth, Ansel Adams and other photographic artists. Working with two or three photographs per image, she began refining the layered, photo-collage technique that has become her trademark. This layering, performed either in the camera or in the darkroom, creates a richly textured, evocative image. She works with still life subjects, including human figures that are often only vaguely visible. She works in both black and white and color, using large format cameras. The color images use light, filtered through color-transparent materials to create semi-abstract images. Many of her works are macro-photographs, giving a new perspective to seeing and interpreting familiar subjects. The black and white prints are textured, rich and dark; the color work is likewise rich and saturated. The images use few straight lines, and the overall characteristics could be described as sensual, mysterious, layered, textured, sensitive—more like prints or paintings than the usual photography.

BROWN, LAWRIE (Photographer)
424 Ocean View Ave., Santa Cruz, CA 95062

Born: 1949 *Awards:* NEA Photographers Fellowship *Collections:* Polaroid Corporation; Center for Creative Photography, Tucson *Exhibitions:* San Francisco Museum of Modern Art; Oakland Museum *Education:* San Francisco State University; San Jose State University *Dealer:* Marcuse Pfeifer, NYC

Known for a project in which she painted food, and photographed it beside commercially colored foods,

Philipp Branum, *Bower Bird Blues,* 14 x 12, mixed media

John Bruce, *Pa Bear,* 20 x 24, charcoal drawing

Janice Rae Brown, *Dennie,* 24 x 36, oil

she has continued to flirt with our notion of nature through a series of painted plants. For her cibachrome "Plantscape," she spent days painting and primping a single "chosen" model. Each plant is set in a complementary environment of painted background panels with colored paper or fabric cut-outs suspended in front. Photographing the scenes became a study of color and the illusion-creating potential of selective focus. Her current work explores modern psychosocial relationships in vignettes that suggest reality, yet are open to interpretation. These scenarios are orchestrated to examine cultural and perceptual aspects of our society.

BROWN, THEOPHILUS (Painter)
468 Jersey St., San Francisco, CA 94114

Born: 1919 *Awards:* 1st Prize, Los Angeles County Annual *Collections:* Metropolitan Museum of Art, NYC; Hirshhorn Museum, Washington, D.C. *Exhibitions:* John Berggruen Gallery, San Francisco; Maxwell Davidson, NYC *Education:* UC-Berkeley; Atelier Leger, Paris *Dealer:* John Berggruen Gallery, San Francisco

Throughout his long career, he has consistently been a figurative painter. He paints either in acrylic or in oil, mostly on canvas but sometimes on paper as well. He also draws with various black and white media. For his larger works, he usually makes studies, though he normally finds it necessary to depart radically from them in the creation of his final painting. He has traveled widely and studied in Paris.

BRUCE, JOHN A. (Painter, Printmaker)
5394 Tip Top Rd., Mariposa, CA 95338

Born: 1931 *Collections:* Smithsonian Institution, Washington, D.C. *Exhibitions:* Butler Institute of American Art *Education:* Art Center College of Design; Chouinard Art Institute

He was trained as a commercial illustrator and graphic designer; his style is photo-realistic. His subjects are people who live in the fantasy of the past, such as men who hunt with black-powder and muzzle-loaders, and Indians who dress as their grandparents did, when they attended powwows. Working on either canvas or masonite panels, he draws with charcoal or pencil, underpaints with a thin wash of medium and color and then works impasto with either a bristle or sable brush. He is able to impart presence to his subjects through a realistic, richly detailed approach. Influences include Rembrandt and Sargent.

BRUCE, RANDALL (Ceramist)
1832 Hollyvista Ave., Los Angeles, CA 90027

Born: 1950 *Awards:* Honorable Mention, Clay, Glendale College *Exhibitions:* Gallery Eight, San Diego; Craft and Folk Art Museum, Los Angeles *Education:* Los Angeles City College

He is best known for earthenware vessels treated with lava and luster glazes. Highly unpredictable when fired, these glazes produce a range of colors and a bubbly, frothy surface. Since this surface is so colorful and intense, he keeps the clay forms simple and graceful, with smooth lines and elegant shapes. He has studied with Lee Whitten and Robert Kibler, but his technique and approach are more akin to that of Beatrice Wood. Fascinated by the glazed surface's capacity to reflect the surrounding environment, he constantly experiments with new glazes and firing procedures.

BRUKOFF, BARRY (Photographer)
310 Industrial Central Building, Sausalito, CA 94965

Born: 1935 *Collections:* American Broadcasting Corporation, NYC; Bank of America, San Francisco *Exhibitions:* Elaine Horwitch Gallery, Palm Springs; Gallery Minoru Shirota, Tokyo *Education:* School of the Art Institute of Chicago

His photographs fall into two categories. One aspect of his work is directly related to his painting and designing. He delights in photographing fragments of walls, streets, posters and other objects that people pass without noticing. His work presents these by-passed treasures in ways that expand the limits of visual awareness and the appreciation of beauty. The other aspect of his work has to do with travel and architecture: photographing areas in which man and nature have interacted. He has been drawn to Stonehenge, Machu Picchu, Angkor Wat in Cambodia and villages of the Greek Isles—all places where the power and interplay of man and nature are evident. He feels that his work is an exploration of beauty in many different forms. His artistic philosophy is aligned with John Garner's statement that "true art is moral: it seeks to improve life ... art rediscovers, generation by generation, what is necessary to humanness."

BRULC, D. (VAPOUR, MEL) (Video Artist, Mixed Media Artist)
14420-A Walnut St., Suite 281, Berkeley, CA 94709

Born: 1946 *Awards:* A. Durer Research Grant, Germany *Collections:* Winston Collections *Exhibitions:* East Bay Media Center, Berkeley; Monterey Museum of Modern Art *Dealer:* Artsupports, Inc., Berkeley

Throughout his career, he has been an innovator in film and video. In the 1960s he developed the "VapourDye" (tm) print technique. In the 1970s he unveiled a new body of work dealing with environmental structures and involving masses of participants. In the 1980s, he moved to California, changed his name to Mel Vapour, and launched his "ARTOFFENSIVE" on the West Coast. In this series, he confronted his viewers with cast paper icons covered with messages such as "Don't Take Art From Strangers." Most recently he has been experimenting with psychic video works, i.e., confrontational video campaigns, sublimation research and the integration of computer and video techniques.

BRUNER, RICK (Photographer)
291 Adams St., Oakland, CA 94610

Born: 1951 *Collections:* Museum of Modern Art, NYC; Museum of Contemporary Art, Chicago *Exhibitions:* Eye Gallery, San Francisco; Presshouse Gallery, Sonoma *Education:* U. of Northern Iowa; Wayne State U. *Dealer:* Frank Relations, San Francisco

Using a variety of cameras and materials to produce each image, he combines Polaroid SX70 prints, previous 35mm shots (as well as ones taken for the specific project at hand) and hand-drawn and found images. When the final arrangement is finished, he rephotographs the collage with a 4 x 5 camera, to preserve color fidelity. He selects and combines elements along formal and thematic lines, permitting the viewer enough leeway for multiple and individual interpretations.

Jennifer Bain, *After the Darkness,* 72 x 78, oil on canvas and metal

Suzanne Brower, *Ecstasy,* 18 x 24, oil

BRUNNER, PHOEBE (Painter)
69 La Venta Dr., Santa Barbara, CA 93110

Born: 1951 *Awards:* "Meet the Artist" Fellowship, Santa Barbara Museum of Art *Collections:* Glenbow Museum of Art, Calgary, Canada; United Technologies, Hartford, CT *Exhibitions:* Louis Newman Gallery, Beverly Hills; Robert Berman Gallery, Santa Monica *Education:* College of Creative Studies, UC-Santa Barbara *Dealer:* Robert Berman Gallery, Santa Monica

She invokes art's psychological and emotional power of communication through surrealist landscapes that are just outside the familiar. Fishes fly through air thick with fumes. Below, rows of industrial refinery tanks number into infinity. In another painting, the fish hover over leveled tree trunks, and in another, a brilliant copper orb illuminates lonely urban rooftops from its mountaintop perch in an ominous sky. These unsettling images connote an alien past or future in which humans have lost control of their environment. First with acrylic paint, and now oil, her palette utilizes texture, color and pattern to affect a haunting, evocative quality.

BRUTOSKY, C.S.J. VERONICA (Painter)
2530 W. Alamos, #114, Fresno, CA 93705

Born: 1932 *Awards:* Finalist, Mixed Media, International Art Competition *Exhibitions:* USC; Plum's Gallery, Fresno, *Education:* Otis Art Institute; Cal. State-Fresno *Dealer:* Plum's Gallery, Fresno

She has been influenced by Vermeer's light and by the beauty and presence in Fantin-LaTour's floral paintings. In her still lifes, she conveys an exquisite light and peace. She has also explored qualities of power and exaggeration in figurative paintings, reminiscent of the Mexican Muralists. Recently, she has pursued a love for color and light, by incorporating calligraphic flows of energy into spacious skyscapes. She has also produced a series of political paintings and installations called "Choice/No Choice." These works involve the choices of roles men and women have in choosing war and peace. She is a Sister of St. Joseph of Carondelet.

BRYANT, MONICA (Painter)
2625 Fir Park Way, Santa Rosa, CA 95404

Born: 1950 *Awards:* 3rd Place, California Works, California State Fair *Education:* U. of Hawaii; Maryland Institute of Art

Her work has been influenced by the pluralism of the 1970s. Her classical education in materials and techniques at the University of Hawaii, and her academic drawing classes at the Maryland Institute, complement her admiration for the conceptual work of Joseph Beuys and Christo, and the work of Jenny Holzer and Squeak Carnwath. Her recent work on mahogany is narrative and personal. Her best known works are her monotypes, of such things as high heels and dresses, and her seven-foot standing sculpture of an apron.

BUCHMAN, ROY (Painter)
911 4th St., #B, Santa Monica, CA 90403

Born: 1952 *Exhibitions:* Orlando Gallery, Los Angeles; Downey Museum *Education:* Syracuse U.; Otis Art Institute

He developed an interest in the graphic arts after leaving architectural school in the early 1970s. After studying at Atelier Garrigues, in the south of France, he began painting in oil. Major influences are Eakins, Hopper and Stella. He now paints from sketches and from photographs of everyday life in Los Angeles. His style is, at once, narrative and symbolic. He creates a unique surface by stretching the canvas over a constructed form, curving the canvas in unexpected ways. Linework and color constantly shift, as the basis of single point perspective is repeatedly challenged. The canvases impose their own rhythm on the viewer.

BUDD, ERIK (Painter)
402 9th St., N.W., Fosston, MN 56542

Born: 1949 *Awards:* Purchase Award, 27th Midwestern Invitational Art Exhibition, Moorhead, MN; Bronze Medal, Oil and Acrylic Painting, International Art Competition, Los Angeles *Collections:* North Dakota State U., Fargo; Lamar U., Beaumont, TX *Exhibitions:* California State University Art Museum, Long Beach; Laguna Art Museum *Education:* Concordia College; U. of North Dakota, Grand Forks *Dealer:* Francine Ellmann Gallery, Los Angeles

Influenced by the works of Francis Bacon, Robert Rauschenberg and Robert Motherwell, he developed an expressionist style early in his career. At the same time, he became interested in the writings of Carl Jung, Joseph Campbell and James Joyce. Trusting in the intuition and the subconscious, he began painting pictures of animals and people in that instant before something has occurred—capturing the subjects in the moment of decision. Once quite representational, his works have become increasingly abstract. Experimentation with razor blades, house paint brushes, whisk brooms and other unconventional applicators has altered the texture of his paintings, making the subjects appear blurred and ill at ease in their surroundings. His recent work, *Burying Martin Luther*, is a black comedy of two characters, laying a third to rest.

BUKOVNIK, GARY (Painter, Printmaker)
1179 Howard St., San Francisco, CA 94103

Born: 1947 *Awards:* George Bunker Award, American Society of Museum Publications; Award of Merit, San Francisco Arts Commission *Collections:* Metropolitan Museum of Art, NYC; San Francisco Museum of Modern Art *Exhibitions:* Brooklyn Museum; Museum of Art, Carnegie Institute, Pittsburgh *Education:* Cleveland Institute of Art *Dealer:* Staempfli Gallery, NYC; Allport Gallery, San Francisco

He paints large-scale, botanically accurate flowers. His colors are fearlessly exuberant and his watercolor style is a blend of botanical accuracy and a passionate romanticism. His choice of a floral subject matter was partly inspired by their taboo in the serious art world, but more importantly he finds in live flowers an infinite variety and subtlety. The works are informed by artists from several centuries. His subjects are those of Chardin and Fantin-Latour. Like Demuth, his brushwork is fluid and his subjects are isolated against stark white backgrounds. Like O'Keeffe, he renders flowers closely and brings them near abstraction.

BULITT, PATRICIA (Mask Maker, Performance Artist)
2138 Mckinley, Berkeley, CA 94703

Born: 1949 *Awards:* NEA Choreography Fellowship; Woman Artist Award, Botree Productions *Exhibitions:* Berkeley Art Center *Education:* UCLA

Her contemporary artistic expressions have roots in ancient cultural contexts. Her performance works are rich collaborative efforts that celebrate the body as

Veronica Brutosky, C.S.J., *Rehearsal for Dante,* 16 x 20,
oil on canvas. Photograph: E.Z. Smith

Joan Ingoldsby Brown, *Dreams IV,* 16 x 20,
silver gelatin photograph

sculpture in motion; they incorporate dance, choreography and ethnography. In *Tundra Trance*, she became an escort for the soul at death. Some works involve shamans and honor and explain Eskimo beliefs. Her masks are forms she uses in storytelling. They are strips of paper that cross the face with scripted and calligraphic tones. She uses temporal material such as rice, sand and other natural elements, which cause a reflection and change in a manner inherent to themselves.

BULLOCK, BENBOW (Sculptor)
153 Pfeiffer St., San Francisco, CA 94133

Born: 1929 *Awards:* Purchase Award, 6th Annual Henry Moore Exhibition; Hakone Open-Air Museum, Japan *Collections:* AT&T; Bramlea Corporation *Exhibitions:* San Francisco Museum of Modern Art, Fort Mason; New York Univeristy *Education:* Wesleyan U.

His works are steel or aluminum geometric constructivist sculptures painted in bright colors. Black is not in his vocabulary. Shapes such as circles, spheres, crescents, cubes and pyramids occur frequently in his work. Some of his sculptures weigh over three tons. His work is in the tradition of the Bauhaus and De Stijl, and more recently he has been influenced by Anthony Caro and Chillida. Much of his work features the use of whimsical eletic titles that draw on classical mythological and comtemporary themes. His sculpture *They Laughed at Columbus* was selected from 537 entries worldwide to become part of the permanent collection of the Hakone Open-Air Museum. His work refelcts insights of a well-travelled philosopher.

BULLOCK, EDNA (Photographer)
155 Mar Vista Dr., Monterey, CA 93940

Born: 1915 *Awards:* 1st Place, Monterey Peninsula College Second Annual Photography Contest; President's Award, California Insurance Group Photographic Competition *Collections:* Bibliotheque Nationale, Paris; Center for Creative Photography, Tucson *Exhibitions:* Neikrug Gallery, NYC; Museum of Photography, Antwerp, Belgium *Education:* UCLA *Dealer:* Josephus Daniels Gallery, Carmel

She began her career shortly after the death of her husband, photographer Wynn Bullock, and her first series involved close- ups of wood knots and knot holes, which resembled human faces. She now specializes in photographing the human form in a natural outdoor environment. Concentration is on the male nude, in an effort to develop an aesthetic and emotional response to the nude as an integral part of the relationship of time and space to nature and the elements. Using either a Hasselblad 500cm or a 4 x 5 Tachihara camera and working exclusively in black and white, she endeavors to capture the model's natural and spontaneous reaction to his environment.

BUNDREN, EVELYN (Woodcarver)
13663 Torray Pines, Auburn, CA 95603

Born: 1920 *Awards:* 1st Place, California State Fair *Exhibitions:* Crocker Art Museum, Sacramento; California State Fair Art Gallery

She was schooled in woodcarving by her brother, an artist recognized by the Smithsonian for the brilliance of his own work in wildlife figures. Her subjects are primarily bird figures. The surfaces of the life-sized figures are carved in three- dimensional detail and painted in natural colors to appear extremely life-like. She uses bass wood, a traditional hard wood suited to

detailed carving, and tupelo wood. Feet and legs are made with wire and hand-tooled, and the pieces are mounted on driftwood. She is also beginning to explore the use of lost wax in the creation of original pieces.

BUNNELL, KATHIE S. (Stained Glass Artist, Painter)
P.O. Box 838, Bolinas, CA 94924

Born: 1941 *Collections:* Mt. Hamilton Peace Center, San Jose; John Denver, Aspen Co. *Exhibitions:* First Unitarian Church of San Francisco; 3228 Gallery, San Francisco

She creates naturalistic and abstract images in stained glass and watercolor. Her stained glass work is considered pioneering by her peers, not so much for technical innovation, as for the breadth of her expression in glass and her ability to use the medium to express ideas and emotions. After extensive studies with Judith North, she developed processes of designing around found objects, called "glass sketches and biomorphic compositions." Her paintings revolve around mandala forms and water-holding vessels. Her works are infused with a deep respect for nature and an understanding of life processes.

BUNTON, ETH (Painter)
935 Cocopah Dr., Santa Barbara, CA 93110

Born: 1924 *Awards:* Award of Distinction, Faulkner Gallery, Santa Barbara *Exhibitions:* Santa Barbara Arts Council; Kenwood Gallery, Westmont College, Santa Barbara *Education:* U. of London *Dealer:* Astra Gallery, Santa Barbara

After formal training in an impressionistic style, she developed an interest in landscape, using acrylic and oil in a rather abstract, painterly approach, with a strong emphasis on design. Influenced by extensive study with Robert Frame, she worked in strong, bright colors with sharp contrast. Gradually she toned down her colors, and used a more limited palette. Later, she consciously brightened her palette again, but not to the original color strengths and contrasts. Her recent work has developed in two directions: she has been painting in watercolor, using a free, wet style and clear, bright colors; she has also been creating minimalist landscapes in oil. Although these works refer to natural forms, they are rendered in a sparse, abstract style with empty shapes in the upper and lower portions of the canvas, and a central area of obscured form and color.

BURBANK, NANCY A. (Painter)
108 Belcrest Dr., Los Gatos, CA 95032

Born: 1930 *Awards:* Selected for Calendar, National Association of University Women *Exhibitions:* San Francisco Art Festival; San Jose State University *Education:* San Jose State U. *Dealer:* Sperling Gallery, San Jose

She is best known for her curvilinear paintings, two half-circles connected by two straight lines. Her use of the lozenge shape is the result of a figure painting class she attended in the early 1970s. She began to see squares, rectangles and other sharply angled figures as antithetical to the natural forms that were her inspiration and her subject matter. Along with Buckminster Fuller, she believes that the curved form imitates nature and encourages feelings of spaciousness and freedom. Her painting technique is much like Helen

Helen L. Bellaver, *The Session,* 48 x 65, oil on canvas

Carolyn Berry, *I a Fool?,* 5 x 7 x 2, mixed media (book). Photograph: Susan Scott

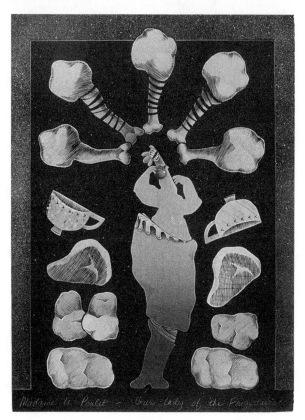

Betty Bates, *Madame Le Poulet, Our Lady of the Frigidaire,*
30 x 22, linoleum cut print. Courtesy: Citadel Print Center Gallery

Fred L. Berensmeier, *Spirit Rock,* 20 x 26, drawing.
Courtesy: Standing Bear Gallery

284

Gary Bates, *Lunar Kecherscmitt,* 168 x 132 x 68, steel boiler-plate.
Photograph: Jens Selvig

Suzanne Bloomfield, *untitled,* 48 x 60, encaustic mix

George J. Bleich, *Old Inspiration Point, Yosemite,* 30 x 40, acrylic. Courtesy: Bleich Gallery, Carmel, CA

Sharon Bender, *January,* 24 x 11 x 7, bronze.
Photograph: Chris Webber

Ken Ball, *Mountain Spirit,* 15 inches tall, bronze.
Courtesy: Gene Autry Western Hertitage Museum,
Los Angeles, CA

Madeline Bohanon, *Sky Dancer,* 43 x 63 (triptych), watercolor. Courtesy: Sierra Galleries, Tahoe City, CA

Vonnie Brenno, *Man in Blue Striped Hat,* 38 x 48, oil on canvas

Frankenthaler's: a combination of acrylic paint applied to raw canvas. Influenced by the works of O'Keeffe, Stella, Rothko and Morris Louis, she uses bright colors and organic, overlapping forms. She strives to create unity from the unusual surface shape, the use of color and the painting's composition.

BURCH, CLAIRE (Painter, Filmmaker)
2747 Regent St., Berkeley, CA 94705

Born: 1925 *Awards:* Grant, City of Berkeley; 1st Prize, North Shore Art Center, Guild Hall, Easthampton, NY *Collections:* Brooklyn Museum; Berkeley Art Center *Exhibitions:* Regent Press Gallery, Oakland; Galerie L'Antipoete, Paris *Education:* Washington Square College, NYC *Dealer:* Ivan Karp, O.K. Harris Gallery, NYC; Regent Press Gallery, Oakland

Watercolor and pencil drawings of figures and ghostly landscapes mix surreal elements with painterly concerns in subtly hued and gracefully drafted fashion. Sometimes working with assemblage, she creates portraits by a funky layering of discordantly surprising paintings, drawings and writing. A novelist, poet and independent filmmaker, her works may be matched to pages of a manuscript of poems or she may alter the images by animating the paintings. A recent series, "Postscript to the Livermore Thousand," depicts pieces of the human body floating on serene landscapes of the mind, a tribute to the protesters who blocked the gates of the Livermore Laboratory in 1983. Peter Schiedahe of the *New York Times* said of her work, "The graceful, economic drawings depict men and women sitting or lying in a state of sensuous alertness. The intimacy is unforced and infectious . . . a totally original style." Her book of images, *Solid Gold Illusion* is available from Regent Press Gallery in Oakland.

BURCHARD, JERRY (Photographer)
1014 Greenwich, San Francisco, CA 94133

Born: 1931 *Awards:* NEA Fellowship; NEA Photo Survey Grant *Education:* California School of Fine Arts

He has long been experimenting with extended night exposures, which have only reached popularity in the last five years. His dreamy compositions seem deliberate, yet intuitive in approach. There is a symbolic and mystical essence, as in the pictorialist genre, where light and form are more symbolically prominent then the objects themselves. "Some things get so overexposed that they turn into new objects," he notes. The photographs exude personal emotion. The settings are often dramatic; Casablanca, Thailand, Shanghai. *Monsoon Thailand*, a piece shot in a luxuriant rain forest, becomes a romantic metaphor, yet the precise meaning is left open-ended. Having worked mostly in black and white, he now experiments with color film, making forays into fragmented views of the human body, often sexual in nature. Although there is less exposure and less distortion, these works remain characteristically mysterious and personal.

BURDEN, CHRIS (Conceptual Artist, Performance Artist)
c/o Ronald Feldman Fine Arts, 33 E. 74th St., New York, NY 10021

Born: 1946 *Collections:* Long Beach Arts Museum; Museum of Modern Art, NYC *Exhibitions:* Riko Mizuno Gallery, Los Angeles; 112 Green St., NYC

Education: Pomona College; UC-Irvine *Dealer:* Ronald Feldman Fine Arts, NYC

In Chicago's Museum of Contemporary Art, he lay under an angled sheet of glass for forty-five hours; he called this conceptual performance piece *Doomed*. Primarily known for putting himself in violent and threatening situations, he once had himself "crucified" to the hood of a Volkswagen. He has been shot in the arm with a rifle during a performance, as well as being arrested by the Los Angeles Police for yet another sensational piece. Often recording these performances on film, he has been featured live on American public television and European television stations. He uses experiences like this, from elements found in American culture, to test his own "illusions or fantasies about what happens." He insists that the performances are art, not theater, both because he creates a visual image, and because he actually experiences what is performed.

BURDEN, SHIRLEY (Photographer)
8826 Burton Way, Beverly Hills, CA 90211

Born: 1908 *Exhibitions:* Museum of Modern Art, NYC; G. Ray Hawkins Gallery, Los Angeles

He started his career in working for R.K.O. Pictures, directing a picture on whaling and producing "She," which starred Helen Gahagan Douglas and was nominated for an Academy Award. After the Second World War, he opened up a studio for still photography in Beverly Hills. His work has been exhibited all over the United States, including the Museum of Modern Art and the Eastman House. His photographs have also been collected into several books including *God Is My Life*, *The Vanderbilts In My Life* and *Chairs*. Magazines that have published his work include *House and Garden*, *The Architectural Forum*, *Art and Architecture* and *McCalls* as well as such trade journals as *Modern Photography* and *Infinity*.

BURG, JEAN (Painter, Printmaker)
3666 Longridge Ave., Sherman Oaks CA 91423

Born: 1934 *Awards:* Boston Printmakers; White House Collection *Collections:* Standard Oil; IBM *Exhibitions:* La Jolla Museum; Barbican, London *Education:* Otis Art Institute *Dealer:* Orlando Gallery, Sherman Oaks

Her first professional works were influenced by Moholy-Nagy and other Bauhaus artists. Geometric abstraction became prevalent in her work throughout the 70s. Recent work has become looser and more expressionistic. Three-dimensional aspects are present in both painting and printmaking. She constructs her paintings out of kydex, a flexible plastic. She cuts the plastic into forms, paints them, drills holes in them, and then boards the pieces together. Large and colorful, they are similar in shape to Frank Stella's wall pieces. Her three-dimensional prints are etchings which she has cut, folded, and curled into abstract forms.

BURGER, LORE (Paper Artist)
26581 Basswood Ave., Palos Verdes, CA 90274

Born: 1933 *Collections:* Imperial College, London; U. of Colorado, Boulder *Exhibitions:* Palos Verdes Art Center Collector's Gallery *Education:* U. of Colorado

It was in 1971, at a lecture in Los Angeles, that the artist first came into contact with papermaking as an art form. Since that time, she has developed assemblage and sculptural applications that have earned admiration from critics in America and Europe. Some

Benbow Bullock, *They Laughed at Columbus '89,* 96 x 180 x 24, Painted Steel.
Courtesy: Hakone Open-Air Museum, Japan

Monica Bryant, *Dance With Me,* 36 x 84, oil on mahogany

of her earliest pieces combined cotton linters and found objects in texturally intriguing collages. Later, when deckled edges on paper strips distinguished her style, she moved to three-dimensional work. A 300 lb. weight cotton rag backing has replaced more delicate formats. Tree bark and twigs, pieces of twine, found objects, fabric or metal are sewn and tied to the structure. Building of layers and fixing paper to stand on its edges lend dynamic tension to each art work.

BURKHARDT, HANS (Painter)
1914 Jewett Dr., Los Angeles, CA 90046

Born: 1904 *Collections:* Hirshhorn Gallery, Washington, DC; Guggenheim Museum, NYC *Exhibitions:* Oakland Museum; Jack Rutberg Fine Arts, Los Angeles *Education:* Cooper Union, NY *Dealer:* Jack Rutberg Fine Arts, Los Angeles

This abstract expressionist painter was born in Basel, Switzerland. In 1924, he came to New York, where he studied at the Cooper Union and with Arshile Gorky. In the 1920s and 1930s he developed a fundamental interest in the figure, which has since been the hallmark of his work. In 1937, he moved to Los Angeles, and although he left New York too early to be considered a member of the New York School, his drawings and paintings of the last five decades show the strong kinship he developed with the artists of that group. His figurative drawings are not studies for paintings but rather fully resolved works in their own right. He is a professor emeritus at California State University at Northridge.

BURNETT, JOHN (Painter)
200 Avery Lane, #5, Los Gatos, CA 95030

Born: 1956 *Exhibitions:* Festival of Art in the Redwoods, Gualala *Education:* Cal. State-Hayward

An early exposure to the paintings of Salvador Dali and Yves Tanguy encouraged him to follow his own surrealistic impulses. The carefully mixed colors and modeling gave his early surreal oil landscapes a photographic smoothness. His portraits and figures were inspired primarily by Basque painter Joaquin Mir and are more impressionistic. He paints his moody landscapes in segments, starting with sky, then clouds, proceeding through the farthest mountains or water; he then works toward the foreground, painting shadows first and finishing with the highlights. Some of the more recent landscapes show the impressionistic qualities of his portraits. Portraits consist of brushstrokes which, though broad and loose at first, become gradually tighter and more specific as the image is brought into focus. They thus have an abstract quality when viewed closely.

BURNHAM, MARDI (Painter)
1835 McAllister St., San Francisco, CA 94115

Born: 1953 *Collections:* Westcap Financial; Spott & Kunse *Exhibitions:* Auburn Art 37; Avenue of the Arts, Belmont *Dealer:* Allrich Gallery, San Francisco

Trained initially as a printmaker, then as a painter, she began to combine the two processes. These first works consisted of a print that had been painted, then scratched, rubbed and sanded to reveal the original images. After working five years in a museum setting, in which she was surrounded mostly by classical artifacts, her work evolved to its current level. Using layers of papier maché and found objects, she excavates back through the layers to "find" the objects within.

BURNHAM, PHEBE (Painter)
1120 Pepper Dr., #152, El Cajon, CA 92021

Born: 1920 *Exhibitions:* Foothills Gallery, La Mesa; Cottage Gallery, San Diego *Education:* Swain School of Design, MA; New York Art Students League; Columbia U. *Dealer:* Decorative Arts, Inc., Oklahoma City, OK

She received formal training in the fine arts, which led to work as a portraitist and art teacher. She then opened the Eyeglass Arte jewelry business, which crafted and distributed art jewelry to museum shops across the country. Returning to the fine arts, she experimented with a variety of techniques, before settling on a complex mixed-media method. She has recently been using an ink resist, combining gouache, ink and pastel. The primary composition is created in gouache on a bright pastel paper. She then applies a layer of ink, which is subsequently washed off, resulting in a woodcut-like appearance. Occasionally, pastel is added to enhance detail or lend special interest. Her works are figurative and naturalistic, often with a historical subject and theme.

BURNS, JOSIE (Painter)
8745 Indiana Ave., #C, Riverside, CA 92503

Born: 1946 *Exhibitions:* Gilbert Gallery, Riverside; Arlington Art Center, Riverside *Education:* College of the Dayton Art Institute; U. of Dayton

She has been most interested in spatial theory work, and though her orientation has been surrealistic, some abstract or representational elements do appear. Her paintings are puzzles of design and spatial problem-solving, with gray fields and non- subjective rock-like imagery; her palette tends toward the cooler colors. Now exclusively a fine artist, she has also worked in advertising and commercial art and design. She is dyslexic and believes that the same perceptual defect that caused her dyslexia also influences her artistic vision.

BURRITT, BARBARA (Painter)
4554 Cedar Lake Rd. #4, St. Louis Park, MN 55426

Born: 1947 *Awards:* First Bank Award, Tri-State Competition, Minneapolis *Exhibitions:* Bloomington Art Center, Minneapolis; Worth-Ryder Gallery, Berkeley *Education:* Minneapolis College of Art and Design

Her early technique, heavily influenced by Degas, Monet and Manet, was dreamy and concerned with the rendition of light and color. She was strongly affected by a major studio fire in 1983, and since then, her style and approach have undergone a dramatic transformation. No longer satisfied with painterly depictions of everyday life, she has sought to capture the archetypal images and relationships of the subconscious. Viewing herself as a visionary artist, she paints freely, using a full palette to render these powerful images, drawn form the core of human experience. These psychic narratives, influenced by the works of Edvard Munch and William Blake, have lately featured human images, drawn from myths and dreams.

BURTON, SCOTT (Sculptor)
c/o Max Protetch Gallery, 37 W. 57th St., New York, NY 10019

Born: 1939 *Collections:* Saatchi Collection; S. and C. Gilman Jr. Foundation *Exhibitions:* Baltimore Museum of Art, Baltimore, OH

Education: Columbia U.; NYU *Dealer:* Max Protetch Gallery, NYC

Gerald F. Brommer, *Trevi Fountain,* 22 x 30, watercolor. Courtesy: Fireside Gallery, Carmel

Lilliana Braico, *Homage to Matisse Floor Screen,* 60 x 80, acrylic on canvas.
Courtesy: Braico/Lewis Gallery

For the last decade and a half, he has used furniture forms to elucidate and explore pragmatic social concerns. He has stated that his work is a rebuke to the art world, which he believes has neglected its responsibility to be concerned with the aesthetic quality of the visual environment. His 1970s *Bronze Chair* was derived from a Queen Anne chair originally used in a street tableau; other found-object furniture pieces such as Adirondack chairs were recast in formica to explore the relationship between the utilitarian and art. Later, the historical influences of constructivism, de Stijl and the Bauhaus emerged in more serious works. His chairs do not adhere to a single style, rather they explore the function and essential aesthetic qualities of diverse styles. Works of the 1970s share a concern with massive form and heavy material, as is visible in his hot-steel-rolled furniture and rock chairs. Recent works are lighter, more linear and dynamic.

BUSHNELL, BRENT (Painter, Sculptor)
1170 S. Van Ness #1, San Francisco, CA 94110

Born: 1940 *Exhibitions:* Oakland Museum; San Francisco Arts Council *Education:* San Francisco State U.

His most recent works are three-dimensional "superstructures" that stand alone. Canvas is stretched over shaped, constructed frames and painted abstractly in oils. His abstractions are drawn from impressions of spiritual states of mind; however, he does occasionally work representationally and figuratively. His sculpture is done plaster and incorporates wood and mirrors. In both painting and sculpture, his handling of the medium is discernibly energetic, tactile and passionately expressive through his use of texture and surface.

BUSHNELL, KENNETH W. (Painter)
2081 Keeaumoku Pl., Honolulu, HI

Born: 1933 *Collections:* Honolulu Academy of Art; Contemporary Arts Center, Honolulu *Exhibitions:* San Francisco Museum of Modern Art; San Diego Museum *Education:* UCLA; U. of Hawaii *Dealer:* April Riddle, Los Angeles

His work, with its roots in the constructivist and neoplastic tradition, is often responsive to specific site requirements. These pieces present studies in the balance of physical forces, tension/compression and gravity/buoyancy. Materials often include stretched canvas painted with oil or acrylic, then physically connected by wooden, fiberglass or plexiglas linear members. Recent work, which continues his concern with architectonics, consists of a triangular grid, in which triangular canvases are held in tension by calculated geometry and intuitive color relationships. Studies for larger works are often postulated by paper relief sketches, lithographs or etchings.

BUSKIRK, MARY BALZER (Weaver)
53 Via Ventura, Monterey, CA 93940

Born: 1931 *Collections:* Victoria and Albert Museum; Museum of Contemporary Crafts, NY *Exhibitions:* American Crafts Invitational, Seattle; Elements Gallery, Greenwich, CT *Education:* Cranbrook Academy of Art, Bloomfield Hills, MI; U. of Minnesota, Minneapolis

A painter early in her career, she seeks in her weaving the expressive and abstract qualities available in painting. Among her first influences were the Scandinavian Rya rugs for their color and texture; the traditional pattern weavers in America, for the loom-woven structure of their work; the textiles of pre- Columbian Peru,

for the infinite variations of technique, to which she was introduced by the writing of Anni Albers; and the color and composition studies of Paul Klee. She has recently been working primarily in wool and silk and taking her subject matter from sketches of the mountains and the desert. She uses the traditional techniques from tapestry to weave a discontinuous weft, but departs from those techniques in her use of a balanced warp and weft structure for complex designs. She also employs techniques uncommon to tapestry weaving and uses an extremely wide variety of weights and textures of yarn.

BUTLER, JACK (Photographer)
113 E. Union St., Pasadena, CA 91103

Born: 1947 *Awards:* NEA Fellowship *Collections:* San Francisco Museum of Modern Art; Los Angeles County Museum of Art *Exhibitions:* Los Angeles County Museum of Art; San Francisco Museum of Modern Art *Dealer:* Min Gallery, Tokyo

He collages, paints and re-photographs pictures taken from print media, in order to construct photographic images that mirror questions about society, specifically the representation of relationships between men and women. His three series "Excitable Pages 1978-1983," "Together Series/The Look (1984)" and "Western Wear" address the exploitation of women in advertising. In his recent series, "The Trial," he uses found black-and-white glossy photographs of an actual trial. He was formally trained in photography, design and advertising but developed his individual post-expressionist photographic style through and interest in the multimedia works of the 1960s and 1970s. He is Assistant Professor of Art at California State University at Los Angeles.

BUTTER, TOM (Sculptor)
c/o Curt Marcus Gallery, 578 Broadway, 10th Fl., New York, NY 10012

Born: 1952 *Awards:* NEA Grant; New York Foundation Grant *Collections:* Indianapolis Art Museum; Albright-Knox Art Gallery, Buffalo *Exhibitions:* John Berggruen Gallery, San Francisco; Pence Gallery, Los Angeles *Education:* Philadelphia College of Art; Washington U., St. Louis

His works display an interest in duality. Early pieces combine organic form and geometric shape, while later works combine the opacity of wood with the translucent qualities of fiberglas; floor and wall sculptures from 1986 incorporate skeletal and surface concerns. The floor pieces speak of an autonomous vertical presence, existing in and yet not aggressively occupying space. The wall sculptures are more dynamic with surface undulations and rough edges.

BUTTITTA, PATTI (Painter, Mixed Media Artist)
818 College Ave., Ste. C, Santa Rosa, CA 95404

Born: 1950 *Exhibitions:* Santa Rosa Junior College, Santa Rosa, CA Cultural Arts Council of Sonoma County, Sonoma, CA *Education:* Sonoma State U., Sonoma

Three-dimensional design, drawing and zen have been major influences on her work. Her serigraphy incorporates various photographic techniques such as the "cropping" eye of the photographic lens and the quality of selection and abstraction found in photography. Her work also explores the print edition as a means of developing variations on a theme, with in-

Phebe Burnham, *Port of Ensenada,* 22 x 28, oil

Roy Buchman, *The Balance of the Initiate,* 16 x 32, oil on canvas

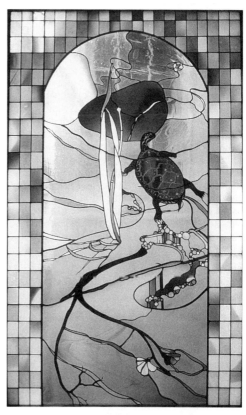

Kathie Stackpole Bunnell, *Turtle Listening,* 84 x 48, stained glass. Courtesy: San Francisco Zen Center

fluences from Japanese printmaker Hamaguchi and painters David Hockney and Wayne Thiebaud. She concentrates on composition, form and color, and emphasizes a work's design aspects. Her graphic design art is found on wine labels, brochures, and posters.

BYINGTON, MARY (Collage Artist)
P.O. Box 1558, Santa Barbara, CA 93102

Born: 1948 *Awards:* Fulbright Scholarship *Collections:* Maniktala Associates; I. Magnin *Exhibitions:* Los Llanos, Santa Fe; Stewart Gallery, Sydney, Australia *Education:* U. of Nebraska, Lincoln; Nanzan, Japan *Dealer:* Franz-Pagel, Lincoln, NE

Her interest in fiber and color led her into paper-making and three-dimensional forms of fiber. The process itself, which she discovered working with fiber-reactive dyes on silk, became a focus in her work. The intellectual was completely denied, but for an interest in the symbolism of visual rhythms, such as those in zig-zags. This interest, in part, came about as a result of her studies of primitive societies and of the work of Picasso and O'Keeffe. Zen philosophy, too, was incorporated in her work. Today, Roland Barthes' ideas of language as sign or symbol occupy her time and serve as a source of her artistic investigations. Her medium remains painted silk collage, though she has introduced the use of black and white photos, turned into transparencies. Her line drawings are used over and over to generate a sense of transparency, of seeing though, seeing under.

CADDEN, WENDY (Painter)
P.O. Box 1274, Oakland, CA 94604

Born: 1945 *Awards:* Lehman Printmaking Award *Collections:* Cabo Frio, Brazil *Exhibitions:* Forum Gallery, NYC; Elaine Benson Gallery, Bridge Hampton, NY *Education:* Antioch College *Dealer:* Kate Dole, Los Angeles

Her early work drew from a range of multi-cultural figurative traditions. In these boldly colored paintings and drawings, she emphasizes the power and complexity of women, a concern that continues in her recent work. During the same period, she illustrated Indian artifacts found in the Southwest, responding passionately to Indian political realities and giving these pieces forcefulness and solidity. Her current work is founded on her deep familiarity with Mexican culture. Her prints, large monotypes, vibrant oil pastel drawings and six-foot-high woodcuts are dominated by musicians in action and by morbid yet cheerful collages. Through these images she addresses a multitude of problems: loss, bigotry, self-hatred, violence.

CAHILL, MUGS (Painter, Sculptor)
1028 N. Kenmore Ave., Los Angeles, CA 90029

Born: 1961 *Exhibitions:* Barnsdall Art Gallery, Los Angeles

Prior to a study of commercial forms as an artistic medium, the artist experimented with the absence of color, as a means to generate feeling. A study of the great philosophers led the artist to regard humor as a common thread linking all human existence. In the artist's work, humor serves as a raison d'etre. Wall and floor pieces are made of wood, metal, window shade plastic and other mundane materials. The small pieces often feature some play on words, with the larger pieces playing off the smaller ones.

CAJERO, MEG HUNTINGTON (Painter)
11850 Hartsook St., N. Hollywood, CA 91607

Awards: Cash Award, Lewis Newman Gallery; Cash Award, National Watercolor Society *Collections:* Robinson's Corp.; Hyatt Regency *Exhibitions:* National Watercolor Society; Village Gallery, Orinda *Education:* U of Arizona; Otis Art Institute *Dealer:* Hunsaker/Schlesinger, Los Angeles

Influenced by Vermeer, Eakins and Carolyn Brady she has worked in transparent watercolors since 1980. Her still life paintings of light and glass in abstracted visual spaces are made with attention to mood and atmosphere. Some pieces depict texture and pattern as seen through transparencies or light. Each work is on d'-Arches watercolor paper and is created using traditional watercolor techniques, taking between sixty and two hundred hours. Her recent paintings have been larger and now include diptyches and triptyches with forty-by-sixty-inch panels. Her early work was in theatrical lighting design and direction, clay and fabric.

CALAMAR, GLORIA (Painter)
P.O. Box 844, Summerland, CA 93067

Born: 1921 *Awards:* NEA Grant *Collections:* Santa Barbara Museum of Art; Mt. St. Mary College, Newburgh NY *Exhibitions:* Los Angeles County Museum of Art; San Francisco Museum of Modern Art *Education:* Otis Art Institute; Art Students League

Growing up in the art colony of Woodstock, New York, she modeled for many famous artists and learned much about art even before attending art school. She learned the method of the modern academy—practice and theory, drawing and painting—at the Otis Art Institute, and at the Art Student's League of New York, the *atelier* atmosphere encouraged individuality. Upon completing her work there she traveled through Europe on a four-month painting trip that began in Naples and ended in Trondheim. When she returned, she began exhibiting her paintings and started teaching at various colleges and universities. She developed an audio- visual presentation that demonstrates her individual approach to painting. Included are works in watercolor—one on painting trees and another on painting in Portugal, Spain and France; and works in oil depicting Santa Barbara Harbor and the medieval city of Chinon, France. The audio-visual work inspired her to write three books on painting.

CALDERA, LESLIE (Assemblage Artist)
12331 Muir Court, Whittier, CA 90601

Born: 1951 *Exhibitions:* Los Angeles County Museum of Art; Santa Barbara Contemporary Arts Forum *Education:* Cal. State-Fullerton *Dealer:* Palm Press, Whittier

After college, he settled on assemblage/collage as the primary medium for his expressions. Throughout the 1980s, the works have become more and more subtle. The emotional content has been of paramount importance, with formal concerns being of little significance; the focus is on the objects themselves, how they're juxtaposed, the picture they make. He has since branched out into other media. A book of collages, *Visions of Paradise*, created for graphic reproduction, was produced in the fall of 1987. He also became part of an international network of artists that used the mail system as the forum for their art, the "postal art net-

Lore Burger, *Monument Valley,* 30 x 60 x 4, handmade paper, mixed media

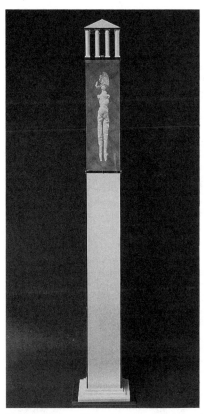

Francis Berry, *Hero 36,* 72 x 12 x 12, mixed media, sculpture. Assisted by: Gregory Costopoulos

Douglas Bremner, *Bronze,* 60 x 72, welded bronze

work." He has experimented with performance art in his typically freewheeling style.

CALLIS, JO ANN (Photographer)
5129 Westwood Blvd., Culver City, CA 90230

Born: 1940 *Awards:* AVA Award; NEA Grant *Collections:* Museum of Modern Art, NYC; Los Angeles Museum of Contemporary Art *Exhibitions:* 1981 Whitney Biennial; Des Moines Art Center *Education:* UCLA *Dealer:* Glenn-Dash Gallery, Los Angeles

Her early work, influenced by her interest in surrealism, had strong psychological overtones, both theatrical and anxiety-provoking. By means of light and texture, objects and people were photographed in both color and black and white, with an emphasis on sensuality and formalism. She recently has been working on photo-linen to produce one-of-a-kind photographs in which the image and the frame work together to form the piece. Expressive clay sculptures of objects traditional to Western painting are made, then placed in simple environments designed to parody their formal roots. Often humorous and ominous simultaneously, these photographs explore ideas of sexuality, objectivity and representation.

CALVERT, SHIRLEY (Painter)
1957 Bluebell Lane, Fallbrook, CA 92028

Born: 1934 *Awards:* Best of Show, Southern California Expo; 1st Prize, Fallbrook Art Association

She enjoys working in both watercolor and oil. When painting in oil, she concentrates on a controlled, expressionistic, representational style and the use of bright, vivid colors. Her watercolor painting is more abstract and experimental, with a looser, free-flowing application of color. Her subject matter includes scenes of every day life, especially human figures in familiar settings.

CAMARATA, MARTIN (Painter)
531 Meadowlark Dr., Turlock, CA 95380

Born: 1934 *Awards:* Fulbright Fellowship, Rome *Collections:* Oakland Museum; Palace of the Legion of Honor Museum of Fine Art *Exhibitions:* McKissick Museum, SC; Oregon Museum of Fine Art, Eugene *Education:* New York U.; Academie Belli Arte, Rome

Influenced by Hogarth and Goya, his figures interact in a heightened modern reality, exposing the darker side of human desires and motivations with wry humor. The humor is expressed through extreme situations that only imply the hidden emotions to the viewer. His style is expressionistic, and Sandra Langer has called his technique "faultless drawing, immaculate application of color, refined spatial compositions and irreproachable artistic technique . . . Camarata's art is not for the squeamish." His most recent series comprises fragmented, Guston- like landscapes that present a sardonic view of life in the wasteland, probing for reality through pieces that depict its veneer.

CAMHI, MORRIE (Photographer)
95 Marshall Ave., Petaluma, CA 94952

Born: 1928 *Awards:* NEA Grant; Calif. Council for the Humanities Grant *Collections:* San Francisco Museum of Modern Art; Tucson Center for Creative Photography *Exhibitions:* San Francisco Museum of Modern Art; Oakland Museum *Education:* UCLA *Dealer:* Min Gallery, Tokyo, Japan

He almost invariably works with large themes, using body language and environment as portrait adjectives.

He prefers black-and-white photography and favors a use of light that suggests drama and form; often he includes the actual light source in the photograph. He invites viewers to search for detail in photographs of dimly-lit areas. "Espejo" ("Mirror") was a broad visual inquiry into Mexican-American life, especially in small towns in California and New Mexico; "Petaluma" also explored small-town life. "Jews of Greece" portrayed an all-but-forgotten remnant of the Holocaust. "AD:vantage" relates to people who compose and place personal classified ads. He is currently working on "Prison Experience," a three-sided exploration of the prisoners, staff and family at a typical American prison. He has also written extensively, primarily as a critic.

CAMINCHA (Collage Artist, Painter)
723 Moana Way, Pacifica, CA 94044

Awards: Merit Award, Art Guild of Pacifica; Best of Show, Presidio of San Francisco *Education:* San Francisco State U.

She paints primarily in brightly colored acrylics, draws with pen and ink, and makes collages. Her sophisticated, simple figures are rendered in the explosive colors that exhibit the artistic inspiration of her native Peru. The works of Goya and Renoir have also influenced her realistic style. She has recently completed a series of 11-by-8-inch paintings and has been busy with a new series of 30-by-40-inch acrylics on canvas that reflect her travels around the world.

CAMIRE, RICHARD (Painter)
1342 Green St., #1, San Francisco, CA 94109

Born: 1948 *Exhibitions:* Clara Hatton Gallery, Fort Collins, CO; Rancho Santiago College, Santa Ana *Education:* San Francisco Art Institute; Art Institute of Boston

During the 1960s, he studied the classical approach to oil painting. During the mid-1970s, influenced by Clyfford Still and Mark Rothko, he discarded the brushes and small-format easel painting of that style. Using trowels, he applied oil paints to large canvases, spreading the paint with squeegees. He began employing geometric shapes and integrating them with color-field backgrounds. Currently he has replaced the color fields with gesture. He builds up layers of paint to reveal glimpses of his wet-into-wet and wet-into-dry processes. His colors tend to range from somber grays and earth tones with slashes and accents of vibrant color to high-chroma contrasts that he seeks to orchestrate into a readable unity.

CAMPANARO, JUDI (Painter)
3320 E. University, #1068, Mesa, AZ 85213

Born: 1946 *Collections:* Professional Software Corporation; Wendy's Corporate Office, Bakersfield *Exhibitions:* Ventura Arts Council; Blanchard Gallery, Santa Paula *Dealer:* Crooked Arrow, Phoenix; Naked Horse, Scottsdale, AZ

A native Californian, she studied privately with Marguerite Hardeman, Mary St. Clair Baxter and Joseph Cota. Her early landscapes were executed in a realist manner and were influenced by the Impressionists' treatment of light and color, as well as the softness of their approach. She also owned and taught at the Hobbit School of Art in Ventura. A recent move to Arizona has marked a shift to paintings with Southwestern and Native American themes. The style too has become more abstract and more surreal, inspired

Dalmar Campbell, *Prototype (Story Hill Project),* 40 x 108, ferrous metals

Victoria Creech P.S.W.C., *Grandmother's Pride,* 24 x 36, oil monoprint and pastel

by Native American culture, the region's natural beauty, and the more gentle pace of life in the Southwest. In addition to the Impressionists, she has admired the work of Georgia O'Keeffe. "I want my work to allow viewers to feel at peace with themselves and one with the universe," she says.

CAMPBELL, DALMAR J. (Sculptor)
4576 Yaqui Gulch Rd., Mariposa, CA 95338

Born: 1939 *Awards:* Honorable Mention, San Joaquin Art Annual; Best of Show, Arbor Art Gallery Invitational, Merced *Exhibitions:* San Joaquin Art Annual *Education:* Cal. State-Fresno

He is an admirer of Alexander Calder and Salvador Dali, whose ferrous sculptures are made from discarded materials. Commissioned to build a sculptural fence for the Story Hill Honeymoon Hotel and Botanical Garden in Mariposa, he welded together parts of broken gears, old axles and rusted skeletons of cars and trucks to create sixteen 9-by-40-inch historical panels. In *Life Line*, he used tail pipes and old pumps to graphically represent the human heart, veins and arteries. Among his animal sculptures are iron butterflies, caterpillars and dogs. He also paints with oils on primed and unprimed canvas.

CAMPBELL, JO (Glassworker)
4 Fawn Court, Gillete, WY 82716

Born: 1950 *Awards:* Art in Public Building Award *Exhibitions:* Nicolaysen Art Museum Invitational Show; State Capitol Show *Education:* South Dakota State U.; Parsons School of Design

She began working in glass after she graduated from college. Borrowing from Narcissus Quagliata and Richard Posner, the two most significant artistic influences on her work, she produced realistic figurative pieces using flat-glass techniques. She experimented with sandblasting and etching to alter glass surfaces while developing a more painterly technique and working with fused glass pieces. In her recent work, she uses open-kiln techniques to create abstract and contemporary designs in full spectrum.

CAMPBELL, RICHARD (Painter, Printmaker)
25640 Huckleberry Dr., Calabasas, CA 91302

Born: 1921 *Awards:* Cleveland May Show; Los Angeles Festival of Arts *Collections:* Theater Guild of America *Exhibitions:* H.M. DeYoung Museum; Butler Institute of American Art *Education:* Cleveland School of Art; UCLA *Dealer:* Gallery West, Los Angeles

His early work was expressionistic and figurative. His largest body of work was done in oil on canvas. During the 1970s he completed a series of etchings. In 1981 he experienced a catastrophic disease. This experience caused him to change his artistic direction. His work now evolves out of dreams and meditation. His present work is done on white using bright colors and is abstract expressionistic.

CAMPION, BARRY (Painter)
1044 Palms Blvd., Venice, CA 90291

Born: 1954 *Collections:* Security Pacific Bank, Los Angeles *Exhibitions:* Los Angeles Institute of Contemporary Art; Citrus Gallery *Education:* Cornish Institute, Seattle

Her early work frequently placed organic abstract forms in a simple field of color. Often the shapes suggest recognizable forms but remain, in the final analysis, ambiguous. In all of her paintings, including the early ones, she uses acrylic paint, built up through glazes and augmented with dry pigments, which are rubbed into the surface. Recently, her forms have become more complex and placed in a setting suggestive of a landscape. She points to Indian Mogul paintings, for their treatment of forms in a landscape, as her primary influence.

CAMPOPIANO, GARY L. (Painter)
5345 8th St., Carpinteria, CA 93013

Born: 1947 *Awards:* 2nd Place, National Orange Festival, San Bernardino *Collections:* Cal. State-Fresno *Exhibitions:* Haddad's Fine Arts, Anaheim; Faulkner Gallery, Santa Barbara Public Library *Education:* Cal. State-Fresno *Dealer:* Mark Christianson Gallery, Los Olivos

He is best known for his landscapes of rural California, which highlight the contrast between the buildings and machinery, and the gently rolling hills. Drawn to the Shandon-Cholame area, east of Paso Robles, he has painted many of his works on location there. His smoothly figurative style has been influenced by American realist painters Hopper, Scheeler and Wood; he paints from a vivid pastel palette. He has recently been painting a series of still life enlargements (four by five feet) of electronic components.

CAMPUS, PETER (Video Artist)
c/o Paula Cooper Gallery, 155 Wooster St., New York, NY 10012

Born: 1937 *Awards:* NEA Grant; Advanced Visual Studies Fellowship, M.I.T. *Exhibitions:* Paula Cooper Gallery, NYC *Education:* Ohio State U.

In the late 1960s, he left a career in commercial film and television to pursue a career as an artist. He is noted for his creation of powerful, emotionally charged visual fields. In the 1970s, he focused on creating videotapes, which feature the artist performing an activity that continually alters the image. The closed circuit video installations, concerned with confrontations of the self, incorporate projections of the viewer's image in an altered state. In the late 1970s, he turned to working with projected slides in order to focus on the image rather than time. A 1987 photo-projection at the Paula Cooper Gallery consisted of images of single rocks enlarged so as to appear as planets.

CANFIELD, NOEL (Sculptor)
1205 Mercedes Ln., Santa Barbara, CA 93101

Born: 1960 *Exhibitions:* Richard/Benett Gallery, Los Angeles; Brattelboro Museum of Art, VT *Dealer:* Richard/Bennet, Los Angeles

Previous to his current figurative sculpture, he worked two- dimensionally, beginning with drawing, then gradually moving to painting. He became acquainted with tools through construction work, and began expressing himself in three-dimensional works. Focusing on the human form, and influenced in material by an artist's poverty, he welded scrap steel into recognizable constructions. He finds a raw energy inherent in scrap, and believes that by constructing recognizable human forms from industrial detritus, he can convey messages about man and the evolution that has brought us into the industrial and space age.

CANTOR, RUSTY (Painter)
2512 9th St., #14, Berkeley, CA 94701

Exhibitions: Brand Galleries, Los Angeles; Institute of American Indian Arts Museum, Santa Fe, NM *Education:* Art Students League

Ande Lau Chen, *Islands and Channel,* 40 x 80, acrylic and paper on canvas

Camincha, *Faces of California,* 30 x 40, collage

She has painted and drawn abstractly since she was a child. Her colors are taken from the beauty of the sunset and from nature's precious stones. She fills her work with the symbols of metamorphosis and femininity that she has gathered from the feminist movement and American Indian culture. Influenced by Kandinsky and Georgia O'Keeffe, she is an expressionist, who must make her views tangible. She paints on raw, stretched canvas, and achieves depth and luminescence in her work by staining her canvas with layers of thin acrylic paint. Her colorful fiber pieces suggest American Indian art, and have an aboriginal quality that is at once mythic, exotic and sexual.

CANTRELL, KITTY (Sculptor)
P.O. Box 890, Escondido, CA 92025

Born: 1955 *Awards:* Juror's Choice Award; 1st Place in Sculpture, San Diego Wildlife Show *Exhibitions:* Merrill Lynch Corp.; World Wilderness Congress *Dealer:* Biota Gallery, Los Angeles

With no formal art training, she was first influenced by the wildlife paintings of Carl Runguis and the sculpture of Frederic Remington. Her early narrative wildlife sculptures were depictions of animals in their natural habitats. In 1985, she started working at a foundry and began bronze shell casting, experimenting with different patinas and the limits of bronze itself. Rather than attempting realism, she tries to capture an animal's personality in her 20- to 24-inch-high pieces. Currently she concentrates on overall form and on the contrast between heavy textures and smooth areas.

CANTWELL, CHARLES A. (Painter)
560 Sierra Ave., Mountain View, CA 94041

Born: 1949 *Awards:* Scholarship, San Francisco Art Institute; Ellen Hart Bransten Memorial Scholarship *Exhibitions:* U. of the Pacific, Stockton; Diego Rivera Gallery, San Francisco *Education:* San Francisco Art Institute

At the time he entered formal training, he was most heavily influenced by the boldness of Francis Bacon and the graphic technique of Ivan Albright. In 1983, he began making random abstract marks, using powdered charcoal with no composition in mind. Relying on subconscious images, he refined the marks into recognizable and semi-recognizable organic forms, the central object being human or human like. He has adapted this technique to oils or dry pigment on large canvas or paper. His major theme is the human condition, his view of which has been influenced by his twelve years as a U.S. Army Green Beret medic. Influenced by Lucian Freud's obsessive use of delineation to create tension, he uses a similar obsessive rendering of forms, as a metaphor for the control man must constantly enforce on his animal tendencies. His images depict the results of uncontrolled human emotion. He has recently been working on a seven-paneled, room size piece that is more figurative and playful than his past work.

CAPONIGRO, PAUL (Photographer)
Rte. 3, Box 960, Santa Fe, NM 87501

Born: 1932 *Awards:* Guggenheim Fellowship; NEA Grant *Exhibitions:* San Francisco Museum of Modern Art; Photography Gallery, La Jolla *Dealer:* Andrew Smith Gallery, Santa Fe

After musical studies early in his career, the influence of photographers Minor White and Benjamin Chin steered his interest toward their medium. Eventually he developed a unique, poetic style depicting movement, typified by large-scale silver prints that capture the magnificence of nature. Close-up, often abstract renderings of the natural environment convey the creative forces behind his work. A founding member of the Association of Boston University Heliographers in New York, he has taught at Yale and other major universities, in addition to publishing numerous books, including a Time-Life series and a critically acclaimed portfolio. "Through the use of the camera, I must try to express and make visible the forces moving in and through nature—the landscape behind the landscape," he says.

CAPRASECCA, LESTER (Painter)
Studio A, 1641 San Pablo Ave., Berkeley, CA 94702

Born: 1950 *Collections:* Lehman Brothers; Plaza Pacific Equities Inc. *Exhibitions:* Centennial Hall, Hayward; Inter Art, San Francisco *Education:* U. of Wyoming; California College of Arts and Crafts *Dealer:* Inter Art, San Francisco

Early influences were Morris Lewis and Frank Stella. He works quickly, painting with thick strokes against a monochromatic surface. His palette is made up of earth tones, blacks, whites, graphite grays, violet oxides and burnt siennas; he paints with acrylic on canvas. His abstract grids reflect his constantly changing moods. Each painting is made up of two or more independent panels and, taken together, they translate into a sort of impressionist/minimalist diary.

CARABAS, LESLIE C. (Textile Artist)
823 Mendocino Ave., Berkeley, CA 94707

Born: 1944 *Exhibitions:* Boston University Art Gallery; Center for Contemporary Art, Kansas City, MO

Influenced by the traditional art of quiltmaking, this self-taught fiber artist works with commercially produced fabrics, cutting and piecing, producing appliqué and weaving fabric. Intense color and color contrasts of black, white and gray fabrics characterize the work. Sewn with a sewing machine, many pieces are reversible, with different images on each side. She is interested in creating a sense of space and depth in her pieces. Various objects, generally abstract, sit on different spatial planes, yet interact with each other. Her black and white pieces feature a varying scale accomplished with a variety of fabrics and surface design sizes. The colorful works occasionally consist of two separate quilt tops, which are cut apart and sewn or woven together to form a grid pattern. She produces small wall hangings through large-scale pieces for corporate settings.

CARAKER, FRANCES (Drawer)
5690 E. Austin Way, Fresno, CA 93727

Born: 1950 *Awards:* Dean's Medalist Nominee, California State U., Fresno *Collections:* Air Force Art Collection, Pentagon *Exhibitions:* Figtree Gallery, Fresno; California State U., Fresno *Education:* California State U., Fresno

She explores the mechanized world as it encroaches on nature. Her larger drawings are images of machines, animals, and bones brought together into broad combinations. The smaller works resemble blueprint drawings of compressing machines that seem to metaphorically squeeze animals out of existence. To make the work, she rubs fields of blue pastel into the surface of watercolor paper (45 by 62) and illustration

Lester Caprasecca, *Lazy L Red,* 55 x 42, acrylic on canvas.
Courtesy: Glen Millward

Kitty Cantrell, *Follow the Leader,* 26 x 19, bronze

board (30 by 40). She then divides the pieces into rectangular areas of drawing. She considers herself a postmodern conceptualist and has been influenced by Larry Rivers, Andy Warhol, the faculty at California State University-Fresno, and the technical drawings of Leonardo da Vinci.

CARDENAS, CAROLYN (Painter)
915 Milwood Ave., Venice, CA 90291

Born: 1953 *Awards:* Chautauqua Institute Award for Painting; Juror's Award, Simard Gallery, Los Angeles *Collections:* Nelson Art Museum, Kansas City, MO *Exhibitions:* Art Institute of Southern California, Laguna Beach; Sierra Nevada Museum of Art, Reno *Education:* Drake U.; U. of Kansas, Lawrence *Dealer:* Koplin Gallery, Los Angeles

Working in egg tempera, she depicts modern life with a conceptual intensity that is matched by her use of color. She paints both extremely detailed figures and interiors, with a view to combining the methods of Renaissance painting with contemporary life. Updating "American Gothic" portraits, she has recently switched her format to a larger scale, and has begun working on alter pieces. Another recent series features soap opera icons. In her work, there is a sense of the spirituality of painting, as was present in both Medieval and Renaissance religious art, which reveals an essence of magic and contemplation where it is not typically sought. Using perspective, she creates distance and awe for her viewers, and an opportunity to examine their own world through her prism.

CAREY, RYAN (Sculptor, Mixed Media Artist)
2430 Ronda Vista Dr., Los Angeles, CA 90027

Born: 1945 *Awards:* Mayor's Certificate of Appreciation, Los Angeles *Collections:* Security Pacific National Bank, Los Angeles and Chicago; Hilton Hawaiian Village, Honolulu *Exhibitions:* Los Angeles City Hall, Main St. and Bridge Galleries; Gump's, San Francisco *Education:* Chouinard Art Institute *Dealer:* Patton/Duval, Los Angeles

As a sculptor/constructivist, he frequently uses found/altered objects in various combinations or in conjunction with his mixed-media material to produce vessel-like forms. From assemblages of objects with manipulated surfaces, his work has progressed to constructions in which vessels and attachments unite with metaphorical potential. He has employed such disparate elements as metal, glass, ceramic, leather, plastic, beads, rope, feathers, bone, tires and fabric in his work. Recent work includes a group of limited edition bronzes, which are lost wax cast.

CARL, JOAN (Sculptor)
4808 Mary Ellen Ave., Sherman Oaks, CA 91423

Born: 1926 *Awards:* Design Award, Ceramic Tile Institute; National Orange Show, San Bernardino *Collections:* Raleigh Museum, NC; North East Ohio Museum, Cleveland *Exhibitions:* Norman Feldheym Gallery, San Bernardino; Fresno Museum *Education:* Cleveland School of Art; School of the Art Institute of Chicago *Dealers:* Thinking Eye, Los Angeles; R.F. Temple, Scottsdale, AZ

Themes of her Jewish heritage are prevalent in public and private works. Many sculptures present explicitly religious subjects. In others, such as the 7-foot-tall *From Generation to Generation*, or the 3-by-2 1/2-foot cedar piece entitled *My Brother's Keeper*, she depicts Jewish family themes by weaving figures together. Her public works are site specific, made of such materials as welded steel, brazed bronze, cast bronze, clay and a variety of hard woods and marbles. She has completed commissions for temples and churches throughout America as well as Israel, including a sculpture for Mount Sinai Memorial Park in Hollywood. She also draws and paints.

CARLANDER, JOHN (Painter)
743 Palermo Dr., Santa Barbara, CA 93105

Born: 1943 *Exhibitions:* Westmont College, Santa Barbara *Education:* Concordia College, MN; Bowling Green State U. *Dealer:* L. Rossbach, Santa Barbara

His early works were representational. With formal study in college and graduate school, he went through periods of abstraction and non-objective painting, before returning to representational painting in the form of photo-realism. He has a painterly approach. His subjects are normally a combination of natural subjects and architectural references, though he occasionally incorporates the human figure. For a time, his canvases were dominated by the European scenes he found while traveling on the Continent. Recently, a brightly lit urban Californian subject matter has been predominant. His medium is acrylic on canvas.

CARLETON, CAROLYN AND VINCENT
(Fiber Artists)
1015 A Greenwood Rd., Elk, CA 95432

Awards: Award of Excellence, California State Fair; "Best Contemporary Rug Design," Roscoe Product Design Award *Collections:* Kohler Co., WI; Brunswick Building, Chicago *Exhibitions:* Design '87, Galleria Design Center, San Francisco; American Craft Museum *Education:* California College of Arts and Crafts, Pacific Basin Textile School *Dealer:* Kneedler Faucher, CA & CO; Hendon, Inc., NYC

They have recently been working in a combination of Navajo and colonial multi-shaft weaving techniques to create limited-edition rugs and tapestries, and have also designed a 22-harness loom with a draw system to expand their use of picture designs. The recent works emphasize borders combined with smaller-scale, non-repetitive motifs. These designs are accented by the use of Persian hues of blue, pine and ochre highlighted with jewel reds and mauves. Dyes are hand-mixed, and all materials are hand-dyed. Their continued exploration of damask pattern techniques has resulted in reversible works whose complex combinations of hue and shade, balanced with elegant design and color, create a shimmering, reflective effect when viewed.

CARLSON, LANCE (Photographer, Printmaker)
P.O. Box 25144, Los Angeles, CA 90025

Born: 1950 *Awards:* NEA Visual Artist Fellowships; Polaroid Corporation Materials Grant *Collections:* San Francisco Museum of Modern Art; Polaroid Corporation, Offenbach, Germany *Exhibitions:* National Museum of American Art, Washington, DC; Cal. State-Fullerton *Education:* Cal. State U. *Dealer:* Fahey-Klein Gallery, Los Angeles

Graduate work in sociology and studies in phenomenology influence his choice of subjects. He is interested in how a viewer's perception of a work connotes economic and political biases, trends, and constraints. Since 1983, when he began making mural-sized prints, he has attempted to break away from traditional photographic practice and presentation. He

Ryan Carey, *Soloist,* 6 x 24 x 14, limited edition (350 pieces) bronze cast. Photograph: Don Miller

Gene Collins, *Queens,* 50 x 90 x 2, oil on canvas with ceramic insert

has continued to make large-scale prints, working now on photo-linen. He hand colors the image after it has been transferred to the fabric. In late 1987, he used a 20 x 24 Polaroid camera to make large photographs of commodities such as example, Cuisinarts, coffee-makers, and jewelry. His most recent work is in lithography, drawing prints based on the commodity photographs.

CARLSON, PAUL (Painter)
1150 N.W. Alder Creek Dr., Corvallis, OR 97330

Born: 1947 *Collections:* United States Air Force Academy, Colorado Springs *Exhibitions:* Seal Rock Art Gallery, Seal Rock, OR; The Mole Hole, Carmel *Education:* United States Air Force Academy *Dealer:* Pegasus Gallery, Corvallis

His art career began at Carswell Air Force Base, where he worked in the maintenance crew painting impressionistic landscapes with great rapidity on U.S. Air Force property with an airbrush. During this period, his work came under the influence of Maxfield Parrish. After receiving his discharge, he began teaching high school art and raising chickens. With this latter occupation, he took to painting realistic, finely detailed pictures of both the day and night sky on the chickens' eggs. He also creates miniature realistic landscapes ranging in size from 1 by 1/2 to 4 by 6 inches. He uses acrylic glazes to insure an extremely smooth surface with no visible brushmarks.

CAROOMPAS, CAROLE (Painter, Performance Artist)
758 E. 14th St., Los Angeles, CA 90021

Born: 1946 *Awards:* NEA Grant *Collections:* Security Pacific Bank *Exhibitions:* Whitney Museum of Art; Cal. State-Northridge *Education:* USC; Cal. State-Fullerton

Since 1972 she has used a conceptual approach to painting through the use of non-traditional materials and forms. This has included an interest in impermanent installations, uncommon art materials and processes, and an interest in the structure of "sets." In her sets, several pieces exist, each complete in itself. At the same time, each refers to the set's collective elements. She has often combined this formal structure with informal materials and in this way she has expanded her narrative concerns and introduced personal and cultural references as oppositional elements. She has combined structure, image and text as cross-references to fragmented narratives. Recent paintings on canvas and drawings are psychological landscapes that examine the relationships between women and men. These works reflect on the past and propose contemporary questions about women and men and their social/sexual roles and relations.

CARPENTER, EARL L. (Painter)
P.O. Box C, Pinewood Art Studio, Munds Park, AZ 86017

Born: 1931 *Awards:* John F. and Anna Lee Stacey Scholarship Fund, Pasadena; Bank Purchase Award, Valley National Bank, Phoenix *Collections:* Valley Bank, Phoenix; Museum of Northern Ariz. *Exhibitions:* Wadle Gallery, Santa Fe, NM; Gallery of the West, Jackson, WY *Education:* Art Center College of Design; Chouinard Art Institute

In his landscapes, he is not concerned with topographical renditions but rather with their ethereal qualities. His paintings emphasize the effect of light and atmos-phere on the shapes found in nature. The Grand Canyon, only two hours from his studio, serves as a constant source of inspiration. To prepare for a large work in oil, he first executes a small study in watercolor at the actual site. He also photographs the scene in 35mm to use as a reference back in his studio. In the oil work, broad strokes come first, with masses of color kept free of detail for as long as possible. He then paints in contrasts and smears areas of the painting to explore the shape of the images. *Canyon Thunder*, in oil on canvas, portrays a dramatic storm over the canyon, painted in vivid hues of orange, blue, green, and gold.

CARPOU, PETER C. (Painter)
639 Lincoln Way, #1, San Francisco, CA 94122

Born: 1950 *Awards:* Individual Residency Grant, California Arts Council & Arts-in-Corrections, San Quentin Prison; Grant, William James Associates, Santa Cruz *Collections:* Crown College, Santa Cruz *Education:* UC-Santa Cruz

Influenced by music and poetry, he painted abstractly while at school. Soon after leaving, he began painting still lifes and landscapes, concentrating on structure and color. These fundamentals, in turn, led him back to abstraction and—in combination with two years of sculpture study—implanted the notion that scale and color might be approached in an open-ended way. His recent work is intimately involved with his Prison Arts Residency at San Quentin. In his abstract painting, a dynamic tension gathers solemnly to a watchful presence. Though often dark, his image is one of hope. Aside from these cryptic abstractions, he draws portraits of San Quentin inmates and of the children and adolescents at the two San Francisco treatment centers where he works.

CARRERE, ROBERT (Painter)
1427 E. 4th St., Los Angeles, CA

Born: 1962 *Exhibitions:* Gene Sinser Gallery, Los Angeles; Rembrandts Restaurant, Los Angeles *Education:* Otis Art Institute

His early work was influenced by Van Gogh and Gauguin. It consisted of impressionist paintings of figures in an urban landscape: people in the park, in coffee shops and on the streets. The surface was executed in bright primary and secondary colors and short, thick brushstrokes. After he left school, and began painting the downtown landscape of Los Angeles, his work blossomed into pure urban landscape, in natural colors with accents of bright pigment. His rendition of sky and of light has been influenced by the landscapes of Monet, Cezanne, Turner and Constable. He uses layers of paint (medium glaze), applied wet-on-dry in thick brushstrokes.

CARROLL, CATHERINE S. (Painter)
1641 San Pablo Ave., Berkeley, CA 94702

Born: 1950 *Exhibitions:* Mendocino Arts Center; Fine Arts Museums of San Francisco *Education:* UC-Berkeley; UC- Santa Cruz

Whether a scene of Mount Davidson, a panorama of San Francisco at sunrise or a gestural interpretation of a woman with a fan, her works are informed by her architectural studies. The paintings frequently employ a wash technique with oil on canvas, and surfaces vary from the layered construction of the focal point to areas of raw, exposed canvas. There is an emphasis on the city, from abstractions of buildings under construc-

Phebe Burnham, *Diver's Eye View,* 20 x 24, mixed media. Courtesy: University of California
Marine Biology Laboratory, Catalina, CA

Jennifer Bain, *Autumn Trilogy,* 64 x 165, oil on canvas

Helen L. Bell, *Andalusian Dream* 25 x 75 x 5, handmade paper and metal construction.
Courtesy: Sheraton Raincross Hotel, Riverside, CA

Buskirk, *Gods at Play Series/White Sands II,* 44 x 44, wool, silk, acrylic paint

Raye Bender-Klinefelter, *Genesis in Blue,* 30 x 23, watercolor. Courtesy: Florence Ross

Sarah Biondo, *Pacific Tide,* 21 x 32, oil, enamel, acrylic and silk screen ink on canvas

Nick Boisvert, *Bright Angel Interplay,* 29 x 46, acrylic on canvas

Tom Brooks, *North Wales,* 12 x 24, pastel on paper

Evelyn Bundren, *Ring Neck Pheasant,* full scale, wood and oils

Kathie Stackpole Bunnell, *Childhood Design,* 27 x 40, stained glass

Wilsdon Brenner, *Big Sur Valley,* 31 x 67, acrylic on gatorfoam

Tze Ying Chen, *Woman,* 48 x 60, oil and acrylic

Brian Frank Carter, *Manscapes,*
34 x 48, acrylic

Alice Corning, *Torso,* 31" high, stoneware.
Photograph: Mel Schockner

Lester Caprasecca, *Lazy T Turquoise,*
58 x 21, acrylic on canvas

Steven V. Correia, *Southern Lights,* permanent kinetic
laser sculpture. Photograph: Art Fox

Victoria Creech P.S.W.C., *Wind Beneath Her Wings,*
36 x 28, pastel

Dalmar Campbell, *Lifeline,* 96 x 50 x 65, ferrous metal

Mario Castillo, *Resistance to Cultural Death:*
An Affirmation of My Past, 36 x 24, acrylic

Camincha, *The 13 Coins,* 18 x 24, acrylic on canvas

Mary Czarnecki, *Center Stage,* 72 x 48, oil on canvas

Mary D. Chabiel, *untitled,* 36 x 48, acrylic on canvas

Sue Cazaly, *Tulips,* 4 x 6, photograph.
Courtesy: Bay Gallery, Mendocino, CA

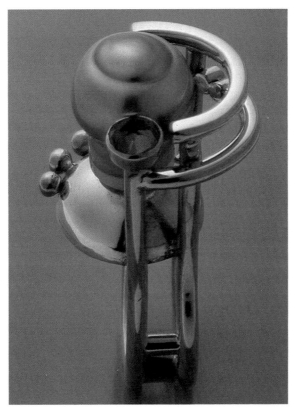

Joyce Clements, *Sun Temple III (ring),* 39 x 18mm, 14 carat
gold, sterling silver, pearl, amethyst, tourquoise, garnet

316

Robin Coventry, *Golden Glory,* 20 x 15, pen and watercolor.
Courtesy: Dr. George Abbott, Carmel, CA. Photograph: Phil Miller

Judi Campanaro, *Medicine Woman,* 16 x 20, oil

Peter Carpou, *A.M. Carson Section, San Quentin,* 48 x 42, oil on canvas

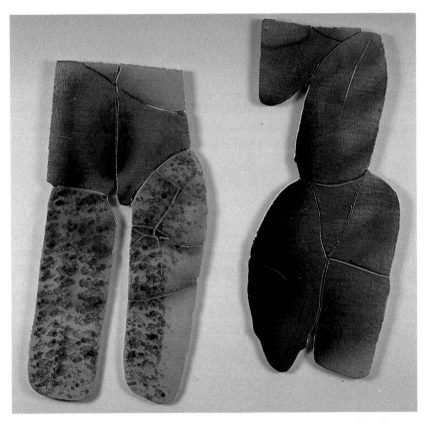

Katy Cauker, *Elemental Dance,* 14 x 32, each section, glazed porcelain tile.
Courtesy: Gerald Senogles. Photograph: Douglas R. Smith

Georgina Clarke, *Gypsy Om,* 75 inches diameter, acrylic on canvas.
Courtesy: Dr. Paul Rubenstein

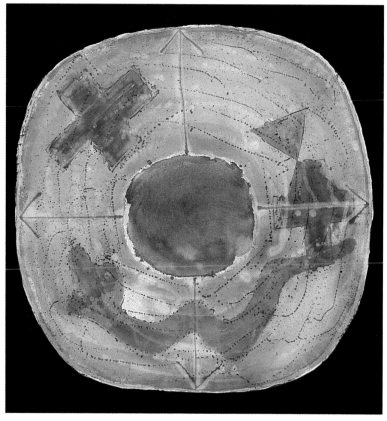

Cantor, *Prayer Shield #1,* 66 x 66, acrylic on canvas

Fay Conn, *Dusk,* 48 x 48, oil

Tom Cummings, *Pink Patio,* 72 x 72, oil on canvas

tion to aerial views incorporating massive amounts of geographical information and rendered in a thick impasto. In all the pieces, composition is the paramount consideration, and the balance, form, harmony and rhythm are achieved through the process of painting.

CARSON, PLEASANT (Painter)
1142 Buchanan St., San Francisco, CA 94115

Born: 1941 *Exhibitions:* Crown Zellerbach Building, San Francisco; Sargent Johnson Gallery, San Francisco *Education:* City College of San Francisco

His initial influences were "comic" book artists of the EC group and pre-*Mad* comics: Jack Severin, Jack Davis, Wallace Wood and Frank Franzetta. Later influences included Picasso's Blue Period; Mexican muralists Rivera, Orozco, Siqueiros and Camarenas; and Dali, Tanguy and Magritte. In the early 1960s, he began to explore color, as well as to develop a finer approach to pen and ink composition. His mixed-media compositions are essentially two-dimensional, employing found objects such as cloth, door latches and barbed wire. The primary media for his paintings are oil and alkyd on canvas or panel, and acrylic, ink and collage on paper. His imagery includes birds, human figures and machine parts, rendered in earth tones and bright yellows, blues and greens.

CARTER, BRIAN F. (Commercial Illustrator, Painter)
649 Edgewood Ave., Mill Valley, CA 94941

Born: 1939 *Awards:* Purchase Award, San Francisco Art Festival; Readership Award, AT&T Advertising Illustration *Collections:* Coyote Point Museum; Oakland Museum *Exhibitions:* California Museum of Art, Santa Rosa; Talmadge Galleries, Placerville *Education:* Academy of Art; Art Center College of Design

After formal training, he worked commercially for ten years. At the same time, he pursued a fascination with the paintings of Turner and Parrish and the draftsmanship and dream rendering of Dali. He found enthusiastic audiences for his work in Europe, and upon his return to the U.S., he continued to paint both fantasy portraits and large murals for museums. Technically realistic, he works with illusionistic themes. His natural world reveals something fantastic. Landscapes and figures merge. He paints with acrylics over a blue and white negative and uses glazes to give his colors a luminosity reminiscent of Maxfield Parrish.

CASSELL, BEVERLY BACH (Painter)
2202 W. 20th St., Los Angeles, CA 90018

Born: 1936 *Awards:* Featured Artist, *Quarry West Collections:* Georgia Museum, Athens; Mitsubishi Corporation *Exhibitions:* The Contemporaries Gallery, NYC; Henderson Museum, Boulder, CO *Education:* U. of Georgia, Athens; New York U. *Dealer:* Bob Venger, Los Angeles

After moving to New York City in 1960 she shifted from her early abstract expressionist training and began a singular pursuit of oil figuration influenced by Giotto's compressed pictorial space. Working with a fresco-like deliberation she aimed toward a contemplative quality of understatement. She moved west in 1967. Through the dark canyons of her current Los Angeles nightscapes are vast expanses of coppery shadows and geometric extravagances of gold and yellow lights. Her night city twinkles and glitters; mountain roads, smeared with car lights, emerge in the foreground with folksy humor. She explores her af-

finity with 17th Century Chinese monumental landscapes in a series of ink paintings on oversized rice papers. Celebrating inclusiveness, she draws her titles from Walt Whitman.

CASTELLANOS, LEONARD (Painter, Sculptor)
P.O. Box 1718, Taos, NM 87571

Born: 1943 *Awards:* NEA Fellowship *Collections:* Congressman Esteban Torres *Exhibitions:* Los Angeles County Museum of Art; Santa Fe Museum of Art *Education:* Chouinard Art Institute

Although traditional themes have always dominated his art, a wide variety of media are utilized. Originally influenced by the Mexican muralists Orozco, Siquieros and Riviera, he now decorates *retablos* and pine furniture that he has built with flower and animal motifs. He also draws spirit figures on paper, representing the historical background of northern New Mexico. Recent works use a palette of earth tones, adobe, rock and wood to create "earth structures." Other projects include large canvas acrylic stains, wood sculpting and photography.

CASTELLINI, MARY M. (Commercial Illustrator)
465 Ridge Rd., Tiburon, CA 94920

Born: 1923 *Awards:* Educational Foundation Grant for Project and Research, Washington, D.C. *Collections:* Dominican College of San Rafael; A.A.U.W. Educational Foundation *Education:* U. of Washington, Seattle; Dominican College of San Rafael *Dealer:* Kenwood Florist

Her herbariums are plant specimens that have been dried, pressed, identified and classified. Her mounts allow the viewer to see the plant in its entirety including the texture, delicacy and life that a photo drawing or a brief walk in the woods cannot give. Her book, *Herbarium . . . A Noetic Herbal Expedition*, is a portfolio of Marin County plants. She printed each of the color plates in her book from a real flower mount. The book also contains poems composed by her son, Egar Castellini. In 1980, her pressed and mounted cutting *Zinfandel* was photographed for the cover of *Graduate Woman* magazine. She is a life member of the American Association of University Women.

CASTILLO, MARIO (Painter)
1153 W. 65th Pl., Los Angeles, CA 90044

Born: 1945 *Awards:* 1st Place, Painting, Museum of Science and Industry, Chicago; Film Grant, American Film Institute *Collections:* City of Chicago; Illinois Bell Telephone Co. *Exhibitions:* Institute for Hispanic Cultural Studies, Los Angeles; Prairie Gallery, Chicago *Education:* California Institute of the Arts; School of the Art Institute of Chicago

His combined abstract and figurative works include the pre- Columbian, the colonial and the contemporary avant garde. Although he occasionally uses the imagery and symbolism of his Mexican heritage, he more often explores his culture through the unstated and implied. Employing juxtapositions of various systems overlaid on neo-cubist ground, he makes references to art history, especially to his own earlier artworks. One of the first artists to begin painting murals as public art in Chicago in 1964, he has recently been probing the inner states of the mind, reflecting anxieties, feelings, emotions and intellectual perceptions. These canvases, incorporating collage, writing

Sue Cazaly, *The Shed*, 5 x 7, photograph. Courtesy: Bay Gallery, Mendocino, CA

Mario Castillo, *Hohokamgram,* 37 x 27, mixed media

and conceptual and body art, depict human faces as systems within themselves.

CASWELL, JIM (Ceramist)
2208 Cloverfield Blvd., Santa Monica, CA

Born: 1948 *Awards:* NEA Fellowship; Artist in Residence, The Manufacture of Sevres, Paris *Exhibitions:* Jan Baum Gallery, Los Angeles; Laguna Beach Art Museum *Dealer:* Jane Corkin, Toronto

After studies in both the decorative and fine arts, he decided to concentrate on ceramics. This decision allowed him to combine his plastic sensibility with a highly decorative and figurative surface treatment. By the late 1970s, he had tired of the circular, cylindrical, traditional forms and the muted colors of his early work. Brilliantly luminous glazed coloring and extremely angular forms characterized his new style in vases and wall relief platters. The abstract patterns, which echo human, animal, plant and mineral forms, enliven, define and contradict the work's surface and form. Recently, two years of research in Paris have expanded his technical and aesthetic concerns and given him a new sense of the role and history of his art.

CATCHI (Painter)
2 Grist Mill Lane, Manhasset NY 11030

Born: 1920 *Awards:* Dr. Maury Leibowitz Art Award; Accedemia Internazionale di Lettere Science & Arts, Florence, Italy *Collections:* Senator George McGovern; Hofstra University *Exhibitions:* U.S. Congressional Show; House of Representatives

A colorist, she has painted primarily landscapes, particularly Italian landscapes that she views from a summer studio in Italy. She conveys the lushness of Italian summer greenery by choosing warm colors (whites, yellows and light greens) and bathing each scene in light. She studied in New York under Leon Kroll, whose murals of justice are on display in Washington. The artist's works, despite her background in New York, have almost no trace of that city's modern art style. She is opposed to abstractionism, and unlike the harsh, disturbing works of some of her peers, the artist's own works are as happy, springy and airy. Her works bring to mind the joviality of John R. Neill's illustrations in the *Wizard of Oz* books.

CATES, RUTH GALLOWAY (Painter)
P.O. Box 160, Weott, CA 95571

Awards: Best of Show, Ink People Show *Exhibitions:* Humboldt Cultural Center; Humboldt State U. *Dealer:* Mac Mezzanine Gallery, Fort Bragg

She works as a watercolorist in both representation and figuration. Currently, the work concerns two main subject matters. One series concentrates on the Redwood, madrone and oak forests of Northern California; these are approached as brocades of light, color and shape. Another series comprises pastel and acrylic on canvas flowers. In these works, the acrylic painting is overlaid in pastels to make the texture of the petals tangible. Her main influences have been Georgia O'-Keeffe and Andrew Wyeth.

CAUKER, KATY (Ceramist)
P.O. Box 923., Jacksonville, OR 97530

Born: 1949 *Awards:* Grant for Art in Public Places, Oregon Art Commission *Exhibitions:* Rogue Gallery, Medford, OR *Education:* East Texas State U. *Dealer:* Jill Halley, Corona Del Mar

She creates bas-relief mosaic murals by drawing and sculpting slabs of wet porcelain and cutting irregularly shaped tiles as it dries. She was inspired by both painters and sculptors. Her early work was at its best in the raw, unfired stage of sculpted clay. After studying more contemporary and abstract artists (George Segal, Georgia O'Keeffe, Stella, Kandinsky, de Kooning) she developed an interest in color and how it changes the emotion of form. She now adds color to her sculpted, drawn on, carved in clay by spraying on glazes. She often includes a figure and a landscape. "I like to communicate the most emotion and movement with the fewest lines."

CAULFIELD, GAIL (Sculptor)
36 Front St., San Rafael, CA 94901

Born: 1944 *Awards:* Cash Grant, Marin Arts Council; Cash Award of Excellence, Berkeley Art Center *Exhibitions:* California Crafts Museum, San Francisco; Lillian Paley Center for the Visual Arts, Oakland *Education:* San Francisco State U.; Bridgewater State College

She became a professional studio potter in the mid-1970s, after several years of informal training. In 1977, she entered a graduate program, but it was not until she had been out of school for several years that her work became predominantly figurative. Living in the Bay Area where other figurative clay artists were working, she saw some of the possibilities of large-scale ceramic art. Her first series of figures were assembled from wheel-thrown forms, and are reminiscent of the Japanese Haniwa figures and ancient female fertility stone sculptures. Wishing to increase her understanding of the human form, she returned to school to study figure drawing; her ceramic figures became more and more realistic. Since 1987, however, the work has been evolving again. While the three-dimensional form continues to resemble actual forms, the surface textures and coloration have gone in a non- realistic direction, with, for example, some figures having rock-like or concrete-like surfaces, even though they are human figures.

CAVAT, IRMA (Painter)
802 Carosam Rd., Santa Barbara, CA 93110

Awards: Fulbright Fellowship *Collections:* Flint Museum, Flint, MI; Hirshhorn Museum, Washington, DC *Exhibitions:* Kennedy Galleries, NYC; Feingarten Gallery, Los Angeles *Education:* New School for Social Research, NYC *Dealer:* Feingarten Gallery, Los Angeles

Originally a sculptor, she began painting with Balcomb Greene, Hans Hofmann and Willem de Kooning. She slowly moved from Abstract Expressionism to figuration in a transition largely inspired by her discovery of Italian Renaissance painting and the work of Giorgio Morandi. In the past ten years, her paintings have become more realistic. She uses a wax technique that produces luminous glazes reminiscent of Flemish still-lifes. A recent series of paintings depicts the prenuclear and post-nuclear world, combining broad expanses of sky with symbols of civilization such as Stonehenge. Her most recent work is in painted assemblage using a trompe l'oeil technique. She cuts objects from wood, paints them in oil, and then mounts them on a surface, thus giving a three-dimensional appearance to a flat object.

Katy Cauker, *Valley Views,* 36 x 408 x .5, triptych, glazed porcelain, three sections.
Courtesy: City of Medford, Oregon. Photograph: Douglas R. Smith

Rodney Chang, *Analytic Wash,* 16 x 19, cibachrome. Courtesy: Soho Too Gallery, Honolulu, HI

CAZALY, SUE (Photographer)
537 Jones St., #1022, San Francisco, CA 94102

Born: 1932 *Exhibitions:* Gallery F22, Santa Fe, NM; Phoenix Art Museum *Education:* Ohio U. *Dealer:* Bay Gallery, Mendocino

Influenced by Ansel Adams and her teacher, Dorr Bothwell, as well as by the soft light of Southern Ohio region where she received her M.A., she uses the soft-image effect to transform the harsh Southwestern light into a soft, romantic scene. She spends much of her time in the wilderness, and her work reflects her growing alarm at the over-development of the California landscape. She has recently been working on three books of photography and text. In one, she portrays the foothill country of California in soft color prints. In another, she combines black and white photographs with a poetic text that honors nature. In the final, old barns are her subjects.

CELIS, PEREZ (Painter, Printmaker)
714 Broadway, New York, NY 10003

Born: 1939 *Awards:* Prize, International Grand Prix of Painting, Monte Carlo; Swift Engraving Award, Museum of Modern Art, Buenos Aires *Collections:* Museum of Modern Art, NYC; E.F. Hutton, NYC *Exhibitions:* Wildenstein Gallery, Buenos Aires; Museum of Fine Arts, Caracas, Venezuela *Education:* School of Fine Arts, Buenos Aires *Dealer:* Anita Shapolvsky

An Argentinian from Buenos Aires, he lived and worked in Paris before moving to New York City in 1983. Since the 1950s, he has painted abstractions. His work in the 1980s depicts great geometric planes. Some stand horizontally, bisecting the canvas against an equally vivid, multi-colored active background. Others—triangular and bursting from the borders, prow-like—appear to move against the canvas. Still others, tall and rectangular or sharply triangular, teeter beyond the confines of the otherwise rectangular composition, balance on a corner or appear to be riding the crest of a somber sea.

CELMINS, VIJA (Painter, Graphic Artist)
c/o Gemini G.E.L., 8365 Melrose Ave., Los Angeles, CA 90069

Born: 1939 *Collections:* Whitney Museum, NYC; Museum of Modern Art, NYC *Exhibitions:* Whitney Museum; Los Angeles County Museum of Art *Education:* Herron School of Art; UCLA *Dealer:* David McKee Gallery, NYC; Gemini G.E.L., Los Angeles

Born in Latvia, she came to Indiana as a child, eventually studied there, and later moved to California. Images in wood and enamel sculpture, as well as drawings, derive from her perception of the California landscape. She seeks to recapture "some remembered light or feeling" from the past. Graphite drawings of seas, galaxies and deserts reflect a long preoccupation with the tension between surface and depth, motion and stillness. These unified surfaces of graphite on acrylic ground simultaneously depict abstract designs and illusionistic deep space, resulting in a balance between abstraction and the recognizable image.

CHABIEL, MARY (Painter)
235 N. 6th St., San Jose, CA 95112

Born: 1920 *Collections:* St. Patrick's Church, San Jose; Guadalupe Church San Jose *Exhibitions:* Hispanic Development Center, Dorhmann Bldg., San Jose; Santa Clara County Fairgrounds, San Jose *Education:* San Jose State U.

After a life devoted to raising her family and meeting her professional responsibilities as an assistant draftsman for Santa Clara County, she went back to school to pursue her love of learning and art. After she took introductory art courses, her professors encouraged her to explore her predisposition to multi-color design. The result was a series of more than fifty folk masks and expressions. These works have been exhibited throughout Northern California. Her work has evolved from these small felt-tip drawings to 3-by-6-foot oil and acrylic paintings composed of colorful folk-art motifs and images. Her Hispanic cultural heritage is apparent in the bright, exotic colors and folk-art images of these paintings. Recently, she has completed a number of watercolors and oils on silk and other fabrics. The watercolors are floral compositions, while the the fabric paintings are of a more religious nature and have been exhibited at numerous church functions.

CHAET, VICKY (MEYER) (Painter)
339 Frederick St., San Francisco, CA 94117

Born: 1941 *Awards:* Artist-in-Residence, Ragdale Foundation, Lake Forest, IL; Carnegie Fellowship, Stanford U. *Collections:* Wm. Bonifas Fine Arts Center, Escanaba, MI; Sundown Design, Ltd., San Francisco *Exhibitions:* Richard Sumner Gallery, Palo Alto; Bergman Gallery, Chicago *Education:* U. of Massachusetts *Dealer:* John R. Manning, San Francisco

Her early figure drawings' draftsman-like quality is also well displayed in some of her early architectonic sculpture pieces. She has worked in several media, including computer art, sculpture and more recently, acrylics on canvas. Best known for her color and composition, she has executed portraits, self- portraits, landscapes and abstract figures, in an array of palettes, from vivid to muted. Her unusual flexibility and command of the figure is also displayed in these various modes. In all her work a rigid formalism underlies her engaging expressionism. The totality of her work speaks to her personal artistic journey and to the struggle for balance between the moving and static energies of life.

CHAFFEE, MARTA (Painter)
14458 Sunset Blvd., Pacific Palisades, CA 90272

Born: 1936 *Awards:* Finalist, Olympic International Art Competition *Collections:* Security Pacific National Bank; Bank of America *Exhibitions:* Art Space, Los Angeles; Long Beach Art Association *Education:* Occidental College; Otis Art Institute

She is a landscape artist who draws in soft pencils and paints with oils. With her simple, almost oriental, expressionistic style, she conveys a feeling of place, rather than a specific site. Characteristic are such images as mountains, a coast, a waterline against the sand or a road moving through a canyon. The level of abstraction varies in her largely realistic approach. In her paintings, she applies the medium in thick layers, as well as thin washes. In her drawings, her forms are erased almost as much as they are drawn. Her studies of dense undergrowth are peculiarly effective. The best works are minimal, economical and gentle.

Mary D. Chabiel, *untitled,* 36 x 48, acrylic on canvas

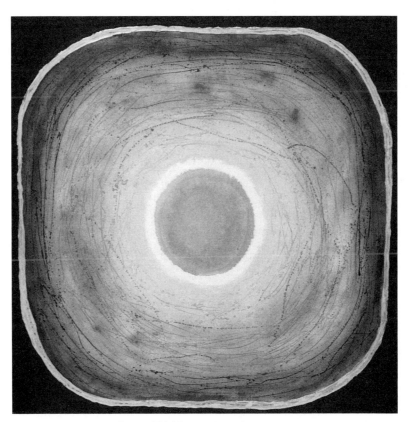

Cantor, *Prayer Shield #14,* 60 x 60, acrylic on canvas

CHAN, PHILLIP P. (Painter)
5225 Edgeworth Rd., San Diego, CA 92109

Born: 1946 *Awards:* NEA Individual Artist Award *Exhibitions:* San Francisco Museum of Modern Art; Palace of Fine Arts, San Francisco *Education:* UC-Berkeley

During the early 1960s, his interest in Richard Diebenkorn and the Bay Area Figurative Artists led to a formal modernist style. In his series of "anti-paintings" during the late 1970s, he ironically commented on the state of painting by asserting the material nature of paint itself. By the early 1980s, he again became concerned with icons. Though the images in this phase were at first minimal, by the late 1980s, his figures suggested the groundlessness of modern existence. With tension between faith and doubt, they are literally beings with wings that cannot fly. Recent figurative painting is a decomposition and re-integration of sexual and primitive themes.

CHANCO, PAULETTA M. (Painter)
12 Greenside Way, San Rafael, CA 94901

Born: 1959 *Awards:* Hayes-Jacobs Prize, UC-Berkeley; Emerging Artists' Award, Women Artists Gallery, San Francisco *Exhibitions:* Redding New Works Gallery, Redding; Worth Ryder Gallery, UC-Berkeley *Education:* UC-Berkeley *Dealer:* San Francisco Museum of Modern Art Rental Gallery

The imagery—organic elements with forms becoming progressively abstracted—is derived from her life and from nature and photographs. Color, the primary expressive vehicle, is used intuitively, not to achieve greater naturalism but to express emotion and form. Structure is achieved when the colors are perceived abstractly as separate entities in themselves. She achieves these abstracted, organic shapes by alternately layering brightly colored oil paint with darker elements. Her work is inspired by certain aspects of Chinese landscape painting, and she strives to strike a balance of airiness with darker voids in space. She also shares the Chinese aesthetic concern for the importance of the elusively expressive, in contrast to the solid and permanent forms of the Western aesthetic.

CHANDLER, ELIZABETH (Painter, Printmaker)
1240 11th Ave., San Francisco, CA 94122

Born: 1941 *Collections:* Nordstrom's, Sacramento; Jupiter Realty, Los Angeles *Exhibitions:* Pie Gallery, San Francisco; Stanford University *Education:* Stanford U.

She received formal training in drawing, painting and printmaking, but her early work was primarily in photography. She resumed painting in 1970, working in oil, acrylic and monotype until 1983. In the mid 1980s, her work showed the influences of photography, ancient rock painting and the work of Nathan Oliveira, the pieces exploring the relation of figures or groups of figures to their environments. Using acrylic on gesso, she investigated both depth of surface and surface textures by building up many translucent layers of paint. The environments in her figurative work eventually became more important than the figures themselves, and she began to produce abstract landscapes. These pieces reveal references to such artists as Matisse, Mondrian and Klee. She selects a "cast" (e.g. a star, a palm tree) and places it in a variety of moods and compositions, concerning herself with color, space, gestural brushwork and flat shape rather than with form and rhythm.

CHANEY, HOWARD W. (Painter)
7732 Belgrave Ave., Garden Grove, CA

Born: 1940 *Exhibitions:* La Mirada Festival of Art; Pine Tree Gallery, Traveling Exhibit *Education:* Famous Artists School

Influenced by the techniques of fine arts and commercial illustrators, he has investigated many avenues of artistic expression, such as acrylics, pen and ink, pencil and, recently, watercolor. Painting from a limited palette which includes indigo, burnt sienna and aurelian yellow, he creates forest-, sea- and landscapes. He uses a wet-on-wet technique, and prides himself on his ability to render detail. Yosemite Park and the Carmel-Monterey coast are the subjects of his recent paintings.

CHANG, DICKENS (Painter)
162 South Ash St., Ventura, CA 93001

Born: 1948 *Collections:* City of Los Angeles; City of Santa Monica *Exhibitions:* Carnegie Museum of Art, Oxnard; Tarbox Gallery, San Diego *Education:* California Polytechnic U.

His early work was extremely precise and controlled, with almost all emotion sublimated into a style which harmoniously blended clean figures with abstract lines and forms that were no less mannered. As he developed, the traditional and modern elements in his work grew more at odds with each other. For a while he lived in New York City and used plastic machine-made objects to punctuate the highlights of his paintings. The control that made his early work seem emotionless soon gave way to a free-for-all, cathartic style that exploded on the canvas. One constant running through both his early and later work is a narrative element that carries the imagery along in a linear fashion. He is well-known and widely exhibited in Taiwan.

CHANG, RODNEY (Computer Artist)
2119 N. King St., Suite 206, Honolulu, HI 96819

Born: 1945 *Collections:* Nishi Noho Gallery, NYC *Exhibitions:* I.D.E.A. Gallery, Sacramento; Amsterdam Art Gallery, Berkeley *Education:* Northern Illinois U.; Union Graduate School *Dealer:* Soho Too Gallery, Honolulu

The originator of the theory of "pixelism," he is best known for computer graphics that merge computer abilities with human artistic expression. He works by returning computer images to their human antecedents, using computer art as the basis for paintings. He has been experimenting with the transfer of computer art to lithography. The holder of ten college degrees, he tries to express a holistic approach to life in his work. Besides computer art, he has been working with a wood sculptor to create a six- by nine-foot wooden relief, in which he has attempted to freeze light and shadow in solid form.

CHANG, WAH (Sculptor)
9805 Palisade Dr., Carmel, CA 93923

Born: 1917 *Exhibitions:* Lawrence Gallery, Sheridan, OR; Wing Gallery *Dealer:* Carmel Art Association

Known nationally for his prints and etchings, puppetry and sculpture, his prolific career has spanned nearly sixty years. The child of two graphic artists and later the ward of noted artist Blanding Sloan, he developed

Beverly Cassell, *Now I Pierce the Darkness,* 39 x 50, oil

Dickens Chang, *Jazz in N.Y.,* 30 x 40, acrylic on canvas. Courtesy: Dr. F. Meronk

an early familiarity and aptitude for block printing, etching and painting. He was staff artist of the Cavalcade of Texas during the 1936 Texas Centennial, taught art in the Honolulu WPA program and worked on exhibitions for the San Francisco World's Fair in 1939 before joining the Walt Disney Special Effects Department on such films as "Bambi," "Fantasia" and "Pinocchio." Later film work included masks and headdresses for "The King and I," "Can Can," and "Cleopatra," special effects for "The Time Machine" and "The Seven Faces of Dr. Lao," and puppetry for a 1947 educational feature dealing with the moral implications of the atom bomb. Interest in the environment has since led him to design bronze sculptures of endangered animals using the lost-wax process of metal casting. Realistic work often focuses on children and the sensitive bond between animals and their young. He has also experimented recently with more abstract forms.

CHANGSTROM, BETH (Ceramist, Painter)
690 Highland Ave., Penngrove, CA 94951

Born: 1943 *Awards:* Award in Ceramics, ArtQuest *Collections:* James Jones Memorial Collection, Pomona *Exhibitions:* Oakland Museum of Art; Kurland/Summers Gallery, Los Angeles *Education:* Claremont Graduate School *Dealer:* Susan Cummins Gallery, Mill Valley

Initially she produced functional ceramics with decoratively painted surfaces. A few years ago, she began to paint seriously, rendering the figure with acrylic on clay platters. From there, she began to assemble clay and painted wood elements. These assemblage works gradually evolved into a more iconic form, with an altar-like, painted ceramic frame around paintings that featured abstract human figures. She now divides her time between producing commercial works and fine art. The latter consists of glorifying the objects and rituals of everyday life. Although her recent work has focused on the cup, she uses other subjects as well, placing them in a painted and assembled setting to create a dialogue between two and three dimensions.

CHAPMAN, NEIL (Photographer)
7890 El Toro Way, Buena Park, CA

Born: 1950 *Awards:* Golden Globe Award, Orange County Advertising Federation; Merit Award, Orange County Advertising Federation *Collections:* Bibleothique Nationale, Paris; U. of California, Riverside Collections *Exhibitions:* Galerie Perspectives, Paris; Fresno Metropolitan Museum *Education:* Cal. State-Fullerton *Dealer:* Susan Spiritus Gallery, Newport Beach

Interest in the work of Ansel Adams and Diane Arbus led to study with Robert Routh, Eileen Cowin and Darryl Curran, in order to develop traditional craft techniques. He later experimented with image overlays using applied color on computer generated formats. Photographs and photo-styled still lifes are fed into the computer. A hard copy of the resulting transferred image is made into a clear transparency, then a lithograph negative, which is developed as a photograph. The print has a richness in tone similar to old-fashioned lithographs. The computer's use is not evident in the final product; it is simply a device used in conjunction with the camera to achieve a desired effect. Subjects continue to explore the social statement and the individual portrait. In emotional studies,

such as *Conflict* and *The Sneeze*, personal dynamics are scrutinized in minute detail.

CHAPPELL, WALTER (Photographer)
P.O. Box 8736, Santa Fe, NM 87504

Born: 1925 *Awards:* NEA Fellowship *Collections:* Metropolitan Museum of Art, NYC; Stanford University Art Museum *Exhibitions:* Whitney Museum, NYC; Sun Gallery, San Francisco *Dealer:* Andrew Smith, Santa Fe

After studying architectural drawing, he worked in various arts, including music and painting, and published a book of poetry entitled *Logue and Glyphs* in 1948. In the early 1950s, he spent three years recovering from tuberculosis, during which period he decided to concentrate his artistic efforts in photography. He studied with Minor White and published *Gestures of Infinity*, a book of poetry and images. He spent three years as Curator of Prints and Exhibitions at George Eastman House before founding the Heliographers Gallery Archive in New York City in 1962. He soon moved to New Mexico, where he photographed the nude figure and the Southwestern landscape while studying Native American ceremonial life. His later experimental work involved electrophotography, particularly high-voltage, high-frequency electron imagery of plants. He has been awarded three National Endowment for the Arts Fellowships.

CHARLASCH, ALICE (Photographer, Painter)
38245 Calle Arrebol, Murrieta, CA 92362

Exhibitions: Los Angeles Art Association; Woman Space, Los Angeles *Education:* Cal. State-Northridge; UCLA

Always fascinated with the abstract quality of the miniature world, she began painting microstructures using acrylics in the 1960s. In the early 1970s, she used polyester resins to create abstract crystal sculptures. Since 1980, her work has involved the photography of microscopic crystals. By manipulating chemical formulae, she has expanded the variety and content of crystalline abstract form. Her recent work falls into five categories: crystal drawings—causing crystals to grow within a drawn line; crystal landscape; master imagery, influenced by Klee, Magritte and Giacometti; abstraction and hybrid form; and calligraphy as a framework for crystal growth.

CHARLES, ROLAND (Photographer)
1837 S. Cloverdale Ave., Los Angeles, CA 90019

Born: 1941 *Awards:* Mayor's Certificate of Appreciation, Los Angeles; Recognition of Dedicated Service, City of Long Beach *Collections:* Long Beach Historical Society; Michael Jackson *Exhibitions:* Bridge Gallery, Los Angeles City Hall; Museum of African-American Art, Los Angeles *Dealer:* Black Gallery, Los Angeles

During the protest era of the 1970s, with a background in fashion, editorial and advertising photography, he began documenting black lifestyles, focusing on historically and culturally significant images. In the early 1980s he began incorporating collage, hand-tinting and display design into his photography. More recently he has expanded the work to include audio-visual installations. His subjects, though still relevant to the black experience, have evolved to include broader images of the urban cultural landscape.

Elizabeth Chandler, *Hey diddle diddle . . .,* 22 x 30, monotype

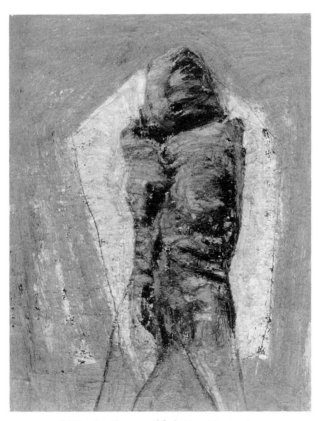

Phllip P. Chan, *untitled,* 28 x 22, oil sticks

CHARLOT, MARTIN (Painter, Illustrator)
P.O. Box 161, Kaneohe, HI 96744

Born: 1944 *Awards:* Fellow In Perpetuity, Metropolitan Museum of Art, NYC; Perpetual Member, Hawaii Film Board *Collections:* Metropolitan Museum of Art, NYC; State of Hawaii *Exhibitions:* De Mena Gallery, NYC; Contemporary Arts Center, Honolulu

Known primarily as an oil painter and muralist, he paints figurative works that express a fruitful spiritualism. He apprenticed with his father, Jean Charlot, who during the 1920s and 1930s taught the art of the mural fresco to Diego Rivera and the entire school of Mexican painters. He often depicts the variety of races and peoples that populate present-day Hawaii, in restatements of Christian stories that function as commentary on current social and political issues. His rich botanical details create a mystical, surrealistic quality, intensified by vivid colors that glow with the luminous light of the tropics. "Stars In Paradise" captures the quiet gentility and dignity of the old Waikiki, peopled by Hollywood stars with island connections.

CHARTERS, CYNTHIA (Painter)
P.O. Box 816, West Sacramento, CA 95605

Born: 1949 *Awards:* Artist's Residency, Yosemite National Park *Collections:* Diepenbrock Collection, Sacramento *Exhibitions:* Contemporary Realist Gallery; Fresno Arts Center *Education:* UC-Davis *Dealer:* Michael Hackett; Contemporary Realist Gallery, San Francisco

Her recent work has primarily focused on *plein air* landscapes of the Sacramento River Delta; she explores other landscape subjects less frequently. The paintings evoke an almost photographic brilliance of light, a result of her use of dramatic purples, blues and other deep tones that express the emotional power hidden beneath the Delta's surface calm. In *Randall Island Palms*, a landscape of talm palms, the light seems to be reflected in the air that surrounds it, rather than seen clearly itself. This effect is heightened by the image's liquid reflection in the river, which, though distorted by ripples, appears more "real." Palpable emotion is unmasked through strong, highly expressive brushwork.

CHATELAIN, MARTHA (Sculptor)
833 G St., San Diego, CA 92101

Born: 1935 *Awards:* Merit Award, California Women Artists; Best of Show, La Quinta Arts Festival *Collections:* IBM Corporation, La Jolla; Bank of America *Exhibitions:* Gallery Beni, Kyoto, Japan; Westmont College Art Center, Santa Barbara *Education:* Chouinard Art Institute, Los Angeles; UCLA *Dealers:* Mano Gallery, Los Angeles; Janet Disraeli, San Diego

She creates wall sculptures of paper, which she herself makes of pure cotton fiber. While still wet, she folds, creases, pulls, slashes, tears, layers and textures the paper. These compositions are abstract—often bilateral and asymmetrical in appearance—and are colored with acrylic paint, mica powders and translucent or opaque glazes, or left in the white of the paper in its pristine state. Earlier works were in pastel shades, more recent pieces in bolder hues. Natural materials such as birch bark or melaleuca are sometimes incorporated into a design. Her white, uncolored, 5-by-4-foot piece *Beyond Separation,* for

example, has the appearance of a shirt-front grabbed and pulled upon, with great diagonal folds drawn from the perimeter to the center. The folds cast shadows below their ridges, the flat expanses on either side aree mbossed patch-like and the throat is folded and crumpled like a lace cravat.

CHEN, ANDE LAU (Painter)
638 Westholme Ave., Los Angeles, CA 90024

Born: 1932 *Awards:* 1st Place Painting, Princeton Art Association *Collections:* 1st Interstate Bank, Los Angeles; Hawaii State Collection *Exhibitions:* Jacqueline Anhalt Gallery, Los Angeles; Starkman Gallery, NYC *Education:* Columbia U. *Dealer:* The Art Loft, Honolulu

The abstract collage paintings of Tseng Yu Ho were a decisive influence that led her to collage, this early work a blend of Oriental perspective and Western abstract. Hand-made and painted papers are incorporated into her paintings. The crumpled papers give an impression of geological mass and deep crevasses; landscape textures are captured by air-brushing acrylics into the papers. She has recently been exploring the use of color to define form, the fibrous textures of the hand-made papers taking on new importance. In this newer work, she glazes metal leaf and rice papers with acrylic paints that are air-brushed in multiple layers, creating luminous landscapes often set in the Oriental screen format.

CHEN, TZE Y. (Painter)
13131 Arabella Dr., Cerritos, CA 90701

Born: 1960 *Exhibitions:* U. of California Gallery, Irvine *Education:* UC-Irvine

The painter studied fashion design in Taiwan but switched to fine art upon immigrating to the U.S. in 1983. The "sculptural painting" technique used was first introduced by a professor at the University of California. The artist soon made personal alterations on this style, seeking out varied exuberant color combinations to better represent, "my colorful, strange dreams of art." Applying "trash" relief elements to paintings provides further textural interest. Clay sculptures mirror the abstract style of the paintings. While ceramic sculpture affords unique expressive opportunities, painting remains the favorite and primary discipline.

CHENG, KAI BOB (Painter, Sculptor)
14 Westminster Ave., Venice, CA 90291

Born: 1940 *Exhibitions:* Santa Barbara Contemporary Arts Forum; Taipei Museum of Fine Art *Education:* UCLA *Dealer:* Krygier/Landau Contemporary Art Gallery, Los Angeles

Alternating between assemblage sculpture, acrylic paintings and constructed mixed-media reliefs, he "experiments" his work into completion. A variety of found objects are worked into paintings or sculptures that refer to ethnic, scientific or musical subjects. Inspired by the marriage of sculpture and painting in the work of Joseph Cornell, he frequently layers somewhat clichéd paintings of landscapes or seascapes with constructions evocative of ancient cultures. One such piece, *Reflections on a Mask*, uses painted details of a wave's froth as the base for a mask constructed from thin pieces of wood. Other paintings incorporate animals from Africa's Serengeti Plain in lush California landscapes, evoking a sense of spontaneity and fluid surrealism.

Tze Ying, Chen, *Friendship,* 2 pieces, 24 x 36, oil and acrylic

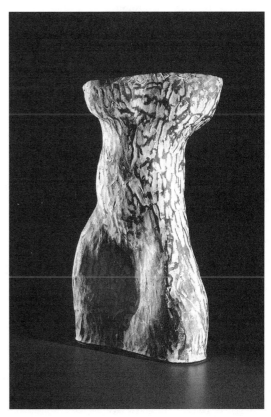

Maude Church, *Doing Lunch: Nocturne,* 60 x 36, acrylic on canvas

Alice Corning, *Torso,* 13" high, stoneware. Photograph: Mel Schockner

CHERIN, LOTTE (Sculptor)
P.O. Box 786, Malibu, CA 90265

Born: 1947 *Collections:* Prince Charles, Prince of Wales; Long Beach Public Library *Exhibitions:* Gallery of Contemporary Metalsmithing, NYC; Jane Aron Art Center, Mills College, Oakland *Education:* California State U.; Mills College

This jeweler, silversmith and sculptor has been attracted to a broad range of materials, frequently combining metal with more fragile materials. Equally comfortable working with precious metals or with steel and aluminum, she creates pieces in a variety of sizes—from those that fit in the palm of the hand to those that won't fit through a doorway. The range of materials is matched by the range of subjects—from hand-fabricated, one-of-a-kind abstracts to to limited-edition bronze castings in the shapes of animals. The metals are occasionally anodized or painted, and more fragile elements are lacquered; she sometimes uses mixed media elements in contrast to the pure metals. One recent work is a site-specific, seven-by-three-by-three-foot aluminum abstract sculpture.

CHERNY, TERESA (Sculptor)
3634 Seventh Ave., Apt. 8E, San Diego, CA 92103

Born: 1929 *Awards:* 3rd Prize, Arte y Cultura, Mexico City; Anthony Busachi Award *Collections:* Presidio Exploration Inc., Denver *Exhibitions:* Galeria Mizrachi, Mexico City; San Diego Public Library *Education:* Universidad Motolinia, Mexico City; Universidad Feminina, Mexico City *Dealers:* Galeria Mizrachi, Mexico City; Knowles Taibox, Sura, Mexico City

After formal training in interior design and decoration, she worked with sculptor Don Jose Bardasano, and chose bronze as her medium. Her sculptures of women are elongated, slim, sophisticated, graceful and faceless. Line, in her work, replaces decoration; shape replaces identity. Her women are exultant, alone and introspective, intertwining with men, or in groups, consoling and sharing with each other. She works without a plan (drawing or model), creating the original piece in clay or plasticene and leaving foundry workers to mold and pour the bronze and apply the patina. Each piece has a rich green or bluish tone and takes six to eight weeks to complete.

CHESNEY, LEE (Painter, Printmaker)
14601 Whitfield Ave., Pacific Palisades, CA 90272

Born: 1920 *Awards:* Fulbright Senior Research Award, Tokyo; Francis G. Logan Medal and Prize, Art Institute of Chicago *Collections:* Chicago Art Institute; Wadsworth Atheneum, Hartford *Exhibitions:* U.S. Cultural Center, Paris; Yoseido Gallery, Tokyo *Education:* U. of Colorado; U of Iowa *Dealer:* BIMC Gallery, Paris

Early paintings and prints featured symbolic figuration, which gradually came under cubist discipline. An interest in automatism and psychic states persisted throughout the 1950s, with linear and planar elements dominant. After he moved to Los Angeles from the midwest in the 1960s, his painting showed an increased formal emphasis, a simplification of means and an exploration of iconic imagery. In the early 1970s, a further relocation to the South Pacific launched a fifteen year study of color, light and space, which resulted in large, exuberant, expansive, open canvases. Linearity and darkness were replaced by soft, nearly flat shapes (usually disks or doughnuts) drifting over seas of color.

Oil and paint seemed to become light, which, in turn, seemed to dissolve into spirit. Richness and variety of surface supported color brilliance. Since his recent return to California, a new, specific, threatening imagery has shouldered its way into his painting.

CHICAGO, JUDY (Painter, Sculptor)
c/o ACA Galleries, 21 E. 67th St., New York, NY 10021

Born: 1939 *Awards:* NEA Grant *Collections:* Brooklyn Museum; San Francisco Museum of Modern Art *Exhibitions:* Whitney Museum, NYC; San Francisco Museum of Modern Art *Education:* UCLA *Dealer:* ACA Galleries, NYC; Shidoni Gallery, Tesuque, NY

Minimalism and color fields characterized her style when she studied in Los Angeles in the early 1960s. All of her work has a femininist perspective, offering new insights into the role of women in art. She is best known for her mixed-media presentation *The Dinner Party,* a triangular table, each side forty-eight feet long and each displaying thirteen place settings that address the subject of women in society. Each plate was painted with a flower in a style derived from Georgia O'Keefe, and each was set for a particular woman of historical prominence. The flowers' similarity to female genitalia contributed to the controversy and acclaim over the work. "I am trying to make art that relates to the deepest and most mythic concerns of humankind. I believe that . . . feminism is humanism," she says.

CHIEN-ERIKSEN, NANCY (Painter)
113 Rice Lane, Larkspur, CA 94939

Born: 1949 *Awards:* Ballantine Award, Sci-Fi Fantasy Publishers *Collections:* Fountain Grove Inn, Santa Rosa *Exhibitions:* Harvest Festival; California Renaissance Pleasure Faire *Education:* UCLA

During her studies at the University of Padua, Italy, and at the Academy of Fine Arts in Venice and in Florence, she found kindred spirits in the Mannerist painters of the early 1500s. By the 16th and 17th centuries, religious icons often evolved into secular or pagan fantasy images; this is a phenomenon that crosses thematic lines of philosophy in her work. She credits her sense of bold spontaneity, however, to her Chinese heritage of disciplined brush painting, which she has combined with the Western traditions of detail and emotional expression. Expanding ideas of flowing movement via creatures, fantastic or realistic, she incorporates various media in layers onto cotton rag board. Using ink, watercolor, watercolor pencil, pastel and ink again, she applies three-dimensional items, such as feathers, to add a final textural component.

CHILDRESS, GAYEL (Painter)
3298 E. Ojai Ave., Ojai, CA 93023

Born: 1940 *Awards:* 1st Place Oils & Watercolor, 18th Annual Adah Callahan Juried Art Show *Exhibitions:* Ojai Art Center, Ojai; New Media Gallery, Ventura College

Monoprints and watercolor, acrylic and oil paintings number among this artist's works. Early pieces are primarily watercolors that incorporate collage, resists, airbrush and glazes. The work is sometimes abstract and sometimes representational—the latter comprising figures, landscapes, and still-lifes. Her later watercolors have been nudes. One such painting presents the ladies of the *Ojai Garden Club*; a light social criticism characterizes the treatment of the pieces. She has recently

Tom Cummings, *At the Beach,* 24 x 47, oil on board

Nancy Chien-Eriksen, *The Three Graces,* 48 x 72, acrylic and ink on canvas

been painting primarily in acrylic and oil. For these, she lays down simple shapes with a fast-paced brush in flat colors with under- glazing. Her work shows the influence of Van Gogh, Gauguin and Kandinsky.

CHING, PATRICK (Painter, Commercial Illustrator)
P.O. Box 87, Kilauea, Kauai, HI 96754

Born: 1962 *Collections:* Kaiser Hospital; Hawaiian Telephone *Exhibitions:* Leigh Yawkey Woodson Art Museum, Wausau, WI; Natural History Museum of Los Angeles *Education:* Otis Art Institute; U. of Hawaii

He is a painter, sculptor, commercial illustrator and part-time U.S. Fish and Wildlife Service ranger who is interested in wildlife preservation. He explores the remote areas of Hawaii and studies native plants and animals in their natural habitat before depicting them. The subject of his recent works are the endangered wildlife and flora of Hawaii. He works in a wide range of media—sculpting in clay and painting with pastels in a realistic style. He is currently studying under the surrealist painter John Pitre.

CHISM, DWIGHT (Sculptor, Multimedia Artist)
819 Cayuga St., Santa Cruz, CA 95062

Born: 1957 *Collections:* Stanford U.; U. of California, Santa Cruz *Exhibitions:* Janus Gallery, Los Angeles; Afro-American Museum, Los Angeles *Education:* U. of California, Santa Cruz *Dealer:* Nikki Lee of Los Angeles, Felton

While still in school, he became very interested in West African art, especially as practiced in Gambia, Senegal and Nigeria. He received a grant, and traveled to Africa to study traditional Mandingo wood carving techniques. This experience deeply impressed him; African images and motifs echo throughout his subsequent work. As a watercolorist and graphic artist, he has employed a battery of collage and design techniques to create what he calls new age cultural forms. As a sculptor, he works in bronze, creating iconic pieces, which mix various surface textures and patinas to evoke a sense of "reading" the sculpture. His work details the victories and heartbreaks of people of color and their struggles to attain freedom.

CHRISTENSEN, TED (Painter, Printmaker, Potter)
573 3rd St. East, Sonoma, CA 95476

Born: 1911 *Awards:* 1st Prize, Oregon Society of Arts *Collections:* Harwood Foundation, U. of New Mexico, Taos; St. John's College, Santa Fe, NM *Exhibitions:* Village Gallery, Orinda, CA; Westview Gallery, San Jose *Education:* Otis Art Institute; Museum School, Portland, OR *Dealer:* Village Gallery, Orinda, CA

He paints impressionistic landscapes and waterscapes in a variety of media—oils, acrylics, watercolors and, recently, pastels. Scenes of his extensive travels in Europe, Mexico, Hawaii, California, the Pacific Northwest and the American Southwest furnish the subject matter for his works, which are often done on location. He began to paint after his injury-related discharge from the Army during World War II, in which he served as a machine-gunner.

CHRISTENSEN, WES (Painter, Printmaker)
1195 Montecito Dr., Los Angeles, CA 90031

Born: 1949 *Awards:* NEA Fellowship *Exhibitions:* U. of Hawaii, Hilo; The Design Center of Los Angeles *Education:* Cal. State-San Francisco; Cal. State- Long Beach *Dealer:* Space Gallery, Los Angeles

Influenced by Robert Bechtle and film historian, Raymond Durgnat, he uses a small format, miniaturist technique to present realistic portraits and narrative situations. His narratives ambivalently encourage subjective viewer response; his titles, like Magritte's, are intended to be tangential and evocative, rather than explanatory. Often he includes an idiosyncratic iconography of literary, art historic and personal referents. Modernist and film conventions also influence his compositional decisions. His strong interest in archaeology, especially Mesoamerican, has led to work illustrating the monographs of several scholars.

CHRISTIE-PUTNAM, COLLEEN (Painter, Papermaker)
1524 7th Ave., Oakland, CA 94606

Born: 1956 *Collections:* AT&T; RCA Records Corp. *Exhibitions:* San Francisco State U.; Mendocino Arts Center *Education:* California College of Arts and Crafts

Her abstract paper pieces are made primarily of pure cotton fiber—some with the addition of abaca, a Japanese bast fiber. She soaks sheets of 100% cotton rag (linters) in warm water, where they soften to a wet mush. This mushy pulp she treats with either pigments or fiber reactive dyes. After rinsing the dyes from the fibers, she puts the pulp in buckets, and beats and softens it with a bench-mounted mixer. She pours this beaten pulp onto a screen, working upside-down, like a monoprint. When the piece is entirely laid out, she squeezes as much water as she can from the pulp, and leaves the rest to air dry. To the dried paper she applies alternate layers of acrylic medium and acrylic paints, creating a fully colored illusion of depth and texture. She has an extensive education in the fields of textiles, ethnic dress, ornamentation and 20th century art history.

CHRISTO (Environmental Artist, Sculptor)
48 Howard St., New York, NY 10013

Born: 1935 *Collections:* Museum of Modern Art, NYC; National Museum of Art, Osaka, Japan *Public Installations:* Wrapped Coast, Little Bay, Australia; Wrapped Walkways, Kansas City *Education:* Fine Arts Academy, Sofia; Vienna Fine Arts Academy *Dealer:* Jeanne-Claude Christo, NYC

Born in Bulgaria, he came to Paris in 1958 and began to wrap objects and packages. In the early 1960s, he gained recognition with huge assemblages of oil barrels, and upon moving to New York City in 1964 completed a series of "Store Fronts." Since then, he has wrapped monuments, buildings and landscapes all over the world, redefining the meaning and scope of art. One of these works was *Running Fence 1972-76*, an 18-foot-high, 24 1/2- mile-long fabric fence that ran across the California countryside. The recent *Surrounded Islands, Biscayne Bay, Greater Miami, Florida, 1980-1983* used six-and-one-half million square feet of pink, woven polypropylene fabric. Works in progress include *The Umbrellas, Joint Project for Japan and the U.S.A., Wrapped Reichstag, Project for Berlin,* and *The*

Ted Christensen, *Napa Valley, Winter,* 15 x 22, acrylic. Courtesy: West View Gallery, San Jose, CA

Alice Charlasch, *untitled No. 22,* ©*1985,* 22 x 28, photomicrography

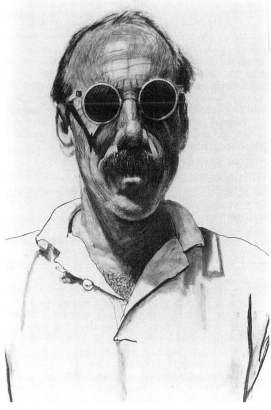

Julia Couzens, *Michael Himovitz,* 30 x 22, charcoal on paper

Mastaba of Abu Dhabi, Project for the United Arab Emigrates.

CHRISTY-RODGERS, LISA (Painter, Sculptor)

2314 Goodwin Ave., Redwood City, CA 94061

Born: 1955 *Exhibitions:* San Jose State College; Griner College, Portova Valley *Education:* San Jose State College

She has introduced modern techniques into the established equestrian art field with bronze sculptures and paintings in oil. Polychroming is used with sculptures to enhance movement, and a third dimension is added to two-dimensional works. Oils focus on cameos of action rather than full figure poses. Recent paintings are influenced by Diego Rivera's use of line, color and composition. Voluptuous women are portrayed with attention paid to the full roundness of their bodies. Large canvases accentuate mass and spontaneous postures; surroundings are slightly erotic, and movement is emphasized. Traditional canvas preparation and painting technique stress the naturalness of her live models. Yellows, raw sienna and burnt umber add warmth to an honest, unashamed sense of femininity.

CHUN, JEFFREY W. (Painter, Commercial Illustrator)

5326 W. 139th St., Hawthorne, CA 90250

Born: 1960 *Exhibitions:* Apache Cultural Center and Museum; Lion Art Studios, Laguna Beach *Education:* Cal. State-Long Beach *Dealer:* Lion Art Studios, Laguna Beach

After studying fine arts and illustration at California State University at Long Beach, he worked in the Southern California area as a fine artist and commercial artist, completing commissions for such diverse clients as movie production companies, advertising agencies and the Apache Cultural Center/Museum in Arizona. He has recently been involved in painting a series on figure skaters, which he hopes to show before the next Winter Olympics. This long-term project will take four years and involve a variety of media, including charcoal pencils on colored boards, a combination of watercolors and pastels and oils on traditionally prepared canvas.

CHURCH, MAUDE (Painter)

5412 Bryant Ave., Oakland, CA 94611

Born: 1949 *Awards:* 1979 Outstanding Woman of the Year Award *Collections:* Bonino Collection, Palm Springs; Shaw College, London, England *Exhibitions:* Pacific Grove Art Center; Wrubel Gallery, Berkeley *Education:* California College of Arts and Crafts; Byam, England *Dealer:* Andrea Schwartz, San Francisco

In her early oils, her background in pop art and color-field abstraction is evident. Her interest in rich, bold colors and simplified forms continued as her work progressed from abstraction to landscapes. These paintings in the Romantic- visionary tradition focus on color relationships—dramatic compositions with attention to the figure placed in a landscape at a particular point in time and space. She has recently been working in acrylic on canvas, in pastels and in all drawing media. These recent pieces use neon back-lighting to lend a particular luminosity to the colors. Themes center around social commentary on California lifestyle, but also include series on palm trees and redwood landscapes.

CIRICLIO, S.E. (Photographer, Sculptor)

535 Haddon Rd., Oakland, CA 94606

Born: 1946 *Awards:* San Francisco Arts Commission Special Merit Award; NEA Fellowship *Collections:* San Francisco Museum of Modern Art; Oakland Museum *Exhibitions:* M.H. DeYoung Memorial Museum, San Francisco; San Francisco Art Institute *Education:* Calif. College of Arts and Crafts; Mills College

Following strong formalist and technical training in photography, she turned to color and photography's relationship to, and existence in, the everyday environment. As a result, her work began to explore how a viewer interacts with the photograph as object. She first made one-of-a-kind books and puzzles and then moved into large-scale photo fabric installation pieces. She continues to explore the relationship between photography and the everyday environment in numerous small color photographs. Her own residential neighborhood serves as the subject matter for pieces that range from flat wall works, each using a few dozen photographs, to book and table pieces, each using several hundred photographs, to room-size installation pieces with several thousand photographs.

CLARK, ETTA (Photographer)

29 Martling Rd., San Anselmo, CA 94960

Born: 1942 *Awards:* 1st and 2nd Places, Golden Gate Transit *Exhibitions:* Marin County Civic Center; San Francisco International Airport

She took up photography as a hobby while raising her three children. In the early 1980s, she began photographing portraits of older athletes. These black-and-white portraits were compiled in a book, *Growing Old is Not for Sissies*. For the last three years, she has been working on a project, *Swimmers and Swimming*, making Cibachrome prints from slides. She shoots above and below the water with Tri-X and infrared film loaded into Olympus and Hasselblad cameras. These photographs of young and old swimmers engage the viewer's attention, recreating the interaction she feels when looking through the viewfinder into her subject's eyes.

CLARK, GEORGE LUTHER (Painter)

1104 3rd St., Hermosa Beach, CA 90254

Born: 1908 *Awards:* Merit Scholarship, Art Students League of New York; Merit Scholarship, Otis Art Institute *Collections:* San Raphael Cattle Company, Patagonia, AZ *Exhibitions:* Fowler Mills Gallery, Santa Monica; Nelson Rockefeller Gallery, Costa Mesa *Education:* Art Students League of New York; Otis Institute of Art *Dealer:* Los Angeles County Museum Rental Gallery

Shortly after completing his formal art training, he walked across the United States. This odyssey has provided a background for his work, which is drawn entirely from memory and imagination. Landscapes, harbors, inland waterways and farms of the American East, West and South are intensely personal records that document his personal experiences as a traveler, longshoreman, house painter and farmhand. Documenting the simplicity of his experiences, he seeks through the use of traditional methods to create a contemporary feeling in the paintings. Expressing a feeling of innocence and charm, he attempts through design and color to intensify the immediacy of a memory of a particular experience. He has begun

Alice Cronin, *Delphi,* 32 x 40, acrylic, mixed media with monotype chine colle

Jeff Chun, *Morning Stretch,* 15 x 20, prismacolor and charcoal pencil on illustration board

recently to experiment with abstraction, exploring the use of symbols to represent farms, houses, people and animals.

CLARK, RICK (Ceramist)
173 Downey St., San Francisco, CA 94117

Born: 1954 *Awards:* Crafts Award, Art in the Park, San Francisco *Exhibitions:* San Francisco Art Commission Gallery; De Young Museum Art School Gallery, San Francisco *Education:* U. of Oklahoma; Santa Fe Workshops of Contemporary Art

He developed an interest in color-field abstraction during his early work as a painter. When he progressed to work in ceramics, he built on this interest and applied his color abstraction skills to three-dimensional work. He has recently completed a series of ten abstract ceramic altarpieces using the raku process, which he chooses for its spontaneity. His works have a Mayan and pre-Columbian influence, which he effects by using the centuries-old potting techniques. He uses this ancient style in an urban setting to create urban works with cross-cultural links.

CLARKE, GEORGINA (Painter)
P.O. Box 4261, San Pedro, CA 90731

Born: 1935 *Awards:* Merit Award, Art Students League, NYC *Collections:* Techsteel Corporation, Atlanta; Mr. Gazanfar & Rani of Hunza, King & Queen of Hunza State, India *Exhibitions:* Hyatt Regency, Long Beach; Southern California Contemporary Art Association, Los Angeles *Education:* San Francisco Art Institute

The artist's work embodies her search for universal truth and its expression in tangible form. Her painting *Om Mandala* received international recognition after Unicef distributed greeting card reproductions of it worldwide. Her interpretation of the Buddhist graphic symbol of the universe, Om Mandala, has become a leitmotif she continues to explore. A certified yoga instructor, she experiences painting as an opportunity to commune with the supreme consciousness of the universe. The ethereal quality of her work can be traced to her extensive training in color theory, as well as her mastery of airbrush technique. Her large-scale paintings of cloud and space phenomena glow with inner luminosity, and evoke the vastness of limitless space.

CLAUSSEN, JAMES (Painter, Printmaker)
878 Green Ave., San Bruno, CA

Born: 1953 *Collections:* National Museum of Fine Arts, Rio de Janeiro; Pratt Institute, NYC *Exhibitions:* Library of Congress, Washington D.C.; Soker-Caseman Gallery, San Francisco *Education:* U. of Washington; Kansas City Art Institute *Dealer:* Don Soker, San Francisco

His traditional academic training acquainted him with the figurative and narrative principles he developed as a surrealist. Now, as more of a formalist, he uses inanimate objects as subjects, juxtaposing them in strict compositions, which focus on spatial relationships and visual balance. He uses color to complement these forms, and to add texture to the painting's physical presence. As a printmaker, he uses only his own drawings on stone lithographs. Here, he uses colors and forms to highlight the stone's texture, rather than imposing a design unrelated to the medium. Whether working on stone or canvas, he strives for movement and emotion, through blended colors and exacting shapes.

CLEMENT, JOYCE (Jeweler)
P.O. Box 324, Bolines, CA 94924

Born: 1942 *Awards:* Fine Crafts Award and Grant, Marin Arts Council; Jewelry Award, Marin Society of Artists, Open Sculpture and Crafts Exhibition and Competition *Collections:* Oakland Museum *Exhibitions:* Susan Cummins Gallery, Mill Valley; Fisher's Custom Design Jewelry *Education:* UC-Berkeley; Gemological Institute of America

Seeking a creative outlet while pursuing her doctorate, she began to make jewelry over ten years ago. Early work featured simple organic forms in sheet metal. She now creates geometric, consciously designed pieces in a variety of precious metals, stones and gems. Nature, the relationships among people, the characteristics of her chosen materials, the desires of her clients and the jewelry-making process itself all fuel her creative imagination. She places her work in the fine arts and crafts category, and cites Wendell Castle's woodwork as an inspiration. She calls her pieces of jewelry "small sculptures," believing that only her insistence that they be functional differentiates them from fine art.

CLENDANIEL, NANCY (Photographer)
853 N. Citrus Ave., Los Angeles, CA 90038

Born: 1949 *Exhibitions:* Los Angeles Photography Center

Following formal training as a painter, she moved into theatrical photography, doing production stills at Long Wharf and other theatres in New Haven, Connecticut. Her move to California followed a stint as house production photographer in Chicago. On the West Coast, she has worked for and photographed such notables as John Davidson, Ray Charles, Jerry Lee Lewis and Manhattan Transfer. Her concert photography is done primarily on location, although she also executes studio portraits occasionally. Working from the premise that form is defined by light, she tends to look for the chiaroscuro and avoids technical manipulation of the image. Director of the non-profit organization Women in Photography, she also takes pictures in the travel photography genre, including a series of images of racetracks in Great Britain.

CLOSE, CHRISTIE (Painter)
P.O. Box 1070, Capitola, CA 95010

Born: 1945 *Collections:* TRI L Associates, Saratoga; Stevenson & Prarie, Attorneys, San Diego *Exhibitions:* Tager Gallery, Santa Cruz; Villa Montalvo Center for the Arts, Los Gatos *Education:* Fresno State College; Cabrillo College

Her work is compounded of a number of divergent influences: her drawing teacher H. Ikemoto; Salvador Dali's illustrations for the Jerusalem Bible; and the pre-World War I works of Austrian painter Egon Schiele. She works in watercolor, exporing ways to expand the traditional limits of watercolor practice. She also works with metallic crayon and watercolor pencil, and has explored the dissolution of the rectangular format and its concomittant restraints on composition. Recent paintings verge on abstraction, and feature images of islands and of the Monterery Bay Peninsula. She has been exhibiting and marketing her work since 1975, and, since 1987, has produced several interior acrylic murals by commission.

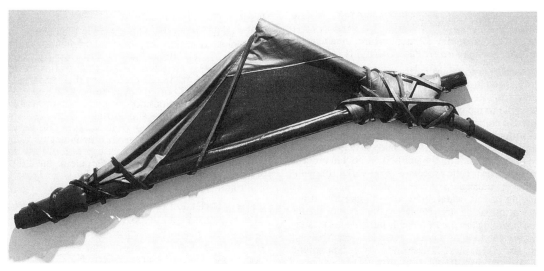

Victor A. Cohen-Stuart, *untitled,* 48 x 120, canvas, wood, masking tape, acrylic

Brian Frank Carter, *Manscapes,* 34 x 48, acrylic

Joyce Clements, *Sun Spots (ring),* 1.5 x .7, 14 carat gold, citrene, diamonds. Photograph: Mel Schockner

341

CLOSE, CHUCK (Painter)
271 Central Park West, New York, NY 10024

Born: 1940 *Awards:* Fulbright Fellowship; NEA Fellowship *Collections:* Museum of Modern Art, NYC; Whitney Museum *Exhibitions:* Los Angeles County Museum of Art; California Museum of Photography, Riverside *Education:* U. of Washington School of Art; Yale U. School of Art & Architecture; Academy of Fine Arts, Vienna *Dealer:* Pace Gallery, NYC

Large-scale photo-realist portraits of faces in black and white gained him recognition in 1967. A grid system was used to transfer the photographic image as accurately as possible to the canvas. Similar giant faces were also painted in color, employing layers of the three primary colors much like the color-printing process of photography, a process visible in *Mark.* Since 1972 grid systems have often been left on the finished product in order to emphasize the artistic process. A large variety of media have been utilized in the execution of these works, including pastels, watercolors, oils, "fingerprint drawings," printmaking and collage. A number of techniques, including the use of a highly intricate grid system to create the look of a computer- generated drawing, have also been used. These innovative experiments have turned portraits into icons, expanding the concept of portraiture.

CLYMER, ALBERT ANDERSON (Painter)
P. O. Box 2278, Yountville, CA 94599

Born: 1942 *Awards:* 1st Place, Berkeley Museum; 1st Place, Laguna Beach Festival of Art *Collections:* Newport Museum; Levi Strauss Co. *Exhibitions:* Pallas Museum of Fine Art; Exhibition of American Art, Chautauqua, NY *Education:* Texas A & M; Napa College

Most recently, his subject matter has emphasized the mysticism of American Indians and derives from his childhood in the Southwest. These paintings lay outside the tradition of Western art, focusing on a pure expression of medium and an investigation of form. He paints in a representational style with a freedom of gesture that borders on the abstract. His simple palette and highly articulated tonal variations reflect his background as a watercolorist.

COAR, NORLYN (Painter)
P.O. Box 3697, Manhattan Beach, CA 90266

Born: 1949 *Collections:* San Francisco Hilton; Westin Maui Resort Hotel *Exhibitions:* Toluca Lake Galleries, Burbank; Stables Gallery, Taos, NM *Education:* UC-Santa Barbara *Dealer:* Courtyard Collection, Los Angeles; Fidelity Arts, Los Angeles

In the 1970s, she was concerned with both the function of the mythological and the interaction of seen and unseen worlds. Working with bands of color, she created fluid spaces that changed densities as one "world" modulated into another. By the 1980s, her imagery had evolved into scenes involving nymphs, satyrs, muses and earthscapes. These works, too, resolved into a meeting or unification of physical and spiritual realms. She usually works with watercolor and metallic gouaches on textured rice paper. Interweaving structure and form, she often paints representationally abstract images over a grid or imposes that structure on her imagery.

COBURN, DWIGHT (Painter, Sculptor)
15 Easton Ct., Orinda, CA 94563

Born: 1948 *Collections:* Seattle Art Museum *Exhibitions:* Harleen/Allen, San Francisco; Davidson Gallery, Seattle *Education:* Wayne State University *Dealer:* Harleen/Allen, San Francisco

After spending ten years immersed in the abstract expressionist tradition, he returned to figuration. Influences, as he made his way into neo-figurative expressionism, included artists Philip Guston and James McGarrell. Initially color was the major structural component, but gradually he became interested in designing the composition around an image to tell a story. Roberto Matta and Anselm Kiefer became major influences at this time. He works in both acrylic and oil on large canvases, from 6-by-9-feet to 10-by-12-feet. His years as an abstract expressionist are still apparent in his gestural style. His palette includes a bold use of primary colors, offset by large areas of black and white.

CODY, BRUCE J.(Painter)
2130 E. Noble Pl., Littleton, CO 80121

Born: 1941 *Collections:* CitiCorp, NYC; Mountain Bell, Denver *Exhibitions:* American Artist Competition, NYC; Grand Central Gallery, NYC *Education:* U. of Wyoming, Laramie; Washington State U., Pullman *Dealer:* David Epstein, Berkeley

In the 1960s, after many years of abstract painting, he developed a series of surrealistic etchings and lithographs that led him to a renewed focus on the figure and landscape. By 1973, he was focusing on plein air landscapes, and this work progressed to images of urban Denver and of Southwestern landscapes. He begins with lean washes and gradually employs more paint, and his surfaces are lush with impasto. In his finely tuned color modulations, he runs the gamut from subtle shifts of grays to clear, full-spectrum hues. Using oils on linen, he has achieved a painterliness beyond the normal confines of verisimilitude.

COHEN, HELEN (Sculptor)
P.O. Box 769, Groveland, CA 95321

Born: 1930 *Awards:* NEA Fellowship; Small Sculpture, Triton Museum *Exhibitions:* U. of California, Davis; Fresno Art Center and Museum *Education:* San Jose State U.; California College of Arts and Crafts

For years of she painted in oil and watercolor; then, the lectures of Sam Richardson on the definition of sculpture inspired her to begin working in three dimensions. Her mixed- media pieces explore the relationship of everyday objects to their contexts and to their value as carriers of memory. A vintage hairdryer stands divorced from its historical moment until a look through its air vent reveals a beauty parlor of the 1950s, complete with turquoise and pink plastic styling chairs. A washroom, a kitchen and a motel room occupy a paper towel holder, a toaster and a shaving kit. The objects are never exotic or unusual, their outside-in rooms never contain inhabitants. Rather the viewers' incipient presence is implied, or that of their mother, grandfather, aunt, by a discarded shoe, food on the table, crumpled paper towels. The voyeurism felt from peering through cracks at such meticulous detail gives her work a surrealist quality; careful lighting and, often, an accompanying soundtrack of music or banal news reports add to the sense of deja-vu. She constructs all pieces within the

Norlyn Coar, *Horse,* 48 x 60, watercolor and metallic gouache on rice paper.
Courtesy: San Francisco Hilton Hotel

Lee Chesney, *untitled,* 22 x 30, acrylic, gouache, watercolor on d'Arches paper. Courtesy: Mrs. Bett Chesney

interiors herself from clay, heavy watercolor paper, balsa wood and wire.

COHEN, KNOX (Painter)
Rt. 22, Box 934, Tyler, TX 75704

Born: 1943 *Education:* East Texas State U.

His major influence is Van Gogh; other inspirations include Klee, Chagall and Picasso. He began painting in 1963, soon moving to acrylics for ease of clean-up. His style, which he calls "visionary" or "contemplative," has developed independently of pressures from the artistic mainstream. He shows a passion for vibrant colors and a full palette, and has done works on aluminum with oil and acrylic that play tricks with light because of the metal's reflective properties. A good example of his bold use of color and light is *New Wave Lao-Tsu.* He has studies art history with Paul Kelpe, one of the founders of the American Geometric Abstract school.

COHEN, MARGERY (Painter)
760 B Pierce, Albany, CA 94706

Born: 1952 *Collections:* BAIR Associates- International Trading, San Francisco; Donelly/Colt Publications, Hampton, CT *Exhibitions:* Sushi California, Berkeley; Magic Theater, San Francisco *Education:* Windham College

She spent her reclusive childhood sketching introspectively. Showing evidence of the influence of New York abstract expressionism during the 1950s, these images became strictly abstract while maintaining their own distinctive style. Hundreds of square panels emulsified with oil and varnish convey a sense of liquid movement. The mid-1980s presented a time for deeper self expression. Childhood images emerged, at first superimposed on the abstract pieces, later taking over completely. In all the work, her stream-of-conscious approach to applying paint remains the same. Her recent work is often described as disturbing, surrealistic, humorous and psychological.

COHEN, SHARON (Video Artist, Computer Painter)
124 W. 93rd St., #8E, NYC 10025

Born: 1965 *Exhibitions:* California Arts, Valencia *Education:* California Institute of the Arts

Student work went beyond traditional drawing and painting, and into the realm of video. She mixed original music and poetry with drawing, painting, live action video and propped subject matter. She has recently returned to drawing and painting via a computer "paintbox." This medium uses photon paint instead of traditional media. She approaches the computer like a canvas or sketch pad, working with the same formal concerns those media demand. At the same time, she takes advantages of the computer's special properties. She is interested in unifying her psychology with the flawless rendering of a computer.

COHN, BONITA (Ceramist, Photographer)
1538 Jones St., San Francisco, CA 94109

Born: 1947 *Awards:* 2nd Prize, Photography Contest, Bay Guardian; Award of Merit, Ceramics, Hayward Festival of the Arts *Exhibitions:* ARC Gallery, Chicago; California Crafts Museum, San Francisco *Education:* San Francisco Art Institute; Alfred University

As a potter, teacher and artist, she has been involved in clay for over eighteen years. She specializes in marbleized porcelain—a medium for exploring patterns in natural formations. Neriage, an ancient technique of laminating colored clay, affords her the pleasure of interpreting the landscape with her bare hands. She makes bowls and plates, each one uniquely blending classical thrown forms with her version of marbleized clay. Her work in photography also involves the interpretation of landscapes; she finds her work in clay feeding her ideas in photography, and vice versa.

COIT, MADELIN (Painter)
Contemporary Artists' Services, 9520 Jefferson Blvd., Culver City, CA 90232

Born: 1943 *Collections:* Security Pacific Bank, Los Angeles; Port Authority of New York and New Jersey, Washington D.C. *Exhibitions:* Sylvia Haimoff White Exhibition Annex, Los Angeles; Eloise Pickard Smith Gallery, UC-Santa Cruz *Education:* U. of Connecticut, Storrs

She paints the light of Southern California after the Rococo and Flemish Masters. Like Jan Van Eyck, she concentrates on the reflective qualities of oil paint in order to capture the liquid atmosphere of the coast. Her "First Light" paintings deal with visual illusion and disorientation in space. Hundreds of layers of oil and clear lacquer allow light to enter the surface and bounce back, creating a confusion of background and foreground. Clouds do not interrupt subtle color fields of sky, but the sensual presence of water in the air is evident. Through an assemblage technique, her "Ablate Series" peels away layers of experience to expose its foundations. The formal surface is defined with drafting tape, then pigment is added and the tape is removed. The canvas may be redefined with additional tape, pigment and gestural drawing. While measures are taken to insure the life of the piece, certain materials are not worked in this manner so that they fall to the bottom of the frame, leaving behind a tan mark, an echo or memory.

COKE, VAN DEREN (Photographer)
California College of Arts and Crafts, Oakland, CA 94681

Born: 1921 *Awards:* Guggenheim Fellowship *Collections:* Museum of Modern Art, NYC; San Francisco Museum of Modern Art *Exhibitions:* Oakland Museum; Phoenix Art Museum *Education:* U. of Kentucky; Indiana U.

His photography has been influenced by Man Ray, Christian Schad, Richard Hamilton and Andy Warhol. Early black-and-white work employed the "flash" technique, in which he flashed a white light in the darkroom as the print was developing. This tended to blur the literalism of the image, while it retained its link to reality. Max Ernst-style juxtaposition can be seen in *U.S. Highway 441,* an image of a wrecked car at the peak of a hill, with a Coca-Cola sign lying below it. His later autobiographical work makes references to art, rather than banal, every-day events. He began to use color, again with the "flash" technique, producing exotic browns, plums and grays. Henry Holmes Smith says of his work ". . . Urban man can always see, without half- looking, irrational terror, cruelty, carelessness and waste. Coke's themes are based on those psychological reaches that we must now include in what we call 'reality,' and he uses this matter with great distinction. Coke's urban art is genuine, disturbing and true."

Helen Cohen, *Trash Can,* 24 x 11 x 14, mixed media

Fay Conn, *The Garden,* 18 x 24, etching

COLBURN, SAM (Painter, Draughtsperson)
375 Asilomar Blvd., Pacific Grove, CA 93950

Born: 1909 *Awards:* 1st Place in Watercolor, Monterey County Fair; 1st Place in Watercolor, Pacific Grove Museum of Natural History *Collections:* Monterey Museum of Art *Exhibitions:* Santa Barbara Museum of Art; William Kargus Fine Art, Carmel; Carmel Art Association *Education:* Chouinard Art Institute

Empathy is the basis for his relationship with subject matter. His media are watercolor, pencil, pencil and India ink wash, and occasionally oil. He has never been interested in literal representation and his technique has become looser over time. Watercolor is his favorite medium and he dilutes the paint with a lot of water. When he draws people or animals, he tries to capture the feeling of his subjects. He is increasingly involved with organic form. His more abstract interest in geometric shapes is shown in his use of farm buildings. He has been influenced by John Marin and Charles Burchfield.

COLE, ANASTASIA (Painter)
341 Occidental Ave., Burlingame, CA 94010

Born: 1938 *Awards:* Grant, San Mateo Foundation *Exhibitions:* King Charles Gallery, Burlingame; Metro Contemporary Gallery, San Mateo *Dealer:* King Charles, Burlingame; Metro Contemporary Gallery, San Mateo

Early work was as a fashion illustrator and display artist in Detroit. Since moving to California, she has used a variety of techniques, including collage, oil, silk-screen, etching and mixed media. She decorated the only Chinese mortuary in San Francisco's Chinatown. Her paintings range in subject matter from impressionistic to abstract. The mix of her craft and art background allows her to create new forms of collage. Her large acrylic abstracts have a natural, poetic feeling. When traveling, she uses watercolors to capture the light surrounding her subjects.

COLE, BERNADETTE (Painter, Ceramist)
81 Terrace Walk, Berkeley, CA 94717

Born: 1913 *Awards:* Purchase Awards, Painting and Pottery, California State Fair *Collections:* Crocker Art Museum, Sacramento *Exhibitions:* Oakland Museum; Art Works Gallery, Fair Oaks *Education:* San Francisco State U.

Working with different media and techniques, she paints semi- abstract land- and seascapes. Her wheel-thrown pottery and ceramic sculptures feature a variety of subjects, presentations and construction methods. Here, her main interest is in high-fire reduction glazes, celadons and copper reds, and in other low- and high-fire and oxidation glazes. Her work in ceramics comprises intricately decorated, inlaid plates and sculptures of animals. The latter have reached quite large sizes, and are designed for garden decoration. Hippos, buffaloes, bears, frogs and, more recently, cats are her most common subjects. Recently, she has been working on a series of inlaid plates which feature pelicans and other sea birds, set against large abstract areas of color. She has also done a sizable body of work in raku.

COLEMAN, WINFIELD (Painter)
159 Central Ave., San Francisco, CA 94117

Born: 1944 *Awards:* Best in Class, Marin County Exposition, San Raphael; NEA Grant *Exhibitions:* Open Studio, San Francisco; Southern Exposure Gallery, San Francisco *Education:* Cornell U.; Harvard U.

Raised in the Pacific Northwest, he was exposed early to Asian and regional art styles. After formal training in anthropology and abstract expressionism, he developed a style influenced by Sotatsu, Audubon and Matisse. During this time, he worked in a style based on the abstraction of natural forces, and worked mostly in oil on unprimed canvas. Fascinated by the confluence of science, mysticism and art, he re-evaluated the relationship between thought, subject and technique. The works of Georgia O'Keeffe and later research on Plains Indian art reinforced these interests. His art is covertly political, with an emphasis on the complex, diachronic interdependencies of the natural world. Working with pastel on colored grounds has led to an oil technique, which combines scumbling, glazing and wetbrush over a veil to enhance the harmonic effects of color.

COLLINS, DAN (Painter)
13150 Mulholland Dr., Beverly Hills, CA 90210

Born: 1954 *Awards:* Award of Excellence, Museum of Science and Industry, Ontario *Exhibitions:* Museum of Neon Art, Los Angeles; Los Angeles Municipal Art Gallery *Education:* Art Center School of Design

At 18, he supported himself by sketching portraits at arts and crafts shows. He soon began to paint in cafes, both in the U.S. and in Europe. The cafe paintings were portraits, but they also involved the treatment of the interior and exterior spaces of the cafe. In this period, he worked at night, following an interest in artificial light. His later work has moved from cafes to other interior locations such as pet shops, galleries and hobby shops— environments that include neon, electrical gadgets, sculpture and complex fixtures. These paintings usually include a portrait of the building's owner. Recently he has begun making large-scale works in oil on canvas with pieces of wood affixed to the canvas, creating a storefront or a landscape. These relief paintings still contain businesses and owners, real or imaginary.

COLLINS, DENNIS J. (Painter)
97 Spring Rd., Watsonville, CA 95076

Born: 1940 *Awards:* Award of Excellence, California Expo, Sacramento *Collections:* Cellocon Corp., Belmont; San Jose Public Library *Exhibitions:* Ohlone College, Fremont; Arizona State U., Tempe *Education:* San Jose State U.

Trained as a photo-realist, he was inspired by the emotional tension of Degas, Eakins, Wyeth and Raffael. He is a colorist known for his watercolor technique; his work derives emotional power from altered images and a rich painterly style. In figurative work, he recreates the brilliantly highlighted, un- posed figures that typify casual photographs; in his works from nature, he concentrates on the microcosm, rendering the point where abstraction and realism meet. He has recently been working on a series of cacti and succulents for a book on the botany of the American Southwest.

COLLINS, EUGENE (Multimedia Artist)
4943 Oak Park Way, Santa Rosa, CA 95409

Born: 1935 *Exhibitions:* Downey Museum of Art; Maple Woods Community College, Kansas City, MO *Education:* San Jose State U. *Dealer:* Union Hill Arts, Kansas City, MO

Winfield Coleman, *In Deep Water,* 19 x 25, pastel

Richard Camire, *Double Blind Study,* 54 x 96, oil on canvas

In the late 1950s, he was influenced by abstract expressionism. After military service, he resumed his studies and felt the pull of the 1960s movements: pop, hard edge and California funk. At the same time, he became interested in figuration. While teaching college in the 1970s, he began experimenting with etching and raku. His present work consists mainly of mixed-media paintings, printmaking and raku. Interested in layering ideas, techniques and materials, he incorporates cast life masks, ceramic inserts, wood constructions and found objects into painted surfaces, which are themselves enriched by sand and collage elements. He is currently most interested in the work of Robert Rauschenberg, Jasper Johns and Robert Hudson.

COLLINS, J. (Painter, Printmaker)
1223 Wilshire Blvd., #129, Santa Monica, CA 90403

Born: 1949 *Awards:* First Northwest Film Festival Award *Exhibitions:* Portland Art Museum; Pioneer Square, Seattle *Education:* U. of Oregon, Eugene; California Institute of the Arts

His previous work has ranged from printmaking and film projects to location works. Philosophical influences include Marcel Duchamp, John Cage, Robert Rauschenberg and Andy Warhol. Film projects include "Pit Viper," the "Filmosophy" works at UC-Davis, and his continuing performance project, "Visual Pursuit." Location works include *Nixon Headquarters*, a recreation of a 1960 Republican headquarters, during the 1980 presidential campaign. His non-representational collage/acrylic works center on a visualization of specific events in time, i.e. what a "Glimpse," "Snapshot" or "Passing Fancy" is like. The recent "Modern Hieroglyphics" monoprint series makes innovative use of color laser copiers.

COLLINS, JIHMYE (Painter)
1827 Midvale Dr., San Diego, CA 92105

Born: 1939 *Awards:* Finalist, Willoughby Senior Memorial for Deserving Artists *Exhibitions:* Villa Montezuma Gallery; Several Shades of Blue, La Jolla *Education:* Indiana U., Indianapolis

His artistic career began at the age of five. Throughout adolescence, he did portraits, physical movement drawings, and still lifes. In college he became fascinated with Charles White's profound expression of African American culture. His present paintings show a concern for the dignity of African Americans and other oppressed groups. His style is representational and he attempts to reflect the mood of the subject by developing a natural, cultural relationship and by using an unrestrained technique of multiple strokes. His multiple layers of color give the work a three-dimensional effect. He paints primarily with watercolor, but is also adept with oil and pencil drawings.

COLLINS, J.P. (Painter, Mixed Media Artist)
640 Octavia, #4, San Francisco, CA

Born: 1963 *Collections:* Mills College Collection *Exhibitions:* Silverwood Gallery, Costa Mesa; Aligator Gallery, San Francisco

Impressed by Matisse and Hopper, his pieces display a refined sense of line. He works in mixed media, including charcoal on wet gesso, acrylic paint on masonite, oil on canvas, and linoleum block prints. His subject matter is the urban landscape. *Water Works,* for example, is a painting of a gray water pipe, rendered on two pieces of wood, joined at a ninety-degree angle. A stenciled arrow contrasts with a drawn,

buffalo-like creature, pitting the formal against the expressive, the post-modern against the primitive. The gray color scheme, echoed formally in the architectural forms taken from the urban skyline, is symbolic of the impersonality of the city, and the ascension of the corporate over the personal.

COLLINS, TIM (Sculptor)
1466 San Bruno Ave., San Francisco, CA 94110

Born: 1956 *Exhibitions:* San Francisco Art Commission Gallery; Bay Front Park, Mill Valley *Education:* San Francisco Art Institute; U. of Rhode Island

His early work focuses on translating personal experiences— surfing, sailing, fishing and diving—into sculptural pieces. Eventually, the artist began to view studio work as divorced from "real-life experience." His emphasis therefore shifted to creating on-site pieces that explore and are consequently defined by site-specificity—in particular sites where water meets land. The sculptures frequently employ architectural spaces and objects, for instance a wooden shack, and incorporate water in some way. The pieces generate a quiet, spiritual space that invites awareness of place, of relationship and of seeing.

COLMAN, ALEXANDRA (Painter)
P.O. Box 50453, Santa Barbara, CA 93150

Born: 1942 *Awards:* 1st Prize, State Capital Museum, WA; 1st Prize, Angeles Arts in Action *Collections:* Hilton Hotel Corporation; Port Angeles Port Authority *Exhibitions:* Lynn Kottler Gallery, NYC; Galerie Triangle, Washington, D.C. *Education:* Sorbonne

From the very beginning of her interest in painting, she has portrayed the land and sea. Her work has progressed from charcoal drawings to watercolors, to paintings on silk (influenced by studies with Sakura Jameson), and finally back to works on paper and board. Her studies in Paris have had the greatest influence on her work. Her recent acrylic, pastel and mixed-media works reflect her original involvement with the paintings of Cezanne and Kandinsky. Fusing abstraction with a realistic observation of nature, her perceptions constantly restructure the visual world. Her method of preparing board with raw pigment and then combining acrylics with pastels for her subject is unique.

COLWELL, GUY (Painter)
The Rip-off Press, P.O. Box 4686, Auburn, CA 95604

Born: 1945 *Awards:* 1st Prize, Art in the Park, San Francisco *Exhibitions:* Triton Museum, Santa Clara; La Pena Cultural Center, Berkeley

Even while painting abstract and psychedelic colorism during his two years at the California College of Arts and Crafts, he felt that abstract modernism was heavy on image but empty of meaning, purpose or feeling and constituted a wasteland of aesthetic confusion. His style matured during two years in federal prison for refusing the draft. American social realists Wood, Sloane and Hopper, and the precise craftsmanship of Van Eyck, Bosch and Durer provided more constructive models as he developed a gritty, expressionistic realism that made strong statements about a world that must be changed. *Race Street,* painted shortly after his release in 1970, depicts a bloody race riot heavily populated with distorted figures and grotesque figures in livid oil colors. Later watercolors imbue erotic subjects with the same hot energy. He is also

Dennis J. Collins, *Sempervivum Calcareum,* 25 x 33, watercolor. Courtesy: Tim and Barb Zollin- Malm

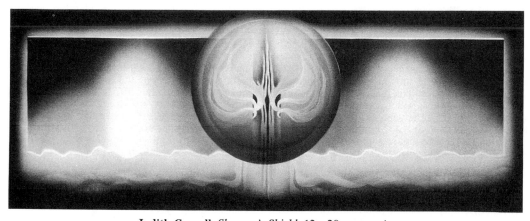

Judith Cornell, *Shaman's Shield,* 12 x 30, watercolor

known for his drawings in the adult Rip-Off Comix, and for court sketches of political and social trials throughout the 1970s. Recent work is less violent than his street scenes, and often moves into surrealism and erotic humor. A search for more positive images has led to nature images and wildlife art.

CONN, FAY (Painter)
1705 Westgate Ave., #8, Los Angeles, CA 90025

Awards: International Art Competition, Glendale; Award for Silkscreen, Brand Museum, Glendale *Collections:* Ms. Julie Mulvaney, Venice, CA; Markman Family, Venice, CA *Exhibitions:* Jewish Federation, Los Angeles; Unitarian Church, Santa Monica *Education:* Tyler School of Art; UCLA

Influenced by the precision and intimacy of the Dutch masters and by the lighter color palette of the Impressionists, she attempts to create a harmonious image using these seemingly disparate approaches to oil painting. At the same time, she does not limit herself to the seen world, sometimes using these techniques to portray dreamlike and fantastic images. Her palette is becoming lighter as she works toward a more refined and accurate style, perhaps influenced by Jan van Huysun. A painting of a bouquet of flowers on a table is reminiscent of the Impressionist's approach, only tighter. She uses both oil and oil pastels. Her line drawing of an egg beater is included in the text *Drawing on the Right Side of the Brain*, by Dr. Betty Edwards.

CONNELL, WILL (Sculptor)
P. O. Box 334, Glendora, CA 91740

Born: 1935 *Awards:* 1st Place, Annual Los Angeles Citywide Competition; 1st Place, Hillcrest Show, Los Angeles *Exhibitions:* Los Angeles Barnsdale Gallery; Depot Gallery, Yountville *Education:* UC-Berkeley *Dealer:* Los Angeles Contemporary Art Gallery

After working for fifteen years as a aerospace engineer, he began sculpting, using his engineering experience to explore new techniques and materials. Following a period during which he carved marble and wood, he discovered resin casting and set out to synthesize this technique with the use of wood and other materials. Typical sculptures are hollow and constructed by the reverse casting of resins on a mangrel. He then embeds wood mosaic designs to give the shape texture and color. The forms of the sculptures are abstract and organic, with a sense of lightness that is enhanced by the materials and by the smoothness of surface. The mosaics are not limited to rectilinear designs, but rather follow the sculpture's form to create mood and suggest contrasts in surface texture.

CONNER, BRUCE (Painter, Filmmaker)
45 Sussex St., San Francisco CA 94131

Born: 1933 *Awards:* NEA Grant; Guggenheim Fellowship *Collections:* Los Angeles County Museum of Art; San Francisco Museum of Modern Art *Exhibitions:* North Point Gallery, San Francisco; Los Angeles Museum of Contemporary Art *Education:* Brooklyn Museum Art School; San Francisco Art Institute *Dealer:* Smith Andersen Gallery, Palo Alto; Fraenkel Gallery, San Francisco

Early assemblages were made of photographs, feathers, fur and veils of fabric—silk, lace and chiffon. These surrealist works concerned humor, eroticism, fetishism, horror and death, most memorably in a figure of a baby doll in a high chair, scorched black as if destroyed at Hiroshima. Later work has been more direct and formal—in black-and-white drawings and paintings which seem to come from drug-induced visions. Many of these intricate designs are mounted on scrolls and framed in silk, a reminder of the earlier fetishistic works. His films have been exhibited extensively.

COOK, ANDY (Painter, Commercial Illustrator)
31423 Meadowbrook Ave., Hayward, CA 94544

Born: 1964 *Awards:* Best in the West; Gold Key Award, Oakland Museum *Collections:* Western Independent Bankers, Oakland; Hewlett Packard, Palo Alto *Exhibitions:* Diego Rivera Gallery, San Francisco Art Institute; Goodman Gallery, San Francisco *Education:* Calif. College of Arts and Crafts; San Francisco Art Institute

His early large-scale pencil drawings were influenced by surrealists Salvador Dali and Paul Delvaux. Later, painting in acrylics and oils, he experimented with abstract and representational depictions. Some of these works involved collage and wash techniques. He studied airbrush techniques and traditional painting with Tom Akawie at the San Francisco Art Institute. He has since followed a classical approach to composition and concentrated on technical perfection. His "Art of Bodybuilding" series consisted of six larger-than-life bodybuilding figure studies painted with acrylics on wood. This was influenced by Hellenistic and Italian Renaissance figures. He is currently combining traditional and modern techniques of brush, airbrush, and collage in paintings laden with personal artistic struggle.

COOK, LIA (Fiber Artist)
c/o Allrich Gallery, 251 Post St., San Francisco, CA 94610

Born: 1942 *Awards:* NEA Fellowship; NEA Special Project Grant *Collections:* American Craft Museum, NYC; Museum of Modern Art, NYC *Exhibitions:* San Francisco Museum of Modern Art; San Jose Museum of Art *Education:* UC-Berkeley *Dealer:* Allrich Gallery, San Francisco; Gallery Three, Austin, TX

Her early large-scale woven hangings employ a variety of materials including cotton, wool and polyurethane fibers. Working with an airbrush, space dyeing and photographic transfers, she gives the impression of an underweave. In the late 1970s, she paused from these ribbed constructions and dye techniques to develop a series of small studies that she called "pressed weaves". These works employed post-weaving dyes and finishing processes to create shimmering low reliefs. More recent hangings in industrial rayon gain a three-dimensional quality from wads of foam inserted horizontally during the weaving process. The fabric is washed and hammered into shining relief before dotting on translucent dyes and opaque prints.

COOK, MICHAEL (Painter)
292 Coventry Rd., Kensington, CA 94707

Born: 1953 *Awards:* NEA Fellowship; Illinois Arts Council Fellowship *Exhibitions:* New Museum, NYC; Museum of Contemporary Art, Chicago *Education:* Florida State U.; U. of Dallas; U. of Oklahoma *Dealer:* Janet Steinberg Gallery, San Francisco; Iannetti/Lanzone Gallery, Inc., San Francisco

He worked in a figurative style from age 12 until college, at which time his works began to take the form of paintings on paper, canvas and masonite informed by mainstream issues stemming from conceptual and

Dede Coover, *Civilization–Puppets on a String,* 27 x 24, ink

Bruce Cody, *City Grids,* 46 x 54, oil on canvas. Courtesy: Carol Siple Gallery, Denver, CO

minimalist art. In this work, he began dealing with technology and its impact on culture and civilization, exploring the medium of video. His work since 1979 has been characterized by the contrast of ideas such as alchemy and particle physics, as if the vehicle of painting were an electron accelerator. His cycles of paintings address issues such as nuclear weapons research and use, food irradiation, war and love. He employs saturated colors, painted on a tar-like surface that literally sucks the paint into the canvas. For example, "Suite 71645" is a series of nine paintings that incorporates images from Soviet civil defense manuals evoking the ambiguity that exists between ideas and the ramifications of these ideas taking a physical form. The artist incorporates images from throughout the world into his work.

COOPER, CARLISLE (Painter)
286 N. Ashwood Ave., Ventura, CA 93003

Born: 1919 *Exhibitions:* Faulkner Gallery, Santa Barbara; Ventura County Government Center *Education:* School of the Art Institute of Chicago

Influenced by the colorists Boris Anisfeld and William Mosby, and by Isobel McKinnon Rupprecht (a student of Hans Hoffman), he has developed a stylized approach to figure painting. His work combines both eternal and contemporary themes, stong color and, often, surrealist references to outer space. Using only acrylic paints, he develops his large paintings from small gouache color studies. He builds with opaque paint, and later adds numerous color glazes for enrichment. He has exhibited in over twenty-five one-man shows throughout the world (Los Angeles, Atlanta, Berlin), including a July, 1989 exhibition in Munich.

COOPER, LOUISA S. (Painter)
1000 S. Bayfront, Balboa Island, CA 92662

Born: 1931 *Awards:* 1st Prize, Orange County Fair *Collections:* Southland Corporation; San Juan Capistrano Mission *Exhibitions:* American Artists Professional League; Knickerbocker Artists *Education:* UC-Irvine

Her work has developed out of an appreciation for traditional styles of lasting experience, reflecting her background in art history and the influence of her mother, a professional artist. Her paintings also are informed by her interest in archaeology, travel and architecture. Strongly influenced by European and American post-impressionism and the contemporary Northeast school, she uses oils in loose realism on large, square-format canvases. She is presently concentrating on her native Hawaii, capturing the natural color and vibrancy of the islands' foliage and mountains and the sea and sky. The realistic, representational work displays concern with color and form, with an impressionistic approach to the landscapes that underscores a sense of lightness enriched by flat, built-up colors.

COOPER, RON (Sculptor)
P.O. Box 667, Ranchos De Taos, NM 87557

Born: 1943 *Awards:* Theodoron Award, Guggenehim Museum, NYC *Collections:* Guggenheim Museum, NYC; Stedelijk Museum, Amsterdam, The Netherlands *Education:* Chouinard Art Institute *Dealer:* Ace Contemporary Exhibitions, Los Angeles

All of his work is characterized by the playful investigations of positive and negative space, voids and volumes. His most recent works are a series of portrait lamps and vases in cast bronze. In these pieces, the physical material of the sculpture exists purely to define and shape the negative space around itself—infusing the subject (a profile portrait) with an epheral presence, an illusion drawn from figure-ground perceptual psychology.

COOPER, RUFFIN (Photographer, Photo-Construction Artist)
285 Chestnut St., San Francisco, CA 94113

Born: 1942 *Awards:* Merit Award, New York Art Directors *Collections:* Bank of America; Chase Manhattan Bank *Exhibitions:* Brooklyn Museum; McAllen International Museum, McAllen, TX *Education:* Boston U. *Dealer:* Galerie Bast, Paris

A former writer, his first photographs were landscapes influenced by Ansel Adams; architectural icons such as the Golden Gate Bridge and the Statue of Liberty soon became his main subjects. In these photos, he uses color and scale in the manner of Frank Stella to reveal the more fragile elements of seemingly strong structures. He has recently begun combining photography with sculptural techniques, cutting apart his hand-colored photos of buildings and reshaping them using wire, metal and plastic. He has also created multi-image compositions influenced by David Hockney that combine human and non-human forms in a textural, contrasting process.

COOPER, SUSAN (Painter)
509 Eudora St., Denver CO 80220

Born: 1947 *Awards:* Artist-in-Residence, Roswell Museum, NM; Guest Resident, Yaddo, Saratoga Springs, NM *Collections:* Denver Art Museum; Roswell Museum, NM *Exhibitions:* Inkfish Gallery; Center for Contemporary Art, Los Angeles *Education:* UC-Berkeley *Dealer:* Paula Hughes, Inkfish Gallery, Denver

At Berkeley her oil still lifes and portraits were influenced by Elmer Bischoff and R.B. Kitaj. In 1974 she was commissioned by the School of American Research in Santa Fe to reconstruct a pueblo. In 1975 she moved to Denver and spent time doing landscapes, abstractions and two years of figuration. Returning to landscapes in the early 1980s she began experimenting with the third dimension creating what she calls "illusionistic, still- life installations." Composed of hard woods, such as maple and birch, they are constructed to appear two-dimensional but painted to appear three-dimensional. Often including references to art, she contrasts the commonplace (still lifes) with the grandiose (paintings and books).

COOVER, DEDE (Painter, Printmaker)
3008 Twin Oaks Rd., Cameron Park, CA 95682

Born: 1917 *Awards:* Humble Oil Co. Award; Manhattan Savings Bank *Collections:* International Science and Technology Magazine; Scovill Mfg. Co., Danbury, CT *Exhibitions:* Silvermine Guild of Artists, Silvermine, CT; American Can Corporation, Richfield, CT *Education:* Woodbury U. *Dealer:* Virginia Barrett, Chappaqua, NY; Gallery Talmadge, San Francisco

While studying with Fred Mitcham at the Dallas Museum of Art, she left her early realistic style and began to work abstractly. In the 1960s, she moved to the New York area, and was exposed to the color, design and shape of 20th century painting. She weaves bright-shaped segments of continuous color into tapestry-like paintings, leaving the viewer to

Dede Coover, *Floating World I,* 36 x 36, oil

Kitty Cantrell, *Beachmaster,* 14 x 10 x 9, bronze

Judith Cornell, *Illumined Matter,* 24 x 22, watercolor

Ande Lau Chen, *Mountain Glow,* 47 x 53, acrylic and paper on canvas

Helen Cohen, *Cake Box,* 7 x 9 x 9, mixed media. Courtesy: Braunstein/Quay Gallery

Martin Charlot, *Stars in Paradise,* 73 x 101, oil on linen

Helen Blair Crosbie, *Burt Reynolds L.A.,* 9 x 15, bronze

Dickens Chang, *It's Your Turn to Fly,* 40 x 50, oil on canvas. Courtesy: Dr. F. Meronk

Phillip P. Chan, *Annunciation,* 22 x 28, oil sticks

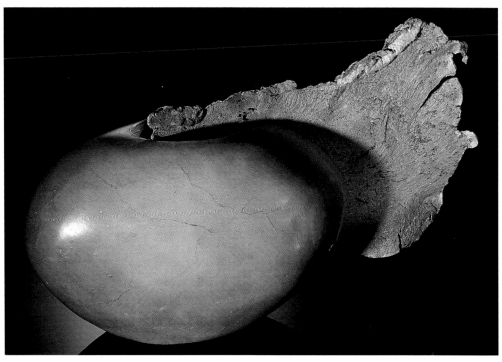

Ryan Carey, *Spirit Mother,* 17 x 26 x 8, mixed media construction. Photograph: Don Miller

Meg Huntington Cajero, *Mirage,* 22 x 30, transparent watercolor. Courtesy: Hunsaker/Schlesinger Gallery

Beverly Cassell, *Yamashira,* 25 x 102, oil on canvas

Keith Crown, *The Little Roads of Arroyo Moranda–Near Taos, NM,* 21 x 29, watercolor. Courtesy: Gallery Elena, Taos, NM

Maude Church, *Evolution: Foot Chart (Tribute to Julia Morgan),* 48 x 60, acrylic on canvas

Richard Camire, *Blue Ribbon,* 72 x 108, oil on canvas

Lee Chesney, *Last Dance,* 96 x 144, acrylic on canvas. Courtesy: Mrs. Bett Chesney

Bruce Cody, *By the City-Side,* 44 x 66, oil on canvas. Courtesy: Kaiser Permanente, Denver, CO

Winfield Coleman, *Wind,* 48 x 72, oil

Julia Couzens, *Calliope,* 60 x 128, oil on canvas

Alice Charlasch, *California Graffiti Series No. 36,* ©*1982,* 22 x 28, photomicrography

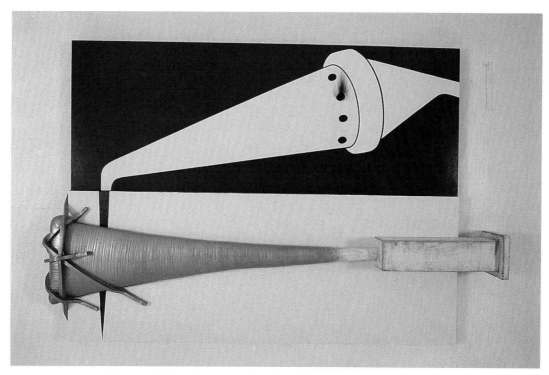

Victor A. Cohen-Stuart, *untitled,* 72 x 96, wood, masking tape, acrylic

Dennis J. Collins, *Echeveria Leucotricha,* 20 x 28, watercolor. Courtesy: Nafisa Taghioff

James Crable, *Commercial St., San Francisco II,* 31 x 42, cibachrome Courtesy: J.J.Brookings Gallery

Frances Caraker, *Whale/Jonah Myth,* 45 x 62, pastels and prismacolor pencils on watercolor paper

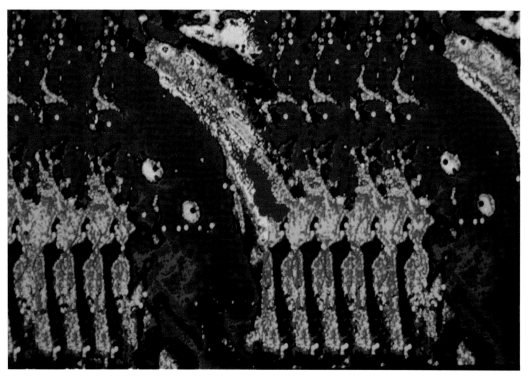

Rodney Chang, *Assembly,* 16 x 19, cibachrome Courtesy: Soho Too Gallery, Honolulu, HI

Martha Chatelain, *Explorations II,* 36 x 60 x 4, handmade paper wall sculpture

Ted Christensen, *Valley Storm,* 24 x 36, acrylic. Courtesy: West View Gallery, San Jose, CA

Jeff Chun, *Erin,* 48 x 30, oils

Norlyn Coar, *Dory #1,* 48 x 72, oil on canvas

Gene Collins, *Mi-Wuk,* 60 x 91 x 3, oil on canvas with sand, ceramic and skull insert

Alice Cronin, *East of Tokaido,* 26 x 40, acrylic, mixed media with monotype

Elizabeth Chandler, *A View from the Castle,* 30 x 44, monoprint

368

reconstruct her shimmering landscapes and florals. Some of her oil and watercolor works are abstract landscapes of pure design. Her black-and-white ink and acrylic work is bold in linear movement. Recently painting in oils, she creates abstract configurations of circles that are at once oriental and modern.

CORA, VLADIMIR (Painter)
c/o B. Lewin Galleries, 210 S. Palm Canyon Dr., Palm Springs, CA 92262

Born: 1952 *Awards:* Grand Prize, First Ibero-American Biennial, Monterrey, Mexico *Collections:* Centro de Arte Moderno, Guadalajara; Departmento de Bellas Artes, Guadalajara *Exhibitions:* Museum of Modern Art, Mexico City; Carillo Gil Museum, Mexico City *Dealer:* B. Lewin Galleries, Palm Springs

He has been acclaimed as one of the finest contemporary Mexican artists; his work has been exhibited throughout the U.S. and Latin America. Primarily using heavily textured oils and acrylics on canvas, he works in a rich abstract-expressionist style. He paints from a varied palette: cool greens, blues and purples; iridescent yellows and greens; and bold primary colors. Much of his imagery revolves around abstracted female nudes.

CORNELL, JUDITH (Painter)
15 Pearl St., Sausalito, CA 94965

Born: 1941 *Awards:* Institute of the Noetic Sciences, Sausalito; NEA *Exhibitions:* Marin Civic Center Galleries, San Rafael; City College of San Francisco *Education:* Nazareth College; State U. of New York, Alfred; Columbia Pacific University

Originally a ceramist, she explored many traditional and non-traditional approaches to clay, most notably color work in porcelain and low-fire clay. During the middle to late 1970s, she experimented with incorporating clay figures and painted canvas structures. She now paints in oils and watercolors, working within the Abstract Expressionist school. Light, color and luminescence are the main focuses of her work, and she evokes a quality of spirituality through the use of abstract color fields and glazes. She is also an art educator, and she encourages her students to improve their work through expanded artistic consciousness gained through visualization exercises and other innovative methods.

CORNING, ALICE (Ceramist)
209 Ethel Ave., Mill Valley, CA 94941

Born: 1943 Exhibitions; Worden Gallery, San Francisco; Mill Valley Library

She uses glazes to express the deep connection she feels with nature. From the ceramic traditions of China and Japan, she has taken a vessel orientation and an appreciation for the infinite possibilities for refinement presented by that simple form. Since the early 1980s she has been making on a series of more complex slab-built triangular vessels. Geometry and balance are primary in these pieces. Her recent works include torso vessels, in which the form of the figure acts as a metaphor for the figure/ vessel of life. She works in both porcelain and stoneware and reduction fires her pieces to Cone Ten.

CORREIA, STEVEN V. (Glass and Laser Light Sculptor)
P.O. Box 294, Topanga, CA 90290

Born: 1949 *Awards:* Edwin F. Guth Memorial Award of Merit, I.E. Society of North America; International Lighting Design Award of Merit, I.E. Society of North America *Collections:* Metropolitan Museum of Art, NYC; Smithsonian Institution, Washington D.C. *Exhibitions:* Los Angeles Olympics; Kentucky Derby Museum, Louisville *Education:* U. of Hawaii; UCLA

He works with light and space, crystal and glass objects. *Southern Lights* in San Diego is the first permanent, site-specific, kinetic Laser Sculpture in the U.S. It interacts with the architecture and environment in an ever-changing dance of light, visible for fifteen miles, two hours every night. His second permanent Laser Light Sculpture, for the San Diego Design Center, premiered in October, 1989; it interacts with the first to form a monument to San Diego's northern gate. "Firelight" and "Starlight" are his two series of limited edition optical lead crystal sculptures.

COST, JAMES PETER (Painter, Printmaker)
P. O. Box 3638, Carmel, CA 93921

Born: 1923 *Awards:* Franklin Mint Golf Medal *Collections:* R. W. Norton Museum, Shreveport, LA; Monterey Museum of Art *Exhibitions:* R. W. Norton Museum *Education:* UCLA *Dealer:* Betty Jo Cost

He began his career as an abstractionist and a set designer for MGM. Studies of more traditional methods of work led to a complete shift in style to rigorous realism that concentrates on landscapes. The landscapes are primarily in watercolor, though he also does a small number of serigraphs. He first thoroughly sketches in very thin oil on board, paper or canvas and then lays on watercolors, oil glazes and occasionally pastels. He considers technique as a support for the subject matter, which is the most important element in a work. Seascapes and other scenic paintings reveal a use of detail and light reminiscent of the Dutch Old Masters, particularly Pieter de Hooch. The composition comprises an vibrant, kinetic inter-relation between elements that involves the viewer and is accentuated by the use of up twenty-two colors in his palette.

COTINOLA, BERNADETTE (Painter, Sculptor)
11727 Sundale Ave., Hawthorne, CA 90250

Born: 1959 *Exhibitions:* Santa Monica Art Show; Affair in the Garden, Beverly Hills

As a young child, she studied the work of her idols, Norman Rockwell and Carl Faberge. Collecting books, cards and calendars, she was inspired by their work; eventually, she developed her own style, working not on canvas, but on rocks, wood, bones and, her favorite, eggs. Using acrylics, she works on a collection of exotic egg shells, including ostrich, rhea, swan, alligator and emu. With intricate precision, selected portions of the egg painting are sculptured by a special process. The result is a lace-like, three dimensional form of shadow and light.

COTRELL, RUSS (Painter, Mixed Media Artist)
9842 Hamilton #3, Huntington Beach, CA 92646

Born: 1951 *Exhibitions:* Bevel Cut Gallery, Corona del Mar *Education:* School of the Ozarks

He uses oils, pastels, airbrush, and resin in a slightly abstract impressionist style. The work is figurative and often includes collage elements, such as hot glue, gold leaf, copper leaf and alligator paper. He often paints two or three works, then cuts them up and assembles them into another complete piece. He works intuitively, using a bright palette of reds, oranges and greens with black, and he strives for a fresh, expressive appearance. Paintings are framed in acrylic. He sees the role of modern art changing from a fulfillment of expressive needs to an answer to commercial demands.

COUZENS, JULIA (Painter)
P.O. Box 2641, Sacramento, CA 95812

Born: 1947 *Awards:* Public Art Grant, Sacramento Metropolitan Arts Commission; Increase Robinson Graduate Fellowship, Cal. State-Sacramento *Collections:* Humboldt Arts Council *Exhibitions:* Downey Museum of Art, Los Angeles; Crocker Art Museum, Sacramento *Education:* UC-Davis; Calif. College of Arts and Crafts, Oakland *Dealer:* Himovitz/Salomon, Sacramento; Jeremy Stone, San Francisco

Her work has focused on drawings of the figure, with a particular emphasis on a graphic energy that would materialize qualities transcending mere pictorialization. She came to believe in the power of drawing as an end in itself and the image of the human figure as the classic vehicle for artistic expression. Her media and forms include wood construction using both found and ready-made material such as garden trellises, and painting with relief materials such as plaster and sand. She does not seek obvious formal consistency in her work or her style, and she is working in figuration and abstraction, painting and sculpture. Her drawings are large, direct, confrontational images of faces. The paintings, on the other hand, are abstract. She uses a variety of oil paints, as well as spray and enamel paint. She also often uses hand-made stencils to create an image, the process of paint removal becoming as much an act of painting as is the application of pigment.

COVENTRY, ROBIN W. (Painter)
P.O. Box 195C, Rt.2, Templeton, CA 93465

Born: 1944 *Collections:* Glasgow Art Gallery and Museum; Coast Gallery, Big Sur *Exhibitions:* Stanford U.; Royal Scottish Academy, Edinburgh *Education:* Glasgow School of Art

He was trained at the Glasgow School of Art. In his early "Changing Face of Glasgow" series, he documented the destruction of that city's old tenement buildings against a background of sterile high rises. This culminated in a TV feature on his art, and illustrations for Scottish newspapers. He moved to the U.S. in 1972, and has continued to work with watercolors and pen and ink. His technique simplified, and he focused on abstract illusions, seen in the shapes of trees, landscapes and rocks. The interplay of realism and nature's pure abstraction is a continuing theme in his work; he is interested in the adventures of the inner mind. His lyrically abstract drawings are influenced by the cave paintings at Lascaux, and, in his mixed media work, he distorts scale, changes color and arranges objects such as flower heads, metal scraps and peace badges in abstract ways.

COWIN, EILEEN (Photographer)
3918 Van Buren Place, Culver City, CA 90230

Born: 1947 *Awards:* NEA Fellowship *Collections:* Museum of Modern Art, NYC; Los Angeles County Museum of Art *Exhibitions:* Los Angeles County Museum of Art; Whitney Museum, NYC *Education:* Illinois Institute of Technology *Dealer:* Jayne Baum Gallery, NYC; Roy Boyd Gallery, Santa Monica

She stages, arranges and directs scenarios for the camera. In many of her early pictures, she explored the symbolic portrayal of emotions. The works were photographic fictions, dramas and plays about relationships, and the influences ranged from Robert Rauschenberg and Jasper Johns to "Father Knows Best" and "Ozzie and Harriet." The recent work is more involved with gesture and pose, straddling the line between reality and fiction. Her main concerns are the way in which media represents life and the reinterpretation of art-historical themes. The pieces range in scale from 8-by-10 inches to 4-by-5 feet and are in both black and white and color.

COX, ALVIN L. (Sculptor, Printmaker)
150 G St., No. 2, Arcata, CA 95521

Born: 1944 *Awards:* Outstanding Achievement in 3-D Design, Institute of American Indian Art *Exhibitions:* Keeping the Home Fire Burning, Eureka; Humboldt Cultural Center, Eureka *Education:* Institute of American Indian Art; U. of Kansas

While in formal training as a painter, he worked in the figurative style of C.M. Russell and Remington. Now a sculptor, his stylized work concentrates more on form and texture than on detail. With his wood and cast-metal figures, familiar realistic forms are given an abstract interpretation to create a "dreamlike" effect. His past experience manifests itself in the limited amount of color which he adds to many of his two- to three-foot wooden sculptures. Although current projects are not influenced by any specific movement, a great deal of time is spent observing the work of his peers.

CRABLE, JAMES (Photographer)
261 Green St., Harrisonburg, VA 22801

Born: 1939 *Awards:* Virginia Prize for the Visual Arts; First Prize Gold Medal, 1984 Los Angeles International Art Competition *Collections:* IBM Collection, Charlotte, NC; Equitable Life Assurance, NYC *Exhibitions:* J.J. Brookings Gallery, San Jose; Monterey Peninsula Museum of Art *Education:* Rochester Institute of Technology; Chelsea School of Art, London *Dealer:* J.J. Brookings Gallery, San Jose

After formal training in painting and printmaking, he began experimenting in the early 1970s with various photographic approaches. Using the still photographer's techniques of framing, focus and exposure, he started to arrange color prints into large-scale grid compositions. His recent work, "People and Architecture," presents urban man in relation to his contemporary architectural environment. The complex creations merge a series of photographs from the same location, each individual unit showing different people moving into, along or out of the same architectural backdrop—sidewalks, doorways, stairways, subways and escalators. Although his media is photography, his work reveals the strong influence of such painters as Mondrian, Leger, Klee and Noland.

CREIGHTON, LYNN (Sculptor)
9127 Encino Ave., Northridge, CA 91325

Born: 1938 *Exhibitions:* L.A. Art Gallery; New York Century Gallery, Sylmar *Education:* Cal. State-Northridge; Temple University

She began working with clay as a potter, but in searching for new forms, she discovered that sculpture provided a broader and more exciting field for investigation. Maximizing the plastic qualities of clay, she set

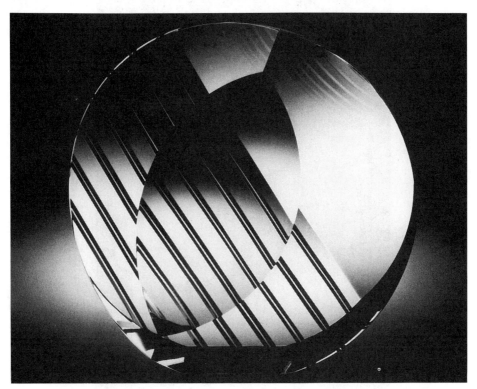

Steven V. Correia, *Arc,* 7" diameter, optical lead crystal. Photograph: Art Fox

Peter Carpou, *Athena,* 36 x 44, oil on canvas

Martha Chatelain, *Possessing,* 40 x 28 x 4,
handmade paper wall sculpture

Robin Coventry, *Dreaming Plant,* 11 x 15, pen and watercolor.
Courtesy: Dr. George Abbott. Photograph: Phil Miller

Martin Charlot, *Ko Ke Hanau Hou,* 60 x 100, oil on linen

James Crable, *Columbus Circle, NY, NY,* 49 x 43, cibachrome
Courtesy: J.J. Brookings Gallery

out to create "what the life force might look like." Her sculptures are dynamic and organic, evoking the nature of primeval life forms. Surrounded by beds of natural stones, the singular shapes of *Sibling* and *Emerged Couples* appear to have been lifted directly out of the landscape, their creviced and craglike surfaces suggesting the powers of nature. Other works, such as *Pod* and *Flower,* make reference to the evolution of cellular structures and speak to the force of growth in the universe.

CRIONAS, GEORGE (Painter, Etcher)
4753 Abargo St., Woodland Hills, CA 91364

Born: 1925 *Awards:* American Artist of Renown *Collections:* Sony Corporation; Caesar's World, Las Vegas *Exhibitions:* Visions Gallery, Morro Bay; Great Lengths Gallery, Los Angeles *Dealer:* Larry Yaker, Los Angeles

He is best known for his paintings, lithographs and etchings of clowns. Working in a style inspired by Lautrec, he works in oil and acrylic, on canvas and 300 lb. rough, artistico fabriano paper. His interest in clowns and circuses began with a childhood wish to pursue a circus career. Many of his works feature clowns in non-circus settings, such as a clown jazz band performing on the street. His paintings include elements of whimsy, as well as realistic emotion; he has also created abstract collages using this same imagery. He believes that everyone is at least part clown, and will soon be participating in a documentary on the art of clowning.

CRISPO, DICK (Painter)
511 Lighthouse, Pacific Grove, CA 93950

Born: 1945 *Awards:* First Prize, Calif. State Fair; Pan American Graphics Award, Mexico City *Collections:* Museum of Western Art, Tokyo, Japan; Museum of Modern Art, Mexico City *Exhibitions:* U. of Guadalajara, Mexico; UNESCO, NYC *Education:* Trinity Hall College and Seminary *Dealer:* Carmel Art Association, Carmel, CA

His primary influences are derived from his love of folk art and from murals by artists such as Diego Rivera. He is currently working in a variety of media that explore an interest in time and space, an interest that is related to the spirituality of his training as an ordained priest. Social commentary and the interplay of body, mind and spirit are common themes. Works are in oil, acrylic and watercolor. His imagery deals primarily in allegorical abstractions, embodying mythical and religious references in images of angels, devils and serpents. Major projects include a half-mile-long mural created in conjunction with inmates at Soledad Prison. The mural incorporates symbols that simultaneously represent unity and diversity: a synagogue in Cincinnati, the Bronx Zoo, the Golden Gate Bridge. His murals are found in such diverse places as churches, prisons, and restaurants. He also does portraits, etchings and silkscreen work.

CROCKETT, BILL (Painter)
45 Sharon St., San Francisco, CA 94114

Born: 1949 *Exhibitions:* Chrysler Museum, VA; Janet Desrailli Gallery, San Diego *Education:* Maryland Institute

His earliest training was dominated by the Washington/Yale school of color, of which Albers was a member. In his early paintings, he integrated these color-analysis influences with a love for the abstract

landscapes of Turner and a fondness for the supernatural depictions of Frederick Church. Works have grown to the six-by-ten-foot scale. He has recently completed a series of paintings depicting the quality of light changes, as it travels through fog, or when fog is evaporating. In these abstract landscapes, he captures the quality of color as it is acted upon by light passing through a moist atmosphere.

CROMPTON, PETER (Painter)
2129A Channing Way, Berkeley, CA 94704

Born: 1956 *Awards:* 1st Prize, California State Fair; 1st Prize, Humboldt State U. *Exhibitions:* Berkeley Art Center; California State U., Hayward *Education:* Stanford University *Dealer:* Convergence Gallery, San Francisco

After moving to Palo Alto to attend Stanford in 1974, he was influenced by the techniques of the Bay Area Figurative painters. Since then, he has drawn on sources, from German Expressionists Beckmann and Nolde to Italian Renaissance painters Piero della Francesca and Giovanni Bellini, in their approach to the figure. These works are done primarily in acrylics on paper or board constructions. In some instances, the paintings are constructed in three dimensions, with several planes in shallow relief that create an effect similar to that of a stage set. Preferring a greater spontaneity than the constructions allow, he concurrently works on large pastel or charcoal drawings. These depictions of over-life-size figures, usually nude in a landscape setting, recall the Roman and Renaissance frescoes that he studied on an extended trip to Italy in 1984.

CRONIN, ALICE (Painter, Printmaker)
139 Tunnel Rd., Berkeley, CA 94705

Born: 1929 *Exhibitions:* Berkeley Printmakers, Berkeley ; Art Center, Berkeley *Education:* UC-Berkeley *Dealer:* Kala Institute, Berkeley

Her early abstract expressionist prints and paintings are explorations of abstraction and figuration. After studying Chinese brush painting, she began to paint and print in a more gestural manner. Since 1984, she has worked primarily with monotypes and papermaking, often combining them with chine-colle and acrylic brushpainting. Her abstract themes are characterized by dynamic brush strokes, calligraphic signatures, and strong episodic colors over black and white backgrounds, while her figurative works are more colorful and subtle. In her seascapes, she achieves a convincing ocean light by using luminous washes of atmospheric colors.

CROSBIE, HELEN BLAIR (Sculptor)
1919 E. Claremont St., Phoenix, AZ 85016

Awards: Medal of Merit, National Society of Arts and Letters *Exhibitions:* Portraits Inc., NYC; C.G. Rein Galleries, Scottsdale, AZ *Education:* Masssachusetts College of Art *Dealer:* O'Meara Gallery, Scottsdale

This sculptor's format of xhoice was initially the portrait bust, by commissions were difficult to obtain. With her shift to small, ten to twenty inches, full-body bronze portraits came offers from such personalities as William Paley, John P. Marquand, and Margaret Sullivan. The artist's rough, impressionistic style captures the essence of her client. She models the majority of a piece during casual sittings where the subject is asked to "sit and chat, naturally." A pose, or stance presents itself as she develops a feel for the sitter's

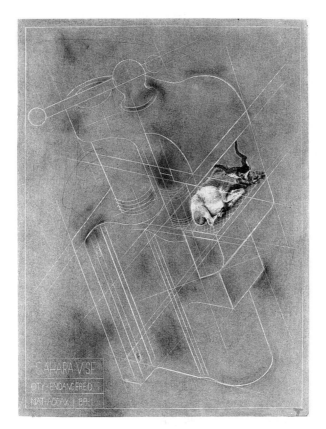

Frances Caraker, *Sahara Vise,* 40 x 30, pastels and prismacolor on illustration board

Helen Blair Crosbie, *Lester Mayfield–Wyo.* 14" high, bronze

personality. After the sculpture is cast, buyers express amazement at the likeness of the sculpture to its subject.

CROWN, KEITH (Painter)
819 Edgewood Ave., Columbia, MO 65203

Born: 1918 *Awards:* Purchase Award, National Watercolor Society *Collections:* Phillips Collection, Washington, D.C.; U. of Arizona Museum of Art, Tucson *Exhibitions:* Long Beach Museum of Art; Art Institute of Chicago *Education:* School of the Art Institute of Chicago

He belongs to America's generation of Abstract Expressionists and though he developed in isolation, his aspirations were akin to theirs. His paintings always represent objects. If his subject is a landscape, he paints it on location. Color and shape are the phenomena that most concern him. Throughout his career he has endeavored to contribute to the usage of materials. He was one of the first to employ aerosol spray paint and now paints with an airbrush and watercolors. His works are exhibited and collected widely. His main influences are Cezanne, Matisse, Marin and Van Gogh.

CRUIKSHANK, SALLY (Animation Artist, Painter)
15143 Hartsook St., Sherman Oaks, CA 91403

Born: 1949 *Awards:* 1986 American Film Institute Maya Deren Award for Independent Filmmaking; NEA Grant *Collections:* Yale Art School *Exhibitions:* Museum of Modern Art, NYC; USSR-Bay Area Cartoon Exchange *Education:* Smith College; Yale School of Art at Norfolk

Since 1971 she has been making bizarre, colorful animated films that have attracted a cult audience. Films such as *Quasi at the Quackadero, Fun on Mars*, and *Make Me Psychic* have been shown nationwide in theaters and on cable television. Influenced most strongly by cartoons of the 1930s and underground comics, she has created a wild fantasy world of color, motion and strange inventions, using the traditional cel technique in untraditional ways. Because she creates virtually all of the art work herself and also possesses an obsession for detail, it may take her as long as three years to complete a three-minute film. In addition to the animation, the artist also paints in gouache and oil in a spin-off style from her movie work, and creates painted sculpture out of cardboard and foam.

CRUISE, SHARON (Draughtsperson, Painter)
P.O. Box 1367, Upland, CA 91785

Born: 1947 *Awards:* Honorable Mentions, Millard Sheets Wildlife Exhibit, Redlands *Exhibitions:* Kohl Galleries, Upland; State of California, E.D.D., Ontario *Education:* Chaffey Jr. College

She is a photo-realist; her favorite subjects are animals, domestic and wild; her media include: acrylic, oil, watercolor, colored pencils, pen and ink, airbrush, mixed media, charcoal, pastel and markers and scratch board. She has illustrated publications, ranging from technical and medical to science fiction, fantasy and cartoons. She has recently begun working with sand-etching, silkscreening and stained glass. Among her influences are Rembrandt, Michelangelo, Leonardo da Vinci, Robert Bateman and Richard Ellis. During the early and mid-1980s, she owned and operated a small graphic arts business.

CUMMINGS, TOM (Painter)
3211 Calle Cedro, Santa Barbara, CA 93105

Born: 1949 *Exhibitions:* De La Guerra Gallery, Santa Barbara; County Bowl, Santa Barbara

The self-taught artist's initial landscape and still-life paintings described a flat, naive style. These oil works were confined to smaller formats than his recent, figurative pieces. Modigliani's influence is evident in the artist's treatment of portraits. More painterly than previous work, his elongated, mannered treatment of the subject emphasizes gesture and line. In some places, the oils are thinly applied, producing a wash-like, watercolor effect. Although his palette covers a wide range, his typical background is flat and cool. An air of unforced playfulness runs through the body of his work, whether the painting is figurative, landscape or still-life.

CUNNINGHAM, ALBERT (Painter)
49 Conrad St., San Francisco, CA 94131

Born: 1920 *Collections:* States Lines *Exhibitions:* Crocker Museum, Sacramento; De Young Museum, San Francisco *Education:* San Francisco Art Institute

He is known for his landscapes and waterscapes, most often painted in earth-toned watercolor, and sometimes in black ink. These pieces, done in a variety of styles, evoke a strong spirit of place and emphasize the structure of things. He started out a realist, painted and sketched in the South Pacific as a Marine, and was influenced by George Post, Rex Brandt, Richard Yip, Darrel Austin and Grant Wood. Recently, he has been working in a more abstract, impressionistic style and has been experimenting with painting in a hypnotic trance.

CURRERI-CHADWICK, DYANA (Painter)
375 Douglas St., San Francisco, CA 94114

Born: 1952 *Awards:* 1st Prize, Northern California Annual *Exhibitions:* Museo Italo Americano, San Francisco; Art Bridge, Kobe, Japan *Education:* Cal. State U. *Dealer:* Himovitz/Solomon, Sacramento

Following formal training under Bay Area artists Oliver Jackson and Carlos Villa, she developed a series of works using line and color to depict evidence of energy patterns in nature. Atmospheric light and shadow patterns dominated her large-scale paintings in the 1970s, as did the ideas in Fritz Capra's *The Tao of Physics*. She began to explore motion and energy through color and line in a minimal style. Primary colors, acrylic paint and graphite were here principal media, although she frequently explored variations on a small scale. She continues to work on canvas sized with rabbit skin glue with oil stick and paint. She uses jagged lines and strong color to make emblematic abstractions influenced by the urban environment, the subconscious and occasionally dreams. Repeated calligraphic line, overlapping forms and spontaneous, blended areas of high color typify her current work.

CURRY, MARK (Painter, Sculptor)
500 Landfair Ave., Los Angeles, CA 90024

Born: 1956 *Exhibitions:* Coop Coffee House, Los Angeles *Education:* UCLA

The son of an artist, he paints on anything that doesn't move too much. Canvas, wood, cardboard and telephone poles all qualify as surfaces for female nudes, human faces and landscapes with people and animals in them. Often, he spots his landscapes with

Meg Huntington Cajero, *Mirage II,* 22 x 30, transparent watercolor. Courtesy: Hunsaker/Schlesinger Gallery

Keith Crown, *Baldwin Hills, Los Angeles, California,* 22 x 30, watercolor

plops, blobs and splotches of color. Oils are his primary medium. His major influences include European painting and a high school art class, in which he had to draw a wine bottle over and over again. He struggles to make his pictures resemble what he sees.

CURTIS, ART (Painter)
2647 Magnolia Ave., Los Angeles, CA 90007

Born: 1946 *Awards:* 1st Place, Unpublished Illustration, Society of Illustrators of Los Angeles; Purchase Award, Brand XI Watercolor Show *Collections:* U. of Arizona, Tucson *Exhibitions:* Rose Cafe and Gallery, Venice; Annual San Diego International Watercolor Exhibition *Education:* Cal. State-Long Beach *Dealer:* Michelle Isenberg, Corporate Art Consultant, Los Angeles

In training to be a commercial illustrator, he became interested in watercolor. Influences from the art world, at this time, included Edward Hopper and Jean Folon. As he began to make fine art, he found the watercolor medium particularly suited for recreating the colors and shadows of the semi-arid environment of Southern California. His work has change in scale: from small, 11-by-14-inch commercial art pieces to large, 30-by-40-inch or 40-by-60-inch fine art watercolors. Images from the inner city and industrial areas, as well as a rich variety of desert and garden plants, are the subjects of recent paintings. He has been occupied with a series depicting the diners of downtown Los Angeles. These paintings speak for the street people and their lifes—scenes that most of us assume do not exist in car-oriented California.

CURTIS, DENNIS W. (Painter)
262 1/2 S. Main St., Los Angeles, CA 90012

Born: 1943 *Collections:* Hyatt Executive Offices, Chicago *Exhibitions:* Laguna Beach Art Museum Invitational; Double Rocking G Gallery, Los Angeles *Education:* Art Students League; UC-Berkeley *Dealers:* Double Rocking G Gallery, Los Angeles; Volid Gallery, Chicago

He works by covering the canvas with oil paint and applying a densely pigmented encaustic material. He then removes certain areas of the wax, exposing the color and form beneath. The bright, carnival-type colors are well-modulated by both the dark and the light waxes with whihc he works. He paints figures and still lifes, preferring a single, dominant subject. His paintings usually feature a portrait, in which the subject holds a personal or defining object. He cites the drawings of Raphael, the paintings of Vermeer and Velasquez and the contemporary ideas of Duchamp and Jasper Johns as the major influences on his style and approach.

CUSENZA, ANNA (Printer)
252 Chattanooga St., #3, San Francisco, CA 94114

Born: 1949 *Exhibitions:* Vida Gallery, San Francisco; La Mamelle, Inc., San Francisco *Education:* San Francisco State College

She credits Edvard Munch, Toulouse-Lautrec and William Blake for providing her with a vision of color, shape and form. Her first prints were done from etchings on zinc and copper plates; these were followed by soft pastels and acrylic paintings, and later she began spray painting and working with xeroxes. The work subsequently underwent dramatic transformation as she became involved in the process of instant imaging, combining the photo- copying process with airbrush painting. She is currently continuing to work with photo-generated processes, and she has recently completed a work involving black-and-white Polaroids, xeroxes, motion and photomurals. She increasingly combines highly graphic media, creating strong contrasts with black-and- whites.

CUSHMAN, PAM (Painter)
3663 Christian Valley Rd., Auburn, CA 95603

Born: 1929 *Awards:* Best of Show and Magazine Cover, Almond Growers Blue Diamond Art Exhibit, Sacramento; Best of Show, Placer County Art Show *Exhibitions:* Old Church Gallery, Meadow Vista; AFCH Galleries, Auburn Faith Community Hospital *Education:* Kansas State U.; Sierra College

She did not begin to study art until her children had reached their teenage years. She is now gaining recognition as a watercolor artist. Her appreciation of skillful draftsmanship, unusual images and abstract forms has strongly influenced her style. Many of her early paintings were abstract, but when she developed an interest in photography and started painting from the pictures she had taken, the watercolors became more realistic. Light and shadow now form the only abstractions in her realistic paintings. Floral works show a great interest in design. All of her subjects—from a generator at an old gold mine, to a discarded doll among the rocks—must deeply affect her emotionally before she decides to capture them on canvas.

CUTTER, DOROTHY (Painter)
290 Cypress Ave., Morro Bay, CA 93442

Collections: Justin Dart; Leonard Firestone *Exhibitions:* Hutchins Gallery, Cambria; San Luis Obispo Art Association *Dealer:* Zantman Art Galleries, Carmel; Hutchins Gallery, Cambria; Story Collection, Las Alivos

Her most influential training was with artist Richard Diebenkorn. She spent a period exploring abstraction, followed by another studying, and her current work is something of an evolution of the two. Working with mixed media, she appropriates scenes from everyday life: a cluster of potted flowers; chairs and a table set on a patio backgrounded by a bay filled with boats; the plates and books in a dining room cabinet. Despite the apparent representational quality of the work, the subject is always subservient to the arrangement of shapes and color. The paintings thus become a meeting place for her earlier distinct interests in abstraction and figuration.

CZARNECKI, MARY (Painter)
240 Mt. View Ln., Mill Valley, CA 94941

Born: 1957 *Awards:* Grant, Barbara Deming Memorial Fund, Brooklyn, NY *Collections:* Mills College Art Gallery, Oakland; Primetime Publicity, NYC *Exhibitions:* Barbar Gillman Gallery, Miami; American Zephyr Gallery, San Francisco

A continuity of prismatic colors and fluid gestural strokes dominates her figurative and non-objective abstractions. The works are abstract expressionist. There is an unbridled exuberance of form, color and overall design. Her figurative "Big Women" series was a group of large dramatic statements about the condition of women. These are oil paintings of women of power, strength, healing abilities and vibrancy.

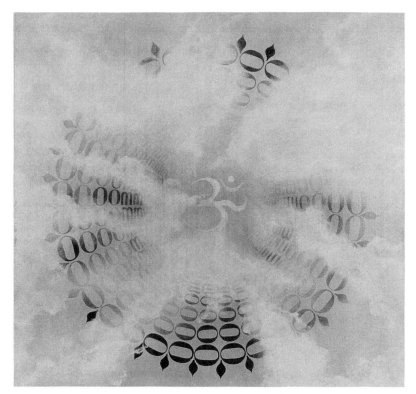

Georgina Clarke, *Himalayan Om,* 30 x 30, acrylic and oil on canvas.
Courtesy: Dr. Paul Rubenstein

Mary Czarnecki, *Mary's Midnight Ride,* 36 x 36, oil on canvas

DAE, GAYLE (Commercial Illustrator)
13610 N. Scottsdale Rd. #10-234, Scottsdale, AZ 85254

Born: 1941 *Awards:* Best of Show, Mid-Cities Festival; Special Judge's Award, Manto Art Show *Collections:* Appleton Gallery of Arts; Northland Chapel *Exhibitions:* Wildlife Artists of Wisconsin; Women of Wisconsin in the Arts *Dealer:* Renoir, Phoenix

Using a palette of soft colors combined with detailed figuration, she realistically depicts scenes from the wild with the human figure, exploring the circular forms of nature as they relate to the connection of man and animal. A recent series on endangered species addresses the fragility of nature. She has progressed from colored-pencil works to oil on canvas, and the works have become increasingly stylized; she develops layers of colors using a combination of Albers' color theory and the natural colorations of the desert. Backgrounds are tinted or black gesso glazes, further highlighting her images' brilliant hues and fine details.

DAHLQUIST, BOB (Painter)
3030 Pualei Circle/207, Honolulu, HI 96815

Born: 1922 *Awards:* Best of Show, Hawaii Watercolor Society *Collections:* Bank of Hawaii; Honolulu Savings and Loan *Exhibitions:* Village Gallery, Maui; Laguna Hills Gallery *Education:* Otis Art Institute; Art Center College of Design *Dealer:* The Livingston Galleries, Hilton Hawaiian Village; The Village Galleries, Lahaina, Maui

He is a former television professional; his career included stints as art director, scenic artist and graphic artist. Now retired, he paints Hawaiian land and seascapes. His watercolor technique has been influenced by S.C. Sedpool, Millard Sheets, Rex Brand and Joana Irving. Waterfalls, wildlife, Hawaiian villages, resorts, sporting events and forests all occupy his purist brush. His palette is filled with oranges, greens and burnt yellows. He loves the beauty of Hawaii and his work reflects his feeling for the islands.

DALEY, MARGARET (Painter)
1147 Dolores, #2, San Francisco, CA 94110

Born: 1949 *Exhibitions:* Southern Exposure Gallery; Color Box Gallery, San Francisco

Although she is formally trained, her style rapidly shifted to visionary surrealism after she moved to the Bay Area. Her paintings, drawn from dreams and a visionary perspective, present photo-real images in evolved forms and settings. She works from a vividly colored palette, using acrylics on canvas. The continuing themes in her work are magic, women and spirituality, and rebirth.

DAME, DIANE (Sculptor)
3580 Soda Canyon Rd., Napa, CA 94558

Born: 1946 *Collections:* Los Medano College *Exhibitions:* Dorothy Weiss Gallery, San Francisco; Zaks Gallery, Chicago *Education:* UC-Berkeley

Originally a painter, she was attracted to the sensuous, tactile quality of clay. She was initially influenced by the California funk tradition of Robert Arneson and David Gilhooley, producing visual puns with high-gloss surfaces. Study with Peter Voulkos brought about an evolution to clay tablets or "stele," in which the surfaces are rubbed with oxides and earth and objects are pressed in. Some include drawings, while others are purely abstract. Her most recent steles evoke a concern for the integrity of natural materials in a format reminiscent of Rothko and of the Rosetta Stone. The pieces, which are not overly manipulated, allude to the elements of fire, water, air and earth, and speak to the spiritual or subconscious through a purely abstract presentation.

DANIEL, JAY (Photographer)
Box 1232m, San Rafael, CA 94915

Born: 1952 *Awards:* Best in Show, Photography, Falkirk Annual Exhibit *Exhibitions:* Artisans, Mill Valley; Portfolio published in *American Photographer Education:* UC-Berkeley

A former bacteriologist, he decided to abandon his career at the Pacific Med Center to pursue his first love, photography. He is best known for the "Naked Cafe," a striking series of photographs of fifty people with and without their clothes. Each subject is presented against a draped background, striking the same pose in both the nude and the clothed picture. Although humorous at first glance, the work forces viewers to confront their feelings about cultural norms, expectations and the sociological functions of clothes. He is also an accomplished commercial photographer, equally comfortable working in color and black and white. He shoots in both small and large formats, using Canon 35mm cameras and Norman studio lighting. Considered a fine technician and conceptualist, he often employs an array of darkroom techniques such as multiple imaging, aerial masking, handcoloring, airbrushing and chemical processing, to achieve the desired effects. Citing the influences of Ansel Adams, Edward Weston, August Sander and Diane Arbus, he chooses to work only with people.

DANIEL, LAVI (Painter)
4411 Grand View Blvd., Los Angeles, CA 90066

Born: 1954 *Exhibitions:* Corcoran Gallery, Newport Harbor Art Museum, Newport Beach; Long Beach Art Museum *Dealer:* Jame Corcoran, Los Angeles

His work is a form of theatrical figuration, which explores the tensions between abstraction and representation. His paintings focus on the relationships among figures as a means of suggesting the conditions of the inner self.

DANIELS, JAN (Potter)
410 Hacienda Ct., Los Altos, CA 94022

Collections: North Central Washington Museum *Exhibitions:* Fresno Art Museum Gallery; Olive Hyde Gallery, Fremont

Her pieces show the influence of her research and studies in Japan as well as her strong interest in Southwest Indian art. She employs a number of techniques to give her vessels a primitive, bare-bones look. The pieces are almost without exception coil-built and fired with organic materials. The color and surface embellishments are influenced by the firing process itself—in which a high-fire clay body is low-fired. This leaves the clay porous, tactile and open to further coloration due to atmospheric conditions. The forms themselves vary, and may be open or closed, quiet or disturbing, male or female, rough or smooth, organic or geometric; they are not passive.

DAR, DINA (Painter, Xerographer)
3573 Adamsville Ave., Woodland Hills, CA 91364

Born: 1939 *Awards:* Master Artist, Gayle Givvs Giesen Trust, Pasadena Art Workshops; 2nd Prize, Painting, House of Zionists of America, Tel Aviv *Exhibitions:*

Ann Garat Ducey, *Dispersion,* 40 x 60, watercolor. Courtesy: Banaker Gallery

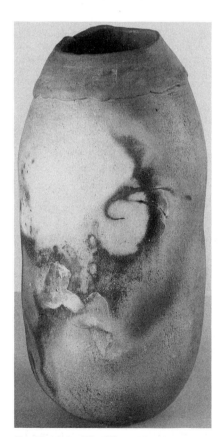

Jan Daniels, *The Wave,* 13 x 6, clay

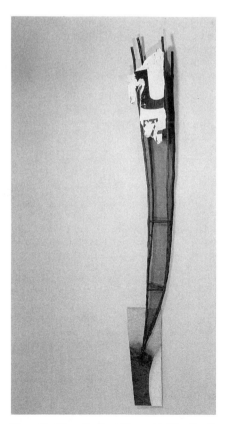

Steve DeGroodt, *Fast Forward,* 78 x 9 x 7, enamel, paper, wood, aluminum screen. Courtesy: Paul Ruscha

Lelieudit, Paris; The Jewish Museum, NYC *Education:* Cal. State-Northridge; Art Center College of Design

A Jew born in Poland during World War Two, she made large abstract expressionist field paintings during the 1960s and early 1970s. In the mid-1970s, she discovered the color Xerox machine and began manipulating food imagery. By 1980, having received a packet of family pictures, she had begun using the Xerox machine to make collage-like holocaust picture stories. Using snapshots, letters, handkerchiefs and flowers, her compositions in pale pinks, blues and blossoming bright reds are poignant celebrations of mortality and regeneration. She has recently completed a book of xerography, poems and acrylic paintings entitled *A Book of Roses and One Dream.*

DARROW, PAUL (Painter, Collage Artist)
Dept. of Art, Scripps College, Claremont, CA 91711

Born: 1921 *Awards:* NEH; Ford Faculty Research Grant *Collections:* Times Mirror Co., Los Angeles; Los Angeles County Museum of Art *Exhibitions:* Sao Paulo Biennial; San Francisco Museum of Art *Education:* Claremont Graduate School; Colorado Springs Fine Arts Center *Dealer:* Miriam S. Deane, Laguna Beach

He is a painter, muralist, watercolorist and draughtperson. His satirical drawings on the human condition involve human forms, surrounded by minimal elements of landscape. Always seductive in technique, he humorously alludes to his own vulnerability and that of his fellow man. Eastern metaphysical influences are evident in his mystical "Mandala" paintings and prints. He is also well known for his work in mixed media. He is a professor with and a former chairman of the Art Department at Scripps College in Claremont.

DASHIELL, DAVID (Installation Artist)
400 Duboce, #411, San Francisco, CA 94117

Born: 1952 *Awards:* NEA Fellowship *Collections:* Long Beach Museum of Art; Los Angeles Institute of Contemporary Art *Exhibitions:* Southern Exposure Gallery, San Francisco; Beyond Baroque, Venice *Education:* Calif. Institute of the Arts, Valencia *Dealer:* Ellis/Irwin Associates, San Francisco

Studies with John Baldessari, Vito Acconci, Lynda Benglis and Yvonne Rainer led to work in video, performance, installation and bookworks. He focuses on the arbitrary nature of language and human organizational structures. His early video entitled *Ulysses* presents a series of landscape stills, spiraling out from an unmarked center spot and accompanied by narratives of the title character's life. His work has developed into illustrational structures that incorporate drawings, paintings and found objects such as binoculars, light bulbs, fake fur and naugahyde. Projects often use literary and scientific models to create shadows of logic and meaning. A recent work, *Lover's Discourse*, recalls Goethe's and Roland Barthes' investigations of obsessive love, taking its title from a book by Barthes. The work is a circle of eighty surrealistic, cartoon-like paintings surrounding a small table, onto which a copy of the Barthes book has been bolted. A recording of the suicide soliloquy from Goethe's *Sorrows of Young Werther* plays over the scene.

DATER, JUDY (Photographer)
P.O. Box 79, San Anselmo, CA 94960

Born: 1949 *Awards:* Guggenheim Fellowship; NEA Grant *Collections:* San Francisco Museum of Modern Art; Museum of Modern Art, NYC *Exhibitions:* Santa Barbara Museum of Art; De Saisset Museum, Santa Clara *Education:* UCLA; San Francisco State U.

In her early work, which concerned the human figure and the portrait, she employed a 4 x 5 view camera to make penetrating, insightful images of the male and female face and figure. The prints are rich and luminous, with an emphasis on deep, inky black tones and chiaroscuro lighting. In 1978, she began using color as well as black-and-white and working with different camera formats. Departing from the single image, these works employ several photographs in sequence or groupings, sometimes with text. Recent works are large, multiple-print images with narrative references, created with both the wall and the book in mind. Her underlying curiosity about the psychology and emotional make-up of people is still uppermost in the content of her work.

DAVAULT, ELAINE (Mixed Media Artist)
326 N. Coast Hwy., Apt. H, Laguna Beach, CA 92651

Born: 1955 *Awards:* 1st Place, Honorable Mention, Newport Harbor Art Festival, Newport Beach; Who's Who in the West, Palette Award, Laguna Beach *Exhibitions:* Orange County Center For Contemporary Art; Laguna Beach Museum of Art *Education:* Indiana U.; Art Institute of Southern California *Dealers:* Michelle Morgan, Irvine

She studied under Ray Jacob. Her light-hearted, multimedia, post-modern, surrealist work is divided into three parts. First, using the technology of the 1980s to manipulate paper, retouched photos and transparencies, she creates two-dimensional collages that are at once high-tech and classical. Second, she combines wood forms, paint, photo-collage and found objects into large "Anti-Anxiety Art," three-dimensional constructions. Finally, she has developed cubic plexiglas "Little Theatres." Resembling fine-art pop-up cards, these self-contained, post-modern environments are fun to play with. "My view of art is something you can enjoy," she says.

DAVENPORT, HOULGATE (Painter)
4165 Wake Robin Dr., Glen Ellen, CA 95442

Born: 1928 *Awards:* 1st Award, Painting, Marin Society of Artists; Show Award, San Francisco Museum of Modern Art *Exhibitions:* Wing Gallery, Los Angeles; Tokyo Museum of Modern Art *Education:* USC; San Francisco Art Institute *Dealer:* Interart, San Francisco

At the San Francisco Art Institute, she was most influenced by Richard Diebenkorn's color and paint surfaces and the moody quality of Elmer Bischoff's work, and she tried to incorporate these elements into her own figurative landscape paintings. She later realized that she was most interested in the light between figures, both setting them off from the background and binding them to it. Gradually, figures have disappeared completely into color fields with shapes joined by light. She now paints primarily in acrylic, watercolors and gouache, using transparent glazes to build up areas of complexity and depth. Other methods include scratching through the paint and adding homemade paper, sand and gesso.

Elaine Davault, *Creature Palace,* 14 x 18, mixed media.
Courtesy: Jan Duncan, Corona Del Mar, CA

Arabella Decker, *Pregnancy: A Crowded Condominum,*
18 x 24, ink on paper

DAVID, VIVA (AWEE-PA-NO) (Sculptor)
P.O. Box 1537, Cambria, CA 93428

Born: 1946 *Exhibitions:* Contemporary Southwest Galleries, La Jolla; Big Mt. Support Native American Art Show *Education:* Cooper Union, NYC; Art Students League, NCY *Dealers:* Contemporary Sourthwest Galleries, La Jolla; The Gallery, Harmony; Suma Sil Gallery, Cambria

She began her professional career painting abstracts of the human form in oils. She also worked in stone carving and created primitive influenced silk-screen before beginning to work in wood. Within roots, burls, branches and knots came visions of an ancient tribal past. Transforming the wood with oil colors, wood bleach and her own beadwork; her Native American subjects evoke the memories of a universal heritage. She has just completed her first bronze and is currently producting paper castings of her high relief carvings, some of which are over five feet tall. Her brilliant mastery of wood carving allows her to expand upon her visions and to create ever more complex images.

DAVIDSON, ABRAHAM A. (Photographer)
1516 Addison St., Philadelphia, PA 19146

Born: 1935 *Awards:* Group 17 Prize in Photography, Detroit Institute of Arts *Education:* Harvard U.; Boston U.

Since the mid-1950s, he has made black-and-white photographs. His subject matter generally consists of land- and cityscapes, either with or without figures. He does no nudes or still lifes, and portraits only rarely. Politics generally do not interest him—an exception being the hooded figures who marched in a parade commemorating the 20th anniversary of Hiroshima. He often attains a sense of poetic detachment and isolation. His favorite subjects are small, strategically-placed figures in old parts of a city, sometimes beside ruined monuments. Trying for bizarre, strange, but not completely fantastic situations, he creates mildly surreal works.

DAVIDSON, CECELIA (Painter)
837 Flower Ave., Venice, CA 90291

Born: 1949 *Collections:* Xerox Corporation, NYC and Los Angeles; Hilton Hotel, Los Angeles *Exhibitions:* Schwartz Cierlak, Santa Monica; Art Rental Gallery, Los Angeles County Museum *Education:* Fontebonne College *Dealer:* Francine Ellman, Los Angeles; Trabia-McGafee, NYC

Her recent works in oil and mixed-media monotypes explore the cycles of birth, death and creation. Loosely structured landscapes set primary figures in scenes evoking dream states. Vibrantly colorful areas, laid down with loose brushstrokes, abut broad areas of gold leaf. The psychological abstraction of her work reflects the influence of Matisse and Max Beckmann. From Matisse and Diebenkorn, she learned the emotional impact of color, and a rigorous emphasis on composition. The figurative elements of her work were developed during ten years of formal training, drawing from the figure.

DAVIS, JAMES, G. (Painter)
Rancho Linda Vista, Box 160, Oracle, AZ 85623

Born: 1931 *Awards:* Commission, Container Corp. *Collections:* Metropolitan Museum of Art, NYC; National Gallery, Washington, DC *Exhibitions:* Shoshana Wayne Gallery, Santa Monica; Tucson Art Museum *Education:* Wichita State U. *Dealer:* Riva Yares Gallery, Scottsdale

His images are anxious and provocative, rendered with painterly sensitivity and highly developed technique. He presents a world of ominous stillness in which familiar objects, often household appliances, achieve a disquieting effect; he often presents a confrontation between the animate and the inanimate, between man and his environment. His figures fluctuate across different planes, adding to the disconcerting atmosphere in his work. Though his work is intellectually challenging, he never loses touch with his concern for painterly sensuality—his paintings transcend the starkness of their subject matter through high energy, startling colors and sheer physical tension. The significance of his work lies in his juxtaposition of incompatibles, which he places at odds with each other.

DAVIS, KATIE (Painter)
4109 N. Ellen Dr., Covina, CA 91722

Born: 1926 *Awards:* Gold Medal, San Gabriel Fine Art Show, 1987 *Exhibitions:* San Gabriel Gallery *Education:* East Los Angeles College

She is a portrait painter, influenced by the Old Masters of Europe. The paintings of Velazquez and Sorolla have been particularly important inspirations for her works. Her interest in portrait painting dates from her early childhood in Laguna, when an artist working on the cliffs near her house painted her portrait and entered the painting in the 1936 Laguna Festival of Arts. She prefers painting directly, using quick-drying paint and finishing a portrait in one sitting. Her teachers have included Joyce Pike, Claude Ellington and Sergei Bongart. Her own teaching takes place in her home studio in Covina.

DAVIS, STARR (Painter)
20681 Leonard Rd., Saratoga, CA 95070

Born: 1942 *Awards:* Northern California Watercolor Competition; Los Gatos Art Association *Collections:* Alaska International Art Institute, Anchorage; San Jose Arts Commission *Exhibitions:* Fresno Metropolitan Museum; Gallery House, Palo Alto *Education:* Beloit College; School of the Art Institute of Chicago

Work centers on the colors and rhythms felt from experiencing landscapes. In her watercolors, nature's spontaneity is reflected by letting pigment settle into pools and dry into patterns. Highlights on trees and water can also be revealed by scraping off wet paint with a knife. Like Matisse, she searches for "exactly the delicate order of shape in which the color and form of nature best agree." Complementary colors are counterbalanced— red with green, yellow foliage with branches of violet. Lately her play with earth images has extended into her work with ceramics. Clay is squeezed into zig-zag folds that appear as layers of mountains. In the traditional Raku pottery process, a glowing piece is lifted from the kiln and swung in a cool breeze so that the glaze crackles. It also may be placed into a container lined with rice hulls which ignite and smoke the clay black, producing a sense of actual rock formation.

DAVIS, WILLIAM C. (Painter, Ceramist)
17038 Community St., Northridge, CA 91325

Born: 1930 *Awards:* Purchase Award, Moor Park College; Purchase Award, Cal. State-San Luis Obispo *Exhibitions:* Security National Bank, Los Angeles;

Martine Deny, *Tangu III,* 43 x 29, monotype, oil sticks

Awee-pa-no Viva David, *Deer Spirit,* 26 x 15, redwood burl.
Courtesy: Sid Fridkin

American Ceramic Society, Brand Library, Los Angeles *Education:* USC *Dealer:* Story Collection, Los Olivos

Native American forms, styles and images are continuing motifs in his work. His early formal training was in painting and printmaking. He began working with clay in 1948, first modeling, then progressing to the potter's wheel and hand-building techniques. His current style is a contemporary interpretation of Native American myths, stories and folklore. These are translated onto ceramic vessels, accompanied by mixed-media drawings and fused colored glass forms. Each piece of a trio is formally, narratively and thematically related to the others.

DAWSON, SHARON (Painter)
P.O. Box 1411, Middletown, CA 95461

Born: 1960 *Awards:* 2nd Place, Wildlife, Holly Daly/Herman Pal Beach Art Galleries *Exhibitions:* Stary Sheets Art Gallery, Guala; Buffalo Bill Western Art Show & Auction, Cody, WY *Dealer:* Stary Sheets Gallery, Guala

Her early painstaking works were pointillist, photo-realistic western drawings, executed with small-sized rapidograph pens. The forty to one hundred hours of eye-straining labor that each piece demanded wore her down and she began painting in oils. Her first paintings were realistic and overly technical. Abstraction has since become an element of her work and given her a sense of freedom. She strives to render a true nature. Her palette contains eighty colors and she paints a thick impasto. Recently, she has been working with watercolors. Her figurative subjects include hands at a piano, *Dancing Keys*, and *Baby on the Beach*.

DAY, JANET E. (Painter)
Star Route, Whitethorn, CA 95489

Born: 1953 *Exhibitions:* Hale Gulch Trade Fair; Benbow Arts Fair *Education:* Southern Oregon School of Art; Mendocino Art Center *Dealer:* Culture Crafts, Garborville

As a child, he painted and drew with his father's supplies. In adolescence, he rendered detailed studies of plant life with pen and ink. In 1973, he began taking classes in watercolors, and at first struggled to paint realistically. He found that he loved colors and the way they blended. He moved to impressionism and painted landscapes. He now finds his greatest inspiration in nature. His paintings are clear, realistic and full of light. He uses wet-into-wet techniques, and his bright colors are often more brilliant than those of his subjects. During the past few years, he has painted scenes of the "Lost Coast," as well as images of gardens and wildlife.

DAY, L.S. (Painter, Printmaker)
654A N. Dillon St., Los Angeles, CA 90026

Born: 1935 *Awards:* Market St. Program, Long Beach Museum *Collections:* Betty Parsons Collection, NYC; American Masters Collection, Los Angeles *Exhibitions:* Jacques Seligman Gallery, NYC; American Masters Collection, Los Angeles *Education:* Rochester Institute of Technology; Art Student's League *Dealer:* In Formulation, Los Angeles; Iori Okura, NYC

Since the 1960s, he has serially developed four ongoing, somewhat unrelated bodies of work. The contemplative, blue monochrome series, "Space Concept," was the beginning of his exploration of symbolism and minimalist surrealism. This work has recently tended toward a large format. The paintings in his "Barney's Beanery" series were developed from intensive street and location drawings and show a colorfully expressive and flatly figurative style. The "Walking Man" series is a major body of work in an expressionist mode; it represents a psychological treatment of the inner man. Finally, the abstract "Diamond Series" are kinetic-light mandalas painted in mixed-media, influenced by Pollock, Mark Tobey and Oriental schools of calligraphy. Produced serially and without drawings, these spontaneous, expressionistic works continue to involve an adventuresome brush and spray technique on varying polished metallic surfaces.

DEAL, JOSEPH (Photographer)
3540 Watkins Drive, Riverside, CA 92507

Born: 1947 *Awards:* NEA Fellowship; Guggenheim Fellowship *Collections:* Museum of Contemporary Art, Los Angeles; Oakland Museum *Exhibitions:* The Photographers Gallery, London; Otis Art Gallery, Los Angeles *Education:* Kansas City Art Institute; U. of New Mexico

Originally from the Midwest, he is drawn to landscapes, architecture and nature. In his panoramic landscapes, he seeks to reveal man's exploitation of the land. This theme of man's domination over his environment arose in the 1970s and is crucial to his prints. Along with several of his contemporaries, he exhibited a series of his photographs at the International Museum of Photography in 1975 in an exhibition entitled "New Topographics: Photographs of a Man-Altered Landscape." Another series, "Beach Cities," is revealing for its depiction of man-inhabited beaches characteristic of Southern California.

DEAN, JOYCE (Printmaker)
1025 Carlton St., #7, Berkeley, CA 94710

Born: 1945 *Exhibitions:* Traveling Exhibit, Pacific Grove Art Center; Member Show for Society of Printmakers *Education:* UC-Berkeley; Vancouver School of Art

Originally a figure painter, she switched to printmaking while at school in Vancouver. She became intrigued by Japanese woodcuts and the effect achieved by layering oil-based colors in relief printmaking. The Japanese influence is still apparent in the abstract, softly colored monoprints of her recent work. She uses plexiglas plates to make the prints characterized by organic forms, leaves, plants, and rocks and other abstract elements, such as torn Japanese paper. She also works with respresentational linocuts in her "Americana" series of prints. This series includes portraits and small businesses, such as a corner grocer and a Chinese laundry.

DEAN, NAT (Painter)
3435 Army St., Suite 214, San Francisco, CA 94110

Born: 1956 *Awards:* Best of Show, San Francisco Museum of Modern Art; Merit Award, California Institute of Arts *Collections:* San Francisco Museum of Modern Art; The Getty Trust *Exhibitions:* LACE, Los Angeles; Jose Drudis-Biada Gallery, Mt. St. Mary's College, Los Angeles *Education:* San Francisco Art Institute; California Institute of the Arts

Her work is concerned with an exploration of the complexities that occur between one's private inner world and the external world. In the early 1970s, her work

Mila del Potro, *Tree Mentis,* 24 x 30, acrylic

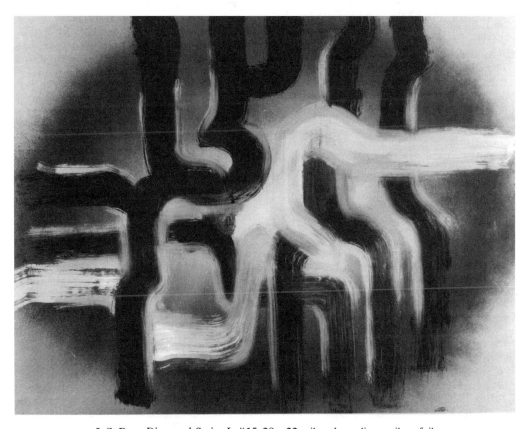

L.S. Day, *Diamond Series I–#15,* 28 x 22, oil and acrylic on silver foil

consisted of abstract paintings on canvas and paper; through the later 1970s, it evolved into more representational painted paper fans, envelopes and booklets. Eventually she built book-like constructions that incorporated traditional hand-binding techniques and figurative images. This led to dual and trifold boxes containing painted acrylic panels and acid-etched glass panes, and later to large-scale screens made of mirrored panels with sandblasted images. Her recent work—large-scale drawings in graphite on paper—is a conscious departure from the technically complex and difficult sculptural materials. The drawings seek to touch the viewers' "vocabulary of personal experience" while revealing the artist's struggle to come to terms with her own experience.

DEANE, GREGORY, H. (Painter)
4057 Fabian Way, Palo Alto, CA 94303

Born: 1938 *Collections:* Nordstrom, San Francisco; Syntex *Exhibitions:* Nordstrom, San Francisco; Silk Dynasty Corp., Los Angeles *Education:* San Jose State U.

His early works were mostly representational: in particular, large and even life-sized portraits. The transition to his current non-objective style was slow. Over the last dozen years he has grown in both abstract vision and artistic confidence allowing him to express his prolific ideas with an increasing sense of spontaneity. Inspired by American Expressionists Paul Jenkins and Franz Kline, and the object collages of Robert Rauschenberg, his style is both intricate and bold, but at the same time non-confrontational. Corporate buyers have been increasingly attracted to his work, but the mainstay of his enthusiastic following is still the private collector.

DEBSKA, ANNA (Sculptor)
1924 Willow Tree Ct., Thousand Oaks, CA 91362

Born: 1929 *Awards:* 1st Prize, International Art Festival, Budapest; 2nd Prize, International Sculpture Festival, Italy *Collections:* Apparel Mart Grand Hall, Dallas; Diamond Shamrock Corporation Building, Dallas *Exhibitions:* Museum of Science and Industry, Los Angeles; Fine Art Acquisitions, Los Angeles *Education:* Academie des Beaux Arts, Warsaw

She was one of Poland's best known artists when Texas businessman and art collector Trammel Crow commissioned her work for his offices in Texas. She now lives in this country, sculpting animals, especially horses in motion. She creates a wax mold, which is then cast in metal and used to create bronze statues. These pieces are finished with a lifelike patina. She also uses the technique of covering a metal or wooden armature with a concrete substance, using a type of bronze wash to finish the surface. Her forms are emotional and naturalistic, full of energy and life—pure juxtapositions of forms, shapes and spaces. Her recent work includes a horse sculpture for the National Arabian Horse Show in Kentucky, and a mythological piece, *Unicorn With Lady.*

DECKER, ARABELLA (Sculptor, Painter)
P.O. Box 370-648, Montara, CA 94037

Born: 1942 *Exhibitions:* U.S. Representative, International Artists Exhibition, Finland; Sculpture Representative, Year of the Woman, Stanford U.; BIS Women's Art Festival

The tension-filled landscapes of Bosch, Edward Munch, Kathe Kolbwitz and Goya are her most important influences. She sculpts in bronze, fiberglass and acrylic, trying to capture the moment between decision and action. In some pieces, such as *Rite to Life,* which features a woman with several babies, she creates composite images, evoking the essence of feeling. Similar works include *The Card Party,* where four women play cards at a table, and *Anticipation,* in which a lonely woman sits under a lamp waiting for her husband to return. She has recently been working on a series of paintings—*Stompin' Mama, Smother, Flycatcher* and *Jonestown Madonna*—focusing on how women cope alone with the conflicting pressures in their lives.

DECTER, BETTY (Painter, Sculptor)
5412 W. Washington Blvd., Los Angeles, CA 90016

Born: 1927 *Collections:* Edron Fixture Corp., NYC; Ivey's Department Store, Gainesville, FL *Exhibitions:* Brand Library Art Gallery, Los Angeles; Bonwit Teller, Beverly Hills

Her images derive from events she has lived through; she evokes images from memory, painting not to recreate a literal, external reality, but an emotional one. This calls at times for a distortion of figure and object. Her paintings are large, though she never uses a brush larger that one-and-a-half inches wide. The works are primarily in acrylics, sometimes incorporating Oriental paper, foils and metallic powders. She lays down layer after layer, working not from a specific image but from an emotional force. The resulting works reveal the influence of Gustav Klimt, Egon Schiele and Edvard Munch.

DEESE, RUPERT J. (Ceramist)
P.O. Box 126, Claremont, CA 91711

Born: 1924 *Awards:* Everson Museum *Collections:* Everson Museum; Boston Museum *Exhibitions:* Stary-Sheets Gallery, Gualala; Beretich Gallery, Claremont *Education:* Pomona College; Claremont College *Dealer:* Barbara Beretich, Claremont

At Scripps College, he studied ceramics with Richard Petterson and sculpture with Albert Stewart. For several years, he made his living as a potter. In 1964, he joined the design staff of Franciscan Dinnerware, and concentrated on the development of shapes in ceramic dinnerware. He also designed crystal for Tiffin and stainless steel flatware for Amefa-Holland. In 1984, he resumed full-time work as a studio potter. His primary interest remains in the forming of stoneware vessel shapes on the potter's wheel and the application of appropriate surface patterns. His clay is a vitreous, fine-textured dark brown stoneware, fired to cone five.

DEFEO, JAY (Painter)
Dept. of Art, Mills College, Oakland, CA 94613

Born: 1929 *Awards:* NEA Fellowship; Adaline Kent Award *Collections:* San Francisco Museum of Modern Art; Oakland Museum *Exhibitions:* Museum of Modern Art, NYC; San Francisco Museum of Modern Art *Education:* UC-Berkeley *Dealer:* Gallery Paule Anglim, San Francisco

Early influences include abstract expressionists and the work of primitive peoples, while later influences of the Italian Renaissance and of Japanese painting are also visible. New works combine intense textural concerns with a very disciplined and structured attitude toward space. Imagery has always been largely abstract, alternating between a sense of landscape and a more figurative point of view.

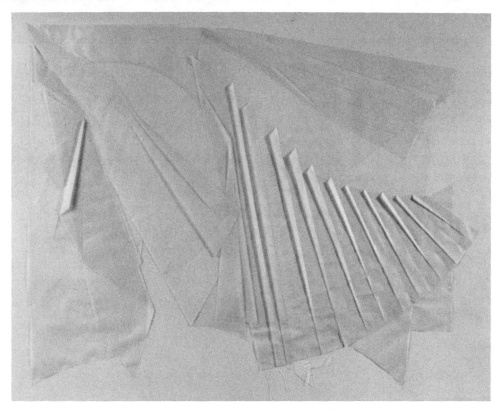

Carmine DeVivi, *Arctic Series #1,* 32 x 37, sewn papers. Photograph: Michele Maier

Rupert J. Deese, *Planets Jar,* 9 inches wide, stoneware. Courtesy: Galleria Beretich

DE FOREST, ROY DEAN (Painter, Sculptor)
P.O. Box 47, Port Costa, CA 94569

Born: 1930 *Awards:* NEA Fellowship; La Jolla Art Museum Purchase Prize *Collections:* Art Institute of Chicago; San Francisco Museum of Modern Art *Exhibitions:* Fuller Goldeen Gallery, San Francisco; Whitney Museum, NYC *Education:* California School of Fine Arts; San Francisco State College *Dealer:* Fuller Goldeen Gallery, San Francisco; Allan Frumkin Gallery, NYC

Several of his early series of drawings in marker or pastel on large paper depict the development of such themes as romance and friendship. He then turned to painting on large canvases in series alluding to pulp westerns or philosophy treatises. Whimsical, naive interpretations of the figure in landscapes characterize much of his recent work. He calls himself an "obscure visual constructor of mechanical delights" who seeks to depict the "phantasmagoric micro-world" in which he travels. Media have recently included ceramics, painted clay and wood mounted on stretcher frames. He has worked with Robert Arneson in a project called "The Bob and Roys," a cooperative effort to create ceramic dishes and lamps.

DEFRANCE, JIM (Painter)
239 S. Los Angeles St., Los Angeles, CA 90012

Born: 1940 *Collections:* La Jolla Museum of Art; Fredrick Weisman Collection, Santa Monica *Exhibitions:* Jan Baum Gallery, Los Angeles; Cirrus Gallery, Los Angeles *Education:* UCLA; U. of Colorado *Dealer:* Jan Baum Gallery, Los Angeles

This artists' earlier pieces dealt with color behind the canvas— a pervasive gray and brown with rectangular slits cut in the surface, and the underside of the painting done in a bright color which when lit from above reflected onto the wall behind the canvas. Recent works concern the surface color's vibrant properties. The color and light of these pieces bounces out, confronting the viewer. Layers of color are applied one over the other until a new, effervescent pastel is generated just off center from the primary source. Across these fields, diagonal lines describe triangles, parallelograms and trapezoids, or fragments of these shapes—the lines creating vibrations between the surrounding rich color fields and the outlined shapes.

DEGENHART, PEARL C. (Painter, Sculptor)
P.O. Box 142, Trinidad, CA 95570

Born: 1905 *Exhibitions:* Frank Lloyd Wright Library, San Rafael; Cultural Center, Eureka *Education:* Columbia U.

This artist's paintings range over a diversity of subject matter and style. They derive from realism, fantasy and to abstraction. Oil is the primary medium, varying in viscosity to suit the needs of the painting. When left thick, the paint is applied with a brush and palette knife. Humor is common to several of the paintings.

DE GROAT, GEORGE (Painter)
P.O. Box 306, Carmel Valley, CA 93924

Born: 1917 *Awards:* Ford Foundation Grant *Collections:* Ira Gershwin; Edward G. Robinson *Exhibitions:* Monterey Peninsula Museum of Art; Pasadena Art Museum *Education:* Newark School of Fine Arts *Dealer:* Landell Gallery, Carmel

After investigations into formal realism, abstract expressionism and the figuration of the Bay Area school, he has focused on figurative painting, which he combines with a concern for abstract shapes. Working wet on wet in oil, he develops large, abstract shapes on the canvas that are worked using warm and cool colors to produce the figurative imagery. Although his work is done primarily as an expression of his subconscious and is not literal in content, he does make exceptions. One such work, a painting paying homage to Hammurabi, the first recorded lawmaker, was done in yellow to symbolize justice through enlightenment. Recent explorations have involved sculpting in bronze.

DEGROODT, STEVE (Painter, Sculptor)
P.O. Box 861026, Los Angeles, CA 90086

Born: 1948 *Exhibitions:* San Francisco Museum of Modern Art, Rental Gallery; Simard & Halm Gallery, Los Angeles

In 1971, he graduated with a degree in the visual arts; he then became a professional composer and musician. By the end of the decade, he had come full circle, resuming his visual art, with mixed-media paintings on wood, metal and paper in a series investigating retinal dialogues. 1984 was a pivotal year as a result of intense experiences during his travels in the South Pacific, in particular, Papua New Guinea. At this point, he began to explore more sculptural elements and assemblage. In these pieces, forms fashioned primarily from found branches are sometimes wrapped with veils of aluminum screen. In *Tumora (Tomorrow)*, a small wooden outrigger is attached to the bottom half of a 5-foot-tall canvas, splashed with thin layers of cerulean blue. Half-tone media advertisements are added to some of the pieces, often speaking to the erosion of traditional South Pacific cultures.

DE HERAS, JOHN (Painter, Mixed Media Artist)
3544 Beethoven St., Los Angeles, CA 90066

Born: 1931 *Awards:* NEA Fellowship; Fulbright Scholarship *Collections:* Ateneo, Cultural Hispanica, Madrid; California State U. Foundation *Exhibitions:* Hippodrome Gallery, Long Beach; University Art Museum, California State U., Long Beach

After formal training in a figurative mode, influenced by the works of Vuillard, Bonnard and Matisse, he developed a style based on the "combine" paintings of Rauschenberg and Jasper Johns. The work, "assemblage," became a style of its own. While on a Fulbright Grant to Spain in the early 1960s, he became interested in the work of Antoni Tapies, Manolo Millares, Saura and other Spanish artists. At this time, the work became more sculptural due to the influences of Marcel Duchamp and the "found object." Returning to the U.S., he progressed from assemblage to large paintings using mixed media. After a brief period of neo-figurative work, the illusion aspect gave way to a bold front of strong color and interlocking shapes of ambiguous definition. He has recently been using a combination of oil paint, canvas, paper, wood and cement.

DELANEY, LIN (Painter)
7492 Baldwin Dam Rd., Folsom, CA 95630

Born: 1941 *Awards:* Best of Show, Roseville Art Center and Museum; 1st and 2nd Places, Forrest Farms Art Festival *Exhibitions:* Crocker Art Museum, Sacramento; Auburn Art Center

After doing both graphic art and fine art, she has chosen to concentrate on fine art. Her visual style is

Omar d'Leon, *Figures,* 14 x 22, inks

John de Heras, *Room With a View,* 41 x 29,
acrylic and charcoal on paper

best described as loose board handling in watercolor. She builds layers of pigment to achieve a strong, dense background, preferring to let the work evolve on its own into one of her favorite subjects, either an enlargement of a small, delicate object, or calligraphic line work. Her more recent paintings are figurative, abstract and colorful, and she has experimented with pastels and collage. She has been especially interested in making studies of the interiors of flowers.

DELAP, TONY (Sculptor)
225 Jasmine St., Corona Del Mar, CA 92625

Born: 1927 *Awards:* NEA Fellowship; Purchase Prize, Long Beach Museum of Art *Collections:* Museum of Modern Art, NYC; Los Angeles County Museum of Art *Exhibitions:* Whitney Museum, NYC; Jan Turner Gallery, Los Angeles *Education:* California College of Arts and Crafts; Claremont Graduate School *Dealer:* Robert Elkon Gallery, NYC; Janus Gallery, Venice

He began as a painter, but turned to sculpture in the early 1960s. After working exclusively in sculpture for ten years, he combined sculpture with painting to create "wall-hanging paintings" employing a variety of media, including wood, canvas and acrylics. One of his primary concerns is the edge: "I developed a hyperbolic, paraboloid, wooden edge that changed course as it continued around the canvas, much like a Mobius strip." In this way, the wall becomes an integral part of each work. In *Jaipur Jinnee*, the wall is also integrated into the work through experiments with different geometrical shapes and negative space.

DE LARIOS, DORA (Multimedia Artist)
8635 Washington Blvd., Culver City, CA 90232

Born: 1933 *Awards:* Silver Achievement Award, Y.W.C.A. for Art, Los Angeles; Certificate of Honor, Women in Design International, San Francisco *Collections:* Fredrick Nicolas, Los Angeles; Security Pacific Bank *Exhibitions:* Barnsdall Municipal Gallery, Los Angeles; Calif. Craft Museum, San Francisco *Education:* USC

Her recent body of work has been a joyous explosion of color on multi-layered wood constructions. She uses bright, primary colors in acrylic similar to those in Mexican art. Images range from the representational to the highly abstract. Among the materials she works with are plexiglas, brass, porcelain, clay, cement and gypsum board. Her designed sculptures of stainless steel and carved plexiglas are fabricated by other artists. She considers herself an "architectural artist," creating commissioned work for specific architectural sites. Projects include a mural of wood, gold leaf and porcelain for a hotel lobby, and a series of wall pieces —including one with a pair of cheetahs inside that come together in the shape of a woman.

DE LEON, V. MICHAEL (Jewelry Maker, Body Sculptor)

Born: 1940 *Awards:* Best of Show, Mill Valley Fall Arts Festival *Exhibitions:* Eureka Design Center *Education:* U. of Colorado

Very early forays into the plastic arts were influenced by Dali, Tanguy and the ecology prints of James Audubon. He painted, drew and did some bronze casting before moving to the San Francisco Bay Area in 1966. There, he came under the influence of funk and shamanistic-psychedelic art. Welding and wood carving, fiberglass and plastic casting were soon added to his media repertoire, as an interest in the nature of

consciousness influenced his design conceptually. As a complement to his visual and tactile awareness, he developed a sense of letting form reveal itself by working the field of action with respect for the media. Once discovered, organic growth is allowed to direct the evolution of the piece. After studying pottery in England, he became involved in the Marin County craft revival and began working with cast jewelry and body sculpture. The wax work necessary for jewelry casting lends itself to his fluid creative process.

DELOS, KATE (Painter)
1518 California St., Berkeley, CA 94703

Born: 1945 *Awards:* Jerome Foundation Fellowship for Printmaking; California State U. Distinguished Artist Forum *Collections:* San Francisco Museum of Modern Art; Newport Harbor Art Museum *Exhibitions:* Lang Gallery, Scripps College, Claremont; Prieto Gallery, Mills College, Oakland *Education:* UC-Berkeley; San Francisco State U. *Dealer:* Eaton/Shoen, San Francisco

Her work is about ideas, not the picture of things; she explores myth and idea by using image over and over again. The rich earth colors of her painted faces become entrances, beautiful in their own way, but mere portals to a place of contemplation. She chooses such images as the moon and the lily for her visual archaeology. The forms of her faces in her oils and monotypes reveal the influence of her African travels; her colors evoke the lights of California. She has recently been working on a series of paintings concerning the couple—confronting problems of similarity and divergence within the pairing.

DELOYHT-ARENDT (Painter)
2617 N. 58th St., Scottsdale, AZ 85257

Born: 1927 *Collections:* Thunderbird Bank; IBM *Exhibitions:* Invitational Plein Air Festival, Catalina Island; National Watercolor Association *Education:* U. of Missouri, Kansas City *Dealer:* Mammen II Gallery, Scottsdale, AZ; Gallery 203, Taos, NM; Galerie Le Shea, Montecito, CA

She has fourteen years of experience as a commercial artist producing black-and-white images for reproduction work, and this provides her with a particular sensitivity in her color painting. Working primarily on location, she creates representational paintings, with colors closely approximating those before her. The oil and watercolor pieces are done in an impressionistic style, leaving the viewer to provide the details of the scene.

DEL POTRO, MILA (Painter, Ceramist)
765 Neilson St., Berkeley, CA 94707

Born: 1946 *Collections:* Progressive Asset Management, San Francisco *Exhibitions:* Gallery House, Palo Alto; Novart Gallery, Madrid; Del Bello Gallery, Toronto *Education:* Madrid U. *Dealer:* Virginai Breier, San Francisco

She is a clinical psychologist and self-taught fine artist, and her creative inspiration is facilitated by unconscious processes that manifest themselves through diverse media. She integrates drawings into her clay work, using the clay as if it were a canvas and then breaking it up into collage. She identifies with primitive cultures and chooses their themes for her work. Also influenced by Picasso, she uses childlike colors, as in her depiction of a woman's face in her monoprint

Betty Decter, *Portrait of the Artist as Max Beckman,*
life size (installation). Photograph: Janice Felgar

John A. de Marchi *Focused Concept,* 30 x 24 x 32, machined
aluminum, steel, alkyd oils. Photograph: Don Cabrall

paper collage *Primitive Persona*. She is currently working on large-scale murals.

DE MARCHI, JOHN A. (Sculptor)
3740 Roblar Rd., Petaluma, CA 94952

Born: 1941 *Collections:* Saks Fifth Avenue, San Francisco; Sonoma State U., Sacramento *Exhibitions:* Museum of Modern Art, San Francisco; California Museum of Art, Santa Rosa *Education:* UC-Santa Cruz *Dealer:* Ianetti Lanzone Gallery, San Francisco

The artist's solidly constructed metal sculptures offer metaphors for many elements of the human condition. The immediate precision and cold, mechanized lines of his work are tempered and humanized by the warmth of applied color. His clever manipulation of such principles as tension and balance allow for easy recognition of each structure's meaning. In *Tension*, two opposing steel hooks pull two links taut within a long, open, rectangular structure. The piece creates an overwhelming emotive impact of tension, but the artist's optimism is manifest in signs of hope. The sides of the steel rectangle are defined only by four relatively thin rods, whose tapering points add to implications of escape, and the entire structure appears mobile on its heavy, cylindrical base. Like Leonardo da Vinci, the artist does not separate art from technology or discount either discipline's usefulness to man. His kinetic pieces allow the viewer to become directly involved with a structure.

DEMOSS, MAX (Sculptor)
26593 Lake St., Hemet, CA 92344

Born: 1947 *Awards:* Best of Show, Bowers Museum, Santa Ana; Best of Show, San Bernardino Museum *Collections:* Chicago Sun Times *Exhibitions:* IAC Fine Arts, Los Angeles; Viridian Gallery, La Jolla *Education:* Cal. State-Long Beach; Claremont College, Claremont *Dealer:* IAC Fine Arts, Los Angeles

After painting in a minimalist style in the late 1960s and working as a conceptual artist in the early 1970s, he became interested in using the human figure as a narrative symbol. He cast figures himself in bronze, allowing the casting process to be incorporated into the work. This resulted in exposed rough-cast surfaces, flashing and mold lines, giving the figures a loose, expressive quality. As his work progresses, figures have evolved into fragmented, life-sized pieces suspended on steel poles. In the recent "Saints and Martyrs" series, life-sized bronze torsos are pierced with crossing steel rods that suspend the torso above the viewer.

DENMARK, GARY (Mixed Media Artist, Printmaker)
1516 Dolores St., San Francisco, CA 94110

Born: 1953 *Collections:* Boston Museum of Art *Exhibitions:* Erickson/Elins Fine Arts, San Francisco; Sonoma State University, Rohnert Park *Education:* U. of Wisconsin, Madison *Dealer:* Smith/Anderson Gallery, Palo Alto

Formal training in printmaking, work in collage and mixed media, the influence of photo-realism and the discovery of Kurt Schwitters and synthetic cubism shaped his aesthetic. Early work consists of collage-like compositions based on references to architecture and detritus, placed within a geometric structure. The palette is intense, influenced by the light of California. Three-dimensional wall constructions, incorporating printed and painted paper, wood, aluminum and various found materials have become his focus. He is concerned with the principles of geometric abstractions and implied symbolism. The forms themselves create reality and space, where before these were only suggested through visual illusion.

DENY, MARTINE (Painter, Printmaker)
7955 W. 4th St., Los Angeles, CA 90048

Born: 1954 *Awards:* Bourse du Governement Francais; Finalist, Artquest *Collections:* Banque Internationale de Luxembourg; Graham & James, Los Angeles *Exhibitions:* Galleria Cortina Milano; Chuck Levitan Gallery, NYC *Education:* U. of Paris; USC *Dealer:* Wade Gallery, La Cienega

She first worked in watercolors, attempting to express ever-changing forms in this fluid, transparent medium. As a great admirer of Helen Frankenthaler, Jackson Pollock and the German Expressionists, she felt the need to work on increasingly large surfaces. While working with Ruth Weisberg, she became fascinated by monoprinting, due to the metal plate's greater resistance (relative to paper), and to the opportunity to work with a roller. When working with canvas, she first applies paint with her fingers, changing later to a brush. Working from a palette dominated by primary colors, she combines fields of color in irregular, vaguely geometric shapes, which appear to be in a state of transformation. She uses oil sticks to finish the work, drawing strong lines through and around the free-flowing forms and colors. She describes her work as the expression of feeling, the destruction of the image and the transformation from fear to hope.

DERJUE, RITA (Painter)
2539 Ridge Rd., Littleton, CO 80120

Born: 1934 *Awards:* Colorado Council of Arts; Museum of Art, Syracuse, NY *Collections:* Munson-Williams Gallery; Proctor Institute, Utica, NY *Exhibitions:* Littleton Historical Museum, Littleton, CO; Ohio State U., Newark *Education:* Rhode Island School of Design; Cornell U. *Dealers:* Panache Gallery, Denver; Parker-Blake Gallery, Denver

Following her formal training, she became fascinated by two German expressionist movements from the turn of the century: the Blue Rider group and Die Brucke (the Bridge). During the 1960s, the New York school influenced her style. Over the years, her work has become more abstract, more experimental and more concerned with civilization's impact on nature. One category of work comprises large, stretched canvasses approximately 5-by-4 feet, painted on both sides and suspended from the ceiling. Another group of works, "The Billboard Paintings," comments on the needless commercialization of the Colorado landscape. For these paintings, she mixed dry pigments with polymer emulsion (so that she could work with transparencies) and layers of color and form. She works by painting numerous watercolor sketches of her intended subject. The watercolors are similar to jottings in a notebook; they help to clarify her thoughts as she prepares to begin a new painting.

DERN, CARL (Sculptor)
58 Park Rd., Fairfax, CA 94930

Born: 1936 *Awards:* Fellowship, Hand Hollow Foundation *Collections:* IBM; U. of California *Exhibitions:* UC-Davis; Gallery 454 North, Los Angeles *Education:* San Francisco Art Institute; UC-Berkeley *Dealer:* Gallery 454 North, Los Angeles

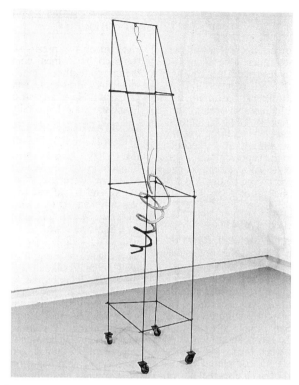

Carl Dern, *Spiral Structure, 1988,* 82 x 15 x 22, steel, bronze

Paul Darrow, *Mandala I,* 22 x 30, color lithograph

His sculpture reflects the subjective, precarious perceptions humans have of each other. One of his two ongoing series was inspired by his childrens' drawings. In these large, brilliantly colored, complex human figures, he employs a childlike spontaneity and economy of line. Since 1985, he has also been making a series of allegorical human figures. The form of these anthropomorphic pieces allows him to bring out the figure's stance, energy, movement and presence without the formal prejudices the representational figure brings. His materials include wood, stone, bronze, steel, paper, enamel, latex and acrylic paints. Most of his sculptures may be exhibited out of doors.

DESANTIS, MARY (Painter)
3732 23rd St., #4, San Francisco, CA 94114

Born: 1942 *Awards:* Honorable Mention, Artworld, San Mateo *Exhibitions:* San Francisco Arts Festival; Fobbo Gallery, San Francisco

Early work in oils was mostly introspective. After experimenting with wood sculpture, papier mache, stained glass and block printing, she took up watercolors. Her works are on-the-spot paintings of life in movement. Still lifes and San Francisco's cityscape, zoos and boats dominate. She has been influenced by the beauty of life, and her work displays a colorful impressionistic sense. She recently completed a series of blue papier mache fish and ocean pieces that appear to hang in mid-air.

D'ESOPO, MARCIA (Painter)
1218 N. Beverly Glen, Los Angeles, CA 90077

Awards: NIDA Grant, Venice *Collections:* KCET Television, Los Angeles *Education:* San Francisco Art Institute

She calls herself a Social Realist, presenting each subject in both its internal and external environments. The work of Edvard Munch has had a great deal of influence on her portraits, as she particularly employs the use of shadows and unrevealed space to express a subject's environment and personality. Her palette consists of brilliant colors. She has also begun to make sepia ink line drawings that concentrate on line and form, in a style reminiscent of Japanese art. Paintings which exuberantly explore the nuances of the featured character through the use of graceful lines reflect the influence of her experiences as a dancer.

DESOTO, LEWIS (Photographer)
96 Panorama Dr., San Francisco, CA 94131

Born: 1954 *Awards:* 1st Place, Annual All California Juried Exhibition, Orange County Center for Contemporary Art *Collections:* Los Angeles County Museum of Art; Museum of Modern Art, NYC *Exhibitions:* Friends of Photography, Carmel; Silver Image Gallery, Seattle *Education:* Claremont Graduate School; UC-Riverside *Dealer:* Silver Image Gallery, Seattle; Jones/Troyer/Fitzpatrick Gallery, Washington, D.C.

Influenced by the earthworks of Smithson and de Maria and the photographs and sculpture of Richard Long, he began in 1981 to introduce elements of performance, sculpture and text into his photographic pieces. Addressing the ideas of time and transformation, the particular and the infinite, he situated his work generally in the landscape and incorporated long exposures, silhouettes of his body, projections and colored light. Recent work, especially the "Tahualtapa Project" embodies the idea of a transformation of a site—Mt. Slover in California—into the substance of civilization—cement—through photographs surrounded by frames, comprising the "substance" of meaning: feathers, marble and cement, as well as sculptures, drawings, installations and public project proposals. He is an associate professor of art at San Francisco State University.

DE STAEBLER, STEPHEN (Sculptor)
21 Bret Harte Rd., Berkeley, CA 94708

Born: 1933 *Awards:* NEA Fellowship; Guggenheim Fellowship *Collections:* Oakland Museum; Neuberger Museum, Purchase, NY *Exhibitions:* San Francisco Museum of Modern Art; Renwick Gallery, Washington, D.C. *Education:* Princeton U.; UC-Berkeley *Dealer:* CDS Gallery, NYC; Berggruen Gallery, San Francisco

The properties and characteristics of the material he works with are integral to his art, and while studying with Peter Voulkos, he was introduced to clay and discovered its potential. During the 1960s, he worked primarily with this material, developing a series of sculptures associated with landscape imagery. This work was low-relief and installed on the ground or flat against a wall. The most important aspect of these sculptures was their visual integration with their environment. He has since moved from low-relief sculpture to free-standing forms. In the more recent work, he combines an architectural sense of structure with organic shapes related to the figure, and he continues to explore more complex relationships between the figure and its non-figurative environment.

DETAMORE, ROBERT C. (Printmaker)
512 Spencer St., Barnesville, GA 30204

Born: 1947 *Awards:* 2nd Place, ArtQuest; Purchase Award, Galleries Elect, Los Angeles *Collections:* Brooklyn Museum of Art; High Museum of Art, Atlanta *Exhibitions:* Valerie Miller and Associates, Los Angeles; Pratt Graphics Center, NYC *Education:* Georgia State U.; U. of Georgia, Athens *Dealer:* Valerie Miller, Los Angeles

For the past few years, his surrealistic intaglios have been involved with space and its manipulation. Starting from deep space that adhered to rigid systems of perspective, he moved towards more compressed, textural areas and greater ambiguity. These settings house discordant, at times, humorous juxtapositions of figurative and historical imagery, including references to measurement and scientific instruments. His printing process begins with simple line etching, and progresses through darkening stages of aquatint until certain images are scraped out of the blackness in the manner of mezzotint. The image is then translated into color.

DEUTSCHER, LUDELL (Ceramist, Sculptor)
670 C East H. Street, Benicia, CA 94510

Born: 1927 *Awards:* 1st Prize, San Francisco Art Festival; San Francisco Potters Award *Collections:* Mills College, Oakland; City of Walnut Creek *Exhibitions:* California Polytechnic U.; Banaker Gallery, Walnut Creek

As a potter, she found satisfaction only when her work took sculptural form. In 1972, she began devoting full time to clay, and to handmade paper sculpture. After coloring paper pulp with dye or pigment, she forms it in plaster molds, or casts against the found objects she uses as molds. Techniques include spraying or couch-

Ludell Deutscher, *Exfoliation,* 36 x 24 x 12, stoneware clay.
Photograph: Grey Kinder

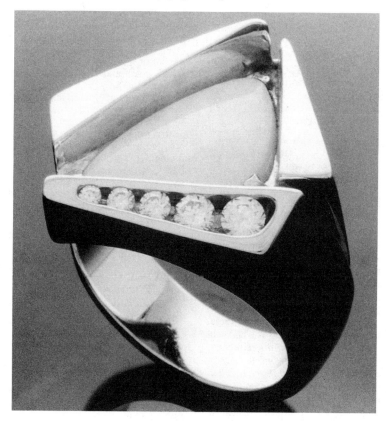

Glenn Dizon, *Try Angles,* opal and diamond ring

ing, sometimes using thin layers of paper or strips of fiber in the mold before backing them with layers of pulp, in order to achieve a multidimensional effect. She also includes wood and metal separately and in combination with paper. Freestanding paper sculptures are mostly figurative; wall pieces are usually more abstract. Her study of primitive art by traveling throughout the world has influenced her sensual, organic imagery. In a recent paper piece, the photograph of a waterfall is inserted into the convex side of the back half of a man's body.

DEVEREUX, MARA (Painter)
5653 1/2 Hollywood Blvd., Los Angeles, CA 90028

Born: 1932 *Awards:* Scholarship, Otis Art Institute *Exhibitions:* Brooklyn Museum; Los Angeles County Museum *Education:* Otis Art Institute *Dealer:* Gaye Blair, Beverly Hills

Trained in a traditional setting, she has always worked in oils. She was influenced by Kandinsky, and became a hard edge abstract painter in 1963. Between then and 1970, she progressed from flat surfaces to five-sided box paintings. Since 1970, she has walked the long road back to realism, producing only drawings until 1980, when she was again drawn to hard edge abstraction. She currently intersperses abstract paintings with highly realistic landscapes, portraits and still lifes. Abstraction and realism are tied together in her work, each battling for primacy.

DEVINE, MARY ANN (Sculptor)
4535 Vanalden Ave., Tarzana, CA 91356

Born: 1935 *Awards:* NEA Fellowship *Collections:* Library of Congress, Washington D.C.; Long Beach Museum of Art *Exhibitions:* Marjorie and Herman Platt Gallery, Los Angeles; Ankrum Gallery, Los Angeles *Education:* UCLA; Cal. State-Long Beach *Dealer:* Ankrum Gallery, Los Angeles

Trained in painting and printmaking at UCLA in the late 1950s and early 1960s, she was introduced to sculpture by Robert Cremean. Profoundly influenced by Kenneth Clark, who lectured on campus, she pledged allegiance to the human figure in a symbolic context. She created an "Eve" series while studying bronze casting and stone carving at California State U., and later incorporated concrete to enlarge the scope and scale of her work. As a contemporary artist engaged in a dialogue with the past, she uses ancient materials to evoke ancient ideas. An original technique allows her to cast concrete with elaborate inlay to create large intarsia panels. She feels that myth and archetype transcend time and culture by virtue of their birth in common experience, and often uses fragmented forms reminiscent of archaeological remains to suggest the classical notion of spirit durable beyond the dissolution of body. She has worked extensively with small bronzes. A traditionally intimate form of art, it is designed to be handled and reflects, in its metallic strength, both the fashions of its day and the continuity of history. Recent work includes a series of carvings that explore feminine sexuality. Alabaster fragments of goddesses are animated by abstract drapery and inlaid with gemstones and gold. Delicate pink Venus figures are coifed, civi-

lized and contained, while raw orange baccantes twist, turn and leap in a hungry dance celebrating the flesh.

DE VIVI, CARMINE W. (Mixed Media Artist)
290 Rose St., Danville, CA 94526

Born: 1929 *Awards:* Thornton-Oakley Gold Medal, U. of Pennsylvania *Collections:* Du Pont Corp., Wilmington, DE *Exhibitions:* Philadelphia College of Art; Civic Arts Center, Walnut Creek *Education:* Philadelphia College of Art; U. of Pennsylvania

In graduate school at the University of Pennsylvania, the artist worked with Angelo Savelli, Piero Dorazio and James House, Jr. Under these influences, the early work tended toward masses of built-up color. Soon known as a colorist, the artist almost immediately turned to working in abstracted images, made up solely of whites and off-whites. Interested in different types of paper, the artist created works that integrated paper architecturally into them, often by hand-sewing the paper into the canvas, sometimes in combination with plexiglas and transparent plastics. When successful, these later works trick the eye into seeing much greater depth than is actually there, and various images seem to float magically above the main bodies of the paintings.

DEVRIES, NANCY L. (Photographer)
P.O. Box 64424, Los Angeles, CA 90064

Born: 1956 *Collections:* Atlantic Richfield Permanent Corporate Art Collection; John Portman & Associates, Atlanta *Exhibitions:* Artists Society International Gallery, San Francisco; The Art Store, Los Angeles *Education:* UCLA

She began studying graphic design in 1974, then found herself gravitating more towards photography. Her design background has had a profound influence on her photography, specifically in her perception of space, color and composition. Early on, she was influenced by the work of artist Victor Vasarely, for his use of color, geometry and optical perspective. Her study of form, light and color have led her to architectural photography, creating what she calls architectural abstractions. These images are often seen by isolating architectural details within the compositional frame of the camera, producing a piece with graphic visual impact. She also experiments with various processes to radically change the actual color of a space or object. Thus, abstract views of reality become a kind of found art, originating from her perception and reaction to the subject.

DICKINSON, ELEANOR CREEKMORE
(Painter, Video Artist)
2125 Broderick St., San Francisco, CA 94115

Born: 1931 *Awards:* National Society of Arts & Letters; Distinguished Alumni, San Francisco Art Institute *Collections:* National Museum of American Art; San Francisco Museum of Modern Art *Exhibitions:* Corcoran Gallery of Art; Smithsonian Institution, Washington D.C. *Education:* U. of Tennessee; San Francisco Art Institute; California College of Arts and Crafts *Dealers:* Hatley Martin Gallery, San Francisco; Michael Himovitz Gallery, Sacramento

She is essentially a draftsman; although she works in a variety of media, these are usually linear, and color is employed for its value, not its hue. The act of drawing is most important, along with the excitement of unplanned composition and discovery. Her subject is always figurative, and her style is expressionistic realism.

Warren Dreher, *Little Lake St., Mendocino,* 19 x 25, chalk pastel on paper

Charles Dickson, *Uprooted,* 156 x 60 x 60, A.B.S. plastics, rigid vinyl

Joe Draegert, *La Balancoire,* 60 x 40, acrylic on hardboard. Courtesy: Erickson & Elins/Fine Art

Among the subjects of her major series are old and young lovers, animals, revival meetings, models and illness and death. Her exhibition "Revival!" comprised 2,000 objects interacting with each other in paintings, drawings, photographs, slides, holograms, artifacts and videotapes. Her most recent traveling exhibition, "The Crucifixion Series," shows huge foreshortened figures with upraised arms in pain and praise, 10 feet high in pastel on black velvet.

DICKOW, JEAN (Painter)
9 Hidden Valley Rd., Lafayette, CA 94549

Born: 1936 *Collections:* Walnut Creek City Hall; U.S. Coast Guard, San Francisco *Exhibitions:* Valley Art Gallery, Walnut Creek; Alta Bates Hospital, Berkeley *Education:* UC-Berkeley *Dealer:* Interart, San Francisco

Whether figurative or non-objective, landscapes dominate her work. Inspired by Monet and Cezanne, she renders the Contra Costa landscape in a neo-impressionist style, with blues, pinks, purples and greens. She works in acrylic on primed and unprimed canvas, and uses a mixture of water pastel and acrylic on paper. She is most interested in the play of light—the way it diffuses the land and water into limpid, tranquil images. She hopes to explore the abstract in her future work.

DICKSON, CHARLES (Sculptor)
423 E. Rosencrans, Compton, CA 90221

Born: 1947 *Awards:* John C. Fremont High School Hall of Fame for Art *Collections:* Golden State Mutual, Afro-American Art Collection; Curtis Junior High School, Carson *Exhibitions:* Palos Verdes Art Center; Afro-American Museum

As a young boy he began carving wood. He later studied drawing and painting with Charles White and developed a style influenced by African and Asian art. His media of that time consisted of wood, bronze and plaster. In 1983, he began sculpting with high impact styrene plastic, a clear material often used in packaging products such as batteries. He soon added urethane foam to the plastic and discovered a medium that could be formed quickly on a very large scale while remaining light and strong. The female form is the subject of his recent work. He continues to use the new medium as a means of expressing his African American heritage.

DIEBENKORN, RICHARD (Painter)
c/o M. Knoedler, 19 E. 70th St., New York NY 10021

Born: 1922 *Awards:* Gold Medal, Pennsylvania Academy of Fine Arts; National Institute of Arts and Letters *Collections:* Metropolitan Museum of Art, NYC; San Francisco Museum of Modern Art *Exhibitions:* Whitney Museum, NYC; De Young Memorial Museum, San Francisco *Education:* California School of Fine Arts; Stanford U.; U. of New Mexico *Dealer:* M. Knoedler, NYC

Early still-life and interior and figurative paintings during World War II were influenced by modern French painters such as Matisse and Bonnard. Contact with artists in California and New York transformed his work to a non-objective, energetic style that evolved quickly from geometric abstraction to a more expressionistic mode. In his large, expressionist canvases, such as in his "Ocean Park" series, he tends to use areas of color rather than line, arranging pictorial space asymmetrically into large open areas with smaller active areas and abstracting specific elements from the landscape as a whole. In recent years, he has become increasingly independent from abstract expressionism and has shown concern for more literal subject matter. He recently completed a set of prints at Crown Point Press.

DIEHL, GUY LOUIS (Painter)
4161 Sacramento St., Concord, CA 94521

Born: 1949 *Awards:* Purchase Award, Alameda County Art Commission *Collections:* City Hall Building, Oakland; Alameda County Art Commission, Oakland *Exhibitions:* Jeremy Stone Gallery, San Francisco; Oakland Museum *Education:* Cal. State-Hayward; San Francisco State U. *Dealer:* Jeremy Stone Gallery, San Francisco

Acrylics and watercolors on canvas are realistic renderings of contemporary leisure activities, such as *Edge of Pool with Mondrian Towel.* Formal symmetrical compositions are full of the intense sunlight of summer, deep shadows and brilliant colors. Although figures are not present, personal belongings indicate their presence. Small-scale still lifes are classically painted with wit and humor. Subject matter consists of everyday objects—food, books, shells, flowers, paper airplanes—bathed in intense light and surrounded by painterly shadow and reflection. These unpretentious works have been compared to the paintings of Bay Area artists Wayne Thiebaud and Mark Adams.

DIKE, PHIL (Painter)
2272 N. Forbes Ave., Claremont, CA 91711

Born: 1906 *Awards:* Purchase Prize, National Watercolor Exhibition; 1st Prize, Watercolor, Butler Institute of American Art *Collections:* Metropolitan Museum of Art, NYC; Phoenix Art Museum *Exhibitions:* Los Angeles County Museum of Art; Scripps College Lang Galleries *Education:* Chouinard Art Institute; Art Students League *Dealer:* Richard Challis Gallery, Laguna Beach

Though he also paints in oils, he is best known as a prominent California Watercolorist, responsible along with Rex Brandt, Millard Sheets, Dong Kingman and others for the popularity of the medium in California beginning especially in the 1930s and 1940s. As with later movements, the area's distance from the international art centers allowed for the freedom to explore media and styles not necessarily in vogue; in addition, the sky, sun and water lent themselves especially to watercolor treatment. These elements are the consistent theme of his watercolors, and over the years he has distilled the images through precise compositions and brilliant colors to simplified shapes that approach pure abstraction. His influence has also been felt as a teacher at the Chouinard Art Institute, the Brandt-Dike Summer School of painting and Scripps College. Critic Janice Lovoos says, "Dike's recurring themes of sea, sky and shoreline, birds, sea life and beach fragments never lack variation, nor do the striations of color streaming across the picture plane of his painting surface."

DILL, GUY GIRARD (Sculptor)
819 Milwood Ave., Venice CA 90291

Born: 1946 *Awards:* Theodoron Award, Guggenheim Museum; NEA Fellowship *Collections:* Museum of Modern Art, NYC; Museum of Contemporary Art, Los Angeles *Exhibitions:* Guggenheim Museum; Arco Center for the Visual Arts, Los Angeles *Education:*

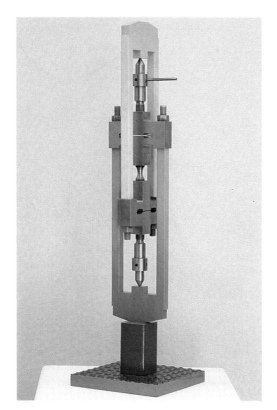

John A. deMarchi, *Push Comes to Shove,*
37 x 10 x 10, machined and welded steel,
alkyd oils. Photograph: J. de Marchi

Susan Dobay, *Venus,* 24 x 36, acrylic and oil on canvas
Courtesy: Style Connection Gallery, Encino

Mila del Potro, *Vulcan's Cameo,* 16 x 12 x 9, ceramic

John Drooyan, *Lullaby for a Monster, from the series,*
"Altar Egos", 40 x 25, mixed media, photo-sculpture assemblage

Awee-pa-no Viva David *White Buffalo Calf Woman,*
48 x 18, redwood burl. Courtesy: Sid Fridkin

Charles Dickson, *Stepping in, Stepping out, Stepping on,*
144 x 60 x 66, high impact styrene plastic, urethane, foamcore

L.S. Day, *Walking Man Series, N.Y.: "Big Red",* 21 x 31, auto laquer and pastel on paper

Glenn Dizon, *Opal and Diamond Woman's Ring,* 14k gold

Paul Darrow, *Woman with Ribbons,* 24 x 39,
colored pencil on paper

Elaine Davault, *Avalon,* 14 x 18, mixed media

Carl Dern, *Standing Figure, 1988,* 42 x 10 x 8, rock, steel, bronze

Martine Deny, *Hillside Ave.,* 39 x 51, oil sticks on canvas

Ludell Deutscher, *Shadow,* 96 x 60 x 48, mixed media,
paper fiber, burlap. Photograph: Michele Maier

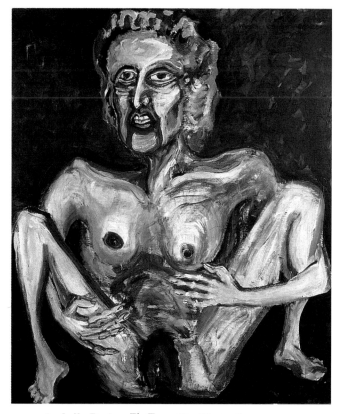

Arabella Decker *Fly Trap,* 48 x 60, acrylic on canvas

Marie Ducasse, *d'Orient,* 24 x 20, serigraph

Jan Daniels, *Voices,* 11" each, clay

Betty Decter, *Double Sided Kimono,* 216 x 216, acrylic. Photograph: Janice Felgar

Omar d'Leon, *Avocados,* 16 x 20, oil, wax

Carmine DeVivi, *Arctic Series #4,* 32 x 40, sewn papers. Photograph: Michele Maier

Ruth Mary Dugan Reid, *Crystal and the Mockingbird,* 30 x 38, mixed media. Courtesy: Crystal Reid

Elly Drees, *Mannequin III,* 24 x 30, oil

Barbara Dougherty, *Lagoon,* 30 x 40, goauche

Veronica diRosa, *#2 Blue on Yellow,* 60 x 84, polychromed steel plate. Photograph: Jock McDonald

John deHeras, *Cenotes,* 10 x 13, acrylic on paper

Cecelia Davidson, *The Last Journey of Isolde,* 74 x 120, oil and gold leaf on paper mounted on wood

Laddie John Dill, *untitled, From "Death in Venice,"* 48 x 96, oil on canvas. Courtesy: James Corcoran

Joe Draegert, *Nastro Di Azzurro Da Notte,* 45 x 48, acrylic on hardboard.
Courtesy: Erickson & Elins/Fine Art

Marnie Donaldson, *Maria's Friends,* 24 x 30, watercolor

Warren Dreher, *Waiting,* 19 x 25, chalk pastel on paper, 1985

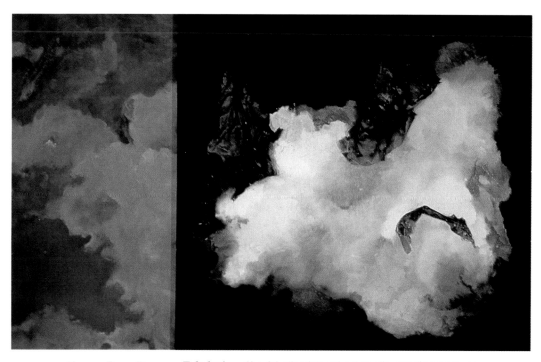

Noreen Dean Dresser, *Exhaltation,* 60 x 96, dipytich, mixed media, acrylic on canvas

Ann Garat Ducey, *Possession in Great Measure,* 40 x 60, watercolor, Courtesy: Banaker Gallery

Bonnie Dunn, *Tahoe Rocks,* 16 x 20, photogragh

Chouinard Art Institute *Dealer:* Flow Ace Gallery, Los Angeles

He constructs architectonic structures in scale, from such materials as metal, marble, concrete and wood. Beginning in 1971, the circle served as a fulcrum for the compositions. Later the column was added as a "connection and icon." He preserved the natural colors and surfaces of the media in order to provide his works with "real-energy." Now more interested in the combination of planes, surfaces and shapes and in working with space and scale to create works of visual harmony, he seeks to unify his chosen forms—the circle, the beam and other elements—in order to create "an integrated icon or shape."

DILL, LADDIE JOHN (Painter, Sculptor)
1625 Electric Ave., Venice, CA 90291

Born: 1943 *Awards:* California Arts Council Grant; NEA Fellowship *Collections:* Los Angeles County Museum of Art; San Francisco Museum of Modern Art *Exhibitions:* Santa Barbara Museum of Art; Long Beach Museum of Art *Education:* Chouinard Art Institute *Dealer:* Charles Cowles Gallery, NYC; James Corcoran Gallery, Los Angeles

An early influence on his work was the environmental art of Robert Irwin. In 1986, he created light and sand pieces in a horizontal format, installations made of glass, neon and sand that appeared to be aerial views of landscape. Experiments with painting led to a rectilinear format with the addition of architectonic shapes to the landscape imagery. In 1975, the format was vertical, suggesting "a figurative reference achieved by a more formal architectural structuring," and two years later he produced a vertical "Door" series. Paintings now reflect both landscape and architectural imagery. His media are cement polymer, glass, silicone and oil on canvas; he has also made drawings in pastel, oil and graphite on rag paper.

DIMICHELE, DAVID (Painter, Installation Artist)
2718 Petaluma Ave., Long Beach, CA 90815

Born: 1954 *Awards:* Artist-in-Residence Grant, City of Long Beach; Phi Kappa Phi *Collections:* Laguna Art Museum; Security Pacific Bank *Exhibitions:* Laguna Art Museum; Security Pacific Bank *Education:* Cal. State-Long Beach; UC-Santa Cruz

He endeavors to place the present in a historical context of advancing technology, abstracting and arranging such disparate images as stone tools, machine parts and space probes. The work is a combination of an early interest in non-objective juxtapositions and an imagery he derives from pre-historical and historical epochs and contemporary life. His early paintings were either loose, gestural abstractions in the abstract expressionist vein, or hard-edged, rectilinear shapes similar to that evoked in early European abstract painting. This early work emphasized contrasting analytical and intuitive modes of thinking.

DIN, SEITU (Painter)
537 Jones Box 8489, San Francisco, CA 94102

Born: 1952 *Collections:* American Savings and Loan Association, Oakland *Exhibitions:* Detroit Historical Museum; Richmond Art Center

The former Arthur Sanders III bases his cubist, allegorical work on a strong African-American heritage. He appropriates the forces and images of his interrelated cultures and places them in opposition, without

however creating tension. Influenced by the works of Paul Klee, his abstract style takes everyday visual objects and transforms them until they deliver messages—his children become trees, his houses children. In one work, the will to succeed is etched on a child's face. He fills his palette with unusual yellows, oranges, greens, purples and blacks, most often working in watercolors but also frequently using oils, gouache, inks, dyes, pastels, pencils and new materials.

DINGUS, MARITA T. (Sculptor)
5812 S. 331st St., Auburn, WA 98002

Born: 1956 *Collections:* Seattle Arts Commission *Exhibitions:* Ankrum Gallery, Los Angeles; Tallahassee National Gallery

One of the upcoming talents of the Seattle art scene, she follows the tradition and philosophy of Black African art. Her sculptural works have a voodoo look to them and an aura of ritualistic shamanism. Each has a raw vivacity that makes it an imposing presence in any room. Her figures are built from scraps and tatters of cloth that she collects. Each wears a painted mask, which she ties on with glittering bits of cloth regalia. In 1988, she was featured as part of Seattle's Black History Month celebration. She has exhibited widely and she is candidate for the American Academy of Arts and Letters.

DINNEN, GARY (Painter, Computer Animator)
1730 27th St., Sacramento, CA 95816

Born: 1953 *Awards:* 3rd Place, Visions of the U.S., American Film Institute *Exhibitions:* Gregory Ghent Gallery, San Francisco; San Francisco Museum of Modern Art, Rental Gallery *Education:* Cal. State-Sacramento *Dealer:* Michael Himovitz, Sacramento

He had already studied painting and drawing for ten years when he began working with computer-generated images. The computer enabled him to work quickly through ideas, and he produced many colorful, expressionist works and animated shorts. Recently, he has been spending more time with his painting, concentrating on producing oil, etching and watercolor works with deep color saturation. He frequently uses human or animal forms, with a bend toward narrative and personal fantasy.

DINUR, DORIT (Painter, Collage Artist)
3190 Carnegie Place, San Diego, CA 92122

Born: 1948 *Exhibitions:* Perspectives Gallery, San Diego; La Jolla Art Association

She was a chemist and a teacher, but felt restless and dissatisfied; a few art classes began to convince her to rethink her career. She paints and constructs collages that connect the microscopic world of atoms and molecules to the macroscopic world of people and societies. Her work shows the influences of Matisse, children's drawings and Middle Eastern art. Floral motifs swirl through her pieces, although they appear in a more abstract form. She uses junk mail, other found materials, oil, acrylic and enamel paints on a variety of surfaces, including paper, canvas, chairs and rugs. Her work is bright and colorful— an expression of her optimism—and a constant surprise to her.

DIRKS, JOHN (Sculptor, Furniture Artist)
5120 Alzeda Dr., La Mesa, CA 92041

Born: 1914 *Awards:* 1st Prize, National Arts and Crafts Show, Pomona; Best in Show, San Diego Artists' Guild Exhibition *Collections:* Walbridge Collection, La Jolla *Exhibitions:* San Diego Museum of Art, Focus Gallery;

San Diego State U. Gallery *Education:* San Diego State U.; Claremont Graduate School

During the last twelve years he has worked with the light- gathering and conducting properties of clear, translucent and semi-translucent acrylic. Sometimes incorporating wood into his non-geometric constructions, he attempts to eliminate the stereometric monotony found in some modern sculpture and architecture. He holds the attention of the observer with changes of rhythm, rather than through a repetitious beat. In recent sculptures, he has returned to small abstracted animal forms. Reflecting his childhood interest in animals and birds, he combines laminated curved elements with carved parts to produce a sense of inner life in his three-foot-high pieces.

DI ROSA, VERONICA (Painter, Sculptor)
5200 Sonoma Highway, Napa, CA 94559

Born: 1934 *Collections:* Mr. and Mrs. Cornelius Vanderbilt Whitney; San Francisco Museum of Modern Art *Exhibitions:* Whitney Museum (Private); Crocker Art Museum, Sacramento *Education:* Emily Carr School of Art *Dealer:* Oberon Gallery, Napa

After formal training in art and graphic design, she painted non-commercial watercolors, with figurative and landscape subject matter, eventually developing a complex, surreal vocabulary of juxtaposed reality and fantasy, representing the inner as well as the external world. Concurrently, commercial work included writing and illustrating books on food and wine, and making wine art (labels, posters, logos, letterheads and ads). Much of this was based on landscape and figurative work in watercolor. In 1987, after years of working primarily on paper, she started mixed-media sculpture: at first, with miniaturized objects and landscape references; but finally, in full scale. She devised animal motifs in 1/4-inch polychrome steel—specifically life-size herds of sheep and cows in familiar configurations, but unfamiliar colorations. Influences have been primarily the realities of the agricultural environments of her childhood and adult years.

DISTEFANO, JOAN (Glass Artist)
329 Lewis, Oakland, CA 94607

Born: 1946 *Exhibitions:* San Francisco Art Commission *Education:* San Francisco Art Institute

She was a painting major, who found that the frustrations of painting were better solved through the medium of glass. Influences include the minimal line work and crisp starkness of contemporary German masters. From work to work, colors vary widely; in any specific, almost monochromatic piece, she varies shades subtly. Her early work was decorative; in her present expressionistic mixed-media constructions, she combines flat glass with wood, steel, paper and barbed wire, producing lively works that change through the day and evoke a wide range of emotions. Her stained glass pieces are often free standing. Her work has been collected and exhibited in Paris and Nairobi.

DI SUVERO, MARK (Sculptor)
c/o Oil & Steel Gallery, 3030 Vernon Blvd, New York, NY 11102

Born: 1933 *Awards:* Longview Foundation Grant; Art Institute of Chicago Award *Collections:* Whitney Museum, NYC; Art Institute of Chicago *Exhibitions:* Los Angeles County Museum of Art; San Diego Museum of Art *Education:* U. of California *Dealer:* Oil and Steel Gallery, NYC

Constructivist and baroque elements are synthesized in order to explore space, motion, gravity, balance and structure. Massive public works are spatial sculptures constructed out of wide-flange steel I-beams welded or bolted together. Viewer participation is invited by the inclusion of movable portions that can be climbed upon. Smaller, human-scale sculptures are comprised of balanced pieces and variable elements. The smallest works—puzzle pieces—are elaborate calligraphic shapes cut out of steel, which the viewer can assemble.

DIXON, WILLARD (Painter)
5 Belloreid, San Rafael, CA 94901

Born: 1942 *Awards:* Purchase Prize, San Francisco Art Festival *Collections:* Oakland Museum; Metropolitan Museum of Art, NYC *Exhibitions:* William Sawyer Gallery, San Francisco; Gallery 454 North, Los Angeles *Dealers:* William Sawyer Gallery, San Francisco; Gallery 454 North, Los Angeles; Fischbach Gallery, NYC;

Drawing inspiration from the Western landscape, he uses considerable detail and large canvases to create vast scenes that may be filled with train tracks, buildings, trucks or figures. Distinguished by his use of atmospheric perspective and light between the landscape and the observer, his works often evoke feelings of particular weather conditions or times of day. He manipulates spatial depth to create illusions of distances and of the placement of the observer, whose vantage point may be indoors, outside, alone or below the painting. Unlike most realists, he also reveals his personal involvement in the painting. His use of perspective and illusion follows in the tradition of 19th-century Romanticism. Although he was once considered a photo-realist, his recent work takes a more painterly and imaginative approach.

DIZON, GLENN R. (Jeweler)
P.O. Box 386, San Rafael, CA 94901

Born: 1953 *Awards:* 1st Place, Award of Excellence, National Metal Arts Competition, Metal Arts Guild; Award of Excellence, International Art Competition, NYC *Exhibitions:* Union Street Goldsmith, San Francisco; Contemporary Art Market, Santa Monica *Education:* Revere School of Jewelry Arts

The artist's admiration and respect for the properties of each individual gemstone is the primary inspiration behind his sleek jewelry designs. His first pieces encouraged him to pursue jewelry-making while completing his business degree in college. On the advice of several colleagues, he enrolled at Revere, and this remains a major factor influencing his current designs, providing the finishing touch to his technique. While nature and music inspire many of his creations, he maintains an instinctual sensitivity to the intrinsic nuances and qualities of the stones themselves.

D'LEON, OMAR (Painter)
P.O. Box 3125, Camarillo, CA 93011

Born: 1939 *Awards:* Gold Medal, Nicaragua; Silver Medal, Guatemala City *Collections:* Museum of Modern Art of Latin America, Washington D.C.; Carnegie Arts Museum, Oxnard *Exhibitions:* Museum Tauroentum, France; Art Institute of Chicago *Education:* School of Fine Arts, Managua

Deeply emotional and expressive, his work pursues beauty of both color and form through the interaction of human figures in moments otherwise overlooked in everyday human activities. A sense of magical realism

Veronica di Rosa, *First Cow,* life-size, 1/4"steel plate, automotive enamel. Collection: Saintsbury Winery

Marnie Donaldson, *Sheep,* 22 x 30, watercolor

pervades the jewel tones he achieves through as many as twenty layers of scored oil paint and beeswax over crayola. Uncompromisingly full and round, his figures of women cross the boundary of impressionism and abstraction, belonging to neither one clearly. This is particularly true of his pen and ink studies. Compared by critics to Picasso, Degas, Gauguin and Zuniga, he explores line and pattern with a continuity that underscores the unique combination of contemporary and classical sensibilities evident in the pieces. Inspired by his native Nicaragua, he maintains a sense of anonymity and mystery in the lyricism of his voluminously draped figures that involves the viewer through a shared emotional resonance and a search for semblance.

DOBAY, SUSAN (Painter)
125 W. Scenic Dr., Monrovia, CA 91016

Born: 1937 *Collections:* KFAC Radio, Los Angeles *Exhibitions:* Contemporary Museum of Fine Art, Budapest *Dealer:* Style Connection, Encino

Working in several different styles, the Hungarian, born artist paints on canvas with acrylic, ink, oil, modeling paste and mixed-media. Frequently her subject is the human experience: man's passions, his moods and his predicament. Occasionally she deals with philosophical subjects, rural scenes, impressions, landscapes. In *Science*, spherical bodies rotate in a prison of closed curves. In *My Newborn Child*, a naked man surrounded by tombstones raises his infant child to the lilac colored horizon. She recently began experimenting with ideas of infinity and trying to put feeling into her combination of geometric and figurative shapes.

DONALDSON, MARNIE (Painter)
1022 Bale Ln., Calistoga, CA 94515

Born: 1945 *Collections:* California Savings and Loan, San Francisco *Exhibitions:* National Watercolor Society; Rocky Mountain Watercolor Society *Education:* UC-Davis; Oregon State U.

A fourth-generation Californian, she has been influenced by the California school of watercolor. She paints loosely with watercolors and chooses subjects that range from landscapes and waterscapes to figures and animal studies. While the work is representational, she establishes an almost abstract design by moving close to her subject matter. Her figures or animals run off the edges of the paper, creating positive and negative spaces. She thinks of herself as a "bit of a colorist" and mixes her colors on the paper instead of the palette. She is a full signature member of the National Watercolor Society.

DOOLIN, JAMES (Painter)
2020 N. Main St., #232, Los Angeles, CA 90031

Born: 1932 *Awards:* Guggenheim Fellowship; NEA Fellowship *Collections:* Contemporary Art Museum, Honolulu; Australian National Gallery *Exhibitions:* Los Angeles Municipal Gallery; Koplin Gallery, Los Angeles *Education:* Philadelphia College of Art; UCLA *Dealer:* Koplin Gallery, Los Angeles

His early works, known as "Artificial Landscapes," were abstract color field paintings with references to urban architectural forms. In 1970, he departed sharply from abstraction with a series of realist landscape and figure paintings that culminated in a large and complex four-year project: a hyper-realistic representation of a shopping mall from the air. Since 1980, his landscape paintings have moved away from sharp realism and are more concerned with relationships of color and light. The most recent urban landscapes have often included groups of figures and display a heightened interest in the theatrical nature of city streets and artificial lighting.

DOPP, SUSAN MARIE (Painter)
4401 San Leandro St., #2B, Oakland, CA 94601

Born: 1951 *Awards:* Artist in Residence, Roswell Museum and Art Center *Exhibitions:* Pence Gallery, Davis; San Francisco Museum of Modern Art *Education:* San Francisco Art Institute

In recent years, she has experimented with a wide range of media, including printmaking, sculpture, assemblage and multimedia installations. Her latest work includes small paintings in oil on gesso panels using the Renaissance technique of underpainting with layers of oil glazes. These highly detailed, surrealist paintings are executed in a limited palette, which includes glowing ruby red and emerald green. She also uses more contemporary techniques such as collage, wax relief and texturing to finish these paintings. Her imagery is dreamlike in appearance and psychological in content.

DORN, VIRGINIA (Painter)
95 Evergreen Dr., Orinda, CA 94563

Awards: 1st Award, Artist Embassy Gallery, San Francisco; San Francisco Women Artists, National Women's Caucus for the Arts *Collections:* Wells Fargo Bank, San Francisco & San Jose *Exhibitions:* Labaudt Gallery, San Francisco; Trinity Gallery, Berkeley *Education:* U. of Minnesota; Cal. State-Hayward *Dealer:* San Francisco Women Artists Gallery

She has progressed from ink drawings of zoological dissections to extreme realism and portraiture and to abstract landscapes and "musical abstractions" in acrylic and mixed media. The artist has always used strong color and bold forms to create intense, abstract images that embrace in opposition the energetic and the reposed, exploring the possibilities of flat planes and deep space. The surfaces of her landscapes are enriched by a variety of techniques: glazing, blotting and rubbing with brushes, plastic cards, sponges, paper towels and the hands and fingers. She aims to recreate in the viewer the feelings evoked by her memories of the landscapes she has seen.

DOTSON, REBECCA (Painter)
49 Maple Ave., Fairfax, CA 94930

Born: 1947 *Awards:* 1st Place, Roanoke College, VA; 1st Place, Photography, Ruckesson Corporation, San Francisco *Exhibitions:* Marin Arts Guild, Larkspur; Marin Artist Society, Ross *Education:* Columbus College of Art & Design

Working towards developing an individual style of painting, using a number of different media, his work has evolved from simple flat areas of color into a more intricate, decorative image. With experience as a commercial artist, he did his first figurative studies in oil, within the action painting tradition. He began working in watercolor, and, influenced by Matisse, he started focusing on pattern as an essential element in composition. His still lifes of fruit and flowers are inspired by the patterns inherent in the subjects. While pattern provides the structural foundation of these paintings, color provides the theme. Using an intense palette, he juxtaposes bright, concentrated colors with cool,

Bonnie Dunn, *Banana Leaf,* 16 x 20, photograph

Susan Dobay, *Broken Necklace,* 24 x 36, acrylic and oil on canvas. Courtesy: Attila Bokor

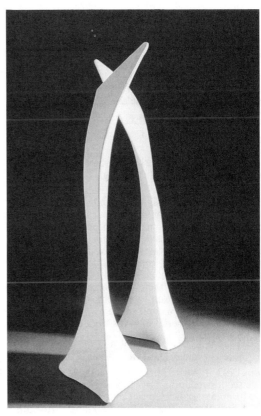

Madelyn Engle, *Pegasus Wings: White Series,* 92 x 62 x 60, canvas and wood

transparent ones. In recent work, he is returning to large oil paintings based on classical literature.

DOUCET, MELVIN A. (Painter)
4097 Buckingham Rd., #B, Los Angeles, CA 90008

Born: 1954 *Awards:* Artist of the Month, Bunker Hill Art League *Exhibitions:* Second Annual Black Artist Show, Gosky Gallery, Hollywood; Afro-American Museum, Los Angeles *Education:* Los Angeles City College

Picasso, Cezanne and Dali are the strongest influences on his work. He prefers working on a large surface, experimenting with perspective, composition and form. Using a combination of acrylics, applied with a palette knife and colored washes, he achieves a rough and smooth surface. Along with a mix of hot and cool colors, this variable texture creates a three-dimensional effect. His recent painting, *Love Dance*, features a dancing woman, foregrounded against a group of African drummers.

DOUGHERTY, BARBARA (Painter)
P.O. Box 152, Carpinteria, CA 93013

Born: 1949 *Awards:* 1st and 3rd Prize, Water Media, Death Valley Art Show *Collections:* Barclay's Bank; Litton Industries *Exhibitions:* Westlake Plaza Hotel; Red Lion Hotel, Santa Barbara *Education:* University of California; University of New York

From 1970 to 1978, she worked with three-dimensional forms in clay. After moving to California, she apprenticed with Frank M. Hamilton and began working in egg tempera and gouache. Influenced by George Innes and Georgia O'Keeffe, her present works are large, sweeping landscapes, painted in warm vibrant tones depicting a muted earth. She layers paint in a an impressionistic way and uses color to create a quality of light and a feeling of mood. She chooses the landscapes that are disappearing, done "on-site". One series was inspired by an area south of Buffalo. Another by the strawberry fields of California.

DOUGHERTY, MICHAEL (Sculptor)
P.O. Box 152, Carpinteria, CA 93013

Born: 1934 *Awards:* 2nd Prize, Allentown Festival, NY; 1st Prize, Orchard Park, Festival, NY *Exhibitions:* The Copenhagen Gallery, Solvang; The Judith Gallery, Solvang *Education:* Fordham U.

While a Jesuit seminarian in the South Pacific islands, he met an island sculptor who encouraged him to feel the shape of sculpture in wood. Since then, he has created wood sculptures designed for the observer to touch. Using a variety of hard and exotic woods, he has explored concave and convex shapes, positive and negative space. The process begins by building wooden pieces and laminating them. He then rasps and subtracts wood until a strong form emerges. He is now having his originals cast in bronze to produce limited editions. His latest series involves wooden spheres.

DOUKE, DANIEL W. (Painter)
5151 State University Dr., Los Angeles, CA 90032

Born: 1943 *Awards:* James D. Phelan Award, San Francisco Foundation *Collections:* Newport Harbor Art Museum; Art Museum, California State University, Long Beach *Exhibitions:* Oakland Museum; Museum of Modern Art, NYC *Education:* Cal. State-Los Angeles *Dealer:* O.K. Harris, NYC; Tortue Gallery, Santa Monica

His early photo-realistic paintings of California swimming pools were done in the three primary colors entirely with airbrush, the images candidly reflecting and recording the Southern California environment. Recent work addresses the dilemmas of truth and reality through a balance between abstraction and reality. Constructed stretched canvases are transmuted through various painting techniques into what seem to be mundane used cardboard cartons or, in more recent works, thick plates of painted cold-rolled steel. Colors in these trompe l'oeil works have progressed from muted tones to bright pink, yellow, magenta and blue. His work continues to evolve toward material illusionism, exploring the vague boundary between contemporary painting and sculpture.

DOWD, ROBERT (Painter)
5653 1/2 Hollywood Blvd., Los Angeles, CA 90028

Born: 1936 *Collections:* Federal Reserve Bank, Washington, D.C.; Johnson Museum, NYC *Exhibitions:* Riverside Art Museum; Newport Harbor Art Museum, Newport Beach *Education:* Center for Creative Studies *Dealer:* Koslow Rayl, Los Angeles

His work, along with that of Andy Warhol, Jim Dine and Roy Liechtenstein, was included in the first pop art exhibit, "New Paintings of Common Objects," curated by John Coplans at the Pasadena Art Museum in 1962. Fascinated by the formal and substantive limitations of postage stamps and currency, he altered imagery and words, creating surrealist, dadaist works in their place. More recent paintings have concerned quantum particle theory. Combining abstract and representational elements, these works explore the subatomic realm where an object is an event, a state of perpetual becoming.

DOWLING, TOM (Painter, Multimedia Artist)
P.O. Box 4214, Balboa, CA 92661

Born: 1949 *Collections:* Laguna Art Museum *Exhibitions:* Newport Harbor Art Museum, Newport Beach; B.C. Space, Laguna Beach *Education:* UC-Santa Barbara; UC- Irvine *Dealer:* Works Gallery, Long Beach; Foster Goldstrom, Oakland, NYC

Influenced by the works of Braque and Picasso, he creates complex pieces, which juxtapose the real with the illusory, and the geometric with the disorderly. He applies acrylic paint in broad, gestured brushstrokes to large ovals of aluminum or stainless steel; then he sands and marks the metal surface, creating a slightly holographic effect. He affixes narrative photographs of the human form, or of religious icons to the surface— an element which recalls his experience in the film industry. The contrasting themes and media (narrative and abstraction, two-dimensional and three-dimensional visual surfaces, paint and metal) together form a tightly bound aesthetic vision, open to multiple readings and varying visual perceptions from different perspectives. Among his recent work is a large outdoor sculpture constructed from steel and glass.

DOWNEY, MARIA (Painter)
9548 Farm St., Downey, CA 90241

Born: 1954 *Collections:* City of Newport Beach Chamber of Commerce *Exhibitions:* San Francisco Museum of Modern Art; Matrix Gallery, Sacramento *Education:* Rosary College, Florence, Italy *Dealer:* Vladimir Sokolov, Laguna Beach

Influenced by the colorful rhythms of Van Gogh and the powerful subject matter of Munch, she uses oil on

Elly Drees, *Paris Winter,* 24 x 36, oil

Anna Debska, *The Wolf,* 84" high, bronze

linen, and fluorescent chalk on thick museum rag-board for her paintings, drawings and political cartoons. She has recently been working on a "Warriors" series, focusing on the wars going on around the world. Although these pieces are political, they are non-partisan, expressing the horror of war and its human costs, without attempting to fix blame.

DOWNS, DOUGLAS (Sculptor)
405 Alder St., Pacific Grove, CA 93950

Born: 1945 *Awards:* 1st Prize, International Exhibition, Miniature Painters and Sculptors Society, Washington, D.C.; 1st Prize, National Miniature Show, New Mexico *Collections:* King Karl Gustaf, Sweden; President Ronald Reagan *Exhibitions:* May Gallery, Scottsdale; Gallerie de Tours, San Francisco *Education:* Claremont Graduate School; Whittier

Influenced by both Arp and Brancusi, he imbues his sculptures with a sense of negative space. Insides become outsides and outsides become insides in a shifting, Moebius strip dialogue between space and form. He employs mythic and American Indian imagery in his intimate figurative work. Strongly influenced by Jungian archetypes, he features the interplay of dancing forms in these works. In *Dance of the Buffalo,* a buffalo dancer becomes a buffalo and vice versa. Birds of prey dominate his abstract work. "[These] Space Birds have no detail but are still recognizable as bird forms." He recently began working on a series of abstract birth forms.

DRAEGERT, JOE (Painter)
2339 3rd St., San Francisco, CA 94103

Born: 1945 *Awards:* Rome Prize in Painting; Yale Fellowship *Collections:* San Francisco Museum of Modern Art; Oakland Museum *Exhibitions:* Gregory Kondos Art Gallery, Sacramento; Redding Museum and Art Center *Education:* Kansas City Art Institute; UC-Davis

He has been influenced by Wayne Thiebaud and American still life painters from the Peale family to James Rosenquist. His own larger-than-life still lifes bespeak the influence of Northern California's strong lighting, chromatic coloring and obsession with natural abundance. His subjects include the standard vases, flowers and fruit, but his paint application sets him apart. He applies paint in an almost glaze-like surface using brushwork hatching to create color/form contingencies beyond the image itself. The white of the underlying gesso lends his colors a bold, fresh quality. His media include acrylic on board and pastel on paper.

DRAKULICH, MARTHA (Sculptor)
16640 N. 34th Dr., Phoenix, AZ 85023

Born: 1931 *Exhibitions:* Arizona Ceramic Artists Association; Phoenix Public Library Gallery

Coming to the United States from Europe in the mid-1970s without any formal art training, she has created a sculptural technique by manipulating fiber, which she spins and dyes herself, into landscapes, depicting waterfalls, trees and scenes of the four seasons and the desert. These wall sculptures may be either abstract or as realistic as nature and are made to suit the mood of the milieu. Three-dimensional frames of wicker, stoneware, wood and metal add to the unique beauty. Other sculptures include religious figures with bisque heads and hardened textiles. She also designs decorator items.

DRAZY, FLOVIA (Painter)
1105 S. Sherborne Dr., Los Angeles, CA

Born: 1918 *Collections:* Wadsworth Veterans Hospital; Chapel in the Canyon, Canoga Park

This prolific artist and teacher has exhibited her work both in the United States and in Europe. Born in Chicago, she attended art schools in Milan, Warsaw, Tokyo, Nice and Paris. Working in oil on canvas, she has a realist figurative style, influenced by the Impressionists' use of light and color. She has also written and produced a film series, "Art As You Like It," and another series on cassette about color and oil painting. This latter series will soon appear in book form.

DREES, ELLY (Painter)
784 St. Katherine Dr., Flintridge, CA 91011

Born: 1929 *Awards:* 1st Place, Verdugo Hills Art Association; Certificate of Honor, Centre International D'Art Contemporaine, Paris *Exhibitions:* Graphic Showcase, Pasadena; Artistic Endeavors, Simi Valley *Education:* Parsons School of Design

Her formal training included classical art training in anatomy, color, perspective and related areas. She also studied design, and her first work in commercial art was for wallpaper design companies. After several years, during which she didn't paint at all, she returned to art, taking several classes as refreshers. At this point, she was quite fascinated by the Impressionists, especially Monet. Their use of flickering light and shadow inspired her new work. She often makes several preliminary sketches of her subject, usually either a figure or a landscape. She then transfers the images to canvas using a light charcoal. A dripping wash is applied as underpainting, and then the main work is executed in a wet-on-wet a la prima technique. She is most concerned with mood and feeling and strives to achieve a sense of freedom through painterly brushwork.

DREHER, WARREN (Painter)
1576 Sunnyvale Ave., #41, Walnut Creek, CA 94596

Born: 1948 *Exhibitions:* Vorpal Gallery, San Francisco; Diane Sassone Gallery, Laguna Beach *Education:* Rhode Island School of Design

After studying sculpture, he began working exclusively in chalk pastel, due to its clay-like qualities and its ability to capture the fleeting spontaneity of light. Studying with Jack Tworkov and Budd Hopkins in the mid-1970s gave him a new concern for surface and geometric implications, which continues to this day. In the late 1970s, he moved to California and began a series (now numbering in the hundreds) of light-filled, architectural landscapes. He works with chalk pastel on Canson paper, and builds the pastel, layer by layer, working fixative all the way through the painting. In the last few years, he began working in oil, thus allowing some work to be done on a larger scale. Pastels, however, are still his main focus. Major influences on his work include Edward Hopper, Charles Dwyer and the early pastels of Michael Mazur.

DRESSER, NOREEN D. (Painter)
The Studio, 849 Fell St., San Francisco, CA 94117

Born: 1953 *Collections:* Human Relations Association, La Jolla; North Hall, Antioch College, Yellow Springs, OH *Exhibitions:* Pacific Graduate School of Psychology, Menlo Park; Bade Museum, Berkeley *Education:* Claremont Graduate School; Antioch College *Dealer:* Hatley Martin Gallery, San Francisco

John Drooyan, *The Omnivores of the Lagoon,* 20 x 20, mixed media: photo-sculpture assemblage

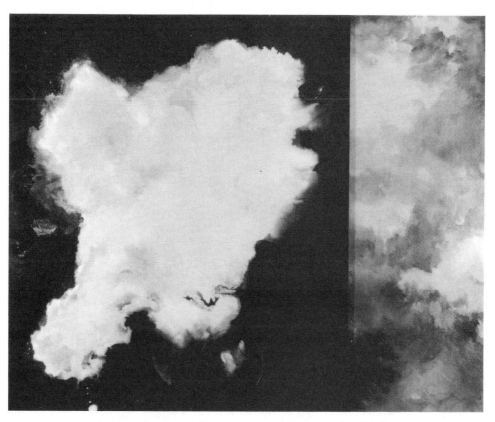

Noreen Dean Dresser, *Arise (diptych),* 60 x 72, mixed media, acrylic on canvas

She studied painting and drawing for two years in northern Europe, Italy and Greece, before returning to the U.S. to complete her formal art education. Working in cultural affairs, she did research and assisted with the mounting of exhibitions featuring contemporary and traditional African and Asian art. These experiences broadened her artistic vision, leading her to seek out a more spiritual, universal approach to post-modern art. Her spiritual, expressionist style combines the intensity of Blake's vision with the contemplative mode associated with Zen painting. Formally, her work incorporates western chiaroscuro with eastern, mystical washes and free organic line. The painting space hovers between the surface marks and illusory space. Subtle shifts in color and suspended particles in the ink/acrylic further accent the sense of change, movement and timelessness.

DROOYAN, JOHN N. (Photographer, Sculptor)
4608 19th St., San Francisco, CA 94114

Born: 1952 *Exhibitions:* San Francisco Museum of Modern Art; Union Gallery, UC-Davis *Education:* Stanford; San Francisco Art Institute

He was initially drawn to art by the work of the Surrealists; his photographic art has been a search for visual representations of the world, whose meanings transcend objective reality. In 1983, he was commissioned to make chapter-opening art for a set of math textbooks. In the process of designing, building and photographing lightweight sculpture (based on mathematical ideas) in Death Valley, he uncovered a personal vision, based upon the perceptual experience that occurs in the photographic representation of sculpturally defined space. Using found objects as source material, the subject of his art is "meaning"—as one might ascribe to the vast realm of manmade things (with an inclination towards an anthropomorphic interpretation that can be traced to a knowledge of primitive and Mexican Indian Art, and the influence of the painter, Rufino Tomayo). Drawing, painting and assembling three-dimensional objects on the surface of his photographs, he utilizes photography's refined descriptive capabilities to address "simultaneously the real and the fictitious that echoes the paradox of objective identity in pictorially defined space, which Magritte explored."

DUBIN, JORG R. (Multimedia Artist)
818 Bluebird Cym Rd., Laguna Beach, CA 92651

Born: 1955 *Collections:* Laguna Beach Museum of Art; Modern Museum of Art, Irvine *Exhibitions:* Los Angeles Municipal Art Gallery; City of Brea

He is a multimedia artist whose main concerns are value, strong shape and architecture. He often implies a utilitarian approach in his terra cotta clay vessels. In his oil paintings, he deals with social, as well as architectural, themes. One of his series of paintings might be called "Still Life With Gun." In these works, he juxtaposes the image of a shiny revolver with such middle class icons as bowling balls, John Deer hats, Bibles and grenades. He has recently been creating a series of cast concrete vessels and wall pieces. Among the works he admires are Scott Moore's paintings and Kris Cox' and Richard White's ceramics.

DUBOIS, EMILY (Textile Artist)
4701 San Leandro St., #8, Oakland, CA 94604

Born: 1946 *Awards:* NEA Fellowship; Ford Foundation Grant *Collections:* Albuquerque Museum;

Hewlett-Packard Corp. *Exhibitions:* Fiberworks Center for Textile Arts, Berkeley; Allrich Gallery, San Francisco *Education:* California College of Arts and Crafts *Dealer:* Miller/Brown Gallery, San Francisco

Her training included traditional crafts-oriented textile education, field work and research in the historical and contemporary textiles of Asian cultures, as well as studio work in drawing, painting and sculpture. Years of tai chi practice and an interest in Chinese philosophy have strongly influenced her current work. Her woven pieces in a variety of colors feature the rippling, waving forms of nature, particularly feathers, water and cloud formations. These natural forms express growth and energy in motion. Using a combination of weaving and dyeing processes, the woven canvas and the image are created simultaneously. Techniques include: ikat, dyed and discharged warp and weft; various bound and stitched resist processes, applied before and after weaving; painting with dyes, pigments and discharge chemicals; brocade; and various complex, computer-controlled weave structures. Because the techniques mirror the images both visually and structurally, the images arise naturally from the processes themselves.

DUBOIS, JESS E. (Painter)
6791 1/2 Quebec, Commerce City, CO 80022

Born: 1934 *Exhibitions:* George Phippen Show, Prescott, AZ; The Hawk Gallery, San Diego *Education:* Colorado Institute of Art

For years, he has painted the people and landscapes of the Southwest. He paints on location and from memory. He has recently been experimenting with a variety of colors in pastel, oil and acrylic. In addition, his "Children of the Sun" series, pastel portraits of Native American children, continues to challenge his abilities.

DUCASSE, MARIE (Printmaker)
354 Parrott Dr., San Mateo, CA 94402

Born: 1929 *Awards:* Silver Award for Merit *Collections:* Ford Motor Company; Northwestern Memorial Hospital, Chicago *Exhibitions:* Pacific Art League; Society of Western Artists *Education:* College of San Mateo; Providence College of Nursing *Dealer:* Miriam Perlman, Inc., Chicago

Born in Seminole, Oklahoma in 1929, she came to art after a career in nursing. She began her formal art training in 1981 at Skyline College. Later, at the College of San Mateo, she studied under Deborah Rumer, Joe Price, Allen Appleton, Phyllis Wheaton and Judy Morley. Eventually, she developed her current realistic style of printmaking. She works in several printmaking media and her prize-winning serigraph, "d'Orient" is a still life of a flower-patterned oriental vase with three tomatoes sitting at its base and a wall-hung fan behind it. She has exhibited widely in the West, and her work is held in several corporate collections.

DUCEY, ANN GARAT (Painter)
1023 Dyer Dr., Lafayette, CO 94549

Born: 1939 *Awards:* Ruth Winn Award, San Diego Watercolor Society *Collections:* IBM; Westpac Banking Corp. *Exhibitions:* National Watercolor Society; West Coast Watercolor Society *Education:* UC-Berkeley; California College of Arts and Crafts, Oakland *Dealer:* Banaker, Walnut Creek

Cecelia Davidson, *Zeus and Athena,* 22 x 30, mixed media monotype

Marie Ducasse, *Monnies and Mibs,* 20 x 24, serigraph

Her pastel-colored windows invite the viewer to observe her abstract skies. In these paintings, she seeks to present gentle connections to a representational world. She evokes the solitary quiet of dusk or the break of dawn in landscapes, which include deserts, oceans, mountains, rocks or clouds. In her watercolors, mountainous shapes float in ambiguous space, with only a base line to establish the idea of a horizon. In recent work she features hexagram configurations from the Chinese Book of Wisdom. In each hexagram, she contrasts shifting organic textures with the structural hard edges.

DUDAS HALEY, REBECCA A. (Ceramist, Painter)
31756 Country Club, Porterville, CA 93257

Born: 1948 *Exhibitions:* American Craft Council Show, San Francisco; Festival of the Lake, Oakland *Education:* International College; Ohio Dominican College *Dealer:* Wild Blue, Melrose

Originally a ceramist working with high-fire clays and glazes, she took up painting during the mid-1970s when she didn't have access to a kiln. These paintings concentrated on circular forms and mandala patterns. She began working with clay again, and developed the clay pieces as painting surfaces. She forms dishes from low-fire clay slabs, and uses low-fire glazes for decoration. Designs include zebra stripes, polka dots and combinations of contrasting hard-edged geometric patterns.

DUDLEY, JACK (Painter)
460 Panorama Dr., Laguna Beach, CA 92651

Born: 1918 *Collections:* Coca Cola Company *Exhibitions:* Esther Wells Collection, Laguna Beach; Demille Galleries *Dealer:* Esther Wells, Laguna Beach

Responding to a personal interest in Latin America, he began traveling and painting in Central and South America. This led to other trips; eventually he would paint in Europe, the Caribbean, the Orient and the Middle East. Always interested in color effects, he continues to experiment with a technique he calls "broken color," wherein many layers of pure color are applied to the painting surface, with grayed color at the end. Because of the heavy applications of oil paint, he paints on untempered masonite, rather than canvas. A recent series of 4-by-6-foot paintings is of sand dunes, which upon closer inspection, reveal themselves to be subtle, abstract female figures. This is accented by a real figure that walks amidst the them.

DUDLEY, NELSON (Mixed Media Artist)
10262 Pimlico, Cypress, CA 90630

Born: 1938 *Exhibitions:* Chapman College, Orange; Laguna Beach Gallery *Education:* U. of North Carolina *Dealer:* Anbeum Gallery, Los Angeles; Art Resource Group, Newport Beach

He is best known for his strongly crafted, mixed-media pieces made from envelopes on canvas. He lays out white envelopes and colors them with ink and gouache. The envelopes are then arranged in a predesigned pattern and glued to the canvas. Constructed with coats of varnish, glue and plastic, the envelopes form intricate textures. When finished, the work is framed and covered. Rendered in the full spectrum of color, these collages are an intensely personal expression of his view

of the world, its consistency, orderliness and directedness.

DUGAN REID, RUTH MARY (Painter, Mixed Media Artist)
2216 Kelton Ave., Los Angeles, CA 90064

Born: 1942 *Exhibitions:* Jonathan Club Art Walk, Los Angeles; Unitarian Church, Santa Monica

She creates easily, drawing what she sees and layering images from microcosm to macrocosm. She starts with a printed pen-and-ink drawing, then works it with airbrush, pastels, watercolor, textile paints and metallics, developing hallucinogenic imagery and geometric and symbolic substructures within forms. She also videotapes the entire creative process. Recently, she has been using luxury frames and mountings to add a sculptural dimension to her work. She has also been exploring the possibilities of fantasy art and animation.

DULLANTY, PATRICK (Painter)
2323 K St., Sacramento, CA 95816

Born: 1927 *Exhibitions:* Van Staveren Fine Art, Sacramento; Crocker Art Museum, Sacramento

He began his career in the 1950s as a freelance artist, photographer and animator working on 16mm film. He then took up printmaking and exhibited his work— abstract and non-objective lithographs, linocuts and serigraphs influenced by Pollock, Picasso and his friend Wayne Thiebaud—throughout the country. In the 1960s, he began to paint in oil, and by the 1970s, he was painting the landscapes and waterscapes of Sacramento and the Pacific Northwest that comprise the bulk of his work. He paints these in a representational style influenced by impressionism, and his work reveals the enduring influences of Homer, Henri, Balthus and, above all, Thiebaud.

DUMAS, JACK (Painter)
14111 Occidental Road, Sebastopol, CA 95472

Born: 1915 *Awards:* 2nd Place, National Wildlife Art Show, Washington, D.C.; Alaska Wildlife Audubon Exhibition *Collections:* Weyerhaeuser Timber; Reader's Digest *Exhibitions:* California Academy of Sciences; National Cowboy Hall of Fame *Education:* Cornish Art School and Seattle Academy of Arts; Chouinard Art Institute; Art Center College of Design *Dealer:* Christopher Queen Galleries, Duncan Mills

He created editorial art and story illustrations for thirty-five years, and he brings to his wildlife paintings the craft he learned with this experience. Before painting, he researches the subject, studying as many as thirty pieces of reference material to achieve an accurate depiction. All of his paintings are done in oil. The subjects range from present-day scenes of birds, fish and grizzlies in their natural habitats to old-west scenes such as that of a stagecoach storming up a hill and pursued by Indians. Most paintings feature a single animal in its natural environment. Although his experience as an illustrator continues to inform his realist style, his most recent work sometimes are slightly less detailed.

DUNITZ, JAY (Photographer)
20110 Rockport Way, Malibu, CA 90265

Born: 1956 *Collections:* Museum of Modern Art, NYC; National Museum of American Art, Washington, D.C. *Exhibitions:* Jayne Baum Gallery, NYC; Santa Monica College Photography Gallery *Education:* San Francisco Art Institute; Hampshire

Ruth Mary Dugan Reid, *Frank Morgan,* 11 x 14, felt-tip pen. Courtesy: Crystal Reid

Michael Dougherty, *Clear,* 50 high, mahogany

College, Amherst, MA *Dealer:* Jan Kesner Gallery, Los Angeles

In his early realist paintings, he experimented with the texture, shape and geometry of elements when juxtaposed and rendered in larger-than-life detail. He found it difficult to reach desired visual intensity and spatial tension through any single medium until he noticed the unexpected spectrum of metal surfaces in his color photograph of a deteriorating refrigerator. He photographed his "Kroeber Series" of oxidized metal constructions in daylight, and later found that the colors had been generated by friction, as a result of over-grinding. With a gas torch and a grinder, he created color patterns on metal, then moved from steel to titanium, niobium and tantalum and found an "electric paintbrush" that could create shifts in hue through varying voltage. These controlled metal plates are photographed under quartz halogen video lights by a process of multiple exposures at a range of f- stops, shutter speeds and light positions that can take up to four weeks. The resulting 30-by-40-foot Cibachrome magnifications give the texture and intensity of the subject startling depth, and resemble abstract impressionist paintings under glass. The "Pacific Light" series captures California's brilliant atmosphere with an evocative lyricism that transcends its technical novelty.

DUNN, BONNIE (Photographer)
P.O. Box 368 Felton, CA 95018

Born: 1945 *Awards:* Sponsorship, Santa Cruz Arts Commission; 1st Place, Professional Division of Photography, Santa Cruz County Fair *Collections:* Bargetto Winery, Soquel; Twin Hills Winery, Paso Robles *Exhibitions:* Santa Cruz Art Gallery; Santa Cruz Government Center

She photographs natural objects on color film at close range using only natural lighting. Her earlier works were primarily California landscapes, but now through macro-photography, her subjects appear almost abstract. Her favorite shots are leaves, rocks and pools of water. Her use of natural lighting accentuates the textures, forms and colors of her subjects. She tries to capture the simplicity of nature in its abstract patterns. "The picture is not just the forest, but the veins of life within a solitary leaf," she says.

DUNN, CAL A.W.S. (Painter)
Rt. 9 Box 86L, Santa Fe, NM 87505

Born: 1915 *Awards:* Honorable Mention, New Mexico Watercolor Society; Distinguished Achievement Award, A.A.R.P. *Collections:* New Mexico Museum of Fine Art, Santa Fe; The Albequerque Museum *Exhibitions:* Ballentines's Art Project, Seal Beach; Indian Trading Post, Lone Pine *Dealers:* O'Brien's Art Emporium, Scottsdale; Gallery of the Southwest, Taos, NM; Wichita Gallery of Fine Art; 16 East Gallery, NYC

A competitive watercolorist since the 1930s, he worked as an industrial filmmaker until 1979. Earliest work depicted the typical barns of the era, but becoming bored by regional ruralism, he began to vary his approach. During a period of abstraction, he painted on masonite with spray-can enamel. Since moving to Santa Fe in 1976, he has returned to landscapes, using acrylics on both masonite and three-hundred-pound watercolor paper. His works are influenced by Goya and El Greco and by his work as a filmmaker, and are remarkable for

their composition—the Southwest's awesome churches, skies and mountains loom over the viewer.

DUNN, RUTH M. (Painter, Photographer)
1740 7th Ave., Sacramento, CA 95818

Born: 1910 *Awards:* Special Award, Northern California Arts Membership Show *Exhibitions:* Yosemite Renaissance National Open Art Exhibit; Carmichael Artists League National Open

She painted her early on-location landscapes with oils. During this early period, she also studied anatomy, figure and portrait painting. Later, she stumbled into pastels, doing sketches at first and finally moving on to landscapes, portraits, animals and birds. She now studies watercolors and paints with Jim Estey. Her canvases often deal with such topical subjects as the Year of the Dragon or the Olympics. She also continues to work with pastels and has started additional classes in pastel painting, which is the medium with which she wins the most awards. The most important thing that she has learned is how studying art expands your brain by bringing to light beauty in objects previously considered ugly.

DURAND, NICOLE (Sculptor)
1095 Karella, Laguna Beach, CA 92651

Born: 1957 *Exhibitions:* Palms Springs Art Center; Lakeview Art Center *Education:* University of Paris

Though he has a degree in management, his expertise in oil painting and sculpture is primarily self-taught. Working in the European tradition, he attended various art schools in France and Italy, including Pietrosanta, known for its famous stone carving studios. Initially, he stood on the strength of his oil painting, working for the high bourgeoisie of Lyon with frequent exhibitions in St. Tropez and Venice. Much of the work resides in the homes of private collectors in Switzerland, Italy and France. While he remains most skilled as a painter, he works now primarily in stone sculpture. The array of sculptures are of various colors of alabaster, carved with an eye to capturing feminine beauty.

DUSTYN (Painter, Commercial Artist)
6739 Pollock Rd., Linden, CA 95236

Born: 1951 *Awards:* Purchase Award, Stockton Art League Haggin Exhibit *Exhibitions:* Open Studio, Stockton; Lodi Art Center *Education:* Sacramento St. U.

Her abstract landscape style has been heavily influenced by Van Gogh and O'Keeffe. Attempting to capture the emotional energy of land forms, she translates their majestic shapes into mystic visions rendered in vibrant oils on canvas. She is most comfortable painting the foothills of eastern California and New Mexico. She works from a muted palette of peach, lavenders and pale greens. Also a commercial artist, she designs and illustrates brochures, logos and posters for clients in California and New York.

DWYER, FLORENCE (Painter)
5025 Woodminster Ln., #202, Oakland, CA 94602

Born: 1945 *Awards:* Robert Rauschenberg Foundation Grant; Grant, Artists Fellowship, Inc., NY *Collections:* J'nette Gardens Gallery, Oakland *Exhibitions:* Ariel Gallery, NYC; Creative Growth Gallery, Oakland *Education:* Lone Mountain College *Dealer:* J'nette Gardens Gallery, Oakland

She likes to tell of her childhood in Chicago, where her earliest artistic influences came from an enjoyment of her Holy Card collection. She had never heard of a woman artist, and believed that if she wanted to become an artist, she would have to change into a man and paint Holy Cards. As she grew older, she was drawn to the works of Magritte, George Tucker, Bosch, Rousseau and the Flemish masters. Her work now reflects both her personal experiences and her personal interpretation of the world. Although some of her paintings are autobiographical, she hopes that many could be narratives taken from the life of any woman facing the challenges of contemporary society. She is influenced by the works of many female and male artists, but she is even more impressed with the strength, courage and endurance of women artists throughout history.

DZERIGIAN, STEVE (Photographer)
838 E. University Ave., Fresno, CA 93704

Born: 1948 *Awards:* 2nd Place, Nikon International Photography Contest; New Photographics/85, Central Washington University *Collections:* Ansel Adams Gallery; Nikon House *Exhibitions:* Chautauqua Art Gallery; Spectrum Gallery *Education:* UCLA

The main body of his printed work consists of Cibachrome photographic prints made from color negatives characterized by modified reversals of value and hue combined with the juxtaposition and overlapping of sharp edges and soft movement. The common and the uncommon in the world of people, events and things appear as shadows or altered mirror-images. Chance, movement and long available light exposures are utilized in the production of this work. Only superficially representing objective reality, these pieces are intended to rekindle feelings of the illusive qualities behind or in the midst of everyday experience.

EASTMAN-ROAN, CYNTHIA (Painter, Printmaker)
1243 Raymond Dr., Pacheco, CA 94553

Born: 1944 *Awards:* 1st Place, Georgia Miniature Art International; Montana Miniature Art International *Exhibitions:* Ruth Carlson Gallery, Mendocino; Hammons Gallery, Kensington *Education:* Diablo Valley College

She creates limited edition, hand-embossed watercolors of bare trees, flowers, landscapes and the Golden Gate Bridge. Using them somewhat like printer's plates, she hand cuts her embossing plates, gluing them together to form a reverse image. The watercolor paper is immersed for twenty minutes, then hand-embossed into the selected dimensional pattern. After it has dried she turns the formed design over and paints it with watercolor. She also paints international award-winning miniatures of seascapes, and is a signature member of the Society of Western Artists. She has recently been doing an impressionistic boat series in acrylic, and working on signature membership in Miniature Artists of America.

EATON, PAULINE (Painter)
10 Alta Mira Ave., Kentfield, CA 94904

Born: 1935 *Awards:* Redlands Hospital Award; Grumbacher Gold Award *Collections:* Citicorp, Chicago; Mercy Hospital, San Diego *Exhibitions:* Mondavi Winery Gallery, Sonoma; Neville Sargent Gallery, Chicago *Education:* Northwestern U. *Dealer:* Neville Sargent Gallery, Chicago

Painting in watercolor, she has always sought to reconnect the individual figures in her painting to the essence of life and the universe. Early paintings developed from such ideas and metaphors as the "Warp and Woof of Existence," "Threads of Reality," "The On-Goingness of Creation" and "Connectivity." Although she has always painted broadly enough that the original conception of the work does not become lost in the final product, she has also paid great attention to detail to preserve the clarity of her line. After she moved from San Diego to Northern California, her work became concerned with transition and the act of tearing up one's roots. She used images of trees, often uprooted ones, to reflect her own solitude and fragility in the world.

EDERY, SIMON (Sculptor)
2519 Polk St., San Francisco, CA 94109

Born: 1948 *Exhibitions:* Centre Georges Pompidou, Paris; New York Film Festival *Education:* San Francisco Art Institute

After formal training in math and physics, he decided to explore the mind through film and sculpture. Early work involved scrap metal for heavy work, and modern stained glass. A interest in Samuel Beckett has strongly influenced the philosophical and performance aspects of his work. Film/performance pieces have become more informal, as three choreographed dances projected onto the same screen and accompanied by live dancers confuse live action with the illusory reality of the silver screen. Similar dichotomies are explored in his unwearable mask sculpture. Realistic faces of resin, plaster or clay are decorated with gold and silver leaf and mounted on mirrors or glass. He also designs and builds functional art furniture in plaster and sheet rock.

EDGE, DOUG (Painter, Sculptor)
635 N. Alisos St., Santa Barbara, CA 93103

Born: 1942 *Awards:* NEA Fellowship *Collections:* Museum of Modern Art, NYC; Security Pacific *Exhibitions:* Gallery 454 North, Los Angeles; Laguna Art Museum *Dealer:* Earl McGrath, Los Angeles

His works, with titles such as *If, What's the Big Idea?* and *Grey Matter,* combine sculpture and painting. Creating both relief and freestanding pieces, he usually works with wood for the easy way in which it interacts with paint. His subject matter is wide-ranging: landscapes, hills, deserts, frozen tundra, even oceans; figures, symbolic and archetypical; and abstract design. But through all the works runs a questioning spirit and a conviction of the interconnectedness of all things that often allows him to mingle diverse elements almost seamlessly. Influenced largely by Eastern philosophies and primitive tribal cultures, his images seem to arise out of that ephemeral boundary separating waking and sleeping.

E'DRIE, LORRAINE (Painter)
1809 1/2 W. Bay Ave., Newport Beach, CA 92663

Born: 1934 *Awards:* San Bernardino Museum *Collections:* Barco Engineering; Executive Motor Home Corp. *Exhibitions:* San Bernardino Art Museum; National Arts Club, NYC *Education:* U. of Irvine *Dealer:* Bevel-Cut Gallery, Corona Del Mar; Cove Gallery, Laguna Beach

She is an impressionist, who paints contemporary forms in jewel-like colors. Her subjects are often flowers and coastal areas. Two of her paintings were featured in *Yacht Portraits*, published by Sheridan House. She begins her work by drawing large impressionistic forms on 300lb. paper. Medium and small shapes then fall into place. She describes her subjects through negative space and uses a lot of white. She balances warm colors with light values, and adds cool colors with complementary hues. Often color becomes its own subject. She has a lifetime teaching credential from the University of Irvine, and she conducts an annual workshop at Asilomar in Carmel.

EDWARDS, ERIKA (Painter)
2010 Las Tunas Rd., Santa Barbara, CA 93103

Born: 1929 *Exhibitions:* Gallery de Silva, Santa Barbara

Part of a group of painters called Nature Preserved, she paints endangered landscapes, and presents shows to inform the public. Always intrigued with the beauty and mystique of nature, she expresses this fascination by rendering views of the city, foothills and immediate coast. Sailing with her friends, she makes excursions to the Channel Islands, where she can witness untouched, rugged wildness. These experiences add to her sensitivity when painting, whether her subject be a small wild flower or an expansive landscape. Her paintings are realistic, and reflect her keen sense of color and balanced composition. Recently, she has found herself captivated by water scenes and the play of reflected images.

EDWARDS, FLORA (Painter, Printmaker)
3935 N. Country Club Rd., #28, Tucson, AZ

Born: 1944 *Awards:* New Artist of Tucson *Collections:* DIA Foundation; Museum San Cristobal de las Casas *Exhibitions:* Presideo Art Gallery, Tucson; Women Craft Gallery, Tucson *Education:* Rhode Island School of Design; U. of Arizona *Dealer:* Ken Nelsen, Tres Piedras, NM

Her work is an expression of forms derived from universal ideas. She often looks for practical solutions and has developed intuitive abilities. Her guiding principles are freedom of thought, exploration and research. Her media include painting, sculpting, ceramics, video, weaving, music and cooking. She makes her dyes and colors herself and uses color to reveal the organic reality of a subject, abstracting and strengthening characteristic forms. The beauty of surfaces gives the viewer an irresistible urge to touch them. Among her recent influences are travels in the Middle East and her twenty-year experiences with Mayan Indian culture. She is now sculpting and combining that medium with fiber art. She has also collaborated with many of the leading musicians and poets in the Americas.

EGER, MARILYN R. (Painter)
1295 E. Peltier Rd., Acampo, CA 95220

Born: 1953 *Awards:* 1st Place in Oils, 2nd Place in Sculpture, Delta Boats Show, Stockton; 1st Place in Oils, Honorable Mention in Drawing and Printmaking, Lodi Art Annual *Collections:* Gulf Oil Chemicals, Pittsburg, KS *Exhibitions:* Stockton Fine Arts Gallery; Accurate Art Gallery, Sacramento *Education:* Cal. State-Stanislaus

After formal training in drawing, she began to learn the principles of impressionist brushwork and its emphasis on light and color. This interest prompted her to begin painting from direct observation while on location. The present influences on her work include Georgia O'Keeffe, Wayne Thiebaud and Charles Movalli. Using color to evoke an emotional response, and line to create a sense of sensual movement, she paints close-ups of flowers. She has recently been working on a series of oil paintings of the calla lily. These studies emphasize the sensations of reflected light, substructure and mood changes.

EGGERS, BARBARA (Paper Artist)
475 Montgomery Rd., Sebastopol, CA 95472

Born: 1926 *Exhibitions:* Reese Bullen Gallery, Humbolt St. College, Arcata; Mendocino Arts Center *Education:* UC-Berkeley *Dealer:* Harleen & Allen Fine Art Gallery, San Francisco; Swan Gallery, Philadelphia

During the 1950s and early 1960s, she painted the figure in oils, in an abstract expressionist manner. During the 1970s, she began doing etchings and lithographs. By the mid-1970s, her prints and paintings had become completely abstract. At the same time, she began making her own paper for printing. Her recent works are cast paper pieces. During the paper making process, she takes specially made monotypes and embeds them in the still-wet paper. These "hits" act much in the same way as underpaints. In many cases, positive and negative images seem to jump back and forth. About her work there is an interplay of active and passive, of energy across and in and out of a flat surface.

EIFERT, LARRY (Painter)
344 Main St., P. O. Box 127, Ferndale, CA 95536

Born: 1946 *Collections:* Redwood National Park; U.S. Navy, Centerville *Exhibitions:* The Eifert Gallery *Dealer:* Eifert Gallery

He is trained exclusively through his family and spent his youth traveling with his mother, the noted American naturalist and author Virginia Eifert. Consistent with his belief that art should provoke controversy, he works to raise America's consciousness of environmental issues. Gouache is his preferred medium, and he often paints on colored paper. His recent work, in deep greens and blacks, centers on the redwood forests and is part of a preservation effort. Other subjects include rare birds that nest in old-growth redwoods. He renders these animal subjects to communicate the flawlessness of birds, plants, oceans and mountains, reflecting the influence of environmentalists such as Rachel Carson. Much of his work in recent years has comprised large-scale murals, including an 800-square-foot ceiling mural of plants and birds. He continues to travel regularly to wilderness areas and up the western coast of the North American continent to maintain his connection with the spirit of his paintings. His technique ranges from transparent background washes to opaque applications for detailed areas.

EINSTEIN, CASSANDRA (Painter, Video Artist)
581 1/2 Windsor Blvd., Los Angeles, CA 90004

Born: 1937 *Collections:* Whitney Museum, NYC; Museum of Modern Art, NYC *Exhibitions:* Space Gallery, Los Angeles; Whitney Museum, NYC *Education:* Chouinard Art Institute; San Francisco Art Institute

Influences on her oil, acrylic, watercolor and pastel paintings include De Kooning, Matisse, Picasso and Van Gogh, as well as the traditions of Greek sculpture. Her figurative work is slightly surreal, and the use of

Marilyn R. Eger, *Bottle Study I,* 18 x 24, oil

E'drie, *Island Vista,* 22 x 30, watercolor. Courtesy: Larry Dotson Gallery, HI

color, light, emotion and expression is a response to visual experience. In addition to canvas, she paints on wood and film and experiments in video art.

EIS, RUTH (Painter, Multimedia Artist)
5401 Belgrave Pl., Oakland, CA 94618

Born: 1920 *Awards:* Honorable Mention, San Francisco Women Artists *Exhibitions:* San Francisco Art Museum; Lillian Paley Center of Visual Arts, Oakland *Education:* Lone Mountain College

She had traditional academic training in Europe, and a career in commercial art in New York; the abstract expressionist character of Bay area art in the 1950s and 1960s prompted a decisive change in her style, subject matter and approach. Recently, she has been interested in three-dimensional, environment-oriented soft sculpture and shaped textiles. These colorful, abstract assemblages are constructed from fabrics, buttons, threads, ribbons and other found materials.

EISEN, JUDITH A. (Painter)
P.O. Box 142, Guerneville, CA 95446

Born: 1942 *Awards:* Fellow, Royal Microscopal Society, London; Who's Who in Holography *Collections:* Bernstein Collection; Hutchinson Collection *Exhibitions:* Museum of Munich, West Germany; Smithsonian Institute, Washington D. C.; *Education:* San Francisco State U.

She is a landscape artist who works in oil on linen, and also a pioneer and teacher of holographic processes. Her recent work is partially inspired by sumi painting (influenced by a trip to China and Tibet), particularly in her exploration of watercolor-like effects of oil on unprimed linen. While often representational and exact, her works interject internal realities and emotional content in the interplay of raw areas of canvas left exposed between glazed, worked areas. Colors are restrained but naturally rich; her palette commonly runs from sepia greens and Prussian blues to rose and crimson. The intensity of her frottage and fine brush work, combined with the layers of glazes, creates landscapes that seem to emanate energy at a level of microscopic movement. The intensity of her landscapes is founded on her experience as a holographer and on the works of Monet, Bonnard, Ernst and Dali.

EISENBACH, DIANE (Ceramist, Painter)
4480 Euclid Ave., Apt. P, San Diego, CA 92115

Born: 1960 *Exhibitions:* Gallery Eight, La Jolla; Perspectives Gallery, San Diego *Education:* San Diego State U. *Dealer:* Glass Growers Gallery, Erie, PA

Her work in photography led her to develop a focused view of the intricacies of nature. Influenced by plant, animal and marine life, she began to use clay forms as canvases, on which to paint and draw the natural images. The work was executed in earthenware and low-temperature underglazes, with an emphasis on color and surface design. Later work in clay is an attempt to combine painting and sculpture. The forms are usually amorphous shapes which suggest waves, fins or other aquatic ideas. Her recent works dispaly a more painterly surface—the result of her study of the works of Georgia O'Keeffe. Her artwork is about the details of nature that often go unnoticed.

EISENBERG, ROBERTA (Painter)
202J E. Stevens St., Santa Ana, CA 92707

Born: 1940 *Exhibitions:* Fresno Art Museum; Laguna Art Museum *Education:* Philadelphia College of Art;

Boston Museum School of Art *Dealer:* Space Gallery, Los Angeles

The familiar yet provocative settings in her paintings allude to man's presence amidst the drama of life and nature. Expressively painted landscapes are built up carefully, layer by layer, using a limited palette with areas of color spontaneously breaking through the richly painted surface. Gestural lines within the landscape refer to figures and forms in nature. The work develops as a result of an intuitive and intellectual process. The strong brushstrokes evoke a feeling of motion, sometimes dissolving entirely into abstraction.

EISENSTAT, BENJAMIN (Painter)
3639 Bryant St., Palo Alto, CA 94306

Born: 1915 *Awards:* Harrison Morris Prize, Penn. Academy of Fine Arts, Philadelphia *Collections:* Philadelphia Museum of Art; New Britain Museum of American Art, New Britain, CT *Exhibitions:* Mangel Gallery, Philadelphia; San Francisco Art Institute *Education:* Penn. Academy of Fine Arts, Philadelphia; Albert Barnes Foundation, Merion, PA

Early paintings explored techniques ranging from a gentle impressionism in landscapes to a volatile expressionism in urban scenes. Influences include Bonnard, Kokoschka and de Kooning. Since he moved to California, his palette has lightened, and his subject matter has expanded. Colors are high-key, with emphasis on cadmiums, oranges and yellows, and his painting style has become an expressionistic realism. He primarily paints busy urban scenes and landscapes, occasionally doing murals as well. *End of Day* depicts downtown Philadelphia in a soft, brushy rendering that captures the movement and flow of the urban landscape. California works include studies of urban San Francisco, as well as beach and sailing scenes and a series of horse show paintings.

EISENSTAT, JANE SPERRY (Painter)
3639 Bryant St., Palo Alto, CA 94306

Born: 1920 *Awards:* George E. Dawson Medal, Philadelpia Watercolor Club; Mary Smith Prize, P.A.F.A. *Collections:* William Penn Charter School, City of Philadelphia *Exhibitions:* Philadelphia Art Alliance; Olive Hyde Gallery *Education:* Pennsylvania Academy of Fine Arts *Dealer:* Newman Galleries, Philadelphia

Whether it be sculpture or cartooning, or any of the various manners of painting and illustration, her primary criterion is quality. When painting in oils, her work is expressionistic. In watercolors, which she has concentrated on for the past ten years, her work is more in the manner of Charles Demuth. As a student at the Pennsylvania Academy of Arts, she was influenced by Henry McCarter who stressed radiation and interaction of color. As a teacher herself, she emphasizes the importance of negative space. This influence is seen in her own work where she uses fractured images to create an illusion of light and space.

ELDER, LAUREN (Environmental Designer)
5809 Ayala Ave., Oakland, CA 94609

Born: 1946 *Awards:* Isadora Duncan Dance Award, San Francisco; Outstanding Achievement/New Directions in Theater and Technical Achievement Award, Bay Area Theater Critics' Circle *Exhibitions:* Bay Area Dance Series, Laney College, Oakland; Oakland

Cynthia Eastman-Roan, *Lotus of a Thousand Nights,* 24 x 30,
watercolor, prismacolor and mixed media.
Courtesy: Ruth Carlson Gallery, Mendocino, CA

Ruth Eis, *Trees,* 26 x 30, oil on board.
Courtesy: Jack Langer, Oakland, CA

Museum *Education:* UCLA *Dealer:* San Francisco International Art Management, San Francisco

A visual artist, she synthesizes a wide variety of media in an ongoing process of experimentation with production and performers. She has seventeen years of professional experience in drawing, painting, sculpture, graphic arts, photography and scenic design. She prefers using commonplace and recycled materials, such as washing machines, refrigerators, shopping bags and Venetian blinds in order to explore the transformational and symbolic possibilities they contain. Her methods have been heavily influenced by the physicality and improvisational techniques learned from performers. She has worked with performance artist Nina Wise on projects sponsored by MOTION, originally a women's performance collective. The duo produced seven major theatrical works, which examined the complex social, political and spiritual dilemmas of contemporary American society from a woman's perspective.

ELDERS, KENT (Painter)
440 N. Stanley Ave., Los Angeles, CA 90036

Born: 1957 *Awards:* Silver Medal, Grumbacher Inc. *Collections:* Washington and Jefferson College, Washington, PA *Exhibitions:* Laguna Beach Museum of Art; Double Rocking G Gallery, Los Angeles *Education:* Bowling Green State U.

He was influenced by Agnes Martin and Jules Olitski and works with combined paint media. His construction painting of the late 1970s was a color-field handling of a canvas and its projecting wood supports. By the 1980s, he had begun noticing Ed Moses' grid paintings, and using oil color to achieve a shallow depth of field. Working with high contrast, he allows the viewer's eye to travel through layers of interrelated colors. He paints thickly with a knife and brush, using related undertones on a dark canvas. He paints his rectangular subject in the same manner as he paints the background field, thus producing a dissolving ghost image. These canvases are as large as 6-by-7-feet, and can take up to a year to complete.

ELDRIDGE, JAN (Painter, Draughtsperson)
2472 Tennessee St., Vallejo, CA 94591

Born: 1932 *Exhibitions:* Gallery Route #1, Pt. Reyes; Accurate Art Gallery, Sacramento

Most of her early formal training emphasized academic realism. After mastering this aesthetic, she began using an Oriental approach, minimizing the details in landscape paintings. In a later series of acrylic paintings and oil crayon drawings, the major theme was *Les Calvaires*, the sculptural tableaux of the Stations of the Cross commonly found in front of many churches in Brittany. These works marked the beginning of a preoccupation with the combination of positive and negative shapes. A close value relationship with muted color produced a merging of the subject with the background, and an overall mystical feeling. Soon, the empty space became so important that the figures almost disappeared. The catalyst for her most recent work is the Pere La Chaise cemetery and the cathedrals of France. In a charcoal drawing series, each contains some reference to monuments, headstones and arches placed in ambiguous space, creating a sense of quiet and mystery. A series of abstract collages consist of three or more layers of torn and cut papers stained with ink and watercolor, which have a glow reminiscent of stained glass windows. Her choice of subjects, a preoccupation with empty space and a preference for increasingly abstract forms are attempts to destroy or dissolve the perceived world to reveal more intangible realities.

ELIAS, SHEILA (Painter, Sculptor)
2323 E. Olympic La., New York, NY

Born: 1945 *Collections:* Brooklyn Museum of Art; Laguna Beach Museum of Art *Exhibitions:* The Louvre, Paris; Stella Polaris, Los Angeles *Education:* School of the Art Institute of Chicago *Dealer:* Paula Allen Art Gallery, NYC

In 1984, as part of her "American Icons" series she painted the seven-foot-long *Two English Girls*—a study of two faces of the Statue of Liberty. More recently, she has been concerned with making beauty out of ugliness. She now makes abstract pieces with some figurative imagery out of canvas and hand-made paper. She applies paint in a vividly colored, sensuous mix of acrylic, oil, resin and other media. Often, she paints over photo-emulsions and includes black-and-white xeroxes in the work. She also makes site-specific sculptural installations that are totemic in form. She has been influenced by Matisse, as well as by rigorous studies of life drawing while training formally at the Art Institute of Chicago.

ELINSON, HENRY D. (Painter)
997 Benito Ct., Pacific Grove, CA 93950

Born: 1935 *Awards:* Gold Medal, Milan, Italy *Collections:* San Francisco Museums of Fine Art; Palace of the Legion of Honor, San Francisco *Exhibitions:* Pratt Institute, NYC; Museum of Tokyo *Dealer:* Paule Anglim, San Francisco

Born in the Soviet Union, he emigrated to the United States in 1973. His early work was abstract but figurative. In 1980, he abandoned the figure and began an investigation of form and color. He has since returned to the figure, and his work has been called "primitive," "symbolic" and "totemic." Pastel has been his primary medium for over three decades, although he also works with pen and ink, frottage and collage. In his most recent pastels, he has layered various images, the animate as well as the inanimate, one on top of the other, creating canvases full of floating objects and figures contained within a finite plane.

ELLIASON, ANTHONY (Painter)
3624 California St., San Francisco, CA 94118

Born: 1953 *Exhibitions:* Galerie Emmanuelle Davide, Paris; Maxwell Gallery, San Francisco *Education:* U. of British Columbia, Vancouver, Canada *Dealer:* David Raymond

His only formal training is ten years study under Tchin Chiao, a Chinese master who was exiled in Canada after the cultural revolution. In oil and watercolor, he is self-taught. He has been influenced by Rembrandt's ability to explore the limits of paint, of and for itself, in the manner of a modern artist, while still acknowledging the object world and it appearance. His own work is principally, though not exclusively, representational. He creates a tension between the discipline of representational appearance and the limitless possibilities of paint, in experimental, often accidental combinations. Thus, the work takes on a life of its own, apart from its subject matter.

ELLIOT, LAURA (Painter)
2708 Webster St., No. 3, Berkeley, CA 94705

Roberta Eisenberg, *Entanglement,* 38 x 50, mixed media on stonehenge paper

Benjamin Eisenstat, *Learning the Course, Woodside,* 22 x 30, acrylic

Born: 1950 *Collections:* Playboy Enterprises, Atlantic City, NJ; Security Pacific, Los Angeles *Exhibitions:* Richmond Art Center; Mills College, Oakland *Education:* UC-Berkeley; San Francisco State U. *Dealer:* San Francisco Museum of Modern Art Rental Gallery

An early training in abstraction led to lush paintings on large canvases and paper, in which forms appeared to float in space. Pale, creamy colors gave way to harsher contrasts, as she began to explore an expressive figurative style with a brooding, existential mood. In these paintings, primitive, androgynous figures are suspended within isolated environments. This sense of confused spirituality has since found gentler, more fully rendered images in her emblematic landscapes. Deep space replaces layered, multihued background, in which trees, mountains, vegetation and solitary figures combine persuasively into a stark primeval garden. These minimal images contain an enigmatic metaphorical power, highlighted by the use of sanguine reds and earthtones. Influenced by Tibetan Buddhist writings, this work examines man as a natural phenomenon that must find its place in the rhythmic order of nature, and addresses the anxiety of separation from the organic experienced by contemporary society.

ELLIOTT, VIRGIL (Painter)
4803 Spring Hill Rd., Petaluma, CA 94952

Born: 1944 *Awards:* Thomas Leighton Award, Pastel Society of the West Coast; American Portrait Society Certification *Exhibitions:* California Museum of Art, Santa Rosa; Sacramento Fine Arts Center *Dealer:* Haakman Gallery, Palm Springs

While still a child, he was tutored, via correspondence, by Robert Fawcett, Harold Von Schmidt and others; he then spent years researching the techniques of the Old Masters. He painted impressionistically in Heidelberg between 1963 and 1965, gradually evolving a style in which the classical and impressionist approaches are reconciled. He now works primarily in oils (occasionally pastel), using people as a vehicle for conveying a feeling, mood or thought. Systematically employing opaque, translucent and transparent paints, he achieves different optical effects. Imagined settings are made to appear real, and a story is suggested. The artist adheres more closely to the classical concepts of pictorial harmony than to any current trends in art.

ELLIS, MARILYN (Painter, Photographer)
621 Begonia Ave., Corona del Mar, CA 92625

Born: 1932 *Exhibitions:* Orange Coast College, Costa Mesa; Costa Mesa Art League *Education:* Cal. State-Fullerton; UCLA

She has been and continues to be influenced by impressionist colors and abstract feelings of space and color. Imagery arises out of many different combinations of color strokes and color fields, a give-and-take with the blank surface of the white canvas or Arches paper. Her images subtly emerge to the surface rather than being preconceived attempts to reproduce past impressions. Her media has been and continues to be acrylic, oil, pastels, lithography inks in monotypes, watercolors, pencil, India ink and mixed and experimental media. She has done extensive travel photography in Europe, including both black-and-white prints and color slides, and she has taught art history both in the U.S. and abroad.

ELLIS, STUART (Video Artist, Mixed Media Artist)
830 N. Gardner St., Los Angeles, CA 90046

Born: 1947 *Exhibitions:* James Turcotte Gallery, Los Angeles; Warner Arts Center, Woodland Hills

He began his career in Amsterdam, where he studied painting and produced many pastel works and detailed pencil drawings. He later moved to Los Angeles, where he developed an interest in film and video production. He now concentrates primarily on video, exploring new techniques and technology. His current work incorporates video, music and animated collages and paintings. He makes these works with cut paper, markers and glass. Influenced by Dali and Van Gogh, the images of fish, birds and human beings metamorphose throughout the piece. The works are extremely surrealistic, with a strong, satirical narrative. Other influences on his work include Walt Disney, African art and Norman Rockwell.

EMENS, JANE (Mixed Media Artist)
3339 Santiago St., San Francisco, CA 94116

Born: 1951 *Exhibitions:* Sincere Technologies Gallery, Oakland; Fiberworks Gallery, Berkeley; *Education:* Oberlin College; John F. Kennedy U., Orinda

Her early training was in painting and geology, a combination that began to coalesce when she studied fibers and related mixed-media construction work with the Bay Area fiber movement. This push into new materials allowed her artistic expression and intellectual interest in geology, archaeology, mapping and conceptual experience to come together. Forming warped "fragments" of papier mache, which are then layered with handmade and Japanese papers, she adds lines and symbols that relate to ideas of mapping or creating petroglyphs. Their abstract quality speaks of a woman's personal iconography in the present, and are not derivative of any past culture. The fragments are then arranged on the wall, contained within pencil lines drawn directly on the wall surface, or arranged on the floor with papier mache "stones" in conceptual configurations reminiscent of a Zen garden.

EMERTON, ANTHONY (Multimedia Artist)
P.O. Box 14404, Santa Barbara, CA 93107

Born: 1952 *Awards:* Arts Council of Great Britain Performance Grant *Exhibitions:* Ellman Gallery, Los Angeles; Mendenhall Gallery, Whittier *Education:* Leeds, England *Dealer:* Francine Ellman, Los Angeles

A concern for illusion and reality has dominated his work. In 1979, he began making small sculptures and paintings that acted as metaphors for these issues. In the 1980s, he spent several years doing performance art and, though he has now returned to sculpture, the theatrical element remains in his aggressive distortions of perspective. He draws his technique from the Baroque, while the contents are more related to modern German art. He combines wooden objects with drawings and paintings of constructed wooden objects. Though he spent time in several art colleges, he considers himself self-taught.

EMERY, DONALD EDWARD (Multimedia Artist)
520 Mildas Dr., Malibu, CA 90265

Virgil Elliott, *The Dreamer,* 24 x 30, oil. Courtesy: Emiko Namiki Collection, Tokyo

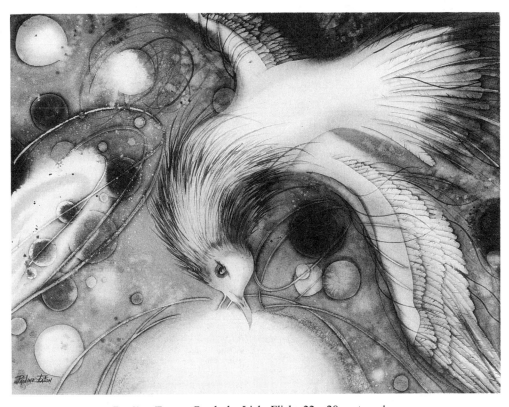

Pauline Eaton, *Catch the Light Flight,* 22 x 30, watercolor

Born: 1943 *Awards:* Aleliade International Festival of Photography; Printing, Cracow Print Biennial, Poland *Collections:* Executive Life Insurance, Los Angeles; International ICM, Beverly Hills *Exhibitions:* Alternate Space Exhibition, Sumitomo Bank, Los Angeles; Santa Monica College *Education:* Cal. State-Long Beach *Dealer:* Los Angeles County Museum of Art Rental Gallery; Hunsaker/Schlesinger, Los Angeles

There is a great deal of variety in his work, both in terms of media and expression. His life experience and relation with nature are his main subjects, although he seeks to interpret nature, not reproduce it. His sense of design and composition, and his knowledge of materials and processes enable him to use a variety of techniques to express his feelings about the people and places in the world around him. He works in a range of materials including gouache, screen printing, linocut and mixed media printing and painting. His baby daughter has lately been a favorite subject.

ENGEL, DESIREE (Papercaster, Printmaker)
1515 Camino Los Robles, Fullerton, CA 92633

Born: 1921 *Awards:* Honorable Mention, Hillcrest Fine Arts Festival, Whittier; 2nd Place, La Habra Art Association *Exhibitions:* Gallery 57, Fullerton; The Gallery, Los Angeles *Education:* Cal. State-Fullerton

She uses her own handmade paper as support for printmaking techniques, especially relief etching. She incorporates multiple viewpoints in her work, thus opening the possibility for multiple interpretations. Her imagery takes the form of layers, earth strata, rocks and clouds, periods of time and cultures, which build their reality on the tradition of previous cultures. Another frequent theme in her work is duality, expressed in the frequent use of positive and negative images and in the attention given to negative as well as positive images. She works in white, dark brown, black and gray. Recent pieces deal with the Holocaust, death and the process of breaking free.

ENGEL, HANA BARAK (Painter, Sculptor)
P.O. Box 2031, Redondo Beach, CA 90278

Born: 1954 *Awards:* Certificate of Excellence; International Art Competition, NY *Exhibitions:* T. Gallery, Marina Del Rey; Carnegie Art Museum, Oxnard *Dealer:* Five Seasons C.V., New Orleans; Ariel Gallery, NYC

Drawing themes from her imagination and from the reality of her immediate surroundings, she attempts to convey commonality and uniqueness while at the same time examining her own existence as a woman. She renders her subjects, normally women, in a style she calls "minimalism figuration," which involves recognizable but not realistic images rendered with rich, vibrant colors in oil paint. The style also conveys moods of quiet, sensuality and harmony. Recently, she has also been sculpting wood, stone, bronze and cement. Her work has been included in *Women Under Discussion*, a book about women artists in California.

ENGLAND, ANNE R. (Painter)
387 Jasmine St., Laguna Beach, CA 92651

Born: 1938 *Awards:* Purchase Award, Jacksonville Museum of Art, FL; 2nd Prize, So. California Jazz Exhibition, Costa Mesa *Collections:* Batholomew Collection, Pet Milk, San Francisco *Exhibitions:* Alison Creek Art Group, Mission Viejo; Sawdust Festival, Laguna Beach; Bevel Cut Gallery, Newport Beach *Education:* Florida State U.; Long Beach State U.

Although she was formally trained in oils and acrylics, she enjoys the freedom and spontaneity of watercolors. Anne pursues compositions using three-dimensional and flat shapes to produce patterns of values that read as objects. Painting from a palette that emphasizes blue, mauve, purple, pink and lavender, she renders picket fences, lattice work, flowers and California landscapes and coastlines. Her work, "The Crystal Cove" series, is nostalgic, impressionistic and highly reminiscient of the old California and the quaint cottages that have attracted generations of painters to the California Coast.

ENGLE, MADELYN (Painter, Sculptor)
3750 Riviera Dr., San Diego, CA 92109

Born: 1943 *Collections:* E.F. Hutton, San Francisco; Hilton Corporation, San Diego *Exhibitions:* Riggs Gallery, Los Angeles; Circle Gallery, San Diego *Education:* U. of Missouri *Dealers:* Mary Moore, La Jolla; Anuska Smith, San Diego

Her early works were distinguished by a romantic use of watercolor techniques applied to oils. Eventually, she came to use an almost Oriental style of brushwork to depict rustic Midwestern subject matter. Early influences included Wyeth, Van Gogh and Turner. She spent several years investigating large iron and brass forms, using oxyacetylene welding. Concurrently, her canvas work began to include collage and often became three-dimensional. She has since invented a means for using the monoprint process to produce large images on canvas. Recently, she has returned to sculpture, creating soaring, abstract forms with clean, complex curves, by stretching raw canvas over redwood armatures, or casting in bronze. Stripped of all recognizable figuration, the works take on a spiritual energy, enhanced by their execution in pure white or bronze.

ENGLUND, N. JONAS (Painter)
P.O. Box 1274, Kaneohe, HI 96744

Collections: Volvo; Texaco Scandinavia *Exhibitions:* New Sweden Anniversary *Education:* Berklee College of Music, Boston

A native of Sweden, he pursued a career in music before turning to painting, touring and recording with the Scandinavian rock group Strasse. A sudden decision to paint professionally coincided with an equally fortuitous choice of endangered exotic birds as subject matter, and very quickly the artist achieved a dominant position in the field of ornithological art. Within the works, birds painted with a photographic sharpness and realism are set against bright fields of color, or in absurd surrealist situations. In all cases a sense of levity pervades the treatments, which the artist intends to evoke a pleasurable response in the viewer. The comic tone is also reflected in his suggestions of animal character: many of his works depict pairs of birds interacting in ways that, although neither saccharine nor overtly anthropomorphic, have a resonance in the human experience of the viewer. To achieve the sharpness and accuracy of an Audubon while maintaining bright and decorative coloration, the artist works in acrylics and uses live birds as models. Likewise, he makes use of multiple studies in planning and executing a work, so that each is a deliberate and clear rendering of a bird in a precisely orchestrated composition.

ERDMAN, BARBARA (Printmaker, Mixed Media Artist)

N. Jonas Englund, *King Macaw,* 24 x 18, print

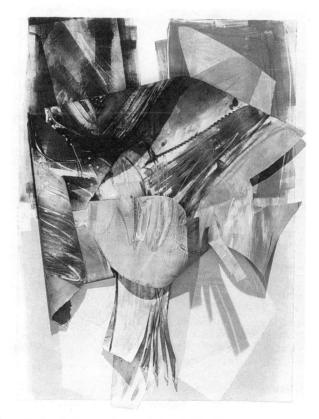

Barbara Erdman, *Alternatives to Origami,* 30 x 23, sculpted monoprint

1070 Calle Largo, Santa Fe, NM 87501

Born: 1936 *Collections:* Museum of Fine Arts, Santa Fe, NM; IBM Corporate Collection, NYC *Exhibitions:* Berkeley Art Center; Scottsdale Center for the Arts, Scottsdale, AZ *Education:* Cornell U.

She is an abstract expressionist who is particularly involved in the painting of odd-shaped canvases and multiple images. These often interlock to create large tableaux. She recently began a series of monoprints and drawings which concentrate on her concerns with spatial issues both in terms of color and of the visual embodiment of infinity. Other works include three-dimensional monotypes constructed by printing on both sides of one sheet of paper, manipulating it into a sculptural form, and sometimes affixing it to another monoprint used as a background. She believes that abstract expressionism is the most direct way to deal with the problems of painting, drawing and printmaking. For the past ten years she has also been working in photography.

ERICKSON, E. DALE (Draughtsperson, Printmaker)

499 Alabama St., San Francisco, CA 94110

Born: 1942 *Collections:* Achenbach Foundation, San Francisco *Exhibitions:* Steven Thomas Gallery, San Francisco; Joseph Chowning Gallery, San Francisco *Education:* Art Institute of Chicago; San Francisco State U.

His drawings and prints are mainly concerned with a classical-surreal approach to expression. Since the late 1970s, these have been geometric forms made from ropes and drapery. He intends the works to have a classical, formal meaning and to present viewers with a challenging and engaging appearance. His prints are characterized by a hatch system that evolved from his handling of the etching needle. When finished, he often colors the backgrounds of his prints and uses a pencil to assure a rendered, almost sculptural texture.

ERICKSON, KIMBERLY (Mixed Media Artist)

2372 Riverside Dr., Santa Ana, CA 92706

Born: 1958 *Awards:* Grant, California State U., Fullerton *Exhibitions:* Whittier Museum; Humboldt Cultural Center, Eureka *Education:* Cal. State–Fullerton

After researching a variety of textile techniques, she used a multimedia approach to create a series of ethnic influenced ceremonial vestments. She then began incorporating such non-fiber materials as wood, cast aluminum and glass into the work. Her earlier experiences in dye processes made the subsequent transition to aluminum anodizing (also a dye process) a natural means of incorporating color into her cast metal reliefs. Her recent sculptural wall pieces echo the vestment form.

ERICKSON, MARK (Painter)

495 Clementina St., San Francisco, CA 94133

Born: 1955 *Exhibitions:* San Francisco Art Institute; Stockton Art Museum *Education:* San Francisco Art Institute *Dealer:* Hanson Galleries, Mill Valley

His work investigates the distinctions between abstraction and realism, creating a playful and often lyrically colorful vocabulary of non-representational images. He applies both iridescent and fluorescent acrylics, enamels and chrome paints to paper or canvas. The resulting image appears to be a view entirely from a window, from which can be seen gestural lines, dots and abstractions floating above and casting shadows on a rich, flat background. This exploration of real depth through seemingly non-objective compositional elements achieves a childlike and dizzying sense of rhythmic interrelationships and hidden discovery beneath a somber illusion of urban life.

ERICKSON, ROBERT (Furniture Maker)

17790 Tyler-Foote Rd., Nevada City, CA 95959

Born: 1947 *Awards:* Design Award, "Art of Crafts," Denver Art Museum *Collections:* Yale University Gallery; Los Angeles County Art Museum *Exhibitions:* Gallery Fair, Mendocino; Kurland/Summers Gallery, Los Angeles *Education:* U. of Nebraska

He is well known for his carefully crafted chairs and other furniture built primarily from domestic hardwoods, including Pacific madrone and black locust. Mainly self-taught, he began woodworking while he was an undergraduate in Nebraska, but his professional career started when he moved to the mountains of California, where he spent 1969 working with craftsmen Ed Stiles and Roger Somers. They introduced him to the designer/craftsman approach to woodworking, which includes principles of design, execution and marketing. He gathers wood from the forests near his home, as well as from small saw mills in California and Nebraska. His designs have been influenced by contemporary furniture makers, especially the Swedish. His trademark is a comfortable floating buck seat. Another specialty is the traditional three-legged chair, first made in Rui, Norway.

ERL, JANET TARJAN (Painter)

312 Anderson Rd., Yreka, CA 96097

Born: 1957 *Awards:* Best of Show, Los Angeles Audubon Society; Merit Award, Pittsburg Watercolor Society *Collections:* Sacramento Science Center; City of Yreka *Exhibitions:* American Artists Professional League; Los Angeles Audubon Society Wildlife and Environmental Art Exhibit *Education:* UC-Davis

Trained in abstract expressionism, she soon came under the influence of such Pop Artists as Wayne Thiebaud and Robert Arneson, and began to make pop art sculptures. Later, she painted watercolors in which she depicted rocks and roots as sculptural forms placed in abstract landscapes. In these impressionistic landscapes, she was influenced by the lyrical Chinese landscape painters of the 17th century. In her more recent paintings of illusory objects, she seeks to achieve an enhanced sense of form and space by controlling of texture and surface, using a technique which involves several layers of washes.

ESAKI, YASUHIRO (Printmaker)

11 San Antonio Ct., Walnut Creek, CA 94598

Born: 1941 *Awards:* First Prize, Miami International Graphic Biennial *Collections:* Boston Museum of Fine Arts; Brooklyn Museum *Exhibitions:* San Francisco Museum of Modern Art; Brooklyn Museum *Education:* Lone Mountain College

Her primary media are drawing and painting. Early works featured isolated objects portrayed in a still-life manner. She drew ropes, leaves, towels and brown paper bags without any trace of time or place in them. In recent works, she uses colored pencils over a layer of acrylic. She draws sheets, variously creased, folded over, flattened out or bunched up. With the sheet as a starting point, she freely modifies its shape in the drawing for compositional emphasis.

ESCHNER, STEPHEN (Painter)
1927 Lakeshore Ave., Los Angeles, CA 90039

Born: 1953 *Collections:* Levine Collection, Kitchner, Ontario *Exhibitions:* Gorky's, Los Angeles *Education:* Syracuse University

Though he received formal training in abstract expressionism, he remained a figure painter throughout school, finding ways to apply the various techniques to flat, proportionately rendered figure drawings. Influenced by Hans Hofmann, Van Gogh and various painters from Leon, his style reflects the idyllic themes of the expressionists, while maintaining his individual expression via the figure.

ESOIMEME, JAMES E. (Painter, Sculptor)
P.O. Box 773, Oakland, CA 94604

Born: 1950 *Awards:* Gold Medal Sculpture, Gold Medal Mixed Media, San Mateo County Art Fair Competition *Exhibitions:* Alameda County Fairground Arts Competition, Pleasanton; California State Fair Competition, Sacramento *Education:* San Francisco State U.

His work incorporates African themes, motifs and images with contemporary Black American experiences.

ESSICK, AMY (Mixed Media Artist, Paper Artist)
46 Mt. Devon Rd., Carmel Highlands, CA 93923

Born: 1957 *Exhibitions:* Biennial Paper and Clay Exhibit, Memphis, TN; Stockton National *Education:* Ohio U., Athens *Dealer:* Walter/White Gallery, Carmel

Drawing subject matter from underwater themes, boats, architecture and natural forms, she combines recognizeable and abstract imagery in unexpected ways. Her technique of handmade paper drawing is the culmination of years of formal training in fiber processes, painting and printmaking. Color is an important element of the work and is made from combining different colors of permanently pigmented abaca/cotton pulp. The colored pulps create the image and the support through various pouring, lamination and stencil techniques. Following drying/pressing processes, she may continue work with watercolor or colored pencil. In addition to the handmade paper drawings, she is involved with monotypes, drawings and watercolor paintings.

EVANS, ALEXANDER (Neon Artist)
3275 Laguna Canyon Rd., Ste. Q, Laguna Beach, CA 92651

Born: 1953 *Awards:* Artist of the Year, Laguna Beach Civic Organization; Best Booth and Best Display, Sawdust Festival, Laguna Beach *Exhibitions:* Festival of the Arts, Laguna Beach; Elan Gallery, Laguna Beach *Education:* Art Institute of Chicago; Southern Illinois U.

Early work was in painting and sculpture. A trip to Las Vegas, with its panorama of brightly colored signs, inspired a fascination with neon. He taught himself to work the medium by studying the theory behind the works of Nikola Teslas, and the practical applications of George Claude. Influenced by art nouveau, he incorporates the warm, eerie glow of neon into the media of plastic and metal, mixing old forms with new ones. In his work, light and color appear to emanate

from nowhere and continuously breathe new life into his inanimate pieces.

EVANS, DEAN (Painter)
22 Eastbrook Ct., Clayton, CA 94517

Born: 1961 *Exhibitions:* Gallery Six, San Jose; Sacramento Regional Arts Festival *Education:* San Jose State U.

His paintings are at once familiar and elusive; his collage technique subjects visual memories from his childhood to technical experimentation. The influence of Helen Frankenthaler and Jay De Foe can be seen in these works, which incorporate elements of surrealism and organic abstraction. The pieces are highly detailed and contain much illusion, creating an interaction between figure and landscape that is real, though not literal. He is comfortable with a variety of media, and his paintings are often a combination of charcoal, colored chalk, graphite and acrylics—the use of acrylics, however, is restricted to dark colors.

EVARISTO, PETE (Painter)
4535 34th St., Suite B, San Diego, CA 92116

Born: 1955 *Awards:* NEA Grant; Artists Guild Exhibit, San Diego Museum of Art *Exhibitions:* Rather Art Center, San Diego; San Diego Museum of Art

In the late 1970s and early 1980s, he made three-dimensional reconstructions from formal arrangements of common objects that he scavenged from the ruins of American homes. Avoiding any evidence of formal art training in these works, he encouraged each viewer to interpret the object in terms of his or her own past experiences. He has recently been influenced by tantric art of Asia, world cultures, interpersonal relationships and the full moon. He now paints large, mixed-media canvases with imagery somewhere between abstraction and figuration. He is also a neighborhood artist, and he is deeply involved in the revitalization of the community in which he lives.

EVART, ELEANOR (Sculptor, Ceramics)
22628 Valley View Dr., Hayward, CA 94541

Born: 1920 *Exhibitions:* Mills College, Oakland; UC-Berkeley *Education:* UC-Berkeley

After working with Fred Bauer at Mills College in Oakland and then with Peter Vaulkos at Berkeley, she began making 8-by-8-foot ceramic-tile murals with deep-carved bas-reliefs. These figurative, sculptured murals have a dreamlike quality that the artist has enhanced by her studies of European technique. She high-fires colored washes in a gas kiln. Her recent work has comprised small groups of tiles on which she has made sgraffito drawings of dancer Isadora Duncan, a recent inspiration being August Rodin's drawings of Isadora Duncan. She is currently experimenting with low-fire colors and clay.

EVE, ELIZABETH (Painter)
512 Frederick, #31, San Francisco, CA 94117

Born: 1959 *Awards:* Honorable Mention, "Artist's Liaison," Santa Monica *Exhibitions:* Joseph Chowning Gallery, San Francisco; Perel Cuisine Gallery, Tiburon *Education:* San Francisco State U. *Dealer:* Joseph Chowning, San Francisco

Her works emphasize detail, revealing the paintings' underlying emotions. At one point, she used spackle on masonite to give the paintings added dimension. Now she works in acrylics, using every color except black. She believes that black stops the eye. Instead, she uses deep purples, blues and browns, which draw the eye deeper into the painting. Subjects include apartments, street scenes, floral still lifes and portraits. Current work includes a series of life-size nudes, realistically rendered but painted with distorted, vivid colors. She was recently included in the *International Catalogue of Contemporary Art*.

EVERETT, BRUCE (Painter)
9247 Franklin St., Chatsworth, CA 91311

Born: 1942 *Collections:* Yale U., New Haven, CT; Aldrich Museum of Art, Ridgefield, CT *Exhibitions:* Los Angeles Institute of Contemporary Art; Jan Turner Gallery, Los Angeles *Education:* UC-Santa Barbara; U. of Iowa *Dealer:* Jan Turner, Los Angeles

Early abstract expressionist works gradually incorporated elements of representation, and by 1968 he had begun working directly from photographs, resulting in monumental photo-realistic depictions of manmade minutiae such as gum wrappers and a box of thumbtacks. In 1973, he shifted his focus to natural phenomena and spent three years capturing a precise image of a flowing creek. Since that time, landscapes have predominated as subject material, although the smooth precision of monumental photo-realist canvases has been tempered with a looser and more textural and expressive technique. This results in works that maintain a representational clarity from a distance yet display a multiplicity of approaches to pigment application in close-up. Subjects likewise combine traditional landscape environments with mundane social elements such as roads, rails, signs. Through such images, the artist attempts to evoke in the viewer a sense of connectedness with the depicted scene, and thereby to impart upon the landscape a significance beyond the merely pictorial. His work reflects a dichotomy of subject and technique that attempts to honor both, and in so doing, reflects the artist's professed love of both the act of painting and the image produced.

EVERHART-DAVIS, MARILYN (Painter, Ceramist)
61 Merrydale Rd., San Rafael, CA

Born: 1930 *Collections:* Blind Friends Art Works *Exhibitions:* Sister Kenny Institute, Philadelphia; Art in the Park, San Francisco

She is a visually impaired artist who works in several media. She paints brilliantly colored realistic canvases in oils. These images of landscapes, life experiences and recurring dreams have a mystical quality about them that comes in part from an overall light source. Upon careful examination, they often reveal hidden scenes or persons in the background. Her burnished Native American pottery is in the form of large jugs up to 4 by 7 feet. She also makes personalized canes and chess sets for the blind complete with holes in the board for the pieces and braille on the sides. She normally completes her paintings in one session. Among her influences are Renoir and Mary Cassatt.

EVERSLEY, FREDERICK JOHN (Sculptor)
1110 W. Washington Blvd., Venice, CA 90291

Born: 1941 *Awards:* NEA Fellowship; Artist in Residence, Smithsonian Institution *Collections:* Guggenheim Museum, NYC; Oakland Museum *Exhibitions:* Whitney Museum, NYC; Santa Barbara Museum of Art *Education:* Carnegie Mellon University

His early works are cast, multicolored, multilayered resin sculptures. The works were primarily transparent, although later pieces were translucent or opaque. Shapes were geometric and explored properties of the parabola; many consisted of large parabolic lenses. Several of these same shapes were executed in large (up to 35-feet high) outdoor pieces constructed of stainless steel. Recent work consists of multiple triangular elements arranged to form large curvilinear arcs in space. The indoor pieces utilize layers of metal triangles alternating with clear plastic triangles. All of his work, past and present, deals with concepts of energy, particularly solar energy. He has also been working on a series of large architectural-scale transparent oil flowing fountains.

EVERTS, CONNOR (Painter)
The Market, 2351 Sonoma, Torrance, CA 90501

Born: 1926 *Awards:* International Painting Exhibition, Tokyo *Collections:* Museum of Modern Art, NYC; Art Institute of Chicago *Exhibitions:* Los Angeles Municipal Art Gallery; Luminous Images *Education:* Universidad de las Americas; Courtauld Institute *Dealers:* Paul Gallery, Tokyo; Ruth Bachofner, Los Angeles

After toying with abstraction in the late 1940s, he moved to Mexico, where he visited archaeological sites and studied pre-Columbian art. Later he worked as a mural assistant to D.A. Sequieros. After leaving Mexico, he studied art history at the University of London. Upon his return to California, he began a series of large scale (8-by-20-foot) collage drawings. In the 1970s, his work became more psychologically oriented, and he moved toward a more reductive and abstract style. He spent several years as an artist in residence at Cranbrook Academy, where he painted works that seemed entirely white. In 1981, he returned to California and his work became brighter. His recent paintings are almost decorative, with diverse images mixed into a highly activated, brightly painted surface.

EWING, EDGAR (Painter)
4226 Sea View Ln., Los Angeles, CA

Born: 1913 *Awards:* Goldwyn Award; Florsheim Award *Collections:* San Diego Museum of Art; Los Angeles County Museum of Art *Exhibitions:* Carnegie International; Art Institute of Chicago *Education:* School of the Art Institute of Chicago *Dealer:* Esther Bear, Santa Barbara

He emphasizes chromatic and tonal qualities in his ambiguous presentations of figurative forms. His media are oil and acrylic, on canvas or gesso board. His paint application has become, over the years, increasingly simple and direct. Most recently he has had a one-person exhibit at the Fisher Gallery. He has been a faculty member at the Art Institute of Chicago, at the American Academy in Rome and at Carnegie-Mellon U. He taught at the University of Southern California for three decades and was made Distinguished Professor Emeritus of Fine Arts in March of 1987. He has studios in both Athens and Los Angeles.

FABIANO, DIANE FABIAN (Painter)
5624 Las Virgenes Rd., Studio 16, Calabasas, CA 91302

Born: 1952 *Collections:* Laser Institute, Van Nuys; Massachusetts General Hospital, Boston *Exhibitions:* Aubes 3935 Galerie, Montreal; Tarsh Gallery, Tar-

Claire Falkenstein, *Forum (Memorial to A. Quincy Jones),* 600 x 840 x 216, Port Orford cedar logs

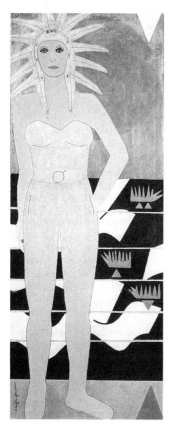

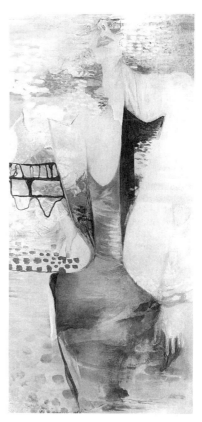

Diane Fabian Fabiano, *The Planet Series: Mars,* 22 x 28, fabric dyes and acrylic paints with simulated gems

Beatrice Findlay, *Blonde in a Purple Skirt,* 48 x 24, oil on canvas. Photograph: Janice Felgar

zana *Education:* California College of Arts and Crafts; Cal. State-Northridge *Dealer:* Tarsh Gallery, Tarzana

After multifaceted training in painting, as one of her first creative projects, she set out to paint a visual catalogue of the feminine archetypes. Influenced by Modigliani in content and style and by Hans Hoffman in color, her first works were realistic, oil-portrait busts of fertility goddesses. As her images became more simplified, stylized and two-dimensional, she began painting in acrylics. At this time, she began grouping her figurative series by character types and wrote socio-political feminist themes for them. Her figurative work progressed to life- sized, full bodies of the feminine image now encompassing wisdom and knowledge. Her contemporary fertility goddess is balanced—seductive while strong; gentle but powerful. On primed canvas, she uses fabric dyes, acrylic paints, glitter and simulated gems, creating a flat but luminous image.

FACEY, MARTIN (Painter)
2625 Malpais Ave. S.W., Albuquerque, NM 87105

Born: 1948 *Awards:* Guggenheim Fellowship in Painting *Exhibitions:* Tortue Gallery, Santa Monica; Ivory-Kimpton Gallery, San Francisco *Education:* UCLA *Dealer:* Tortue Gallery, Santa Monica; Ivory-Kimpton Gallery, San Francisco

His early work was an eclectic fusion of abstraction and representationalism, suggesting a dreamlike and surreal evocation of the California experience: sunglasses, swimming pools, the movie industry and physical beauty intermingled with such images of violence and death as guns, skulls and burning hillsides. These and other unlikely combinations of figures and objects often appear arranged on table tops. For a time, his paintings depicted crypt-like images—entombed and wrapped figures and skeletons. More recently, his work is departing from overtly figurative surrealism to a more symbolic structuring of color and form, evocative of ancient and mysterious arts and mandalas.

FAIRLEY, LEZA (Photographer)
9358 Olympic Blvd., Beverly Hills, CA 90212

Born: 1957 *Exhibitions:* San Francisco Art Institute; California Institute of the Arts *Education:* California Institute of the Arts; San Francisco Art Institute

After formal training in painting, film and photography, she chose to work with black-and-white photography and text. Early influences were the portraits of Judy Pater and Imogen Cunningham. She works mainly in the South, taking pictures of poor blacks. She brings a love of her subjects to her work; one series depicts the plight of black women on cotton farms. She has lately discovered the photographs of the depression era Farm Security Administration and now hopes to continue their work.

FALKENSTEIN, CLAIRE (Sculptor, Multimedia Artist)
719 Occan Front, Venice, CA 90291

Collections: Museum of Modern Art, NYC; San Francisco Museum of Modern Art *Exhibitions:* Loyola Mary Mount College, Los Angeles; Los Angeles County Museum of Art *Education:* UC-Berkeley *Dealer:* Jack Rutberg Fine Arts Gallery, Los Angeles; Anita Shapolsky, NYC

She has had a varied and distinguished career, creating sculptures in metals, molten glass and wood, as well as

paintings and drawings in various media. The crux of her approach is an exploration of curved, relativistic space, as opposed to geometric, Euclidean space. As such, her pieces are an artist's rendering of the natural world, as revealed by modern science. Consistent metaphors in her work include "the moving point" (alluding to Einstein's relativity), "interstices" (referring to the spaces contained by matter) and "the never-ending screen" (representing the expanding, seemingly infinite universe). Her works include: fountains which mimic the form of water; sculptures that refer to the infinitesimal and the infinite; stained glass windows that convey a sense of the voluptuous rendered in metal and colored glass; and multi-media, two- dimensional pieces that partake of the recognizable and the abstract.

FARBER, GERTA (Painter)
5727 Claremont, Oakland, CA 94618

Born: 1927 *Awards:* Honorable Mention, East Bay Watercolor Society Exhibit, Holy Names College, Oakland; Merit Award, Oakland Art Association Exhibit *Exhibitions:* First Federal Savings, Oakland; Marin Art Center *Education:* Chouinard Art Institute

Although she has been a professional painter for many years, she divided her time between fine art and architectural illustration until the early 1980s. After a move to the Bay area, she dedicated herself to watercolor painting. Her expressionistic portraits, landscapes and still lifes display the Fauvist influences of Matisse and Derain. She works with models, and uses vivid colors to remind the viewer of often overlooked colorings and shadings.

FARIS, MARJORIE B. (Printmaker)
4296 #J Wilkie Way, Palo Alto, CA 94306

Born: 1932 *Awards:* Honorable Mention, Matrix Workshop California Women Artists; Honorable Mention, California State Fair *Exhibitions:* Monterey Museum of Art; Triton Museum, Santa Clara *Education:* UC-Davis; Stanford U.

Her work has moved from abstraction to figuration and back again, always maintaining a sense of highly charged inner and outer landscape. During the late 1970s, she created collage pieces with wood, cloth, drawings and other materials attached to large canvases. She now works in monoprints, or with oil or acrylic on paper, frequently mixing the media to produce painted prints. Her exploratory use of materials courts chaos which may eventually reveal such familiar places as: caves, forests, waterfronts or buildings. These areas may, on occasion, be inhabited. She wants radiance of color, movement and the presence of composition to co-exist successfully. All of this must be counterpoised with an underlying sense of serenity.

FARRINGTON, REED (Painter)
P.O. Box 1263, Carmel, CA 93921

Born: 1938 *Exhibitions:* Carmel Art Association; Janice S. Hunt Gallery, Chicago *Education:* San Francisco Art Institute *Dealer:* Janice S. Hunt Gallery, Chicago

Originally influenced by such American Abstract Expressionists as de Kooning and Pollock and such California figure painters as Diebenkorn and Park, he has worked on a progression of problems inherent in

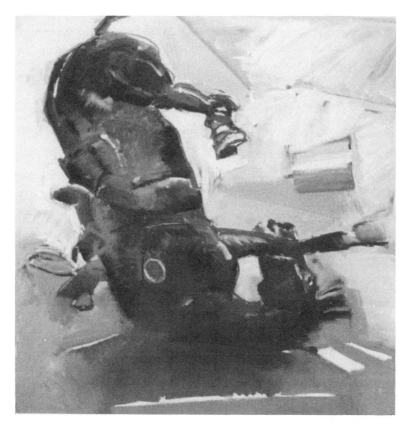

Farrington, *Good Golly, Miss Molly,* 36 x 36, oil on canvas

Corey Fowler, *Joy,* 20 x 24, pen and ink

the contradictory nature of those influences. He now paints a wide range of subject matter including the non-objective. The works are large and painterly and are done exclusively with oils on canvas.

FARROW, AL (Sculptor)
P.O. Box 2574, San Rafael, CA 94912

Born: 1943 *Collections:* Modesto Lanzone, San Francisco *Exhibitions:* Brockman Gallery, Los Angeles; Monterey Peninsula Museum of Art *Dealer:* Himovitz/Salomon, Sacramento

In the early 1960s, the work of German expressionist sculptors Wilhelm Lehmbruck and Ernst Barlach led him to a figurative style concerned with making social commentary. His works from this period are in clay, wood and stone. For a time, his pieces evolved from social commentary into figurative abstraction, and during this period, which lasted into the late 1970s, he began experimenting with cast bronze and welded steel. He build a foundry in 1978, and in 1984, he returned to his earlier interest in social issues, adopting a future-historical perspective. The work is characterized by delicate surface detail and color, the figures aged by time and the perils of the human condition.

FAUST, AMY K. (Jeweler)
10 Arkansas St., Suite H., San Francisco, CA 94107

Born: 1960 *Exhibitions:* San Francisco International Airport; San Francisco Folk and Craft Museum *Education:* State U. of New York, New Paltz

She is a jeweler who has been influenced by architecture, Japanese design, and natural forms and textures. Her pieces usually are abstractions derived form architecture, and combine a sculptural depth with the innate beauty of materials like silver, gold, slate and steel. She works with tones and textures rather than blatant color. Since 1984, she has collaborated with various jewelry artists, creating both production and one of a kind pieces, as well as doing jewelry repair. She currently maintains a studio and show room in San Francisco, and does free-lance jewelry designing for a major jewelry and gift company.

FAUTH, BETTE LAVERNE (Painter)
808 University Place, Riverside, CA 92507

Awards: Visual Artist Award, Riverside Cultural Arts Association *Collections:* Fortmann Gallery, Florence, Italy; Thiel College *Exhibitions:* Fortmann Gallery, Florence, Italy; UC-Riverside Faculty Club *Education:* Claremont Graduate School; Escuela Centro Lorenzo de Medici, Florence, Italy; NYU

Her early interpretations of impressionism eventually developed into an abstract expressionist style. She has studied at the Claremont Graduate School, the Art Students League and in Florence. During her study with James Pinto and Fred Samuelson at Instituto Allende in Mexico, she began introducing the glorious colors of the area into her still-developing style. The works had unusual and vibrant color combinations and semi-abstract fantasy imagery. She recently has been working on two series of acrylic paintings. In the first, strange figures and animals exist in a medieval and early renaissance-style environments. The others are semi-abstract fantasy landscapes in subtle color combinations.

FEASEL, DONALD (Painter)
2040 Fell St., San Francisco, CA 94117

Born: 1953 *Collections:* Gallery Paule Anglim, San Francisco; Dr. Stephen Kalkstein, El Cerrito, CA *Exhibitions:* Gallery Paule Anglim, San Francisco; Pro Arts, Oakland *Education:* UC-Berkeley *Dealer:* Gallery Paule Anglim, San Francisco

His initial influences were the ceremonial and otherworldly still lifes of 17th-century Spanish painters Cotan and Zurbaran. His interest later shifted to the more visceral and expressionistic treatment of still-life subjects in Goya's late painting. Of late, the self-contained silence and stillness of his earlier still lifes have led to portrayal of objects within a fluid, painterly field and to a willingness to sacrifice distinctness of form in order that objects can locate themselves through the act of painting. His works are dark, impastoed renderings of such objects as fish heads, lamb hearts and vegetables.

FEESE, RICHARD (Sculptor)
4905 U St., Sacramento, CA 95817

Born: 1947 *Exhibitions:* Mendocino Art Center; Jennifer Pauls Gallery, Sacramento *Education:* Cal. State-Sacramento; Sacramento State College *Dealer:* Jennifer Pauls, Sacramento; William Sawyer, San Francisco

As a sculptor, he is comfortable with both plaster and wood, fashioning fish and birds and casting a mountain in plaster of paris. Much of his imagery is inspired by his journeys into the wilderness, the events and places he experiences finding expression in his sculpture. His works also incorporated found objects, which he then paints or inscribes as parts of a larger artistic statement. The work is often humorous and sometimes erotic, with parts that move or doors that open.

FEINER, GEORGE LEOPOLD (Painter)
6000 Coldwater Canyon, #13, N. Hollywood, CA 91606

Born: 1933 *Awards:* NEA Fellowship *Exhibitions:* Platt Art Gallery, Los Angeles; ISC Gallery, UCLA *Education:* State College, Crakow, Poland; Academy of Fine Art, Cracow, Poland

His oil and acrylic paintings portray mythological characters such as Apollo and Zeus in deep golds and blues. These works are influenced by Italian and Renaissance art as well as contemporary art. He explores the potential of expression through color, painting not only portraits but also still-life compositions and constantly striving to master the abstract vision of a painterly space wherein figures move and objects are alive. Major works include a series of twelve portraits of Greek gods. His surrealistic works juxtapose elements such as Greek gods and clowns in sophisticated narratives of transformation. *Three Graces* depicts a sculptured head, with the faces of two women shown in profile in the background. The predominant colors are grays, browns and pale blues.

FELCIANO, RICHARD (Sound Sculptor, Environmental Artist)
1326 Masonic Ave., San Francisco, CA 94117

Born: 1930 *Exhibitions:* Ft. Worth Art Museum; Whitney Museum, NYC *Education:* Mills College; U. of Iowa

His early fascination with sound as a spectral and spatial phenomenon led him to make indoor and outdoor environments. Bell sounds, electronics sounds, programmed location of sound and Doppler shifts were key elements in his installations for the Fort

Anna Debska, *Colt in Emotions,* 16" long, bronze. Courtesy: The Diamond Shamrock Building, Dallas, TX

Claire Falkenstein, *Montage Section,* 108 x 240 x 96, copper and Lexan plastic sheeting.
Courtesy: Eileen Norris Cinema Theatre, USC-Los Angeles

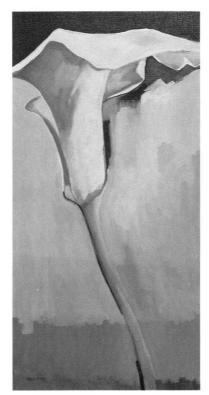

Marilyn R. Eger, *Calla Lily V*, 48 x 24, oil

Madelyn Engle, *Pegasus Wings #1 and #3 (Diptych),*
72 x 60 x 60, bronze

Virgil Elliott, *Melancholy,* 40 x 30, oil on panel.
Courtesy: Clifton J. Buck-Kaufman Collection, Cotati, CA

Cynthia Eastman-Roan, *Monique,* 16 x 20, acrylic

Roberta Eisenberg, *Archipelago,* 54 x 68, oil on canvas

Pauline Eaton, *Encounter of Worlds,* 30 x 40, watercolor

Ruth Eis, *The Stickpin,* 9 x 12, collage

Benjamin Eisenstat, *Van Ness St., San Francisco,* 26 x 36, acrylic

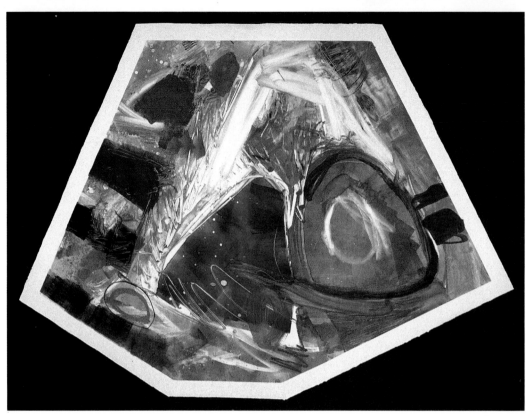

Barbara Erdman, *Orange Room with a Window on Space,* 28 x 38, mixed media, monoprint

Bruce Everett, *Oak Grove #2,* 60 x 90, oil on canvas. Courtesy: Jan Turner Gallery, Los Angeles

N. Jonas Englund, *Macaw Vision,* 20 x 30, serigraph

E'drie, *Cameo Coastline,* 30 x 40, watercolor. Courtesy: Bevel Cut Gallery, CA

Diane Fabian Fabiano, *The Planet
Series: Earth,* 72 x 28, fabric dyes and
acrylic paints with simulated gems

Beatrice Findlay, *Terpsichore,* 60 x 40, oil on canvas

Bob Freimark, *Fertile Cresent,* 65 x 46, acrylic

Helen Feyler-Switz, *Gateway 4,* 12 x 10 x 5, bronze

Carl Fieber, *Sapphora,* 26 x 13 x 13, clay-raku.
Courtesy: Magidson NYC Gallery, NYC

Deanna Forbes, *I'll show you mine if you give me yours,*
30 x 22, mixed media on paper

Corey Fowler, *The Open Sea,* 38 x 46, acrylic

Leland Fletcher, *Construction 1A:11,* 192 x 120 x 120, steel.
Courtesy: Musée de La Sculpture en Plein Air, Maubeuge, France

Catharine Phillips Fels, *Blackleg Dance: Return on Musicians to the Kiva,* 24 x 23, silk screen print

John Freeman, *Dia de los Muertos,* 66 x 53, oil

Patsy Foard, *The Flags Fly Over,* 36 x 36 acrylic

Farrington, *Pool at Redondo,* 36 x 36, oil on canvas

Michael Frank, *Seven Figures,* 94 x 96, mixed media

Dolly Ci Wai Fong, *Longevity Peach,* 13 x 18, watercolor on rice paper

Beverly Fredericks, *Homage to Inness,* 36 x 48, oil on canvas.
Courtesy: Mr. and Mrs. James Browne, San Marino, CA

Marjorie Faris, *Encounter,* 30 x 42, acrylic and charcoal

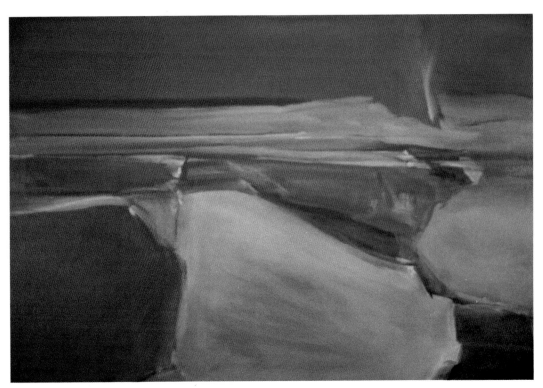

Vera Felts, *Winterset Red,* 24 x 36, oil

Mel Fillerup, *Elk Crossing,* 24 x 48, oil

Worth Art Museum, Boston City Hall, Grapestone Gallery and the San Francisco Opera House. Recent research into psychoacoustics has fanned his interest in timbre as a constructive element. He now employs acoustical illusions such as the Shepard scale and is attempting to establish a musical parallel to the works such visual artists as Josef Albers.

FELDMAN, BELLA (Sculptor)
12 Summit Lane, Berkeley, CA 94708

Born: 1940 *Awards:* NEA Award; Cabot-Lyman Trust Award *Collections:* Oakland Museum; University Art Museum, Berkeley *Exhibitions:* San Jose Museum of Art; Ianetti/Lanzone Gallery *Dealer:* Space Gallery, Los Angeles

For many years, she used organic forms to explore notions of paradox and time, these forms having been inspired by a lectureship in Uganda. In 1986, she visited the Mayan ruins in the Yucatan and was deeply affected by their terrible beauty. Thereafter, she continued with the same concerns but based her forms on man-made architecture, carts and machines. Recently, her work has been in steel, although she occasionally uses bronze and aluminum. The works appear dense and solid but are entirely fabricated from sheet. She also often includes fragments of industrial forms, although never in an unaltered state.

FELICIA (Sculptor)
208 Grant St., #103, Denver, CO 80203

Born: 1926 *Collections:* Channel 6 Television, Denver, CO; Western Images, Santa Ana *Exhibitions:* National Arts Club, NYC; Adagio Gallery, Palm Springs *Education:* School of Visual Arts, NYC *Dealer:* Adagio Gallery, Palm Springs

Her career began as a painter, working in watercolor and acrylic. In the mid-1970s, she began to work on bronze sculpture, learning the technique of lost-wax casting while working at a foundry. Her subjects are primarily Indian women and children, executed in both bronze and hand-made cast paper. Creating movement with innovative free forms, she begins with detailed, realistic faces and creates the work around them as an extension of their expressions. A high-polish effect is often used in contrast with areas of deep texture, adding color to the piece in patinas of green and brown. She is influenced by sculptor Alan Hauser.

FELIX, NELSON (Draughtsperson, Mixed Media Artist)
c/o Barbara Lorimer, 3006 Aurora Ct., Santa Rosa, CA 95405

Born: 1954 *Awards:* 2nd Prize, III Art Salon of Rio, Ministry of Culture, Funarte, Rio de Janeiro, Brazil *Collections:* Nynex Corporation, NYC; Museum of Modern Art, Rio de Janeiro *Exhibitions:* Scott Hansen Gallery, NYC; Galerie Charles Sablon, Paris *Dealer:* Barbara Lorimer, Santa Rosa

In the late 1970s, new elements such as cut-outs, collages and rubber stamps entered his work. Previously clean surfaces and homogenous lines suddenly incorporated elements of fragmentation and repetition. Now he works only on paper and is producing large drawings of heavily applied graphite and mixed media, including lead, gold leaf, acrylic and pastel. These works are abstractions of nature with a single image continued across three or more sheets of paper. These human and animal forms evoke a powerful presence.

Timeless images of a single face, a tree, a mountain or other natural subject present a spiritual essence, suspended on the white ground, but caught on one corner of the paper's edge. Currently, he teaches drawing at the University of Santa Ursula.

FELIX, SUSAN DUHAN (Ceramist)
1436 Berkeley Way, Berkeley CA 94702

Born: 1937 *Awards:* Citation from the California State Legislature *Collections:* Kirball Museum, Los Angeles; Museum of Contemporary Crafts, NYC *Exhibitions:* Magnus Museum; Berkeley Art Commission *Education:* U. of Connecticut

Created with the ancient processes of pit-firing and smoke-firing, her works abstract and expand the forms and themes of ancient Judaic ceremonial objects. She eschews glaze, her pitted pieces bearing the distinct evidence of fire, their irregular color and textures giving them a unique sensuality. Her uncommon firing method and her simple ancient lines create a sense of age in her pieces. In *The Prayer Space*, a walk-in, seven-branched menorah, the artist creates a unique, environmental piece reminiscent both of Stonehenge and of Jewish tradition. Another piece, *Vessel*, depicts three ceremonial bowls.

FELS, CATHARINE P. (Painter, Printmaker)
P.O. Box 3165, Taos, NM 87571

Born: 1912 *Awards:* Northwest Printmakers; San Francisco Museum of Modern Art *Collections:* State Library of New Mexico, Santa Fe; Museum of Art, Santa Fe *Exhibitions:* Museum of Northern Arizona, Flagstaff; Taos Connections, Denver *Education:* USC *Dealer:* Burke Armstrong Fine Arts, Taos, NM; Elinor Oldham, Albuquerque

After studying with Margaret Peterson in Berkeley, she turned toward figurative work and became interested in architectural subjects. She uses gouache in the field, and often paints in flat color. Her print media include woodblock, etching and silk screen. She has produced several books of her works. *End Time* features prints of Mayan ruins; *A Balkan Byzantine Notebook*, with text by Carl Sheppard, consists of drawings of Byzantine buildings in Bulgaria, Yugoslavia, Rumania, Turkey and Greece. She is a member of the Taos Seven, a group of women painters who exhibit together.

FELS, DONALD (Multimedia Artist)
30002 Issaqnah-Fall City Rd., Fall City, WA 98024

Born: 1946 *Awards:* Fulbright Fellowship *Exhibitions:* Ivory/Kimpton Gallery, San Francisco; Foster White Gallery, Seattle *Education:* Wesleyan U. *Dealer:* Shoshana Wayne Gallery, Los Angeles

From a young age, he studied with Adelaide Foggs, who had a large impact on his work, especially by encouraging him to experiment with a wide range of materials and media. He later assisted her in her studio, and the interest she instilled in him in working with many different types of media has remained. In the 1970s, his first showings were multimedia performance pieces dealing with walls. In the late 1970s, he began making small paintings using paper culled from Italian posters. His later two- and three-dimensional work involved large-scale mixed-media pieces constructed out of plywood, fiberglas, wood and cloth. These pieces, created by the layering of diverse materials, work through an interplay of surface and spatial structuring.

FELTER, SUSAN (Photographer)
Santa Clara University Art Department, Santa Clara, CA 95053

Born: 1945 *Awards:* Guggenheim Fellowship; 1st Place, Ann Arbor Film Festival *Collections:* San Francisco Museum of Modern Art; Bibliotheque Nationale, Paris *Exhibitions:* De Saisset Museum of Art, Santa Clara; Robert Samuel Gallery, NYC *Education:* UCLA; UC-Berkeley

She is best known for documentary photographs of rodeo riders and circus performers in which she explores the myth-value of these highly charged "kitsch" images. Straight-faced cowboys project a ruggedly virile surface illusion intensified by her use of saturated color. Influenced primarily by her parents, Berkeley figurative painter June Felter and filmmaker Dick Felter, she experimented throughout the 1970s with movie and photo pieces along the lines of fantasy filmmaker Fellini, documentary photographers such as Brassai and the surreal documentary of N. White. Her manipulation of fiction and desire continues in more personal directions through hand-drawn figures and self-portrait photo-collages produced on computer. Fantasy landscapes show a figure in an often menacing environment. Simple icons suspended in deep space, or a frenzy of characters tangled within a densely marked field create a sense of narrative drama. Vibrant color is preserved by photographing the images rather than printing them conventionally on paper. The computer allows her to make drastic changes in a drawing and enlarge portions or break up a single work so that it is seen as a sequence of multiple images. It has for her the perfect synthesis of filmic and photographic properties.

FELTS, VERA (Painter)
2930 Nutmeg St., San Diego, CA 92104

Born: 1927 *Collections:* Amera Cosmetics Corp. *Exhibitions:* Knowles Gallery, La Jolla; Gray Gulls Gallery, Grayland, WA *Education:* UC-San Diego; Southwestern College, Chula Vista *Dealer:* Knowles Gallery, La Jolla

Her training in drawing and design included work in painting, collage, printmaking and alternative materials. After moving to the San Francisco Bay area in 1964, she was influenced by Richard Diebenkorn, David Parks, Elmer Bischoff and Tom Holland. Using acrylic, oil and pen, she began to work boldly; her primary concerns are the formal elements of painting and uses of color. Her initial approach to the canvas is oblique, with an emphasis on spatial relationships. Her use of color contrasts solidity with transparency in highly accessible, non-representational landscape-like paintings.

FENSTERMAKER, DONNA (Printmaker)
2434 E. 23rd St., Oakland, CA 94601

Born: 1952 *Collections:* Mills College Library, Oakland *Exhibitions:* Dennis R. Smith & Associates, San Francisco; ProArts, Oakland *Education:* California College of Arts and Crafts

She works in drypoint, to which she sometimes adds monoprint. Her colorful landscape prints express her inner search for space. These works often feature volcanic activity and earthquakes, and cracks and crevices in the earth's surface. Influenced by the works of Frankenthaler, Irwin and Diebenkorn, she works in a variety of materials, including oils, acrylics, pastels, graphite and charcoal on paper. A layering technique provides her works with a heavy line, which gives the impression of submerged content. She takes great joy in her work, the act of marking the plate and the resulting line on the paper.

FENZI, WARREN S. (Furniture Maker)
c/o Fenzi Design, 600-C Ward Dr., Santa Barbara, CA 93111

Born: 1947 *Exhibitions:* Architectural League of New York; Workbench Gallery, NYC *Education:* School of Visual Arts, NYC; Buckinghamshire College, High Wycombe Bucks, England

After receiving formal training in sculpture, he studied wood lamination techniques at the graduate level in England. He also studied furniture design with Swedish designers Karl Erik and Jan Ekselius and Italian designer Carlo Bartoli. In 1979, he opened his own studio for commissioned freestanding furniture. His pieces were characterized by simple, elegant and formal lines. He made his functional works from domestic and exotic hardwoods with some lacquer detail. Recent areas of work include stainless steel and glass in conjunction with hardwood, maintaining all the classical design reference points and technically astute hand joinery.

FERGUSON, BARCLAY (Painter)
P.O. Box 1552, Carmel, CA 93921

Born: 1924 *Awards:* Best of Show, West Coast Biennial, Monterey Museum of Art, and California State Fair; Ascended to the Jacobite peerage for furthering the cause of Scottish art *Collections:* National Air & Space Museum, Smithsonian Institute, Washington, D.C.; Prudential Insurance Co. of America, Newark, NJ *Exhibitions:* James Yu Gallery, NYC; Monterey Peninsula Museum of Art *Education:* Glasgow School of Art, Scotland; U. of Guanajuato, Mexico *Dealer:* J.J. Brookings Gallery, San Jose

His background and education is in the fine art tradition, with emphasis on drawing, painting, murals and wood engraving, and his work is influenced by contemporary film, television and pop art. Early paintings were in the impressionist and post-impressionist styles. His semi-abstract Mexican paintings were combined dreamlike and realistic elements, with one shape recognizable, another not. In Canada in the early 1960s, he developed his own type of abstract expressionism or New Realism, revealing the influence of the California way of life. In a period during which he lived in New York City, his works portrayed cast iron buildings. He subsequently returned to California and began painting board games and tin toys. In 1986, he became involved in his present series, "Industry & Technology," influenced by Sheeler. In these works, he depicts old American industrial power plants, oil and chemical plants, cement plants, or storage and water tanks. Rather than departing from New Realism, he is adding abstract, impressionistic, post-impressionistic and computer-art styles, tied together by an overall geometric grid.

FERGUSON, SARAH (Painter)
17 Westall Ave., Oakland, CA 94611

Born: 1956 *Awards:* 3rd Prize, Santa Cruz Art League; Honorable Mention, San Bernardino County Museum, Redlands *Exhibitions:* Museum of Natural History, Pacific Grove; Matrix Gallery, Sacramento *Education:* California College of Arts & Crafts; On-

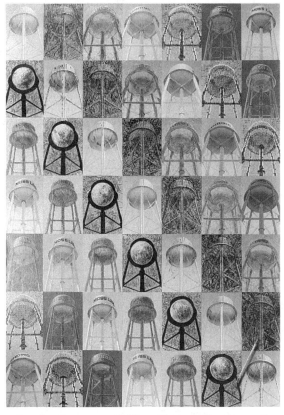

Barclay Ferguson, *49 Water Towers,* 60 x 42, acrylic

George Leopold Feiner, *3 Graces,* 39 x 39, oil on canvas

tario College of Art, Toronto *Dealer:* San Francisco Museum of Modern Art Rental Gallery; The Collectors Gallery, Oakland Museum

Shamans with horned masks, two-headed animals, transparent pregnant beasts, spirals, spears and hand prints constitute some of the prehistoric images that appear on canyon and cave walls in the deserts of the Western U.S. The artist is deeply influenced by these images, witnessed first-hand in the environment where they have stood for hundreds, sometimes thousands, of years. She assimilates these images, creating her own historical record, but giving her pieces titles that reflect the site with which she is working. The colors are those found in the varying rock surfaces, the symbols grouped as they originally appear. Mixing media, she blends sand and gesso on heavy, hand-made paper, then applies watercolor as an underpainting. The painting is then built up with soft pastel and set with a strong casein fixative.

FERGUSON, THERESE (Draughtsperson)
908 Tularosa Dr., Los Angeles, CA 90026

Born: 1928 *Awards:* Honorable Mention, Spring Art Exhibit, Pacific Art Guild *Exhibitions:* Spring Art Exhibit, Pacific Art Guild; Spring Art Exhibit, Westchester Municipal Center *Education:* Catholic U. of America

Her earlier work in watercolor combined an American realist style with impressionist influences. More recently, she has been working in Pentel crayons, producing floral still lifes, portraits and scenes of modern daily life. These drawings are characterized by simple lines and forms rendered in bright colors. Newly retired from a lengthy teaching career, she now plans to devote herself full-time to making art.

FERNANDES, MANOEL (Draughtsperson)
c/o Barbara Lorimer, 3006 Aurora Ct., Santa Rosa, CA 95405

Born: 1944 *Awards:* "Premio Viagen ao Exterior," VI Salao Nacional de Artes Plasticas, MEC, Funarte, Rio de Janeiro *Collections:* Museum of Modern Art, Sao Paulo *Exhibitions:* International Art Fair, Los Angeles; California State U., San Luis Obispo *Education:* MacKenzie U., Sao Paulo *Dealer:* Barbara Lorimer, Santa Rosa

During studies in Italy, the U.S. and Brazil, his attention was focused on the magic of theater. For years he designed stage settings before venturing into the fine arts. His drawings of charcoal and white pastels display a wide range of subtle tonal change and a rich surface. Primarily figurative, these drawings incorporate abstract images from Brazilian folklore and children's fables to suggest theater, magic show or carnival performances. While depicting a circus atmosphere, the dreamlike drawings seem to foreshadow calamity.

FERRANTE, LISA (Painter, Mixed Media Artist)
P.O. Box 858, El Prado, NM 87529

Born: 1953 *Awards:* Ford Foundation Travel Grant *Collections:* Prudential Insurance Company, Los Angeles; Security Pacific Bank, Los Angeles *Exhibitions:* Malinda Wyatt Gallery, Venice; City Hall, City of West Hollywood *Education:* UC-Davis; UCLA *Dealer:* Newspace, Los Angeles

Interested in art from an early age, she has been influenced by many different artists and styles. Her work incorporates diverse elements from Chinese and Japanese art, the paintings and life of Georgia O'-Keeffe, the intaglio prints of Kaethe Kollwitz and the portrayals of human isolation in Goya's paintings. At present, she paints and works with woodcuts, creating images of the people and beliefs of northern New Mexico. Many of her paintings, executed in bright, primary colors, and assemblages made of balsa wood and tin, draw on Christian imagery and Latin American beliefs and superstitions.

FERRARI, DIEDRE (Painter)
116 E. Acampo Rd., Acampo, CA 95220

Born: 1954 *Exhibitions:* ArtSpace, San Francisco; Indian Gallery, Folsom

In the past, she has worked in clay, creating three-dimensional, textured objects. Her current work in painting—oil with mixed media—has been influenced by Klee, Miro and other Impressionists and modern realist masters. She strives to use all possible visual elements, especially space, shadow and texture. Her paintings are quite contemporary and often take the form of figure and color studies.

FETTER, NEWELL (Painter)
108 Escobar Ct., Los Gatos, CA 95032

Born: 1930 *Exhibitions:* Zellerbach Gallery, San Francisco *Education:* Cleveland School of Art

Her early work contained non-objective images rooted in nature. Abstract landscapes of wheat fields and deserts had high horizons and open space. Color and light were very important; she used bright accents on a monochromatic palette of oils and acrylics. She has since diversified in style and subject matter. After living in Africa for three years, she completed a series of paintings examining the lives of a timeless people within a turbulent world. Earthtones and representational, but not realist, figures effect an ethereal quality. More recent still lifes are ink, pastel and collaged paper on rice paper. Flowers from a garden are viewed through windows or on tables. Bright, intense colors and careful detail mark a definite change in style.

FEYLER-SWITZ, HELEN (Sculptor)
660 Curtner Rd., Fremont, CA 94539

Born: 1935 *Awards:* Purchase Award, Hayward Forum of Arts; Best of Show, Southern California Juried Sculpture Exhibition *Collections:* City of Hayward; Chabot College, Hayward *Exhibitions:* Accurate Art Gallery, Sacramento; Editions Limited Gallery, San Francisco *Education:* Cal. State-Long Beach; USC *Dealer:* The Barlett Gallery, Pleasanton

She began working in geometrics in 1965. Her talents were quickly recognized, and she was invited to the Royal Academy of Fine Arts at The Hague to work with its director, J.J. Beljon. Her style has since evolved into organic geometrics: large elegant pieces, defined by smooth, strong lines that echo architectural and landscape forms. Her technique emphasizes pure form and medium integrity. Working in concrete, wood and bronze, she often carves directly into the sculpted forms. Her works are recognizable, yet mysterious, giving viewers the impression that, although they may understand the form in one way, other interpretations are possible. Turning aside from the more crassly commercial aspects of the contemporary art scene, she has dedicated her present efforts to ecological concerns. One recent piece in the series, *Endangered Species*, is a

Helen Feyler-Switz, *Pyramid "E",* 21 x 24 x 19, concrete

Carl Fieber, *Akhisar,* 26 x 18 x 18, clay-pit fired

6-foot-5-inch bronze gateway, symbolizing the oblivion awaiting many animal species and, perhaps, humanity itself. She has also worked in collaboration with landscape architects for the cities of Los Angeles and San Jose.

FIDLER, SPENCER (Printmaker)
226 W. Picacho, Las Cruces, NM 8805

Born: 1944 *Awards:* Ljubljanin Biennial, Yugoslavia *Exhibitions:* International Print Biennial, Cracow, Poland *Education:* U. of Iowa, Iowa City *Dealer:* Adair Margo, El Paso, TX

He studied under Mauricio Lasansky and began his career as an abstract expressionist. He has since moved to a figurative expressionism based on a combination of Greek and contemporary myths and allegories. Layered forms create slightly figurative flat shapes and silhouettes; the colors are expressive and symbolic. In his major work, several intaglio plates contribute to the form and color of the image. He has produced a tryptich which explores the underlying relationship of domestication, cultivation and insanity.

FIEBER, CARL (Ceramicist)
47-625 Melekula Rd., Kaneohe, HI 96744

Born: 1944 *Collections:* State of Hawaii Foundation on Culture and the Arts; Magidson Gallery, NYC *Exhibitions:* Jeremy Solomon Gallery, Los Angeles; Honolulu Academy of Art *Dealer:* Magidson & Associates, NYC

The rough beauty the artist achieves in his raku and pit-fired ceramic work reminds one of pottery unearthed at archaeological excavations around the world. The vessel struck him as an ideal format because of its metaphorical and practical links between ancient, current and future civilizations. Each vessel begins as rolled coils of clay, which are pinched and smoothed into a graceful pottery form. The piece is then fired in an electric kiln. The artist wires and sprays the piece with copper glaze before firing a second time in a special fiber kiln. Upon reaching the maturing temperature, the vessel is placed in a straw-filled container to weather smoke and live flames. The combination of these steps imparts the rich, "aged" patina for which his work is recognized.

FIEDLER, LUC (Sculptor)
1184 Longfellow, Campbell, CA 95008

Born: 1961 *Exhibitions:* National Metal Arts Exhibition, Kentfield; Marin Society of Artists Open Fine Arts Exhibition, Ross *Education:* Southern Illinois U., Carbondale

As an undergraduate at Southern Illinois University at Carbondale, he studied art history, metal-smithing and foundry work. Later, he combined these sciences into an iconographic mimesis of man's technology. As he described it, "I've used the writings of Dante in cooperation with the silicon chip industry." Among his sculptural and technical influences have been Michael Todd, Stephen De Stable and Thomas Walsh, his foundry teacher at S.I.U. He continues to work abstractly and he has recently been making a psychoanalytic review of man with the aid of spiritual alchemy and Carl Jung's book on symbolism.

FILLERUP, MEL (Painter)
P. O. Box 938, Cody, WY 82414

Born: 1924 *Awards:* Gold Medal, American Indian and Country Artists, San Dimas; Member, Society of

Animal Artists *Collections:* National Cowboy Hall of Fame *Exhibitions:* Frye Museum, Seattle; Dahl Museum, Rapid City, SD *Education:* U. of Wyoming

Dominated by light and by rigorous impressionistic brushwork, his Western landscapes are often drawn from history. His use of dramatic skies and lighting are reminiscent of mid-19th-century landscapes, yet are uncompromisingly direct and contemporary in composition. *Moosemeadow, Pelican Creek and Yellowstone Lake* is an example of this, showing a vast sky with still water and marshland in the foreground and moose standing in the midground; deep shadows and flat color enhance the mood. Moved by the beauty of the landscape, he evokes the wonder and magnificence of the Western and Northwestern American landscape with a touching honesty that allows the viewer a personal experience of relationship to the land and permits the subject to speak for itself.

FINDLAY, BEATRICE (Painter)
3606 Amesbury Rd., Los Angeles, CA 90027

Born: 1941 *Collections:* Everson Museum, Syracuse, NY; National Museum of Art, Warsaw, Poland *Exhibitions:* Schiller-Wapner, New York; Museum NECCA, Brooklyn, CT *Education:* U. of Manitoba *Dealer:* Eva Pape

Her human figures evoke a sense of motion and complex form grounded in cubist sensitivities, inviting the viewer to participate within an imaginative framework. She particular emphasizes vibrant color combinations, such as blue, orange and red, to communicate strong emotions without violence. Her work since the 1970s shows the influence by Ernst, Bellmer and Monet; her technique varies depending on the basic concept, and she works both in oils and in acrylics on canvas and paper. New works, including triptychs, explore images that express the mystery of the soul and the non-physical aspects of life.

FINE, JUD (Sculptor, Conceptual Artist)
713 S. Gladys, Los Angeles, CA 90021

Born: 1944 *Awards:* NEA Grant; Contemporary Art Council New Talent Grant, Los Angeles County Museum of Art *Collections:* Guggenheim Museum, NYC; Los Angeles County Museum of Art *Exhibitions:* Art Institute of Chicago; La Jolla Museum of Art *Education:* Cornell U. *Dealer:* Ronald Feldman Fine Arts, NYC

During the 1960s, he earned undergraduate and doctoral degrees in history; he did not receive a degree in sculpture until 1970. In his experimental mixed-media pieces, he parodies art and language, often with fragments of text or photographs in combination with stenciled images and colored shapes. *Discourse* is a booklet hung from a chain on the wall, containing a convoluted argument which ends where it begins. More recent sculptures continue an interest in history and language. The architectonic piece *Horizontal Pillar* is constructed from a 160-foot-long horizontal steel pillar with elements of straw and wood attached by string and wire. Accompanying drawings depict monolithic structures along with written explanations of mankind's existence and its relationship throughout history to the structures he has built.

FINGADO, PAMELA (Printmaker, Mixed Media Artist)
851 Seaview Dr., El Cerrito, CA 94530

Born: 1947 *Awards:* Award of Excellence, CCAFT Annual Works on Paper *Collections:* IBM Corporation *Exhibitions:* Richmond Art Center; Sun Gallery, Hayward *Education:* Cal. State-Hayward

She concentrated on printmaking in school, but upon graduating she revived an earlier interest in collage. Working in her studio, she began experimenting with chine colle and viscosity printing and with incorporating found objects in her work. She also experimented with making paper. Recent hand-made pieces reflect her new interest in fiber and her continuing interest in surface pattern. Strings are dipped in paper pulp, then woven in an interlacing pattern and put through a press. The colors are mostly subdued blues, purples and pinks. Paper continues to offer her the flexibility necessary to explore spontaneous gestures, as well as the regularity and control of grid- or rectangular- patterned works.

FINLEY, JEANNE (Multimedia Artist)

Born: 1955 *Awards:* NEA Fellowship; Phelan Video Award *Collections:* Museum of Modern Art, NYC; La Jolla Museum of Contemporary Art *Exhibitions:* Institute of Contemporary Art, Boston; San Francisco Museum of Modern Art

After formal training in photography, she began to work with narrative slide presentations. These presentations developed into video works or were incorporated within multimedia installations, while still maintaining a narrative basis and often based on true stories. Through the use of factual, social and cultural information combined with personal narratives, the work explores the tension between personal experience and identity and the social and cultural conditions that simultaneously shape and challenge that identity. In *Common Mistakes*, one section begins with the word "Error" and then proceeds to show a young girl pick up a knife, stumble on a carpet, fall and impale herself.

FINNEGAN, GARNETTA (Painter, Printmaker)
5322 Doty Lane, Placerville, CA 95667

Born: 1935 *Awards:* Janet Langmard Award, Oakland Art Association; Purchase Award, Mother Lode Art Show *Exhibitions:* Oakland Art Association Gallery; Djurovich Gallery, Sacramento *Education:* Chobot College

Although originally solely a painter, she has become increasingly involved in printmaking, primarily etchings and drypoint. Intrigued by the element of surprise and by experimentation with the process, she is exploring the combination of a printed image with torn-paper collage and embossing. She seeks an overall mood, and her subjects include figurative and natural images—persimmons and blooming dogwood being particular favorites. Her paintings, done in oil using an expressionistic technique, develop a nonliteral connection between people and nature, through motifs of nudes in the landscape and more personal subject matter.

FINNEY, VERNON (Painter)
5749 Riverton Ave., North Hollywood, CA 91601

Born: 1924 *Collections:* Mr. and Mrs. Bobby Darin; Mr. Vincent Price *Exhibitions:* El Camino College, Torrance; Carter/Sarkin Gallery, Los Angeles *Education:* Oklahoma U.

His training is grounded in the drawing techniques of the Old Masters, but he approaches his subjects through a positive surrealism. Landscapes are recreations of memory combined with an exploration of nature's possibilities. His figurative work begins with live models, the images of whom are later altered and symbolized to fit the idea and space. For example, his otherwise realistic nudes, which he renders in pencil or oils, are hairless, underscoring their symbolic nature. Non-figurative work includes the "Ancient Future Ruin Series." Imaginary mountain ridges exhibit faint signs of previous civilizations, remarking on our own ephemeral culture. Clean skies with yellow cliffs and colors that fade from one to another, deepened by umber shadows, heighten the sense of familiarity and point up the uncertainty of our vision.

FISCHL, ERIC (Painter, Printmaker)
c/o Mary Boone Gallery, 417 W. Broadway, New York, NY 10012

Born: 1948 *Collections:* Metropolitan Museum of Art, NYC *Exhibitions:* Museum of Contemporary Art, Los Angeles; Los Angeles County Museum of Art *Education:* California Institute of the Arts *Dealer:* Mary Boone Gallery, NYC

In paintings and drawings, the psycho-social self is explored through the use of taboo subject matter, such as themes of sexuality, often capturing figures in self-conscious and awkward moments. The prints, too, contain a narrative sensitivity without telling an actual story; in the sequence "Year of the Drowned Dog," the figures are always about to take action and the scenes are full of possibilities.

FISHBEIN, ANNE (Photographer)
12616 Mitchell Ave., #5, Los Angeles, CA 90066

Born: 1958 *Exhibitions:* Art Institute of Chicago; Printworks, Chicago *Education:* Yale U. *Dealer:* Printworks, Chicago

Influenced by Robert Frank and Garry Winogrand at Yale, she is a classic street photographer who shoots primarily in black and white in the 35mm and medium formats. She travels around the country by foot, car or train and searches for material by involving herself in the environment. In her nostalgic visual narrative of the old Route 66, she plays on the contrasts between the romanticized West and the real West. Using a six-by-seven-cm Makina Ploubel and a 35mm Leica, she documented the patchwork quilt of rustic towns, religious revival meetings and tourist stops that remain along the old highway.

FISHGOLD, SUSAN (Painter, Printmaker)
132 Remsen St., Brooklyn, NY 11201

Born: 1949 *Collections:* IBM; National Museum of American Art *Exhibitions:* The McIntosh Gallery, Atlanta; Nexus Contemporary Art Center, Atlanta *Education:* Queens College; Brooklyn College *Dealer:* McIntosh Gallery, Atlanta; Joy Moos Gallery, Miami

After formal training in realism and expressionism, she developed an expressionistic style influenced primarily by the work of Vincent Van Gogh and Georgia O'Keeffe. Her medium is monotype and though pictorialism is an important element of her work, she has always been primarily concerned with color. She sees color as the expression of the movement within a form, the life under the skin of the image. "I have found that use of the monotype process as opposed to direct application by brush, frees the color to some extent from the edges of form," she says. She is a member of the New York Artists Equity Association and the Foundation for the Community of Artists in New York City.

FISHMAN, BARBARA (Sculptor, Papermaker)
4533 Rhode Island St., San Diego, CA 92116

Born: 1934 *Exhibitions:* San Diego Art Institute; Spectrum Gallery, San Diego *Dealer:* Art Consultants West, San Diego

She makes a California version of Japanese paper using imported fibers and incorporates this in her sculptured wall reliefs. In these pieces, she endeavors to translate archetypal feminine experiences into works that speak to everyone. Some of her female masks, made from live models, have facial "hash marks" to typify the universality of their experience. She is influenced by her travels and may incorporate found materials such as sisal, feathers, leaves and bones into the relief or the paper itself. Occasionally a piece will be the result of a "glorious failure", such as *Undelivered Messages*, in which linen paper accidentally spoiled and turned brown when applied to oak boards.

FISKIN, JUDY (Photographer)
10615 Blythe Ave., Los Angeles, CA

Born: 1945 *Awards:* NEA Fellowship; Nominee, Award in the Visual Arts *Collections:* Museum of Modern Art, San Francisco; National Museum of American Art, Washington, D.C. *Exhibitions:* Newspace, Los Angeles; Castelli Graphics, NYC *Education:* Pomona College; UC-Berkeley *Dealer:* Newspace, Los Angeles

She photographs architecture as if it were sculpture. Her prints are so tiny (2 3/4 inches square) that they serve as objects. Her desert landscapes, Hollywood bungalows and amusement parks have a faded glory about them. In her recent series, "Dingbats," depicting the classic wood and stucco Los Angeles apartments of the 1950s and 1960s, all of the buildings are pictured from the front, emphasizing a graphic two-dimensionality. She has recently begun to photograph furniture from the decorative arts collections of major museums. She uses a 35mm camera and black-and-white film to produce high-contrast prints.

FITCH, STEVE (Photographer)
870 Helen Ave., Ukiah, CA 95482

Born: 1949 *Awards:* NEA Fellowship *Collections:* Oakland Museum; Museum of Modern Art, NYC *Exhibitions:* University Art Museum, Berkeley; San Francisco Museum of Modern Art *Education:* UC-Berkeley; San Francisco Art Institute; U. of New Mexico

He is chiefly concerned with photographing emblems of America's Southwest, as is evident in his publication *Diesels and Dinosaurs*. Highways and strip developments are predominant interests. His photographs tend to concentrate on drive-in movies, theaters, neon signs, billboards, motels and facades of buildings. He prefers to photograph at night, and thus he uses a variety of light sources, including the headlights of a vehicle, artificial light (neon or street lights) and moonlight. He also produces large-format color prints that are highly saturated with color. He seeks to achieve pulsating, luminous colors that sharply radiate through the darkness of a foreboding desert night. Natural and artificial lights illuminate these vacuous landscapes with penetrating glimmers of light.

FITZWATER, TOM (Painter, Sculptor)
P. O. Box 847, Greenfield, CA 93927

Born: 1943 *Collections:* Salinas Civic Center *Exhibitions:* Monterey Peninsula Museum of Art; Friends of

Photography Gallery, Carmel *Education:* Cal. State-Long Beach

Influenced by the artists of the American West and particularly the paintings of Thomas Eakins and the sculpture of Augustus Saint-Gaudens, his early work reflects an interest in the classical traditions of painting and sculpture. Current work shows a concern toward achieving sharper, photo-realistic statements of a deep, psychological nature. He explores the conditions of life in relation to moods, emotions and action, creating an internal connection with the viewer. Realistic figuration in landscape is the predominant theme of the paintings and sculptures. He created a life-sized bronze statue of John Steinbeck for the Salinas Civic Center. His monumental work includes a triptych commemorating the founder of the National Parks, John Muir. This greatly detailed, high relief shows Muir looking over a vast range of mountains and forests. The sculpture is cast in polyester resin and colored realistically. A recent painting is set at the turn of the century, depicting the haying season in a local valley.

FLAVIN, DAN (Installation Artist, Sculptor)
P.O. Box 248, Garrison, NY 10524

Born: 1933 *Awards:* Copley Foundation Grant; National Foundation of Arts and Humanities Award *Collections:* Museum of Modern Art, NYC; Whitney Museum, NYC *Exhibitions:* University Art Museum, Berkeley; Whitney Museum, NYC *Dealer:* Leo Castelli Gallery, NYC; Margo Leavin Gallery, Los Angeles

A series of minimalist structures he calls "blank, almost featureless square-fronted constructions with obvious electric lights," was begun in 1961. Later works employ fluorescent lights exclusively, without "constructions," sometimes rendering the light fixtures invisible. He now seeks to dissolve flat surfaces and restructure space. Artificial "installations" emphasize the characteristics of the rooms he works in.

FLECHTNER, MICHAEL (Neon Sculptor)
5837 Hazeltine Ave., Van Nuys, CA 91401

Born: 1951 *Awards:* Ford Foundation Grant *Exhibitions:* White's Old Town Gallery, Pasadena; Museum of Neon Art *Education:* Wichita State U.; Columbus College of Art

He was formally trained in sculpture, and his early work was in wood, steel, ceramics, painting and printmaking. In 1985, he learned how to fabricate neon and began to create three- dimensional forms with neon tubing. He developed new techniques, which allow the medium to support its own weight. In the whimsical *Pop Shark*, he used serial animation to give the illusion of a 4-foot shark being catapulted from an oversized toaster. In *Dinosaur Head*, he used a gear/motor mechanism to physically animate his subject's jaws and tongue. As the viewer approached the piece, a beam of light was broken activating a jaw motor and a micro-switch that lit the pupils, teeth and tongue.

FLETCHER, KEVIN (Painter, Printmaker)
3317 Alta Vista Ave., Santa Rosa, CA 95405

Born: 1956 *Awards:* Artist in Residence, Frans Masereel Foundation, Kasterlee, Belgium; Ford Foundation Grant *Collections:* Portland Art Museum; Cincinnati Art Museum *Education:* Syracuse U.; Miami U., OH *Dealer:* J. Noblett Gallery, Boyes Hot Springs; Elizabeth Leach Gallery, Portland, OR

Leland Fletcher, *Construction 1A:16 (maquette),* 198 x 156 x 270, steel

Jane Fusek, *Jungle Stories,* 40 x 26, ink drawing

Fingado, *#9,* 20 x 16, collage

Following a short tenure in northern California, where landscape became an ever more powerful influence, he shifted from figurative woodcuts and etchings, executed in a somewhat expressionistic mode and influenced by Beckmann and Heckel, to a more painterly and planar tendency comparable to and aspiring toward the atmospheric landscapes of Hodler and Duvenech. He began, in 1983, to employ monotype as a plein air medium. After several trips to Belgium, Italy and Switzerland, having lived for two years in Portland, where he painted outdoors regularly, the artist has decided to work with locations that evoke a certain mystery and tension. He administers a color range that encourages and evokes the mood of the bittersweet sadness of a nightfall in autumn, with hues of blue dominant. Work is currently more informed by the Barbizon School than by any modern movement except perhaps German painters like Kiefer and Lappertz. Figures have disappeared and architectural structure looms as a reminder of mortal existence.

FLETCHER, LELAND (Sculptor)
P.O. Box 335, San Geronimo, CA 94963

Born: 1946 *Collections:* De Saisset Museum, U. of Santa Clara; Cal. State-Long Beach Art Museum *Exhibitions:* Intersection Gallery, San Francisco; Otis Art Institute, Los Angeles *Education:* U. of Minnesota

During his studies of metal sculpture under the direction of Wayne Potratz at the University of Minnesota, he began to explore the use of temporary sculpture installations, including outdoor sites. The earth works of Robert Smithson were also an influence. After moving to California in the early 1970s, he created a conceptual organization, the Department of Art Works. He used construction materials and a blend of performance and installation to create what he called "art zones." At present, he constructs large, permanent metal sculptures in conjunction with "art zones." The materials used for these endeavors include heavy construction equipment, sand, gravel, earth, wood and other materials. Adapted to every site, his metal sculptures and "art zones" are exhibited throughout the U.S., Canada, Europe and South America.

FLETCHER, MARGUERITE O. (Painter)
197 Bryant St., #3, Palo Alto, CA 94301

Born: 1946 *Awards:* Knudson Fellowship; National Lutheran Women Study Grant *Exhibitions:* Rental Gallery, San Francisco Museum of Art; The Corridor, Menlo Park *Education:* Stanford U.

She was influenced by each of the very different styles of Stanford painters Frank Lobdell, Nathan Oliveira and Keith Boyle. What interests her most is the transition from representation to abstraction. Soon after she had finished her formal art training, she began a process that consisted of alternating between field work and exploration and distillation in the studio of these images and all of their formal content. In the field, at specific landscape sites, she executes very literal small-format drawings in gouache and pastel or oil-on-paper paintings; then, in the studio, she spends time developing, editing and culling images before committing them to a larger surface. She soaks, stains, wipes, brushes and draws with oil crayons, or fingerpaints the surfaces of large and small pieces, always striving to keep the painting alive by working in the zone between abstraction and representation.

FLIERS, AMANI (Painter, Photographer)
450 Toulumne Ave., #2, Thousand Oaks, CA 91360

Born: 1939 *Awards:* Purchase Award, City of Thousand Oaks; L.A. City Award for Multicultural Poster *Collections:* City of Thousand Oaks *Exhibitions:* B/C Space Gallery, Laguna Beach; Cal. State-Northridge *Education:* Cal. State-Northridge

She combines painting and serial photographs to explore both the dual nature of perception and the objective/subjective fragmentary aspects of photography. Early work used large sheets of transparent film placed over painted metal plates. Multiple images of the same subject are arrayed in a cubist manner. The photographic element of her work declined in importance and has become more of a footnote or counterpart to the abstract drawings. She has recently been moving towards a more painterly quality in her work. Her palette is full of calm blues, brick reds and dark greens; her subject matter emphasizes oriental motifs, abstractions and personal experiences.

FLYNN, MARIDEE HAYS (Painter)
2026 Stockton St., Napa, CA 94559

Born: 1944 *Awards:* Special Award, Stockton Art League *Exhibitions:* E.B. Crocker Art Museum; Robert Else Art Gallery *Education:* California State U.

Her works are primarily water media on paper, and oil on stretched and unstretched canvas, and her subjects are internal landscapes, achieved through either line drawings or color media. The works include elements that are representational—references to body forms and word formations—as well as elements that are non-specific and non-figurative. Some pieces stress solely internal rhythms contrasted against the external world of the canvas. The canvases are large and intense, filled with "electric" lines. The drawings, although smaller in size, are much like the paintings, and drawn in a manner similar to a jazz singer's "skat" style. The works have a nebulous feel, expressed by the use of floating planes. The pieces are dense, with little space left unworked, but what emerges out of the nebulous floating planes is an overall sense of balance.

FOARD, PATSY (Painter)
3030 Pualei Circle, #110, Honolulu, HI 96815

Born: 1935 *Awards:* Royal Culture Arts Gallery *Exhibitions:* Hawthorn Gallery, Melbourne *Education:* U. of Hawaii *Dealer:* Art Loft, Honolulu

Her first formal training came at the Royal Melbourne Institute of Technology in Melbourne, Australia, where she was born and raised. Later, she spent three years in Europe, where she found the landscapes of Italy and Iceland a stimulus for the development of a fluid abstract expressionist style. When she returned to Australia, her paintings again reflected that continent's strong color and light. In 1978, she moved to Hawaii permanently. She took her M.A. at the University of Hawaii and today she finds Hawaii's sea, ships, buildings and landscape a stimulus for abstract serigraphs, colographs and acrylic paintings.

FOEY, BILL W. (Painter)
248 Washington St., Red Bluff, CA 96080

Born: 1950 *Awards:* 1st Award, Sunshine Fair, Red Bluff; 1st Award, Orland May Art Festival *Exhibitions:* State Office Building, Sacramento; Le Gallery, Red Bluff *Education:* Chico State U.

His main artistic emphasis has always been watercolor. After his initial realistic style, he adopted a spon-

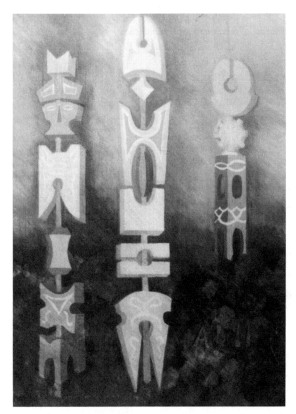

Patsy Foard, *Hawaii Totem,* 36 x 30, acrylic

Dolly Ci Wai Fong, *Bamboo,* 18 x 13, watercolor on rice paper

taneous, loose impressionist style greatly influenced by the works of Claude Monet and Vincent Van Gogh. He began to explore a more instantaneous, quick form of painting, attempting to adapt the impressionist oil and canvas techniques to watercolor and heavy paper. Using bright reds, yellows, oranges, greens and blues applied in thick, heavy brushstrokes, he combines spots of pure color and long wriggles to blend the clean charm of Monet and the exaggerated organic forces in Van Gogh.

FOGG, WILLIAM (Painter)
1162 E. 3rd St., #18, Long Beach, CA 90802

Born: 1953 *Exhibitions:* Long Beach City College; Rio Hondo College, Whittier *Education:* Art Center College of Design

Initially an illustrator, he later rejected commercial work in favor of painting. He started by painting photo-realistic pieces, but gradually his series of drawings and paintings began to distort the human face and figure. The overt sexuality and violently distorted bodies in his works have brought censorship and prevented the exhibition of some of the pieces. His recent work has been in acrylic on small canvases, usually 5-by-7 inches. The images are highly rendered and meticulously detailed—although with soft edges—looking much like a tinted or retouched photograph. These recent paintings continue to focus on the human face and form, but are somewhat less grotesque than the early pieces.

FOLEY, PETER FRANK (Painter)
845 Maple St., South San Francisco, CA 94080

Born: 1947 *Awards:* James D. Phelan Award *Collections:* Oakland Museum; Mills College Gallery Collection, Oakland *Exhibitions:* San Francisco Museum of Modern Art; Pacific Art League, Palo Alto *Education:* California College of Arts & Crafts; San Francisco State U. *Dealer:* Rolando Castellon, San Francisco

He describes his work as neo-archaeologist—an expressionist's view of historical decay accelerated a thousand times. In this way, he simultaneously presents the past, present and future. Dissatisfied with canvas's inability to tolerate extensive surface reworking, he began constructing multimedia paintings on plywood sheets. These works are constructed from clay and mud, wallpaper, wallboard and oils and enamels in bright primary colors. His paintings are characterized by subtly-textured clay surfaces covered with random marks, colors and tones. Deeper layers, defaced images and faint linear shapes sometimes push to the fore, creating a multidimensional appearance. He cites the works of Rauschenberg, Oliveira, Rothko and Beuys as major stylistic and thematic influences.

FONG, DOLLY CI WAI (Painter)
627 Windemere Isle, Alameda, CA 94501

Born: 1939 *Exhibitions:* First National Bank, Alameda; Great Western Savings, Alameda

She paints watercolors, often on rice paper, of plants and animals, especially birds and bamboo, in the manner of traditional Chinese brush painting. Cho Chien Chow, a famous artist in her native Canton, taught her first, and in Carmel, California she studied with the master artist Chen Yiu Por. Her earlier work was more structured and formal; her later work, showing Western influences, is characterized by broader and more fluid brushstrokes and greater open space. The principle of Yin and Yang, the male and female aspects of being that inform most Chinese art, influences the development of form in her work.

FOOSANER, JUDITH (Painter)
2736 Hillegass Ave., Berkeley, CA 94705

Born: 1940 *Awards:* Summer Residence Grant, Yaddo Artists and Writers Colony, Saratoga Springs, NY; U.I.A.C. Grant, California College of Arts and Crafts, Oakland *Collections:* Newport Beach Museum; Albuquerque Museum *Exhibitions:* Jeremy Stone Gallery, San Francisco; Everson Museum of Art, Syracuse, NY *Education:* UC-Berkeley *Dealer:* Michael Dunev, San Francisco; Space Gallery, Los Angeles

Beginning with arbitrarily placed black or colored lines, she scrubs medium into the canvas with a cheap, nubby-bristled brush. As she scrubs the lines, the brush acts as a confrontational medium between line and space. New shapes and spaces are called into being and movement begins to occur. With short linear strokes, she then applies thick hues of paint where rhythms of space and line marry to produce elementally forceful movement. She has recently been producing large-scale, non-objective, charcoal drawings.

FORBES, DEANNA (Painter)
442 Casanova Ave., Monterey, CA 93940

Born: 1940 *Awards:* 1st Prize, Monterey Peninsula Museum Biennial; 1st Prize, Triton Museum of Art Competition *Collections:* Oakland Museum of Art; de Saisset Museum *Exhibitions:* Monterey Peninsula Museum of Art; Oakland Museum *Education:* San Francisco Art Institute *Dealer:* Michael Himovitz Gallery, Sacramento

Her large non-objective oil paintings of the early 1960s gave way in 1968 to thinly painted, quirky acrylic and watercolor still lifes of fish heads, knives, razors, pigs' heads, masks, Mexican skull candy and familiar objects. In 1978, influenced by Frank Lobdell, Jack Jefferson, Frida Kahlo and Francis Bacon, her work took on a more personal and psychological turn. Animals, snakes, self-portraits and solitary, masked, bound and mutilated figures appeared on her dark canvases. In paintings of oil on canvas and in drawings of casein, crayon and colored pencil on tough or smooth paper, she layers, incises, scrapes and sponges the surface, creating richly worked pieces.

FORBES, JANET L. (Photographer)
1601 Oakwood Ave., Apt. A, Venice, CA 90291

Born: 1928 *Awards:* 1st Place Black & White, 2nd Place Color, Scarab Club, Detroit *Exhibitions:* Halstead Gallery, Birmingham, MI; Otis Art Institute, Los Angeles *Education:* Center for Creative Studies, Detroit

Over a period of time, an emerging interest in movement developed in her photographs. Using the female nude form, she began to examine different aspects of movement and the challenge of capturing it in a medium that is fundamentally static. A large body of early work ventured into this territory in a series of black-and-white photographs—a medium, she says, best suited for isolating elements of motion. A recent work uses ritualistic objects in conjunction with drawings, which themselves have been photographed and

Deanna Forbes, *The Core of Melancholy, The Skin of Mania,*
30 x 22, mixed media on paper

Michael Frank, *Down the Stairs,* 22 x 29, monoprint

are presented alongside the drawing and the actual objects. In this work, the viewer is engaged in the question as to what is really real, what can be taken as source, what illusion.

FORESTER, RUSSELL (Sculptor, Painter)
2025 Soledad Ave., La Jolla, CA 92037

Born: 1920 *Collections:* Guggenheim Museum, NYC; La Jolla Museum of Contemporary Art *Exhibitions:* Modern Art Center, Zurich, Switzerland; Herbert Palmer Gallery, Los Angeles *Education:* Institute of Design, Chicago

Sculptures are built of plywood covered with Colorcore. His work makes extensive use of miniature neon bulbs as well as LEDs (light emitting diodes)—lights normally found in electronic components. In daylight, the lights are subservient to the colors and shapes of the sculptures' exterior volumes and interior shapes; in lesser, ambient light, his lights create their own spaces and fill them with vibrant colors. The scale of the work belies the actual size of the sculptures, some of which stand as lilliputian skyscrapers, others as dynamic, complex interior spaces. Melinda Wortz of *Artnews* wrote, "The mood of Forester's sculpture is both nostalgic and futuristic.... He combines the modernist's infatuation with straight line and smooth surface, and the postmodernist's willingess to play with form and mix metaphor."

FORNEY, DARRELL E. (Painter)
1125 I Street, Sacramento, CA 95814

Born: 1933 *Awards:* NEH Grant *Collections:* Purdue University; Crocker Art Museum *Exhibitions:* Newport Harbor Art Museum, Newport Beach; California College of Arts and Crafts

His work is grounded stylistically in cubism and in geometric, hard-edged imagery. He creates a sensibility at the same time real and surreal, combining the perceptual and the conceptual. New works pay homage to Stuart Davis and Ralston Crawford. Working from sketches, photographs and found objects, his flat, blended colors and cubist fragmentation create a dynamic, visual "jazz" of form, color and line. Another current series depicts a fictional character, Bacon Eddy, and is titled "The Bacon Eddy Show." The series explores Bacon Eddy's life from the good to the nefarious, from the cradle to the grave. This figurative series is rendered realistically in subdued pastels, with bright colors of red, green and blue. From 1972 until 1986, his body of work centered on large-letter painted-word pictures, such as *Greetings from...*, with striking colors and images of real or imagined vacation spots.

FORTE, FRANCESCA (Photographer, Videographer)
P.O. Box 11511, Oakland, CA 94611

Born: 1956 *Collections:* National Holistic Institute, Emeryville; City Arts Workshop, NYC *Exhibitions:* Whitney Museum, NYC; Susan Caldwell Gallery, NYC *Education:* School of Visual Arts, NYC

Her early subjects were humanistic studies of gamblers and the mentally ill and tranquil scenes in the Catskill Mountains. She worked her way through art school as a photojournalist and documentary photographer. Soon thereafter she began her self-portraiture series, which is a life-long body of work. In a recent series of mandala-textured photographs, she emphasizes water, movement and design. She is also producing videotapes on humanistic subjects.

FOSTER, BARBARA (Printmaker)
3532 Mirasol Ave., Oakland, CA 94605

Born: 1947 *Awards:* Phelan Art Award, San Francisco Foundation *Collections:* Mills College Art Gallery, Oakland *Exhibitions:* World Print, San Francisco; CCAC Gallery, San Francisco *Education:* UC-Santa Barbara; San Francisco State U.

While still in school, she was influenced by Charles Sheeler and Bonnard. Her small lithographs contain a photographic image that is overdrawn and manipulated, which forms an image that intimates another.

FOULKES, LLYN (Painter, Assemblage Artist)
6010 Eucalyptus Lane, Long Beach CA 90806

Born: 1934 *Awards:* Guggenheim Fellowship; New Talent Purchase Grant, Los Angeles County Museum of Art *Collections:* Whitney Museum, NYC; Museum of Modern Art, NYC *Exhibitions:* Whitney Museum, NYC; Art Institute of Chicago *Education:* Chouinard Art Institute *Dealer:* Asher/Faure Gallery, Los Angeles

Believing in the most direct approach to art, he seeks to give art validity "in an over-stimulated world." Because he refuses to become "a product for art's sake," he is difficult to categorize. His media have included assemblages of such materials as polyethylene, wood, paper and enamel, and paintings in oil and acrylic. A humorist, he founded a group called "Llyn Foulkes and the Rubber Band" in the 1970s. He stands on the fringes of pop art with repeated monochrome images of eroded rocks, to which he applies labels, such as postcards.

FOWLER, CORKY (Painter)
200 42nd St., Manhattan Beach, CA 90266

Born: 1944 *Exhibitions:* The Frame Stop, Manhattan Village Mall, Manhattan Beach

After two decades of international travel and a professional skiing career, he was compelled to rekindle his childhood passion for art. Greatly moved by the beauty of the many locations he has visited, he endeavors to share his memories and responses with his viewer through acrylic, watercolor and pen and ink work. Though he is primarily self-taught, an admiration for Modern Realists John Stobart and David Shephard helped steer him toward natural realism in his own painting. Skillfully capturing a variety of geographically peculiar color and light, the artist imparts a strong emotional impact to each image. In a 3-by-4-foot painting of an ocean-going sailboat, he presents a serene, perfect day, complete with turquoise sky and brilliant white sails.

FOX, HEIDI (Commercial Graphic Illustrator)
116 1/2 Murphy St., Grass Valley, CA 95945

Born: 1954 *Collections:* Drummond House, Nevada City, CA *Exhibitions:* Open Studio, San Francisco; Artists' Co-Op Gallery, San Francisco *Education:* California Institute of the Arts, Valencia; San Francisco Art Institute

Focusing on facial expressions and the portrayal of feeling through color and form, she renders angels in oil and watercolor. Brightly colored angels on horseback, angels with animals and an angelic woman whose hair is full of butterflies and birds have been among

Bob Freimark, *Canyon Wall,* 107 x 110, tapestry. Courtesy: Mr. and Mrs. John De Andrea

Darrell Forney, *Bacon Eddy,* 72 x 50, acrylic

Catharine Phillips Fels, *House with Palm Tree,* 11 x 17, woodcut

her canvases. She has been influenced by Gustave Dore, Remedios Varos and Albrecht Durer. She also takes commissions for the photo-like portraits she does in stipple, or dot matrix. Her greeting cards are published by Renaissance of Maine and she has illustrated both *The Where-to-Go Guide* of Grass Valley and the children's book, *The Heart That Followed Me Home*.

FOX, JOHN W. (Sculptor)
2262 Hidalgo Ave., Los Angeles, CA 90039

Born: 1950 *Collections:* Arizona State U. Art Collection; Ohio State U. Art Collection *Exhibitions:* Los Angeles County Museum of Art; Eilat Gordin Gallery, West Hollywood *Education:* California Institute of the Arts

He initially trained as an environmental designer under the tutelage of Buckminster Fuller. At the same time, he studied abstract expressionist painting, working with sheet metal, plastic or other materials instead of paint on canvas. Recently, he has been influenced by the work of Mexican wood carvers. Their imaginative designs have prompted him to develop a simpler way of creating. He cuts flat shapes from plywood and assembles them into three-dimensional volumes that hang on the wall or stand on the ground. He sprays the surfaces with enamel, either leaving them unfinished or treating them with a light color wash.

FRANCIS, SAM (Painter)
345 W. Channel Dr., Santa Monica Canyon, Los Angeles, CA 90402

Born: 1923 *Awards:* Tamarind Fellowship; Dunn International Prize, Tate Gallery *Collections:* Guggenheim Museum, NYC; Museum of Modern Art, NYC *Exhibitions:* San Francisco Museum of Art; Albright-Knox Art Gallery, Buffalo *Education:* UC-Berkeley; Atelier Fernand Leger *Dealer:* Smith Anderson Gallery, Palo Alto

After prolonged formal study, he had his first solo show in 1952 in Paris. This early work consisted of abstract paintings with large areas of color light in tone. Soon the tones became more vivid, with areas of color bleeding into each other. A trip around the world in 1957 perhaps influenced his artistic career most. Cool colors, thinly applied and arranged in asymmetrical segments on the canvas, seem to recall the Japanese tradition. During the 1960s, he became increasingly occupied with lithography. His Oriental tendencies continue, with the clarity and starkness of form and composition related to the minimalists.

FRANK, MICHAEL (Painter)
P.O. Box 46066, Los Angeles, CA 90046

Born: 1961 *Awards:* Los Angeles County Museum of Art *Collections:* Panza Collection, Italy *Exhibitions:* Richard Bennett Gallery; Colorado Place *Education:* UCLA; Cranbrook Academy

Despite his extensive formal training, he retains a spontaneity and an innocence in the determination of line. His sharp-edge relationships and voluminous forms suggest an affinity to Picasso and de Kooning. He works on mammoth surfaces, exploring questions of abstract and academic figuration. Working without any prior sketches, he attacks his surface with impasto, bold lines and often contrasting media. He renders the abstract real by layering events, thoughts, impulses and al-

lusions. The pieces are dense with passages, and are detailed with reactive paints, which are juxtaposed with quiescent, dormant spaces.

FRANKOVICH, TOM (Painter)
2034 29th St., San Diego, CA 92104

Born: 1951 *Awards:* Juror's 1st Award, La Jolla Art Association Annual Exhibit; 1st Award, San Diego County Artists Exhibition *Collections:* Hotel Intercontinental, Inc.; Western Digital Inc. *Exhibitions:* San Diego Museum of Art; Riverside Museum of Art *Education:* San Diego State U.; Southern Illinois U. *Dealer:* Beasley Gallery, San Diego

Three primary forces characterize his work: freedom of brushwork and gesture; the exclusion of obvious representational subject matter; and the pursuit of a rhythmic orchestration of line, color, shape and form. He derives much of his inspiration from intuition, translating his intuitive feelings into internalized rhythms that are in turn used to create a visual vocabulary. Comparing himself to a composer for whom silence is as important as sound, he creates paintings in which the passive negative or blank space is as important as the positive or filled space. His images move in relation to open space, creating a delicate balance between active and passive, light and dark, large and small, silence and activity.

FRARY, VIVIAN (Painter, Jewelry Maker)
P.O. Box 1540, Burney, CA 90613

Born: 1941 *Awards:* Special Award, Green Valley Show *Exhibitions:* Myndseye Unlimited, Chico; Fredric Rash Gallery, Laguna Beach *Dealer:* Pauline Brown, Sacramento

At the age of five, she began to study painting with her grandmother. Since then, she has developed her own style, which is influenced by Native American—particularly Cherokee—art. Her fluid, colorful paintings display her love of texture and form. She has also designed and made jewelry.

FRASER, FRANCES HOLLINGER (Painter)
7152 Fenway Dr., #31, Westminster, CA 92683

Born: 1935 *Awards:* Anaheim Cultural Arts Center; Hesperia Western Art Show *Collections:* Pentagon Coast Guard Collection *Education:* Art Students League

She works in an almost photographic manner, painting what she sees and feels. Her portraits are in the grand manner. Often, costumes play an important element, especially in her Civil War scenes. Her search for subject matter sometimes takes her to the mountains to attend meetings of mountain men and Indians. She has studied under Shinjiro Nakamura in Tokyo and under William Yelland of Orange, California. Her other influential teachers include John Howard Sanden, Thomas Fogerty and Betty Edwards. She comes from a family that immersed itself in music, poetry and painting.

FRASHESKI, ANDY (Photographer)
4701 San Leandro St., Oakland, CA 94601

Born: 1950 *Exhibitions:* Nikon Gallery, Zurich, Switzerland; San Diego Art Institute *Education:* U. of Pacific *Dealer:* Josephus Daniels Gallery, Carmel

His university years exposed him to many of the great literary and visual artists in the world. He began photographing in color, but was so impressed by the print quality achieved by master photographers Adams

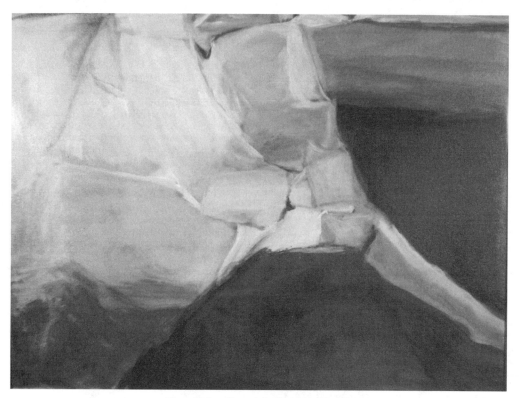

Vera Felts, *Strand Series,* 40 x 48, oil

Beverly Fredericks, *A New Day,* 30 x 40, oil on canvas. Courtesy: Universal City Bank of America

and Weston that soon he went to black and white. His travels in Europe, especially those in Greece, provided the inspiration that would truly launch his work. His "Red Period" is an on-going series of hand-colored black-and-white images that uses the color red to connect the blood of Christ and the blood of women. As the series has progressed, he has been able to mask off specific areas for hand-coloring with watercolors. The result is seamless, with no change in the gloss of the silver emulsion so that the photograph looks like a color print. The typical use of red is sparing: the only red in an image of a crucifix in Mexico is in the blood; in an image of a woman baring her legs, only her shoes are red.

FREDERICK, WALTER (Painter, Printmaker)
1322 20th Ave., San Francisco, CA 94122

Born: 1942 *Awards:* Honorable Mention, International Cultural Competition, Los Angeles *Exhibitions:* International Cultural Competition, Los Angeles; Phoenix Gallery, San Francisco *Education:* Academy of Art College, San Francisco *Dealer:* Lake Gallery, Tahoe City

He spent his childhood in the art museum in Buffalo. Its predominantly abstract collection left him with an abiding love of strange, often incomprehensible art. In 1970, he decided to pursue a career in art; he spent the next several years becoming acquainted with the great diversity of the Western art tradition. His style has evolved into a simple, evocative idiom, characterized by basic forms and resonant color. Attention is focused on the interaction of masses in space which parallel, in an abstract manner, the universal forces acting invisibly in nature. He has recently completed a diptych: a field of blue-black, with a centrally positioned area of lighter blue. While the work was inspired by abstract impressionism, it has a rather more traditional feel. He cites Clifford Stills, Barnett Newman and Mark Rothko as major influences.

FREDERICKS, BEVERLY (Painter, Printmaker)
8227 Westlawn Avenue, Los Angeles, CA 90045

Born: 1928 *Collections:* Bank of America; University of Texas *Exhibitions:* Warner Fine Art, Los Angeles; Barton Gallery, Akron, OH *Education:* Colorado Springs Fine Art Center *Dealer:* Louis Newman Gallery, Beverly Hills; John Lane Gallery, Poughkeepsie, NY

She studied with Boardman Robinson, Emerson Woelffer, Vaclav Vytlacil and Italian printmaker Georgio Upiglio. Her work, primarily landscapes in oil and watercolor monotypes, are in the traditions of American Tonalists, such as George Inness and William Keith, and the Impressionists. The colors within a picture are muted and are narrow in their range of intensity—creating the moods of meditation, quiet and poetry she seeks to evoke. She has painted both scenic views of the present and historic scenes from across America.

FREDIANI, JULIE MARIE (Painter)
2850 Bellflower Dr., Antioch, CA 94509

Born: 1956 *Awards:* Artist of the Year, Delta Art Association; 3rd Place, Watercolor, Las Juntas Artist's Art Show *Exhibitions:* Upper Room Studio Gallery, Antioch; Antioch Civic Arts Commission *Education:* UC-Davis *Dealer:* Lombardo's Interiors, Antioch

She has a traditional watercolor style, using a wet-on-wet technique in soft hues followed by stronger and darker colors. Subjects include California landscapes, landscapes of forests, abandoned buildings and childhood memories of trips to various parts of the country. She serves on the executive board of the Delta Art Association, an organization involved in art education for children and adults, and is a member of the Society of Western Artists.

FREE, K.K.
2664 Great Highway, San Francisco, CA 94116

Born: 1930 *Exhibitions:* Oakland Art Association; Club 9, San Francisco *Education:* Banff School of Fine Arts; University of Notre Dame *Dealer:* F.J. Michaels Gallery, San Francisco

Seeking rigorous physical and spiritual art instruction, the artist studied in Japan and Korea for several years. This Oriental influence is still apparent in the brilliant palette and inch-thick brush strokes of the watercolor and oil paintings. The images—flowers, plant and animal life and birds of all sorts—are rendered to produce an emotionally rich evocation of nature. Recent work includes "The Great Question," a series of oil paintings that explore metaphysical expressions of nature.

FREEDMAN, STEPHEN (Ceramist, Sculptor)
3740 Wade St., Mar Vista, CA 90066

Born: 1953 *Collections:* Long Beach Museum; Oakland Museum *Exhibitions:* West Australia Museum of Art; Lizard Harp Gallery, Pasadena *Education:* U. of Western Australia *Dealer:* Lizardi/Harp, Pasadena

Originally trained as a ceramist, he found that sculptural and literary forms insinuated themselves into the traditional formats of classical pottery. The result has been a fusion of surrealist literary concerns, minimalist sculpture and classic ceramic forms. From minimalist hypnotic abstraction, the work has developed into a more sophisticated cipher, dealing with content versus mass and three-dimensional writing. While he still works in clay, the vessels, installations and sculptures have the presence of metal and stone.

FREEMAN, EARL H. (Painter, Draughtsperson)
240 S. Valencia St., #1, La Habra, CA 90631

Born: 1915 *Exhibitions:* Sherwood Gallery, Santa Monica; Frame of Mind Gallery, Calabasas

He greatly admires the French avant-garde artists and the German Expressionists, and believes that Picasso's work liberated art from its traditional constraints. He works in oil, acrylic and ink on paper, creating humorous, figurative drawings and paintings. His palette is strong and simple, and the numerous figures are drawn with strong lines and detailed shading.

FREEMAN, JOHN (Painter)
851 Alvarado, San Francisco, CA 94114

Born: 1938 *Exhibitions:* Gallery Space, San Francisco Arts Commission; Schneider Museum of Art *Education:* San Francisco Art Institute

Since 1970, he has evolved the flat picture plane of his earlier color-field work into spatial, figurative compositions. A brilliance of color and a concentration on light link the pieces to his earlier work. He currently divides his time between portraits and landscape. The portrait series depicts character in rigorously open composi-

Mel Fillerup, *Crossing the Divide,* oil

John Freeman, *Betsy Miller and the Mural "Infinity",* 36 x 50, oil

tions lit with abundant sunlight, while the landscape paintings convey mood. Influences include Kokoshka, with whom he studied, and Cezanne.

FREEMAN, MEG (Painter)
1740 Burnell Dr., Los Angeles, CA 90065

Born: 1955 *Collections:* State University of New York Art Gallery, NYC *Exhibitions:* Los Angeles County Museum of Art; University Fine Arts Gallery, Las Vegas *Education:* State U. of New York

Her angular nudes, sharpened by hard graphic lines, recall Gustav Klimt's Japanese-influenced handling of the female figure. She focuses on mood in her works, rather than image, cropping her figures (usually confrontational, emotional, provocative) into restrictive settings. The stark, empty surroundings—a room with a chair as the only prop—evoke a cool isolation particular to New York, where the artist studied for several years. She balances this mood of isolation through facial expression and color. Experimentation with color in abstract collage has enabled her to manipulate color particularly—she softens her hard nudes with pastels, giving the strongly isolationist images a touch of optimistic human warmth.

FREIMARK, ROBERT (Painter, Printmaker)
539 A, Dougherty Ave., Morgan Hill, CA 95037

Born: 1922 *Awards:* New Talent in the U.S.A. Award, *Art in America*; Ford Foundation Grant *Collections:* British Museum; Boston Museum of Fine Arts *Exhibitions:* Art Institute of Chicago; Stanford U. Bechtel Center *Education:* Cranbrook Academy of Art *Dealer:* Aartvark Gallery, Philadelphia; Editions Ltd., San Francisco

He is perhaps most widely known for his experimentation with the new Czech media "Art Protis" and for his attempts to liberate tapestry from its conventional crafts limitations. From 1960 to 1968, he executed a suite of color serigraphs depicting each of the fifty states in the Union. During the 1970s, he created tapestry installations for museums and corporations. He regularly returns to Czechoslovakia to complete works. He has recently been working on a suite of 500 watercolor paintings of pristine California, portraying isolated locations that have not been "improved " by modern man. In 1989, he completed his "Hawaii Suite."

FREUDENBERGER, LAURE (Jeweler)
8085 Cibola Ct., San Diego, CA 92120

Born: 1952 *Awards:* 1st Award, Professional Jewelry Without Stones, Del Mar Gem and Mineral Show; Nominee, A.S.I. Art Achievement Award in Jewelry, Artists International Gallery, San Francisco *Exhibitions:* The Art Scene, San Diego; Brandon Gallery, Fallbrook *Education:* San Diego State U.

After sculpting a series of large, dramatic projects, she turned to the design and execution of equally powerful statements on a smaller scale. She creates jewelry using electrically charged niobium and titanium. These dynamic pieces, which she regards as wearable art, display her concern with light, color and movement. She works with both representational and abstract designs, creating light-weight necklaces, collars and other items in vibrant blues and pinks. She considers herself a realist, and cites the works of Arlene Fische and Sandra la Berge as major influences on her style and approach.

FREY, VIOLA (Ceramist, Painter)
663 Oakland Ave., Oakland, CA 94611

Born: 1933 *Awards:* NEA Fellowship *Collections:* Whitney Museum, NYC; San Francisco Museum of Modern Art *Exhibitions:* Seattle Art Museum; Wenger Gallery, La Jolla *Education:* Tulane U. *Dealer:* Rena Branstein, San Francisco

In the 1950s, her ceramic pieces were influenced by the then- current interest in Japanese pottery, but in the 1960s, she started exploring the iconographic potential of her art and turned to overglaze painting to enhance her pieces. She used paint to add depth to the surface of her objects, and she also used china painting to establish a complex of interrelated forms on her base structure. Her drawings and paintings deal more directly with her own experience. In these, she combines the very small with the very large to achieve a dynamic interplay of various characters and situations on a single surface. Fritz Eichenberg's paintings of Manhattan have had a strong influence on these later works, as has urban mural art.

FREYMUTH, URSULA (Ceramist, Sculptor)
14406 Mandolin Way, Nevada City, CA 95959

Born: 1945 *Collections:* The Titus Mill Collection, Hopewell, NJ *Exhibitions:* Chico Museum; Nevada County Arts Council Gallery *Education:* Art Student's League; San Francisco Art Institute

Growing up surrounded by European folk art and having nearly always lived a rural life style, she has used both glazed and unglazed ceramics to explore her relationship to the primal elements and to the animal world. Her early work contained images of wolves, snakes and birds and explored her own experience as mother, lover and empty vessel. In her recent pieces, she studies universal and ancient archetypes through the technique of pit-fired pottery, using, native clays, slips, tools and fuel that she finds in the Sierra Nevada foothills near her home. She is currently working on large clay masks adorned with feathers, sticks and wool. All of her work shows concern for inner transformation; as an instructor working with disturbed children and mentally disabled adults, she desires to facilitate self-understanding through the process of creating art.

FRICKMAN, FRANCES (Sculptor)
P. O. Box 4663, Santa Barbara, CA 93140

Born: 1923 *Awards:* Honorable Mention, Sculpture, Santa Barbara Art Association; Art History Award, San Diego State College *Exhibitions:* El Bethel Exhibit, Dallas; Santa Barbara City Library *Education:* Claremont Graduate School

A sculptor, she found that bronze was the best medium in which to render her works, which centered on the theme of children at play. Although her sculptures begin with actual photographs or drawings of children, her principal concern lies in the capacity of her material and the various ways in which it can be teased or drawn out. In her later work, she also began exploring abstract themes, carrying her preoccupation with the art form itself further. With this move, she began exploring the aesthetics of papier maché and colle. She also began experimenting with the use of color on three-dimensional surfaces. Probably the largest influence on her work was John Stenson, the artist under whom she

Michi Fujita, *Winter Lake,* 48 x 36, acrylic. Courtesy: San Francisco Women Artists Gallery

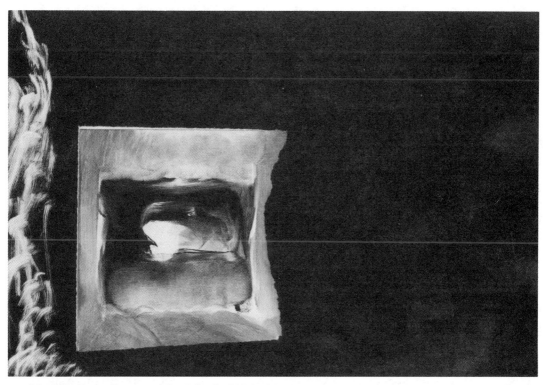

Marjorie Faris, *Dreams of the Animals #18 for Margaret Atwood,* 8 x 12, monoprint with chine collé

studied at Claremont, but her work also shows the mark of the years she spent as a fashion illustrator.

FRIED, HOWARD LEE (Sculptor, Video Artist)
1101 Georgia St., Vallejo, CA 94590

Born: 1946 *Awards:* NEA Fellowship *Collections:* Stedelijk Museum; San Francisco Museum of Modern Art *Exhibitions:* University Art Museum, Berkeley; Museum of Modern Art, NYC *Education:* Syracuse U.; San Francisco Art Institute; UC-Davis *Dealer:* Paule Anglim, San Francisco

A seminal figure in the overlapping fields of video, performance and installation art, he has earned an international reputation particularly in video. However, because of their structural nature, his works are best discussed as sculpture. Generally, his method involves the objectification of social or psychological process. He accomplishes this by constructing metaphors which in some sense equate physical structures with psychological phenomena. Earlier works tend to be autobiographical and to focus on the complexities of decision-making and the process of learning. Recent pieces are concerned with group dynamics and external societal issues.

FRIEDLER, HOWARD (Sculptor)
2255 Hearst Ave., #2, Berkeley, CA 94709

Born: 1952 *Awards:* 2nd Place, People's Choice, "Art in the Park," Golden Gate Park *Exhibitions:* Falon Building, San Francisco; California Visions, Sausalito

His love for sculpture and surrealism grew throughout his college years, as he studied Michelangelo and Magritte. He had been working in stone and wood, when a jeweler suggested that he try carving on gemstones and ivory. Now he sculpts exclusively inside quartz crystals, using a dentist's drill, equipped with a diamond burr. His imagery includes people, dragons, castles, mermaids, centaurs and other figures, both real and mythological. Through the past several years of experimentation, he has learned about sphere magnification, multiple imagery of facets and figure distortion of the internally sculpted image—all of which are critical to the finished appearance of the work. A recent piece, just 4 by 3 inches in size, features an island with nine lounging mermaids. He finds this medium endlessly exciting, because although the carvings are solid, the images pulsate and move with each change of perspective.

FROULA, BARBARA (Painter)
108 W. Byers Pl., #208, Denver, CO 80223

Born: 1955 *Awards:* Rotary Scholar; Award of Honor, Historic Denver, Inc. *Collections:* Anschutz Corporation, Denver; Citicorp USA, Denver *Exhibitions:* Savageau Gallery, Denver; Cogswell Gallery *Education:* Auburn U.; Royal Danish Academy of Fine Arts *Dealer:* Image Conscious, San Francisco

She is best known for her cityscapes in watercolor. In these, she seeks to create a sense of place, depicting the geometry of buildings, especially old ones. She renders the play of light and shadow over their surfaces, the detail and patterns created, and how the structures become the backdrop for human activity. To achieve a harmony of color in her painting, she uses a few basic pigments and mixes them to create more.

Her work is influenced by Edward Hopper, although his paintings are more somber than her often whimsical creations.

FRUDDEN, RICK (Jeweler)
232 Ivy Dr., Orinda, CA 94563

Born: 1955 *Awards:* 2nd Place, Sacramento State Fair *Exhibitions:* Pacific States Craft Fair, San Francisco; Banaker Gallery, Walnut Creek *Education:* San Francisco State U. *Dealer:* Elaine Potter Gallery, San Francisco

He credits his high school crafts teacher, Richard Gompf, with introducing him to jewelry-making, craft shows and competitions. He uses a lost wax casting technique, using a pin tool and exacto knife to form the piece from wax, then casting it in 14k, 18k and 22k gold. The settings usually have a carved or cabochon centerstone, with small facet stones to accent the design. He has traveled extensively, collecting images and ideas—not to mention precious and semi-precious stones, which he uses in his jewelry. He has been particularly fascinated by the cultures, religions and arts of the Asian countries. He has recently been making rings and necklaces with Mexican opals and fire agate.

FUJITA, MICHI (Painter, Batik Artist)
195 Bella Visto Dr., Hillsborough, CA 94010

Born: 1922 *Awards:* International Artist of the Year, Los Angeles; 2nd Award, California State Fair *Collections:* Japan Airline, San Francisco; Sumitomo Bank of California *Exhibitions:* Oakland Museum; California State Fair *Education:* Academy Art College, San Francisco *Dealer:* San Francisco Women Artists

Before coming to the United States from Japan, she had designed kimonos and studied batik and dyeing methods from such well known artists as Rinzo Takii. Today, she paints landscapes, does batik on canvas and makes sculpture. Her landscape paintings are a symbolical representation of her own emotional life. She paints these works on cotton, silk and sometimes wool, and uses candle wax for the white areas and imported dyes for colored images. Her batiks also deal in landscape imagery. Her bronze sculpture, *A Child and a Mother* is a large abstraction.

FULLER, STEVEN V. (Mixed Media Artist)
10941 Fair Oaks Blvd., Fair Oaks, CA 95628

Born: 1951 *Exhibitions:* Rara Avis Gallery, Sacramento; Slant Gallery, Sacramento *Dealer:* Art Works Gallery, Fair Oaks

Though he had always experimented with drawing, and later with logo illustration, he never took his art seriously until his introduction to late Austrian Expressionist Egon Schiele. Interest in the German Expressionists, Dadaists, Abstract Expressionists and Picasso followed, and a painting style emerged combining figurative and abstract qualities with an emotional use of intense color. He heavily layers oil pastel over a rough graphite or charcoal sketch on 4-ply rag board or cotton paper, leaving plenty of white space exposed. Then, he washes watercolor over the picture, mopping sporadically. After it dries, he improvises by scraping the stained oil pastel. Recent work on large handmade paper includes acrylic painting, though most pieces are still mixed media. Subjects usually deal with the human condition; oriental portraits reflect his interest in Asia. *Nagasaki Too*, a recent raku ceramic sculpture of a tiny figure in

Barbara Froula, *A Visit to Capitol,* 16 x 30, Watercolor. Courtesy: Savageau Gallery

David Gallegos, *5 Lakes II,* 40 x 60, oil

meltdown comments quietly on our capacity for inhumanity.

FULMER, CHARLES W. (Photographer, Mixed Media Artist)
1798 Sunridge Dr., Ventura, CA 93001

Born: 1942 *Collections:* Anne Veis Memorial *Exhibitions:* Buena Ventura Art Association, Ventura County Government Center; Cultural Center, Port Hueneme *Education:* Cal. State-Northridge; UCLA *Dealer:* Costo Deloro, Ventura

He was originally a painter, but the work of photo-artist Jenny MacMillan inspired him to explore photography. He prefers working with mixed media, including elements of drawing, painting and photography. He photographs human figures in classic poses, then adjusts the images using pastels, acrylics and photo-processing chemicals. In this way, he creates individualistic expressions of humanism.

FULTON, JACK (Photographer)
109 Orange St., San Rafael, CA 94901

Born: 1939 *Awards:* Buck Foundation Fellowship, Marin Arts Council; Eugene Atget Award, Ville de Paris *Collections:* San Francisco Museum of Modern Art; Bibliotheque Nationale, Paris *Exhibitions:* Oakland Museum; International Center of Photography, NYC *Dealer:* Silver Image, Seattle

The artist combines elements of art history, creative writing and engineering/architecture to produce photographs whose art context is truncation rather than abstraction. He eliminates as much as possible from his images while keeping them totally referential. Alongside and on top of his photos, he often appends drawings, materials and writings from the stream-of-consciousness school. His interest in poetry aids him with the brevity of his image making. Today he produces large Cibachrome images from slides taken in the American West, Alaska and Europe. Recently, he completed a book with words and a black-and-white portfolio of San Francisco transvestites. He has recently been working on color prints of France, using the negatives from Fuji 1600 high speed film to make "pointillist" images.

FUSEK, JANE (Painter, Printmaker)
1388 Berkeley Way, Ukiah, CA 95482

Born: 1948 *Awards:* Purchase Award, Sonoma State U. *Exhibitions:* Pacific States Print and Drawing Exhibition; Art Space National Exhibition, Sacramento *Education:* UCLA; Sonoma State U.

In the past, she allowed her subconscious to emerge through spontaneous drawings. She filled her freely drawn lithographs and paintings with composite figures, made from forms of animals, rocks, plants, birds and dancers. In 1988, she began making large ink drawings, finding in the brush-and-black-ink medium an unequaled freshness, immediacy and power. No matter what the medium, the images remain spontaneous, and she is currently integrating a black-and-white interplay of positive and negative spaces into all the work. She is continuing with her paintings and lithographs while also creating collages into which she now incorporates watercolor, gouache, pastel, bits of drawing or prints and handmade paper.

GAD, SIMONE (Multimedia Artist)
4235 1/2 Avocado St., Los Angeles, CA 90027

Born: 1947 *Awards:* CRA Grant *Collections:* Foundation for Performance, NYC; Los Angeles Institute of Contemporary Art *Exhibitions:* Otis/Parsons Exhibition Gallery, Los Angeles; B-1 Gallery, Santa Monica *Dealer:* Neo Persona Gallery, NYC

Since the middle of the 1970s, her work has centered on Hollywood—its past and the enduring, iconic value of the images it has created. Her assemblages incorporate memorabilia and vintage found objects from Hollywood's past and reveal the influence of such pop artists as Andy Warhol and Lucas Samaras. As she progressed, her works grew larger, finally resulting in the creation of several major installation pieces. She has also included self-portraits in her assemblages, an example of which is *3 Simones with Black Cats,* in which she included her own portrait next to portraits of Simone Simon and Simone Signoret. She has also done self-portraits with Cyd Charisse and Brigitte Bardot.

GAGLIANI, OLIVER (Photographer)
605 Rocca Ave., S. San Francisco, CA 94080

Born: 1934 *Awards:* NEA Grant; Fisher Grant, University of Arizona *Collections:* Museum of Modern Art, NYC; San Francisco Museum of Modern Art *Exhibitions:* Monterey Peninsula Museum of Art; Josephus Daniels Gallery, Carmel *Education:* California College of Arts and Crafts; California School of Fine Arts

His photographs capture the essences of the objects in the world around us. Trained in music and later self-taught in photography under the influence of the West Coast school, he orchestrates his palette of gray tones to draw forth the life within a chair, a broken window, a fallen wall, a vine scaling the height of a tree. "From these objects in the world, from their own lives which often far outlast our own," he says, "we can acquire a wisdom which would otherwise be inaccessible to us. It is the photographer, through the medium of light, who must confront these objects directly, not as he would like them to be, but as they are in themselves." Carefully and precisely composed, the images in his photographs are both abstract and concrete, a tension that provides for metaphor.

GALE, BILL (Painter, Sculptor)
1335 N. Fairfax Ave., West Hollywood, CA 90046

Born: 1952 *Exhibitions:* Los Angeles Municipal Gallery of Art *Education:* U. of Arizona

In 1978, after formal training in figurative painting and drawing, he began exploring mixed-media techniques. He incorporated elements of light and water into large-scale sculptures, thereby adding a psychological dimension, and involving the viewer. He was an early and frequent participant in the Furniture as Art Movement. Since 1985, he has returned primarily to painting, depicting the Southern California landscape, using pastel colors and the iconographic emblem of the palm tree. Though he is still concerned with architectural imagery, his most recent work deals with painterly issues of texture, color relationships and light and shadow. He has been inspired by movements as diverse as quattrocento Italian art, Bauhaus, constructivism, and streamline moderne architecture.

GALE, GAYLE (Sculptor)
1335 N. Fairfax Ave., West Hollywood, CA 90046

Simone Gad, *Self Portrait with Brigitte Bardot,* 40 x 50 x 10, mixed media collage/
assemblage. Courtesy: B-1 Gallery. Photograph: Roger Marshutz

Emily Gordon-Nizri, *Torn Paper, Torn Lives,* 12 x 16, oil on panel

Born: 1952 *Exhibitions:* Los Angeles Municipal Art Gallery; Los Angeles Museum of Art *Education:* Otis Art Institute; U. of Arizona

Influenced by the conceptual art of the late 1960s and early 1970s, as well as by interests in fashion, stone lithography and printmaking, she transforms various high-tech, man-made materials (plastics, rubber, vinyls), iridescent fabrics and other mixed media into colorful, soft, wearable sculpture. Her current concerns are primarily sculptural, and her pieces can function in the gallery or be worn as avant-garde clothing and accessories (fake snake belts, tropical fish purses, space tunics). She is also active in performance, and she often collaborates with her husband, sculptor Bill Gale. She is currently working on a series of wearable "Space Age Kachinas" (masks), drawn from autobiographical experiences.

GALLEGOS, DAVID MAES (Painter)
50 A Ash Ave., San Anselmo, CA 94960

Born: 1954 *Awards:* Distinction/Honor, IFRAA Arts and Architecture Awards Competition *Collections:* Richmond Art Center; Redding Museum and Art Center *Exhibitions:* Robert Mondavi Gallery, Napa; Redding Museum and Art Center *Education:* Cal. State-San Francisco; California College of Arts and Crafts

His art reflects an elemental and essential respect for nature. The works are primarily landscapes, painted in watercolor, oil and graphite, although he creates cityscapes as well. His style has moved among differing schools of painting; at present, it reflects a blend of realist and impressionist elements. From a deeply attuned sense of nature, he paints landscapes fraught of spirituality. He also does serious and concentrated studies of sunsets.

GALLI, STANLEY W. (Painter)
P.O. Box 66, Kentfield, CA 94914

Born: 1912 *Awards:* Hall of Fame, Society of Illustrators, NYC *Collections:* Palm Springs Museum; Weyerhaeuser Co., Tacoma, WA *Exhibitions:* Charles and Emma Frye Museum, Seattle; Crocker Museum, Sacramento *Education:* San Francisco Art Institute; Art Center College of Design *Dealer:* Calvin Vander Woude Gallery, Palm Springs

He is a "Designed Realist" whose early work during the 1930s was influenced by Italian Renaissance painters, the French Moderns of the time and, most of all, by his subject matter which included wildlife, early Spanish California and the Italian scene. Work proceeds from many small tempera studies of thoroughly investigated subjects and generally progresses to a large canvas. Oils, acrylics and, sometimes, watercolors are his media; his recent subject matter continues to deal with Spanish California and the Tuscany area of Italy where he lives part of the year. Contemporary influences include Milton Avery and Ben Shahn.

GALLICK, EUGENE C. (Installation Artist)
224 High St., Moorpark, CA 93021

Born: 1945 *Awards:* Chain Scholarship *Exhibitions:* Los Angeles Institute of Contemporary Art; Moorpark College Administration Building *Education:* California Institute of the Arts; Cal. State-Northridge

His installations explore the use of found objects in our environment and organize them into new environments. Performances, writings and installations combine to comment on such issues as pollution, technology and the overwhelming realization of our human condition and its frailty.

GALLOWAY, KIT (Video Artist)
700 Cedar St., Santa Monica, CA 90405

Born: 1948 *Awards:* NEA Fellowship; American Film Institute Fellowship *Collections:* Museum of Modern Art, NYC; Long Beach Museum of Art *Exhibitions:* Museum of Contemporary Art, Los Angeles; Museum of Modern Art, NYC *Education:* U. of Paris

In Europe, he worked with the Videoheads video collective, creating the first video theater in Europe to incorporate live action and videotape into multi-channeled shows and installations. Projects included a series of 12 interactive video installations for the Sony France showroom on the Champs Elysees, and a collaborative undertaking with Salvador Dali to produce a three-dimensional video system. With partner Sherrie Rabinowitz, he works under the name Mobile Image to explore and develop the unique properties of state-of-the-art communications technologies. In 1980, he and Rabinowitz created *Hole-In-Space: A Public Communication Sculpture.* A three-day, life-sized, unannounced, live satellite link allowed spontaneous interaction between the public on the East and West coasts. Video cameras and rear-projection screens were installed in display windows at the Lincoln Center for the Performing Arts in New York and at the Broadway department store in Los Angeles. Passers-by could see, hear and talk with people on the opposite coast, almost as if they were standing on the same street corner.

GALTON, HERTA (Painter)
13806 Oxnard St., Van Nuys, CA 91401

Born: 1914 *Exhibitions:* U. of Kansas, Lawrence; Herta Galton, Van Nuys *Education:* Hoffmann School of Painting, Vienna; The Academy of Fine Arts, Vienna; U. of Kansas, Lawrence *Dealer:* Bolsover Gallery, London

Born in Austria, she did not come to America until 1962. There remains in her work a European sense of family and city. She celebrates cities as centers of civilization. Her buildings are living structures which mirror the grace, learning and generosity of their human inhabitants. Her figures are abstract, almost geometric. Since moving to California in 1976, she has begun to incorporate such California icons as palm trees into her work. The pieces are large (up to 6 feet) in which she builds up a rough surface from pure oil paints. She has been influenced by the technique of Hundert Wasser, Klimpt and Schiele and by the whimsical quality of Paul Klee.

GAMBINI, WILLIAM (Painter, Construction Artist)
P.O. Box 12146, San Diego, CA 92112

Born: 1918 *Awards:* Grant, Mark Rothko Foundation *Exhibitions:* 10th St. Cooperative Exhibition, NYC; Thomas H. Neumaier Gallery, San Diego

He first received notice as a member of the New York school of painting when, in 1956, he was actively involved in the organization of the 10th St. Cooperative Gallery. Working with oil, acrylic, pencil, charcoal, pastels, watercolor, gouache and mixed media, he paints and constructs on canvas, paper, wood, glass, plastic, metal and corrugated and bristle board. Concern and

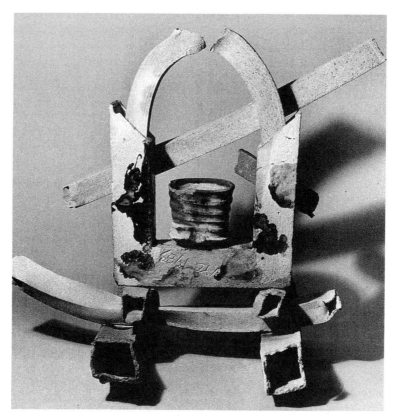

Gerrish, *Ahmednagar Rocker,* 18 x 20, ceramic. Photograph: Grey Crawford

Stanley W. Galli, *They Met Kearny at San Pasqual,* 36 x 36, charcoal and color on gesso

feelings come first in his work; method follows. Figures dominate the surface of his paintings—and time and space become vast and generous, the mood large and mystic. He has been influenced by Turner, Cezanne, Van Gogh and Picasso.

GAMBLE, SHEILA (Painter, Fiber Artist)
311 Shoreside, Pacifica, CA 94044

Born: 1943 *Awards:* Excellence Award, Art Guild of Pacifica; Grant, Peninsula Community Foundation, Burlingame *Collections:* California State Art in Public Buildings Commission, San Jose; Valley Bank, Pocatello, ID *Exhibitions:* San Francisco Academy of Fine Arts; San Mateo Arts Council Gallery, Belmont *Education:* San Francisco State U.

Influenced by sculpture fiber artists, Magdalena Abakanowicz and Barbara Shawcroft, she has worked in fiber sculpture since 1970. She has also worked with pen-and-ink watercolors, progressively pushing natural forms toward abstraction. While integrating fiber, papermaking and watercolors into mixed-media constructions, she also continues to weave relief tapestries of wool, reeds and rope. An artist-in-residence, she is active in the San Francisco Learning through Education in the Arts Project (LEAP), and is strongly committed to providing uncommon art experiences for children.

GARABEDIAN, CHARLES (Painter)
c/o Ruth S. Schaffner Gallery, 128 W. Ortega St., Santa Barbara, CA 93101

Born: 1924 *Awards:* NEA Fellowship; Guggenheim Fellowship *Exhibitions:* Whitney Museum, NY; Rose Art Museum, Waltham, MA *Education:* UC-Santa Barbara; USC *Dealer:* Ruth S. Schaffner Gallery, Santa Barbara; Hirschl & Adler Modern, NYC

Unswayed by current styles, he employs a variety of media in innovative ways, including combinations of paper collage, watercolor, drawing and colored resins poured and hardened directly on the surface. Narrative works often suggest scenes of violence or eroticism heightened by a melodramatic mood. Although his approach has gone through many changes, he has always dealt in some way with the figure and with the theme of freedom—the struggle to obtain it, what it means to possess it, and its limitations. In 1978 he began "Prehistoric Figures," a series lasting several years characterized by primitive-looking figures in enigmatic landscapes and similar to the earlier *Islands No.2.*

GARBER, DEBORAH (Painter)
1105 G St., Petaluma, CA 94952

Born: 1955 *Awards:* Honorable Mention, National Air and Space Museum; 2nd Prize, Triton Museum of Art Competitive Drawing Exhibition, Santa Clara *Collections:* UC-Berkeley; Quad City Arts Council, Rock Island, IL *Exhibitions:* Bank of America, San Francisco; National Air and Space Museum, Washington D.C. *Education:* Rhode Island School of Design *Dealer:* Allport Gallery, San Francisco; Dubins Gallery, Los Angeles

After formal training in printmaking and illustration, she began using pastels to depict landscape. Now working in acrylics as well, she creates luminous landscapes that are characterized by abstract elements. Trees and houses punctuate her vividly colored landforms, which are overhung by richly painted skies. She is fascinated with "the geometry, harmony and random quality of nature in general and landscape in particular," and she is now experimenting with large and small formats on both paper and canvas.

GARCIA, ELENA (Painter)
543 Felton Way, San Luis Obispo, CA 93401

Born: 1955 *Exhibitions:* "Jazz and All That Art on Filmore," San Francisco; Art-A-Fair, Laguna Beach *Education:* California Polytechnic U., San Luis Obispo *Dealer:* Morfett, San Francisco; Gallery Martieli, Atlanta

She spent several years refining her drawing technique before she began painting in 1983. A sixteen-month South Pacific cruise inspired a series of paintings, which depict the people and settings of the South Pacific Islands. In these works, she combined a succession of color washes with drybrush detail. Painting from a limited palette, she uses traditional techniques, such as drips, splatters, salt spindles, carving, frisket and blotting, and non-traditional techniques, such as fingerpainting, painting directly from the tube, mixing and collaging gold leaf, in a realist manner. A recent series of cattle skulls, for example, is more abstract, yet still representational, moving away from her characteristic photo-realist technique.

GARCIA, RUPERT (Painter)
c/o Anne Kohs & Assoc., Inc., 251 Post St., Suite 540, San Francisco, CA 94108

Born: 1941 *Awards:* San Francisco Art Commission Award of Honor for Outstanding Achievement in Printmaking *Collections:* National Museum of American Art, Washington, DC; San Francisco Museum of Modern Art *Exhibitions:* Oakland Museum; San Francisco Museum of Modern Art *Education:* San Francisco State U.; UC-Berkeley *Dealer:* Iannetti/Lanzone Gallery, San Francisco

The artist was active in the Chicano-Latino cultural movements of the late 1960s and early 1970s and first became known for his socially conscious posters and prints. He developed a bold silk-screen style that subverted many of the pictorial devices and premises of pop art in order to serve his own aesthetic and ideological ends. Since 1975, he has worked primarily with pastels on paper and more recently with oil paints on canvas. He continues to use media images, making large-scale diptychs and triptychs and frequently including images of protest, outrage, and injustice—which he combines with his own memories and reflections in order "to create a forum where moral and spiritual dilemmas can be addressed."

GARLIN, NAN (Painter)
16250 Mustang Dr., Springville, CA 93265

Born: 1929 *Awards:* 1st Place, Watercolors, Society of Western Artists Annual, Fresno *Exhibitions:* Society of Western Artists Annual, Oakland

Her watercolors are transparent and impressionistic. In her intimate florals of minimized subjects, she demonstrates a careful attention to negative space and receding areas. Sometimes working abstractly, she employs a variety of additional media, including ink, colored pencil and opaque watercolor. Her palette varies widely, and, in landscapes, she will occasionally use subdued, limited, moody colors. She has recently been painting an imaginative series of Southwest cliff

Deborah Garber, *Flux,* 30 x 40, acrylic on canvas

Susan Goldsmith, *Nancy,* 22 x 30, pastel and pencil on paper

dwellings in transparent watercolor and ink. "Rather than telling a story," she says, "I strive for feeling and mood."

GARNER, TODD (Ceramist)
2830 E. 5th St. #2, Long Beach, CA 90814

Born: 1953 *Exhibitions:* Palos Verdes Art Center, Rancho Palos Verdes; Chapman College *Education:* California St. Polytechnic U.; Cal. State-Long Beach

Painting dominated his early work, which was strongly influenced by the moods explored in the works of Joseph Turner and Francis Bacon. He then discovered clay as a means to express his images and techniques in three dimensions. His most recent work moves in two directions. The first, a series of ceramic helmets, is the result of his life-long fascination with Celtic mythology and his own Scottish ancestry. He constructs the helmets from overlapping slabs of clay, paints them with acrylics, then supports them on long sticks. Arranged in a line, they comprise the installation entitled *Sentinels*. In addition, he also constructs what he calls ceramic "leaf" cups, made from clay thrown on a hard surface and formed into thin sheets. These are then draped over an obloid and glazed in bright metallic colors. When finished, they resemble flames issuing from a burner.

GARROD, RICHARD M. (Photographer)
2121 San Vito Circle, Monterey, CA 93940

Born: 1924 *Awards:* New Talent U.S.A., *Art-in-America Exhibitions:* Vision Gallery, San Francisco: Spectrum Gallery, Fresno *Education:* UC-Berkeley *Dealer:* Josephus Daniels Gallery, Carmel

During the middle decades of 20th century, he was inspired by the tonal range in the contact prints of the large-format photographers—Adams, Weston and Evans. The sensitivity and beauty of this work led to a long period of large-format work and a special concentration on printmaking. He worked primarily in outdoor photography of natural and man-made landscapes. Subsequently, he came to believe that smaller-format work would permit a more refined, aware vision. His landscapes have become increasingly abstract, yet he remains grounded in reality, the reference point for understanding his designs and images.

GATNIK, KOSTJA (Painter, Multi-Media Artist)
480 Utah. St., San Francisco, CA 94110

Born: 1945 *Collections:* Museum of Modern Art, Ljubljana, Yugoslavia *Exhibitions:* Lone Wolf Gallery, San Francisco; Pacific Presbyterian Medical Center, San Francisco *Education:* Academy of Fine Arts, Ljubljana, Yugoslavia

While still a student, he executed a series of underground cartoons, which established his reputation as one of the most promising contemporary Yugoslav artists. He collected these cartoons in a book, *Magna Purga*, which quickly sold out and has since become a collector's item. He established himself as a free-lance artist, working in graphic design, photography, stage design and, especially, book illustration. His hyper-real style of painting features painstaking technique and close attention to detail, reproducing objects with startling fidelity. The contrast between the realistic details of the objects in his paintings and the underlying images and emotions tickle the eye, and cause the careful ob-

server to rethink the relationship between perception and reality.

GAWNE, CANDICE (Painter, Multimedia Artist)
1061 Avenue C, Redondo Beach, CA 90277

Born: 1949 *Exhibitions:* Museum of Neon Art, Los Angeles; Laguna Beach Museum of Art *Education:* UCLA; El Camino College

She is best known for oil on canvas paintings of surreal landscapes. Completely depopulated, these eerie, dramatic paintings feature a textured, agitated, nearly sculptural surface, which acts to catch the bright light and reflections that play a dominant part in her works. After years of using increasingly bright paints, she eventually decided to incorporate neon into her works. Recent paintings of interiors—hallways with reflective floors, lighted spaces with floors like shimmering water—are three-dimensional, layered wood constructions. The neon tubes are recessed so that only their light is part of the painting.

GENAU, MARLENA (Jewelry Artist)
32 El Gavilon, Orinda, CA 94563

Born: 1936 *Exhibitions:* Concepts Gallery, Palo Alto; Banaker Gallery, Walnut Creek *Education:* New York U.

She creates metal jewelry using gold and silver, and more recently modume-gane or laminated metal. Working from metal sheets, she employs hammers and stakes to stretch and compress the metal into the desired shape. By working with various coloring, buffing and texturing techniques, the artist brings up the distinctive quality of each metal. Her works are a synthesis of traditional forms infused with a more subtle, contemporary look. Her primary concern is simplicity and the idealization of form.

GENELIN, SUSAN (Painter)
13169 Cheltenham Dr., Sherman Oaks, CA 91423

Born: 1939 *Awards:* Honorable Mention, Long Beach Art Association *Exhibitions:* Art Space, Los Angeles; Santa Monica College Art Gallery *Education:* Otis Parsons Art Institute *Dealer:* Art Space, Los Angeles

Inspired by the multicultural stimulus of Los Angeles, she used multiple images with collaged and layered materials in her early work. The inner psychology and complexity of the human experience is the main subject matter of her work, which begins with her own photographs. Collages that include found objects are created, from which human-size paintings are developed. Bas-reliefs are also created with corrugated cardboard, and, finally, a light box may be added. These narrative pieces embody expressions and responses to people and events. They are physical environments, portraying the non-physical, and sometimes secret, components of living. Texture, pattern, color and symbol are used to circumvent the rational, intellectual limits of perception, and encourage total immersion in the world that is created.

GENTRY, DOE (Painter, Jeweler)
2270 N. Beachwood Dr., #8, Los Angeles, CA 90068

Born: 1941 *Exhibitions:* Coalesce Gallery; Wild Blue, Los Angeles

A museum and gallery enthusiast, she is a self-taught artist. Her high-energy paintings, mostly of airplanes, exude a profusion of color and energy, which seems to explode on large canvases. Spiritually pure, slender,

Guiyermo, *Pilatos Se Limpia de Culpas,* 22 x 32, linoleum engraving

Todd Garner, *Pain Sentinel,* 68 x 29 x 14, ceramic and mixed media.
Courtesy: Orlando Gallery

white vehicles are suspended in time and space—flying brushstrokes of hot color. The vibrational quality of these works is equally due to their acrylic execution, and to their soaring composition. The works of Frank Rozasy and Picasso helped to shape her painting technique and approach. She also manufactures jewelry, made from precious metals and gemstones. Employing a wax-casting technique, she has been influenced, in this area, by California and Colorado goldsmiths.

GEORGE, PATRICIA B. (Painter)
4025 Selkirk Ct., Cypress, CA 90630

Exhibitions: Mt. Ada Gallery, Catalina; Interior Design Show, Costa Mesa and Palm Springs *Education:* UCLA

Her landscapes and cityscapes translate energy and solid form through strong color applied with precision by palette knife. Flat colorfields combined with slightly skewed perspective press the compositional planes directly toward the viewer, lending an immediacy of emotion and creating a sense of inclusion in the often exotic settings. Light is almost tangible, pervading the pictures as a key to their lyrical interpretations. Direct and gestural, her applications of bright color are softened by muted sand and sky.

GERDES, PHORA (Sculptor)
12935 E. Rosecrans, Norwalk, CA 90650

Born: 1933 *Exhibitions:* Artist's Society International Gallery; Downey Museum *Education:* Otis/Parsons School of Design

She draws and paints on a three-dimensional scale and uses any material that helps delineate the meaning of the work. This includes a fourth dimension of time and such non-traditional materials as optical illusions and electronics. In her latest work she represents the memories of an elderly woman by sculpting secondary figures with hollow heads. The hollow heads contain the memory in motion. Larry Rivers and Red Grooms helped inspire her sense of movement. The work of Red Grooms also helped her bring humor to the work.

GERLACH, CHRISTOPHER S. (Painter)
820 A Canyon Rd., Santa Fe, NM 87501

Born: 1952 *Awards:* Murray Landscape Scholar Prize, Royal Academy, England; Bank of America Fine Art Award *Collections:* San Diego Museum of Art; Hughes Aircraft, Los Angeles *Exhibitions:* Orr's Gallery, San Diego; Munson's Gallery, Santa Fe *Education:* Cal. State-San Diego; Oxford U. *Dealer:* William Sawyer, San Francisco

He has been influenced by painterly realism in all stages of art history—from the French Impressionists, to the English landscape school, to the twentieth century modes of abstraction. Starting with subjective interpretations of nature, he has worked extensively on location, producing stronger and more painterly work.

GERMAIN, HARRIET MEYER (Sculptor)
350 Beloit Ave., Los Angeles, CA 90049

Born: 1909 *Collections:* Skirball Museum, Hebrew Union College, Los Angeles; Sheraton Hotel, Los Angeles International Airport *Exhibitions:* Artcore Museum, Los Angeles; Artspace Gallery, Beverly Hills *Education:* U. of Oregon, Eugene *Dealer:* Carol Shaff, Los Angeles

She creates a variety of colorful sculptures from handmade papers made of leaves, grasses and natural fibers. Characters from the Hebrew alphabet, figures from Greek mythology and other images from antiquity provide the themes for her work. She forms the paper into three-dimensional sculptures, applies wax to them and then paints them in bright colors from a full palette.

GERRISH, RICHARD (Ceramist, Mixed Media Artist)
Studio One, 2415 S. Santa Fe Ave., Los Angeles, CA 90058

Born: 1947 *Awards:* Purchase Award, American Ceramic National, Downey Museum of Art *Collections:* Fred Marer Collection of Contemporary Ceramics, Scripps College, Claremont *Exhibitions:* Kirvan/Bartoszewicz Gallery, Palm Springs *Education:* Claremont Graduate School

His artworks comprise architectural sculpture in both ceramics and found items, including lamps, scrap metal and other junk yard artifacts. His three-dimensional ceramic wall paintings, usually six-by-eight-feet in size, feature broken and extruded portions, and scrambled, hard-edge lines reminiscent of Pollock and early Stella. These pieces are painted in a dominant rose color, with areas of soft pastels and white highlights. Earlier pieces are more controlled and consist of combined geometric forms arranged around negative space. These table-top sculptures, 18 by 24 inches, are freestanding and made completely of ceramics. Recent work is in the dada tradition.

GERRMAN, ROSALIE (Feathercrafter)
2410 Coronet Blvd., Belmont, CA 94002

Born: 1943 *Awards:* 2nd Place, Art Council of San Mateo Art Show *Exhibitions:* Shady Lane Craft Gallery, Palo Alto; Northwest Discovery Gallery, Bellevue, WA *Education:* San Jose State U. *Dealer:* Shady Lane Craft Gallery, Palo Alto

She delights in the rich colors, textures, and patterns of bird feathers, which have always been a part of her life: as a young girl, she collected the feathers of peacocks and ducks in San Francisco's Golden Gate Park. In the 1960s, she specialized in drawing San Francisco's Victorian houses in pen and ink, but by the late 1970s feathercraft had absorbed her complete attention. In her feather masks, she transforms natural feather material from parrots, pheasants, quails, chickens and other birds—and often also including fur, gemstones and metallic lamés—into design elements. Half-faced masks recreate animals; full-faced masks may be abstract, fantastic or exotic works of Oriental or African inspiration. She takes as much pleasure in the selection of the feathers as she does in the construction of the mask itself.

GERSHGOREN, MILTON (Painter)
1559 S. Stanley Ave., Los Angeles, CA 90019

Born: 1909 *Awards:* 1st Place, California State Fair; Purchase Award, Motion Picture Art Directors, Los Angeles *Collections:* Dallas Museum of Art; Virginia Museum of Art, Richmond *Exhibitions:* Long Beach Museum; Pennsylvania Academy Annual *Dealer:* Heritage Gallery, Los Angeles

Early in his career, after an introduction to the work of Cezanne, Rouault and Soutine, the artist adopted an expressionistic style in his painting. A full, vibrant palette, with the omission of black, was used to investigate scenes and landscapes from pedestrian life. The colors in his musician series were chosen expressly for their correlation to music. Out of his opaque water-

George Leopold Feiner, *The Cristale Space,* 60 x 40, acrylic on paper

Barclay Ferguson, *Power Plant (detail),* 71 x 158, acrylic

Fingado, *Kunumdrum,* 24 x 16, paper

Darrell Forney, *Cool,* 42 x 66, acrylic. Courtesy: Steve Gibson and Iris Yang

Barbara Froula, *Cityscape,* 20 x 30, watercolor

Michi Fujita, *The Four Seasons,* 80 x 56, oil. Courtesy: San Francisco Women Artists Gallery

Stanley Goldstein, *Hillary,* 60 x 35, oil on canvas.
Courtesy: Jeremy Stone Gallery, San Francisco

Phora Gerdes, *Ol' Lady on Cane,* 51 x 20 x 12, mixed media

500

Joseph Goldyne, *Night Pinks,* 9 x 6, monotype on paper.
Courtesy: John Berggruen Gallery

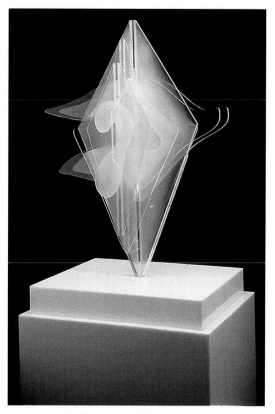

Jackie Greber, *Absolute Zero (-273°),* 32 x 20 x 16, lacquered acrylic

Tricia Grame, *Things in their Season,* 50 x 38,
mixed media collage on paper

Richard Godfrey, *Clara's Song,* 120 x 168 x 300,
mixed media with light, water and fire

Steve Gillman, *untitled,* 163 x 108 x 48, granite

M. Gershgoren, *Woman Seated,* 24 x 30, oil on canvas.
Courtesy: Joseph Hazen, New York

Cheryl Gross, *Tail o' the Pup,* 35 x 39, oil and crayon on canvas.
Courtesy: B-1 Gallery

Ken Goldman, *Crane Reflections,* 44 x 36, veiled watercolor

Stanley W. Galli, *Siena,* 30 x 36, oil

Nori Green, *Celebration,* 35 x 76, ink on Japanese papers with found objects

Joan J. Grant, *Raumgefuihl,* 61 x 15 x 12, mixed media

Patricia George, *Cancun,* 48 x 48, oil with palette knife on canvas

Susan Goldsmith, *Susie II,* 22 x 30, pastel and pencil on paper

Deborah Garber, *Sunswept,* 26 x 36, acrylic on canvas

Emily Gordon-Nizri, *Red Dancer,* 14 x 17, oil on panel

Gerrish, *Triptych with Blue,* 66 x 101, ceramic, brass, neon. Photograph: Grey Crawford

Carl Glowienke, *California Gray Whale,* 36 x 30 x20, bronze. Courtesy: Stephen Schackne

Betty Gold, *Kaikoo IX and XVII,* 108 x 168 x 120, 168 x 96 x 108, welded steel and print.
Courtesy: National Museum of Contemporary Art, Seoul, Korea

Mary Gould, *The Pack,* 5 dogs, 25 x 10 x 20 each, carved foam over wood
armature. Photograph: Jacqueline Paul

Jennifer Green, *Sea Cloud,* 12 x 18, watercolor

Jeff Griffeath, *The Black Swan Theatre Doors,* 28 x 40, airbrushed acrylic on masonite. Courtesy: William Sawyer Gallery, San Francisco

Guiyermo, *Ghost Mine Madrid,* 32 x 40, oil on canvas.

David Gallegos, *5 Lakes I,* 40 x 60, watercolor

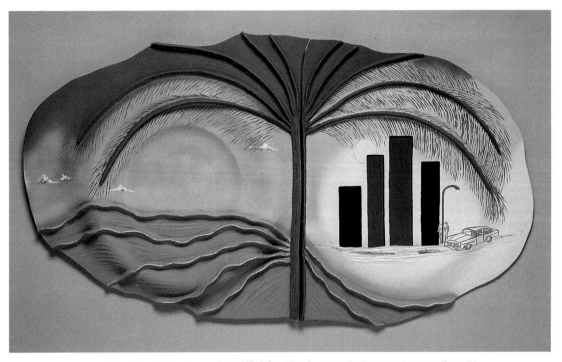

Jennifer A. Gyeltsen, *L.A. III,* 25 x 40 x 3, ceramic (wall sculpture–diptych)

color period of the 1950s came an impasto oil technique. Over the past two decades, the artist's style has become more manneristic. In a series of paintings portraying empty highways, the flatter surface treatment magnifies the sense of isolation. Recent woodcut prints, executed in a one-plate process, contain elements of abstraction.

GEYER, GARY YAKIMA (Painter)
160 View, Ct. A, Aptos, CA 95003

Born: 1940 *Exhibitions:* Triton Museum, San Jose; Eric Erison Gallery, Palo Alto *Education:* UC-Santa Cruz; San Jose College

His early influences were Old Dutch Masters and Surrealists such as Dali and Bosch. He paints in the high glaze style of the Dutch Masters developing a three-dimensional feeling by layering oil underpaints on canvas and linen. A colorist by nature, his high-color spectra give his paintings a vibrancy rarely found in color media. A realist, surrealist and mystic, his works sometimes fall into individual categories and are sometimes combinations of the three classes. He recently began documenting West Coast heritage by painting medium sized (38 by 42 inches) landscapes, seascapes, maritime scenes, and historically accurate nautical portraits.

GEYER, GEORGE (Sculptor)
2323 E. Olympic, Los Angeles, CA 90021

Born: 1935 *Awards:* NEA Grant; Hand Hollow Fellowship *Collections:* Scripps Institute of Oceanography, La Jolla; Security Pacific National Bank, Los Angeles *Exhibitions:* Claremont Graduate School; Site Installation, San Jose State U. *Education:* San Diego State U.; UCLA *Dealers:* Karl Bornstein Gallery, Los Angeles; Works Gallery, Long Beach

He studied ceramics and trained as a craftsman. After several years of making pottery, he became fascinated with what happens to clay during the ceramic process. This led him to study the effects of erosion on natural materials. Done in wood, stone, glass and combined materials, his sculptures—whether presented as outdoor installations or as indoor objects of art—concern the physical process of decay and humanity's relationship with delicately balanced natural forces. In one piece, *Surf Line Erosion,* five slabs of formed earth, sand, Hydrastone and Orzan-S were erected on the tideline of a California beach. Their subsequent erosion by wind and water was documented by Jim Irvine on videotape and by Libby Jennings' slide photography. These documents stand as the record of the completed artistic event: the complete wearing away of the slabs. His other pieces—a ziggurat made of glass, wood, and stone; gravity-influenced glass panels; a series of tilted glass panels—all display the influence of natural forces, captured in these instances in a discrete event. He has recently been working in slate, glass and granite, exploring different geometric arrangements of complement and opposition.

GIBBONS, MICHAEL (Painter)
The Old Vicarage, 140 N.E. Alder, Toledo, OR 97391

Born: 1943 *Collections:* Bank of California Tower, Portland *Exhibitions:* Loran Speck Gallery, Carmel; Frye Art Museum, Seattle *Dealer:* Kirsten Gallery, Seattle; Ruth Carlson Gallery, Mendocino

Entranced by the shapes and colors of his native Pacific Northwest environment, he set out as a teenager to seek a visual expression at one with his feelings and perceptions. An exhibit of Emil Carlsen's paintings and drawings in 1975 has remained the single most profound influence on his approach to landscape painting. Generally small in size, his paintings portray the quiet, softly lit landscapes of Oregon and Gloucestershire, England. He works in highly keyed oils, which he thickly applies in a tonalist manner. He has recently painted a group of fifteen pieces, entitled the "Wintersurf Series." A departure in size and style, these larger paintings, up to 80 by 30 inches, are executed in soft colors—cream, pink, mauve and gray. He feels that his painting is a continual search for a more vivid means of expressing the link between nature and the cosmos.

GIBSON, CATHERINE (Painter, Ceramist)
4 Teakwood Ct., San Rafael, CA 94901

Born: 1907 *Exhibitions:* San Francisco Museum of Modern Art; Michaels Gallery, San Francisco *Education:* U. of Minnesota *Dealer:* Michaels Gallery, San Francisco

For fifty years, she has worked in transparent watercolor after the fashion of Winslow Homer. She has recently focused her attention on subjects that are close to her, her familiarity with the American Indian informing the newer work. "The Hereafter," an exhibit of ceramics and watercolors, featured clay figurines painted and adorned with feathers, fabrics, twines and quills, and watercolors painted in mosaic-bright colors and dancing shapes. Men, birds, lizards, worms, turtles, fish, hand and foot prints and abstract symbols all intermesh within the works. She is currently completing a series of watercolors based on her childhood memories of small-town life in South Dakota and her grandmother's homestead in Montana.

GIL, MATTHEW (Sculptor)
P.O. Box 63, Rumsey, CA 95679

Born: 1956 *Collections:* San Jose Museum of Art; San Francisco Museum of Modern Art *Exhibitions:* Triton Museum, Santa Clara; Ivory/Kimpton Gallery, San Francisco *Education:* San Jose State U. *Dealer:* Ivory/Kimpton, San Francisco; Site 311, Santa Monica

At first, he explored ideas about movement, color and figure in a vast number of feverishly quick kinetic sculptures, which he spot welded in light-gage steel. Through the 1970s and 1980s, he strove for his own interpretations of Tinguely's, Takis's and Cornell's whimsical structures. Gradually he began to develop a unique style. His recent works are massive forms of stone, bronze and plate steel, which have metal parts that move in very subtle ways. He strives to find the visual balance between the large and the small, the mobile and the stationary—a balance where permanence of materials and harmony of space, time and color are one.

GILHOOLY, DAVID (Sculptor)
c/o Smith Anderson Gallery, 200 Homer St., Palo Alto, CA 94301

Born: 1943 *Collections:* Oakland Museum; San Francisco Museum of Modern Art *Exhibitions:* Crocker Art Museum, Sacramento; Palm Springs Desert Art Museum *Education:* UC-Davis *Dealer:* Smith Anderson Gallery, Palo Alto

His humorous anthropomorphic ceramic sculptures of moose, hippos, crocodiles, beavers and especially frogs draw on various humanistic sources—Western, Eastern, Egyptian—to create a wholly unique universe; the playful and satirical approach removes animals and objects from their normal settings, informing them with new and offbeat associations. His "frog culture" includes frogs in outer space, frog vikings, frog Buddhas, and noted frog personalities like Frog Elvis, Frog Tut and Mao Tse Toad; his frog Moses comes complete with a Frog-world Ten Commandments, including "Don't fool around in the God-Frog's presence," and "Stand by your products." Although on the surface his humor may appear to approach the corny, at a deeper level, the personal iconography comments on man's fundamental emotional and psychological regard for animals. A ritualistic signifiance echoes and reverberates through the laughter the works evoke.

GILKERSON, ROBERT (Mixed Media Artist)
P.O. Box 2697, McKinleyville, CA 95521

Born: 1922 *Exhibitions:* Oakland Museum; Long Beach Museum

He constructs mechanical and non-mechanical "monsters" from scrap metal, sheet tin, solder, drift wood and other materials, transforming these cast-offs into colorful, unique, three-dimensional wall-hangings and freestanding sculptures. Entirely self-taught, he began his career as an artist when he was laid off from his job as a grease mechanic at a construction company. Painting by hand or with spray paint, he applies words, phrases and bits of advice, and bright, primary colors to his pieces. Subjects include personal likes and aversions (to doctors and dentists, for example), fairy tales, movies and his observations of the world around him. His whimsical, cartoonish, unlikely assemblages express the subtleties and vulgarities of American culture.

GILLMAN, STEVE (Sculptor)
1765 12th St., Oakland, CA 94607

Born: 1945 *Awards:* Individual Artist's Fellowship, Oregon State Art Commission *Collections:* Portland Art Museum, Portland, OR; U. of Washington, Seattle *Exhibitions:* Richmond Art Center, Richmond; Nelson Gallery, UC-Davis *Education:* U. of Oregon, Eugene

He was strongly influenced by the environmental movement in the San Francisco Bay Area in the late 1960s, and he concentrated on work that would be encountered outside museum and gallery walls. The focus of his recent site pieces has departed from the "object" and moved towards activating a place or the history of place—the goal of his work being to charge the site with a sense of place and mystery. In the abstract installation work, *Stone Poem*, eight granite slabs approximately twelve feet high may be seen as human figures gesturing and posturing. All of his works reflect an overriding concern with the flow of time and with the connectedness of the future to the past.

GIMLIN, BEVERLY (Painter, Mixed Media Artist)
471 Western Dr., Richmond, CA 94801

Born: 1954 *Collections:* S & W Foods, San Ramon; Archer, McCombs & Lagesun, Walnut Creek *Exhibitions:* 2nd International Contemporary Art Fair, Los Angeles; Vorpal Gallery, San Francisco *Education:* UC-Berkeley; California College of Arts and Sciences *Dealer:* Barclay Simpson, Lafayette

The Abstract Expressionists were a dominant influence on her early oil paintings, which became increasingly abstract. She was interested in process painting that combined the intuitive with the spontaneous. Bright organic shapes dominated her canvases, while lines wove through the forms and spaces, creating energetic movements. As she became more involved with process painting, spontaneity became less of a concern. She began to labor over her painted surfaces, scratching and scraping into multiple layers of paint. Her recent work is moody and contemplative, featuring dark and muted architectural forms, simple geometric shapes, and lines occupying ambiguous environments.

GIRARD, LAWRENCE R. (Painter, Commercial Illustrator)
1201 Alta Vista, #309, Santa Barbara, CA 93103

Collections: Rokuroku, Tokyo *Exhibitions:* Honeywell Trade Exhibition; Spectrum Gallery, San Francisco *Education:* Art Center College of Design

He was influenced primarily by James Rosenquist; he prefers oils on rolling, sculptured canvas. His montages are as large as four by twenty feet; they often tell a story and leave the viewer with a message. One of them, based on William Randolph Hearst, brought together a castle, a rosebud and a scene from *Citizen Kane*. In 1983, while developing an oversized oil montage, depicting the evolution of western technology, he developed a process he named Corp Art. In another process called Visionary Art, he used computer chips to produce works such as *Energy One and Two* and *Bonfire on Wall Street*. He has recently made large, abstracted oil paintings of flowers.

GLAD, DEANNA (Painter, Commercial Illustrator)
P. O. Box 3261, Santa Monica, CA 90403

Born: 1942 *Awards:* National Endowment for the Arts *Collections:* Seiko Corp.; Levi Strauss Corp. *Exhibitions:* Janus Gallery, Los Angeles; Biennale of Lausanne *Education:* UCLA

The strong, emotional impact of Edvard Munch's woodcuts and the drawings of Picasso had the greatest influence on her graphic sense. Her work began as abstracted figures or landscapes, often showing multiple images suggestive of different situations or states of being. An interest in strong form, bold color and design coupled with a sculptural quality, led to the development of her bas-relief fabric images in 1971. These often lighthearted, emblematic sculptures combine sewing, appliqué and stuffing to comment on popular culture and icons such as the automobile. The early 1980s marked a return to watercolor and acrylic painting, inspired by travels in rural California and Nevada. These pastoral landscapes are executed in subdued colors with simplified forms of cattle, oak trees and horses. She has recently begun to incorporate bright, intense colors and sharply delineated forms in figurative works often surrounded by borders. Including in this series are images inspired by Greek myths and the Book of Revelations, rendered expressionistically and rooted in traditional wood cuts.

GLEITSMAN, BING (Ceramist)
200 Buzzard Lagoon Rd., Corralitos, CA 95026

Born: 1953 *Awards:* Best in Show, Tempe Fest; 1st Place Westwood Arts Fest *Exhibitions:* Beverly Hills

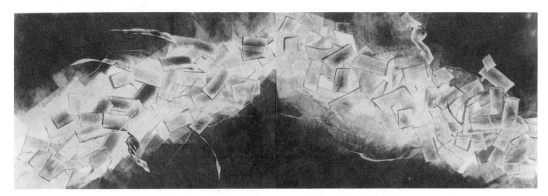

Joan J. Grant, *Space-Time,* 61 x 22, monoprint diptych

Betty Gold, *Kaikoo V* 240 x 276 x 168, welded steel and paint. Courtesy: Sinskey Winery, Napa, CA

Stanley Goldstein, *Cocktails at America,* 23 x 48, black and white acrylic on paper.
Courtesy: Sixth Street Studio, San Francisco

Affair in Gardens; Santa Cruz Art League *Education:* UC-Irvine; Cal. State-Long Beach

After formal training in sculpture, he developed his throwing abilities as a production potter. In 1976, he set up his own clay studio. He focused on developing new colors, hand-painting brightly colored oxides over high-gloss white glaze and using sgraffito (etching into wax) for details. Today he continues to add new colors and techniques. He has returned to his roots as a sculptor, creating abstract vessels with mask-like faces. He is also fulfilling a demand for art as furniture, and he is one of the few ceramists throwing fine porcelain to architectural sizes for both interior and exterior floor lamps, tables and freestanding pieces.

GLOVER, ROBERT LEON (Ceramist, Sculptor)
6015 Santa Monica Blvd., Los Angeles, CA 90036

Born: 1936 *Awards:* Ford Foundation Grant *Collections:* First Federal Savings, South Pasadena; Southern California Container Corporation *Exhibitions:* San Francisco Museum of Fine Arts; Space Gallery, Los Angeles *Education:* Chouinard Art Institute; Los Angeles County Art Institute *Dealer:* Space Gallery, Los Angeles

His ceramic sculpture is formal and abstract, dealing with the natural attributes of clay as both medium and metaphor. Early upright forms were rounded, closed and engraved with designs suggestive of bricks or stonework. These made references to standing stones and conceptually linked the manmade object with the natural. Recent work is modular and composed of units that are placed in natural settings or arranged within an interior space to create a "site." The curving stoneware slabs of his piece *Dial O* are arranged in a circle ten feet in diameter. Connotations of prehistoric earthworks, archaeological sites and techniques, and the natural landscape are activated by these pieces.

GLOWIENKE, CARL (Sculptor)
2316 Bancroft St., San Diego, CA 92104

Born: 1955 *Collections:* Greenpeace Permanent Collection *Exhibitions:* American Cetacean Society Biennial Symposium; Scrimshaw Gallery, San Francisco *Education:* Cal. State-Northridge

He wrote briefly for *ARTWEEK* after taking a degree in music. His subsequent abstract wood torsos were heavily influenced by Moore and Nakian. In 1985, he went to the Sea World Research Center and began studying marine mammals. His work of the period was influenced by Randy Puckett and Jerry Glover. He is presently continuing to study marine mammal anatomy under Larry Foster and is apprenticing in bronze work under Guillermo Castano of Mexico City. His recent, graceful bronze sculptures are large-scale, anatomically accurate depictions of animals. He has recently proposed building a dinosaur playground.

GODFREY, RICHARD (Installation Artist)
Studio 8A, 110 Center St., Los Angeles, CA

Born: 1953 *Exhibitions:* Santa Barbara Contemporary Arts Forum; Muckenthaler Cultural Center, Fullerton *Education:* San Francisco Art Institute

Using a variety of materials, he constructs environmental installations with geometric figures, water, fire and red, black and purple ultraviolet light. These minimalist, post-modern spaces are designed to reverse the traditional western visual style. He takes three-dimensional forms and, utilizing a viewing chamber to enforce a three-point perspective and ultra-violet light to flatten forms, reduces it to two dimensions. In a recent work, *Clara's Song*, a glass flame burns atop an inverted blue pyramid, suspended over water. In another, *Pitch*, blue spheres hover over and around square blue frames, suspended over a raised platform and water. With elemental shapes and substances, these intricately structured works give the illusion of simplicity, while echoing the complexity and elegance of nature.

GOLD, BETTY (Sculptor, Painter)
1324 Pacific Ave., Venice, CA 90291

Born: 1935 *Collections:* Newport Harbor Museum; Palm Springs Desert Museum *Exhibitions:* Milwaukee Museum; National Contemporary Museum, Seoul *Education:* U. of Texas *Dealer:* Natoli Ross, Santa Monica

Her art experience includes painting, drawing, silkscreening, tapestry design, photography and jewelry-making, but she is best known for her outdoor monumental sculptures. Worked in welded steel, her artistic concerns are expressed in both an abstract figurative style and a non-objective, geometric style. Sculptures are either left unfinished or are painted with Rustoleum paints in red, black and yellow. Currently she is working on her painting, using acrylic paint on handmade paper. These geometric works are puzzle-like variations on rectangles.

GOLD, E. J. (Painter)
P.O. Box 1656, Grass Valley, CA 95945

Born: 1941 *Collections:* Museum of Ancient and Modern Art; Connell Foundation for the Fine Arts *Exhibitions:* Museum of Modern Art, New York; Houston Museum of Fine Arts *Education:* Otis Art Institute *Dealer:* Coleman Greene Gallery, NYC; Spiral Gallery, Los Angeles

He has always worked as an experimental artist. The techniques of forced perspective, planar contiguities, color field reductionism and iso-magnification have been important in the development of his work with breathing and soft sculptures. His work has ranged broadly from the figurative to the abstract; in all styles, he has concentrated on gestural refinement. Recent work includes a series of large paintings with figures floating in and out of walls and corridors. Relying on perspective distortions and exposed canvas, they reflect the influence of sumi-e through their use of irreversible lines. A disturbing sense of otherworldliness contrasts with a mood of deep serenity and peace. Also working in small lithographs on his own press, he is collaborating with John Cage on a livre d'artiste to be published in Germany.

GOLD, STUART (Painter, Video Artist)
1749 Vine St., Berkeley, CA 94703

Born: 1949 *Collections:* Achenbach Foundation, San Francisco *Exhibitions:* San Francisco Art Institute; Somh Gallery, San Francisco *Education:* San Francisco State University; UC-Davis *Dealer:* Hatley Martin, San Francisco

His concern with the negative subliminal effects of television has been the basis for his art since the late 1970s. At that time, he portrayed television as an altar in a series of representational etchings. In subsequent drawings and paintings, he developed a style that he calls video syntax, which resembles the video wave and scramble patterns on a television screen when it is mal-

Robert Goldman, *Sunset–La Jolla,* 24 x 30, oil on canvas. Courtesy: Tarbox Gallery

Patricia George, *17 Mile Drive,* 30 x 40, oil with palette knife on canvas

functioning. *Death for Dinner* is a mixed media altar that comments upon the degree to which violence is transmitted via television and, thus, taken for granted. The central portion of the altar consists of a television that plays taped footage, manipulated by the artist, of the 1967 shooting of a Viet Cong prisoner by a general in the South Vietnamese army, a scene that was viewed by Americans both on television and in newspapers and magazines. The left panel of his altar depicts the scene in painted video syntax, while in the right wing, an abstract video pattern suggests the echo of the shooting—the screen gone haywire.

GOLDEN, JUDITH (Photographer, Mixed Media Artist)

4108 W. Camino Nuestro, Tucson, AZ 85745

Born: 1934 *Awards:* NEA Grant; Grant, Arizona Commission for the Arts *Collections:* San Francisco Museum of Modern Art; Los Angeles County Museum of Art *Exhibitions:* Museum of Contemporary Photography, Chicago; Museum of Photographic Art, San Diego *Education:* School of the Art Institute of Chicago; UC-Davis *Dealer:* Andrew Smith, Santa Fe, NM; Etherton Gallery, Tucson, AZ

She creates unusual photographic portraits and self-portraits depicting universal female archetypes. She uses theatrical make-up and oil paint on the models; she paints the print and adds various natural and manufactured collage materials. Her work is an exploration of the masks people wear in everyday life, and how they daily recreate their public identities. At other times, she has recycled found images of celebrities, illustrating the post-modernist blur between public and private, genuine and mediated life. In her recent series, "Persona" and "Elements," she abandons contemporary American culture and turns to mythological themes. The human element unites with vegetation or animals in ways that emphasize timeless connections with the earth.

GOLDEN, SHEILA (Painter, Ceramist)

P.O. Box 183, Penngrove, CA 94951

Born: 1943 *Collections:* Willitts Designs, Petaluma *Exhibitions:* Vorpal Gallery, San Francisco; The Clay Company Gallery, Sebastopol *Education:* Sonoma State U.

She has had a varied career that began with abstract expressionist studies with Morris Davidson in Provincetown, Massachusetts. She has also worked in commercial art and film, and, in the mid-1970s, she created a series of colored-pencil-animations backgrounds for Sesame Street. By the early 1980s, she had returned to painting, this time working in watercolor. These abstract works are inspired by the sun and the ocean, and are rendered in hot colors—such as purples, hot pinks and yellows— against cooler colors, all surrounded by white. Her work as a ceramist consists of organically-shaped vessels which she airbrushes with pastels.

GOLDER, CARLA E. (Printmaker, Draughtsperson)

4144 Telegraph Ave., Oakland, CA 94609

Born: 1949 *Awards:* Jerome Foundation Fellowship, Kala Institute; 1st Prize, Ariel Gallery, NYC *Collections:* Achenbach Foundation for Graphic Arts, San Francisco; Bureau of Art Exhibition, Lodz, Poland *Exhibitions:* Reed Whipple Art Center Gallery, Las

Vegas; Lone Wolf Gallery, San Francisco *Education:* Ohio State U.; San Francisco Academy of Art

She began working principally in mezzotint in 1982, because of a fascination with chiaroscuro and an interest in combining organic and geometric elements. In subsequent years, she has done a number of large pencil and prismacolor drawings using magnolias and succulents as principle imagery. Recently exploring color mezzotints, lithography and silkscreen, her subject matter has broadened, encompassing dolls in addition to plant forms. She pays more attention in her work to the value contrasts of light and shade than in color, and her engraving and dry point techniques enable her to achieve a linen-like surface to her prints.

GOLDMAN, ANNE (Sculptor, Ceramist)

1972 Meadow Rd., Walnut Creek, CA 94595

Born: 1945 *Collections:* Nora Eccles Harrison Museum, Logan UT; City and Art Commission of San Francisco *Exhibitions:* American Craft Museum, NYC; Crocker Museum of Art, Sacramento

She began her ceramics career doing functional stoneware. She is obsessed with textures; her surfaces are smooth, glazed and textural or unglazed. She continued to work with high-fired stoneware because she wanted to retain the feeling of earthiness. Her pieces are wheel-thrown, then sculpted and carved. The highly textured, abstract forms are inspired by rocks, trees, mountains and objects from the sea. She has developed an array of original techniques over the last twenty years: for example, the use of porcelain slips to create highlights and the addition of heavy, sand-clay mixes to produce a natural, eroded appearance. Carving with stones, slate and wood, she introduces an interplay between the work's surface and its form.

GOLDMAN, KEN (Painter)

5057 Lotus St., San Diego, CA 92107

Born: 1950 *Collections:* San Diego Museum of Fine Art *Exhibitions:* Museum of Natural History, San Diego; MOA Center Museum Gallery, Long Beach *Education:* Art Students League *Dealer:* Knowles Gallery, La Jolla

He is one of the few veiled watercolor artists in the U.S., having studied with the media's originator, Liane Collot D'Herbois, in Europe. Incorporating several hundred washes of watercolor pigment, his paintings exude color and light effects that are more organic than traditional watercolor, oil or acrylic techniques. He works from a 44-inch-wide roll of rag paper stretched and stapled to bars. Each painting's subject emerges as the wash process progresses. Imagery includes semi-abstract figures, florals and animals. He also paints portraits and landscapes in oil and pastel. In the landscape paintings, he constantly juggles oppositions: earth's density in relation to light and atmosphere. Color, texture and compositional movement are the relating principles between these forces. In all of his artistic endeavors, he strives to convey the complete ambiance of the subject.

GOLDMAN, ROBERT (Painter)

2851 Capps St., San Diego, CA 92104

Born: 1948 *Awards:* 2nd Place, Regional Exhibition, Scottsdale, AZ *Collections:* The Henley Group, San Diego *Exhibitions:* San Diego Museum of Art; United States International Universities, San Diego *Education:* UC-San Diego *Dealer:* Tar Box Gallery, San Diego

Joseph Goldyne, *Tulips, Dots and Scratches,* 48 x 35,
monoprint and pastel. Courtesy: Magnolia Editions

Ken Goldman, *Portrait of Stephanie,* 40 x 34, pastel

His landscape paintings of the last decade strongly follow traditions set by the Post-Impressionists. The artist prefers to begin his work outdoors, on location in various areas of San Diego or New Mexico. As he roughs out his subject in oils, he commits the light and colors to memory. He completes the piece later in his studio, utilizing a light impasto treatment to highlight various areas. While his latest pieces have strayed from realism, the tone, color and line lend each painting a recognizable sense of place.

GOLDNER, MARCIA (Photographer)
221 Vine St., No. 23, Philadelphia, PA 19106

Born: 1952 *Awards:* Sarah A. Peters Fellowship, Moore College of Art *Collections:* Handwerker Gallery, Ithaca, NY; Humboldt Arts Council, Eureka *Exhibitions:* Los Angeles Municipal Gallery; Vision Gallery, San Francisco *Education:* Moore College of Art, Philadelphia; Temple U., Tyler School of Art

Influenced by avant-garde photographers Bill Larson and Lawrence Bach, she is concerned with a non-traditional exploration into the medium. Once settled into color photography, she became involved with creating illusions, mostly by photographing media images within other photographs, or by simply collaging images experimentally. For example, a layered effect is achieved by using film masks made of grease pencil on clear acetate. In *Portrait of an Aged Beauty*, two dramatic blue eyes in heavy make-up are prephotographed and placed on a woman's face of smaller scale. Most of the artist's work deals with women of all ages, though she has recently begun using totally abstract, non-reality based figures.

GOLDSMITH, SUSAN (Painter)
1 Garden Rd., San Anselmo, CA 94960

Born: 1955 *Awards:* Merit Award, California College of Arts & Crafts *Exhibitions:* Gallery 506, San Rafael; Northern California Print Competition *Education:* California College of Arts and Crafts

After studying printmaking, the artist explored lithography under the guidance of Robert Bechtle. She employed both figurative and non-figurative elements in her compositions, utilizing a full palette. Nature is a constant source of inspiration to the artist, and while recent work contains surreal, humorous touches, the organic forms remain recognizable. Milk cows with flower patterns for spots, and other extraordinary farm animals, frequently inhabit her paintings. In an earlier series she focused on the skulls of animals, while another commissioned project dealt solely with florals. Renoir and O'Keeffe intrigue her, but the work of Joseph Rafael has had the most profound influence on her style.

GOLDSTEIN, STANLEY (Painter)
1458 Page St., #3, San Francisco, CA 94117

Born: 1954 *Awards:* Yale Fellowship *Exhibitions:* Jeremy Stone Gallery, San Francisco; Santa Barbara Museum of Natural History *Education:* UC-Santa Barbara *Dealer:* Jeremy Stone Galley, San Francisco

After college, he worked as a cartoonist, illustrator, sign painter and graphic artist. At the same time, he produced a series of large-scale, dreamlike paintings on the theme of man and woman. Influenced by Hopper, Bechman, Manet and Sargeant, he began to paint directly from life. His everyday subjects include studio and friends, with undercurrents of humor and passion.

He captures light in a manner that seeks to transform the mundane into the beautiful. His paintings are realistic, but the evidence of brushwork is clearly visible. His media are oil, watercolor and acrylic on canvas, masonite, cardboard and paper. Although most of his works are wall pieces, he has also experimented with two- and four-sided paintings.

GOLDYNE, JOSEPH (Printmaker)
1 Maple Street, San Francisco, CA 94118

Born: 1942 *Collections:* Fine Arts Museum, San Francisco; Museum of Fine Arts, Boston *Exhibitions:* John Berggruen Gallery, San Francisco; De Saisset Museum, U. of Santa Clara *Education:* Harvard U.; U. of California *Dealer:* John Berggruen Gallery

The revelation of Degas' monotypes led him to his medium. Unlike the finger-painting approach that characterizes much work done in monotypes, his prints are characterized by delicate lines and highly refined color blending. The small size of many of his earlier prints invites a private scrutiny of the subject matter; objects small in themselves—a flower, a paper clip, a peach, a pair of tweezers—are placed in a corner of a room or simply on a flat, plain surface. His works from the 1970s often juxtapose images from paintings by old and modern masters. Seemingly unrelated, these passages are made to harmonize through manipulation of composition and color. Works in the 1980s comprise drawings and large pastels as well as monotypes. Recent monotypes are much larger and are frequently heightened with pastel.

GOLIGHTLY, DOUGLAS (Painter)
1155 W. Brown Ave., Porterville, CA 93257

Born: 1931 *Collections:* The Milwaukee Journal *Exhibitions:* Margaret E. Rogers Gallery, Santa Cruz; Sunset Cultural Center, Carmel *Education:* U. of Wisconsin, Madison *Dealer:* Reid Gallery, Friday Harbor, WA

His technique has been influenced by the works of Aaron Bohrod, John Wilde and Salvador Dali. He has always worked in oil in a hyperrealistic style. In his work, the forms of nature are transformed to produce new designs and meanings. Subject matter includes people, horses, dogs, cats, birds, still lifes and the nude. His sharply focused paintings are attempts to express the intangible.

GONZALEZ, ARTHUR (Sculptor)
3038 Texas St., Oakland, CA 94602

Born: 1954 *Awards:* NEA Fellowship *Exhibitions:* Oakland Museum; Allrich Gallery *Education:* Cal. State-Sacramento; UC-Davis *Dealer:* Sharpe Gallery, NYC

After training in photorealism and then developing a painting style on organically shaped ceramic slabs, he discovered a facility for creating works out of found objects. Encouraged by Robert Arneson, he moved from there to creating figurative sculpture in the round. Manual Neri also had an influence on this work by supporting his rough style. Eventually, he returned to working with walls, creating sculptures in 180 degrees, using a white wall to double as deep space. His figures, which have an unusual feeling of depth for relief pieces, are usually caught in some action rather than at rest or in a pose. As these pieces developed, he began juxtapos-

Carl Glowienke, *Southern Right Whale,* 20 x 20 x 15, bronze, glass. Courtesy: Stephen Schackne

Mary Gould, *Falcon,* 36 x 12 x 12, plaster, wood, acrylic paint. Photograph: Jacqueline Paul

Nori Green, *Warrior,* 96 x 60, ink on Japanese papers with found objects

ing figures with inanimate objects or with other figures, expressing the idea that time is measured internally and that its measure is determined by our relationship to our surroundings.

GONZALES, D. JUAN (Painter, Sculptor)
14 1/2 W. Pine St., Woodbridge, CA 95258

Born: 1945 *Exhibitions:* State Capital, Sacramento; Haggins Gallery, Stockton *Education:* Delta College, Stockton

Largely self-taught, he believes artists have a responsibility to the community. He admires the Cubists and Dadaists, because of their willingness to expand the bounds of art. His paintings on contemporary themes include a series on the fetus. These bright Daliesque oils on canvases, as large as 58-by-48 inches, depict the fetus, sometimes with a lily, from conception to term. He has recently been working in various canvas sizes and with various media; he has planned a work that will bring together fetus, Last Supper and space imagery. His sculptures are developed from bronze and found objects and they, like his paintings, make contemporary statements.

GONZALEZ, MANUAL (Sculptor)
5120 Pony Express, Camino, CA 95709

Born: 1938 *Awards:* 1st Prize, El Dorado County Fair *Exhibitions:* River Park Gallery, Coloma; Billie G's, Diamond Springs

A self-taught sculptor, he began working with stone at age forty- three, after ten years of painting with acrylics. Overwhelmed by the life-size sculptures he saw on a trip to Zacatecas Mexico, he returned to the States intent on learning the art. Carved from a diverse number of stones and woods, including El Dorado marble, black limestone and Utah and Nevada alabaster, his highly polished surfaces, accented by roughly chiseled formations, reveal the influence of his love for the work of Michelangelo and Rodin. Recent works show an inclination toward pre-Colombian and impressionistic sculpture. He generally carves directly on stone without a model. His works are inspired by childhood memories, the shape of the stone, people and animals and his theological studies, from the time when he was an member of a religious order in the 1960s.

GOODE, JOE (Painter)
P.O. Box 10372, Marina del Rey, CA 90295

Born: 1937 *Awards:* NEA Grant; American Foundation of Artists *Collections:* American Federation of Arts, NYC *Exhibitions:* James Corcoran Gallery, Santa Monica; Pence Gallery, Santa Monica *Education:* Chouinard Art Institute, Los Angeles *Dealer:* James Corcoran Gallery, Santa Monica

After moving to Los Angeles from Oklahoma, he established his reputation in 1961 with a show of milk-bottle paintings, which were followed by series of houses and staircases. During the earlier years, his subjects have included screwdrivers, matches, milk bottles, houses, unmade beds, clouds and windows. In 1978, he moved to the foothills of the Sierra Nevadas, where he made canvases that he blasted with a shotgun. He called this work his "Environmental Impact Series." His recent paintings of forest fires, trees and other natural forces are technically impeccable. He now divides his time between his studios in Venice, California and Springville, California.

GOODMAN, RIMA (Painter)

10548 Blythe Ave., Los Angeles, CA 90064

Born: 1929 *Awards:* Best of Show, Laguna Beach Museum of Art *Exhibitions:* Los Angeles Institute of Contemporary Art; Los Angeles County Museum of Art *Education:* U. of Miami, FL *Dealer:* Classic Artforms, Los Angeles

She began painting in a figurative, expressionist style, which she later combined with abstract expressionist techniques, creating a style in which a strong gestural use of paint is combined with areas of flat, thin staining. This was the style of her "fish paintings," a series of works offering a wealth of symbolic interpretations. She has begun to experiment with the application of wax and collage constructions to her paintings. These recent paintings use feathers, bones and lights attached to the canvas. The representational subject matter is historical, although the placing of paintings "in and on" paintings creates a mysterious effect. The experiments in relief techniques, waxing and construction explore the sense of scale and space and exploit this sense of mystery.

GORDON, MICHAEL (Ceramist, Sculptor)
207 Sequoia Ave., Walnut Creek, CA 94595

Born: 1940 *Awards:* Moses Award, San Francisco Potters Association *Collections:* Antonio Prieto Memorial; Mills College *Exhibitions:* Los Angeles County Art Museum; Eva Chan Gallery, La Jolla *Education:* California College of Arts and Crafts

During his student years, 1959-1967, his work was influenced by Peter Voulkos and the Abstract Expressionists. The three-foot pots he made were thrown in sections; he used slips and oxides to decorate them with abstract forms. In 1973, a fire destroyed all his past work, and for the next three years, he worked at the Berkeley Art Foundry, casting bronze sculpture for many Bay Area artists. Influenced by his foundry work, he has adapted a patina-like color into his classically shaped pots. Using copper and iron in the raku process, he achieves a semi-matte finish with iridescent coppers, blues, purples and golds. He also does commissioned sculpture work.

GORDON-NIZRI, EMILY (Painter)
P.O. Box 125, Oregon House, CA 95962

Born: 1945 *Awards:* Juror's Award, Crocker-Kingsley, Crocker Art Museum; Award of Merit, California State Fair *Exhibitions:* Crocker-Kingsley, Sacramento; California State Fair *Education:* U. of Maryland; Cal. State U.

She manipulates composition and color in work that is an attempt to provoke a contemplative state from the viewer. *Torn Paper, Torn Lives* is a startlingly evocative oil still life of three purple onions sitting on a linoleum surface, wherein shards of glass reflect two grief-stricken figures. Her new series of abstract, non-figurative oil paintings, "Stones of Jerusalem," was inspired by architecture and stone work she saw during a trip to Israel. Her recent painting has been influenced by contemporary magazines and newspapers.

GOTTLIEB, ROSITA (Painter)
12434 Aneta St., Los Angeles, CA 90066

Born: 1930 *Collections:* President Lopez Mateos; Holocaust Museum, Jerusalem *Exhibitions:* Old Jaffa Gallery, Tel Aviv; Instituto Nacional de Belles Artes, Mexico City

Her most recent series of paintings is "Invisible Cities," which continues to explore the more spiritual aspects

M. Gershgoren, *Mountain Cabin,* 30 x 40, oil on canvas

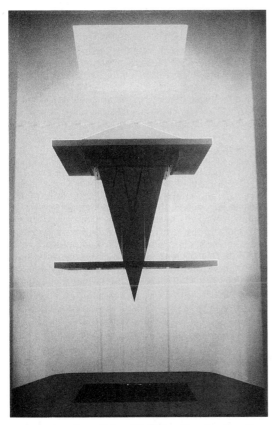

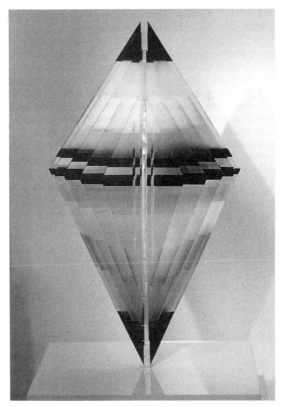

Richard Godfrey, *Trine,* 70 x 30 x 30, mixed media with water

Jackie Greber, *Noetic Reflections,* 27 x 15 x 9, lacquered acrylic

of representational art. Working with a palette knife, she creates paintings in which textures play against her strong use of color. *The Enchanted Forest* is typical of her approach; in this piece, she takes an expressionistic approach to the sequoias that guard the blue sky, highlighted by bright yellow. While vibrant and bold, her work equally exhibits delicacy and sensitivity to the immensity of the subject matter.

GOULD, MARY (Sculptor, Set Designer)
1641 San Pablo Ave., #3, Berkeley, CA 94702

Born: 1923 *Exhibitions:* Walter and McBean Galleries, San Francisco; Center for Visual Arts, Oakland *Education:* San Francisco Art Institute; UC-Davis *Dealer:* Virginia Breier Gallery, San Francisco

A dance student of Martha Graham, she has been influenced in sculpture by the movements and dynamics of dance, the color and strength of the theater, and the human body's expression. All of her work reflects the relationship between dance and sculpture. In her early work, she used fiberglas to build large, figurative forms, covering the forms with fabric, padding and other materials. Her current work is smaller in size. Because of the hazards of fiberglas, she no longer works with that material, instead using plaster, clay, carved styrofoam and cloth maché. Recent work includes a series of fourteen-to-sixteen-inch sculptures of people and a series of life-sized and larger-than-life sculptures of dogs. Both series reflect her concern for movement, dynamics and truth in form. Her set design work includes a recent collaboration with dancer Nancy Bryan on the set pieces for a feminist work entitled *A Living Room*, presented at the Oakland Museum.

GRAEF, ALLEN H. (Glass Artist)
3823 E. Anaheim St., Long Beach, CA 90804

Born: 1942 *Collections:* North Dakota State U.; Alfred U., NY *Exhibitions:* Art-A-Fair, Laguna Beach

He has researched, done extensive work with and manufactures dichroic glass: a two colored glass medium, covered with micro-thin layers of metals, which can be manipulated to produce a variety of brilliant colors. He bevels the German 6mm crystal to make elaborate abstractions, or uses a combination of glasses and techniques to create traditional designs such as fleur-de-lis, stars or original filigrees. The pieces are often elaborate abstractions for private residences. He is the owner of The Glass Bevel in Long Beach, and he currently spends most of his time doing intricate bevels for his studio, as well as researching and developing new products and techniques for the glass industry.

GRAME, TRICIA (Painter, Collagemaker)
234 Montair Dr., Danville, CA 94526

Born: 1946 *Collections:* Harrison & Crossfield Co., NY; IBM, San Ramon *Exhibitions:* 333 Bush St., San Francisco; Art Concepts, Walnut Creek *Education:* College of Arts and Crafts, Oakland; Cal. State-Hayward

She is inspired by the varying luminosities, textures, and color vibrations of nature's abstract elements. Her work is a mixed media collage of color field painting, fabric, oriental rag, and handmade paper. Some areas are serene, other less so, but she balances the whole through a harmony of color which creates a mood or internal feeling. She either paints or pours the pigment and then peels pigment from selected areas to give the

work a sculptural appearance, creating both an earthy and atmospheric effect. She has been influenced by Harold Parish, Helen Frankenthaler, Nathan Oliver, and Robert Rauschenberg.

GRANT, JOAN JULIEN (Sculptor)
2768 Sawtelle Blvd., Los Angeles, CA 90064

Born: 1934 *Exhibitions:* Royal Hiberian Academy, Dublin; Art Rental Gallery, Los Angeles County Museum of Art *Education:* Otis Art Institute *Dealer:* Gloria Delson, Los Angeles

She has been influenced by Kurt Schwitters and David Smith. After leaving graduate school, she juxtaposed steel supports with layered stacks of recycled wood. Gestural and spontaneous, this early concept of "frozen movement" in the form of installations was meant to represent the unconscious manifested in a recognizable form. After a middle period of working on wall pieces, she began experimenting, combining small branches and cut pieces of wood with plexiglas, bronze, copper, aluminum, steel, and traces of paint. These sculptures remain part of her wall-based environments. She is currently working with linear steel parts combined with geometric shapes in wood. She continues to be intensely concerned with the concepts of gravity and the modular in multilateral installations.

GRANTHEM, CLAUDINE (Draughtsperson, Sculptor)
P.O. Box 737, Mountain View Dr., Camino, CA 95709

Born: 1936 *Collections:* Capitol Bank at Commerce Center, Sacramento *Exhibitions:* Crocker Art Museum, Sacramento; Solano Community College, Suisun *Education:* California State U.

Her work turned toward the abstract in the mid-1980s. Influenced by Eva Hesse's use of non-traditional materials, she started using cloth, paper and paint on canvas to alter the surface of her works. These pieces evolved into wall hangings containing references to the human figure. Her drawings became more abstracted and simplified, combining figures with their supporting props. Rendered in acrylic on paper, these works grew increasingly expressive, incorporating oilsticks in black, red and neutral tones. Her sculpture, which either hangs on the wall or lays on the floor, is influenced by the primitive arts of Mexico and Central America. She layers, ties and wraps such materials as cloth, paper, twine, wire and metal around wooden armatures to create abstract figurative images. This cold-forming method includes riveting and hammering strips of metal into forms that allude to masks and shields. Her limited palette consists of black, red, gray, white and ocher in both matte and glossy patinas. Recent drawings refer to these sculptures and consist of figures in shallow spaces.

GRAVES, KA (Mixed Media Artist)
921 W. Lynwood, Phoenix, AZ 85007

Born: 1938 *Collections:* Rutgers U.; Arizona State U. *Exhibitions:* Otis Arts Center; Tempe Fine Arts *Education:* Arizona State U. *Dealer:* Elaine Horwitch, Palm Springs

She works in three-dimensional installations, clay and porcelain masks, and paintings. Her work is influenced by traditional African body painting and by the rich, decorative work of Gustav Klimt, and themes of ritual and costuming predominate in all media. She recently created an installation of art furniture that combines

Tricia Grame, *Descend,* 67 x 41, mixed media
collage on canvas

Gary Yakima Geyer, *Californian on Monterey Bay,*
36 x 30 oil on canvas

raw silks, skunk and fox furs, mule horns and wood carving in a sofa bed intended for practical use. Non-realistic figurative works include wire figures dressed in costumes derived from Russian and Eastern European folk designs. Colors are vibrant and intense against subdued backgrounds.

GRAVES, MICHAEL (Architect)
341 Nassau St., Princeton, NJ 08540

Born: 1934 *Awards:* Progressive Architecture Design Awards; Honor Awards, National American Institute of Architects *Exhibitions:* Museum of Modern Art; Deutsches Architekturmuseum, Frankfurt, West Germany *Education:* U. of Cincinnati; Harvard U.; American Academy in Rome

He is one of America's premier designers of office buildings, public buildings, and private residences. His recent projects include the Portland Building, the Humana Building, the Environmental Education Center at Liberty State Park, the San Juan Capistrano Library, Riverbend Music Center in Cincinnati, the Emory University Museum of Art and Archaeology and Clos Pegase Winery in California's Napa Valley. His other work includes murals, stage sets, installations, furniture and artifacts such as tables and beds. Since 1962, he has taught at Princeton University, where he is Schirmer Professor of Architecture.

GRAY, MAURICE (Printmaker, Sculptor)
21890 Winding Rd., Riverside, CA 92507

Born: 1947 *Awards:* Purchase Award, Zaner Gallery; Purchase Award, San Diego National Print Exhibit *Collections:* Dulin Gallery of Art, Knoxville, TN; J. Paul Getty Trust, Los Angeles *Exhibitions:* Museum of Modern Art, Wakayama, Japan; Museum of Neon Art, Los Angeles *Education:* U. of Colorado, Boulder; U. of Dallas *Dealer:* Artist Trait, Ontario

As an art student in the 1960s, he was caught in the wake of abstract expression, then lured into the hard-edged pop movement. His prints were multicolored and black-and-white "scenes of the crime." Twenty years later he moved from a direct, two-dimensional sensibility into hermetic sculpture. Influenced by Mexican iconography and Egyptian enshrinement, hammered and painted aluminum tombs, up to ten feet tall, hold wrapped figures. A neon element produces an aura around the human form, which may have a coyote or wolf skull. The cloth wrapping is painted with distorted shapes; the sarcophagus is covered with several different colors of oil enamel, then sanded to reveal the layers. Up to 3000 screws per piece are screwed to an underform like rivets. Then their plating is etched away so that they will rust. The result appears as a constructed, freestanding painting, a three-dimensional version of the original prints.

GRAY, ROBERT (Painter)
P.O. Box 836, San Marcos, CA 92069

Born: 1952 *Awards:* Best of Show, Catalina Art Expo, Catalina Island; Del Mar Exhibition *Collections:* Whaler's Museum, Hawaii; Natural History Museum, San Diego *Exhibitions:* Knowles Gallery, La Jolla; Rancho Sante Fe's Historical Inn *Education:* UCLA *Dealer:* Underwater Studio, Rancho Sante Fe

Influenced by the work of Jacques Cousteau, he has focused on rendering the undersea settings and denizens of the Pacific Ocean. His association with Dr. Steven Leatherwood, the head research scientist at Hubbs-Sea World, has given him the opportunity to refine his technique and increase his knowledge of marine life. Using combinations of oil and acrylic, applied with brush and airbrush, he has developed two basic techniques for accurately depicting the underwater scenes. Working in variable light, he layers the paint, sealing layers with soluvar to capture specific visual properties and colors. When completed and viewed under rheostatted light, these works give the illusion of three-dimensionality. He has also experimented with a bubble placed over a painting to make it appear as though the work is being viewed through an aquarium.

GREAVER, HANNE (Painter, Printmaker)
P.O. Box 120, Cannon Beach, OR 97110

Born: 1933 *Awards:* Purchase Award, Boston Printmakers, Boston *Collections:* British Museum, London; Smithsonian Institute, Washington, DC *Exhibitions:* Boston Printmakers; Northwest Print Council & Oregon Arts Commission *Education:* School of Arts and Crafts, Copenhagen; Kalamazoo Institute of Arts, Kalamazoo, MI *Dealer:* Attic Gallery, Portland, OR

After many years working primarily with woodcuts, etchings and lithographs, she has recently turned her attention to oil painting. She draws inspiration from daily life in a small Oregon coastal community, her subjects ranging from people and animals to landscapes and domestic interiors. Early prints include *Puff,* a woodcut in gold, orange and brown portraying a young boy crouched down in a field, blowing on a large seed puff. Another woodcut reflects her experience while living in Maine: A forest of firs at night is rendered in shades of blue contrasting with the light of the moon. Recent work focuses on flowers and interiors. Her palette is now lighter, and she colors by hand.

GREAVES, SUSAN F. (Painter)
15742 Middletown Park, Redding, CA 96001

Born: 1944 *Awards:* John R. Grabach Award, American Artists Professional League, NYC *Exhibitions:* Redding Museum and Art Center; North Valley Art League, Redding *Education:* Los Angeles State U.; Sergei Bongart School of Art, Los Angeles *Dealers:* Jack Meier Gallery, Houston; Roundtree Gallery, Monroe, LA; Adams Art Consultants, Redding

Rich, exaggerated and harmonious colors dominate a painting style she describes as "classicism with color." Early work as an interior designer in neo-classical New Orleans left her with a romantic and classical sensibility, which is apparent in her painting. Her still lifes and florals range from graceful formal arrangements of silver pitchers, urn-shaped vases and roses and lilacs to more stylized contemporary schemes comprising glittering liquid-filled glasses, single pieces of fruit and colored paper bags. She alternates soft and hard edges emphasizing proportion and anatomy in her portraits and scenes of peasant, western and Native American life. In her landscapes of northern California, she makes freer use of color while retaining the essential elements of drawing and perspective.

GREBER, JACKIE (Sculptor)
2155A Mountsfield Dr., Golden, CO 80401

Born: 1940 *Awards:* 1st Place in Sculpture, Emerald City Classic; Award, Arvada Center for the Arts and

Steve Grossman, *Collection Three,* 100 x 95 x 14, acrylic, wood construction, painted oak balls on canvas. Collection of James and Linda Burrows. Courtesy: Jan Baum Gallery, Los Angeles

Susan Greaves, *Old Man's Story,* 24 x 20, oil

Humanities *Exhibitions:* Art and Science Exhibition, Albuquerque; La Jolla Museum of Contemporary Art *Education:* Stanford U. *Dealer:* Inkfish Gallery, Denver; Ariel Gallery, NYC

Because of her scientific background in biology and psychology, (M.A. and Ph.D.) she approaches properties of light and ideas of perception in new ways. She uses constructivist and minimalist principles to explore light, color, illusion and space. In one series of non-objective reflected-light sculptures, she created the illusion of a geometric form suspended in or receding into a deep gulf of space by airbrushing and lacquering several layers of lucite. In another series, she attained an inner illumination by selectively scarring the surface of stacked acrylic sheets. Her interpretations of feminine biomorphic forms reveal a deep affinity with feminist art.

GREEN, JENNIFER (Painter)
P.O. Box 6964, Bend, OR 97708

Collections: National Maritime Museum, San Francisco; African-American Museum, San Francisco *Exhibitions:* Institute of American Indian Art, Santa Fe, NM; African-American Museum, San Francisco *Education:* Academy of Arts, San Francisco

She paints with watercolor, pastel and oil. She painted historical watercolor paintings of old restored tugboats that work in San Francisco Bay and ocean; she painted many workers from different races; she painted a 15-foot dragon on the mainsail of a Chinese Junk. In 1986, The Institute of American Indian Art Museum featured an exhibition of a major Indian work and all her paintings. She is commissioned directly by Indians on the museum staff to paint Indians. She has recently been painting a large mural of Indians from many tribes.

GREEN, MARCELLA (Painter)
3420 Pine Ridge Lane, Auburn, CA 95603

Born: 1952 *Awards:* Traders Award *Exhibitions:* Artcetera Art Show, Auburn; Community Faith Hospital Art Show, Auburn

She began her career as a commercial artist, working in Advertising. While studying photography, she discovered Chinese ink and brush painting, a style that has had a profound effect on her work. She has had five years' formal training in this technique, working mainly on rice paper. Her later work in this technique has incorporated color into the traditional Chinese style. Recently she has begun to paint landscapes and portraits, in watercolor alone and watercolor mixed with the ink and brush technique. These experiments in mixed media have expanded the range of her style and subject matter beyond the traditional bounds of the ink and brush style.

GREEN, MARTIN LEONARD (Painter, Printmaker)
c/o Art Angles Gallery, Orange, CA 92613

Born: 1936 *Collections:* Fogg Museum, Harvard University; Los Angeles County Museum of Art *Exhibitions:* Santa Barbara Museum of Art; Smithsonian Institution *Education:* Pomona College; Scripps College *Dealer:* Louis Newman Galleries, Beverly Hills

Living atop a mountain near Idyllwild, California, he creates oil paintings, intaglio and lithographic prints, monotypes, and cliche-verre. In his oils, he has attempted to synthesize Oriental and Occidental themes. He has experimented with new methods in printmak-

ing, and his monotypes in particular have attracted attention. His work was included in the traveling exhibition "New American Monotypes", sponsored by the Smithsonian Institution.

GREEN, NORI (Mixed Media Artist)
10635 Wilshire Blvd., Suite 204, Los Angeles, CA 90024

Born: 1937 *Exhibitions:* Robertson Gallery, Beverly Hills; Chalfonte St. Giles, San Francisco *Education:* Art Institute of Chicago; Otis Art Institute

She combines inks with Japanese paper, ribbons and found objects to create works whose subject matter is primarily Far Eastern. Her style is theatrical, sensitive and, at times, fragmented. It is comparable to Lautrec in mood, but echoes some of Klimt's passim. Although she worked from models for many years, she now assembles her brilliantly colored, occasionally figurative, works from her imagination. Her love for the Kabuki and the culture of Japan is a key element of her work.

GREEN, PHYLLIS (Sculptor)
800 Traction Ave., Los Angeles, CA 90013

Born: 1950 *Awards:* NEA Fellowship; Canada Council Project Grant *Exhibitions:* Laguna Art Museum; Jan Baum Gallery, Los Angeles *Education:* UCLA; U. of Manitoba *Dealer:* Jan Baum Gallery, Los Angeles

Inspired by the West Coast ceramics movement and by the emerging feminist consciousness in art that encouraged the use of female body imagery, she began in the late 1970s to create figurative mixed-media sculpture that included clay. After her move to California in 1978, she started to incorporate found (live) wood into the works, and in part through the influence of her teacher, Italo Scanga, wood gradually became her predominant material. The figures became larger and more gestural. In the mid-1980s, she began to coat the wood with a cement polymer mixture, the coating process representing the cultural transformation of natural materials. Her approach to form is reductive and is influenced by the surreal 1930s work of Giacometti, as well as by the work of more contemporary artists such as Louise Bourgeois, Joel Shapiro and Nancy Graves.

GREEN, THEO (Painter)
439 49th St., #11, Oakland, CA 94609

Born: 1956 *Awards:* Artist in Residence, Rancho Poetics, OR *Exhibitions:* Minx Gallery, San Francisco; Southern Exposure Gallery, San Francisco *Education:* UC-Berkeley; Cal. State-Sacramento

In his early ink-on-paper drawings, he drew from a "Rorschach" influence, eventually creating large ink-blot canvases. He became influenced and inspired by Arabic calligraphy, and—drawing on the work of Mark Tobey, Brion Gysin, Robert Motherwell and Sam Francis—he developed his own calligraphic style. For several years he explored transparent and opaque calligraphic gestures on paper, using a variety of media. Recently, he has been working on a series of Pollock-influenced, mixed-media paintings. He drips and splashes on large canvases, sometimes creating large (up to ten by twenty feet), irregularly shaped masonite triptychs. Recent influences include Rothko, Pollock and Kline.

GREENE, JACK (Painter)
2141 Lake St., San Francisco, CA 94121

Born: 1940 *Awards:* Bartlett/Paige Traveling Grant *Collections:* Olson Foundation, CT *Exhibitions:* Bos-

Steve Gillman, *Stone Poem (detail),* 6 of 8 stone heights;
96 to 143 inches, granite

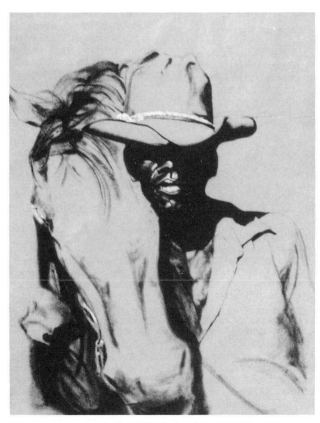

Jennifer Green, *Black Cowboy,* 16 x 22, oil

ton Museum of Fine Arts; U.S. Embassy, Lima, Peru
Education: School of the Boston Museum of Fine Arts
Dealer: The Museum Gallery, San Francisco

His encounters of the psyche are structural abstractions of reality placed at a new juncture of time. His oil paintings of the 1960s were arenas of abstraction—visual events that he pieced together. In 1970, he began using the airbrush to create formalist, sequential structural patterns. By 1976, he had incorporated into the work brush markings and other techniques of creating spatial tensions and varying surface texture. During that period, he used found objects, debris, grids, stencils and drawn images which he enlarged, edited and reconstructed. By the 1980s, he was gathering information with a camera and using slide negatives as the building blocks of his paintings. He has been influenced by Cezanne, Kandinsky, Johns and Tapies.

GREENE, STEPHEN (Painter)
408A Storms Rd., Valley Cottage, NY 10989

Born: 1917 *Awards:* Council of the Arts Award, Washington, DC; Institute of Arts & Letters Award, NYC *Collections:* Tate Gallery; Whitney Museum of American Art *Exhibitions:* Guggenheim Museum; Ruth Bachofner Gallery, Los Angeles *Education:* Iowa State U. *Dealers:* Ruth Bachofner Gallery, Santa Monica; Marilyn Pearl Gallery, NYC

He believes that first there exists the potent visual fact of a painting, drawing the viewer deeply within the work. Further examination then reveals layers of thought and meaning. Similarly, he feels that paint is never merely the embellishment of surface, but also has a power of its own, inextricably linked with the spirit of the work itself. He has recently completed "Enigma," a series of sixteen large paintings. Abstract, mysterious and moody, these works are rendered in the full range of color tones from strong to subtle. The images are evocative of veils, as circular areas of color reveal themselves gradually through layers, painted and structured through the center of the work. He describes these paintings as slightly surreal and highly expressive.

GREENLEAF, JUDITH (Sculptor)
6034 Airport Road, Little River, CA 95456

Awards: 2nd Prize, Gualala Art Center *Exhibitions:* Hatley-Martin Gallery, San Francisco; Mendocino Art Center *Education:* UCLA *Dealer:* Bill Zimmer, Gallery Fair, Mendocino; Deanna Miller, Los Angeles

Her early work was primarily in plastic, often utilizing the natural folding and creasing qualities of resin-dipped fabric to produce organic pieces that combine interior and exterior animal and plant forms. These works comprised both three-dimensional wall pieces and large standing pieces that usually grow from a stem and blossom into sensual, somewhat erotic forms. In the 1970s, ceramics became her primary sculptural material. Current work remains sensual in form, incorporating the natural qualities of the clay with figurative forms. Many of the works combine a strong classical flavor with a contemporary, dynamic, expressive technique. Themes range from comments on natural mythology to a more personal mythology concerning women. Series include life-sized wall-hung porcelains of women; fragments with painted surfaces; large, ceremonial vessels; vases and chalices with figures emerging through rich, subtle metallic surfaces; and large, abstract vessels with a geologic feel. She

works in both high-fire and low-fire materials and is recognized for her rich metallic glazes and lusters. She teaches for the College of the Redwoods and for Santa Rosa Junior College.

GREGORY, ANNE (Mixed Media Artist)
12200 Montecito, D-122, Seal Beach, CA 90740

Born: 1939 *Awards:* Killgore Research Grant; Indiana Arts Commission Grant *Collections:* Portland Art Museum *Exhibitions:* Amarillo Art Center; School of Visual Concepts, Seattle *Education:* Reed College; U. of Washington; Columbia U.

Drawing, painting and two-dimensional design make up her work, which progressed from non-objective painting in oils to acrylic, hard-edged abstracts in the 1960s. In the 1970s, she produced realistic nature studies often depicted on unstretched canvas and treated paper. Printmaking processes are also frequently used to execute the hangings. Her works in calligraphy and the book arts are important aspects of career and have been exhibited in solo shows. Her recent work comprises portraits of neighborhood poets, watercolor still lifes and depictions of landscapes.

GREMEL, JIM (Ceramist)
1625 Kains Ave., Berkeley, CA 94702

Born: 1944 *Exhibitions:* Banaker Gallery, Walnut Creek; California Crafts Museum, San Francisco *Education:* U. of Michigan; Diablo Valley College

His initial experience in functional ceramics and his interest in clean, precisely controlled forms such as Sung Dynasty porcelains led him in 1980 to make a series of large, symmetrical vase forms with Raku-fired monochrome glazes. In 1985, he switched to saggar firing. He continued to expand the size of his forms, and in order to maximize the tension between his tightly thrown forms and the looseness and apparent spontaneity in the colors and patterns of saggar firing, he experimented with surface color and reduction/fuming materials. His recent hand-thrown pieces are ten to forty-two inches tall.

GREY, JEN (Painter)
3728 Lomina Ave., Long Beach, CA 90808

Born: 1951 *Awards:* NEA Grant; California State University Meritorious Performance Awards *Collections:* Harbor National Bank, Long Beach; Security Pacific National Bank, Los Angeles *Exhibitions:* Long Beach Museum of Art; Shakti Gallery, Long Beach *Education:* Maryland Institute; Bradley U.

In the past his work drew from associations with surrealism, chance and internalization. These influences combined to result in mysterious landscape drawings animistically charged and occupied by mundane or revelatory objects. Later works, executed with raw pigments on rock slabs, were 20th-century portable cave paintings, combining appropriate cave iconography with illusionistic renderings of animals and human beings. Recently he has been painting with oil on linen in a series focusing on endangered species. He is redeveloping several of these works as resources for architectural-scale, mixed-media, site-specific installations.

GREY, WHITNEY C. (Painter, Cinematographer)
Rte. #1, Box 356, Scottsdale, AZ 85256

Born: 1949 *Awards:* NEA Grants *Collections:* Smithsonian Institute *Exhibitions:* U. of Aachen Folk Museum, West Germany; Hague, Amsterdam *Education:* Institute of American Indian Arts, U. of New Mexico; Southwest Polytechnic Institute, Albuquerque

This artist of Native American ancestry trained formally at the Institute of American Indian Arts, and he explores and represents the myths of his heritage that have been handed down to him through the elders. He draws upon a wide range of sources for his symbols—the plant and animal kingdoms, inanimate natural objects and human symbolism. The works include references to all Indian cultures. He paints cow skulls and includes feathers and abalone in his watercolors. The palette is brighter in his most recent pieces.

GRGICH, KATHERINE (Painter, Mixed Media Artist)
1659 Ocean Front Walk, Santa Monica, CA 90401

Born: 1958 *Awards:* Best of Show, Brooks Institute *Exhibitions:* Spark Gallery, Venice; Women's Building, Los Angeles *Education:* BFA, Arizona State U.

She paints using a method akin to automatic writing. Feeling that her artistic expression is inspired by a link to a higher spiritual consciousness, she allows her feelings to find their own manifestations in her colorful, free form paintings. She works in pastels, china markers, chalk, acrylics, and spary paints. Among her works is a series of ethereal self-portraits.

GRGICH, SUSAN (Painter)
4520 Via Maria, Santa Barbara, CA 93111

Born: 1933 *Awards:* Jury Award, Santa Barbara Art Association; Exceptional Artist, Atkinson Gallery, Santa Barbara City College *Exhibitions:* Santa Barbara Museum of Art, Rental Gallery; Faulkner Gallery, Santa Barbara *Education:* U. of Oregon; Santa Barbara City College

Early abstract oil pastels and oil paintings show the influence of Kandinsky. Working pencil into the pastels, she has smeared the images and color, giving a soft mysterious effect to the entire composition. From these early explorations, she expanded her repertoire of images to include recognizable forms. Wild animals, insects and amphibians are layered so that they appear and reappear from the depths of a strange atmospheric world. In *Deep Breakfast*, fish faces seem to rise to the surface and fall back again. Often the forms are struggling with each other in a battle for survival.

GRIEGER, SCOTT (Painter)
5102 Franklin Ave., Los Angeles, CA 90027

Born: 1946 *Awards:* NEA Fellowship *Exhibitions:* Mark Richards, Los Angeles; Long Beach City College

Early on, he used well known artistic motifs as raw materials for "Impersonations" and combined sculptures. He soon changed direction and made meticulously rendered, animation-style animals for a short time before retreating to his storefront studio, where he concentrated on the immediacy of communication. Currently, he decals portrait heads onto the surface of corporate logos in an allusion to cubism. His paint handling is rough and expressionistic with a muddy coloring. The work is not confined to a pure rendering of the subject but also toys with psychological and formal elements. Among his influences are Gorky, Fra Angelico and Eco.

GRIFFEATH, JEFF (Painter)
66 Toyon Ln., Sausalito, CA 94965

Born: 1951 *Awards:* Certificate of Merit, Society of Illustrators, Los Angeles *Collections:* IBM; Hughes Aircraft *Exhibitions:* William Sawyer Gallery, San Francisco; Euphrat Gallery, Cupertino *Education:* UC-Santa Barbara *Dealer:* William Sawyer, San Francisco

From 1976 to 1978, he studied airbrush technique from Thomas Akawie, at the San Francisco Art Institute. He had always been drawn to realism. His fascination with reflective surfaces led to a series from 1979 to 1984 of airbrushed photo-realistic "Glass Jar" paintings, "Glass Door and Window" paintings and, later, to paintings of boats and other objects, reflected in the water. Between 1985 and 1988, he worked for a computer graphics software development company. Transferring his aesthetic of realistic, reflected imagery to the computer medium, he used his access to sophisticated computer paint systems and their corresponding 16.8 million colors, to create covers for national computer graphics magazines.

GRIM, THOMASIN (Textile Artist)
1606 Harrison St., San Francisco, CA 94103

Born: 1957 *Awards:* NEA Fellowship *Exhibitions:* California Crafts Museum, San Francisco; Fiberworks Center for Textile Arts, Berkeley *Education:* California College of Arts and Crafts *Dealer:* Braunstein/Quay, San Francisco; Eve Mannes, Atlanta

She is interested in combining traditional weaving technique with anti-modern sentimentality. By using a supplementary warp pick-up, she endows her works with two-dimensionality and painterly surfaces. While not actually tapestry, their effect is similar. Abstract symbols float against fields of black and white, red, green and a range of other colors. In the past, she focused on interpreting veiled landscapes. Recently, she completed a large project, "The Century Plant." This autobiographical work, a pictorial narrative, is a series of 100 twelve-foot squares. Semiotics, the science of signs, is the conceptual base of this effort.

GROAT, JENNY H. (Calligrapher)
P.O. Box 295, Lagunitas, CA 94938

Born: 1929 *Awards:* Award of Merit, Marin Arts Guild Gallery *Collections:* Humanities Resource Center, U. of Texas, Austin *Exhibitions:* Junior Arts Center, Los Angeles; Marin Society of Artists *Dealer:* Signature Gallery, Atlanta

Trained as a musician, dancer and painter, she first achieved notoriety with a series of dance/theater works, including starkly simple pieces, innovative in their multimedia approach. Her concerns continue to be with movement, color, sound and light. Although she sometimes paints her letter-like forms in great detail, more often her gestures are large, sweeping and dance-like. Her abstract works are often named as songs or untranslatable poems, and may have smaller calligraphic gestures which resemble writing. In works with words, she may use brush, quill or reed pen. She frequently uses burnished gold.

GROSS, CHERYL (Painter)
911 8th Ave., Brooklyn, NY

Born: 1953 *Exhibitions:* Brooklyn Museum; La Foret Harajuku Museum, Tokyo *Education:* School of Visual Arts, NYC; Hunter College *Dealer:* B-1 Gallery, Santa Monica

Influenced by Dali, Picasso and New York's East Village art scene, she is known as a social commentator. Although she is not a graffiti artist, she does combine graffiti with crayon and thick layers of paint, applied with a syringe to create pieces that are heavy on mood. Her subjects are the icons of Americana. In a recent series on tabloids, she uses the front pages of Bernard Getz era newspapers, scandal sheets and popular magazines like *Interview* to show how ridiculous and sensational journalism is. Her major work to date, *Tail O' the Pup*, is a hot-dog-shaped Los Angeles hot dog stand.

GROSS, STEWART B. (Painter)
170 St. Germain Ave., San Francisco, CA 94114

Born: 1921 *Exhibitions:* UC-San Francisco; Mesa Gallery, San Francisco *Education:* San Francisco Art Institute *Dealer:* Mesa Gallery, San Francisco

Influenced by de Stael, Kline, Hoffman and Diebenkorn, he is a colorist who began painting full time after retiring from medicine in 1979. His early works were impressionistic, but after he attended San Francisco Art Institute from 1979 until 1982, his small oils on paper were explorations of color and design. These popular pieces, filled with ochres, oranges, blues and greens, were followed by similar 3-by-4-foot paintings on canvas. He is currently making 3-by-8-foot and 4-by-6-foot diptychs on canvas. "My love affair with color and surprise discovery of depth and mystery are sustaining," he says.

GROSSE, STANLEY G. (Painter, Mixed Media Artist)
2476 Harrison St., San Francisco, CA

Born: 1930 *Awards:* 1st Place, San Francisco Bay Arts Award *Collections:* Bank of America, San Francisco; Dean Witter, NYC *Exhibitions:* Gallery 30, San Mateo; Pomeroy Gallery, San Francisco *Education:* California College of Arts & Crafts, Oakland; University of Guanajuato, Mexico *Dealer:* Gumps, San Francisco; Oakland Museum Collectors Gallery; C.G. Rein Galleries

He has always been attracted to the styles, cultures and landscapes of foreign countries. Since his retirement after thirty years in education, he has devoted himself to painting the impressions he has gathered from extensive travel. His style exhibits the diverse influences of Richard Diebenkorn, James Pinto, Antoni Tapies and Alexander Nepote. He works on paper and canvas—30 by 40 inches, 40 by 60 inches and 50 by 80 inches—using mixed-media techniques to create collages. Materials include enamels, oil washes, acrylics, lacquers, inks, prismacolor, oil pastels, charcoal, asphalt and 3M coatings. These are applied, rubbed, scraped and varnished to produce rich colors and textures. His collages reflect an interest in Japanese culture and designs.

GROSSMAN, STEVE (Painter)
417 S. Wall St., Los Angeles, CA 90013

Born: 1954 *Awards:* Ford Foundation Travel Grant; UCLA Art Council Award *Collections:* S&O, World Trade Center, NYC; Security Pacific Bank, Los Angeles *Exhibitions:* Jan Baum Gallery, Los Angeles; Rotunda Gallery, NYC *Education:* Philadelphia College of Art; UCLA *Dealer:* Jan Baum Gallery, Los Angeles

From a foundation of formal training in representational painting based on observation, he progressed to non-representational modes. Since 1980, he has created dimensional paintings characterized by strongly colored surfaces of flat canvas or rigid panels set back several inches behind a loose, geometrical, three-dimensional wooden-frame structure. He uses a variety of colors and painting techniques, amplifying the visual complications of the pieces. More recently, he has added a subtle emphasis on imagery and color shifting to his dimensional paintings while working on flat pieces as well. He works in New York City as well as Los Angeles.

GUMPERTZ, ROBERT (Painter, Cartoonist)
238 E. Blithdale Ave., Mill Valley, CA 94941

Born: 1925 *Exhibitions:* F.J. Michaels Gallery, San Francisco; Northwind Gallery, Mill Valley *Education:* California College of Arts and Crafts

He divides his time between cartooning and illustration and fine art. His cartoons and illustrations have appeared in *The International Dog, Professor Twill's Travels, From Fiddletown to Tuba City, Dream Notebook* and, as a regular Sunday cartoon, in the *San Francisco Chronicle*. These pieces are done with pen and ink and gouache. His fine-art works, paintings of heads and figures, are executed in water-based paints and collage. Using wet and dry wash techniques on a variety of surfaces, he paints non-realistic yet recognizable portraits. These bold, colorful works feature blocky forms and delicately lined detail.

GUNNUFSON, KENT (Photographer)
12257 21st St., Hawaiian Gardens, CA 90716

Born: 1946 *Awards:* Letter of Artistic Recognition, President Gerald Ford *Exhibitions:* Rizzoli's International Gallery, Costa Mesa; Stanford U., Palo Alto *Education:* U. of Colorado *Dealer:* Camera Obscura, Denver

His work focuses on the Rocky Mountains and, to a lesser extent, the people who live in the mountains. Although much of his work is in black and white, his more recent forays into color have proved more challenging to his expressive abilities, because of color's close relation to reality. He has experimented widely with a variety of processing and photographic techniques, particularly ones related to the topography and weather in the mountains. His manuscript, *Photography*, is considered to be the definitive work in this area. *Tracking the Snow-Shoe Itinerant*, a book of black-and-white photographs and accompanying narrative text, chronicles the travels of 19-century Methodist preacher, mail carrier and miner, John Lewis Dyer. The photographs interpret the beauty of the mountains and the unique, rugged conditions of Rocky Mountain alpine life. He cites the works of Bill Simpson, Al Weber and F.S. Smyth as major influences. Recently, he has been working on a series on the rivers of Southern California.

GYELTSEN, JENNIFER A. (Ceramist)
1151 Fernwood Pacific Dr., Topanga, CA 90290

Born: 1946 *Exhibitions:* A. Albert Allen Fine Art Gallery, Palm Desert; Ahwahnee Hotel, Yosemite *Education:* Royal Society of Arts in Business, England

She apprenticed in basic ceramics with Harry Berman, but her style was mainly influenced by the Native

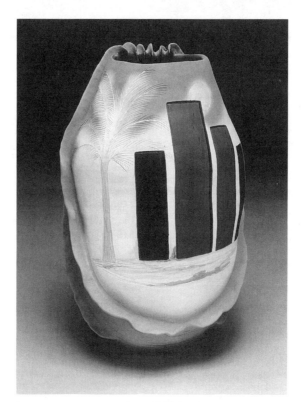

Jennifer A. Gyeltsen, *L.A. III,* 16 x 12, ceramic (vessel)

Phora Gerdes, *Ol' Lady on Cane (detail),*
20 x 51 x 12, mixed media

American potters of New Mexico and Arizona, especially Maria and Julian Martinez and Lucy Lewis. She has always worked in whiteware clay, using the coil and slab method. In her early work, she incised her designs into the clay bodies and used colored underglazes. After making mainly small vessels and bowls, she now concentrates on wall sculptures with accompanying large-scale vessels. Although the technique and clay are the same, the pieces are now sculptural and far more fluid in style. Underglazes are still used for the basic colors, but she now applies them with an airbrush as well as a traditional brush. She has also started using acrylics and oils for highlights. The landscapes and coastlines of the Southwest are her inspiration, and she feels the most important influence on her current work is Georgia O'Keeffe. She tries to create a feeling of tranquility through her sculptures, eliciting the true spirituality of the land that lies beneath the modern society.

HACK, ELIZABETH (Printmaker, Mixed Media Artist)

PO Box 10076, Berkeley, CA 94709

Born: 1954 *Awards:* Artist-in-Residence, Kala Institute, Berkeley; Grant Recipient, Morris Stolsaft Foundation *Exhibitions:* Weir Gallery, Berkeley; Creative Growth Center Gallery, Oakland *Education:* U. of South Carolina; U. of Miami

She creates abstractions in ink and mixed media that evoke landscapes and organic forms. Under the influence of Hokusai, Van Gogh and Chinese brush painting, she developed a technique whereby black ink is applied to paper in small lines that merge and separate to form a background upon which watercolor, acrylic or collage is added. She has recently been using bold colors—blue and yellow especially, and some red—over the foundation of black lines to create contrast and movement between the background and foreground, suggesting explosion. The effect of the whole is intensified by hand-painted etchings; her *Untitled* work is an example.

HAHN, MOIRA (Painter)

439 N. Vista, St., Los Angeles, CA 90036

Born: 1956 *Awards:* 2nd Place, Downey Museum of Art *Exhibitions:* Honolulu Academy of Art; Achenbach Foundation, San Francisco *Education:* Maryland Institute, College of Art *Dealer:* April Sgro-Riddle Gallery, Los Angeles

She studied under Masami Teraoka for five years and was greatly influenced by Teraoka, Ben Sakaguchi and James Rosenquist. In her early work she used watercolors to approximate the surface and color density of lithography. Using satire as a means of social commentary, she buried social issues within historical and visual contexts. She has recently been combining dreams with physical and psychological environments in portraits of herself and friends. Her technique has shifted from her earlier attempt to reproduce the look of certain media, and she is now exclusively involved with conveying her subject's psychological transitions through the sensitivity and transparency of watercolors.

HALEEN, BRENTANO (Computer Artist)

P.O. Box 3227, Rancho Santa Fe, CA 92067

Born: 1954 *Exhibitions:* Computer Industry Overview Conference, Santa Clara; Merideth Long Gallery, NY *Education:* School of the Art Institute of Chicago

He has been influenced by Max Ernst, Van Gogh, and Kandinsky. His early pieces were hard-edge abstractions drawn with prismacolor pencils. He used line relationships and colors to create different feels, moods, and complete thoughts. In 1983, he started making computer-assisted fine art. In 1986, he collaborated with computer composer Christopher Yavelow on a multimedia presentation called *Imaginary Conversations*. All of his work utilizes colors. He is recently began working exclusively with computer generated images output directly to canvas or applied to canvas by means of serigraphy.

HALEM, J-SCOTT (Painter)

2512 Regent St., #6, Berkeley, CA 94704

Born: 1944 *Exhibitions:* John Pence Gallery, San Francisco; Bay Area Art Scene Show *Education:* Art Students League, San Francisco *Dealer:* Orient Express Studio, San Francisco

He spent his first seven years as a student of art studying with the eminent figurative painter, Frank Mason. Inspired by the work of the Old Masters, Rembrandt, Vermeer and Watteau, as well as the early Renaissance artists of Flanders and Italy, he went on to work from nature, the figure, still life and landscape. Since the early 1970s, however, he has been drawing primarily upon images of his imagination, using objects and scenes in a symbolic fashion. *Home Sweet Home*, for example, portrays a human figure with a fish head, carrying a bag of groceries out of a kitchen and into a living room where a mouse, several cats and birds are congregated. As a picture of harmony between species, it is meant to suggest the ways in which evolution is bringing forth nourishment. It is in a like manner that many of his paintings mix myth with fantasy and American iconography. A lover of the technical aspects of painting, he makes many of his of paints and mediums, grinding the pigments himself. In this regard, he has been influenced by the work of Jacque Maroger of the Louvre Museum in Paris.

HALL, DIANE A. (Painter)

4131 23rd St., San Francisco, CA 94114

Born: 1945 *Exhibitions:* New Langton Arts, San Francisco; Maloney Butler Gallery, Los Angeles *Education:* Maryland Institute of Art; Skowhegan School of Painting and Sculpture *Dealer:* Fuller Gross, San Francisco

She was co-founder and member of T.R. Uthco, an avant-garde group of artists who collaborated in performance and video projects for ten years, from 1969 to 1979. This had a direct influence on her work, for she re-entered painting from a more conceptual vantage. Her work is involved with natural phenomena: weather, storms, dawn, dusk, light, atmospheric conditions and especially, space. Her source material is gathered from her travels and experiences in the landscape. Her concerns are perception of space and light. Incorporated into these renderings of light are abstract rectangular planes or lines, either superimposed or juxtaposed, describing a moment of perception. These pictures locate motions of sea and sky as powerful, temporal states of matter observed in freeze-frame. She combines distinct views, in multiple panels or insets within a single panel, so as to orchestrate different atmospheric weights and durations. These are sumptuous conceptual paintings, the weather parsed in sets of prismatic incident, each bearing its load of absence and fullness, rapture and resolve.

Michael Hughes, *Fresh Snow,* 54 x 40, oil on canvas.
Courtesy: Stephen J. Yoder

Thomas Hall, *Mixed Bouquet,* 28 x 22, oil on canvas

HALL, THOMAS (Painter, Draughtsperson)
6024 Broadway, Oakland, CA 94618

Born: 1949 *Awards:* Award of Merit, California State Fair *Collections:* Peralta Medical Center, Oakland; Home Savings, Oakland *Exhibitions:* Los Gatos Porch; Richard Byars, Monticeto *Education:* California College of Arts and Crafts *Dealer:* Sohlman Art Gallery Etc., Oakland

His early work included a variety of media such as oils, watercolors, black-and-white graphics, woodcutting, etching, ceramics, sculpture and photography. He now concentrates on realistic, understated paintings of flowers, plants, landscapes and small animals. He uses photographs as auxiliary tools, but works mostly in the studio and from live specimens. His paintings exhibit a smooth surface, which he achieves with gentle, level brushstrokes and a damar varnish finish. He renders subjects in clear, closely keyed colors, which give the appearance of full daylight. By focusing on the same subject matter over a number of years, his realistic style has evolved into contemporary trompe-l'oeil.

HALLOCK, CAROL C. (Painter)
4715 B, La Villa Marina, Marina Del Rey, CA 90292

Born: 1958 *Exhibitions:* Pacific Art Guild Art Show, Westchester *Education:* Montclair State College

Studies in pointillism and an interest in the works of Seurat, Monet and Braque led her to choose a semi-abstract impressionism as medium of expression. After expanding this early style through use of vivid color and movement, she moved away from conventional subject matter and into free-form abstraction. Using short brushstrokes and various sizes of brushes, she was able to give her work sharp definition. She balances this definition by removing the boundaries between colors through color mixing and blending. She emphasizes color gradations—usually vibrant yellows, blues and greens—in her works by applying thick layers of paint. Her resulting work resembles mountains, with gradations of color fields progressing up the slope.

HALPIN, T. SCOTT (Painter, Installation Artist)
124 Page St., San Francisco, CA 94102

Born: 1954 *Awards:* Parent's Choice Review of Media; Artist in Residence, Headlands Center for the Arts *Exhibitions:* Headlands Center for the Arts *Education:* U. of Iowa; San Francisco State U.

He studied with Maritzio Lanzansky at the University of Iowa Print workshop. This early intaglio work laid the foundation for a private graphic world whose inhabitants are involved in the push-pull of spiritual growth. Subsequent training in painting, sculpture, music and performance led to "New Genre" work, in which he merges different media in a search for new forms. His recent performance opera, *The Blue Shaman,* includes an electric and acoustic score, choral and narrative libretto and paintings for rear screen projection. Its theme is the spiritual quest, the attempt to break through to a more enlightened state.

HAMAGUCHI, YOZO (Printmaker)
c/o Vorpal Gallery, 393 Grove St., San Francisco, CA 94102

Born: 1909 *Awards:* Grand Prix, Lubljana International Print Biennale *Collections:* Museum of Modern Art, NYC; Bibliotheque Nationale de Paris *Exhibitions:* Vorpal Gallery, NYC; Galerie Berggruen, Paris Ed-

cuation: Tokyo U. of Fine Art *Dealer:* Vorpal Galleries, NYC & San Francisco

In 1930, after studying sculpture in Tokyo, he moved to Paris and took up studies in painting and drawing, both on his own and at the Academy Grand Chaumiere. He brought the ascetic qualities of his Japanese heritage to a mezzotint technique and achieved an extraordinary balance between simplicity of subject matter and complexity of technique. At the same time, he inspired new interest in the medium and developed the colored mezzotint. His printing involves a meticulous procedure of engraving copper plates by roughing up their surface with a toothed rocker and burnishing the image with a tool or scraper. This technique produces the tonal rather than linear effect that characterizes his work.

HAMILTON, LARRY (Painter)
465 E. Olive Ave., Merced, CA 95340

Born: 1946 *Collections:* Blueberry Hill Restaurant, Livingston *Exhibitions:* California College of Arts and Crafts Gallery; Merced College Gallery *Education:* California College of Arts and Crafts

He is most interested by the appearance of finished pieces. His main influences have been custom paint jobs on cars, especially candy apple and pearl lacquers. His work is done entirely with airbrush on metal surfaces. He takes slides, usually of people, then makes stencils from the projected image and uses these to paint. His abstract work often involves torching a metal sheet to achieve a wavy effect, which is especially pronounced when painted with pearl lacquer. His portraiture is done on aluminum sheets, which he paints with apple car paints, a gold underpainting and transparent glaze. Although he was once interested in the ideas of Carl Jung, he now takes his inspiration from the teachings of Christ.

HAMMERSLEY, FREDERICK (Painter)
608 Carlisle SE, Alburquerque, NM 87106

Born: 1919 *Awards:* NEA Grant; Guggenheim Fellow *Collections:* Corcoran Gallery, Washington, DC; San Francisco Museum of Modern Art *Exhibitions:* Museum of Modern Art, NYC *Education:* Ecole des Beaux Arts, Paris *Dealer:* Modernism, San Francisco

While he was studying at the Jepson Art School in Los Angeles, a small painting of his was chosen for exhibit at the San Francisco Museum of Modern Art. At the height of the abstract expressionist movement, he was included in an exhibit of abstract classicists that attracted great attention in the United States because of its strong divergence from then current trends. His paintings in this show were minimalistic works of flat, geometric shapes. He has continued to create geometrically-based works, but in the late 1970s and early 1980s, he produced a series of paintings drained of color. In 1986, he made history by refusing to show his paintings at an opening. He mingled with guests at the opening, but on the walls were nothing but the nails on which the paintings were to hang and the titles of the works. He commented simply that he did not want his work to be "visual muzak." The paintings were put on exhibit the next day.

HAMMERUD, JAMES DONALD (Painter)
1825 Cottage Grove Ave., San Mateo, CA

Born: 1953 *Awards:* Scholarships, U. of Mexico, San Francisco Art Institute *Exhibitions:* Hughes Air West, Main Office Building, San Mateo; U.S. Concert and

H. Elton Harris, *Lightfoot,* 11 x 11 x 6, stone, alabaster

Frederick Hammersley, *Need Less to Say,* 45 x 45, oil.
Courtesy: Los Angeles County Museum of Art

Computer Show, Los Angeles *Education:* The College of San Mateo

Fascinated by art from his childhood, he early evidenced a special talent for expressing the marvelous and fantastic. After taking an A.A. in art, he made his living as an electrician, and, influenced by artists like Roger Dean and Syd Mead, painted brightly-colored dragons, waterfalls, exotic mountains and scenes of outer space in oils and gouache. During the late 1970s, he began painting almost exclusively in acrylic, using an airbrush to achieve speed and visual effects. Because of commercial requests, he has recently been making contemporary paintings with hard-edged shapes and forms.

HAMMOND, THEKLA H. (Painter)
1513 Fifth St., Berkeley, CA 94710

Born: 1940 *Awards:* 1st Place, San Francisco Arts Commission *Exhibitions:* Haines Gallery, San Francisco; Worcester Art Museum, MA *Education:* UC-Santa Barbara *Dealer:* Cheryl Haines, San Francisco

For many years, she worked in a non-representational vein; during the past two years, her work has featured abstracted palm tree imagery, as a point of departure for lushly painted, mysterious objects. Over time, the palm has become a central focal point, a particularly expressive symbol. Her fascination with the palm is explored in rich, deep colors in thickly painted oils. While her earlier works were fairly literal interpretations of the palm, her recent paintings are highly abstracted, organic pieces, which concentrate on small sections of the palm, rather than the whole. Despite the strong abstract treatment, the paintings retain a tropical atmosphere. Using the palm motif, she creates powerful works that reflect her fundamental interest in exploring the qualities of paint, surface, color and light.

HAMROL, LLOYD (Sculptor)
901 Pacific Ave., Venice, CA 90291

Born: 1937 *Awards:* NEA Grant *Collections:* Los Angeles County Museum of Art; Smithsonian Institute, Washington, DC *Exhibitions:* San Diego Museum of Art; Los Angeles Municipal Gallery *Education:* UCLA

Influenced by Brancusi and David Smith and by ancient architectural monuments, he creates large-scale participatory public sculptures that people can walk through and sprawl on, engaging the audience rather than confronting it. He is fundamentally concerned with integrating the work with the surrounding architecture and landscape, creating a dialogue between material, form and function. In *Highground,* on the campus of the University of New Mexico, a subtle, elegant circular plane of lawn is pivoting up from the ground on one side and down into it on the other. His works are characterized by clean lines, unobtrusiveness and open expanses.

HANNAFORD, JOHN (Painter)
1102 Coombsville Rd., Napa, CA 94558

Born: 1950 *Collections:* Sonoma State U.; Arizona State U. *Exhibitions:* San Francisco Museum of Modern Art/Museum Rental Gallery *Education:* Cal. State-Sacramento *Dealer:* San Francisco Museum of Modern Art Rental Gallery

In a stylized realism, he renders a slightly distorted mirror image of certain elements of daily life, often as parody. His subjects, he says, are "representative as cultural signifiers in an emblematic sense." Though satirical, these large-scale acrylic paintings reveal the artist's painful but sympathetic awareness of the lack of depth in societal roles. More recently, he has begun to incorporate words as part of the surface itself. He has been influenced by Jasper Johns, Clyfford Still, David Hockney, Robert Arneson, Richard Diebenkorn and Henri Matisse. He currently serves on the faculty of Napa Valley College in California.

HANSON, BARBARA (Painter)
c/o Hank Baum Gallery, 2140 Bush St., San Francisco, CA 94115

Born: 1954 *Exhibitions:* 1078 Gallery, Cal. State-Chico *Education:* Cal. State-Chico *Dealer:* Hank Baum Gallery, San Francisco

Early in her career, she derived inspiration from Renaissance painters Botticelli and Caravaggio. While in school, her style changed from traditional figurative works rendered in oil on canvas to abstract color fields using acrylic on paper. She later returned to figurative subjects, permitting herself only limited autobiographical expression. Recently, she has been working by layering images: a city or dwelling, a figure in the environment, and a symbol of change—a boat, plane, car or other vehicle. This technique allows her to express the complexity of perception and the dilemmas facing mankind today.

HANSON, SUZANNE (Painter)
Contemporary Artist's Services, 9520 Jefferson Blvd., Culver City, CA 90232

Born: 1942 *Awards:* Peninsula Community Foundation Grant; Society for the Encouragement of Contemporary Art Award *Collections:* State of Colorado; Bank of America World Headquarters, San Francisco *Exhibitions:* Ivory/Kimpton Gallery, San Francisco; Orange Coast College Art Gallery, Costa Mesa *Education:* Mills College; U. of Michigan

Large rectangles are bent, folded or pleated and browned by exposure to portray the passage of time, particularly through the representation of industrial garbage. Sheets of canvas, or oatmeal and manila paper are laid outdoors and covered with technological remnants such as broken car parts, dull blades from a food processor or fractured keys from an adding machine. After a certain amount of time, she showers them with inks and powdered pigments, inviting the sun to print photograms around the geometric forms. Dirt and dust randomly mark the composition further. Finally, she removes the objects and outlines their evidence with paint and pencil, preserving actual records of natural urban decay. When presented, these imprints appear as circles and grids etched over elegant surfaces, gaskets spiraling into orbit, classical patterns that serve as metaphors for the designed obsolescence of material and consciousness in 20th-century society.

HARGIS, BOBBY-LOU (Painter, Printmaker)
402 E. Plymouth St., Glendora, CA 91740

Born: 1930 *Awards:* Best of Show & Special Award, Collectors Gallery *Collections:* Lyndon Johnson; Vincent Price *Exhibitions:* Ontario Museum; East Valley Art Association, Arboretum, Pasadena, *Education:* Citrus College, Glendora *Dealer:* Chim. Gregg Art Gallery, La Puente

In the early 1970s she began studying modern art and abstraction under Bob Ueker. She then drew in her own style. She used lines to break up areas of mixed,

Bobby-Lou Hargis, *Unorthodox (triptych),* 30 x 48, acrylics Courtesy: Ontario Museum

Madden Harkness, *At Night,* 54 x 87, mixed media on vellum. Courtesy: Roy Boyd Gallery

flat, harmonious colors. In 1972 she began drawing with Gregg Shorthand to augment the abstract quality of her work. She paints with acrylics on canvas, and uses complementary colors for contrast. The work is action oriented and she continues to develop her Gregg Shorthand style. She now mainly works in triptych on three-in-one canvases. Her current paintings are large enough for museum walls.

HARKNESS, MADDEN (Painter)
1180 N. Catalina Ave., Pasadena, CA 91104

Born: 1948 *Collections:* The Everson Museum, Syracuse, NY; Mr. Ira Levy, NYC *Exhibitions:* Taipei Fine Arts Museum, Taiwan; Forum '88, Hamburg, West Germany *Education:* Calif. College of Arts and Crafts, Oakland; Tufts U. *Dealer:* Roy Boyd Gallery, Los Angeles; Ivory Kimpton Gallery, San Francisco

Photo-realism strongly influenced her early work, which explored the amount of visual information in a painting and the degree of control the artist exercises over the work. She painted in oil on canvas and also did a good deal of drawing. This interest in drawing caused her work to open up in both gesture and content. The plastic film she now employs allows her to work with wet and dry media, combining painting and drawing. She uses oil washes, oil sticks and graphite to produce dark tones and light areas in which the pigment has been removed and the white reflected through the film from behind. Influences include Francis Bacon, Jim Dine and Raphael. In the last three years, she has been working on a series of dark, figurative paintings that generally depict unidentifiable figures in space.

HARPER, JOHN (Painter, Printmaker)
2910 Pioneer Dr., Redding, CA 96001

Born: 1950 *Collections:* Redding Museum; San Jose State U. Art Department *Exhibitions:* Shasta College, Redding; U. of the Pacific, Stockton *Education:* San Jose State U.

After his formal training in traditional printmaking, he began a major body of work utilizing exploratory print processes. Influenced by the works of Robert Rauschenberg and Jasper Johns, he combined serigraphy with direct photo emulsion processes to create a series of prints that dealt with the theme of sustenance. By 1980, his interest in symbolism and story-telling came together in a formal approach of juxtaposing dissimilar objects. This theme continues to dominate his work which now consists of watercolor painting. These large-scale watercolors dealing with images of baskets, fish traps and other containers are orchestrated with images of rulers, tapes and other methods of measurement. The value of his work lies in the tension among the images, rather than in the depiction of the objects themselves. The fact that one object is often painted in color and the other in monochromatics heightens the synthesis of the work.

HARPER, ROB MARCH (Painter)
3099 California St., Oakland, CA 94602

Born: 1942 *Awards:* Artists Society International Art Achievement Award, San Francisco *Collections:* Hallmark Cards, Kansas City; Butler Institute of American Art, Youngstown, OH *Exhibitions:* Yosemite Renaissance National Art Exhibition, Yosemite National Park; Ariel Gallery, NYC *Education:* San Francisco Art Institute; Washington U., St. Louis *Dealer:* Ariel Gallery, NYC

He has been influenced by the Sunday comics, early radio programs and model airplanes. He uses only oil and acrylic on linen, painting with a sharp brush to create hard-edged, vivid images. The juxtaposition of elements creates an abstract effect. Proceeding without any preconceived formula or idea, he works by filling the background with a dominant initial image. Favorite initial ideas include a plane or a landscape (most recently a Yosemite landscape). He paints from a comic-bookstyle palette—very bright, almost Day-Glo, colors. He relates to his art as if it were a bodily function: while the completion of one piece leaves him feeling satisfied, he is never completely satisfied and soon must start another painting. He is currently painting images of Yosemite Valley, contrasting the city with the country. In one painting, for example, W.C. Fields lounges in the valley, with a waterfall in the background.

HARR, PAMELA (Sculptor)
1460 Bear Canyon Rd., Bozeman, MT 59715

Born: 1944 *Awards:* Inducted for Art, National Cowgirl Hall of Fame *Collections:* Congressman Ron Marlenee, MT *Exhibitions:* Squash Blossom Gallery, Palm Desert; Montana Society Congressional Reception, Washington, D.C. *Education:* Oregon State U.

A former physical therapist, she began sculpting after using the medium in therapy programs. Her early pieces in cloth, clay and wire were characters from mythology, fairy tales and Bible stories. In 1971, she moved to a cattle ranch in Oregon and began depicting the western life she saw and experienced. Two years later, she learned bronze casting from western painter and sculptor Ernie Caviness. In 1977, she married and moved to Bozeman, Montana. She currently works full time making wax or clay molds of pioneering women, children and carousel horses. She casts these in bronze at the foundry she owns jointly with her husband.

HARRIS, ANN (Painter)
671 Clubhouse Dr., Aptos, CA 95003

Born: 1927 *Awards:* 2nd Prize, Riverside Art Assoc. Annual Purchase Prize Exhibition, Riverside; 2nd Prize in Watercolor, Santa Cruz Art League, Santa Cruz *Exhibitions:* Rotunda Gallery, Riverside; Montalvo Center for the Arts, Saratoga; *Education:* Pomona and Scripps Colleges, Claremont *Dealer:* Friends of the Arts Gallery, Carmel

She began her career painting in watercolor directly from nature, but since has moved into more abstract work done from memory and reflecting her personal view of the natural world. She continues to alternate between these two approaches, preferring to sketch with paint in line or broad, fluid washes of color, rather than initially sketching in pencil. Images include abstractions of nature, as well as wildflowers, landscape scenes of old houses by the sea and explorations of the High Sierras in winter. A highly transparent watercolor technique and watercolor treatment of acrylics renders her works more impressionistic than realistic. Early paintings favored warm browns, yellows and greens; her current work shows preference for lavenders and pinks.

HARRIS, DAVID (Painting)
1870 Ralston Ave., Belmont, CA 94002

Born: 1948 *Awards:* 2nd Place, California Museum; Best of Show, San Mateo County Invitational *Collections:* Chartered Bank of London, San Francisco;

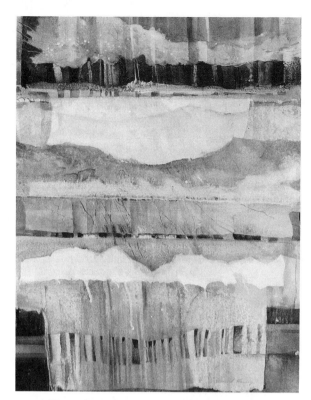

Elaine L. Harvey, *Tapestry: Repose,* 30 x 23,
watercolor collage, bronze powder

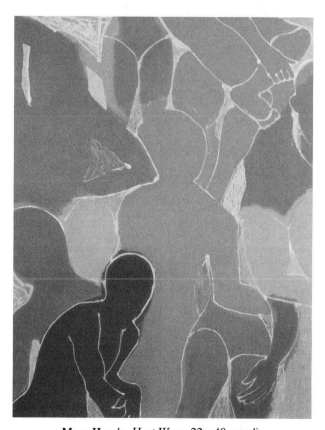

Mary Harris, *Heat Wave,* 32 x 40, acrylic

North Central Washington Museum, Wenatchee, WA *Exhibitions:* A Gallery, Palm Desert; Eva Cohon Gallery, Chicago *Education:* San Francisco State U. *Dealers:* Barry White, Palm Desert; Frisch, Ltd., New York; Louis Newman Gallery, Los Angeles

His early works display the light and impasto techniques employed by the Impressionists, Old Masters and Abstract Expressionists. He works by placing primed canvas in a prone position and applying a succession of acrylic washes in gray, black, red, magenta and green. Using a squeegee and other tools, he controls the pigments, building layers of color into the desired design. These paintings appear as free-floating, wispy tendrils of delicately colored forms. He calls this style colorfield expressionism and cites Helen Frankenthaler and Paul Jenkins as major influences. His non-objective, organic works also show the influences of Eastern mysticism.

HARRIS, H. ELTON (Sculptor)
912 W. Lime St., Lompoc, CA 93436

Awards: 1st Place, Professional Sculptor, Santa Barbara County Exhibition

Lacking formal training, he has found his own style. He catches his subject's outstanding characteristics and allows the viewer's imagination to do the rest. There is a warm rhythmic flow in his sculpture, and he uses the stone's natural characteristics to enhance his work's narrative quality. His media include marble, alabaster, serpentine, onyx, obsidian, steel and wood. Since the mid-1970s, his work has been influenced by Rodin, as well as by the Asian, Eskimo and primitive South and Central American sculpture he has seen while traveling.

HARRIS, MARY E. (Painter, Mixed Media Artist)
5 Shelter Cove, Pacifica, CA 94044

Born: 1917 *Exhibitions:* Art Guild of Pacifica; University Club, San Francisco State U. *Education:* California Institute of Integral Studies; San Francisco State U.

She has studied in this country with Basil Marros as well as overseas with Liou in Taiwan, Kadoguchi in Japan and Rodde in Paris. She has remained an abstract expressionist, believing that this style is the most interesting way to explore the infinite variability of nature. For the last several years, she has experimented with a variety of different techniques and materials, including tissue-paper collage (tearing off paper and leaving dye), masking-tape resist, glue drawing and paint peeling. She works in cool acrylic colors, primarily blue and magenta, using abstract, reflective forms. She also spends many hours each week teaching art to small children.

HARRISON, DIANA L. (Painter)
540 Alabama St., San Francisco, CA 94110

Born: 1956 *Awards:* Raina Gese Award, Stanford University *Collections:* Pacific Presbyterian Professional Corp.; Jan Holloway Gallery, San Francisco *Exhibitions:* Jan Holloway Gallery, San Francisco; Sonoma County Fair *Education:* Stanford University *Dealer:* Jan Holloway Gallery, San Francisco

Her work focuses on both figure studies and cityscapes. Influenced in her figurative work by Degas, Matisse and Cassatt, she works mainly in pastel and charcoal. Her subject matter is primarily family and women, including pregnant women, mothers with children, and mothers in childbirth. For the last three years, her major focus has been on San Francisco cityscapes. Working in oil on canvas and pastel on paper, she captures a specific light quality, color interaction and composition as the primary elements of the painting. Although highly realistic, her lush and vibrant palette and tightly woven compositions make apparent the underlying abstract qualities within these views. The ubiquitous beauty of San Francisco continues to inspire her work.

HART, LISA (Sculptor)
11017 Ocean Dr., Culver City, CA 90230

Born: 1953 *Awards:* Arts Council Award, UCLA *Exhibitions:* Bower Art Museum, Santa Ana; Laguna Art Museum, Costa Mesa *Education:* UCLA; Atlanta College of Art

Her initial training in drawing and printmaking yielded to an interest in sculpture, when she found herself wanting to create three-dimensional objects based on her drawings. Influences included Joseph Cornell's boxes, William T. Wiley's expressive use of line and ideas and Robert Graham's emerging figures. As her work evolved, she found her self turning to natural formations for inspiration for her sculpture. She uses handmade paper to emboss artifacts, which are included on the surface of pod-shaped forms, and then uses wire to protect these fragile forms. As well as paper pods, she also creates fiberglass pods that have a translucent quality. In both instances the wire that encircles the pods becomes a three-dimensional drawing, in which the sculpture appears to float. Some of the works are attached to the wall; larger, 10-by-4-foot works rest on the floor.

HARTE, JOHN (Painter)
P.O. Box 2628, Palm Springs, CA 92263

Born: 1927 *Collections:* Chevron Corp.; Oakland Art Museum *Exhibitions:* Chevron Corp.; UC-Berkeley *Education:* U. of Wyoming; California College of Arts and Crafts, Oakland *Dealer:* William Sawyer Gallery, San Francisco

After a commercial art education he moved to the West Coast and began landscape painting, primarily in oils. For twenty-one years he both painted and worked full time for Chevron. During this period he experimented with abstract, non-objective figurative and realistic work in various media. He is currently painting National Parks, archeological sites, and nature preserves in watercolors. Using fine grade imported watercolor paper and good sable brushes, he creates subtle nuances of color by a series of washes and dry brush techniques. "Watercolor challenges me with its excellent glazing properties and soft freshness. Design and color contrast and, above all, rendering of a good drawing are most important to me."

HARTINI (Painter)
111 Pier Ave., #111, Hermosa Beach, CA 90254

Born: 1956 *Collections:* U. of Iowa Museum of Art *Exhibitions:* SDAI National Juried Exhibition, San Diego; 42cro 9 Gallery, Venice *Education:* U. of Iowa *Dealer:* Artservice, Los Angeles

Originally from the east, her early work was heavily influenced by the works of Nathan Oliveira and Richard Diebenkorn. Her previously serious and studied style gradually opened up as she exaggerated color, line, and form, pushing figures from realistic to figurative. Gradually, forms began to dissolve al-

Hartini, *Love Offering,* 40 x 60, oil on canvas

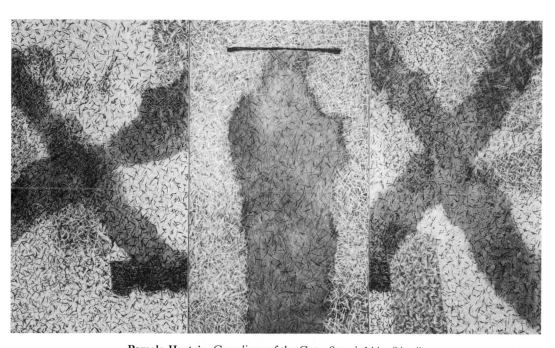

Pamela Hartvig, *Guardians of the Gate: Satori,* 144 x 84, oil

together into fragments of thought, place, sight, emotion, and dream. She considers her work rather quirky in its attempt to convey recognizable narrative and movement, and she sees many references to travel, literature, and history in her paintings.

HARTLEY, CORINNE (Painter)
34 Washington St., Venice, CA 90292

Born: 1924 *Awards:* Purchase Award, National Orange Show, San Bernardino; A.A. Exposition Santa Paula *Collections:* Barbara Mandrel, Gallatin, TN *Exhibitions:* Pasadena Art Museum; Downey Museum *Education:* Chouinard Art Institute; Pasadena School of Fine Arts *Dealers:* Zantman Galleries, Carmel, Palm Desert; Dassin Gallery, Beverly Hills

For many years after her formal training, she worked for leading department stores as a children's and women's fashion illustrator. Still influenced by the colors, thick paint and vibrating brush strokes of the French and American Impressionists, she applies oil with a broad, loose technique, using the figure as the main subject and abstracting the background. She applies watercolor in a wet-on-dry method, with complete technical control but a loose sensibility. In recent large impressionistic works, she depicts the figure within landscapes, seascapes and interior scenes. She is writing a book about her technique and is a well known Los Angeles portrait painter.

HARTVIG, PAMELA (Painter, Printmaker)
560 S. Main St., Studio 10 S., Los Angeles, CA 90013

Born: 1945 *Awards:* Scholarship, California College of Arts and Crafts, Oakland *Collections:* Cole Wheatman Interiors, San Francisco *Exhibitions:* Women's Building, San Francisco; Los Angeles Contemporary Exhibition *Education:* California College of Arts and Crafts; Kala Institute, Berkeley *Dealer:* Wade Gallery, Los Angeles

Influenced by Matisse, Braque and Cezanne, among others, she etched, painted and made photographs for the first few years of her career. Though she is an abstractionist, she always works from drawings or photographs. She paints her wall-sized, textured works with layers of several oil media; the depth she achieves is in the paint and layers, not in her image or lack of it. Her latest influences include Susan Rothenberg and David Hockney. She has recently been painting 9-by-12-inch canvases with gouache and watercolor. She is also printing old etching plates and adding a new series that is more in line with her painting.

HARVEY, ELAINE L. (Painter)
1602 Sunburst Dr., Cajon, CA 92021

Awards: American Watercolor Society, NYC; Rocky Mountain National, Golden, CO *Collections:* Citibank, Los Angeles; Wells Fargo, Los Angeles *Exhibitions:* Allied Artists of America, NYC; National Watercolor Society *Education:* San Diego State U.

In 1984 she began organizing her paintings in a Rothko-like format incorporating figurative elements derived from her own experiences and concepts. Her abstract images frequently deal with the eternal cycles of the earth, as well as with illusion and reality. She combines watercolor media with new materials and techniques, giving her work a unique look. Glazes of transparent color are layered and then contrasted with opaque areas. Metallics are frequently featured, as are additions of rice paper and the more traditional water-

color techniques. Her recent paintings are organized as a series of horizontal rectangles, some suggesting a screen or curtain partially obscuring understanding or perception.

HARVEY, JEANNE (Commercial Illustrator, Photographer)
P.O. Box 4341, Kailua-Kona, Hawaii 96745

Born: 1953 *Awards:* Pele Awards *Exhibitions:* Studio 7 Gallery, Kailua-Kona, Hawaii

She has a formal background and two parents who were artists, and she developed her own unique style of illustration. She draws with an intense clarity of life, and her subjects include animals, still lifes, historical subjects and portraits of people. She prefers the black-and-white media of pencils, charcoal and ink, but she is also adept at pastels and oils. She has also worked as a graphic designer since the early 1970s. Her understanding of media lends itself well to the illustrated style, and she has been able to adapt her style to the various graphic needs of advertising.

HARVEY, NANCY (Weaver)
5834 Riddio St., Citrus Heights, CA 95610

Born: 1939 *Collections:* Arthur Anderson & Co., Oakland; KCRA-TV, Sacramento *Exhibitions:* Sacramento Center for the Textile Arts; Sacramento History Museum

Her weaving was initially influenced by her interest in Native American textiles. Drawn to their strong geometric images, she designed her own pieces, first sketching on graph paper with attention to exact symmetry and bold shapes. Her study of technique expanded to include that of medieval tapestry, and her work then became an exploration in combining the two processes. The recent work has been primarily representational—landscapes and floral images serving frequently but not exclusively as subjects—in color and marked by a strong design. Her many commissioned pieces reveal yet another dimension: the influence of the environment for which they were created.

HARWOOD, STUART (Sculptor)
5901 Pescadero Rd., Pescadero, CA 94060

Born: 1923 *Awards:* Fulbright Fellowship *Collections:* Whitney Museum, NYC; Rochester Memorial Art Gallery *Exhibitions:* Traditionalists Gallery, Brea; Sculpture on the Avenue of the Arts, Belmont

He became known in New York in the 1950s for his large, delicate, semi-abstract woodcarvings, based on human relationships, such as the *Winged Figures* in the Whitney Museum's permanent collection. After a Fulbright in Florence in the 1960s, he began producing large, leather, expressionistic figures and small bronzes. Struggling for two decades with the challenge of creating unique bronzes, he realized that his paper-fiber originals were fresher than the bronzes. He now works with feathers, hair, dryer-lint-felt, plastics and three-dimensional collage. The pieces speak a psychological magic realism with strong folk art references. There is a social import to these works as well; his recent material addresses issues concerning the homeless and AIDS awareness.

HASSINGER, MAREN (Sculptor)
21-20 45th Ave., Long Island, NY

Born: 1947 *Awards:* National Endowment for the Arts *Collections:* California Afro-American Museum *Exhibitions:* Los Angeles County Museum of Art; Cal.

State-Northridge *Education:* Bennington College; UCLA

Inspired by nature, most of her work is site specific, created to communicate the character of the space—both physically and emotionally. Indoor installations are made from natural materials. Outdoor works often include trees juxtaposed with wire rope, imitating and blending with the natural setting in an uneasy coexistence. In one recent piece, the enhancement of a park prompted her to use pear trees as her medium. A circle was created, later shielded by a baffle to allow its discovery and stimulate surprise in viewers. Another planting installation featured weeds created out of steel cable, set into cement ground.

HASTINGS, NINA (Painter)
1286 61st St., Emeryville, CA 94608

Born: 1952 *Awards:* Morilla Paper Award, Louisiana Watercolor Society; Binney and Smith Award, Palo Alto *Exhibitions:* Northern California Watercolor Society; Sonoma Hills Gallery, Petaluma *Education:* California College of Arts and Crafts

The child of an art student, she grew up in France and the San Francisco Bay area. An early bent toward photo-realism led her to consider a career in commercial art. She became disenchanted with commercial art's subject matter, and, after studying metal working, created kinetic sculpture for an "art" factory. Taking up watercolors, she began painting flowers, shells, fabric, glass, toys, fishes and figures. Influenced by Wayne Thiebaud, Thomas Hart Benton and N.C. Wyeth, her colors deepened and light became exaggerated. Things began to appear not quite real, but three dimensional and "juicy." In two recent series, she illustrated scuba divers and fishes of the California coast.

HATTON, AYRIS (Painter)
112 Crescent Rd., San Anselmo, CA 94960

Born: 1947 *Awards:* Honorable Mention, Marin County Fair *Collections:* Mr. and Mrs. Carlos Santana *Exhibitions:* Francoise McCuen Gallery, Marin; Pt. Reyes National Seashore, Marin *Education:* UC-Berkeley; Cal. State-Sacramento

Influenced by her teachers, Elmer Bischoff, Joseph Raffael, William Allan and Gordon Cook, she uses movement in form, strongly contrasting light and a full color palette, to create a dreamy realism, which inspires private memories, and emits a quiet excitement. Her watercolors range from very small to over six feet. Interiors, large cacti, landscapes and light on water form the bulk of her subject matter. She works from photographs or sketches she has made on location, transferring a line drawing to very smooth, hot-pressed rag paper, and applying layer after layer of pigment. "I paint as I would like life to be."

HAUNGS, MARY (Ceramist, Printmaker)
11985 Auberry Rd., Clovis, CA 93612

Born: 1934 *Awards:* 2nd Place, Fresno Fair; 1st Place, Old West Art Show, Clovis *Exhibitions:* Hanford Courthouse; Mendocino Arts Center *Education:* Fresno City College

In her constantly evolving printmaking, she has combined experimental intaglio techniques with equally innovative handmade paper. *Center Core* was a lithograph made with watercolored handmade paper, containing pressed stones. Her subjects range from abstract lines and circles to realistic western scenes.

Her colors range from blues to yellows to browns, and her recent intaglio work involves patinated copper on handmade paper. She also works with clay, sculpts in soapstone and wood, and, after studying Eskimo seal gut work with Pat Hickman, has begun to make bowls and primitive style vases.

HAVEMAN, JOSEPHA (Computer Artist)
P.O. Box 9063, Berkeley, CA 94709

Born: 1931 *Collections:* Art Institute of Chicago; International Museum of Photography, Rochester, NY; *Exhibitions:* SIGGRAPH, San Francisco; Hi-Tech, San Francisco *Education:* San Francisco State U.; UC-Berkeley

She is a constructivist- and cubist-influenced artist, whose primary pictorial concern is with an interplay of structure and illusion, and whose work is intended to challenge popular ideas about form and content in general, and spatial precepts in particular. After twelve years as a painter, she turned to the camera to pursue her abstract art. In 1976, she added other printmaking techniques, producing non-objective color lithographs and serigraphs. She started to utilize computers in 1981, to aid her in the continuing quest for new minimalist compositions, which serve to confine her visual expressions to their most crucial elements, thereby providing a counter thrust to the over-embellished imagery that she sees dominating our culture today. She has taught art and photography for twenty years; she is a free-lance computer graphics designer, consultant and proprietor of the A/PIX computer art and education center in Berkeley.

HAVLENA, JARI (Painter, Collage Artist)
219 S. Juanita, Redondo Beach, CA 90277

Born: 1921 *Awards:* DeYoung Museum, San Francisco; Painting Award, Barnsoall Municipal Art Museum, Los Angeles *Collections:* Bakersfield College; International Theatre Institute, Prague, Czechoslovakia *Exhibitions:* Richard Bennett Gallery, Hollywood; Joslyn Center for the Arts, Torrance *Education:* Angewandte/Kunst, Vienna, Austria; School of the Art Institute of Chicago

Her influences in early works were Mondrian's use of simplified cubistic planes with compositional space, and Klee's color and imagery. Working in a number of media—acrylics, graphic arts, photography—she created abstract geometric images, constructed of planes working within a deep space. She uses both high and low color to establish mood and unify the composition. In her later pieces, she has integrated mixed media and collage elements in geometrically structured compositions. Her major influences remain Mondrian, Klee and Feininger.

HAWKINS, MYRTLE H. (Painter)
646 Bucher Ave., Santa Clara, CA 95051

Born: 1923 *Awards:* Gold Seal Award, de Saisset Art Gallery; 1st Place, National Easter Seal Society Competition *Collections:* Leo Norton Art Collection of Whiteweld and Company, San Francisco; Austin Warburton Collection, Santa Clara *Exhibitions:* Rosicrucian Museum of Art, San Jose; Triton Museum, Santa Clara *Education:* UC-Berkeley; San Jose Sate U.

She attributes the patience she exhibits in painting animals and children to the experience of dealing with physical infirmity. She has always had a fascination with people, animals and the sea. After mastering portraiture, she spent years studying the motion and formation of crashing waves, translating her impressions onto the canvas. Her repertoire of media has expanded from oil to pastel and mixed-media drawing.

HAWTHORNE, GREGORY (Painter)
Mule Canyon-Hwy. 1, Big Sur, CA 93920

Born: 1951 *Awards:* Mayor's Award, Beverly Hills *Exhibitions:* S.R. Holman Gallery, Carmel; Kersting Galleries, Sausalito *Education:* Wayne State U.

Formally trained in both sculpture and acrylic painting, he combines paint, color and sculpture in large (up to eight-by-ten feet) multidimensional dreamscapes. His enthusiastic, neon-lit, constructed sculptures, his collages and monumental foiled portraits and his multi-level reliefs are always colorful, occasionally totally abstract and, more often than not, humorous. He has been influenced by the bright colors of de Forest. The oceanside location of his California studio inspires him to create. In recent paintings he has worked with the interplay between foreground and background, and has imparted a sense of transparency to his metallic-colored figures.

HAY, SHERMAN (Painter)
19076 North Dr., Jamestown, CA 95327

Born: 1948 *Awards:* Grant for Artist in Residence, California Arts Council *Collections:* Dept. of Corrections, State of Calif.; Standard Oil of Calif. *Exhibitions:* ART USA, Western Colorado Center for the Arts; International Art Competition, NYC *Education:* Humboldt State U.; Cal. State-Hayward

After returning from Southeast Asia in 1970, he painted and sculpted geometric forms. In 1972, he began studying lithography and intaglio with Misch Kohn. During the mid-70s, he created prints of expressionistic figures whose surrealistic facial features revealed political implications. By 1979, he had returned to geometric work. Intrigued with architecture and modern technology, he would work with small wood constructions that he painted with acrylic. During this period, he also cast numerous works in concrete and pigmented, handmade paper. His current work is constructivist in principle and environmental in imagery. Large (twelve by ten feet), colorful, poetic and detailed, these wall reliefs are constructed of redwood, concrete and paint. He often makes hand-colored paintings of these same works.

HAYES, FREDERICK (Painter, Mixed Media Artist)
1240 Hayes St. #8, San Francisco, CA 94117

Born: 1955 *Collections:* McGuire and Company, San Francisco *Exhibitions:* Vorpal Gallery, San Francisco; Colorado State U. *Education:* San Francisco Art Institute *Dealer:* Vorpal, San Francisco

Augmented by an interest in the works of de Kooning and Hans Hofmann, his formal training led him to experiment with a variety of found industrial materials. He also constructs objects with paint, wax, paper and canvas. He plays with images of frames and doors, images that conform to the shape of the canvas. In this way, the canvas is integral to the composition and supports it rather than contains it. Making collages with newspaper, he often uses wax to affix paper to the canvas, then rips part of the paper away to reveal the images it has left behind. Although his works are abstract, he maintains a realistic approach as he recreates ordinary objects from unusual perspectives.

HAYWARD, JAMES (Painter)
12241 Broadway Rd., Moorpark, CA 93021

Awards: Guggenheim Fellowship; Japan-U.S. Creative Arts Fellow *Collections:* Los Angeles County Museum of Art; San Francisco Museum of Modern Art *Exhibitions:* Sidney Janis, NYC; Ace Contemporary Exhibitions, Los Angeles *Education:* U. of Washington *Dealer:* Ace, Los Angeles; Modernism, San Francisco

The artist makes paintings, he insists—not political pieces, not pictures, religious objects, intellectual objects, signs, critical illustrations, propaganda or things. Among those who have influenced him are Antonio Tapies, Jackson Pollock, Rembrandt, de Kooning and numerous others.

HEARD, BARBARA (Ceramist, Sculptor)
2235 Milton Ct., San Diego, CA 92110

Born: 1960 *Awards:* 1st Prize, Del Mar Fair; 2nd Prize, Westwood Art Fair *Exhibitions:* Cornado Gallery, Cornado Island; Northern Arizona U. Art Gallery *Education:* Northern Arizona U.

Although she was formally trained in ceramics, she has developed an individual abstract style based on the protruding rock formations of the desert floor. She first molds her medium by hand, then colors, glazes, and fires the work, producing brilliant formations which have an inner strength. The pieces are hollow and were originally made from red clay with sawdust added to make the work lighter and to reduce cracking. She is currently progressing to larger, more stylized forms and installations. She often stacks pieces to produce whole environments. She is works with a low-fire terra-cotta clay.

HEARSUM, TIMOTHY (Photographer)
P.O. Box 22133, Santa Barbara, CA

Born: 1946 *Awards:* 1st Prize, Monterey Museum of Art *Collections:* Metropolitan Museum of Art, NYC; International Museum of Photography, Rochester, NY *Exhibitions:* Nikon House, NYC; College of Creative Studies, UC-Santa Barbara *Education:* Visual Studies Workshop, Rochester, NY *Dealer:* Jan Kesner, Los Angeles; Amy Serit, Palo Alto

After formal training at the Visual Studies Workshop in Rochester, NY, he worked with experimental photo printmaking for many years. During the past decade, he returned to straight photography. He uses the panoramic format to photograph altered places in the West, and the Southwestern landscape. His camera's 3-by-1 proportion gives his large scale pictures a very long horizon line.

HEAVENSTON, MARTHA (Sculptor)
300 Brannan St., #310, San Francisco, CA 94107

Born: 1955 *Exhibitions:* Wita Gardinaer Gallery, San Diego; Circle Gallery, San Diego *Dealer:* Wita Gardiner, San Diego

She has been drawing on clay for the past ten years. Vessels and plates were the basis for her first figurative, narrative pieces. As the figure became more important, she began painting life-sized, wooden sculptural forms with oil. While traveling in Southeast Asia, she became became concerned with art's function, and began to work primarily with cement and clay tile. Adhering shards of tile and large, brightly glazed pieces to a light-weight core, she creates work that is similar in

Heli Hofmann, *Young Lady,* 18 x 18, paper collage

Hawthorne, *The Ascot,* 36 x 48, acrylic

imagery to her wood sculpture, but meant to be used outdoors. In 1989, she completed a commission from the City of San Francisco: to create a 200-foot sculptural wall and a clay tile mural.

HEE, HON CHEW (Painter)
45-650 Kapunahala Rd., Kaneohe, HI 96744

Born: 1906 *Awards:* 1st Prize, Woodcarving & Serigraph, Academy of Arts, HI; 1st Prize, Watercolor, Hawaii Watercolor Society *Collections:* Honolulu Academy of Arts; Hawaii State Foundation on Culture and Arts *Education:* California School of Fine Arts

Gold leaf is a dominant element of composition, and his works appear related to Egyptian and Byzantine traditions of religious iconography. He uses Chinese crossword compositions to computerize rainbow colors and tropical elements and to express his thematic exploration of the "melting pot" of the Pacific Basin. The untarnishable gold symbolizes the communication art makes possible across the barriers of time and culture. He has recently been working on illustrations for a historical book commemorating the centennial of the Chinese community in Honolulu.

HEEBNER, MARY (Painter)
914 Santa Barbara St., Studio 6, Santa Barbara, CA 93101

Born: 1951 *Awards:* Regents Scholar; NEA Artists in Schools Grant *Collections:* San Francisco Museum of Modern Art; IBM, New York *Exhibitions:* Univ. of Oregon Museum of Art; USA Today, Washington, DC Education; UC-Santa Barbara *Dealer:* Allrich Gallery, San Francisco; Shoshana Wayne Gallery, Santa Monica

For the past fifteen years, she has worked within the medium of collage. Her materials include watercolor, earth pigments, charcoal, acrylic and handmade paper. Her recent large paintings on both canvas and paper often incorporate collage materials into the painted surface. In her work, the process is present and visible, linking image, surface and content. She works within the tradition of biological abstraction; her imagery is organic, feminist, and rooted in a belief in the connectedness and interdependence of life. Three concurrent series involving monotypes, charcoal drawings and large-scale chalk drawings augment her work in collage and painting.

HEILIGER, LINDA (Photographer)
3606 Bryant St., Palo Alto, CA 94306

Born: 1941 *Collections:* Bank of America, San Francisco; Apple Computers, Sunnyvale *Exhibitions:* San Jose Museum of Art; Allegra Gallery, San Jose *Education:* Brooklyn College; San Francisco State U. *Dealer:* Lumina Image Management, NYC; Photographer's Gallery, Palo Alto

After training in black-and-white photography with Walter Rosenblum, she was led to color photography by her background in painting. She works in a two-and-a-quarter-inch format with negative film, exploring the nuances of color, light and form. Through an exploration of architectural abstractions and minimalism, she creates images that play with light, color and the yinyang relationship of background-foreground. Her color photography can be divided into three groups. The first and most recent body of work includes a highly abstract, stark sky series, in which the sky is emphasized as an element of form and color. The second group is more complex: these photographs generally contain softer colors that create an intimate atmosphere. The third group is more realistic, and features people in relation to architecture.

HEINECKEN, ROBERT FRIEDLI (Photographer)
UCLA Dept. of Art, 405 Hilgard Ave., Los Angeles, CA 90024

Born: 1931 *Awards:* NEA Grant *Collections:* Pasadena Art Museum; San Francisco Museum of Modern Art *Exhibitions:* International Museum of Photography, George Eastman House, Rochester, NY; Museum of Modern Art, NYC *Education:* UCLA

Founder and head of the photography department at UCLA and long known for his manipulation of photographic technique, lately he has been producing images that challenge the credibility of what might be defined as "non-fiction" commercial television. Working with images from ads, news, talk, game and exercise shows, he juxtaposes TV personalities, sometimes stacking images and making composites of both male and female newscasters, to produce a commentary on the commentators. Of *Newswomen Corresponding (Faith Daniels/Barbara Walters), 1986*, Amy Slaton of Art in America writes, "we see four pairs of headshots of Daniels and Walters stacked in a column, each showing the two women, who look alike to begin with, but who are here seen with matching facial expressions as well: voiceless and clonelike, they appear to be utterly artificial." Producing crude images, Heinecken functions in a parodistic role, himself a "expert pretending to lack expertise."

HEINO, OTTO (Ceramist)
971 McAndrew Rd., Ojai, CA 93023

Born: 1915 *Awards:* Gold Medal, Vallauris Show, France *Collections:* Los Angeles County Museum; Vallauris Museum, France *Exhibitions:* Los Angeles County Museum; Olympic Art Festival, Los Angeles

Education: New Hampshire Craftsmen's School; USC While serving in England with the 1st Air Force, he visited many craftsmen in their studios and developed an interest in the large forms for which he is now well known. His very large, rough bottles, glazed with applewood ash, illustrate his continuing interest and sensitivity to form and texture. In the last few years, working with salt glaze and with fallout ash from woodburning kilns, he has developed a fascination with natural glaze effects. He continues to investigate the perfect relationship between form and finish.

HEINO, VIVIKA (Ceramist)
971 McAndrew Rd., Ojai, CA 93023

Born: 1910 *Awards:* 1st Prize, New York Ceramic Show; Rotunda Gallery, San Francisco *Exhibitions:* Los Angeles County Museum; Saddleback Mountain College *Education:* New York Ceramic College

She is best known for her experimental work with glazes and for her use of native ash materials. Skilled in both porcelain and stoneware, she deals in pottery's pure forms, exploring the correlation between form and glaze. She employs a wood fire to give her works the effects of ash. She organized the ceramic departments at Chouinard Art Institute and New England College, as well as ceramics departments at various other colleges. She currently teaches glaze technology classes.

HELD, ARCHIE (Sculptor)

Hon Chew Hee, *Poi Bowl,* 120 x 240, marble

John L. Holmes, *Mindscape for Twin Suns,* 50 x 50 x 42, foam, steel, resin

P.O. Box 331, Point Richmond, CA 94807

Born: 1955 *Awards:* Jim Marcellus Memorial Award for Sculpture, UCLA *Exhibitions:* Dominican College, San Rafael; Triangle Gallery, San Francisco *Education:* UCLA *Dealer:* Triangle Gallery, San Francisco

After working in cardboard, wood, plastic, fiberglas and mixed media, he discovered metal. He now fabricates abstract, elegant forms in bronze and stainless steel. He begins with solid metal columns, then twists and bends them into curving, organic shapes which incorporate running water into their design. These tranquil, soothing water sculptures display a satiny finish and strong lines.

HELLENTHAL, JOAN (Painter)
854 Martin Rd., Santa Cruz, CA 95060

Born: 1945 *Awards:* Minnie Helen Hicks Prize in Art, Brown U. *Collections:* Paine Webber, NYC; Chevron, Richmond *Exhibitions:* UC-Santa Cruz; Montalvo Center for the Arts, Saratoga *Education:* Brown U.; San Jose State U. *Dealer:* San Francisco Museum of Modern Art Rental Gallery

After she studied drawing in California, the abstract expressionist imagery of her early work became more gestural. She prefers working on a fairly large scale, up to six feet, either on single sheets of paper or in diptych or triptych formats. Along with acrylic or oil paint, she uses charcoal, pastels or paint sticks to energize the painted surface. Themes in her work are inspired by an emotional response to nature, which leads to enlivened abstract forms and striking colors that create a sensation of place, light and flux.

HELLESOE-HENON, JANE (Painter, Mixed Media Artist)
20 W. Gabilan St., #3, Salinas, CA 93901

Born: 1945 *Awards:* 1st Place, San Jose Institute of Contemporary Art *Exhibitions:* Accurate Art Gallery, Sacramento; Minot Art Gallery, Minot, ND *Education:* San Francisco State U.

Her eclectic background—publishing, graphic arts, sculpture and extensive figure studies—resulted in an abstract approach related to Matisse and Beckmann. By the 1980s, she was working with intense color dynamics and compositions, exploring ways to energize mundane objects by manipulating space. The illusion of floating objects in space dominated her work, which was characterized by abstract, non-objective images. She works on watercolor or printmaking paper, using acrylics, pastel, charcoal, palette knife and whatever other materials come to hand. Landscape themes have been pushed further into the abstract by the addition of non-objective shapes and symbols. The tension between the abstraction and the real, the sensuality of her colors and paint handling and the sense of things floating give her paintings force and density.

HELMER, BONITA (Painter)
2233 S. Barry Ave., Los Angeles, CA 90064

Born: 1942 *Exhibitions:* Newport Harbor Art Museum; Gallery Q, Tokyo *Education:* Antioch U.; Otis Art Institute

Study with Francoise Gilot led her to the research and use of symbols in her works, combining such elements as architectural and geometric forms with subtle primitive references. The artist mixes these planar symbols with three-dimensional materials, (for example, alternating layers of paint with wire, texture paint, broken glass and other media) to create a spatial illusion,

heavy with culture-spanning innuendo. A pair of works, *Trio* and *Quattuor*, shows this blend particularly: *Quattuor* balances four plates (from ancient Rome, possibly) around central specks of color. In between the plates, tropical fruits, done in color, alternate with ghosts of wine glasses, colorless and two-dimensional. *Trio* appears to blend the dark colors of an inner-city alley with the clean image of an unused plate. The artist has also designed the set of the modern opera "The XTC of Saint Teresa."

HEMMERDINGER, WILLIAM (Painter)
42-240 Green Way, Suite D, Palm Desert, CA 92260

Born: 1951 *Awards:* NEA Grant; Ford Foundation Grant *Collections:* Federal Reserve Bank, San Francisco; Smithsonian Institute, Washington, DC *Exhibitions:* Whitney Museum, NYC; Los Angeles County Museum of Art *Education:* Claremont Graduate School; Harvard U. *Dealer:* Cirrus Editions, Los Angeles

His early non-objective, calligraphic abstractions utilized a hybrid of markmaking. A student of Oriental languages, he employs writing and pictographic forms that evoke Native American symbology, Oriental language forms and the form of printed and written language. The use of temporal materials and the language mark simultaneously suggests contemporary concerns and eternal order. Most recently, he has introduced a representational architectural field sketch in the veneers of applied color. He works in both New York and Los Angeles.

HEMPLER, ORVAL F. (Painter, Sculptor)
2302 Second St., Santa Monica, CA 90405

Born: 1915 *Awards:* Frank and Alva Parsons Fellowship *Collections:* Los Angeles County Museum of Art; Litton Museum of Visual Arts, Los Angeles *Exhibitions:* New York Watercolor Society; Los Angeles County Museum of Art *Education:* U. of Colorado; U. of Iowa *Dealer:* Mary Browne, Norton, KS

His works in watercolor have been compared to those of Raoul Dufy. His use of color is characterized by a splashy, calligraphic style. Working as a designer-artist for a California ceramics firm allowed him to experiment with materials, which led him into sculpture. Using clays, paints and glazes, with high-firing kilns, he creates "sculptured paintings." In these works, he deals with spiritual, celestial, and abstract subjects.

HENDERSON, J. BRIGHT (Sculptor)
1211 Loma Portal Dr., El Cajon, CA 92020

Born: 1938 *Collections:* Jacques Cousteau Society Headquarters, Norfolk, VA; Mission de Alcala, San Diego *Exhibitions:* Wildlife Gallery, Laguna Beach; Wood Gallery, Coronado *Education:* San Diego State U. *Dealer:* Wildlife Gallery, Laguna Beach

She has worked in a variety of media, but is best known for driftwood sculptures of sea creatures, both real and mythological. She gathers the wood herself in trips to the coasts of California and Oregon. Recently, she has progressed from woods to casting media, particularly cultured marble; wood, though, is still her favorite. Her realistic pieces are rendered with a profound love of nature.

HENDERSON, MIKE (Painter, Multimedia Artist)
P.O. Box 43185, Oakland, CA 94624

J. Bright Henderson, *Loomis,* 18 x 14 x 15,
casting L/E cultured marble

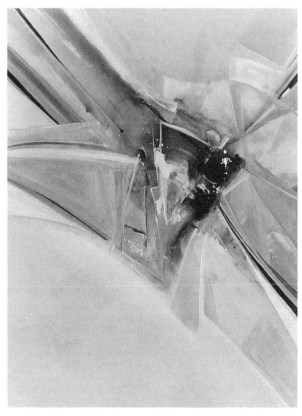

David Harris, *Facets,* 50 x 64, acrylic. Courtesy: Welles Fine
Art Publishing, Palo Alto, CA

Born: 1943 *Awards:* NEA Fellowship; Fellowship, Guggenheim Foundation *Collections:* San Francisco Museum of Modern Art; Oakland Museum *Exhibitions:* U. of the Pacific Gallery, Stockton; Cuesta College Gallery, San Luis Obispo *Education:* San Francisco Art Institute

He has worked in a variety of media including watercolor, acrylic, oil, collage, film and music. His recent main body of work of abstracted natural forms is executed in oil on canvas. Painting from a full palette, he uses knives, brushes and his own hands to apply pigment to the canvas. He also throws, drips and scrapes paint to achieve the desired effect. His social realist approach produces non-figurative works, often focused on prominent political or cultural figures, such as Nelson Mandela and Mother Theresa.

HEREDIA, BETTY REES (Mixed Media Artist)
3053 Bird Rock Rd., P.O. Box 54, Pebble Beach, CA 93953

Born: 1919 *Awards:* Purchase Prize, Foothill College; 1st Prize, Monterey County Art Fair *Collections:* Achenbach Foundation, Palace of the Legion of Honor, San Francisco; Grand Rapids Art Museum, MI *Exhibitions:* West Coast Biennial Open, Pacific Grove Art Center; Ft. Ord Art Gallery *Education:* Antioch U.

She began her art career as a teenager, making linoleum block prints for her high school newspaper. Her subsequent formal training and familiarity with a variety of media have been dedicated to her own self-expression. The Fauves have strongly influenced her energetic, pulsating style. Currently, she uses clay, bronze, steel, concrete, glass, handmade paper and papier maché to create figurative, impressionist, three-dimensional forms. She draws her imagery from the world around her, juxtaposing colors and shapes, then capturing them in ways which depict the day's changing light and shadow.

HERRMANN, RUSSELL (Sculptor)
P.O. Box 882462, San Francisco, CA 94188

Born: 1952 *Awards:* Ford Foundation Travel Grant; Alfredo Orselli Memorial Scholarship, U. of California *Exhibitions:* San Francisco State U.; Southern Exposure Gallery *Education:* U. of New Mexico; UCLA *Dealer:* Joslin Industries, San Francisco; Shidoni Gallery, NM

His sculpture is designed for both human and environmental interaction, but he has also created sculptures for indoor gallery spaces, which utilize human interplay to transform the environment. In these latter works, scrim material is stretched between walls to visually mask the space and therefore alter a viewer's perception of the room. Other works overlook or actually depict the ocean, with waves and wind causing them to move and make sounds by means of cable tethers attached to floats that collide with chimes. One viewer described a sculpture placed outside the Frederick S. Wight Gallery at UCLA as a transformation of a sterile environment into an animated, visually entertaining prelude to the show then on display. It was likened to the works of Joseph Beuys. In one recent piece, he attaches a triangular sailcloth to steel tube supports; the wind then activates the structure into billowing clouds. Attached at the bottom of the sailcloth is a metal weight which swings into chimes, emulating the resonance of Buddhist temple bells.

HERMS, GEORGE (Sculptor)
c/o L. A. Louver, 55 N. Venice Blvd., Venice, CA 90291

Born: 1935 *Awards:* Prix de Rome; Guggenheim Grant *Collections:* San Francisco Museum of Modern Art; Los Angeles County Museum of Art *Exhibitions:* MOCA, Los Angeles; L.A. Louver *Dealer:* L.A. Louver, Venice

His primary work centers on assemblages, although drawings, paintings, prints, photographs, film and sculpture are also found in his body of work. In his early assemblages, influenced most strongly by the work of Wallace Berman and Robert Alexander, he mounts weathered and discarded found objects, employing either great precision or a loose, "tossed-salad" approach. Current assemblage includes *Clock Tower Monument to Unknown*, a large outdoor work 18 by 30 by 40 feet and composed of found rusted steel buoys and a rusted steel column topped by a fabricated triangular clock unit of rusted steel. In many of his works, the presence of a clock or faded newsprint symbolizes the passage of time.

HERNANDEZ, SAM (Sculptor)
345 White Rd., Watsonville, CA 95076

Born: 1948 *Awards:* Phelan Award, San Francisco Foundation; NEA Fellowship *Collections:* Contemporary Museum, Honolulu; New Orleans Museum of Art *Exhibitions:* San Francisco Museum of Modern Art; American Craft Museum, NYC *Education:* Cal. State-Hayward; U. of Wisconsin *Dealer:* Iannetti/Lanzone Gallery, San Francisco

In the early 1970s, he made small assemblages similar to the gentlemanly machines of the 18th and 19th centuries. These elegantly sculpted machines were meticulously crafted of wood, with highly polished surfaces, and encased in felt-lined boxes, but they had no practical function. After traveling to Europe in 1976, he began making more forceful, hand-hewn images with strong emotional impact. He has recently been particularly inspired by the economy of form, construction techniques and surface patina found in tribal and ethnic art and technology. He works primarily in wood and bronze, and he combines organic and geometric forms in a variety of evocative, exuberant, and compelling images "triggered by personal encounters with words, events, phrases, objects and people."

HERNANDEZ, VALERIE (Weaver)
1105 Clinton St., Redwood City, CA 94061

Born: 1950 *Awards:* Gold Award, Textiles, San Mateo County Art Exhibition *Exhibitions:* Mendocino Art Center; Art World International Competitions, San Mateo *Dealer:* M.L. Steinbeck, Arnold, CA

In the late 1960s, she studied with the Navajo Indians, and under their influence, she wove tapestries of unspun or hand-spun wool in their natural colors and featuring a central motif, usually pictorial. In the 1970s, she studied and lived in Central America, where she absorbed the design of that region, particularly that of the Mayans. The recent pieces are hand-dyed and hand-spun, and the natural earth-tones are woven in geometric and overlapping designs that lend the pieces an optical three-dimensionality.

HERNANDEZ-HINEK, SOCORRO (Ceramist, Mixed Media Artist)
P.O. Box 681, Redding, CA 96099

Bonita Helmer, *Complosion,* 60 x 96, acrylic paint and texture on canvas

Russell Herrman, *Mesa Sail,* 120 x 84 x 36, nylon sailcloth and steel spring supports

Born: 1953 *Awards:* 1st Place, Redding Museum Juried Art Exhibition *Exhibitions:* Cherry Street Studios; Shasta College Gallery, Redding *Education:* Cal. State-Chico

Her sculptural forms are derived from organic sources, such as landscapes and organic materials; they represent her spiritual unity with the earth. She works in clay, using plaster casts, slabs and extruded shapes, often combined into one or more units. Some brightly colored pieces are fired four to six times, to achieve the desired effect. Recent ceramic sculptures have been pit-fired, in an attempt to achieve a more naturalistic, less contrived color. Other recent work involved organic collage. For these pieces, she uses thread, fiber, paper, plants, wire, twigs and other organic materials that are the sources of her inspiration. Her paintings revolve around extreme close-ups of flower parts, particularly pistils and stamens. She attributes her interests in spirituality and life beyond death to her Mexican heritage.

HERRERA, BE (Sculpture)
2121 Perkins Way, Sacramento, CA 95818

Born: 1942 *Collections:* Matrix Gallery *Exhibitions:* Artspace, San Francisco; Garden Studio Gallery, NC *Dealer:* Matrix Gallery

Early exposure to Rodin, Moore and Klee and to Chinese ceramics focused her exploration of form and light. The work of Nancy Holt and Eleanor Antin revealed to her the importance of installation in exploring post-modern concerns. Using silk, bamboo, copper wire and paper, she developed constructions that probe the human form as a base "bag of bones." She explored enlarged contexts of intimacy in a series based on the forms of metropolitan subway lines. Her site-specific sculpture studies have led to her current pieces that incorporate cultural symbolism within walled structures, combining wood, aluminum, raw silk and mylar. Present imagery is of angels from all cultures, including Islamic and Buddhist. All thirty pieces in the series incorporate candles at the angels' feet. At its core, her work anticipates and visualizes images of the coming quarter-century.

HERSH, NANCI (Painter)
66-471B Pikai St., Haleiwa, HI 96712

Born: 1959 *Awards:* Purchase Award, Hawaii State Foundation; R.P. Scholz Award, Honolulu *Collections:* State Foundation of Culture and Arts, Honolulu; Hemmeter Collection, Honolulu *Exhibitions:* Honolulu Academy; Haggin Museum, Stockton *Education:* Pratt Institute *Dealer:* Art Loft, Honolulu

Early works were abstract landscapes. Rocks, caves, shells, all became environments. Working in mixed-media and printmaking, she used texture as well as color and form to create personal landscapes. A trip to Hawaii in 1983 influenced a bolder brighter use of color. She began using these colors on a flat black surface heightening their negative/positive relationships. She recently began working on a series of large paintings of meals and also on a series of giant rabbits. These pieces in oil and mixed-media are more painterly and less abstract than earlier works. In them she explores the sensuous qualities of oil while she exploits imagery with a pop quality bringing an ominous tone to everyday events.

HERSHMAN, LYNN (Video Artist, Mixed Media Artist)
1935 Filbert, San Francisco, CA 94123

Born: 1941 *Awards:* First Prize, San Francisco Film Festival *Collections:* Oakland Museum; Palace of the Legion of Honor *Exhibitions:* 1986 Venice Bienalle; New Museum, NY *Education:* San Francisco State U. *Dealer:* Fuller Golden, San Francisco

She uses videotape as a combination of painting and sculpture to produce portrait pieces that activate both the subject and the viewer. The implosion of time in viewing the work and the incorporation of the media as part of the context and composition results in an exploration of process and chance. Recent works—spectator-involvement video disks—have reflected her background from the late 1960s in site-specific sound and light installations.

HERTEL, SUSAN (Painter)
P.O. Box 7, Cerrilos, NM 87010

Born: 1930 *Collections:* Pitzer College, Claremont *Exhibitions:* Pasadena Museum of Art; U. of Redlands *Education:* Scripps College *Dealer:* Joan Ankrum Gallery, Los Angeles; Elaine Horwich Gallery, Palm Springs

She first painted in oils on canvas, with areas of stained canvas, charcoal drawings and some areas of thicker paint. Earlier work as a muralist lent a flatness to the picture plane and an emphasis on the abstract quality of shapes. In 1981, she moved to New Mexico; both her style and subject matter changed. The bright colors, the lyricism and the intricacy of her early work have been replaced by a simpler, more dramatic style and a muted palette. Her paintings display a new interest in light and space and a freer use of paint. Recent subject matter has included horses, dogs, figures with expanses of sky (often night sky) and Southwestern interiors. She strives to find and express the magical in the everyday, to distill complex forms into simplicity.

HERTZ, DAVID (Sculptor)
2908 Colorado Ave., Santa Monica, CA 90404

Born: 1960 *Collections:* Santa Monica College *Exhibitions:* Monterey Museum of Art; Westweek 1988, Los Angeles *Education:* Southern California Institute of Architecture *Dealer:* Sydesis, Inc., Santa Monica; Hokin/Kaufman Gallery, Chicago

He decided to use his formal training in architecture, art and design to create functional works using the materials of construction. He is best known for his interior designs and for furniture made from steel, glass and cast and light-weight concrete. Maintaining the integrity of these materials is an important factor in his work. By juxtaposing the contrasting elements of glass and concrete, he can create a tension which is both structural and psychological. He enjoys the drama of the cantilever and pure forms of geometry which challenge gravity and seem to defy the laws of physics. More recently, he has used the same materials in a series of outdoor public sculptures. These abstract pieces are the products of his desire to create an idealized, immediate expression of the building process.

HERTZ, JO ANNE (Painter, Printmaker)
2852 Colorado Ave., Santa Monica, CA 90404

Awards: Brand Library Art Galleries Award; 1st Place, Craft and Folk Art Museum *Collections:* Warner Records, Los Angeles; Standard Brand Paint Company, Los Angeles *Exhibitions:* Museum of Contem-

Coille McLaughlin Hooven, *untitled,* 9 x 5, porcelain

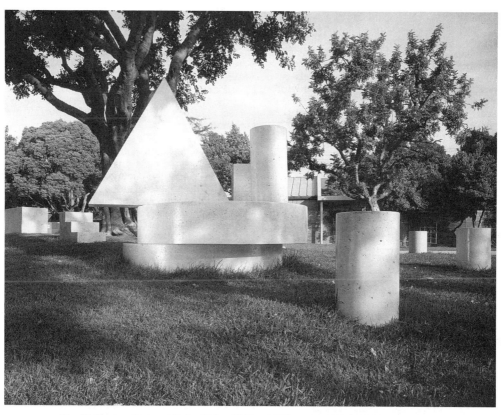

David Hertz, *Abstract Ruin,* 120 x 1200 x 1200, pre-cast lightweight concrete.
Courtesy: Syndesis, Inc., Santa Monica, CA

porary Art, Los Angeles; Los Angeles County Museum of Art *Education:* UCLA

Her works' freedom of movement and generous use of paint reflects the influence of de Kooning and Jackson Pollock and her earlier experimentation in abstract expressionism. But her personal style truly developed when she combined photography with acrylic painting and printing techniques. By translating a photograph onto a silkscreen and printing with a squeegie, she creates a flexible primary image with which she can work the wet ink, then layer and collage until its realism has disintegrated. The result is ambiguous in origin—textured photographic information that is more painterly than an ordinary silkscreen image. Her painting, on the other hand, is more straightforward. She is drawn to figuration for its direct formal considerations and finds the body and the face particularly fascinating landscapes. She has recently explored the shape undulations of the female body in a series of paintings that focus on parts of the nude abstracted by perspective. Like photographs of a moving form, they appear loose and open, rendered by muted whites and greens with broad, gestural brush strokes. She strives in all her pieces to present objects in new ways, and maintains that a personal work achieves meaning only when it communicates.

HERTZ, ROBERT (Sculptor)
1092 Wilshire Blvd., Los Angeles, CA 90024

Born: 1931 *Awards:* 1st Prize, Municipal Art Gallery, Barnsdale Park, Los Angeles *Exhibitions:* U.S. National Fine Arts Competition, FL; Venice Art Walk

After spending years exploring the use of plastic, wood, concrete, steel and low fusing molten metal, he began making loosely figurative and abstract sculpture. Steel edges contained his concrete filled forms. Their size ranged from the table top to the large, site-specific, polychromed outdoor pieces that were often related to specific themes. Cantilevered and projecting structures are a recent special interest. Some works seem to be tilting apart, but stand in balance; in others, triangular shapes have beveled edges or blunted tips. There is a trend toward representational abstraction in his work, and many of his sculptures are designed to take advantage of viewing by parallax.

HERZEL, ANGELIKA (Painter)
1225 N. Poinsettia Pl., W. Hollywood, CA 90046

Born: 1957 *Awards:* Purchase Award, City of Biberach; Riss Municipal Library, Germany *Exhibitions:* Richard Bennett Gallery, Los Angeles; Foyer du Theatre, Valence, France *Education:* Stuttgart Academy of Arts, Germany *Dealer:* Jack Conrad, Los Angeles

Over the past ten years, the artist's exhibitions, commissioned projects and wearable designs have experienced many style and media changes. She is often influenced by the artists and art movements that her studies bring to light; thus, an overview of her career belies her relatively young age. Max Ernst and Magritte provided models for her surreal landscapes executed in tempera, gouache, oil and watercolor. Her style became more ornamental as Gaudi, the Art Deco movement and elements of Eastern art drew her attention. Recent oil paintings reveal the colorist influences of Chagall and Kandinsky. Abstracting elements of her previous landscape paintings, the artist transforms articles of clothing into wearable artwork.

HESS, CRAIG R. (Sculptor)

9863 Amanita Ave., Tujunga, CA 91042

Born: 1944 *Collections:* Milwaukee Mutual Insurance Company *Exhibitions:* Craft Festival, Santa Clara *Education:* Woodbury College

His sculpture has been influenced by his background: in metal work and specialized upholstering; working on the Ice Follies; majoring in Interior Arts; and five years of extensive research and development for Disneyland and Disneyworld adventures. After twenty-one years of experience in sculpting, he still extensively researches each project, including countless reproductions of old cars, carriages, carts, trucks, ships, trains and even carousels. Before ever picking up the torch, he visualizes and creates the subject detail by detail. Working in copper and brass in such fine detail, he must occasionally hold his breath to avoid any movement in the torch.

HEWES, JOHN M. (Painter, Photographer)
230 Madeline Ave., Pasadena, CA 91105

Born: 1958 *Exhibitions:* Laguna Beach Festival of Arts *Education:* UC-Irvine; Laguna Beach Art College

Working from a photographic image on a computer monitor, he uses a variety of paints to capture the image on imported papers. These images are a visual collection of abstract symbols and geometric objects, which are correlated with color to create a flowing visual harmony. The work ranges in size, from 30-by-40 inches to six-by-eight-feet. Other materials, such as typar, polypropylene, nylon, kevlar, resin based and cotton-based photographic materials are sometimes incorporated.

HEWITT, JOHN (Painter)
6155 Lower Lake Rd., Crescent City, CA 95531

Born: 1946 *Awards:* Purchase Award, Asilomar Watercolor Society; Honorable Mention, Texas Watercolor Society *Collections:* State Park at Asilomar; Ingomar Club, Eureka *Exhibitions:* College of the Redwoods Fine Arts Gallery, Eureka; Valperrine Gallery, Madison, WI *Dealer:* Accurate Art, Sacramento

With each painting he intends to evoke a response that transcends an appreciation of technique. Influenced primarily by the California School of Watercolorists, he believes that the beauty of paint on paper is secondary to the impact of the artist's message. Good art will inspire feeling best through a refined use of visual language, he says. To avoid the merely decorative, his traditional approach to landscape emphasizes the relationship between humanity and the environment. A scene is analyzed, interpreted and reproduced with the direct intent of communication.

HEYMAN, JANE (Painter, Collage Artist)
279 S. Beverly Dr., #426, Beverly Hills, CA 90212

Born: 1952 *Awards:* Fellowship, Salmagundi Club, NYC; Pratt Institute Scholarship, Art Students League *Collections:* Staten Island Museum; Madonna *Exhibitions:* Art Works, Santa Barbara; In The Pink, Los Angeles *Education:* Pratt Institute *Dealer:* Steve Handleman, Santa Monica

Early formal works depicted pain and struggle, her own and that of war victims and the victims of self abuse. After moving to Los Angeles, her work took a lighter, almost pop art tone that relied on her strengths in form, structure, color and wit. Incorporating the Los Angeles lifestyle and icon worship, she completed a massive collection of paintings of the pop star Madon-

Emiko Higo, *untitled,* 72 x 240, sculpture

Wayne Hill, *Toy Boat in Pond,* 18 x 24, oil on canvas

na. In a series of pop photo collages, the faces of Warhol, Monroe, Lucille Ball, Divine and Oliver North were repeated in oversized hand-painted film frames. The satirical *The Walking Dead* showed Warhol, Monroe and Presley all holding one-hundred dollar bills, symbolizing the way dead stars are exploited in order to make money.

HEYWOOD, SCOT (Painter)
3552 Beethoven St., Los Angeles, CA

Born: 1951 *Exhibitions:* Newspace, Los Angeles; San Francisco Art Institute *Dealer:* Newspace, Los Angeles

He began his career as a figurative painter and worked in an abstract expressionist style before beginning to paint geometric abstraction and removing all literal references. Since 1985, he has painted in black. His multipaneled canvases of abutted rectangles and diamonds have provoked comparisons with the works of Reinhardt and Kelly. He applies black acrylic paint thinly and flatly, in order to produce an effect that is dense and spaceless. He is interested in an experience of painting that is beyond narration. He has recently been working on a series of flat-surfaced triptychs in blue, green and purple. "Personality in art is vulgar and self-indulgent," he has said.

HICKOK-SCHUBERT, RUTH (Painter)
2462 Senate Way, Medford, OR 97504

Born: 1927 *Awards:* J. Fon Watercolor Award, Hall of Flowers, Golden Gate Park, San Francisco; 1st Place, California State Art Expo, Souverain, Geyserville *Collections:* Monterey Peninsula Museum of Art; Nabisco Brands Inc., San Jose *Exhibitions:* Brea Cultural Center; National Watercolor Show and Exhibition, San Diego *Education:* San Jose State U. *Dealer:* Lyn Shue Village Galleries, La Haina, Maui, HI

She painted in a variety of media until the mid-1970s, when she settled on watercolor. Her work was influenced by the California school of watercolor, as well as by Eric Obek, Joseph Raffael, Millard Sheets and the light, color and freedom of expression in Hawaiian and Californian art. She has been painting in increasingly larger size surfaces, striving to interpret traditional forms with emphases on color, form, design and each subject's particular optical qualities. She is inspired by the natural world and paints close-ups of people, animals, birds, flowers and water. While naturalistic, these renderings are also thoughtful and imaginative, expressing the wonder of nature. She has recently been working on a series of nature studies with a Hawaiian theme.

HIGBY, SHA SHA (Sculptor, Performance Artist)
P.O. Box 936, Bolinas, CA 94924

Born: 1952 *Awards:* California Arts Council Touring Grant; Fulbright-Hays Grant *Exhibitions:* San Francisco Museum of Modern Art; San Jose Museum of Art *Education:* Skidmore College *Dealer:* Hatley Martin Gallery, San Francisco

She presents a unique art form, which she calls "costume sculpture performance." Drawing on her exhaustive studies in Java, Indonesia and Japan, she creates costumes with intricate parts, using exotic materials and techniques from the Orient. Construction of one costume can require up to a year of effort. Performance is presented on a bare stage with minimalist guitar music and bells. In some performances, the audience is given handmade musical instruments to create its own accompaniment. The dance consists of slow, languid movements and the manipulation of toys and puppets. The hypnotic display concludes as she sheds the costume, reflecting the cycles of life, death and rebirth. Her work is influenced by Zen principles.

HIGGINBOTHAM, RAY. S. (Painter)
124 Hiawatha, #14, Santa Cruz, CA 95062

Born: 1951 *Exhibitions:* Politics of Art Show

He is self-taught, and in the late 1970s he started painting cartoons and caricatures. After several years in Asia, he became a follower of Japanese-style color contrast and circle shading. He also became attracted to "ethnic" art's high color contrasts and shadow figures. His current work is often political in nature. Black shadow figures of animals stand in the center of his canvases. He offsets these precisely painted forms with color circles, varied shadows and cloud bank backdrops. He uses pen line separation, and he paints with acrylics and oils on gessoed duck canvas.

HIGHSTEIN, JENE (Sculptor)
c/o Michael Klein, Inc., 611 Broadway, Room 308, New York, NY 10012

Born: 1942 *Awards:* Guggenheim Fellowship; NEA Fellowship *Collections:* La Jolla Museum of Contemporary Art; Guggenheim Museum, NYC *Exhibitions:* Flow Ace Galleries, Venice; Krieger/Landau Contemporary Art, Santa Monica

His sculptures are based upon a minimalism that is infused with symbolism, the attempt being to work with a simple, found minimalist form, as in *The Single Pipe Piece*, a 39-foot-long pipe suspended between two walls. The sculptures, in such materials as wood and cast bronze, are often poetic and humorous. A recent exhibition at the La Jolla museum was a mid-career retrospective of sculpted works and drawings produced within a thirteen-year period.

HIGO, EMIKO (Sculptor)
2161 Stanley Hills Dr., Los Angeles, CA 90046

Born: 1953 *Exhibitions:* Mt. San Antonio Community College Art Gallery, Walnut; Doizaki Gallery, Japanese American Cultural Community Center, Los Angeles *Education:* Tama Art U., Tokyo; UCLA

With a background in weaving and flower arranging, she creates contemporary, environmental sculptures using natural materials such as tree branches and stripped twigs, wooden pegs, and bits of bark. One piece featured a repeated geometric design consisting of two twigs formed into a tepee with other, taller branches waving above. Mark di Suvero is a major influence on her work.

HILL, EILEEN (Painter)
1753 Flint Creek Way, San Jose, CA 95148

Born: 1948 *Collections:* Crocker Museum, Sacramento *Exhibitions:* San Jose Museum; J.J. Brookings Gallery, San Jose *Education:* San Jose State U. *Dealer:* J.J. Brookings Gallery, San Jose

Early work was influenced by Louise Nevelson's assemblage and relief works, and Richard Diebenkorn and Nathan Oliveira's complex color and spontaneous, abstract-expressionist brushwork. In 1970, she stopped painting to study metalsmithing and metal fabrication. Between then and 1986 she produced a large body of jewelry and large-scale metal work. Her recent pieces are a synthesis of metal and paint, structurally similar to jewelry. She fabricates the basic form, applies cast

Nina Hastings, *Bonne Fête Maman,* 22 x 30, transparent watercolor

John Hincks, *What Speaks?,* 29 x 21, vinyl acrylic

bronze elements and then paints the piece with oils. The paint's colors provide her with a wider emotional range than is possible with chemical patination alone.

HILL, SHELLEY (Sculptor)
5024 Otis Ave., Tarzana, CA 91356

Born: 1951 *Awards:* Nominee, San Diego Art Institute National Exhibition *Exhibitions:* Los Angeles County Museum of Art; Los Angeles Municipal Art Gallery *Education:* Cal. State-Northridge; Fashion Institute of Technology, NYC

Educated at a time when pop art and minimalism were popular, she was drawn to the reductive form and raw gesture of Franz Kline's painting. The psychological and dynamic use of space and form, as seen in works by Snelson and Giacometti, influenced the manner in which she approaches her sculpture. Interested in architecture and the human form, she looks for equivalences between the two, as a way to determine the overall shape of her sculpture. She uses incremental color and fragments to emphasize a given form. Working with segments of painted wood and wire, she layers each fragment in a random position, to create a fragile tension between the form as a whole and its segments. In this way, a three-dimensional form is both created and denied.

HILL, WAYNE (Painter, Video Artist)
P.O. Box 1830, Loma Linda, CA 92354

Born: 1942 *Exhibitions:* Ester Wells Gallery, Laguna Beach; Coffee Academy Gallery, San Bernardino *Education:* San Bernardino Valley College

After formal training in the techniques of impressionism, he progressed into abstract expressionism. The majority of his work has been an attempt to bridge the gap between the two movements. His imagined landscapes appeared realistic, but were painted in an expressionistic style. His use of color was influenced by Fauvism. He uses contemporary oil pigments as his medium. He also experiments with computer programs and indirect lighting systems in painting, by which he attempts to present the viewer with more complex dimensions and moods. His river landscapes are studies of the reflections of skies and trees on water.

HILLDING, JOHN (Sculptor)
Box H, Wilkeson, WA 98396

Born: 1944 *Collections:* City of Seattle *Exhibitions:* Seattle Art Museum; Palace of Fine Arts, San Francisco *Education:* Kansas City Art Institute; Maryland Institute College of Art *Dealer:* One Reel, Seattle

He constructs his monumental pop objects out of taped-together, disposable materials, such as polyethylene. These "Disposable Monuments" have included a forty-foot light bulb, a 350-foot extension cord, a thirty-five-foot zipper, a thirty-five-foot faucet and a fifty-foot pencil. He has recently produced large-scale, inflatable polyethylene sculpture that both interacts with the surrounding architecture and adorns specific buildings. In one piece, a huge pencil seems to stick through the corner of a building, like a pencil stuck behind a human ear. He has been influenced by the pop movement and by his instructors, Dale Eldred, George Segal and Robert Morris. He currently teaches at the Art Institute of Seattle.

HILLMAN, BEVERLEY (Mixed Media Artist)
607 Tahos Rd., Orinda, CA 94563

Awards: Merit Award, San Francisco Women Artists *Collections:* Clorox Corporation, Pleasanton; Federal Reserve Bank, San Francisco *Exhibitions:* Second International Contemporary Art Fair, Los Angeles; Palo Alto Cultural Center *Education:* UC-Berkeley *Dealer:* Barclay Simpson Gallery, Lafayette; ART Beasley, San Diego

Learning the monoprint process led to a breakthrough in her work. Her geometric abstract paintings became three-dimensional, as she was able to join spontaneously formed, individually created monotypes into unified constructions. At first, these monotypes were made on rag paper, but as they grew bigger and changed in form and feeling, it became necessary to adjust the process. For the last two years, she has been using aluminum as her base. She monotypes, folds and joins the sheets to achieve the desired shapes and forms. She then joins these pieces with others to form large wall constructions. For a recent commission, she used the same technique to create a paper wall sculpture.

HILLS, ROXANNE (Painter)
510 15th St., #304, Oakland, CA 94612

Born: 1944 *Awards:* MacDowell Colony; Yaddo Foundation *Exhibitions:* Pence Gallery, Davis; Hearst Art Gallery, Moraga; *Education:* California College of Arts and Crafts

She sketches things that excite her, particularly things she finds mysterious, and works rapidly in order to build a rough perceptual analysis. Using this technique, she seeks to capture the subject's spatial relations and its movement and to create a parallel to the forces experienced in nature. Her current subjects are industrial and urban estuaries and waterfronts. Working in oil on canvas, she paints in the tradition of figurative artists, concentrating on landscapes for their depth. She explores the representational quality of the scene through her use of color, allowing the form to show through as naturally abstract. Motion, volume and distance are studied through a use of perspective that is often deceptive, revealing on closer examination an extremeness that is at once masterful in execution and challenging to the viewer's initial perceptions. Her work strives for the harmonious fusion of abstract and representational qualities.

HILTUNEN, JANICE M. (Painter)
P.O. Box 10863, Marina Del Rey, CA 90295

Born: 1947 *Exhibitions:* UC-Berkeley; Pacific Art Guild, Westchester

Highly influenced by realism, her early acrylic paintings and pen and ink drawings were literal, detailed environments of travel and dream imagery. Later, she recalled an earlier interest in impressionism and moved toward a more expressive mode, though strong undertones of realism remained. Later, she produced a series of water images using only a palette knife. Her more recent landscape images repeat and abstract forms with subtle, elegant surface textures. Her media include acrylics, oils, collage, silk screen and other printmaking techniques. Her largest canvases are approximately four by six feet.

HINCKS, JOHN THURSTON (Painter)
6849 Sayre, Oakland, CA 94611

Born: 1943 *Awards:* Sonoma County Fair *Exhibitions:* Court Gallery, Denmark; San Francisco Museum of

H. Elton Harris, *Tryst,* 8 x 8 x 24, marble

Hawthorne, *The Couple,* 48 x 72, acrylic.
Courtesy: Kersting Gallery

John Hillding, *Pencil,* 576 x 72, polyethylene

Wayne Hill, *Aspen I,* 39 x 25, oil on masonite.
Courtesy: Richard T. Stevens

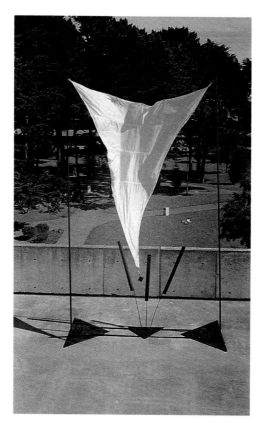

Russell Herrman, *Windchyme,* 168 x 108 x 36,
nylon sailcloth,tube steel & stainless steel attachments

Carol Ann Huboi, *Tiptoe Falls, Southeast Wall,*
Portola State Park, 108 x 156, acrylic

Lynne Streeter, *HOME,* 2 x 3, bronze and marble, 1984

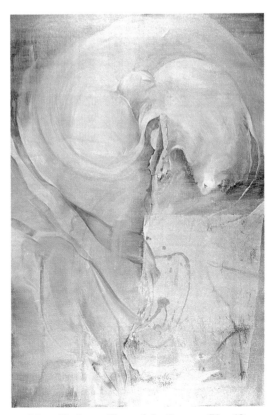

Mary Heebner, *Turn of the Century,* 72 x 48,
acrylic, collage on canvas

Larry Hamilton, *Bette and Earl,* 48 x 72, acrylic lacquer

Nina Hastings, *Picnic Vase,* 22 x 30, transparent watercolor.
Courtesy: Wesley Seeds

Bernard Hoyes, *Hexing Rites,* 35 x 50, oils.
Courtesy: Caribbean Arts Inc.

Elaine L. Harvey, *Land Sea Sky Connections,* 23 x 30,
watercolor collage/bronze powder

Robert Hertz, *Equine,* 40 x 48 x 88, steel and concrete

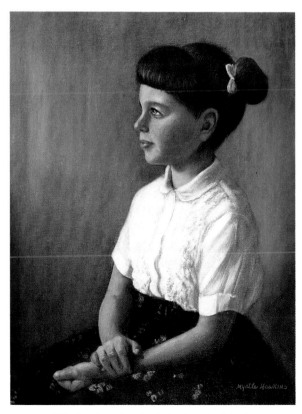

Myrtle Hawkins, *Little Lady,* 18 x 24, oil.
Courtesy: Mr. and Mrs. Charles Perry

Michael Hughes, *The Kiss,* 54 x 40, oil on canvas.
Courtesy: Orlando Gallery

J. Bright Henderson, *Midnight Dancer,* 55 x 50 x 33, driftwood,
redwood burl. Courtesy: Wildlife Gallery, Laguan Beach, CA

Thomas Hall, *Pots of Anemones,* 24 x 20, oil on canvas.
Courtesy: M. Werner, San Francisco

Jim Hutchison, *Proceed as Before,* 48 x 48, oil on canvas

Richard Hornaday, *Dried Flowers and Objects,* 15 x 14, watercolor

Mary Harris, *Sunbathers,* 48 x 48, acrylic & glue

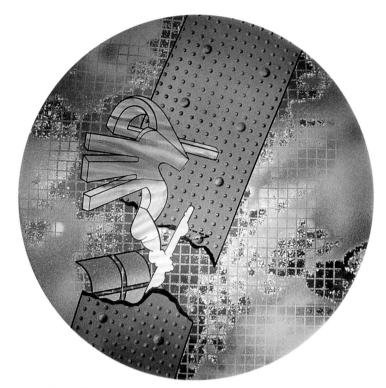

John Hopkins, *Composition 49,* 23-inch diameter, ceramic

Jo Anne Hertz, *Two Sisters,* 48 x 48, silk screen and oil paint

Carolyn Hofstetter, *The Mustard Meadow,* 30 x 30, oil Courtesy: Dr. and Mrs. George Paris

David B. Hoppe, *Ceremonial #2,* 48 x 48, acrylic

John H. Hunter, *Burbank, Where Disney Stood,* 12 x 13, oil on masonite.
Courtesy: Discovery Gallery, San Jose

Heli Hofmann, *Tulip Field,* 22 x 28, oil on canvas

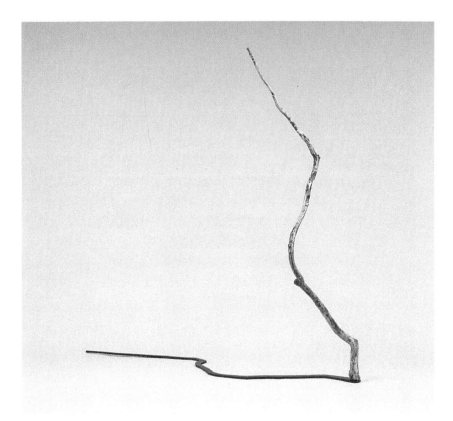

Emiko Higo, *untitled,* 72 x 72, sculpture

Leigh Hyams, *Rio Grande Stones,* partial installation (22 pieces), acrylic on shaped jute canvas

Bonita Helmer, *Threshold,* 60 x 66, acrylic, texture and broken glass on canvas

Hartini, *Land of Shadows (Contests and Battles),* 40 x 60, oil on canvas

John L. Holmes, *Edge III–Bird Flash Beyond,* 22 x 28, pastel and paper

John Hincks, *Guernica Variations,* 27 x 22, vinyl acrylic

Modern Art *Education:* California College of Arts and Crafts

After formal training at the California College of Arts and Crafts, he involved himself in the social experiments of the late 1960s. He then moved to Denmark, where he was influenced by the English pop movement, especially R.B. Kitaj and David Hockney. His eclectic interpretive paintings are populated with fragments, amorphous shapes, symbols and constructions. At times, he interpolates well known works into his own didactic pieces, establishing a metaphorical or allegorical reference. He paints in mixed media on canvas, paper or Masonite.

HINRICHS, ROBERT (Sculptor, Vesselier)
2715 Porter St., Soguel, CA 95073

Born: 1954 *Awards:* 1st Place, Calamari Arts Festival, Santa Cruz *Collections:* Earl of Perth, London; Lorimar Productions, Beverly Hills *Exhibitions:* Gallery 69, Belfast, ME; Artist Society International, San Francisco *Education:* California Institute of the Arts

He has researched the ancient Celtic, Indonesian and Japanese cultures, and his sculptures and vessels are the results of practices and ceremonies he has participated in. In each piece, he combines a "unique revelation" of spirit and form with orientations and influences that are unique to California. He uses textures to create tension and balance so that form, color and size combine with a sense of "shabooi." He works with plastic and wood, and his invention, BOH-massene, (reminiscent of Persian Damascene) augments the wood's imperfection. He has been influenced by Calder and Rockwell Kent.

HIPKISS, CYNTHIA (Ceramist)
18445 Arnold Dr., Sonoma, CA 95476

Born: 1948 *Awards:* San Francisco Art Festival Purchase Award *Collections:* Oakland Museum *Exhibitions:* Galerie Kolczynski, Germany; Richmond Art Center *Education:* California College of Arts and Crafts; Sonoma State College *Dealer:* Arts Guild of Sonoma

Her works are primarily in low-fire white clay and center on humorous figures of plump women ranging up to three feet in height. The figures are brightly glazed and typically involved in a thematic representation, as in *Betty Crocker and Her Hot Cross Buns.* She has recently been creating functional art pieces, such as teapots, as an extension of the figures' frequent references to food, cooking and baking. Other current themes include fish and Mother Goose. The active involvement of her figures in their environments is a lively expression of the more zany aspects of human perception.

HIRD, BETH (Painter)
7547 Terrace Dr., El Cerrito, CA 94530

Born: 1954 *Collections:* Rene and Veronica DiRosa Foundation, Napa; Syntex Laboratories, Inc., Palo Alto *Exhibitions:* Fuller Goldeen Gallery; San Jose Institute of Contemporary Art *Eduction:* Brown U.; San Francisco Art Institute *Dealer:* Fuller Gross, San Francisco

She makes large landscape assemblages, sometimes incorporating the figure. Her subjects are man's destruction of nature and the tapping of the unconscious through the exploration of memory and dreams. The works are often multipanelled. She exaggerates the three-dimensional qualities of foreground objects and blends them into a flat and illusionistically painted distance, in order to draw the viewer into the experience of the painting and emphasize emphasize a feeling of motion and energy. The materials she applies include bamboo, wood, shells, pvc tubing, and eucalyptus and mahogany bark.

HIRSCHFIELD, JIM (Installation Artist)
3600 Wallingford Ave. N., Seattle, WA 98103

Born: 1951 *Awards:* NEA Grant; Rockefeller Foundation Interdisciplinary Grant *Exhibitions:* Eloise Pickard Smith Gallery, UC-Santa Cruz; 80 Langton St., San Francisco *Education:* Kansas City Art Institute; U. of Oregon

He is intrigued with the possibilities of using monofilaments to create ephemeral planes in space and continues to investigate and generate spaces of sanctuary. The monofilaments—often either blue or clear—appear like glass sheets or pools of water and are arranged in varying planes. As the viewer moves through the space, a *moire* effect is created by the layers of monofilament. This establishes a gentle rhythm that is synchronized to the viewer's movement. The viewer becomes involved in the vibrations of light and filament, filtering incoming sensory information discriminately and becoming less cognizant of time and more aware of the encompassing stillness.

HO, RAY (Collage Artist)
5212 18th St., N.W., Gig Harbor, WA 98335

Born: 1939 *Awards:* 1st in Ceramics and Furniture, Port Townsend Art League Annual Arts Festival, OR *Collections:* 1st National Bank of Oregon, Portland, OR; Western Bancorporation, Portland, OR *Exhibitions:* Lawrence Gallery, Sheridan, OR; Art Concepts, Tacoma, WA *Education:* U. of Puget Sound, Tacoma; Central Washington U. *Dealers:* Attic Art Gallery, Portland; Tacoma Art Museum Rental Gallery

He is a collage artist who presents abstract natural designs. His early works resembled rock formations. Over the years, he has developed a translucent painterly technique. He now creates works that resemble landscapes and seascapes, in varying forms and colors. His palette includes violets and lavenders; his most recent pieces have been in variations of natural blues and soft grays. First he dyes a quality rice paper with an oil pigment. He then outlines the designs with water before tearing the paper and layering pieces with a water based glue. He has exhibited widely and he is presently an art instructor at Lakes High School in Tacoma, Washington.

HOAG, JACK (Sculptor)
65 Sleepy Hollow Ln., Orinda, CA 94563

Born: 1929 *Awards:* Oakland Art Museum, Morrison Memorial Medal; Award of Merit, San Francisco Art Festival *Collections:* Oakland Art Museum; International Headquarters, Standard Oil of California *Exhibitions:* California Palace of the Legion of Honor; Pasadena Art Museum *Education:* California College of Arts and Crafts; UC-Berkeley

In 1960 he began designing and sculpting large public fountains and site specific pieces. This formal work involved a variety of materials. He is now exploring the organic world of growing forms, natural events and other examples of changes in energy states. His recent cast bronze sculptures and reliefs are now less heroic in scale and more organic in form. He is pioneering a unique cold casting technique, involving steel-reinforced polychromed elastomers and acrylics. The pieces, generally painted in oils, often feature patterns taken from molds of natural elements such as trees. In his present work, *Cloudburst*, billowing silicon figures emit "rain".

HOBSON, DIANA (Painter)
1316 W. Washington Blvd., Venice, CA 90291

Born: 1948 *Exhibitions:* Nagoya, Japan; Southern California Artists L.A.I.C.A. *Education:* Connecticut College

Influenced by her early exposure to El Greco's *Toledo in a Storm*, she became an abstract artist in her early twenties. By her early thirties, she had discovered a new way to tell a "story" via abstract painting. She currently explores the questions of how and why colors, shapes and lines have the power to move people in desired directions, and what specific elements do so. Her pieces vary from life-size to inspirational-size (ten by seventeen feet) and are done with prime-quality oil paint in a deliberate technique that the works' bravura appearance somewhat belies. Her colors tend to be intense and very alive. She pays attention to good conservation practices and stretches her pieces in their final form. Her heroes include Franz Kline, Kandinsky and Degas.

HOCHBERG, HARRIET (Sculptor)
6636 Neddy Avenue, West Hills, CA 91307

Born: 1920 *Awards:* 1st Prize, Long Island Juried Show *Collections:* Mark Taper Building, Reseda; Laurence Rockefeller *Exhibitions:* Creative Arts Center, Burbank; Brandeis University *Education:* Hunter College; Art Institute of Southport, England *Dealer:* Wilbur Gallery

Whether in etching, drawing or sculpture, her work has always aimed toward purity of line and form. Trained by sculptor Chaim Grass and influenced by Henry Moore and Maillol, she developed her sculpture into simple, strong and rhythmical statements dealing with the human form. She began experimenting with direct wax sculpture for bronze after first working in oil clay and terracotta. Other media have included welded metal, fiberglas and gypsum for large, abstract public sculptures. Her sculptures now reflect a strength grounded in true form. Within this strength, however, the works reveal a sense of lightness, both in the figures' attitude and in the joyful directness of line. Her works are up to four feet in height and emphasize volume, space and form rather than massiveness.

HOCKING, MIRA (Painter)
2500 Lucy Lane #306, Walnut Creek, CA 94595

Born: 1942 *Collections:* Omega Medical Clinic, Walnut Creek; Wilkinson Interiors, Seattle *Exhibitions:* Civic Arts Gallery, Walnut Creek *Education:* UC-Berkeley; Art Students League

Her art is based on spiritual ideals. The power of the symbol is important to her as is a heightened realism that suggests realms beyond the physical. Though her media vary, her work always centers on the power of light and color. This preoccupation with light dictates the structural scaffoldings of her paintings and drawings even as her imagery fluctuates between elements drawn from the external environment and internal events of the imagination. Her media include watercolor, oils, colored pencil, and chalk pastel.

HOCKNEY, DAVID (Painter, Set Designer)
c/o Andre Emmerich Gallery, 41 E. 57th St., New York, NY 10022

Born: 1937 *Awards:* 1st Prize, International Center of Photography, NYC; Guinness Award, London *Collections:* Museum of Modern Art, NYC; Los Angeles County Museum of Art *Exhibitions:* Museum of Modern Art, NYC; Palais du Louvre, Paris *Education:* Bradford College of Art; Royal College of Art, London *Dealer:* Richard Gray Gallery, Chicago; Andre Emmerich Gallery, NYC

Although this British artist was first identified with late pop art, his stylistic tendencies derived from abstract expressionism. Autobiographical works are known for their irony and humor, and a basic theme is the figure in designs and surroundings that explain character. Acrylic paintings are bright and naturalistic but flattened, with a strong sense of pattern. He also creates photographic collages in which fragments are overlapped to create one image, such as *Desk, London, July 1, 1984*. Other accomplishments include drawings, book illustrations, gouaches, lithographs, etchings and aquatints. "Hockney Paints the Stage" was an exhibition of paintings, drawings and displays depicting the various costume and stage designs he has executed for the theater.

HODARA, EDEN (Painter, Multimedia Artist)
24172 Vista d'Oro, Laguna Niguel, CA 92677

Born: 1925 *Collections:* Gutai Museum, Osaka, Japan; Insho Damato Museum of Modern Art, Kyoto, Japan *Exhibitions:* National Academy of Sciences, Washington, D.C.; Los Angeles Institute of Contemporary Art

In May, 1953, she was one of three women included in the first exhibition of "American Abstract Expressionism" in Paris, for which the word "tachism" was coined. While working in Chicago, she became involved with Zen philosophy, and was invited to have a one-woman show at the Yamada Art Gallery in Kyoto. Later, in the 1960s and 1970s, in Pasadena, as part of the California Institute of Technology community, she created technological art. Primarily an artist who needs to comprehend and experiment, she was one of the first to produce and exhibit laser and xerox art works. Reflecting psychological and metaphysical complexities, she cites as major influences Japanese Ukiyo-e prints, Zen, technology and contemporary packaging of ideas and products.

HODDER, MONROE (Painter)
1345 Cowper St., Palo Alto, CA 94301

Born: 1943 *Collections:* Bank of America, San Francisco; Broebeck, Phleger and Harrison, San Francisco *Exhibitions:* Museum Gallery, San Francisco Museum of Modern Art; San Jose Museum of Art *Education:* Vassar College; San Francisco Art Institute *Dealers:* Dorothy Weiss, San Francisco; Jennifer Pauls, Sacramento

After five years in the Far East—Bangkok, Djakarta and Kathmandu—she developed a style using pastels and oils to depict the rich, vibrant landscapes of the Orient. She has since combined the influence of these experiences with European figurative expressionism, particularly the work of contemporary German and Italian artists who juxtapose intense color and fluid, personal imagery. For the past several years, she has concentrated on paintings in which formal concerns are interwoven with an intuitive approach to the figure placed in a natural environment. She often uses a com-

Mira Hocking, *I Wonder Who, I Wonder Where, I Wonder How?,* 22 x 30, watercolor.
Courtesy: Judy Morgenthaler

Jim Hammerud, *Driftwood of a Dream,* 48 x 36, gouache

bination of pastel and "flashe." The latter is a water-based paint with the durability of acrylic and the appearance of tempera. Working in a large scale on a hard surface, the works give the appearance of fresco wall paintings. She seeks to express a continuum of experience in which plant forms, animal life, and humans are integrated in rich and vibrant landscapes that are both primitive and contemporary.

HODGE, GILLIAN (Ceramicist)
11009 Spenceville Rd., Penn Valley, CA 95946

Born: 1927 *Awards:* Silver Medal, 29th Concorso Internationale Ceramica D'Arte Contemporanea, Faenaz, Italy; Best of Show, 32nd Auburn Arts, Auburn *Collections:* Power Collection; Vancouver Art Gallery, Canada *Exhibitions:* Monterey Peninsula Museum of Art; Matrix Gallery, Sacramento *Education:* Ruskin School of Drawing and Fine Art, Oxford U.; Kootenay School of Art, Nelson, BC *Dealer:* Jennifer Pauls, Sacramento

After training in India and at Oxford, she was a painter, but she moved into clay because of an overwhelming concern for dimensionality. Interests in and study of primitive and folk arts dictated an exploration of a variety of media within the ceramic tradition, and her eventual choice of a handmade wood-fired kiln and found glazes is analogous with her exploration of mythic themes and the human condition. The stout and solid figures she makes exemplify the harsh conditions required for their existence—heat, stress, time—and resemble primitive icons. Variations and perturbations inherent in the process—drips, bubbles and cracks—contribute to the heroic transformation of mud into metaphor for life.

HODGES, DEL (Sculptor)
8005 Harlan Rd., Eddyville, OR 97343

Born: 1940 *Awards:* Best of Oil, Oregon Trail National Western Art Show *Exhibitions:* Civic Center, Salem, OR; Oregon State U. *Education:* U. of Oregon *Dealer:* Lou Johnson, Honolulu

After studying both fine and commercial art, he was impressed with abstract expressionism. He put abstract expressionism's exploding brushstrokes into three dimensions using a technique of "spatial imagery" in which the paint is manipulated on sculptural planes. He constructed his pieces primarily from welded steel sheets. Later he commercially packaged his spatial imagery into partially abstract interpretations of wildlife subject matter. He gave his spatial planes a more three-dimensional application and achieved an ideographic unity of animal and environment. His sculptures are made from welded brass, copper and steel sheet.

HOFMANN, HELI (Painter)
5870 Cactus Way, La Jolla, CA 92037

Born: 1937 *Exhibitions:* Women's Art Show, International Center, UC-San Diego

The art education she received in her nine years of West German higher education provided a solid artistic foundation. She most enjoys working in oil on canvas, but has also completed a number of paper collages and silk paintings. These paintings are executed in bright colors and readily display the influences of the French Fauvists and "Der Blaue Reiter" Group. Her figurative works often feature carefully arranged still lifes and faces. The latter have recently become more expressive and stylized.

HOFSTETTER, CAROLYN (Painter)
157 Lois Ln., Palo Alto, CA 94303

Born: 1927 *Awards:* Best of Show, Pacific Art League; Best of Show, City of Sunnyvale *Collections:* City of Palo Alto; Menlo Medical Center, Menlo Park *Exhibitions:* California State Fair; Viewpoints Gallery, Los Altos *Education:* Stanford U.

Her work in watercolor and oil has been influenced by her teachers Eliot O'Hara, Jade Fon, Daniel Mendelowitz, Millard Sheets and Raymond Brose, as well as by contemporary masters Rex Brandt, Jane Burnham and Gerald Brommer. She has developed a realist style, bordering on impressionism and emphasizing overall design and composition. She often works on large canvases. Her paintings are characterized by small areas of realism incorporated into a non-representational composition. She has also been working with collage, working it into watercolors or as an underlayer on canvas for oil paintings or acrylics. Much of her subject matter is derived from sketches and photographs she has used to record her extensive travels. She also enjoys working in oil or watercolor on location.

HOFSTETTER, JANE (Painter)
308 Dawson Dr., Santa Clara, CA 95051

Born: 1936 *Exhibitions:* Christopher Queen Gallery, Duncans Hills; Galerias Euroarte, Lisbon, Portugal

Impressionistic and Oriental influences are visible in her work, though a definite core of design patterns is always discernible. In *Just Weeds,* an accepted National Watercolor Society annual exhibit, there is a focus on dandelions, and bits of foliage anchor an abstracted background to the central image. Her oil, acrylic and mixed-media works are often more abstract, though some structures of the nature-motif are always retained. She is also a versatile landscape artist, and has taught advanced art and design for the last fifteen years.

HOGG, BARBARA (Painter, Printmaker)
1124 Ashland Ave., Santa Monica, CA 90405

Born: 1911 *Awards:* 1st Place, Easter Art Festival, Honolulu; 1st Place, Long Beach Art Museum *Collections:* Laguna Beach Art Museum *Exhibitions:* Talisman Prints Gallery, Laguna Beach; Santa Monica Library *Education:* Honolulu Academy of Arts; U. of Hawaii, Honolulu

At Chouinard, she learned to paint figuratively with acrylics and oils. While studying with Adja Yunkers and John Hultberg, she progressed to abstraction, making serigraphs, and to printing with the intaglio process. Later, she experimented with oil and collage, but she has since returned to making mixed-media monoprints. Today, her images are abstractions of people, flowers, vegetables and animals. In her recent series of monotypes, "Vignettes," her abstracted and realistic images of flowers, vegetables and animals fade toward the edges of the picture. In these and other prints, she creates unusual effects through addition and subtraction of color.

HOGLE, ANN M. (Painter)
45 Meadow Rd., Woodside, CA 94062

Born: 1927 *Collections:* Roy Neuberger Collection, NYC; Bechtel Corp., San Francisco *Exhibitions:* William Sawyer Gallery, San Francisco; Phelan Award Show, Palace of the Legion of Honor, San Francisco

Carolyn Hofstetter, *The Pasta Makers,* 18 x 24, watercolor

Jari Havlena, *Three Moons,* 36 x 60, mixed media, collage. Courtesy: International Theatre Institute, Prague

Education: California College of Arts and Crafts *Dealer:* William Sawyer, San Francisco

She began painting in the style of abstract expressionism, but in the 1960s, influenced by Parks, Diebenkorn and Bischoff, she produced nudes in landscape in a figurative style. During a period of transition, she did "stream of consciousness" paintings concerned more with content than with form; this contrasts with her more recent works, which are more detailed and concerned with issues of painting. For the past decade she has painted large Bay-Area landscapes in oil in a painterly, realist style. These have been both in *plein air* and in the studio, where she refines the work done on site. She has also created large landscapes from imagination.

HOKUSHIN, RANDY (Sculptor)
59-771 Maulukua Rd., Haleiwa, Hawaii 96712

Born: 1951 *Collections:* Honolulu Academy of Art; Contemporary Arts Center of Hawaii *Exhibitions:* Palm Springs Desert Museum; Honolulu Academy of Arts *Dealer:* Monica Lee, Honolulu

He is loyal to clay, and his emphasis over the years has been on vessel forms. His technique has progressed from a fascination and love for glazing to recent works, such as his "primordial" vessels, that have no glaze. The majority of his exploration has involved the raku firing technique, a 16th century firing style. The smoke patterns and fire markings are done with as much deliberation as possible, and sometimes he refires pieces in order to get a specific effect. The process is risky, but satisfaction comes from his sense that he is "painting with smoke." His "Primordial Journey" series of both vessel sculptures and torsos represents an intense study of "painting with smoke." Inspired by Picasso's exhibition at MOMA in 1983, he found himself moving in two opposite directions simultaneously—from perfect vessels to abstractions, which resulted in the "Primordial Puzzle" series and abstract torso figures which moved toward realism.

HOLDSWORTH, ANTHONY (Painter)
3290 Harrison St., San Francisco, CA 94110

Born: 1945 *Collections:* Kaiser Permanente, Oakland; Bramelea Pacific, Oakland *Exhibitions:* Pro Arts, Oakland; Victor Fischer Galleries, Oakland *Education:* Bournemouth College of Art, England *Dealer:* John Chiappolini, San Francisco

Believing that wholesale innovation has given way to a period of reflection and synthesis, he seeks to extract powerful statements about contemporary society from a direct confrontation with the modern urban environment. His works are realistic and he does much of his painting in the settings he depicts. His scenes of Oakland, such as *Contrails* are almost photographic in their illusionism and downbeat in their portrayal of spiritual and cultural desolation. He also paints Columbus Avenue in San Francisco, as well as North Beach, Vesuvio and the City Lights bookshop. "I experience on the street an intensity, an immediacy, that is like jazz," he says.

HOLLAND, TOM (Painter)
28 Roble Rd., Berkeley, CA 94705

Born: 1936 *Awards:* NEA Sculpture Grant; Fulbright Grant; Guggenheim Fellowship *Collections:* Museum of Modern Art, NYC; San Francisco Museum of Modern Art, NYC *Exhibitions:* James Corcoran Gallery, Los Angeles; John Berggruen Gallery, San Fran-

cisco *Education:* UC-Berkeley *Dealer:* James Corcoran Gallery, Los Angeles; Charles Cowles Gallery, NYC; John Berggruen Gallery, San Francisco

He is the son of a painter, receiving additional influence from David Park. His paintings and sculptures are bright, geometric three-dimensional works often in day-glo colors, on and off the wall. *Helli*, in epoxy on aluminum, is one of the larger examples of what he calls painting, even though it is two-sided and free-standing. Layer upon layer is painted and worked, each layer referring to the underlying structure—so that these "standup" paintings at times take on an organic quality. Through this medium he explores the nature of what exists below the surface of matter. Other works include pieces in fiberglass.

HOLMAN, ART (Painting)
Box 72, Lagunitas, CA 94938

Born: 1926 *Awards:* Purchase Award, Standford University *Collections:* San Francisco Museum of Modern Art; Oakland Museum *Exhibitions:* De Young Museum; Smithsonian Institute *Education:* University of New Mexico *Dealer:* Gump's Gallery, San Francisco

After study in New Mexico and on the East Coast, he came to California in 1953. He worked in oils on landscapes and abstractions, progressing to color-field painting in 1957. Returning to landscapes with a strong, abstract approach, his goal currently is a fusion of realism and abstraction that imbues the work with an internal life revealed through formal structuring and composition. Increasingly dense and rich, the pieces evidence a study of Venetian and impressionist painters. Landscape images have extended to astronomical objects, painted with bright bursts of color. The abstract aspects of the work never overtake the identification with natural form. Said Arthur Bloomfield of the *San Francisco Examiner*, ". . . the pictures almost dance . . . [Holman] works with brushstrokes to bring you, in essence, space and light."

HOLMES, GINI (Electrographic Artist)
c/o Hank Baum Gallery, 2140 Bush St., San Francisco, CA

Born: 1949 *Awards:* MIT Council for the Arts *Collections:* Xerox Corporation, Rochester, NY; Northrop Corporation *Exhibitions:* Redding New Works Gallery; Redding Museum and Art Center *Education:* MIT; Stanford U. *Dealer:* Hank Baum Gallery, San Francisco

After formal training in lithography and drawing, she became interested in the influence of technology on art, and of art on technology. This led to several years of experimentation with photography, video, computers and copiers as they related to the creation of an individual print. Now she uses simpler techniques and equipment to create images that synthesize art and technology. With a Canon PC10, an NP-115 and a Xerox Standard Haloid camera, she creates base images that are then drawn, painted and collaged to create narrative images of her life.

HOLMES, JOHN L. (Multimedia Artist)
1719 School Ave., Walla Walla, WA 99362

Born: 1950 *Collections:* Washington State Arts Commission *Exhibitions:* San Francisco Art Institute *Education:* San Francisco Art Institute

Early in his career, the artist's primary goal was to explore the parallels between art and music. As a jazz

Anthony Holdsworth, *Crossroads,* 34 x 40, oil on canvas

Jim Hammerud, *Cosmic Furnace,* 48 x 36, acrylic

guitarist, he became intrigued with the possibilities of finding a visual metaphor for his music. Using various media, including traditional drawing and painting materials, he infused his work with symbols that also spoke to modern cultural conditions. This interest in symbolism remains a strong factor in his recent work, where opposing qualities are highlighted within the same complete image. Metallic resins masquerade as bronze. Foam and that traditionally unlovely material plastic are juxtaposed with painted steel. Neither wholly organic or abstract, these freestanding works suggest calligraphy in their appealing simplicity.

HOLMES, ROSINDA (Painter, Printmaker)
3362 W. Dry Creek Rd., Healdsburg CA 95448

Born: 1917 *Awards:* 1st Place, Sonoma Harvest Fair *Collections:* Dr. Frank Oppenheimer; Mr. Maurice Lapp *Exhibitions:* Lucien Labaudt Art Gallery, San Francisco; Mill Gallery, Petaluma *Education:* Chouinard Art Institute

She is presently working on watercolor landscapes in the realist tradition, as well as returning to her previous background in etching. Her work displays a sensitive, emotional interpretation within the bounds of representational scenes. Reflective, warm tones and glazes are underscored by cooler tones beneath. New works will also begin to combine pastels and collage as she continues to press into the vocabulary of realism.

HOLMES, TIM (Sculptor)
1515 Winne, Helena, MT 59601

Born: 1955 *Awards:* Physicians for Social Responsibility Peace Award, Wallingford, CT *Collections:* Archbishop Desmond Tutu, Capetown, South Africa; Madam Anwar Sadat, Cairo, Egypt *Exhibitions:* Frey Art Museum, Seattle; Paul Mellon Art Center, Wallingford, CT *Education:* Rocky Mountain College *Dealer:* Bob Fitzgerald, Helena, MT

His work has revolved around the human figure and its capacity to generate feelings of compassion and wonder. He has always worked in welded steel and bronze with a variety of styles, techniques and subjects. Typical of his work is a sense of physical motion and spiritual depth. Even his abstract works, from small scale to monumental, share these qualities. He is fascinated by the suggestive effects of obscurity and most recently, he has employed various ways of obscuring the figure to bring out its poignancy. One such suggestive effect is obtained by reducing the figure to shreds or pieces as if barely glimpsed through mist, thick darkness, or eons of decay.

HOLSOPPLE, ALDEN (Sculptor)
23708 Nevada Rd., Hayward, CA 94541

Born: 1943 *Collections:* Warm Spring Civic Center, Fremont; Syntex Corporation, Palo Alto *Exhibitions:* Sun Gallery, Hayward; Moscone Center, San Francisco

His creative process involves the use of multimedia, with the intent to choose materials and a scale suited to the concept of the piece. Presently, his work includes three motifs: experimental designs, clouds and hearts. Two of his most famous pieces involve visual puns that incorporate the heart image: *With Every Beat of My Heart* (which features a heart-shaped snare drum) and *Purple Heart* (which recalls the irony of war and his own experience as a Vietnam veteran). An artist who thrives on constant visual experimentation,

he is now very intrigued with the duality and interplay between written words and visual images.

HOLSTE, TOM (Painter)
Star Route, Box 796, Orange, CA 92667

Born: 1943 *Awards:* NEA Fellowship *Collections:* Guggenheim Museum, NYC; La Jolla Museum of Contemporary Art *Exhibitions:* Los Angeles County Museum of Art; Guggenheim Museum, NYC *Education:* Cal. State-Fullerton; Claremont College *Dealer:* Newspace, Los Angeles

During the late 1960s and early 1970s, he was noted for his large-scale, meditative field paintings. In these works, he allowed layered strokes of sprayed acrylic to accrue on a prepared ground—an exploration of process resulting in a highly sensual spatial image. In 1974 he took a radical step: He began exploring a synthesis of painting and sculpture, characterized by geometric arrangements and frequent shifts in low relief. These painting/sculptures, constructed of cast rhoplex on wood, became larger through 1977 until they started to fragment and become multi-part wallworks implying a strong sense of motion. The works refer both to the dynamic geometric paintings of the Russian Suprematists and to the Kachina icons of desert Indian cultures. His most recent works—mixed-media drawings and paintings of rocks found near his studio in the California coastal mountains—allude to ancient sculptures of animal and human figuration.

HOLUB, LEO (Photography)
3663 21st. St., San Francisco, CA 94114

Born: 1916 *Collections:* San Francisco Museum of Modern Art; National Portrait Gallery, Washington, DC *Exhibitions:* Focus Gallery, San Francisco; San Francisco Museum Modern of Art *Education:* School of the Art Institute of Chicago *Dealer:* Judy Kay, San Francisco

His photographs emanate directly from the forty years of his life that he has been exhibiting as a photographer. In his earlier work, he utilized the five-by-seven-inch format, which did not allow him the mobility that he later gained by shooting with a 35mm camera. Although in his work he does not manipulate the image after shooting through superimposition or other developing "tricks," his work still deals with the medium itself, particularly with the joy of photography and the ability of the medium to take down "notes" from life directly. His photographs function as observations not only of the world but of the pleasure of the photographer observing the world. Although known primarily for his portraits, he has also taken many photographs of San Francisco's urban landscape.

HOLZER, THOMAS (Glass Artist)
P.O. Box 2278, Boulder, CO 80306

Born: 1957 *Awards:* Scholarship, Pilchuck School, Seattle *Collections:* L. Pozner & Associates, Denver *Exhibitions:* Conference of the American Institute of Architects, Orlando, FL; Denver Art Museum *Education:* Cologne College of Fine Arts & Crafts, Cologne, West Germany

Born in Cologne, West Germany, he started his career as a glass artist and designer with a three-year apprenticeship at Karl Dedy Glass Craft Studios near Cologne. He primarily designs stained- glass art for architectural installations, the design determined in the blueprint stages of a building's construction. Works

John Hillding, *Hunting Boat,* 864 x 144

Rosinda Holmes, *Arizona Rose,* 16 x 20, watercolor

include free-hanging glass panels used as exposition pieces. Of late, his focus has moved from stained glass towards exclusively mouth-blown antique glass. He uses lines of lead as one might use brushstrokes in a painting or pencil lines in a drawing, and he creates an illusion of three-dimensionality through large areas of neutral and soft pastels or primary colors in bold free-floating shapes.

HOMER, JESSIE (Painter, Printmaker)
9500 Cherokee Ln., Beverly Hills, CA 90210

Born: 1940 *Collections:* Palm Springs Desert Museum; House of Humor and Satire, Bulgaria *Exhibitions:* Fowler Mills Gallery of Primitive Art; Laguna Beach Museum of Art *Dealer:* Ankrum Gallery, Los Angeles

Self-taught, she paints images from her past, her childhood and her home town in the Helderburg Mountains of New York. The characters, buildings and animals that fill her work are taken from the village of Rensselaerville. Directness, clarity of color and a joyous love of nature characterize her style. She sees herself as a failed realist to whom "things are sometimes more real when 'crickety'." She paints on real linen, and uses high quality woods and polyurethane varnish for her life size cut-outs of cows, dogs and people. Her recent work includes California landscapes, as well as her traditional New York scenes.

HOMLER, ANNA (Performance Artist)
P.O. Box 749, Venice, CA 90294

Born: 1948 *Awards:* L.A.C.E. Interdisciplinary Grant *Exhibitions:* Santa Barbara Contemporary Arts Forum; Wight Gallery, UCLA *Education:* UC-Berkeley *Dealer:* The Cactus Foundation, Los Angeles

Her performance art is a powerful combination of visuals, poetry, music, linguistics and theater. She creates personae from everyday objects and environments in which to investigate her chosen themes, using dream imagery, humor and elements of Jungian psychology. During the early 1980s, after completing degrees in anthropology and linguistics, the artist found a primal root language—"bread language"—and uses it as a way of invoking the collective conscious of her audience. Her former persona, "Bread-woman", was the original, universal earthmother, born of the necessity to have an appropriate speaker of the language. In *Pharmacia Poetica*, songs and stories are presented to the audience as cures for various ailments. The pharmacist prescribes "poeticures" for audience members, which, when sung, are in bread language. "For every malady, there's a melody," she says.

HOOVEN, COILLE M. (Ceramist)
2220 Ward St., Berkeley, CA 94705

Born: 1939 *Awards:* NEA Grant *Collections:* Oakland Museum; National Collection of Fine Arts, Smithsonian Institution, Washington D.C. *Exhibitions:* Quay Gallery, San Francisco; M.H. Memorial de Young Museum, San Francisco *Education:* U. of Illinois

Since 1962, she has worked full-time creating various clay and porcelain pieces. Working with cone-10 porcelain, clear glaze and cobalt brushwork, she builds shoes, gloves, shirts, pillows, etc., as a ground for human or animal imagery. She is fascinated with metamorphic creatures, such as frogs and butterflies. Occasionally, human and animal forms are mixed. In one piece, the small figure of a goat-woman, curled up on a table, contemplates a large, shadow-like bust of another goat—or her own shadow. A small staircase rises to an opening in the shadow's chest, a welcoming, or ominous, entrance. Open to various interpretations, her recent work risks rejection, by departing from her early work in customary vessels.

HOPFE, HENRY KILA (Sculptor)
P.O. Box 343, Waianae, HI 96792

Born: 1949 *Awards:* 1st Place, Hawaiian Mixed-Media Art Show, Royal Hawaiian Shopping Center *Exhibitions:* AMFAC Plaza, Hale Naua III Exhibit, Oahu; Pacific Handcrafters Guild, Oahu

A self-taught sculptor, he finds inspiration for his work in Hawaiian legends, cultural heritage and familial linkages. He is profoundly aware of Hawaiian art forms, and he has committed himself to their perpetuation. He creates sculpture, furniture, boxes, jewelry, art and artifacts from ivory, coral, stone (pohaku) and such native woods as koa, milo, hao and monkey pod. His creations include two "hal ki'i" sculptures of the god Lono made for the F.W. Woolworth store in Waikiki, and a koa, "Wa'a Kaulua" (double-hulled canoe) for the the the New Zealand Minister of Maori Affairs. He is a certified journeyman carpenter.

HOPKINS, JOHN (Sculptor, Ceramist)
23080 Jensen Ct., Grand Terrace, CA 92324

Born: 1947 *Awards:* Cash Award, A.R.T. Beasley Gallery, San Diego; Purchase Award, Art Works Gallery, Fair Oaks *Collections:* Potters Guild, Auckland, New Zealand; Sonoma St. U. *Exhibitions:* Faith Nightengale Gallery, San Diego; U. of Hawaii, Honolulu *Education:* Cal. State-Fullerton; Santa Ana College *Dealer:* Del Mano, Los Angeles; Elaine Potter Gallery, San Francisco

A professor of ceramics and sculpture, he incorporates and synthesizes two kinds of imagery, organic and geometric, in both his sculpture and ceramics. While he has a strong background in classical functional pottery, his main interest lies in the challenges of sculpting. In 1980, however, he started making large ceramic plates, as a way to increase his repertoire of sculptural surfaces. He has not stopped making plates, and his experimentation has led him to develop some innovative ceramic techniques. Each piece of ceramics and sculpture is a careful study in complementary line, form and visual movement. Like Brancusi's sculpture, his work incorporates power and simplicity, and evokes a sense of reverence.

HOPPE, DAVID B. (Painter)
390 Rio Lindo, #111, Chico, CA 95926

Born: 1941 *Awards:* Purchase Award, La Grange National, L. Dodd Art Center, La Grange *Collections:* Minnesota Museum of Fine Art, St. Paul; Yuma Fine Arts Museum, Yuma, AZ *Exhibitions:* Butler Institute of American Art, Youngstown, OH; Rourke Gallery, Moorhead, MN *Education:* Arizona State U., Tempe

A "closet realist," his drawings are small, imaginary still lifes drawn from what he can remember about past observations. With a technique similar to painting, he builds up color with pencils and then works into or over the built-up areas. He has been influenced by Miro and Jim Nutt. His work has a surreal but calm quality intended to reach the childlike qualities of the viewer.

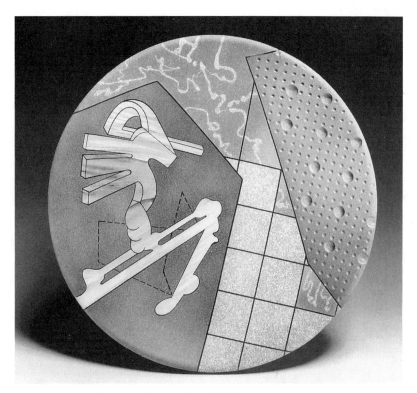

John Hopkins, *Composition 13,* 23-inch diameter, ceramic

Eden Hodara, *Molecular Movement,* 18 x 18, mixed media,
xerox, graphite, paper on canvas

Jessie Homer, *The Deer Hunters,* 18 x 28, oil.
Courtesy: Ankrum Gallery

Myrtle Hawkins, *Pensive,* 24 x 30, mixed media drawing

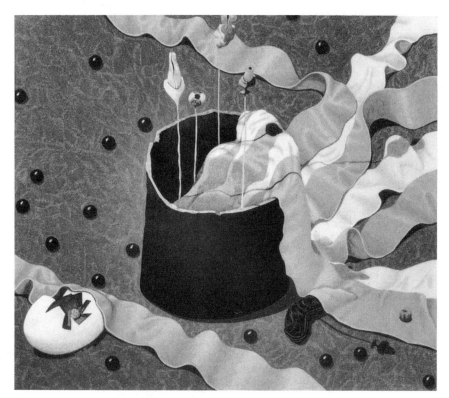

David B. Hoppe, *The Wizard's Egg,* 9 x 10, color pencil

Mary Heebner, *Recognizing Terra Firma,* 60 x 84, acrylic, collage on canvas

Recently he began making large and small figurative acrylic paintings. In one series he depicts an anatomically correct, colorfully adventuresome young girl. He is an art instructor at Chico State University.

HOPPER, STEVE (Painter, Mixed Media Artist)
234 Del Gado Rd., San Clemente, CA 92672

Born: 1952 *Exhibitions:* Orange County Center For Contemporary Art, Santa Ana; Edge Gallery, Fullerton *Education:* San Diego State U.

After exploring abstract images for several years, he began to create pieces in direct response to the contemporary world. Large-scale, abstracted, business-suited male figures are his recurring theme. Although he has begun to use figuration, he retains the expressionistic, painterly surface quality and the "hands-on" look of the abstract work he admires. His collages have a flat, shallow space and tend to be lighter in both appearance and content. Often he includes a humorous caption. His mixed-media paintings, influenced by Matisse and Picasso, have denser surface qualities, are usually on a much larger scale and tend to be less humorous.

HORAN, EDWARD ADEL (Painter)
3753 E. Wethersfield, Phoenix, AZ 85032

Born: 1943 *Awards:* Winner, Murals Competition, Westchester County, NY *Collections:* City of Yonkers, NY; Navajo School, Scottsdale, AZ *Exhibitions:* Arabian Horse Association of Arizona; Sixth Annual Arab-American Television Event, Los Angeles *Education:* Sussex College, England; Da Vinci Art Academy, Cairo *Dealer:* Renoir Gallery, Phoenix

"No picture can equal the beauty of the imagination," maintains this Arab-American painter who draws inspiration and subject matter for his realistic pictures from the English, Arab, and American cultures in which he has lived and worked. Although a painter of landscapes and cityscapes as well, his first love is the portrayal of human beings. Among his paintings are a cowboy on horseback riding a herd almost hidden from view by a cloud of dust and by a blinding sun that sets the scene aglow; the face of a classic Arab beauty, in three-quarter view, gaze intent, one eye almond-shaped and ringed coal black, the other covered by jewels hanging down from a veiled headdress; and three Skid Row bums, sitting idly on the sidewalk, backs against a stone wall, one asleep, another drinking from a bottle, the third withdrawn into the contemplation of a private agony. He has also taught art and worked as a commercial artist.

HORNADAY, RICHARD (Painter, Printmaker)
Dept. of Art, Cal. State University, Chico, CA 95929

Born: 1927 *Awards:* Award of Appreciation, City of Redding; 2nd Award, Kingsley Exhibit, Sacramento *Collections:* Turner Print Collection; Charles Rand Penny Collection; Cal State-Chico; Iowa State University *Exhibitions:* Redding Museum and Art Center; Rosicrucian Egyptian Museum, San Jose *Education:* Iowa State U.; School of the Art Institute of Chicago *Dealer:* Robert Bradbury, Blue Heron Fine Arts Gallery, Chico

In his early work, he conveyed sensations we all have in common through images of anonymous faces, and faces with no features at all. By 1958, he had reduced color to earth tones and had begun using heavy, sand-laden paint applications. He scratched or carved his surfaces, drew and did woodcuts of primitive and archaic forms. In the early 1960s, he incorporated theatrical elements into his painting. With the introduction of acrylic paint in the mid-1960s, his work came closer to the surface, and he started representing everyday figures and objects. From the late 1960s through the mid-1970s, he focused on depicting the inner life through abstraction and microscopic images. In the early 1980s, he reintroduced the figure. His traditional still lifes are vases with abstract backgrounds.

HORTON, LYN (Multimedia Artist)
Harvey Rd., Worthington, MA 01098

Born: 1950 *Collections:* Alexis Smith *Exhibitions:* General Electric, Schenectady; California Institute of the Arts *Education:* California Institute of the Arts *Dealer:* Shippee, NYC; Museum of Fine Arts, Springfield, MA

Working with pastels and painting on paper, large constructions and small sculptural objects, she creates pieces that strike a reconciliation between architectonic and biomorphic form. They allude to the dynamics of illusion vs. reality, of man-made objects vs. natural phenomena and of the artist's "body and soul" interacting with, and through, the environment. In *Still Life With Curves* (1974-5), she juxtaposed photographs of her own body with realistic drawings of still life and landscape. But, in the large, wall-hung constructions she completed in the mid-1980s, geometric forms corresponded directly to body parts. A recent major work, *Essay on Human Relations*, is a group of 100 interrelated, freestanding wood and painted canvas constructions that function as a metaphor for the individual and society.

HORWITZ, CHANNA (Painter)
6060 Clear Valley Rd., Hidden Hills, CA 91302

Born: 1932 *Awards:* NEA Fellowship *Collections:* Los Angeles County Museum of Art *Exhibitions:* Los Angeles Municipal Art Gallery, Los Angeles

In the mid-1960s, she was negatively influence by Lorser Feitelson's hard-edged style. In an attempt to make the hard-edge aesthetically pleasing, she curved the edge, creating a series of black-and-white paintings of circles, squares and shadows. Believing technology to be the artistic tool of the late twentieth century, she began exploring methods of showing motion in a technologically graphic manner. She used graph paper to chart pulses moving through space and time, coloring selected squares to enhance her design. From there, she moved to experiments in subliminal patterns. In these, a basic organizing pattern emerges almost subliminally from color fields and clear grounding patterns, created by the use of repeated lines over bases of color.

HOSS, CAROLE (Painter)
1748 Stoner Ave., Los Angeles, CA 90025

Born: 1941 *Exhibitions:* Visionary Artists' Showcase, West Los Angeles; Visionary Art Gallery, Pasadena *Dealer:* Artquarters, Los Angeles

Her formal, realist style has evolved through surrealism to visionary realism. Her artistic vision has been influenced by the works of Bosch and Dali. She renders form in a detailed, technical way, but what interests her is the spirit which motivates or animates the form. Using a range of realistic tones, she works

Ann Harris, *Western Azalea,* 18 x 24, watercolor. Courtesy: Friends of the Arts Gallery, Carmel, CA

Richard Hornaday, *Port Townsand,* 18 x 12, watercolor

Bernard Hoyes, *Hexing Rites,* 35 x 50, oils. Courtesy: Caribbean Arts, Inc.

with light and transparencies to establish the "other worldly" dimension of the painting. Depictions of women as Creator, Goddess and Sorceress are characteristic of her recent works.

HOUSER, JOHN SHERRILL (Sculptor)
2841 S. Cottonwood Lane, Tucson, AZ 85713

Born: 1935 *Awards:* Elizabeth T. Greenshields Fellowship; Elliot Liskin Award, Salmagundi Club 5th Annual Sculpture and Photography Exhibition, NYC; *Exhibitions:* National Academy of Western Art Exhibition and Sale, Oklamhoma City; Western Heritage Show, Houston; Brand Library and Art Galleries, Glendale *Dealer:* Nicholas Houser, El Paso, TX

He received his early training from his father, Ivan Houser, who assisted in the carving of Mt. Rushmore, and he also studied in Europe and with R.H. Ives Gammell in Boston. Although he was deeply influenced by the 19th-century work of Gericault, Courbet, Goya and Degas, the themes and images of his work are contemporary. As a cultural realist, he lives directly among his subjects, and all works are interpreted from life. He has portrayed such diverse cultural groups as Italian street fakirs, hippies, migrant workers and Native Americans. One of his bronzes, *Barranca Overlook,* naturalistically portrays a Tarahumara Indian from the mountains of Chihuahua, Mexico, and his son perched on opposite sides of a rock. The carefree boy gazes out into space, his feet dangling from the rock. The man, appreciative of the respite in their journey, glances toward the sky.

HOUSTON, MARY ETTA (Painter, Sculptor)
518 Jasmine St., Chula Vista, CA 92011

Born: 1912 *Awards:* 2nd Place, National D.A.R. Art Competition; Gold Medal, Sons of the American Revolution *Collections:* National Women Arts, Washington, DC; Elmhurst Art Museum, Elmhurst, IL *Exhibitions:* Bicentennial Invitational, Texas Fine Arts Association; Gallery International Annual Exhibition, NYC *Education:* Texas Christian U.; Claremont Graduate School

The guiding idea in both her sculpted and painted works is the concept of dissonance, focusing however on a subtlety and contrast that speaks rather than screams. She may juxtapose unrelated colors—yellow-green and orange, for instance—but at the same time make use of a free-flowing construction that softens the starkness. She has produced many bronze and ceramic tile sculptures in addition to her painted works. Among her commissioned works was the painting of a church altar.

HOWARD, STEFANIA G. (Painter, Printmaker)
3567 Mississippi St., San Diego, CA 92104

Born: 1918 *Awards:* 1st Prize, Lenten Festival, First United Methodist Church, Long Beach; Best in the Festival, Lenten Festival, First United Methodist Church, Long Beach *Exhibitions:* San Diego Museum of Art; National Gallery of Scotland, Edinburgh *Education:* Institute of Art, Krakow, Poland

She has been guided by the inspiring, passionate examples of Rembrandt, Turner, Van Gogh and Modigliani. For many years, her representational, spiritual works were created through a unique batik process using wax and acrylic paint on large pieces of rice paper. These monoprints feature classic Christian imagery, themes and icons. More recently, she has completed a large floral triptych in silverpoint.

HOYAL, DOROTHY (Painter, Printmaker)
P.O. Box 3216, Quartz Hill, CA 93536

Born: 1918 *Collections:* NASA; Edwards Air Force Base *Exhibitions:* San Bernardino County Museum; Lancaster Museum *Dealer:* Louis Newman Gallery, Beverly Hills

She was influenced early by the California school of watercolor, and she still looks to those painters for influence. Though she often paints portraits, still lifes and florals in oil, her primary subjects remain landscapes, which she paints in watercolor or monotypes with a watercolor medium. She roams America in her motor home, gathering material for the large, loosely painted scenes of landscape, water and seascape. She then completes the works in in her studio. Her monotypes are a looser extension of her interest in watercolor, and in them she achieves a textural effect not possible in any other medium. She has a permanent installation at the Marriott Hotel in Newport Beach.

HOYES, BERNARD (Painter)
985 Westchester Pl., Los Angeles, CA 90019

Born: 1951 *Collections:* American Embassy, Kingston, Jamaica; Alcan Aluminum Corporation, Montreal *Exhibitions:* Front Porch/Human Arts Gallery, Venice; Museum of African American Art, Los Angeles *Education:* California College of Arts and Crafts

An artist since childhood, he now paints moving, colorful works depicting the people and customs of his native Jamaica. He has worked in many media, including rag and India ink on paper. The swirling forms of the "Rag Series" were often adorned with metallic gold ink, graphite, pastels, and dyes. As he grew older, his art increasingly reflected his Caribbean heritage. By the early 1980s, he had begun the "Revival Series," a group of colorful paintings that expresses his fascination with Jamaica's many religious cults. Most of these works feature full figures in ceremonial dress and are rendered in pure primary hues. Movement is expressed through the positions of the figures and the fall of their clothes. This series represents the profound spirituality of the island religions and the strong connections they foster among the people, their land, and their deities.

HOYLE, JAMES (Painter)
P.O. Box 678, Hanapepe, HI 96716

Born: 1946 *Awards:* 1st Place, Spring Fiesta Art Show, New Orleans *Exhibitions:* Teberon Gallery; Images International of Hawaii, Honolulu *Education:* Ringling School of Art *Dealer:* James Hoyle Gallery, Hanapepe, HI

His colorful, vibrant landscapes show clear impressionist influences. He especially enjoys the mood of landscape, preferring to work outdoors on location. Painting in pastels, he builds thick layers of pink, green and purple hues using quick, short brushstrokes. To overcome the inability of pastels to combine into new colors—an essential characteristic of post- impressionist painting—he developed a technique called scumbling. He applies a dark undercoating to the can-

John Sherrill Houser, *Barranca Overlook (Tarahumara Indians),* 14" high, bronze

Angelika Herzel, *White I,* 16 x 24, oil pastel on paper

vas, fixes it and then applies lighter colors on top. This technique allows him to highlight textures and shadows and to balance light and dark.

HUBER, SPARKLES (Painter, Ceramist)
50 Pleasant Valley Dr., Walnut Creek, CA 94596

Born: 1918 *Awards:* Best of Show, Portraiture, Antioch Fair *Collections:* Pleasant Hill Historical Society Museum; *Exhibitions:* Pleasant Hill Library; Methodist Church, Berkeley

Most of her oil and watercolor paintings are realistic, with a few impressionist and abstract touches. She works from her imagination, most often starting with scribblings and stick figures. Her painted surfaces are thin, and she often works with a palette knife. In addition to portraiture, she paints landscapes and seascapes, which depict the history of the Pleasant Hill area. Her naturally colored ceramic sculptures are hand-built and usually figurative in design. One, for example, depicts a fat woman exercising.

HUBOI, CAROL A. (Muralist)
19222 De Havilland Dr., Saratoga, CA 95070

Born: 1955 *Awards:* Graphic Arts Scholarship, Mission Cities Club of Printing House Craftsmen *Exhibitions:* Los Gatos Art Association; Old Town Art Center, Los Gatos *Education:* UC-Berkeley

Her interest in mural painting was sparked by James McCray at Berkeley. After graduation, she participated in community acrylic mural projects in the San Francisco Bay area. At the same time, took on commissions for frescoes and mosaics of natural and mythical subject matter, done in a illusory/realistic style. In 1986, working under the direction of Richard Haas in New York, she disciplined herself to the techniques of trompe l'oeil mural painting. Returning to California, she used a variety of techniques, such as impressionism, tromp l'oeil and air brush, to complete a series of interior acrylic landscape murals for the Portola State Park Visitor's Center in Woodside. Works in progress involve trompe l'oeil still lifes on exterior walls of private residences.

HUDSON, ROBERT (Painter, Sculptor)
Dept. of Painting, San Francisco Art Institute, 800 Chestnut St., San Francisco, CA 94133

Born: 1938 *Awards:* Guggenheim Fellowship; Nealie Sullivan Award, San Francisco *Collections:* Los Angeles County Museum of Art; Oakland Museum *Exhibitions:* Art Institute of Chicago; Whitney Museum, NYC *Education:* San Francisco Art Institute *Dealer:* Allan Frumkin Gallery, NYC; Hansen-Fuller Gallery, San Francisco

He grew up in the Northwest, and the totemistic reverberations in his painted sculptures reveal the influence of the Native American culture of that region. He was one of the foremost of the '60s Bay Area "Funk" artists, employing found objects in sculptures of welded metal to create seemingly improvisational works full of energy and humorous sensibility. The assemblages vary in their treatment of surface: some surfaces are crumpled and roughly painted, others smooth and lacquered. He collaborated on ceramic works with Richard Shaw in the early 1970s, and later that decade began painting in oils and pastels, these works probing the relation between painting and sculpture by juxtaposing three-dimensional objects with their painted images. The brilliant colors he paints onto a sculpture are meant to highlight and strengthen, rather than supersede, the formal aspects of the piece. Critic Ellen Schlesinger has said, "Hudson mixes various materials with bright, clear colors to create works that combine Rube Goldberg's humorous view of invention with a scholar's passion for the heritage of sculptural concerns. . . . his work is almost a textbook of the ways in which sculptors try to coax, carve and construct matter in order to bring it to life."

HUEBLER, DOUGLAS (Conceptual Artist)
c/o California Institute of Arts, Los Angeles, CA 91355

Born: 1924 *Collections:* National Gallery of Canada, Ottawa; Museum of Modern Art, NYC *Exhibitions:* Los Angeles County Museum of Art; La Jolla Museum of Contemporary Art *Education:* U. of Michigan; Cleveland School of Art; Academie Julian, Paris *Dealer:* Leo Castelli Gallery, NYC; Richard Kuhlenschmidt Gallery, Santa Monica

In the late 1960s, he abandoned the minimalist sculpture that had been his medium in favor of work that conceptually confronts the human condition. In such works as his screenplay *Crocodile Tears*, which consists of storyboards of image and text, he combines photographs, paintings and drawings with text that seems at first contradictory or not clearly presented in the image: "represented above is at least one person whose life is an open book"; "at least three people whom the artist would very likely choose as models for her representation of a 6th-century event, if she were to paint it today." The often humorous, tongue-in-cheek juxtaposing forces the viewer/reader to reflect on the relation between the image and the text, and this reflection reveals a deeper conceptual purpose. By forcing us to question how *this* image and *that* text are related, he transcends the particular, addressing instead the whole relation between image and language, just as in philosophy the liar's paradox—"This sentence is false"—forces one to contemplate the nature of meaning and truth. At one level each piece confronts the culture that glorifies the sound bite, MTV and the sit-com, but at another level each particular piece exists as an element in a meta-language that reveals problematic, contradictory or false preconceptions about art, language and truth.

HUEBNER, MENTOR (Painter)
P.O. Box 41079, Los Angeles, CA

Awards: Purchase Award, Los Angeles City Open Competition; Stacey Fellowship Award *Collections:* State Capitol of California; McColloch Oil Building *Exhibitions:* Smithsonian Institution; New York Museum of Modern Art

He has led a dual career in fine arts and in design for the motion picture industry. His oil paintings are in the post impressionist tradition and his subjects include landscapes, seascapes, and portraits. He has been influenced by Van Gogh, Rembrandt, and Goya. As a designer, he has worked for every major national and international motion picture studio and production company. His work has included special effects opticals, story boards, primary visual concepts, and star portraits. In addition he has designed or conceptualized amusement parks, retirement villages, resorts, and motion picture complexes such as Cinema City. He has taught at Chouinard Art Institute.

HUGHES, MICHAEL (Painter, Photographer)
1001 E. 1st St., #7, Los Angeles, CA 90012

Diana Hobson, *The Dive,* 65 x 45, oil on canvas

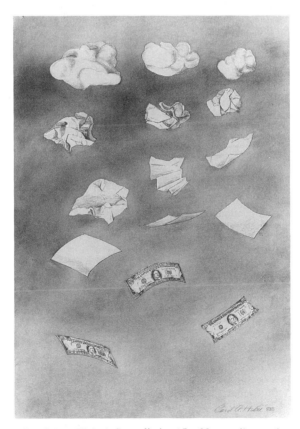

Carol Ann Huboi, *Serenditpity,* 15 x 22, pencil, pastel

Born: 1950 *Collections:* Downey Museum of Art; Carl Schlossberg Collection *Exhibitions:* Orlando Gallery, Los Angeles; West Colorado Gallery *Education:* Otis Art Institute; California Institute of the Arts *Dealer:* Orlando Gallery, Los Angeles

Though his original training was in painting, in graduate school, he exhibited mural-sized black-and-white photographs. He soon returned to painting and created large, black-and-white pieces based on his memories of Vietnam. At the same time, he developed psychologically similar installations dealing with deserted alleyways. The Vietnam work led to an interest in the symbolic possibilities of predators such as wolves. The wolf continues to be his metaphor. The work is increasingly abstract and the paintings tend to be thick, with heavy impasto surfaces, often applied with knife or spatula. His colors tend toward muted blacks, whites and earth tones, though he occasionally uses bright yellows or reds.

HUGHES, RON (Painter)
5937 Fremont St., Oakland, CA 94608

Born: 1955 *Awards:* Honorable Mention, Watercolor Gallery *Exhibitions:* Oakland Museum; American Savings & Loan, Oakland

With formal training in watercolor and oil painting, he initially developed a realistic watercolor style that was influenced by the works of Hugh Wiley and John Turner. After discovering the work of Rowland Hilder in 1979, he began attempting to capture the inspiration of the moment by exploiting the responsive, sensitive qualities of the watercolor medium. He has now progressed into painting subtle tones and harmonious compositions, and he achieves his imagery through a controlled flow of water media. His current watercolor paintings express a controlled feeling of wetness.

HUGHES, SUKEY (Papermaker, Mixed-Media Artist)
1325 Cerro Gordo, Santa Fe, NM. 87501

Born: 1945 *Exhibitions:* West Coast Works on/of Paper, Eureka; Cal. State U.-Sonoma *Education:* Antioch U. *Dealer:* Gallery One of 2nd Street, Denver; Contemporary Southwest Gallery, La Jolla and Santa Fe, NM

In the 1970s, she studied traditional Japanese papermaking with Seikichiro Gotoh. Her book *Washi: The World of Japanese Paper* was published in 1978. She has taught and practiced the craft continuously since 1980, and, in 1987, she developed a method of transforming paper made from living bark fibers into a substance resembling leather. In an attempt to capture the look and spirit of prehistoric Native American apparel, she used this material to create life-size paper garments, pouches, dolls and shields. Recently, she has been dealing in shamanistic themes, and has incorporated Indian and artist-made, aged bones, carved figures, hair, animal teeth and aged feathers into paper/leather work that is an attempt to connect the observer with memories of his or her ancestors.

HULSE, CLINTON (Sculptor)
2900 Silverado Tr., St. Helena, CA 94574

Born: 1948 *Collections:* Saks Fifth Avenue *Exhibitions:* San Francisco Art Institute; Napa County Museum, St. Helena *Education:* San Francisco Art Institute; Columbus College of Art and Design, Columbus, OH *Dealer:* Elaine Horwitch Galleries, Southwest; Miller/Brown, San Francisco

He is a multimedia artist whose earlier works include metallic, woven tapestries, three-dimensional paintings and large, fiberglas wall hangings. His current style originated from a sensitivity to geographic surroundings, and an affinity for natural materials. In 1982, he moved to the Northern California countryside and began carving in the obsidian found in the hillsides and riverbeds of the area. His large-scale obsidian sculptures, often finished with colorful peacock feathers, antlers and other materials, convey a powerful and contemporary image without disturbing its symbolic, primitive value.

HUMPHREY, MARGO (Lithographer, Printmaker)
2938 Adeline St., Oakland, CA 94608

Born: 1942 *Awards:* NEA, 1983; Ford Foundation, 1980-81 *Exhibitions:* Chico State University Art Gallery, Oakland; Fresno Museum of Art *Education:* California College of Arts and Crafts; Stanford U.

The main influences on her work are Haitian artists such as Hippolyte, French Impressionists such as Gauguin, and folk art. Bright primary colors accented with pastel touches combine with graphic presentation of images in her lithographs. These deceptively naive images, such as the leaping tiger in *Getaway,* tell complex and sophisticated stories. The giant, anonymous hands manipulating puppets in *Pencils From China* suggest psychological as well as supernatural meanings. In *Portrait of the Artist on the Way to the Store for More Nectarines and Oranges,* the work's title is incorporated into the image, placed beneath a black silhouette framed by a loose circle of unspoken words, referring to the overlapping personal and public spheres of an artist's life.

HUMPHREY, MARY PACIOS (Painter, Printmaker)
c/o Studio 2, 2898 Glascock St., Oakland, CA 94601

Born: 1934 *Collections:* Achenbach Foundation for the Graphic Arts, California Palace of the Legion of Honor, San Francisco; Art Museum of Santa Cruz County *Exhibitions:* Torsiello Gallery, Oakland; Pacific Grove Art Center *Education:* Massachusetts College of Art; Cal. State-Stanislaus *Dealer:* Djurovich Gallery, Sacramento; Lawson Galleries, San Francisco

Her lengthy career can be broken down into several distinct stylistic periods, each of which has been informed by a sense of the mythological and the erotic. During the reign of abstract expressionism in the 1960s, she chose a more formal, hard-edged style based on the figure. By the 1970s, this hard-edged style had given way to a more explicitly expressionistic style, looser, with less distinct, cruder figures. Since the late 1970s, her work has consisted of large-scale linocuts, which synthesize her previous visual styles. These dramatic, hand-rubbed relief prints are rendered in stark black and white, with limited color for emphasis. She considers these prints to be examples of Spanish expressionism.

HUNNICUTT, TIA (Doll Maker)
58 Minerva St., San Francisco, CA 94112

Born: 1971 *Awards:* Certificate of Appreciation for Outstanding Accomplishments, City of Los Angeles; San Francisco Chamber of Commerce *Exhibitions:* Oakland Museum; Marin Civic Auditorium

After taking lessons from European and American doll artists, she started her own doll company in 1984.

Dorothy Hoyal, *Desert,* 18 x 24, oil

Robert Hertz, *Jo Anne,* 38 x 84, aluminum

George Herms, *Trunk,* 37 x 22 x 7, wood, metal, fabric.
Courtesy: L.A. Louver Gallery

Working primarily in liquid porcelain, she has created over sixty different types of reproduction dolls, as well as a separate line of cloth dolls. Interested in incorporating her own cultural heritage in her work, she has created several dolls of black historical and popular figures, such as Harriet Tubman, Martin Luther King, Jr., Leontyne Price and Diana Ross. She often consults the African American Historical and Cultural Society and the Black History Department of San Francisco State University for information on the clothes and appearance of figures from the period she is recreating in her dolls. She also produces white, Asian and Hispanic figures, with the same careful attention to details. Dolls usually require two weeks to two months to complete, depending on the design and clothing required. Recently, she has been exploring the possibilities of creating vinyl composition dolls with other media.

HUNT, BILL (Sculptor)

7177 Langley Ct., Salinas, CA 93907

Born: 1944 *Awards:* Wildlife Sculptor of the Year, Seagate Foundation for the Arts, Houston *Collections:* Cabrillo Marine Museum, San Pedro *Exhibitions:* Mayhew Wildlife Gallery, Mendicino; Wildlife of the World Gallery, Carmel *Education:* Humboldt State U. *Dealer:* Seagate Foundation for the Arts, Houston

His bronze wildlife sculptures blend his knowledge of animals in the wild with artistic sensitivity and grace. Trained originally as a marine biologist, he began sculpting in metal during his school years. For his first sculpture, a whale, he used an oxygen/acetylene torch, steel welding rod and a block of metal. By the early 1980s, he was sculpting full-time, and had switched to a lost wax casting process. First he creates a fabricated metal armature, over which he melts a coat of hard sculptor's wax; then he chisels, cuts and carves the subject, taking great care to render accurately the animal's anatomical details; a silicon rubber/fiberglas mold is taken from this figure, and used for the duplicates. Cast in bronze, the pieces are painted with patinas in a range of natural colors, and mounted on marble or hardwood. His subjects include turtles, penguins and birds of all sorts, as well as the great sea mammals. Anxious to protect the wildlife that is his inspiration, he belongs to a variety of preservation organizations, including the National Wildlife Foundation and the Audubon Society.

HUNTER, JOHN H. (Painter, Printmaker)

c/o Discovery Gallery, 251 S. 14th St., San Jose, CA 95112

Born: 1934 *Awards:* Fulbright Fellowship *Collections:* National Gallery of Art, Washington, DC; Museum of Modern Art, NYC Exhibitions; Documenta VI, Kassel, West Germany; Chicago International Art Exposition *Education:* Claremont Graduate School *Dealer:* Discovery Gallery, San Jose

A figurative artist, he seeks to infuse ancient themes and motifs with new vigor and substance. Munch, Beckmann, Toulouse-Lautrec and Gauguin are sources of influence and inspiration. He has recently been celebrating the Western landscape, from Colorado to California, working in and amplifying the traditions of such modernists as Marsden Hartley. Clouds and trees often dominate these ornately framed and colorful works, and he occasionally incorporates softened

photo emulsions. His other media include drawing, and printmaking.

HUNTER, MARIANNE KANE (Enamel Art Jeweler)

P.O. Box 260, El Portal, CA 95318

Born: 1949 *Awards:* Award of Excellence, La Quinta Art Association; 1st Place, Beverly Hills Affair in the Garden *Collections:* Ashkenazy Collection *Exhibitions:* National Enamel Guild; National Enamel Society *Education:* Otis Art Institute; UC-Northridge

A self-taught enamelist and jeweler, she has been influenced by studies of painting, dance, literature and botany, as well as by ethnic design and art nouveau. In 1970, she began development of her dry-enamel Grisaille process, a painstaking technique that requires up to twenty-four firings. She has recently been most concerned with small precious objects (jewelry and boxes). These pieces incorporate evocative images, executed with precise enamel work. They feature a diversity of metals, stones in free form cuts and facets, pearls, beads and amber. Each part of her work is rich with color, texture and light, contributing to a cohesive whole.

HUNTER, WILLIAM (Sculptor)

P.O. Box 260, El Portal, CA 95318

Born: 1947 *Collections:* Boston Museum of Fine Arts; Jacobson Collection, Smithsonian Institution, Washington D.C. *Exhibitions:* Renwick Gallery, Smithsonian Institution, Washington D.C.; Del Mano Gallery, Los Angeles *Dealer:* Del Mano Gallery, Los Angeles

Self-taught, he began turning and disc-sanding wood in 1968. Often using imported, exotic hardwoods, his work ranges from complex carved and constructed pieces to simple vessels. Variations on the spiral are a recurring theme, as are orbiting lines, which add dimension to the wood's silhouette and surface, disappearing to draw the viewer in to investigate its origin and destination. Multifluted spirals—the most formally ornamented of all his spiral vessels—are defined by the close, identically curving lines that form a single, pure rhythm.

HURLEY, MAUREEN (Painter, Photographer)

7491 Mirabel Rd., Forestville, CA 95436

Born: 1952 *Awards:* NEA Grant; Grant, California Arts Council *Collections:* Oakland Museum *Exhibitions:* Sonoma State U. Art Gallery, Rohnert Park; Santa Rosa City Council Chambers *Education:* Sonoma State U.

After studying with painter Martin Stoelzel and assemblage artists Inez Storer and Helene Aylon in the 1970s, she explored raku ceramics and glass blowing with potter Thano Johnson. An interdisciplinary artist, she established a career as a poet and, returning to the visual arts arena, used imagery she developed in her writing. A recent body of work consists of woven photographs and paintings inspired by several trips to Central and South America. Using crude watercolor crayons, she manipulates the medium, layering colors, then spraying them with water washes. In her "Tropical Postcard" series, she worked with a brilliant tropical palette, reminiscent of Rivera's last work; turquoise, magenta and orange suggested the need for First World cultures to advance beyond a postcard picture of emerging tropical nations. She has also contributed to group performance pieces with David Best. Other

John H. Hunter, *Christmas Eve,* 16 x 20, oil on panel. Courtesy: Dr. Robert Melnikoff, Los Altos Hills, CA

Stephen Hopper, *Businessman in a Landscape,* 50 x 72, oil, enamel, wax on canvas

Sukey Hughes *War Garment with Medicine,* 25 x 13 x 13, hand-made paper with mixed media

Larry Hamilton, *Summer,* 48 x 72, acrylic lacquer

Lyn Horton, *Essay on Human Relations,* each part 24" in height, mixed media

Jane R. Hofstetter, *Cascade,* 19 x 25, water media. Courtesy: Society of Western Artists

John Harper, *Thicket Trap,* 24 x 20, watercolor.
Photograph: Rick Ray

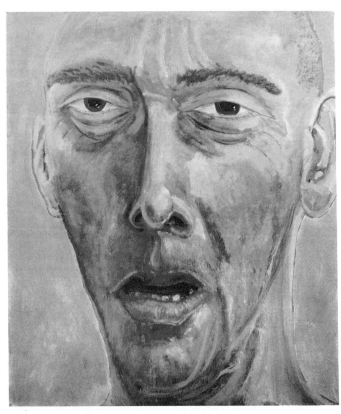

Jim Hutchison, *Survivor,* 72 x 84, oil on canvas

Jo Anne Hertz, *Portait of John Smart,* 1 of series of 4, 36 x 36,
silk screen and oil paint

Jenny Hunter-Groat, *Precept,* 18 x 18, 7-layer serigraph,
original made from sumi ink and gouache

artworks include collages constructed with handmade papers, and watercolor, acrylics and oils. She is a widely published poet and essayist, and has received a grant to exchange poetry and art with Soviet sister city Cherkassy.

HUSBY, MELISSA (Painter)
3037 Myrtle St., Oakland, CA 94608

Born: 1948 *Awards:* Rocky Mountain National Watermedia *Exhibitions:* Whitney Museum, Richmond

During her formal training, she had a specific interest in abstract expressionism. By the late 1960s, she became interested in the works of Paul Klee and Wassily Kandinsky, and she began to orchestrate her work according to structural principles, derived from Kandinsky and from her classical music background. These works evolved from minimalist abstraction on raw canvas to the playful imaging of identifiable forms, in counterpoint with each other, on primed canvas or paper. Presently, her work revolves around spiritual principles and symbols from the unconscious. These paintings speak to a transcendent, fantastic reality and the possible forms and images of multidimensional space. She works in mixed media as well as oils.

HUTCHISON, JIM (Painter)
10515 Tabor St., #3, Los Angeles, CA 90034

Born: 1951 *Exhibitions:* Southern Exposure Gallery, San Francisco *Education:* U. of Colorado; U. of Oregon

After completing a series entitled "Cannibal Abstracts," some twenty 4-by-6-foot paintings with a violent, biological thrust, he embarked on a suite of portraits depicting desperate grief and lunacy, cowardice and distrust. All the paintings are oil on canvas, ranging in size from 9-by-12-inches to 6-by-10-feet.

HUTH, GERALD (Mixed Media Artist)
5895 Anderson Rd., Forestville, CA 95436

Born: 1949 *Collections:* Brooklyn Museum; Vassar College Art Gallery *Exhibitions:* Marin County Civic Center, San Rafael; Luther Burbank Center for the Arts, Santa Rosa *Education:* U. of Pennsylvania

His current work is the result of a journey through many styles and influences. Trained formally as an architect, he began painting when he was twenty. He also began to travel worldwide. He worked originally in an expressionist mode, combining the influences of early 20th-century painting and the primitive art he encountered during his travels. His early works were primarily oil paintings and woodblock prints. In the late 1970s, he began to combine painting and sculpture in an attempt to integrate two- and three-dimensional art forms. Moving through the various facets of expressionism, his work gradually became more abstract, though still tied to depictions of the human condition. He calls this synthetic work "construction/painting." These pieces are combinations of oil paintings on variously shaped canvases and low relief, primarily made of California redwood. They are fluid, organic images based on the human form or on studies of the rhythms of nature. He also addresses these themes in large mixed-media drawings that combine ink, charcoal, pastel, watercolor and collage elements.

HUTTON, KATHRYN N. (Painter, Multi-Media Artist)
1562 Waller St., San Francisco, CA 94117

Born: 1964 *Awards:* Best of Show, U. of Washington Exhibition *Exhibitions:* U. of Washington Art Showing; Southern Exposure Gallery, San Francisco *Education:* U. of Washington

Her early work showed the influence of such painterly and expressionistic artists as Rouault, Kandinsky, Beckmann, Gorky and de Kooning. At first, her paint application was flat, but she eventually moved to a more multimedia approach. She built images through a combination of ideas and processes. She progressed through a series of thickly painted extreme size paintings— monumental to miniature—through collage, assemblages and now sculptures. Along with oil paints, she uses found objects, to create three-dimensional pieces that lie on top of two-dimensional stretched canvases. She also works with a hot glue gun and adds silicon for transparency and dimension.

HUYTS, PETRUS J. (Photographer, Draughtsperson)
6508 Baden Court, Sacramento, CA 95823

Born: 1922 *Awards:* 2nd Place, Sacramento County Fair; Artist of the Month, Northern California Arts Inc. *Exhibitions:* Consumnes River College; California League Annual Open Show

Born in Indonesia, he started drawing at age ten. He later studied and worked at the Topographical Service in Indonesia. As a P.O.W. during World War II, he made money by drawing the family members of the Japanese and Korean Guards. After more than a decade in the Netherlands, he emigrated to California in 1961, where he worked for several companies involved in aerial photography and mapping. He now makes 18-by 24-inch commissioned drawings working from commercial and portrait photographs and using conte crayon or pastel. The works are photo-realistic and "improved to more real." His subjects are frequently Indonesian, although he also addresses other themes.

HYAMS, LEIGH (Painter)
3435 Army, Studio 304, San Francisco, CA 94110

Born: 1936 *Awards:* Fulbright Grant; Residency, Hand Hollow Foundation *Exhibitions:* Ringling Museum of Art, Sarasota; Richard Demarco Gallery, Edinburgh *Education:* University of Guanajator; New College Fine Arts Institute

Above all a colorist, she chose stones as her major subject matter while working on lands of the Southwestern Indians. Her work expresses the particular presence felt in ancient objects and at certain archaeological sites, often through an unusual use of scale and color. Her Minoan pithos and three- and four-part dolmans use shaped canvases and paintings that have the dimensional feel of sculpture. She has recently been working on two series. One is dominated by an imaginary archaeology based on recent studies in the Mediterranean; paintings of ancient vessels in transparent, layered acrylic on heavy jute canvas alternate with larger works. The other, more recent series of shaped canvases explores the flexibility of constructed paintings. The series consists of forty interchangeable canvases, and each of the canvases presents a complete painting in itself that can combine in endless ways with others to create changeable, site-specific, large- or small-scale installations. Among the possible combinations are a Stonehenge-like image, an avalanche and a quiet garden. Her colors are natural—

Anna Homler, *The Hands,* from the ongoing performance *Pharmacia Poetica*

Leigh Hyams, *Dolmen,* 4 pieces, acrylic on shaped canvas. Courtesy: Wilson Collection

Seta Injeyan, *The Moving Arch Series #117,* 16 x 24, charcoal and transparency on paper

Robert Inman, *Chouinard Series #26,* 36 x 48, acrylic

Boris Ilyin, *San Pablo Bay,* 18 x 20, acrylic

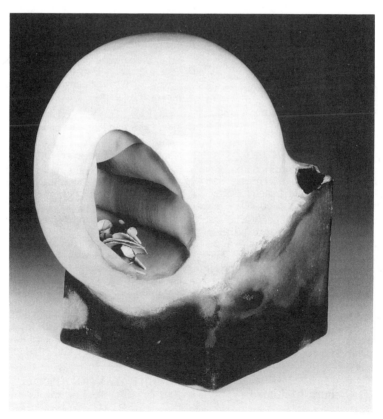

Marilyn Alford Jennings, *Transition,* 18 x 15 x 14, pit-fired clay with glazes

but not limited to naturalistic representation—and incorporate shades of pink, green and orange.

HYATT, IRENE R. (Painter)
545 Pierce St., #1104, Albany, CA 94706

Born: 1924 *Awards:* 1st Place, Gualala Arts *Exhibitions:* San Francisco Women Artists; Gualala Arts She started painting at the age of fifty, studying with Dr. Alex Villumson, who was one of the first teachers to explore the possibilities of right hemisphere drawing. During her ten years of study, she favored bright, colorful oils. Now she works in acrylics and watercolors, drawing her subject matter mostly from photographs. She paints people having a good time, and describes her style as expressionist, rather than photo-realist. Recently she has discovered a new technique using wax paper with acrylic paint. Her recent series, "Florals," comprises eight rather large paintings of flowers in cut-glass vases.

HYDER, FRANK (Painter)
631 N. 2nd St., Philadelphia, PA 19123

Born: 1951 *Awards:* 1988 Pennsylvania State Council Grant *Collections:* Philadelphia Museum of Art; Library of Congress *Exhibitions:* Jessica Darraby Gallery, Los Angeles; The Exhibition Space, New York *Education:* Maryland Institute of Art; U. of Pennsylvania *Dealer:* Michael Dunev Gallery, San Francisco

Combining interests in figurative painting and expressive media such as clay tableau and large-scale wood cut prints, he created his "Plywood Paintings." This form combines the gothic jag of woodcuts with a sensuously painted surface. Alternately painting and carving on large sheets of plywood, he builds the surface into a richly weathered patina. The imagery is figurative and provocative, employing large scale shifts, dramatic spatial relationships and evocative color. A recurrent theme involves a huge hand in the foreground that almost touches a solitary, distant figure, as even more distant figures play in an enormous wave. The works are intended to suggest a private vision of humanity beyond the limits of normal awareness.

HYSON, JEAN (Painter)
950 Franklin, #56, San Francisco, CA 94109

Born: 1931 *Collections:* Oakland Museum; Santa Barbara Museum *Exhibitions:* Legion of Honor, San Francisco *Educaiton:* Art Students League *Dealer:* Joyce Vernon, Rumson Art, Inc., Rumson, NJ

The sensitive and spontaneous styles of her instructors, Yasuo Kuniyoshi, George Grosz and William Baziotes, influenced her at the Art Students League. Her early watercolor works were geometric. Her straight lines converged and intersected; her curved lines were charged with a precariously balanced energy. Recently, she has begun painting more representationally. She now begins with a definite subject matter, and arrives at a Magritte- influenced combination of abstraction and surrealism. Her images of boxes act as metaphors for the inner meanings of societal events. She paints with acrylic and oil; her style is characterized by a precision of line and an intensity of color.

IKEGAWA, SHIRO (Painter, Multimedia Artist)
323 E. Altadena Dr., Altadena, CA 91001

Born: 1933 *Awards:* Purchase Award for Print, Palace of the Legion of Honor, San Francisco; 1st Prize for Print, Los Angeles Printmaking Society *Collections:* Frederick Weisman Co., Los Angeles; Smithsonian Institute, Washington, D.C. *Exhibitions:* Soker-Kaseman Gallery, San Francisco; Shinno Gallery, Los Angeles *Education:* Tokyo University of Arts; Otis Art Institute of Los Angeles County, Los Angeles *Dealer:* April Sgro Riddle, Los Angeles

He creates multimedia works using collage, acrylic and clay. The trout is a recurring image in these works, often juxtaposed with cubes filled with sky and clouds. He also does ceramic plates, which he often breaks and then reconstructs using new glazes, or to which he attaches fur-coated ceramic fish. Japanese characters that refer to dream or illusion often appear in his work. Colors range from deep reds and blues to beige/gold and black/gray tones. One work of acrylic and collage on paper depicts a black trout and a Japanese envelope inscribed with Japanese characters seemingly suspended in a black element flecked with white. A white glow surrounds the fish; above it are Japanese characters in black on gray.

ILYIN, BORIS (Painter)
1951 Las Gallinas Ave., San Rafael, CA 94903

Born: 1918 *Exhibitions:* Ankrum Gallery, Los Angeles; Stanford University Center for Integrated Systems *Education:* UC-Berkeley; Stanford U.

Receiving his early training from a relative, the San Francisco portraitist Peter Ilyin, he developed his technique as a realist over many years, concentrating on the California landscape. In recent years, his interest has shifted to the figure. These works have been inspired by Vermeer and Edward Hopper's vision of spareness and loneliness in American life. His subjects, typically young American business people, sit eating lunch in the noonday sun, uninvolved with each other, balanced between happiness and unhappiness, awareness and the lack of it. Working in acrylic, he often leaves much of the canvas raw, reinforcing the alienation of the figures.

IMMEDIATO, KATHLEEN (Fiber Artist)
3806 Drybread Rd., Cottonwood, CA 96022

Born: 1940 *Exhibitions:* Redding Museum Gallery; National Wool Showcase, Orland

For health reasons, she moved to a farm in the mid-1970s. On her first Christmas Eve there, she was given a newborn lamb as a pet. This gift sparked an interest in breeding sheep to produce fleeces. Currently, she spins yarn by hand, makes sweaters and tends her multicolored flock, which is well known for its premium quality hand-spinning fleeces in a wide range of natural colors. The fibers vary in color from whites, beiges, tans and browns to silvers, blue-silvers and blacks. She has experimented with different techniques of spinning and dying, designing sweaters to take full advantage of the fiber's possibilities. She has developed her own spinning techniques, including a "lock spin" in which the wool fibers are spun with the least disturbance to the fiber's natural layout. Her award-winning, hand-washable sweaters are knitted in solid tones or in complementary colors.

IMPERT, WALTER (Painter)
1001 E. 1st St., #6, Los Angeles, CA 90012

Born: 1948 *Awards:* 1st Prize, Riverside Art Competition *Exhibitions:* Downey Art Museum; Riverside Art Museum *Education:* U. of Denver; Duke U. *Dealer:* Orlando Gallery, Sherman Oaks

Jim Hammerud, *Nucleogenesis,* 48 x 60, acrylic

George Herms, *Clock Tower Monument to the Unknown,* 216 x 360 x 480, sculpture.
Courtesy: L.A. Louver Gallery/MacArthur Park Public Art Project. Photograph: Dennis Keeley

Hon Chew Hee *Royal Hawaiian Family,* 44 x 56, acrylic with 23k gold on canvas

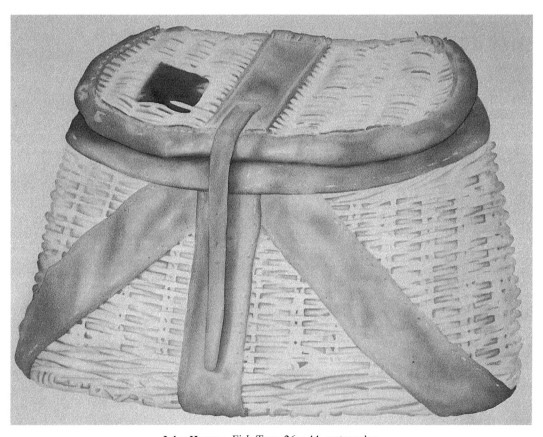

John Harper, *Fish Trap,* 36 x 44, watercolor

Eden Hodara, *Once Upon a Time,* 39 x 30, mixed media on linen

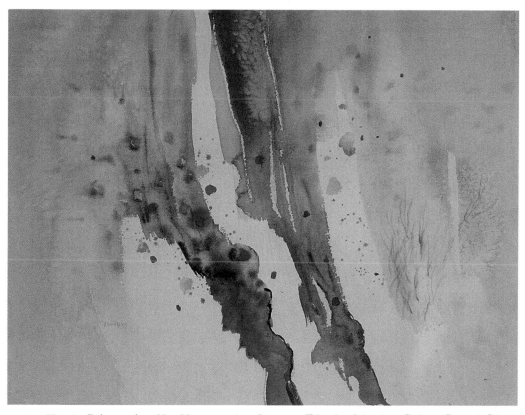

Ann Harris, *Rejuvenation,* 22 x 30, watercolor. Courtesy: Friends of the Arts Gallery, Carmel, CA

Dorothy Hoyal, *Lagoon,* 28 x 38, watercolor

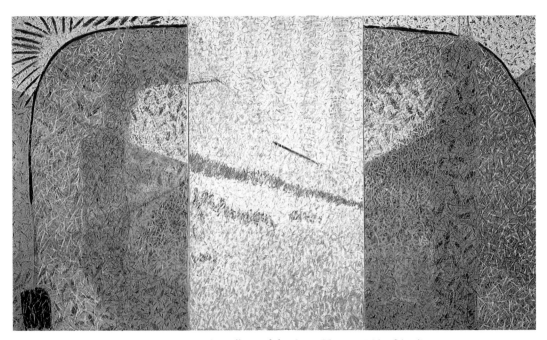

Pamela Hartvig, *Guardians of the Gate: Heaven,* 144 x 84, oil

Mira Hocking, *The Meeting,* 29 x 40, watercolor

John Sherrill Houser, *Mt. Manual Morning (Big Sur),* 30 x 40, oil on panel

Jim Hammerud, *Star Castle,* 59 x 39, oil

Frederick Hammersley, *Same Hear,* 7 x 10, oil

Bobby-Lou Hargis, *Unorthodox (triptych),* 30 x 48 (each canvas), acrylics Courtesy: Ontario Museum

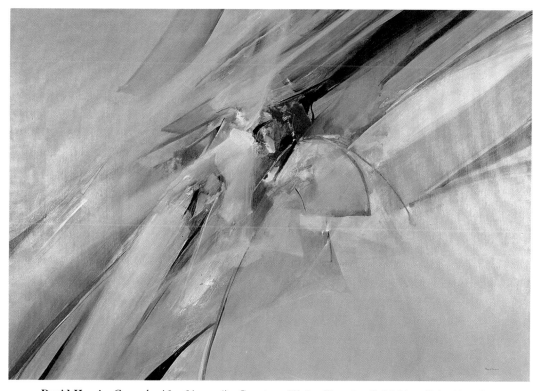

David Harris, *Cascade,* 46 x 64, acrylic. Courtesy: Welles Fine Art Publishing, Palo Alto, CA

Jari Havlena, *Le Paysage,* 36 x 60, oil on canvas

Angelika Herzel, *After the Thunderstorm,* 16 x 24, oil pastel on paper

Jane R. Hofstetter, *Emergence,* 21 x 29, acrylic. Courtesy: American Watercolor Society

Anna Homler, *Buddhas Gae U,* 26 x 42 x 3, mixed media. Courtesy: Elizabeth Abravanel

Stephen Hopper, *Position is 9/10 of the Law,* oil, enamel on paper

Lyn Horton, *Essay on Human Relations (detail),* 100 parts each 24" in height, mixed media

Jenny Hunter-Groat, *Voices From a Bridge,* 30 x 21, watercolor and gouache on paper

Diana Hobson, *Searching for a Level Balance,* 38 x 65, oil

Rosinda Holmes, *Vineyard with Crows,* 10 x 14, watercolor.
Courtesy: Wendy Barr Schmidt, Newport Beach, CA

Sukey Hughes, *Shirt of the Six Crosses,* 52 x 32 x 2, hand-made paper with mixed media

Robert Inman, *Chouinard Series #24,* 48 x 36, acrylic

Boris Ilyin, *By the Waters,* 48 x 48, acrylic. Courtesy: Ankrum Gallery

Seta Injeyan, *Grapevine Mountains,* 12 x 18, mixed media on transparency. Courtesy: Jean Davis

Chris M. Johnston, *10 Years Later,* 21", clay and steel

Johanna Jordan, *#192—Red and Grey,* 240 x 108 x 96,
painted steel

Jo Boot Jones, *River Princess, Coloma,* 22 x 28, oil

Dolly Johnson, *Rose-Coloured Lens—The Actuality,* 30 x 22,
watercolor, acrylic, airbrush, colored pencil, pastel

Yvonne Maree John, *Shapes of Teen Years,* 30 x 24, oil

After training as a non-representational painter with primarily formal concerns, he began to introduce figurative elements into his work. Initially concerned with whimsical, usually surreal images, his work gradually became more realistic and polished. Today he creates highly romantic cityscapes, working primarily in oils and pastels. He anchors his compositions with strong verticals and horizontals, giving his works a solid, classical sense that recalls American landscape painters of the late 19th century. Spiritually, the artist says he owes something to Walt Disney.

INGARGIOLA, INDIA (Painter)
425 Lombard St., San Francisco, CA 94133

Born: 1941 *Exhibitions:* Braunstein-Quay Gallery, San Francisco; Southern Exposure Gallery, San Francisco *Education:* San Francisco Art Institute

Using large-scale canvases, and rich oil colors and technique, her early work is personal, archetypal and narrative. Life-size figures are energetic, brooding, romantic and cryptic, and the paintings exude a dream-like or nightmarish feeling. She cites the influences of Munch, Bocklin, Fuseli, Delvaux, Balthus and Rousseau. Her more recent work is sparse by comparison, devoid of figures, with only an iconographic object to project a haunting presence. The layering of content, accomplished through the layering of paints and glazes, establishes a point-counterpoint relationship between form and content, which contributes to the over-all balance of the piece. Although her work is very personal, the archetypal imagery makes the paintings widely accessible to viewers.

INJEYAN, SETA (Photography Painter)
5610 Pine Cone Rd., La Crescenta, CA 91214

Born: 1945 *Awards:* Purchase Award, Washington State Arts Commission; Best of Show, Art Center Alumni Exhibit, Pasadena *Collections:* Wells Fargo Bank, Los Angeles; Eastern State Hospital, Olympia, WA *Exhibitions:* Santa Barbara Museum of Art; Mona Lisa Gallery, Tokyo *Education:* Art Center College of Design, Pasadena

Influenced by Magritte's imagery, early works dealt mainly with different levels of illusion and reality. The artist worked on both sides of positive transparencies, primarily using watercolors, gouache and chinagraph pencils but also employing airbrush, regular brush and spattering techniques. The medium of transparency allowed him to create a "new kind of reality" based on an existing reality—a developed image on film. He currently concentrates on the sheer vitality of paint on canvas, with the transparency used as an element of collage. He has recently completed a series based on a 1987 trip to Rome.

INMAN, ROBERT (Painter)
11609 Hesby St., N. Hollywood, CA 91601

Born: 1927 *Collections:* IBM, San Francisco; Xerox, San Francisco *Exhibitions:* Umeda Gallery, Osaka, Japan; Ivey Gallery, Los Angeles *Education:* Occidental College; Chouinard Art Institute, Los Angeles

After leaving art school, he spent fifteen years working as a background artist and color stylist in the animation film industry. Influenced by Diebenkorn, Rothko and Frankenthaler, his first works after returning to painting were figurative in concept with a strong color impact. In time, his warmly colored paintings became non-objective. He now calls himself a "constructed action field artist." His acrylic paintings have a strong structural quality, and he creates tension by breaking up structures with color fields and introducing new patterns and forms. Also a printmaker, he makes limited edition collographs and also does some embossing.

IONE, AMY (Painter)
1942 Channing Way #202, Berkeley, CA 94704

Born: 1949 *Awards:* Poster/Publication Illustration, San Francisco Arts Commission 40th Annual Arts Festival *Exhibitions:* Bay Arts, Arts Council of San Mateo; Berkeley Art Center *Education:* Pennsylvania State U.

She works by weaving symbols into a depiction of four-dimensional space, leading the viewer into a reality devoid of rules for linear perspective. "Signs of the Zodiac," a series of twelve ink paintings, reveals the influence of Cezanne, Kandinsky, Mondrian and, particularly, Escher. One painting in this series, *Gemini,* consists of concentric circles of the zodiacal symbol for Gemini, housing an open book and framed by continuous symbols drawn in six ways. This extensive black-and-white work has led her to begin another series of paintings, best described as visual jazz, in transparent and opaque acrylics.

IRMAGEAN (Draughtsperson)
P.O. Box 5602, Berkeley, CA 94705

Born: 1947 *Collections:* Oakland Citizens Committee for Urban Renewal *Exhibitions:* Mission Cultural Center, San Francisco; San Francisco Museum of Modern Art *Education:* California College of Arts & Crafts

Strongly grounded in realism, she was attracted to the works of Kathe Kollwitz, Charles White, and van Gogh. It soon became apparent that emotional and cultural content would be important elements of her style. With references to her racial heritage and to cultural feminism, her energetic drawings are characterized by sweeping drapery, dramatic lines and whirling motion. Repeated images with varying themes merge into a form wherein the interaction among imagination, medium and mood become the motive as well as the subject. She is not concerned with literal translation or the details of background, place and time. Instead, her interest lies in the spirit and the power of the expressive line.

IRWIN, JAMES (Experimental Filmmaker)
564 45th Ave., San Francisco, CA 94121

Born: 1955 *Awards:* NEA Fellowship; Rockefeller Foundation Grant *Exhibitions:* Metropolitan Museum of Art, NYC; San Francisco Museum of Modern Art *Education:* New York U.; San Francisco Art Institute *Dealer:* Canyon Cinema, San Francisco

Although he chooses to work in film because of its eclecticism and experiential impact, the primary influences on his work have been musicians and painters. He has developed various methods for interacting with each stage of the film process. This includes both physical manipulation, such as drawing, painting and assemblage, as well as conceptual strategies such as the introduction of random procedures into his work. Ranging in length from three minutes to an hour, his films are marked by the diversity of techniques he uses to manipulate the plastic element of cinema and by his use of sound. Recurring themes in his films are the loss of self in illusions and the motivating influence of fear. He is best known for a series of films that combine text with image in a complex visual field. These aggressively engage the audience in a direct exchange, employing dark humor and game-like formal properties.

IRWIN, ROBERT (Installation Artist, Sculptor)

10966 Strathmore Dr., Los Angeles CA 90024

Born: 1928 *Collections:* Museum of Contemporary Art, Los Angeles; Whitney Museum, NYC *Exhibitions:* Museum of Modern Art, NYC; Matrix, Berkeley *Education:* Otis Art Institute; Jepson Art Institute; Chouinard Art Institute *Dealer:* Pace Gallery, NYC

An abstract expressionist painter during the 1950s, he later abandoned personal expression for minimalism in the 1960s. He questioned the meaning of image and object in a series of dot paintings, followed by a series of spray-painted discs. In works circa 1968, aluminum convex discs protruded from the wall and were illuminated by floodlights, creating interior and exterior shapes in a composition of shapes and shadows. Installations during the 1970s explored varying arrangements of interior light and space, as in *Portal*. Recent work includes site/architectural sculpture in public spaces. His conceptual approach to art incorporates inquiries into philosophy, natural science and social science.

IVICEVIC, SHARON LYNN (Mixed Media Artist)

17130 Courtney Ln., Huntington Beach, CA 92649

Born: 1933 *Awards:* Juror's Award of Excellence, 17th Annual Works on Paper Exhibition, Southwest Texas St. U., San Marcos; OCAA Award, Orange County Art Association 19th Annual All Media Juried Exhibition, Laguna Beach Museum of Art *Exhibitions:* Irvine Fine Arts Center; Los Angeles County Museum of Art *Education:* San Diego St. College

She casts straw paper pulp onto wood, creating a relief surface approximately three-eighths of an inch thick. When this paper is dried, she brushes parts of the composition with melted beeswax, latex, acrylic, and oil-based paints. She also uses pen and ink and transparent watercolor dyes applied with an airbrush. This variety of media results in a surface rich in texture and color, transparency and opacity, and an unusual metallic patina that belies the fragility of the paper. One goal is to utilize a traditional craft in a unique and painterly manner. More recently, she has been painting tepee forms in oil on linen. These abstract expressionist works deal with the symbolism of the tepee as a metaphor for inner strength and repose.

IZU, DAVID (Painter, Sculptor)

579 Walavista Ave., Oakland, CA 94610

Born: 1951 *Collections:* San Francisco Museum of Modern Art; Carnegie Institute Museum of Art *Exhibitions:* Carnegie International; William Sawyer Gallery, San Francisco *Dealer:* William Sawyer Gallery, San Francisco

He has been influenced by Japanese aesthetics, having lived in Tokyo for one and a half years, and by his teachers Nathan Oliveira and Frank Lobdell. His earliest works were large abstract oil paintings full of floating organic shapes. Eventually, he began to focus on a central column of color which would interact with the surrounding field, sometimes inflecting it with light, sometimes with shadow. He then introduced sand, sawdust and glass shards to add texture. As time progressed, the central column grew more emphatically three-dimensional until he finally dropped off the surrounding color field and stood the column up on two legs. His recent work includes a skinny, freestanding, figurative sculpture made of wood, acrylic paint, cloth, glass and various other materials.

Helen Barker, *Cottage Near Toguay England,* 24 x 30, oil

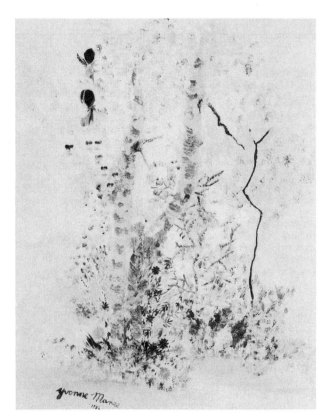

Yvonne Marie John, *N.W. Woods,* 18 x 14, oils

Elmo James, *Minotaur,* 24 x 20, bronze

JACKSON, BOBI (Photographer)
P.O. Box 69775, Los Angeles, CA 90069

Born: 1939 *Exhibitions:* William Douglass Outdoor Photo Exhibit; Venice Public Library *Education:* Santa Monica College

A self-taught photographer, she grew up documenting the landscape of Brooklyn. With her Leica, she was able to capture the scenes: as Canarsie changed from swamp land to the projects in which she lived; as the government huts changed as quickly as the people who lived in them. *Life Magazine* layouts and the *Brooklyn News* were her compositional models, and the work of Ansel Adams persists as an influence to this day. In Greenwich Village, she focused on musicians. After moving to California, the street performers of Venice Beach became her primary image. Her *Tapia Trees* and *The Wave*, taken with a Canon AE1 and black-and-white infra-red film, are perfect examples of Adams' technique.

JACKSON, EVERETT GEE (Painter, Printmaker)
1234 Franciscan Way, San Diego, CA 92116

Born: 1900 *Exhibitions:* Museo del Carmen of the City of Mexico, San Angel; San Diego Museum of Art *Education:* San Diego St. U.; USC

As an oil painter, he has spent his life promoting the values and culture of Mexico. He has for many years painted and studied the Pre-Columbian art and architecture of Central America. In 1965, he became the founding chairman of the Latin American Arts Committee of the San Diego Museum of Art. He is Professor Emeritus of Art at San Diego State University. He has recently been working on a book about his experiences in Honduras. He says that the first step in his creative process is to hold an entire image in his mind. If he is able "to imagine a more pleasing effect at some place within that total image," he then creates that effect. To finish the work of art, he repeats this process until all elements are pleasing together.

JACKSON, LANCE J. (Computer Artist)
4049 Coolidge Ave., Oakland CA 94602

Born: 1953 *Awards:* Society of Newspaper Design *Collections:* Mills College, Oakland *Exhibitions:* C.C.A.T., San Francisco *Education:* Washington University

His early influences were Mayan ruins, Ernst Fuchs and Arnulf Raine. At first, he constructed room environments from pulp paper, resins and various pigments. He then moved to computer generated work. The pieces are archaeological recordings of Americana on disk. He sees his image of a 1968 Pontiac Catalina as a dinosaur from an age gone by, a relic from the height of the industrial consumption age. His recent work is figurative. He uses a Macintosh II with a 13-inch Apple Monitor. His software is a combination of SuperPaint, MacPaint, Adobe Illustrator and Aldus Free hand.

JACKSON-JENKINS, ANITA (Painter)
P.O. Box 330978, Kahului, Maui, HI 96732

Born: 1952 *Awards:* 3rd Place, Oriental Brush Painting, U. of Hawaii Art Festival, Kauai *Exhibitions:* Delta Sigma Theta Exhibition of Black Artists, Brea; Classic Antiquities Gallery, Beverly Hills

She grew up in the Hawaiian Islands, and for many years danced with the Alvin Ailey American Dance Theater. Her artwork began as a way to relax after performances and grueling rehearsals. In the early 1970s, she used only pen and ink, to create flowing graphic forms, interrupted by dimensional pointillistic areas. After an injury ended her dance career in 1980, her painting changed dramatically in format, medium and technique. Using squeeze bottles, she applies one layer of paint at a time, allowing water in varying amounts to run over the canvas. The flowing forms, inspired by the movement of the dance and by Hawaii's clouds, water, sand and skies, are executed in blues and purples, with accents of white, yellow and orange. Currently, she uses watercolors on gesso-soaked muslin for floral still lifes and more abstract compositions.

JACOBS, DIANA (Painter)
3000 Hollyridge Dr., Los Angeles, CA 90068

Born: 1950 *Collections:* Huntington Library, San Marino; Wells Fargo Bank of California *Exhibitions:* Los Angeles Audubon Society; Los Angeles Museum of Natural History *Education:* U. of Pittsburgh; Otis Art Institute *Dealer:* Biota Gallery, Los Angeles

Her interest in Monet led her to work at landscape painting in an impressionist style. By the 1970s, she began studying the content of the landscapes, and making detailed rendering of plants and flowers. She experimented with using these botanical forms in metaphorical and symbolic compositions; she worked in watercolor and pen and ink, a departure from her usual oils. Her recent works are on large sheets of hot-pressed, 140- to 300-pounds. Arches paper. Nudes are rendered in graphite, flowers in watercolor—all in rhythmic compositions, in which the nudes react to the floral forms. The symbolism of the flowers refers to each individual's secret self, a visual message reinforced by the elusive, smudged edges of the nudes.

JACOBS, FERNE (Sculptor, Fiber Artist)
1536 Curran St., Los Angeles, CA 90026

Born: 1942 *Awards:* NEA Fellowship *Collections:* American Craft Museum; The Lannan Foundation, Venice *Exhibitions:* Laguna Art Museum; Oakland Art Museum *Education:* Claremont Graduate School

She creates fiber sculptures using the traditional coiled thread technique. Deeply spiritual, she weaves and collects old weaving and sewing tools, rugs, mats and other pieces in order to feel connected to the works of other women who have lived throughout the ages. Her early pieces were baskets, created with the idea of a receptacle that can both protect and contain. More recent sculptures have moved beyond the traditional basket forms. Some have elongated bodies and multiple openings; others have no bottom, symbolizing passages and entryways. She also works with geological images, rocks and mountains, which symbolize for her the soul of the earth, as well as that part of each individual which is impervious to the transitory. Recently, she has added drawings and collages to the sculptures. These additional materials are attempts to express the feelings of completion and connection engendered by the woven pieces. She seeks to create sculptures that are full of meaning and inviting, yet mysterious.

JACOBS, LAURA ANN (Sculptor)
15 Hermann St., #108, San Francisco, CA 94102

Born: 1960 *Exhibitions:* Virginia Brier Gallery, San Francisco; Northwind Gallery, Mill Valley *Education:* San Francisco State U.

Phillip A. Jameson, *Twin Fetuses,* 30 x 25 x 6,
acrylic on fired clay

Robert W. Jensen, *Five Minutes From the City,*
24 x 18, acrylic on canvas

Using a lost-wax casting technique, she creates bronze sculptures of found objects—specifically, food. She finds that out of its edible context, food can be better appreciated for its varied shapes, colors and textures. These simplistic forms display an Eastern influence and exhibit the effects of time, i.e., erosion, neglect, age and decay. Finished pieces have a ritualistic, ancient appearance.

JACOBS, MIMI (Photographer)
100 Thorndale Dr., San Rafael, CA 94903

Born: 1911 Collections: San Francisco Museum of Art; Oakland Museum Exhibitions: Palm Springs Desert Museum; San Francisco Museum of Art

Early work was in sculpture and weaving; it wasn't until the early 1960s that she turned to photography. She concentrates on portraits of artists. In creating an image, she is unconcerned with backgrounds or props, emphasizing instead the collaboration between subject and photographer. Her goal is to capture the fleeting moment in which her subject reveals a transitory facial expression that is a unique aspect of his or her personality. Her images are frank and deceptively straightforward, and her portraits of Ansel Adams, Raymond Saunders and Betsy Soar explore a wide range of tonal qualities. In addition to photographs of artists, her current work includes children's portraits.

JACOBSON, LINDA (Painter)
758 E. 14th St., 2nd Fl., Los Angeles, CA 90021

Born: 1946 Collections: Palm Springs Desert Museum; U. of Michigan Exhibitions: Cal. State-Los Angeles; Loyola-Marymount U., Los Angeles Education: Art Center College of Design; Otis Art Institute

While studying with Lorser Feitelson, she was influenced by Stonehenge and Henry Moore. She then traveled to the South of France, where she was captivated by the colors and movement of nature and the work of Van Gogh. Her recent abstract landscapes are symbolic expressions of internal psychic states and involve explorations of light and space. She incorporates glazes and calligraphic markings into the work and often scratches through layers of paint and color fields. The results are contemporary metaphysical landscapes that convey a sense of mystery.

JACOBY, VICTOR (Weaver)
1086 17th St., Eureka, CA 95501

Born: 1944 Awards: Purchase Award, Northern California Fiber Exhibit Collections: Marriott Corporation, Richmond, VA; Kaiser Permenante, San Jose Exhibitions: The Art Center, Eureka; College of the Redwoods Creative Arts Gallery, Eureka Education: Humboldt State U.

After a general art and weaving education, he began his career by weaving rugs, which included geometric tapestry sections. He soon became interested in tapestry. His study of the history of weaving and the of work of French artist Jean Lurcat awakened an interest in representational imagery, especially landscapes, flowers and cloth. In his recent, work he juxtaposes representational imagery with geometrical shapes, such as stripes, borders and diamonds. He recently completed a series of tapestries based on trees, in which he concentrated both on details of moss and on the play of light on a tree trunk. He recently began working on a series on forest fires.

JAMES, DINAH CROSS (Painter)
40 Santa Maria, Portola Valley, CA 94025

Born: 1942 Awards: Best of Show, Humboldt State U. Collections: Seattle Art Museum; Arizona State U. Exhibitions: Pro Arts, Oakland; Haggin Museum, Stockton Education: Mills College Dealer: Miller Brown, San Francisco

Visits to volcano craters, and white-water rafting trips down some of the West's wildest rivers inspired the dramatic, moving images of her early work. She used various pouring techniques with unprimed canvas, and acrylic and pastels stains on heavy papers. Since the early 1980s, her imagery has changed as a result of several trips to the Incan ruins of Peru and the Mayan cities of the Yucatan. Her work, now in richly colored oils, is more figurative, with abstracted bone forms, and images from Mayan and Incan art and rituals. These paintings address the spiritual aspects of the earth's cycles of change.

JAMES, ELMO (Painter, Sculptor)
P.O. Box 1467, Valley Center, CA 92082

Born: 1927 Collections: Smithsonian Institution, Washington, D.C. Exhibitions: Norfolk Museum, Norfolk, VA; Cunningham Art Gallery, Bakersfield Education: U. of Mexico; Art Center College of Design

Always a colorist, he created expressionist oil paintings during the 1960s and 1970s. In the 1980s, influenced by the work of Helen Frankenthaler, Franz Kline, Robert Motherwell and others, he began to paint abstractions. In these works, he expresses a great energy and freedom. He applies his acrylic paints lightly and boldly in brilliant color configurations. The sweeping forms of his large canvases emphasize color relationships. He is also a sculptor. His cast bronze figurative sculptures are personal expressions and interpretations of mythological and imaginary themes. He recently used the lost wax process to cast a bronze of the Minotaur.

JAMES, LILLIE (Painter)
1122-A Alakea St., Honolulu, HI 96813

Born: 1952 Awards: Bank of America Achievement Award Collections: Hemmeter Development Corp.; Hilton Hotels Exhibitions: Expo '86, Vancouver, Canada; Marc Glen, Honolulu Education: Alameda College; Fashion Institute of Design, Los Angeles Dealer: Marc Glen, Honolulu

After ten years as an assistant to mural painters in Hawaii and California, she has established herself as a mural painter in Honolulu. Size and color are her primary concerns. She achieves a mood or sense of time by building up layers of oil paint. In her recent oil-on-plexiglas murals, she used brilliant colors reminiscent of Gauguin and created images of Hawaiian people. She also does large (20-by-8-foot) oil-on-canvas landscapes of Hawaii's mountains and California's deserts. She is familiar with costume and fashion design, and her other media include watercolor, ceramics and clay sculpture. She also paints portraits and Southwestern scenes.

JAMESON, PHILIP A. (Ceramist)
c/o Art Dept., Sonoma State U., Rohnert Park, CA 94928

Born: 1952 Awards: Purchase Award, Permanent Collection, Oregon State U.; Direct Purchase, Art in Public Places, State of Washington Collections: State

Barbara Janusz, *Elegant Egrets,* 40 x 60, watercolor. Courtesy: Ron Vandale

Morgan Johnson, *Instrumental,* 24 x 36, oil. Courtesy: Jeff Williams

of Washington *Exhibitions:* Napa College; Sculpture Garden, Palo Alto Cultural Center *Education:* Oregon State U.; Syracuse U.

His slip-cast and hand-built ceramic wall reliefs, measuring 35 by 25 by 6 inches and weighing approximately 75 pounds, are fired and then painted in acrylics using a full palette. He occasionally adds to the pieces, which depict some mutated human or other life form, in order to build up the relief; a pronounced spinal cord is often a central image. Influenced by Max Beckman's *Departure*, his work depicts "people" whose ironic half-smiles seems to mock their distorted form. Many pieces focus on the interaction or encroachment of people upon their environment. This interest has led to two recent pieces, *Nuclear Fetus* and *Nuclear Carnival*, inspired by an incident wherein an inhabitant of an island used for test-bombing later gave birth to malformed children called "jelly babies."

JANOWSKI, KARYN ANN (Painter)
1308 Hayes St., San Francisco, CA 94117

Born: 1958 *Collections:* Tralfamadore Co-op *Exhibitions:* Das Club, San Francisco; Wisconsin Center, Madison *Education:* U. of Wisconsin *Dealer:* San Francisco Women Artists Gallery

She calls upon a wealth of inspiration—from the painters of the Renaissance as well as the Warhol, from the music of Bach and Brahms, and from the theater of Strindberg—to create her portraiture. Under the direction of muralist Caryl Yasko, she produced preliminary drawings and undertook the surface preparation and painting of the Whitewater Historical Mural in Whitewater, Wisconsin. She has assisted in art therapy seminars and coordinated a warehouse studio for visual artists and musicians. Her free-lance illustration work includes a set entitled "Isak Dinesen Illuminations." Skilled in design and layout, she has produced large-format billboard design as well as handbills advertising layouts.

JANUSZ, BARBARA (Painter)
1856 Bellflower Blvd., Long Beach, CA 90815

Born: 1944 *Awards:* Ruth Elliott Award, Women Painters of the West *Collections:* Universal Studios, Los Angeles; Pacific Design Center, Los Angeles *Exhibitions:* Brea Cultural Center; Art-A-Fair, Laguna Beach *Education:* Cal. State-Long Beach

Transparent glazes of watercolor are applied to create a radiance within the painting. Color is often selected on an emotional basis, which evokes a spontaneous reaction in the development of the painting. Her paintings are enriched by association with the sensitivity and style of Robert E. Wood's approach to painting, the dynamic aspects of Rex Brandt's work and the philosophy and depth of Millard Sheets. She gives demonstrations for various organizations and teaches watercolor workshops. Her paintings can be found in private and corporate collections throughout the U.S. and in Paris.

JENKINS, JIM (Sculptor)
500 S. Raymond Ave., Pasadena, CA 91105

Born: 1955 *Exhibitions:* Museum of Neon Art, Los Angeles; Roark Gallery, Los Angeles *Education:* Syracuse U. *Dealer:* Koslow Gallery, Los Angeles

Childhood fascination with both art and inventors crystallized into his kinetic sculptures. They feature a variety of materials, are usually assembled on a large scale and are always set into motion via motors. One such work, *Dena*, is the recreation of a full-size living room in which all of the furnishings move. Recent pieces explore two themes: the television set as cultural icon and the use of figures in seemingly abstract situations that come uncomfortably close to reality. *As the World Turns* exemplifies the first theme: a television set, an easy chair and a remote control channel-changer mimic the orbits of the sun, moon and earth ten feet in the air.

JENKINS, JUDI (Painter)
13140 Lincoln Ave., San Martin, CA 95046

Born: 1946 *Awards:* 3rd Place, Graphics, Santa Clara County Fair; 1st Place in Watercolors, Gilroy Cultural Commission Museum Show *Exhibitions:* Gilroy Museum; A.I.F.S. Center, London *Education:* Gauilan College; San Francisco Art Institute

Among her influences are Andrew Wyeth, Kandinsky and John Porter, her professor at Gauilan College. She paints in watercolors and uses bold colors and reflections to focus the viewer's eye on a central figure. Once focused, the viewer begins to discover the different elements in the painting. She has recently been fascinated with Picasso, and she is now working on color and reflection in the manner of Kandinsky.

JENNINGS, MARILYN A. (Ceramist, Sculptor)
4065 Via Ventura, Red Bluff, CA 96080

Born: 1949 *Awards:* 2nd Place, Ceramics, Redding Art Museum *Exhibitions:* Creative Arts Center, Chico; Tehama County Arts Council, Red Bluff *Education:* Memphis Academy of Arts; Cal. State-Chico

She began working in clay in the mid-1970s and moved into ceramic sculpture a few years later. Sculptors Robert Arneson and Patti Warashina and painter Georgia O'Keeffe have influenced her artistic approach. Her pieces are based on Western landscapes, rocks, rolling hills, ocean cliffs, plants and soft, natural colors. She works with the ideas of Japanese Tsutsumi, or wrapped packages. She uses ceramic, handmade paper and threads, wire and selected natural found objects to explore the Japanese concepts of gift-giving, serenity and the beauty of nature.

JENSEN, CLAY (Sculptor)
951 62nd St., Oakland, CA 94618

Born: 1952 *Awards:* SECA Award, San Francisco Museum of Modern Art; Eisner Award, U. of California, Berkeley *Collections:* Federal Reserve Bank, San Francisco; Security Pacific Bank, Los Angeles *Exhibitions:* San Francisco Museum of Modern Art; Oakland Museum *Education:* U. of Utah; UC-Berkeley *Dealer:* Fuller Gross Gallery, San Francisco

Born in Salt Lake City, he expressed his appreciation of the open spaces of the West in his early sculpture. These works primarily used natural materials, such as wood. When he moved to Oakland in 1977, he was struck by the contrast between the natural and the urban environments, and his sculpture reflected this awareness. He juxtaposed bronze casts of tree limbs with I-beams, using dark metals. Later, he used cut and welded steel plates and beams and cast bronze to suggest the abstract patterns of freeways, alleys and warehouses, combining sculptural and painterly concerns in these works. He applies oil paints to the sculpture, and also marks the works with graffiti and mechanically embossed patterns. The work of late has become more literal and symbolic of a larger idea of the urban environment and cultural challenges.

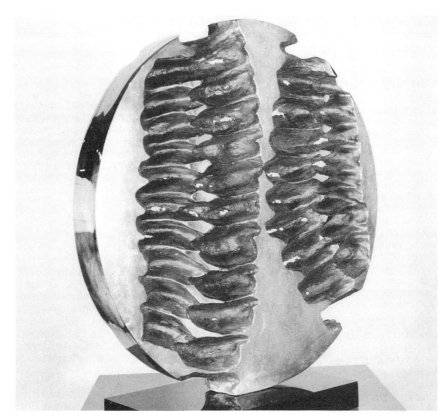

Jimé, *Green Moon,* 30" high, bronze. Courtesy: Louise Matzke Runnings Gallery

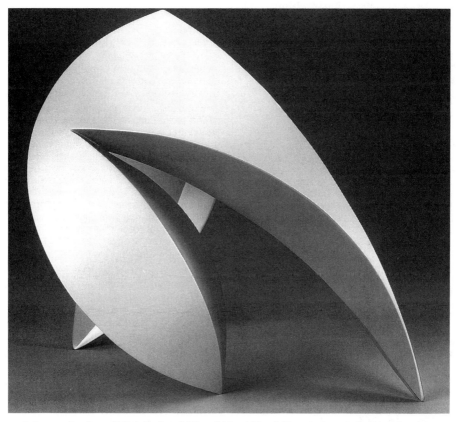

Johanna Jordan, *#184–Red and Blue,* 312 x 180 x 264, polychromed sheet aluminum

JENSEN, ROBERT W. (Painter)
8802 Ashcroft Ave., Los Angeles, CA 90048

Born: 1929 *Awards:* Arts for the Parks, Pacifica Award *Collections:* Copley Library, White House Archives *Exhibitions:* Bower Museum, Santa Ana; U.S. International U., San Diego *Dealer:* Galerie Marumo, Paris & Los Angeles

His paintings have a fast, un-selfconscious, done-on-the-spot appearance, but they are actually meticulously worked-out landscapes, still lifes and portraits that capture beautiful moments in time. He paints with watercolor on paper or acrylic on canvas, often with a bright palette. He is also an avid printmaker, working silk screens, etchings and wood blocks. He has recently been preparing an exhibition chronicling his visit to China. The exhibit comprises paintings and original prints, including an experimental process involving the computer, which he calls "laser prints." He describes himself as a "contemporary American artist with root in the soil provided by the Impressionists and Nabis."

JENSEN, ROCKY K. (Sculptor)
99-919 Kalawina Place, Aiea Heights, HI 96701

Born: 1944 *Awards:* Purchase Award, State Foundation of Culture and the Arts; Congressional Award for Excellence in Hawaiian Art *Collections:* Office of Hawaiian Affairs; Kamehameha Schools, Honolulu *Exhibitions:* Crafts and Folk Art Museum, Los Angeles; California Academy of Sciences, San Francisco

He is known as an expert modern practitioner of traditional Hawaiian wood sculpting and as an advisor in Polynesian art. He sculpts massive faces, figures and masks, some standing twelve feet tall. Carved in Norfolk pine, Brazilian walnut, teak or other native woods, the faces are highly abstracted and composed of smooth planes. They occasionally are decorated with mother-of-pearl inlays, but usually they are plain. Themes include traditional Hawaiian folk tales and characters. Recently, he has been working on a series of large, three-dimensional mixed-media pieces representing Hawaiian gods. The works are executed in wood, plaster and fibers. He is the founder and director of Hale Naua III, Society of Hawaiian Arts.

JERGER, LIEVE A. (Lace Artist)
1840 S. Gaffey St., San Pedro, CA 90731

Born: 1950 *Awards:* Delores Roche Prize of Excellence in Bobbin Lace, International Old Lacer's Guild *Exhibitions:* Pacific Design Center, Los Angeles; Angels Gate Cultural Center, San Pedro *Education:* U. of Antwerp, Belgium

A lace artist of the third generation, she was taught bobbin lace by her mother. In 1976, she began to apply the basic work methods of lace to copper wire. At the same time, she began her life's work: a full-size ceremonial carriage of copper lace: a sculpture of nothing but copper lace. Each of the carriage's eight windows contains a reflected image; each window is a reflection of her own development as a lace artist. She has maintained the traditional tools and techniques of bobbin lace, but by winding her bobbins with wire, she has been able to create three-dimensional, transparent reflective lace objects such as masks, body ornaments, abstracts, kinetic sculptures and the carriage.

JERNBERG, KATHERINE A. (Painter)
3684 Boyer Circle, Lafayette, CA 94549

Born: 1948 *Exhibitions:* Marin County Civic Art Center; Master of Fine Arts Exhibition, Mills College Art Gallery, Oakland *Education:* Mills College *Dealer:* Gump's Gallery, San Francisco; Gallery 30, San Mateo

In the 1960s and 1970s, she was influenced primarily by abstract expressionism and color-field theory. With the addition of some hard-edged elements, her work displayed a balance of unconscious and objective references. An interest in forms and relationships based on natural phenomena developed at this time and continues to this day. After fifteen years of working in acrylics, she returned to oils and began developing more complex uses of color. She seeks in her work to express the difficulty of reconciling the mundane aspects of life with a universal transcendent reality.

JEWELL, HELEN (Painter)
6953 Amberwick Way, Citrus Heights, CA 95621

Born: 1928 *Awards:* 2nd Place, WC California Memorial Show; Honorable Mention, California Open Show *Exhibitions:* Roseville Art Center; Worley-Smith Gallery, Nevada City *Dealer:* Worley-Smith Gallery, Nevada City; The Aesthetics Collection, San Diego

She is largely self taught. After studying with Denna Pro and Gary Pruner, she concentrated on oil landscapes in a realist style. The contrast of light and dark and the effect of color has always interested her. She finds kindred spirits in Georgia O'Keeffe and the early Renaissance painters, like Leonardo da Vinci, who perfected the art of chiaroscuro. Study with Patricia Abraham has left her working exclusively in watercolor, doing large florals in natural settings. Creating flowers larger than life, using color variations to create contrasting areas of light and shadow, she creates drama in a simple floral.

JIMINEZ, JOSE ANTONIO (Sculptor)
619 9th Ave., S. #101, Kirkland, WA

Born: 1938 *Collections:* Xerox Building, Caracas, Venezuela; Pampero Building, Caracas, Venezuela *Exhibitions:* Avanti Galleries, NYC and Rome; SMI/3 Gallery, Rome *Dealer:* Ignacio Jiminez, Kirkland, WA

A Venezuelan born in Spain, he learned foundry and patina techniques at the Lemos Foundry in Caracas. He creates amorphous, rock-like forms from bronze, wood, stone, steel and aluminum. In his pieces, he contrasts smooth and rough surfaces, and his works seem to have been eaten away by a fiery molten lava that is still pouring down its sides. Some have rough sections that seem to have been created by explosions in the metal. "I often give my sculptures names like *Black Hole* and *Internal Sun Explosion*, thus paying homage to that force that masters my brain and feeds it ideas like the strongest drug," he says.

JOHN, YVONNE MAREE (Painter)
10030 Lookout Dr. N.W., Olympia, WA 98502

Born: 1944 *Awards:* Cash and Certificate Awards, Sydney Newspapers *Exhibitions:* Royal Museum of Sydney, Australia; Ventura County Courthouse *Education:* UC-Santa Barbara; Buenaventura College

She was an accomplished landscape artist at a very early age—her work was accepted by the Royal Museum of Sydney in her native Australia when she was only ten. Her early works were influenced by her mother, who was a watercolorist, and by innate representational tendencies. Initial experiments with bluing on board proved overly perishable, and subsequent works were executed in conventional media, including pen and ink. Subject material was plentiful in the Australian landscape. She has worked extensively as a

Stephen Johns, *White Grey Black,* 72 x 72, triptych, oil on canvas

Chris M. Johnston, *Breaking Free,* 12", clay and steel

cosmetologist, and has published numerous short stories and poems. Present works attempt to evoke the spirit of her childhood artistic drives while depicting scenes of the American Northwest. Distinctive subject material includes illusionistic natural phenomena, such as plants that resemble insects, as well as conventional vistas. She is not a prolific artist; her works rely on observation and natural curiosities for their appeal.

JOHNS, STEPHEN (Painter, Printmaker)
P.O. Box 5872, Santa Monica, CA 90405

Born: 1948 *Awards:* Chamber of Commerce, Westwood *Collections:* Hyatt Regency Hotel, New Orleans; Security Pacific Bank, Los Angeles *Exhibitions:* Municipal Art Gallery, Barnsdall Park, Los Angeles *Education:* Chouinard Art Institute; California Institute of the Arts *Dealer:* Tamara Thomas, Fine Art Services, Los Angeles

Over a period of twenty years, his work has evolved from a minimal, geometric study of color gradation on canvas to a more introspective, minimal study of pure geometry, linear composition and textural relief. These abstract pieces are all defined by his application of black, white, gray, primary and secondary colors. His work continues the minimal op-art of Joseph Albers' geometry, the integrated curves and color of Frank Stella and the color spectrum of Victor Vasarely. Strength and simplicity are his aims; he uses optical illusion and raw primary colors to attract the viewer. His media are hard-edge and brushed-on acrylics, on a variety of large, shaped stretched canvases.

JOHNSON, ARDEN (Commercial Illustrator)
1332 Shattuck Ave., Apt. 11, Berkeley, CA 94709

Born: 1953 *Exhibitions:* Art Co-Op Gallery, Berkeley; The Cabaret Gallery, Seattle, WA *Education:* California College of Arts and Crafts; San Francisco Art Institute

Impressionist masters Renoir and Monet were her early influences, in light of her formal studies in impressionism. She traveled in Europe, spending time in Spain and Greece; she found source and inspiration for her work in those experiences. Investing ordinary objects and persons with provocative gestures, she produces pastel drawings with an electric intensity. A sensitive use of pastels, in combination with black backgrounds, gives these images of people and countryside a particular potency, a barrage of color reaching out to engage the viewer.

JOHNSON, D'ELAINE A. HERARD (Painter)
16122 72nd Ave. W., Edmonds, WA 98020

Born: 1932 *Awards:* Honorable Mention, 30th Annual Puget Sound Area Exhibition; Purchase Award, Nova Scotia Art Museum *Collections:* Maritime Museum, Vancouver; Seattle Art Museum *Exhibitions:* Park's Gallery, San Francisco; Centennial Art Gallery, Halifax, Nova Scotia *Education:* Central Washington State U.; U. of Washington

Her art has always been inspired by the mysteries of the sea. Early work showed cellular structures built in layers of transparent color. In the 1960s, she produced poetic interpretations of birds, sea creatures, tidelands, sea-beds, currents, reefs, islands storms and artifacts in the sea environment. During this period, she developed a "self-evolved" water-based medium for expressing liquid space—comprising transparencies, shimmering light, flotations, luminosity, a subtle color spectrum and the feeling of a silent world in a slow-motion ballet. Her point of view has shifted of late to sea cultures of the past in composites depicting ancient religions, legends and myths. Marine icons are enlivened through her documentation of the ancient mythological concepts from which they arose.

JOHNSON, DOLLY (Painter)
16177 Skyline Blvd., Los Gatos, CA 95030

Born: 1949 *Awards:* Honorable Mention, Women's Graphics Competition, Santa Clara *Collections:* California Microwave, Inc., Sunnyvale; National Semiconductor, Inc., Sunnyvale *Exhibitions:* Triton Museum of Art, Santa Clara; Congress Springs Vineyards, Saratoga *Education:* Academy of Art College; Stanford U. *Dealers:* Banaker Gallery, Walnut Creek; Aesthetics Collection, San Diego

She is best known for her abstract landscapes created with her own multimedia technique. Each piece begins with a loose application of watercolor on paper. Next, acrylic paint is airbrushed onto the surface to soften, brighten and seal the watercolor layer. She uses Prismacolor, Verithin pencils and soft pastels to accentuate and blend the colors; metallic paints are often added for extra emphasis. Although these compositions are planned in advance, her response to the media and textures is spontaneous, and the techniques themselves are almost synergistic in nature, each element building upon the other to make each completed piece a unique statement. Her early work in monoprints was influenced by the work of Giacometti, Pollock and de Kooning. Her recent paintings are often compared to those of Georgia O'Keeffe. She is also creating a series of multimedia non-objective "Atmospheres," as well as non-objective monoprints.

JOHNSON, DORIS MILLER (Painter, Draughtsperson)
329 Hampton Rd., Piedmont, CA 94611

Born: 1909 *Awards:* Artist Fund Prize, San Francisco Art Association *Collections:* Piedmont Art Department; *Exhibitions:* San Francisco Museum of Art; Lucien Labaudt Show *Education:* California College of Arts and Crafts; UC-Berkeley

At the University of California, she studied under John Haley, Glenn Wessels, Worth Ryder and Hans Hoffman. Early on, she was considered a member of the "Berkeley School" and her work was sometimes compared with that of Raoul Dufy. She draws her partially detailed ghost towns, street scenes and Victorian houses in a linear style. She then washes the canvas with color in an irregular fashion, using the colors more for their emotional content than for their representational properties. The work is rich in incident and detail and her media include acrylics, oils, gouache, watercolors, ink crayons and pencil. Since the 1960s, she has traveled extensively, painting foreign landscapes and city subjects. She was the founding director of the Art League of the East Bay Saturday Morning Art Classes for Children at the Oakland Art Museum, 1939-1952, and served as president of the San Francisco Women Artists from 1946-1948.

JOHNSON, ERNEST N. (Painter)
3511 W. 115th St., Inglewood, CA 90303

Born: 1941 *Collections:* Los Angeles County Museum of Art *Exhibitions:* Brockman Gallery, Los Angeles; Gallery Plus, Los Angeles *Education:* Cal. State-Carson *Dealer:* Aesthetic Images, Inglewood

Doris Miller Johnson, *Leo the Lion,* 10 x 13, ink on paper

Grant Johnson, *Cube*[3], 40 x 16, mixed media. Courtesy: Mr. and Mrs. Edward Tomoda

Impressionist painters were a strong influence. He prefers to paint the human form and face because of the strong communicative aspects he derives from their simple gestures and facial expressions. He does not consider himself a portrait artist. His use of color is bold. After drying has taken place, he layers color upon color. His recent works are spiritually inspired and religiously motivated. He has moved away from portraits and has attempted to depict more of the intangible world. In one painting, inspired by the Book of Revelations, he depicts an opposing sun and moon over a biblical landscape.

JOHNSON, FRANCIS (Painter)
1124 N. Signal, Ojai, CA 93023

Born: 1924 *Awards:* 1st Prize, California State Fair; 1st Prize, National Watercolor Society *Collections:* Hallmark Fine Arts Collection; Santa Barbara City College *Exhibitions:* Santa Barbara Museum of Art; New Media Gallery, Ventura College *Education:* Cal. State-Chico *Dealer:* Artist and the Outlaw, Ojai

Believing that impressions are what one carries inside oneself from day to day, she has been influenced by Matisse's abstract way of expressing a subject's emotions. In her abstract impressionist paintings, she records her impressions of the relationships of people close to her. In her early work, she used pastel. She soon discovered the strength and power of its pure pigment and began using it almost exclusively. Using her hands or a shammy, she applies the pastels on a slightly textured matte board 32 by 40 inches or 40 by 60 inches. Her palette includes all colors although her shades are often light. She has recently been working on a series entitled "Impressions of People Who Are Close to Me."

JOHNSON, GRANT (Photographer, Video Artist)
P.O. Box 11621, San Francisco, CA 94101

Born: 1949 *Awards:* Western States Regional Arts Fellowship; Award of Excellence, Video Graphics, Broadcast Designers Association, NYC *Collections:* SIGGRAPH/Computer Museum, San Francisco *Exhibitions:* Mill Valley Film Festival; Cory Gallery, San Francisco *Education:* U. of Arizona; Rhode Island School of Design *Dealer:* Stimulus, San Francisco

Toward the end of his formal training in two- and three-dimensional media, he became interested in the fourth dimension as a design element. Video seemed to be the ideal medium with which to incorporate time into his work. He created a form of electronic painting which he called STIMULUS 1-5. By orchestrating visual and aural information over time, he hoped to suggest impressions to the viewer, while leaving the work subjective enough to lead the viewer to the conclusions he intended. His recent work is almost exclusively landscape-oriented, both in video (using single and multiple monitor works, designed for the large, flat wallscreen) and in photography (using aerial photographs of the earth, presented as large Cibachrome prints). He has stopped using the imaging computer for the time being, so that he can be more directly involved in the image-making process. By synthesizing traditional landscape art with modern electronic media, he has produced familiar works, which explore light, composition and color, while adding a new visual perspective and the elements of sound and time. He cites the expressive nature of Pollock, the precision and control of Seurat and the totality of Claude Monet as the primary influences on his work.

JOHNSON, JAY S. (Sculptor)
P.O. Box 12437, San Diego, CA 92112

Born: 1954 *Collections:* Federal Reserve Bank, Los Angeles *Exhibitions:* Phoenix Museum; Thomas Babeor Gallery, La Jolla *Dealer:* Thomas Babeor, La Jolla

His wall-mounted works have been called both painted sculpture and sculptured painting. He creates a tension between two-dimensional painting and three-dimensional surface. His earlier pieces are abstract, and characterized by organic shapes and a limited palette. He has been influenced both by constructivism and by a familiarity with African masks. Recent work has more often been figurative, though in a limited sense. The shape of *Head* creates a human silhouette when placed against a blank, white wall. He has recently created a series of small, unpainted, copper and wood wall pieces.

JOHNSON, JOANNE (Painter)
5984 Willowynd Rd., Rocklin, CA 95677

Born: 1937 *Awards:* Best of Show, Paradise Art Show *Exhibitions:* Signature Gallery, Chico; Bear Flag Gallery, San Juan Bautista

After some formal training, she painted portraits of children and Southwest Indians. After discovering the work of Vermeer, she changed her approach to color and edge: each became softer. During this period, her approach to composition was modeled on that of Wyeth. Then, instead of people, she began to paint wildlife scenes, with unfamiliar settings. Working from a photograph, she does the basic sketch in acrylic on a linen canvas; she blocks in her subject with oils. She completes the background and foreground next; she finishes the work by returning to the subject to add the details that give the painting a photographic realism.

JOHNSON, JUSTINE (Fabric Artist)
2148 Orchard St., Santa Rosa, CA 95404

Born: 1960 *Collections:* Saachi & Saachi Advertising, Taiwan *Exhibitions:* San Francisco Fashion Industry *Education:* San Francisco State U.

She began her career as a costume designer, working with textile dyes to distress the costumes. After school, she was apprenticed to Japanese textile designer Hiroshi Hashido, who taught her the various skills—Japanese yuzen, wax resist and shabori dyeing—on which she has based her subsequent work. She also began painting on finer fabrics like silk organza, and using many colors of dye to achieve different effects. While living in Hong Kong, she developed her own technique of folding the fabrics to create new meanings. She has recently been working on larger paintings, weaving the blocks of folded fabric into each other to create more ideas.

JOHNSON, LEITH (Painter, Printmaker)
810 E. 3rd St., #5, Los Angeles, CA 90013

Born: 1941 *Collections:* Home Savings of America, Long Beach; Union Federal Savings, Long Beach *Exhibitions:* Rental and Sales Gallery, Los Angeles County Museum of Art; Biada Art Gallery, Mount St. Mary's College, Los Angeles *Education:* Millikin U.; U. of Chicago

Influenced by California environmental painters Richard Diebenkorn, David Parks and Ron Davis, the

Geir Jordahl, *Sherman Pass, California,* 8 x 20, silver gelatin print

Dolly Johnson, *Vantage Point II,* 29 x 41, watercolor, acrylic, airbrush, colored pencil, pastel

artist has created a body of work on paper, canvas and wood panels. evocative of the richness and layered qualities of both rural and urban landscapes. Early paintings are an exploration of natural forms, magnified and rendered with layers of transparent color to reveal the organic characteristics of the image. Recent work, which is considered neo-constructivist, reflects the relocation to industrial Los Angeles and a new interest in architectural line and forms.

JOHNSON, MORGAN BURTON (Painter)
938 Hotel Ave., Hayward, CA 94541

Born: 1952 *Awards:* Honorable Mention, Dogwood Arts Festival, Knoxville, TN; 3rd Prize, Downey Art Museum *Collections:* Department of Neurology, UC-San Francisco *Exhibitions:* Erikson Gallery, Half Moon Bay; Fall National, Bakersfield *Education:* Dijon U., France; UC-San Diego; Southern Oregon State College

Although he received no formal art education, his work is refined and varied, including techniques in oil on canvas, linen, glass, cardboard, wood, watercolor and water media, palette knife, collage and encaustic painting. His styles range from classic realism, pointillism and fauvism to abstract expressionism and minimalism. His work in pointillism predates the recent resurgence of its popularity. His recent work involves the combination of pointillism and poetry: a representation of the poetic moment, common to human beings in shared experiences. He has also created a three-volume book, which integrates paintings, poetry and a narrative.

JOHNSON, SHAWNEE B. (Painter)
1310 S. Oak, Calistoga, CA 94515

Born: 1950 *Exhibitions:* Calistoga Book Store; Washington Square Gallery, Yountville *Education:* California Institute of the Arts, Valencia

She is a Native American who has been influenced by O'Keeffe, Warhol and Matisse. She began her career in the early 1970s, working with Judy Chicago and Miriam Schapiro on *Womanhouse*, films, environments and other projects. Through the mid- and late 1970s, she experimented with such media as fabric and glass. Her present work expresses the beauties of nature and the human spirit. She photocopies American and animal images on watercolor paper and colors them with watercolor, gouache, paste and colored pencil. Repetition of images is an important element, and the work is often humorous in its juxtaposition of unlikely images, such as elephants, flamingos and fish.

JOHNSON, STAN F. (Painter)
355 N. Bowling Green Way, Los Angeles, CA 90049

Born: 1907 *Awards:* 1st Prize, California State Fair; Best in Show Award, Westwood Center of the Arts *Exhibitions:* 26th Street Gallery, Brentwood *Dealers:* Mildred Symster Gallery, Newport Beach; Tobey Moss Gallery, Los Angeles

The positive work ethics that guide his painting, sustained him through the pursuit of such diverse occupations as architect, film draftsman, actor, film art director and illustrator. His oil, acrylic and watercolor pieces are strongly influenced by these past experiences. Components of architecture reside in the abstract forms that populate the canvas. His eye for composition and framing was sharpened during his employment as an art director for 20th Century Fox. The artist tries to begin each piece free of any preconceived

ideas. He allows the abstract shapes and random colors to dictate the subject. Lauding the wisdom of the spontaneous subconscious, he maintains that the "perfect painting" would be one in which each viewer perceives a different image. He is a member of the National Watercolor Society, Watercolor West, Watercolor U.S.A. Honor Society and L.A. Art Association.

JOHNSON, TED (Mixed Media Artist)
P.O. Box 1585, San Leandro, CA 91477

Born: 1954 *Collections:* Robert Zucjiaw; Carrie London *Exhibitions:* Southern Exposure Gallery, San Francisco; Drum World, San Francisco *Education:* Mills College; San Francisco State U.

His formal training was in music, dance, theater and art history. He is working toward the visual presentation of his solo percussion compositions by projecting his scores in conjunction with the hanging of his art works. Viewers are given Sony Walkmans and cassettes of his percussion music, to which they listen while walking through a display of his art works and music equipment. He also does mixed media-works with acrylic, paper collage and photography. His recent work is exclusively in metal, which has been the impetus for him to complete a series entitled "Turkish Explosion," as well as to create both abstract and representational works. He has also developed a series of jewelry pieces using metals.

JOHNSTON, ANDREW (Pastel Artist)
2335 Friendly St., Eugene, OR 97405

Born: 1939 *Awards:* Annual Sun River Juried Show, Bend, OR *Collections:* Kidder, Peabody & Co., Seattle; Rainier National Bank, Seattle *Exhibitions:* Oregon Biennial, Portland; Art Expo, Seattle *Education:* U. of Oregon *Dealer:* Pamela Powers, Seattle; Candy Moffet, Eugene, OR

In 1978, he began a transition from abstract expressionism to landscape using pastel as the principal medium. His emphasis has since shifted toward a more color-oriented and simplified compositional approach emphasizing the Western landscape. He has recently been focusing on color composition as opposed to naturalistic color. By simplifying form, he creates a more stylized look with saturated color-shape combinations. A work entitled *Ranch At the Edge of the Desert* is very open in composition. Pastel is used in a painterly way, with veils of transparent color built up in basic shapes. Big landscape surfaces such as mesas and ridges are juxtaposed with buildings rendered small against the vastness of their surroundings.

JOHNSTON, CHRIS (Ceramist)
18294 Avenue B, North Edwards, CA 93523

Born: 1948 *Awards:* Certificate of Recognition, Antelope Valley Arts Council *Collections:* Boron Museum *Exhibitions:* Desert West Juried Art Show, Lancaster; Mendocino Art Center *Education:* Mendocino Art Center *Dealer:* Art Source L.A.

His early pots were tight, functional and carefully crafted. Areas of clay were left unglazed or were glazed with wood or salt to produce random strokes of fire. Shapes were organic and classic, and bits of wood, fiber and artifacts were often embedded in the clay body. More recently he pierces, carves and applies items to the surface of his pots. The pieces incorporate the clays, volcanic ash, tumbleweed and metal objects found in the Mojave Desert where he lives. To allow

Stan Johnson, *Golden Odyssey,* 28 x 38, acrylic on paper board

Jo Boot Jones, *End of the Dance,* 22, glazed ceramic

Andrew Johnston, *Rainy Day Light,* 23 x 35, pastel

the texture of the clay to show through, he glazes his pots only lightly and burnishes the rims for a contrast to the streaks of metallic red in the body. Three tours of duty in Vietnam inspire his art, and he sometimes wraps his pots in barbed wire, in appearance like a crown of thorns.

JOHNSTON, YNEZ (Painter, Printmaker)
579 Crane Blvd., Los Angeles, CA 90065

Born: 1920 *Awards:* NEA Grant; Guggenheim Grant *Collections:* Museum of Modern Art, NYC; Metropolitan Museum of Art, NYC *Exhibitions:* San Francisco Museum of Art; Mitsukoshi Galleries, Tokyo *Education:* UC-Berkeley *Dealer:* Mekler Gallery, Los Angeles; Worthington Gallery, Chicago

Influenced by her travels in Mexico and Europe, her watercolors, oils and etchings of the 1950s and 1960s were rich with complex imagery and displayed a disciplined and somewhat restrained use of color. In recent mixed-media pieces she examines the tactile qualities of the surface. The paintings involve the combination and occasional lamination of diverse materials—oil, acrylic, dyes, encaustic on cloth, canvas and raw silk. The colors are vibrant and the images are composite forms suggesting ambiguous architectural, human, animal and plant shapes. Her influences include Persian and Indian art, as well as such artists as Matisse, Miro, Klee and Picasso.

JOHNSTONE, SANDRA (Ceramist)
101 Higgins Ave., Los Altos, CA 94022

Born: 1937 *Collections:* San Jose Museum of Art; Darling Doodins Institute, Queensland, Australia *Exhibitions:* Potter's Society of Australia; Prieto Gallery, Oakland *Education:* Scripps College; San Jose State U.

A trademark of her work is the single, large, thrown form, which is salt-fired. She feels that the clay exemplifies a kind of paradox—what was once soft, plastic and responsive is altered through the firing process to a hard, inexorable material; and she endeavors to maintain the initial fluidity of the process so that her vessels retain the softness and movement of life. Occasionally after being thrown, the pots are altered, lines are etched in and handles may be added. They are then salt-fired, a process that chemically changes the surface color of the clay by using slips and oxides rather than conventional glazes.

JONES, AMY (Painter, Sculptor)
412 N. Juniper St., Escondido, CA 92025

Born: 1899 *Awards:* Roger Collection Prize *Collections:* New Britain Museum of American Art, CT *Exhibitions:* National Gallery, Washington, D.C.; Art Institute of Chicago *Education:* Pratt Institute *Dealer:* Somerstown Gallery, NY; Katonah Gallery, Katonah, NY

As a young woman, she won a scholarship to the Pratt Institute, where she studied painting. When she left the Institute to marry, she began doing commercial work. At the same time, she began entering competitions and taking commissions to paint murals in post offices. Her images are realistically painted though they sometimes contain surrealistic juxtapositions. Her subjects are diverse. She has done portraits, dramatic scenes, busts and florals. In *Phantasmagoria*, she addressed the mystery of people dressed in Halloween costumes. She works in several media and has been a member of the American Watercolor Society for more than six decades.

JONES, DAVID (Painter, Sculptor)
71 Haight St., San Francisco, CA 94102

Born: 1948 *Awards:* NEA Grant *Collections:* San Francisco Museum of Modern Art; Oakland Museum *Exhibitions:* Whitney Museum, NYC; San Francisco Museum of Modern Art *Education:* UC-Berkeley *Dealer:* Braunstein/Quay, San Francisco

While at the University of California at Berkeley, he studied with Robert Hudson and James Melchert. From 1970 to 1973, he assisted Peter Voulkos in the building of bronze sculptures. Later in the 1970s, he became known as one of the leaders of the "new materials movement." Today he works in a variety of materials, including tinted rubber. He calls his recent works "calculated assemblies" rather than assemblages, since each element has been carefully sought out rather than "found." The idea is to transform the commonplace, and much of the impetus for his work comes from history, philosophy and mathematics. Among his recent works are *Aesthetics Waters Test* and *Sketch for the Aesthetics Waters Test*.

JONES, GEARY & JOHNSON, DAVID (Tapestry Weavers)
8245 S. W. Barnes Rd., Portland, OR 97225

Born: 1953 (Jones); (1956) Johnson *Awards:* Michigan Foundation for the Arts Award; Ford Foundation Grant (Jones); Scholarship, Banff Center; Michigan Council for the Arts (Johnson) *Exhibitions:* G.H. Dalsheimer Gallery, Baltimore, MD; UC-Riverside *Education:* U. of Michigan; Cranbrook Academy of Art (Jones); Colorado State U.; Cranbrook Academy of Art (Johnson)

Each of this pair of artists is an accomplished weaver in his own right. Jones's organic work features sovmak, a centuries-old Russian technique. Johnson's geometric work features hand-dyed wools. Their collaboration brings together Johnson's fascination with pre-Columbian textiles and Jones' expressionistic tendencies. Together, they create abstract, surrealistic landscapes using the full spectrum of color. One example of this is *Synergy*, in which a naturalistic depiction of a mountain range is surrealistically echoed throughout the work. Their collaboration is personally founded on trust and artistically fueled by the attraction of polar opposites.

JONES, JO BOOT (Painter, Sculptor)
P.O. Box 117, Coloma, CA 95613

Born: 1914 *Awards:* Merit Award, Placerville Art Show; 2nd Place, Clay and Sculpture, CASSP *Collections:* UC-Regents; Century Hotel, Los Angeles *Exhibitions:* Oakland Museum; Larkspur Landing Gallery, Marin *Education:* UC-Berkeley

A career in education and psychology separated her early interest in palette knife oil painting, from her work of the 1980s. In 1981, she began exhibiting figurative works, as well as brightly colored, impressionistic, *plein air* landscapes. Her sculptural forms have been influenced by Henry Moore, though her scale is considerably smaller. In the high gloss, blue glaze sculpture, *Midnight Dances*, two stylized dancers (one male, one female) seem to grow from an organic, flower-like form. In her recent paintings, she has employed a blue and green palette, evoking an elusive mystical quality. In *River Princess*, a large heroic look-

Diana Jacobs, *A Drift of Hogs,* 22 x 30, pen, ink and wash. Courtesy: Biota Gallery, Los Angeles

Margaret Kelley, *As An Apple Tree,* 84 x 48, acrylics on canvas

ing woman sits on a throne-like rock and dominates a non-realistic river.

JONES, PIRKLE (Photographer)
663 Lovell Ave., Mill Valley, CA 94941

Born: 1914 *Awards:* Photographic Excellence Award, National Urban League, NYC; NEA Photography Fellowship *Collections:* San Francisco Museum of Modern Art; Art Institute of Chicago *Exhibitions:* Museum of Modern Art, NYC; Focus Gallery, San Francisco *Education:* San Francisco Art Institute

He studied photography under Ansel Adams and Minor White and was influenced in addition by Dorothea Lange, Edward Weston and Alfred Stieglitz. A freelance photographer since 1949, he served as photographic assistant to Ansel Adams for three years. He works in both large and small formats, and is known for his landscapes, in particular those of the American Southwest depicting the beauty of beaches, indigenous vegetation and bodies of water. In contrast to these serene images, he was also involved in a photo-essay project entitled "A Photographic Essay on the Black Panthers" in the late 1960s, presenting a series of photographs on Black Panther gang leaders and their meetings.

JORDAHL, GEIR (Photographer)
P.O. Box 3998, Hayward, CA 94540

Born: 1957 *Awards:* Award of Excellence, California State Fair *Collections:* Museum for Photography, West Germany; Milliken Collection, Ohio State U. *Exhibitions:* Ansel Adams Gallery, Yosemite; Susan Spiritus Gallery, Costa Mesa *Education:* Ohio State U. *Dealer:* J.J. Brookings, San Jose

Influenced by the New Topographic photographers such as Lewis Baltz and Lee Friedlander, his early pictures were abstractions of the urban landscape. Finding his vision expanding wider than the conventional camera, he began working with a Widelux panoramic camera in 1984. He mixes a straight photographic aesthetic with a desire to capture luminescent landscapes filled with vibrant energy. His more natural settings echo traditional landscape photography and turn-of-the-century pictorialists, while remaining strikingly modern. He searches for the emotional landscape where human and natural subjects merge, then realizes these visions in finely printed black-and-white silver prints.

JORDAN, JOHANNA (Sculptor)
1415 6th St., Santa Monica, CA 90401

Born: 1919 *Awards:* International Art Competition; All California, Laguna Museum *Collections:* NEA; Los Angeles Arts and Science Center *Exhibitions:* Long Beach Museum of Art; Laguna Museum of Art *Education:* U. of The Arts, Philadelphia *Dealer:* Northern California, San Jose; Young Gallery, San Jose

Influenced by Rodin and Moore, she fabricates freestanding volumetric maquettes from sheets of aluminum, and enlarges them into stainless steel, corten and carbon steel. At first she worked in a realistic manner, but did not find personal satisfaction until she began to make geometric abstractions. When she found traditional methods too cumbersome, heavy and slow, she began working with sheet aluminum. She creates tension by opposing straight and curved lines. She contrasts bright and neutral colored panels in order to achieve a sleek, finely crafted surface, which she does by spray painting with automotive paints. The pieces appear to be completely different when viewed from one side or the other.

JOSLIN, JERRY (Sculptor)
6960 S.W. Raleighwood Ln., Portland, OR

Born: 1942 *Awards:* Gold Key, Scholastic Art Award, Portland *Collections:* City of Lake Oswego, OR; City of Wilsonville, OR *Exhibitions:* Americana Gallery, Carmel; Sterling Gallery, Ltd., La Jolla *Education:* Portland State U.

Believing that art is the communication of feelings, conscious and unconscious, his current technique explores design that gives meaning to negative space as contrasted with mass or, allegorically, the triumph of spirit over matter. He is a self-taught "recalcitrant romantic" who has been strongly influenced by Rodin, Michelangelo and Norman Rockwell. His sometimes fanciful, but always realistic, pieces often include human figures and wildlife. His early work included stone sculpture. He began bronze sculpture and casting in 1979. He recently completed an outdoor sculptural fountain for the Lake Oswego City Hall and recently began working on a series of figurative works depicting relationships that explore the human condition.

JOYCE, DAVID (Photographer)
990 Madison Street, Eugene, OR 97402

Born: 1946 *Awards:* Oregon Artists Fellowship; Best of Show Award, Maryhill Museum of Art *Exhibitions:* Triton Museum of Art, Santa Clara; Marcuse Pfeifer Gallery, NYC *Education:* U. of Oregon *Dealer:* Marcuse Pfeifer Gallery, NYC; Susan Spiritus Gallery, Newport Beach

Influenced by the work of George Segal and Duane Hanson, he is interested in the interplay of freestanding two-dimensional figures in three-dimensional space. He works with life-size photographic sculpture, printing photographic images on mural paper, mounting them on tempered hardboard and placing them in installations composed of found objects. *Cold Water Flat* features a life-size photograph of a man in a t-shirt and hat sitting before a television. Other elements in the installation include a newspaper at his feet, a battered formica table, a plate, a sink with accompanying cup and toothbrush and other familiar objects. He is concerned with exploring the visual possibilities that are unique to photography—in particular distortion, perspective and the ability to make images of motion that address time using photo-sculptural means.

JURIS, LOLA (Painter)
3200 Buena Hills Dr., Oceanside, CA 92056

Born: 1929 *Awards:* 1st Place Carlsbad/Oceanside Art League *Exhibitions:* International Exhibition, San Diego; La Jolla Fine Arts Gallery *Education:* Syracuse U. *Dealer:* A.R.T. Beasley, San Diego

Early works, created in New York and Boston, bespoke a European heritage and a strong academic background. Painted first in casein and later in acrylic, these introspective statements were done on masonite in muted tones. After a relocation to the West Coast, the work ripened into lush, lyrical watercolors with a floral theme. These large, organic expressions pay homage to Georgia O'Keeffe but are true to the California spirit in their brilliant color and use of natural, local forms. An enlarged microscopic view is a preferred image, but an emphasis on sensuality has

John Killmaster, *Nudes with Sunflowers,* 35 x 35, porcelain enamel fired on steel.
Courtesy: Boise State Gallery of Art

Erika Kahn, *Sash,* 28 x 29, handmade paper, mixed media. Photographer: Herb Dreiwitz

begun to tend towards the erotic. Earlier introspection is evident in the fascination with dark, negative space (the unseen reality), and the direct influence of nature has become more difficult to detect.

JUVE-HU, SUSAN (Painter)
1871 San Antonio Ave., Berkeley, CA 94707

Born: 1945 *Awards:* 1st Place, Livermore California Art Association *Exhibitions:* Humboldt Cultural Center, Eureka; Reese Bullen Gallery, Arcata *Education:* UC-Berkeley

Influenced by the work of William Allan, Jerrold Ballaine and California Realist painters in general, she blends exacting technique with more narrative, emotional subjects. By the mid-1970s, the imagery in her work was dominated by windows and their ability to symbolize the juxtaposition of the self to the other, the inner to the outer and architectural to natural forms. Recent works in watercolor, oil and monotype are replete with ominous and threatening imagery. The windows are increasingly dominated by antlers, branches, fire and water. Her colors have darkened and intensified considerably, parallel to the shift in imagery. The imagery itself continues to be rich in symbol and association. The watercolors, especially, are rendered in controlled multiple layerings with tight brushwork.

KADELL, KATHERINE (Painter, Sculptor)
1344 Londonderry Place, Los Angeles, CA 90069

Collections: Skirball Museum, Los Angeles; Youth Center, Jerusalem *Exhibitions:* Brand Art Galleries, Glendale; University of Judaism, Los Angeles *Education:* Otis Art Institute; UCLA

Born in Vienna, she came to the United States in 1939. Until 1977, she sculpted Henry Moore-influenced abstractions and human forms in bronze, marble, sandstone, terra cotta and experimental materials. In 1977, she began branching out into other media, working in series, and drawing an abstracted symbolism from recent personal experiences. Since 1980, she has created watercolor, collage and mixed-media, handmade-paper assemblages. The monoprints in her recent "Cubus" series were two- and three-dimensional poems in blacks, whites and grays. Among her watercolors, *Shoah* is a fiery, abstract testimonial to the holocaust.

KAHN, ERIKA (Painter, Printmaker)
632 Pacific St., Santa Monica, CA 90405

Born: 1925 *Collections:* Hawaii State Foundation of Culture and Art; Monterey Museum of Art *Exhibitions:* Honolulu Academy of Art; Los Angeles Museum of Science and Industry *Education:* Art Students League; Cal. State-Long Beach *Dealer:* Louis Newman Gallery, Beverly Hills

She considers herself a Pacific Rim artist. She employs an Oriental technique to depict Hawaii's foliage and landscapes. Her sumptuous palette is full of elegant, brilliant colors, which she plays off against delicate mauves and pale, grayed blues and pinks. Her varied media include dyes, paints and prints on handmade papers from China, Japan and Nepal, or on paper she makes herself. Her etchings involve clearly defined, perfectly fused colors. Her collages are paper pieces playfully torn, destroyed and rebuilt into forms that resemble silks, brocades and lace patterns. She works express one of two dominant moods—fragility or

strength. Most recently she has been working with compositions in pastel paper.

KAHN, NED (Installation Artist)
264 Downey St., San Francisco, CA 94117

Born: 1960 *Awards:* Artist-in-Residence, Headlands Center for the Arts, Sausalito *Exhibitions:* Headlands Center for the Arts, Sausalito; New Langton Arts, San Francisco *Education:* U. of Connecticut

He creates works that actively respond to their sites, often making visible an invisible force. As an apprentice to the late Frank Oppenheimer at the Exploratorium in San Francisco, he became interested in the artistic use of natural phenomena. Throughout the mid-1980s, he created over a dozen works dealing with phenomena such as soap-film formations, fluid motion and weather. Inspired by the work of Robert Irwin, James Turrell and Douglas Hollis, he began to work with natural phenomena in a variety of sites. Much of his work involved wind, fog and water. His projects include fog tornadoes in enclosed areas, a fog observatory (a parabolic dish filled with fog that responded to any change in the air currents) and a room in which the windows were fitted with 2000 wind-responsive flaps, revealing the invisible structure of wind in light patterns on the floor, ceiling and walls. Recent work includes the building of a sculpture that uses fine sand and a fan to create a constantly changing, wind-swept landscape.

KAIDA, TAMARRA (Photographer)
School of Art, Arizona State U., Tempe, AZ 85287

Born: 1946 *Awards:* Ferguson Awards, Friends of Photography; NEA Fellowship *Collections:* George Eastman House, Center for Creative Photography *Exhibitions:* Long Beach City College; Security Pacific National Banks *Education:* SUNY, Buffalo *Dealer:* Terry Etherton, Tucson, AZ

She is a photographer who is concerned with issues of personal and societal discovery. "Still Life as Social Landscape" was a series of highly realistic images influenced by 17th Century still life painters of the vanitas tradition and incorporated text and media references. In this work, she addressed social, political and cultural issues. Another series, "Tremors from the Fault Line," were large book pages (19 by 30 inches) composed of photographs and text. These fictional short stories comprise a collective portrait of life in the 1980s in the U.S. She is an associate professor of art at Arizona State University.

KAL, RYUNG (Painter)
49-D, Escondido Village, Stanford, CA 94305

Born: 1959 *Exhibitions:* Diego Rivera Gallery, San Francisco; Long Beach Art Association Gallery *Education:* San Francisco Art Institute; Hong Ik U., Seoul

He has had the opportunity to experience life in several distinct cultural environments: he was born in West Germany and studied in Seoul, Paris and San Francisco. The diversity of his cultural background has enabled the artist to develop a holistic view of mankind—that man is estranged from the natural world by civilization. The central focus of his work, therefore, is to express the emotions common to all people through exposition of nature, the human body and time and space. He hints at man's unnatural modern engagements through depiction of sharp edges of machine parts, among other images. His interest in Elizabeth Muppy's work on geometric canvas has led him to make use of similar geometric arrangements. Through use of such arrangements, he is able to depict both the immortality of nature and the hard edge of modern civilization.

KALISH, SHIRLEY (Printmaker)
4108 Valley Vista Ct., Sherman Oaks, CA 91403

Born: 1920 *Awards:* Honorable Mention, Long Beach Annual *Collections:* Michigan State U., East Lansing; Minot College, ND *Exhibitions:* Laguna Beach Museum of Art; Art Center of the Ojai Valley *Education:* Syracuse University; UCLA *Dealer:* Contemporary Images, Sherman Oaks

Working as an expressionist, she took, as her primary subject matter, the Southern California landscape and environment. Her themes later became more abstract, as she began interpreting Western and Southwestern landscapes in serigraphy. The outdoor work of ancient artists has recently inspired her to work with prehistoric and early historic images. The animals and symbols found in the etchings and drawings of early man are recreated with a contemporary frame of reference. Through these signs, her work and its audience is linked to a past grace, nobility and magic.

KALLAN, LINDA P. (Painter)
496 Cypress Dr., Laguna Beach, CA 92651

Born: 1955 *Collections:* Security Pacific National Bank, Los Angeles *Exhibitions:* Susan Cummings Gallery, Mill Valley; Laguna Art Museum *Education:* UC-Berkeley *Dealer:* Lee Musgrave, Merging One Gallery, Santa Monica

After studying figurative painting with Elmer Bischoff and Joan Brown, she began working abstractly. She soon became influenced by Lionel Finenzer and Richard Diebenkorn and began working with the effects of light on space. Her paintings from this period draw their emotional quality from her use of a window image, which creates an inside-outside effect. She now paints abstracted cityscapes using oil on masonite. Her buildings seem to burst through the ground, and her full use of color evokes the abstract concepts of the works. A recent emphasis on black an white shows in a more elemental manner the tensions between man-made structures and their natural settings.

KALMAN, KEN (Sculptor)
433A Buena Vista East, San Francisco, CA 94117

Born: 1955 *Awards:* Three-Dimensional Award, U. of New Mexico Teaching Gallery *Collections:* U.S. Embassy, Lima, Peru; Tiffany Corporation, San Francisco *Exhibitions:* Gallery West, Los Angeles; Ruth Volid Gallery, Chicago *Education:* Boston U.; U. of New Mexico *Dealer:* Gallery West, Los Angeles; Vorpal Gallery, San Francisco

He constructs large sculptures made of 4-by-4-foot timbers inlaid with 1/8-inch wooden dowels. The dowels are split in half and painted in complementary colors with specific color theories in mind. As the viewer moves around the piece, light, space and motion work in various ways to create optical interplays and illusions. These hard-edged and totemic sculptures range from 3 to 7 feet tall, and are built either as freestanding structures or as wall reliefs. The participatory aspect of the sculptures is important to him, since he believes that one important aspect of art is the relief it can provide to city dwellers bombarded by the dark, gray monotony of the urban environment.

KALTENBACH, STEVEN J. (Painter, Sculptor)
327 I St., Davis, CA 95616

Born: 1940 *Awards:* NEA Grant; Guggenheim Fellowship *Collections:* Allen Memorial Art Museum, Oberlin, OH *Exhibitions:* Idea Gallery, Sacramento; Biola U., La Mirada *Dealer:* Natsoulas & Novaloso, Davis *Education:* UC-Davis

After graduating from UC-Davis in 1967, he moved to New York City, where he joined a group of conceptual artists who created street works, non-objective art and "media manipulations." Returning to California in the 1970s, he immersed himself in visionary painting and performance. Since 1980, the work has been apocalyptic and has drawn on political and Christian concerns. The paintings are large—11 by 18 feet—and depict angels on black linen or black velvet, using airbrush with acrylic paint. The sculptures include marble and bronze figures, or clay painted to resemble marble.

KAMARCK, MARGARET (Printmaker)
118 Pine Ridge Rd., R.R. 1, Brewster, MA 02631

Born: 1917 *Awards:* Juror's Choice, Cape Cod Annual *Collections:* Cape Cod Museum of Fine Art *Exhibitions:* 271 Fine Arts, San Francisco; Perth, Australia *Education:* Corcoran School of Art; Boston Museum School of Art *Dealer:* San Francisco Museum of Modern Art, Rental Gallery; Creations of Cape Artists, Cape Cod, MA

While all printmaking media are appealing to her, she prefers to work with an etching press. Explorations in Japanese woodcutting techniques and sumi drawing are combined with the influence of Matisse in her recent monotypes. Her range of techniques includes chine colle, wiping and scratching into a background of rolled-on color with various tools, stenciling and spritzing. She tries to keep the prints as pure as possible by not working into them after printing. She also does pastel drawings.

KANE, CINDY (Painter)
1735 10th St., Berkeley, CA 94710

Born: 1957 *Collections:* Northern Illinois U.; Delaware Museum of Art *Exhibitions:* William Sawyer Gallery; Jeremy Stone Gallery, San Francisco

While working in Grand Canyon National Park, she became familiar with the Anasazi Indian ruins and the pictographic narration of their lives on canyon walls. Her early works were influenced by her memories of these hieroglyphs, and embellished with symbols from her dreams. The primitive images found in her art depict essential and universal events in the human community: procreation, survival, tribal communion, worship and ritual. Drawing from the tenets of Jungian psychology, she attempts to depict the universal archetypes which underlie all systems of art and narrative. Her paintings begin with a black background, into which she carves figures. Painting around them, she adds melted wax to enhance the impression of figures emerging from primordial forms. Hieroglyphs, characters and other shapes are scratched and chipped into the surface, contributing to the authentic, primeval feel her work exudes. She feels that chipping away at layers of wax, sand and paint is analogous to a peeling away of the many layers of the human psyche.

KANEMITSU, MATSUMI (Painter, Printmaker)

800 Traction Ave., #6, Los Angeles, CA 90013

Born: 1922 *Awards:* National Society of Literature and Art; Long View Foundation *Collections:* Galleria Civica d'Arte Moderna, Turin, Italy; Museum of Modern Art *Exhibitions:* Los Angeles Municiple Art Gallery; San Jose Institute of Contemporary Art *Education:* Art Students League, NYC *Dealer:* Louis Newman Galleries, Beverly Hills

He grew up in Japan, where Oriental calligraphy influenced his early years. As a young artist, he was part of the New York School of Abstract Expressionists. His media were oil paints with knife and brush, and sumi ink with brush. In his recent work, he has combined texture, space and color in freely flowing paintings of earth, wind, air, fire and water. His media are now acrylic on canvas or watercolor and sumi on paper. His colors are either cool or warm, but never both. He has been influenced by Gorky and Jackson Pollock.

KANO, BETTY NOBUE (Painter)

1340 Peralta Ave., Berkeley, CA 94702

Born: 1944 *Awards:* San Francisco Art Festival Exhibition Award; Artists in Schools Grant, California Arts Council *Collections:* Security Pacific Bank, Los Angeles; AT&T, NJ *Exhibitions:* Triton Museum of Art, Santa Clara; Berkeley Art Center *Education:* UC-Berkeley

Her initial interest in the creation of a "subliminal" terrain led to paintings derived from poetry. In these works, words with prismacolor are covered with layers of color and sanded back to suggest and reveal "archaeological" connections. In her later paintings, words give way to wall-like markings, and strong colors are developed into fields. Heavily influenced by Hegel's and Marx's philosophy of dialectics, she produced a series of triptychs—the three parts of which represent thesis, antithesis and synthesis. Since her trip to Cuba in 1985, her paintings have become large—from 6 by 6 to 7 by 7 feet—and are concerned with making a clear, direct and explicitly political statement.

KAPEL, JOHN A. (Sculptor)

80 Skywood Way, Woodside, CA 94062

Born: 1922 *Awards:* Carnegie Fellowship *Exhibitions:* DeYoung Museum, San Francisco; Los Robles Gallery, Palo Alto *Education:* Ohio Wesleyan; Cranbrook Academy *Dealer:* Highlands Gallery of Sculpture, Carmel

Influenced by Henry Moore, he created large, hollow, anthropomorphic forms by cutting and layering flakeboard early in his career. These pieces are thin-walled and give the appearance of rough clay. Subsequently, he fabricated well-hung pieces of painted wood. One such work, *Citadel,* is a hollow, elongated oval with a large "T" figure carved from its middle. The area around the "T" appears roughly finished, with many small, knobby protuberances. These disparate elements convey a variety of simultaneous impressions, at once equivocal and primitive.

KARLSBERG, PORTIA (Painter)

11476 Aliento Ct., San Diego, CA 92127

Awards: Southern California Expo; Honorable Mention, Showcase of Arts, Escondido *Exhibitions:* Knowles Gallery, La Jolla; Southern California Expo *Education:* School of the Art Institute of Chicago; Chicago Academy of Art

She thrives on rigors of the creative process and finds satisfaction in the resolution of artistic problems. Having mastered the art of brushstroke and palette knife painting, she has been researching watercolor and acrylic. Her style is expressionist, and depictions of her active subjects range from the representational to the abstract. Her recent acrylics are very large, while her watercolors are of average size (typically 24 by 30 inches) and her etchings and oil pastels are small (15 by 25 inches). Her other media included monoprints, collages involving print and painting techniques and drip drawings on Belgian linen or pure cotton paper.

KARPEL, ELI (Sculptor)

689 Brooktree Rd., Santa Monica, CA 90402

Born: 1916 *Collections:* Hirshhorn Jewish Museum, NYC; Frank Sinatra *Exhibitions:* Ankrum Gallery, Los Angeles; Pierce College, Northridge *Education:* City College of New York; UCLA *Dealers:* Tobey C. Moss, Los Angeles; Gump's, Los Angeles

He began as a painter, but soon turned to abstract sculpture. His formal subjects are entirely non-objective. He combines the tradition and durability of metal with continuously changing visual effects. He first sculpts in wax, then casts the finished pieces using a lost wax process. He polishes the bronze to create a mirror-like surface, which reflects the environment. He has long taught art at Pierce College in Northridge. "For me," he says, "there is always discovery in the making of a piece of sculpture, and when the process is successful, there is always in it an element of the unexpected."

KARVER, SHERRY (Sculptor, Ceramist)

5363 Manila Ave., Oakland, CA 94618

Born: 1950 *Awards:* Grant Award, Cal. State-Chico; Purchase Award, Westwood Clay National Exhibition *Collections:* California State Teachers Retirement System, Sacramento; Kemper Tool Company, Chino *Exhibitions:* American Institute of Architects, Oakland; Rental Gallery, San Francisco Museum of Modern Art *Education:* Tulane U.; Indiana U.

Having received formal training in ceramics and glass, she began her career as a functional potter in the late 1970s; shortly thereafter, fascinated by the diversity of concepts and techniques achievable in clay, she changed over completely to sculptural expression. The early sculptures were three- dimensional forms dealing with the orderliness of the grid as the underlying element. They emphasized the fragility of the clay and the use of positive and negative space. Ruth Duckworth and Tony Hepburn influenced this early work, the imagery of which often depicted boat forms and decaying buildings. During the 1980s, she began to create wall reliefs, and her imagery became more personal and spiritual. More recently, a central theme in her work has been the light and energy of the human being, and she uses the vessel form as a metaphor for the human body. She draws inspiration from the Kabbalah, from Hebrew mysticism and from her metaphysical studies of quartz crystals, auras and chakras. The works are wheel-thrown, altered and multifired using various techniques. Many are large and architectural, made up of small units.

Kocour, *An Outside Opinion,* 21 x 18, acrylic on board

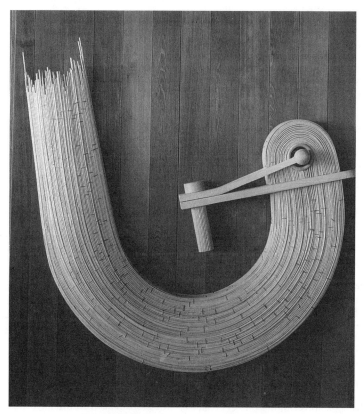

John Kapel, *Counterpoint,* 32 x 40, wood.
Courtesy: Gallery 30, San Mateo, CA

KARWELIS, DONALD CHARLES (Painter)
202-K East Stevens, Santa Ana, CA 92707

Born: 1934 *Awards:* NEA Grant; National Defense Education Act Grant, U.S. Government *Collections:* Los Angeles County Museum of Art; Long Beach Museum of Art *Exhibitions:* Marilyn Pink Gallery; Simar/Halm Gallery, Los Angeles *Education:* UC-Irvine

He is known for paintings and collages that exhibit bold, colorful images emphasized by heavily textured surfaces. A more lyrical approach to abstraction in his early acrylic-on-paper works developed from an interest in ancient Japanese art. Later work includes large-scale acrylic-on-canvas paintings, mixed-media collage on paper, and lithographs, the works exploring the relation of content and object in a balance between figuration and abstraction. In the 1980s, his work has begun to explore the roots of Western Civilization and the foundations of modernism. Dramatic color, striking contrasts of value, invented textures and provocative forms and content continue to be distinctive characteristics of his style.

KASLOW, LISA (Sculptor)
2313-15 Essex St., Baltimore, MD 21224

Born: 1953 *Awards:* John Courtney Murray Fellowship Award, Yale U.; 1st Prize, Lawrence C. Licht Art Award, NJ *Collections:* Rouse and Associates, Beltsville, MD; Baltimore Civic Center *Exhibitions:* Trenton State Museum, NJ; Washington Square, Washington D.C. *Education:* Yale U.; Columbia U. *Dealer:* Cross Creek Gallery, MD

Prior to the development of her sculptural technique, fascination with the human figure in motion motivated years of experimenting with different media. While completing her studies at Yale, the artist became intrigued with the concept of armature as an art form in its own right. Her initial efforts in this format utilized steel rods, which were bent and welded to suit her design. Her later sculptures exhibited a synthesis of many techniques used in the past, including large, cut, steel plate, and vibrant color applied with an airbrush. While sports has been the impetus for a recent series of larger-than-life sculptures, the theme to which she actually directs her tribute is heroes.

KASNOT, KEITH (Illustrator)
9228 N. 29th St., Phoenix, AZ 85028

Born: 1952 *Awards:* Health Sciences Communication Association Award; 1st Place, International Society for Technical Communication *Exhibitions:* Society of Illustrators' Annual Exhibition; Palazzo Bagatti Valsecchi, Milan, Italy *Education:* U. of Texas Health Science Center, Dallas; Indiana U. of Pennsylvania *Dealer:* Ceci Bartels, St. Louis

While studying painting in Austria, he became fascinated by the work of the artists of the Viennese Fantastic school, a style characterized by both ultra-realism and surrealism. His perspective then turned literally "inward," as he began depictions of the human body, an interest influenced by a life-long appreciation for medicine and by graduate studies in medical illustration. His work is an attempt to elevate the field of medical illustration, which has traditionally been viewed as a purely educational medium, to the status of fine art. His depictions assume the feel characteristic of *The Fantastic Voyage* and do not demand medical knowledge in order to be appreciated, but

they are readily accessible from an artistic, aesthetic standpoint. Works are done in vibrant yet naturalistic tones; body parts are often drawn in isolation, appearing against a limbo background. Also an animator, he has among his credits a three-part documentary series for PBS entitled "The Genetic Gamble," and "The Artificial Heart," both of which appeared on *Nova*.

KAU, DAGMAR (Ceramist)
45-207 Mahalani Circle, Kaneohe, HI 96744

Born: 1940 *Awards:* State Foundation on Culture and the Arts Purchase Award; Best in Show Award, Raku Hoolaulea *Collections:* State Foundation on Culture and Arts, Honolulu; City & County of Honolulu

She is a ceramist who works in a variety of media, at times bowing to economic pressures but also finding an outlet in abstraction. She makes functional wares, she says, "because it is what sells." Her double-walled casseroles, buckets and planters are hand-thrown and glazed in earth tones. Recently, she has begun making porcelain bottles glazed with celadons and copper reds and fired again with gold luster accents. Abstraction is important in her Raku sculptures. The sculptures have large, black surfaces with dramatic flashes of luster. In the future, she plans to construct large-scale wall murals using handmade tiles of various shapes and sizes.

KAUFER, SHIRLEY (Painter)
386 S. Burnside Ave., Los Angeles, CA

Collections: Chuck Ross, Los Angeles; Edward Maeder, Los Angeles *Exhibitions:* L.A. ARTCORE, Los Angeles; Health Center, Los Angeles

Her present abstractions combine vivid non-objective color forms in vital hard-edged relationships. She works in oils, and her colors vary from deep reds to high blues in highly emotional and expressive compositions. Her brush work is direct and soft leaving a sense of liquid movement to the forms. In one series, "Pacific Rim," she uses sharp bright clean colors to depict the opposition of elemental forces. She also works representationally in still lifes, emphasizing a similar brush technique combined with a concern for light and form. The artist is also a skilled potter and has completed at least 100 self-portraits.

KAUFFMAN, K.C. (Painter)
1013 Marelene St., Incline Village, NV 89415

Born: 1948 *Awards:* Tosco Corp. Grant; Laguna Beach Festival of the Arts Fellowship *Collections:* Fluor Corp., Irvine; Computer Sciences Corp., Los Angeles *Exhibitions:* Institute of Modern Art, Brisbane, Australia; Tyson Gallery, Utrecht, Holland *Education:* UC-Irvine; Union Graduate School

Her main influence has been the the overwhelming Western American landscape. She identified with the raw power captured by such artists as Arthur Dove, Marsden Hartley, Milton Avery and Georgia O'Keeffe; she profited by the feminist art movement's depictions of women's realities and mythologies. She uses mixed media (acrylic paint, oil paint, oil crayons, oil sticks, conte crayons, soft pastels, colored pencils, charcoal and graphite with turpentine) on paper to create images that range from abstract archetypical shapes to fairly realistic renditions of landscapes and figures, to which are superadded mythologies and sub-conscious sources.

Shirley Kaufer, *Viv in Poncho,* 36 x 26, oil on canvas.
Courtesy: Shoshana Wayne Gallery, Santa Monica, CA

Susan M. King, *Night,* 54 x 48, oil on canvas

KAUFFMAN, ROBERT CRAIG (Painter, Sculptor)

Dept. of Art, UC-Irvine, Irvine, CA 92717

Born: 1932 *Awards:* U.S. Govt. Fellowship for the Arts; 1st Prize, American Exhibition, Art Institute of Chicago *Collections:* Los Angeles County Museum of Art; Pasadena Art Museum *Exhibitions:* Asher/Faure Gallery, Los Angeles; La Jolla Museum of Contemporary Art *Education:* USC; UCLA *Dealer:* Pace Gallery, NYC

His works in the middle to late 1950s were calligraphic, painterly, playfully erotic explorations of abstract, loosely defined forms. These progressed in the 1960s to paintings of sprayed lacquer on vacuum-formed and pressed plexiglas, works in which contours harden and become more defined and in which the forms alternate from erotic organic shapes to geometric and mechanical images, revealing the dual inspirations of Matisse's celebration of pure pleasure and Duchamp's enigmatic mechanisms. The transparent surface and the back-painted lacquer creates an impression of ambiguous space and surface. Recent works have included paintings on silk that expand on the relation between biomorphic or clearly biological images and architectonic shapes—some of which mimic the stretcher bars that support a canvas. Through its manipulation of color, form and space, his work creates a harmony between a timeless idea of physical pleasure and the more culturally specific mechanistic images of our technological age.

KAUFMAN, DONNA J. (Painter, Commercial Illustrator)

3044 Orange Ave., La Crescenta, CA 91214

Born: 1940 *Awards:* Bank of America Achievement Award *Collections:* Mare Island Naval Station *Exhibitions:* Artistic Endeavors, Simi Valley; Disney Studios, Burbank *Education:* Art Center College of Design

As a child, she drew Zulu people and created her own paper dolls. While raising her children, she ran a commercial art business and did work at military bases throughout Northern California. She currently paints lettering in the title department of Walt Disney Studios. Her colorful, non-commercial work is either realistic or based in reality, but eased into design. She prefers oil paints, but also works in pastels, colored pencil and mixed media. Recent works include a realistic color pencil drawing of an old saw mill and pond.

KAVALER, ELIZABETH (Printmaker, Painter)

228 Amherst Ave., Berkeley, CA 94708

Born: 1922 *Exhibitions:* International Exhibitions of Miniature Art, Toronto, CA; Kaiser Center Art Gallery, Oakland *Education:* California College of Arts and Crafts

For many years, she worked as a graphic artist, specializing in lettering and package design for the cosmetics industry. Since her studies with Vredaparis and Kathan Brown in 1965, etching has been her favorite medium of expression. She begins with sketches she makes during her travels and hikes. She then uses at least two or three different plates to make several types of intaglio prints, including line etching, aquatint, and drypoint. She has portrayed the majestic Sierra, the Alaskan mountains and the spectacular cliffs of Yosemite. She has recently been painting stylized Oriental and Asian influenced watercolor landscapes.

KEANE, MARGARET (Painter)

1798 Halekoa Dr., Honolulu, HI 96821

Born: 1927 *Awards:* 1st Place, Printing Industries of America Inc. Graphic Annual Art Competition; Fellow, Society of Western Artists *Collections:* National Museum of Contemporary Art, Madrid; National Museum of Western Art, Tokyo *Exhibitions:* Los Angeles Art Expo; Center Art Galleries, Honolulu *Education:* Jacksonville Junior College; Chaffey Junior College *Dealer:* 4 Unique Art, Redlands

She was the creator of infamous paintings of children with huge, sad eyes during the 1950s and 1960s, although her authorship was not legally affirmed until 1986. These works usually depicted a lone child on a dark street, beach or stairway or looking over fences and barbed wire. They are painted in smoothly applied oils. In addition to the large-eyed children created under the signature "Keane," she also painted, as "MDH Keane," elongated, Modigliani-inspired teenage girls in a lighter palette. Both styles reflect her deepest emotions and her search for answers to life's contradictions. In more recent years, she has painted children who are happier and more serene, introducing tropical foliage and wild animals to the settings.

KEARNEY, KEVIN (Painter)

1401 Illinois Ave., San Francisco, CA 94107

Exhibitions: Haines Gallery, San Francisco; Jeremy Stone Gallery, San Francisco *Education:* UC-Davis; Maryland Institute College of Art *Dealer:* Haines Gallery, San Francisco

In the mid-1970s, he began juxtaposing interiors and landscapes. The opposition of interior and exterior allowed him to engage the viewer on emotional and psychological levels, while bringing up the formal concerns of space, light, color and composition. In 1980, he began integrating the human figure into the work. He now paints with oils on canvas, using a gesso ground and the highest quality paints available. His influences have been the Northern Renaissance and Flemish painters, as well as the Ash Can School of Hopper and Balthus.

KEARNS-WEISS, LAUREN (Ceramist)

10531 Ilona Ave., Los Angeles, CA 90064

Born: 1952 *Exhibitions:* Gallery 5, Pomona; The Clayhouse, Santa Monica *Education:* U. of Oregon; Kansas City Art Institute

In her early work, she emphasized function and form. She was influenced by Japanese pottery and her decorations were simple salt glazes, which led the viewer to the form rather than distracting one from it. Her media were high fired stoneware and porcelain. She has become more interested in color, and her recent porcelain work is highly decorative on the surface. Influenced by European and Japanese techniques, she now hand-paints or airbrushes patterns on her bowls, teapots and jars. Her forms remain simple, elegant and functional. She is a member of the Association of California Ceramic Artists, and she holds credentials as a teacher in California Colleges and Junior Colleges.

KEARSEY, KATHY (Draughtsperson, Mixed Media Artist)

25 McAfee Court, Thousand Oaks, CA 91360

Born: 1958 *Awards:* Bicentennial Award, North Shore Arts Center, Glen Cove, NY *Exhibitions:* Ventura

J. Natasha Kostan, *untitled,* 30 x 40, monoprint, diptych

K.C. Kauffman, *Persephone in Hades,* 24 x 28, pastel, oil crayon

College Art Gallery; Port Huneme Cultural Center *Education:* College of New Rochelle

After formal training in abstraction, she made use of her unconscious feelings and emotions, and took a personal interest in symbolism, to create works of art. Through printmaking, mixed-media drawings, paintings and sculpture, these unconscious feelings were put in a reasoned order. The works of Miro, Kandinsky and Picasso influenced her style. Recently, though, she has been influenced by the work of Claes Oldenburg and Red Grooms. She creates bold, colorful mixed-media paintings and sculptures, of humorously rendered mundane objects, such as mechanical pumps and fire hydrants. Working in a surrealistic style, she has reversed the reality of the scale of these forms, contrasting them with the human figure. Now in a transitional period, she is pursuing the culture and religion of the Southwestern Desert America Indians. She is working to express the feelings of spiritual integration found in their art. These whimsical, symbolic pieces are painted in subtle colors on handmade papers, embellished with dried flowers and tree bark.

KEATING, JOHN MICHAEL (Painter)
P.O. Box 1514, Grass Valley, CA 95945

Born: 1941 *Awards:* Award of Merit, Calif. State Fair, Sacramento *Collections:* Toyota Corporation; Bank of America *Exhibitions:* Crocker-Kingsley Exhibition, Sacramento; Worley-Smith Gallery, Nevada City *Education:* San Francisco Art Institute *Dealer:* Worley-Smith Gallery, Nevada City

There are two principle objectives in his work: first, to render the objects and places that are part of everyday experience, and second, to paint the invisible world—the inner images of feelings, thoughts, dreams, fears and imaginary events. Early works tended to emphasize the latter. *Bridge* shows three different points of view merging into one. On the top of the canvas, the viewer is looking up at the sky; to the lower left, down at a beach with waves crashing against the sand; and to the lower right, straight ahead at a row of trees whose leaves and branches change into water and clouds as the viewer scans the rest of the canvas. By the late 1970s, he abandoned this kind of imagery in favor of more straightforward depictions of nature. Typical of this period is *Airscape*, an acrylic-on-canvas work in earth and sky tones showing mountains, rivers and clouds from an aerial perspective. His recent work, rendered in oil and watercolor, focuses on both the visible and invisible worlds. *Before I Wake* depicts a little girl running across a lonely highway in the Nevada Desert but located simultaneously in a room with four large windows.

KEEFE, PATRICIA E. (Mixed Media Artist)
215 Pinehill Rd., Hillsborough, CA 94010

Awards: 2nd Place, Sculpture, Society of Western Artists *Exhibitions:* Corridor Gallery, Redwood City; Rental Gallery, San Francisco Museum of Art *Education:* San Jose State U.; College of Notre Dame *Dealer:* Metro Centre Gallery, Foster City

Influenced by the works of John Batternburg and Jean Arp, she mixes life-size photographs with constructed and found objects, to make personal and political statements. Her explorations of materials (from bronze to plastic) give direction to her work. A recent series of sculptures depict female deity forms in marble, alabaster, ebony and mahogany. She believes in using traditional materials to express new insights, leading the viewer from the literal and physical to the metaphorical and sublime.

KEEFER, KATHERINE (Ceramist)
1765 12th St., Oakland, CA 94607

Born: 1946 *Exhibitions:* Southern Ohio Museum, Portsmouth; Cheney Cowles Memorial Museum, Spokane, WA *Education:* Washington State U.

She makes non-functional sculpture, using a coil technique to build 6-to-10-foot figures, objects and body parts. She fashions the sculpture more as a tower and form, than as the object itself. She does not glaze these exaggerated, simplified pieces; rather she uses acrylic and oil to paint large fields of color on the fired clay.

KEEFER, PETER (Printmaker)
P.O. Box 1554, Ross, CA 94957

Born: 1933 *Collections:* Citibank, NYC; CBS Television, Los Angeles *Exhibitions:* National Museum of Modern Art, Seoul; Compendium 2 Gallery, London *Education:* California State U.; California College of Arts and Crafts

He has developed a printmaking technique that produces a collagraphic print. The typical plate surface is built up using texturizing media, glues and gels, giving his prints a tantalizing textural edge. He has also experimented with color blending, rolling out two to five connected colors on a flat surface and then transferring from to individual pieces of the masonite-based plate used for printing. His typical subject matter is black-and-white landscape, sometimes delicate, sometimes brash. He constructs serial photographs, collage works and monotypes using this subject matter, arranging the images in planar layers to create depth. His minimalist style is devoid of baggage, allowing his images to affect the viewer clearly and succinctly.

KEISTER, STEVE (Sculptor)
46 Laight St., New York, NY 10013

Born: 1949 *Awards:* Pollock Krasner Foundation Scholar; NEA Fellowship *Collections:* Whitney Museum, NYC; Museum of Contemporary Art, Los Angeles *Exhibitions:* Museum of Contemporary Art, Chicago; Larry Gagosian Gallery, Los Angeles *Education:* Tyler School of Art *Dealer:* Blum Helman Gallery, NYC

His sculptures of wood, pegboard and cardboard that hang from the ceiling by filaments give the illusion, when viewed from different perspectives, of motion through deft manipulation of shape, color and interior and exterior space. In some, panels and shapes are painted in fluorescent colors that reflect the overhead lighting through spaces and gaps in the sculpture. He occasionally employs found objects in the pieces, some of which take on oddly altered geometric forms: boxes, pyramids and rectangles. Critic Suzanne Muchanic comments that the "combination of Cubist space, reflected light and aggressive form is cheeky enough to force contemplation of its presence, and that is an accomplishment."

KEIZER, SUSAN (Painter)
2513 Madrid Ct., Davis, CA 95616

Born: 1940 *Awards:* Kingsley-Witt Award; MacDowell Fellowship *Exhibitions:* Triangle Gallery, San Francisco; City Gallery, Sacramento *Education:* Reed College; Cal. State-Sacramento *Dealer:* City Gallery, Sacramento

John Michael Keating, *California,* 32 x 51, oil on canvas. Courtesy: Worley-Smith Gallery, Nevada City, CA

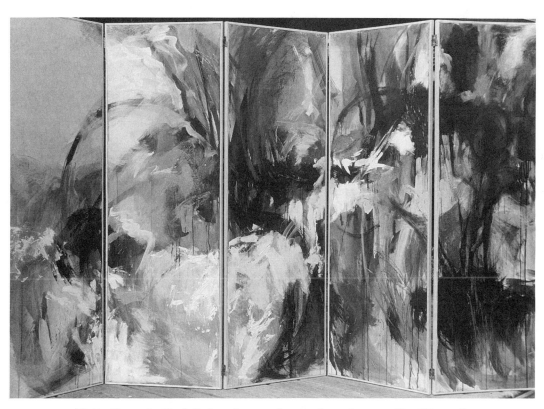

Elaine Kennedy, *Creek Series—Summer Synergy,* 5 panel screen, 60 x 100, acrylic.
Courtesy: Mr. and Mrs. Robert Koda

At first, the Bay Area figurative painters seduced her with their use of line. Her own early works were running pictorial narrative pieces composed of many fragmented, abstracted images and painted with a mix of graphite, chalk pastel and oil stick. Since the work autobiographically reflected process rather than specific life occurrences, she left the underlying marks and shapes visible. The most recent work, which includes paintings on paper and canvas, shows a broader range of color and the images tend to be less flat, more dimensional and have begun to take on an even more primitive organic quality. Her palette is limited and value is often more important than color.

KELL, JEFFREY (Ceramist)
519 N. 11th St., Reading, PA 19607

Born: 1956 *Exhibitions:* Allen Short Gallery, Stockton; Carlyn Gallery, NYC *Education:* West Chester U.; U. of Wyoming *Dealer:* Tesoro Collection, Inc., Los Angeles

He worked as a production potter before his move to California motivated an interest in sculptural forms. All of his work is wheel-thrown, though his pieces often have a hand-constructed appearance. This is due to the impression and slip-trailing techniques that alter the vessel prior to firing. Some pieces may also be coated with terra sigallata, and burnished. Then each goes through a kiln before being placed in an open pit or container with straw, leaves and wood as fuel. The action of the fire on the surface of the form produces striking and often unpredictable results. Since these firing methods generally employ no glazes, a wider range of textures may be achieved. Cloud-like patterns of smoke create interesting relationships between blacks, grays and the natural oyster color of the clay. He is most interested in the articulation of interior and exterior space, surface texture and the primitive power attained by using these techniques.

KELLER, LORETTA (Painter, Sculptor)
1526 Gaywood Dr., Althdena, CA 91001

Born: 1928 *Exhibitions:* Baxter Art Gallery, Pasadena; Barnsdall Municipal Gallery, Los Angeles

She began her artistic career as a self-taught portrait painter. After studying with John Altoon at the Pasadena Art Museum, she combined impression with expression, and achieved the ability to convey the emotions of the person, as well as to depict the likeness. While studying at Caltech, she mastered polyester resin technique, and moved to this sculptural medium from clay. Both Altoon and William Hayter influenced her toward figurative symbolism. The human plight is her abiding concern. Her portraits reflect this directly; her abstract sculptures, indirectly. Their brilliant colors symbolize and evoke emotion. Their contorted, yet balanced, hard-edged shapes symbolize the tensions inherent in the human condition. In two massive works, she inserted softly rounded glass forms to depict human warmth. Knowing that glass and resin cool at uneven temperatures, and that, therefore, the combination results in magnificent fissures, she manipulated the cracks with a vacuum pump so that they formed an inherent part of the work. They stand for struggle and conquest. She has recently been concentrating on expressive portraiture, teaching watercolor painting to the aged and writing a master's thesis based on the experience.

KELLEY, MARGARET (Painter)
1250 Long Beach Ave., Loft 221, Los Angeles, CA 90021

Born: 1954 *Awards:* Rotary Graduate Fellowship, Munich Academy of Art; Gallery Artist-in-Residence, Howart Development Co. *Collections:* Touche Ross; Howart Development Co., Los Angeles *Exhibitions:* Barnsdall Municipal, Los Angeles; Galerie X, Munich *Education:* Cal. State-Long Beach; Academy of Fine Arts, Munich

The artist developed her own visual language of marks and shapes derived from the counterpoint between two landscapes she has inhabited: those of Southern California and Southern Germany. Progression of her personal vision led to increasingly monumental works as the symbols grew and interacted, leading ultimately to a commissioned work the length of a city block. While huge acrylic-on-canvas works have enabled her to explore visually the creation of logic and motion in visual relationships, she has also worked in more intimate media, including ink on paper, cloth and papier maché. She is presently at work in her native California, her works have diminished somewhat in size and become compositionally more clear and assertive, although their focus continues to be upon relationships of images in a visual field.

KELLEY, MIKE (Conceptual Artist)
c/o Metro Pictures, 150 Greene St., New York, NY 10012

Exhibitions: Rosamund Felsen Gallery, Los Angeles; Metro Pictures, NYC *Education:* California Arts *Dealer:* Metro Pictures, NYC; Rosamund Felsen Gallery, Los Angeles

Performance pieces, installations and large-scale drawings and paintings are shocking, and often provoke reactions of fear or revulsion. His humor has been called "brutally comic," as profanity, scatology and paranoia pervade his work. Connected to the "hardcore" culture of Los Angeles, he challenges the definitions of creativity and madness, coming close to anarchy and chaos, recalling the early performances of Chris Burden. He has said that something can "be funny and not funny at the same time, depending on the context," and therefore he parodies everything, from the art world to religion to patriotism.

KELLY, DAVID WILLIAM (Painter)
1745 Selby Ave., #7, Los Angeles, CA 90024

Born: 1956 *Collections:* Koll Company, Irvine *Exhibitions:* Mary Livingston Gallery II, Santa Ana; The Rotation Gallery, Los Angeles *Education:* Royal College of Art, London

His landscape and wildlife paintings combine a naturalist's eye for detail with an abstract artistic approach. Light and leaves, clouds, flowers, water and wildlife are the focus of his large (40-by-60 and 60-by-80-inch) watercolor paintings on handmade paper. Inspired by the work of Joseph Raffael and Katherine Liu, he uses a glazing technique that gives his paintings a depth, which, in some cases, resembles oil paint. Thematically, his work deals with the natural cycle of life

Elmo James, *Singapore Orchid,* 60 x 60, acrylic

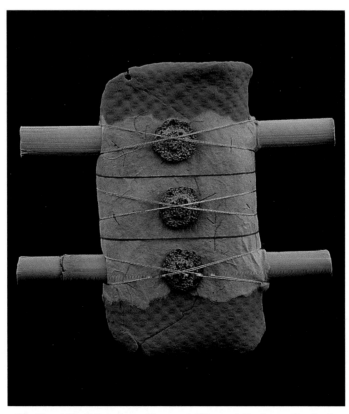

Marilyn Alford Jennings, *Tsutsumi: Wrapped Packages,* 8 x 6 x 3,
clay, handmade paper, threads, natural found objects

Jimé, *Genesis,* 30 high, bronze. Courtesy: Louise Matzke Runnings Gallery

Robert W. Jensen, *Portrait of China Today,* 72 x 84, acrylic on canvas

Morgan Johnson, *Distilled Life,* 36 x 40, oil

Diana Jacobs, *Cattalaya,* 22 x 28, watercolor and graphite. Courtesy: Biota Gallery, Los Angeles

Andrew Johnston, *Trunks,* 27 x 40, pastel

Barbara Janusz, *Autumn,* 40 x 60, watercolor. Courtesy: Rose Strock

Stephen Johns, *Red Yellow Blue,* 36 x 108, triptych, acrylic on canvas

Doris Miller Johnson, *Lunar Safari,* 36 x 48, acrylic on canvas

Geir Jordahl, *Waikiki Beach, Hawaii,* 8 x 20, silver gelatin print

Grant Johnson, *Four Corners,* video wall installation. Courtesy: Stimulus

Margaret Kelley, *The Most Subtle of All,*
84 x 48, acrylics on canvas

David Kelly, *Hawaiian Daze,* 48 x 68, watercolor

Sandy Kinnee, *Japanese Lightning,* 36 x 50,
intaglio on handmade rag paper

Erika Kahn, *December Sash,* 42 x 48, handmade paper,
mixed media. Photograph: Herb Dreiwitz

Sherry Karver, *Inner Explosion,* 96 x 45 x 1, ceramic

Leo Krikorian, *165 BM,* 53 x 39, acrylic on canvas

Zeljko Kujundzic, *Garden of Love,* 33 x 48, integrated media (painting)

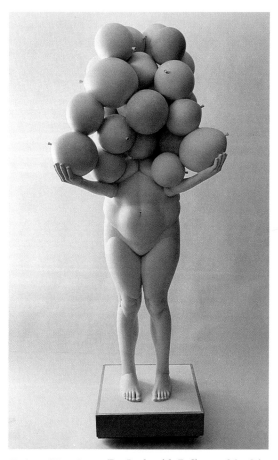

Robert Kingsbury, *Fat Lady with Balloons,* 86 x 36,
papier-mâché. Photograph: Erik Weber

Steve Kursh, *Wild Blue Yonder,* 77 x 42 x 19, polymer on wood and found objects with neon. Courtesy: Donna Ewald

Sheng-Piao Kiang, *Lotus and Mountains,* 36 x 50, mixed media

David Kelso, *Chrome Yellow Light,* 30 x 22, etching, aquatint.
Courtesy: Made in California

Loretta Keller, *The Hat (A Self Portrait),* 36 x 48,
oil and gesso on plywood

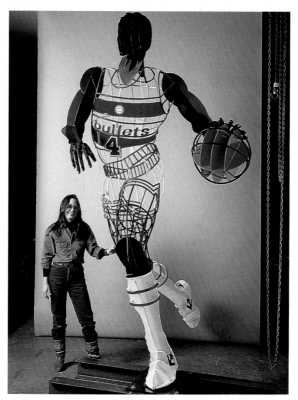

Lisa Kaslow, *Fastbreak,* 138 x 84 x 84, steel with coatings.
Courtesy: Rouse & Associates. Photograph: Alan Browne

Knox, *Acropolis,* 29 x 22, acrylics on canvas.
Courtesy: Mr. and Mrs. Paul Smith

Susan M. King, *The Death of Venus,* 54 x 48, oil on canvas

Bernice Kussoy, *The First Waltz,* 36" high, welded metal

David Kreitzer, *Italian Roses,* 30 x 24, watercolor

Kocour, *The Myth,* 18 x 21, acrylic on board

John Killmaster, *Insight-Out,* 48 x 50, acrylic on canvas.
Courtesy: Boise State Gallery of Art

Shirley Kaufer, *Pacific Rim Series 4,* 40 x 40, oil on canvas.
Courtesy: Shoshana Wayne Gallery, Santa Monica, CA

and death, and he often depicts new life arising from decay and deterioration. His has recently completed a series of large-scale garden paintings, from his personal visual impressions of the Hawaiian Islands.

KELSO, DAVID (Printmaker)
3246 Ettie St., Oakland, CA 94608

Born: 1948 *Collections:* Crown Zellerbach; Rutgers Archives *Exhibitions:* San Francisco Museum of Modern Art; The Grolier Club, NYC *Education:* UC-Riverside *Dealer:* Betsy Senior Gallery, New York

He has committed his energy to printmaking since the early 1970s. He served his apprenticeship at El Dorado Press, and subsequently worked as a printer at Crown Point Press, before establishing his own intaglio workshop, Made in California, in 1980. Richard Diebenkorn, Frank Lodbell and Jack Jefferson remain the most important influences on his work. His exploration of symbolic abstraction in intaglio printmaking is a slow reflective art form, which has required him to relinquish a degree of control to the vagaries of the process. Thus, he must balance the actions of chance, and the psychological ambiguities which surround it, against commitments of intent. He has recently been working in black and white.

KENNEDY, ELAINE (Painter, Printmaker)
954 Peregrine Pl., Anaheim, CA 92806

Born: 1939 *Awards* 1st Award, Brea Civic Center; 1st Place, Chapman College *Collections:* Santa Barbara Savings and Loan; Art Institute of California *Exhibitions:* North Vancouver Civic Center, Canada; Anaheim Cultural Art Center *Education:* Vancouver School of Art

After studying art in Canada, she worked primarily in a realistic figurative manner. Later, as she explored the monoprint medium, the work became freer and more abstracted, progressing to expressionistic acrylics, watercolors and prints depicting the moods and seasons of nature in the Sierras, and through that depiction, man's spirituality. A river by her house serves as a metaphor for life, "sometimes turbulent and unsettled, overcoming obstacles, ever changing, always on a chosen course." She attributes her artistic growth to an attitude of experimentation with media—for instance, combining watercolor with oil pastels through layering. Works have become larger in scale, with acrylics and screens reaching 60 by 100 inches. She has also conducted workshops in painting and monoprinting and has curated a show of fellow Orange County women artists.

KERZIE, TED (Painter)
2606 Purdue Ave., Los Angeles, CA 90064

Born: 1943 *Awards:* California State U. District Artists Exhibition *Collections:* Arco Collection of Visual Arts, Los Angeles; Power Museum, Sydney, Australia *Exhibitions:* Cirrus Gallery, Los Angeles; Nagasaki Prefecture Museum *Education:* Washington State U.; Claremont Graduate School *Dealer:* Cirrus Gallery, Los Angeles

Paintings are executed by a unique process in which large canvases are painted through a small aperture with a taped, dripping border. Canvases are layered in order to create a multidimensional tableau that looks rather like window views of flowers or lush foliage as if seen through a screen. His work recalls impressionist and pointillist landscapes, but remains positively contemporary. A further exploration of color, pointillism and illusion characterizes recent work.

KESSBERGER, ELLEN (Ceramic Sculptor, Painter)
1595 Pacific Ave., Alameda, CA 94501

Awards: 1st Place, Painting, Alameda County Fair, Pleasanton; 1st and 4th Place, Sculpture, Chimerical Gregg Art Gallery *Exhibitions:* Sun Gallery, Hayward; Oakland Museum Collectors Gallery *Education:* U. of Iowa; Colorado State U. *Dealer:* Dorothe Barlett Gallery, Pleasanton

She has been inspired by the provocative shapes and vivid imagery of Judy Chicago, and the bold, rich, sensuous colors of Georgia O'Keeffe's large, floral paintings. Her hand-built porcelain and ceramic sculptures are influenced by the variety of plant, floral and undersea life in the San Francisco Bay area. The rhythmic flowing surfaces and thin delicate shapes give the pieces a buoyant, fascinating quality. The sculptures are designed and built from thinly rolled slabs of either porcelain or low-fire whiteware clay, dried completely and then fired to bisqueware temperatures. These pieces are airbrushed in pastel shades of blue, turquoise, pink, green and golden ambrosia underglaze stains. The entire sculpture is then covered with a low-sheen transparent glaze and fired to vitrification.

KETCHUM, ROBERT GLENN (Photographer)
696 Stone Canyon Rd., Los Angeles, CA 90077

Born: 1947 *Awards:* Grant, New York State Council on the Arts *Collections:* Museum of Modern Art, NYC; San Francisco Museum of Modern Art *Exhibitions:* Santa Barbara Museum of Art; Los Angeles County Museum of Art *Education:* California Institute of the Arts; UCLA

He studied with Robert Heinecken; his early black-and-white work was formal, experimental and manipulative. The color series "ORDER FROM CHAOS" and other early pieces made references to colorist ideas, color-field painting and abstract expressionism. Recent work is documentary and descriptive. Two recent environmental monographs, *The Hudson River and the Highlands* and *The Tongass: Alaska's Vanishing Rain Forest*, have combined a personal aesthetic with political/environmental convictions. He works with transparency film and prints on cibachrome paper.

KHALSA, SANT-SUBAGH K. (Photographer)
630 North G St., San Bernardino, CA 93410

Born: 1953 *Collections:* California Museum of Photography, Riverside; Laguna Beach Museum of Art *Exhibitions:* Newport Harbor Art Museum, Newport Beach; Otis-Parsons Art Institute, Los Angeles *Education:* Maryland Institute, College of Art; Cal. State-Fullerton

Her "Intimate Landscapes" capture the subtlety of experience, through attention to the markings of the land. Light, line, texture and form are her layers of visual information. Her deliberately small prints always take notice of the beauty of minute detail, and, in so doing, invite the viewer to take a closer look. Her gelatin-silver prints are 4 7/8 by 3 1/4 inches; matted prints are 16 by 20 inches. She photographs quickly, and uses landscapes as a neutral channel for her inner and outer essences. She has recently been working on *Khalsa, A Family Portrait,* a book documenting the last fifteen years of the American Sikh community.

KIANG, SHENG-PIAO (Painter, Sculptor)
3774 S. Hazel Ct., Englewood, CO 80110

Born: 1915 *Awards:* U.S. State Department Scholarship *Exhibitions:* City of Boulder, CO; U. of The Pacific *Education:* U. of Colorado, Boulder *Dealer:* Lazy Sun, Maui, HI

She has combined a Chinese calligraphic training with influences from American and European expressionism. As a teen in China, she studied calligraphy and the art of seal carving under several famous Chinese artists. After graduating from college, she came to the U.S. and worked for the United Nations for several years. She was influenced by American expressionism and briefly studied under Max Beckmann, who encouraged her to infuse her traditional Chinese technique with contemporary Western skills. After an extended period of experimentation, she arrived at a calligraphy- based style in watermedia and a variety of papers. She now paints borderless calligraphic lines with traditional Chinese brushes and adds fresh and bright colors to a normally sublime color scheme.

KIBBY, CHARLES (Sculptor)
1084 Trestle Glen Rd., Oakland, CA 94610

Born: 1951 *Awards:* Award of Merit, Carrara, Italy; Residence Fellowship, Wurlitzer Foundation, Taos, NM *Collections:* Rhodes College, Memphis, TN; City of Portland, OR *Education:* U. of Oregon

He has been influenced by Max Bill, Jean Arp and Robert Smithson. His early wave forms, produced in several media, embody metaphorical interpretations of universal processes and man's relationship to them. Since 1979, marble has emerged as his medium, specifically in its laminated form. His creations of spiral helixes, curves and colors have been greatly influenced by Benoir Mandelbrot's invention of fractal geometry. The works range from 24 to 48 inches high.

KIENHOLZ, EDWARD (Painter)
Meineke Strasse 6, 1 Berlin 15, W. Germany

Born: 1927 *Awards:* Guggenheim Grant; DAAD Residence Grant, Berlin *Collections:* Whitney Museum, NYC; Los Angeles County Museum *Exhibitions:* Whitney Museum, NYC; Dibbert Gallery, Berlin *Education:* Washington State College; Eastern Washington College of Education *Dealer:* Galerie Maeght, Switzerland

A self-taught artist, described as being both pop and neo-dada in style, he creates life-size sculptural tableaux that present an unrelenting attack on the repressiveness of complacency towards social and moral issues. His junk assemblages depict individuals in commonplace surroundings in order to create disturbing narratives. Such works as *State Hospital, The Wait, The Beanery* and the notorious *Back Seat Dodge,* a brutal lover's lane scene in which the viewer becomes an unwitting voyeur, deal with society's conditions, institutions and values as they impact upon the individual.

KIILLKKAA, CHRISTIAN (Environmental Installation Artist)
2986 Pine St., San Francisco, CA 94115

Born: 1954 *Exhibitions:* San Francisco Landscape Garden Show; San Francisco Art Commission Gallery *Education:* California Polytechnic Institute

Using indigenous stone, metals and plants, he creates autonomous, site-specific environmental installations. Some of these works feature spiral or circular walkways to provide a sense of movement and relief. A variety of materials combine to form a textured, diverse space: grassy, leafed plants; solid, stick-like bamboo plants; flowers of different types; and water, metal and stone. All are melded into a natural, unified whole. His background in painting, sculpture and art history, combined with a love of the outdoors, provides a fecund foundation for his current endeavors.

KILGORE, MICHAEL (Sculptor)
611 Loma Prieta Dr., Aptos, CA 95003

Born: 1951 *Awards:* Chancellors Award in Art, UC-Santa Cruz; Purchase Award, Long Marine Lab *Collections:* UC-Santa Cruz; Long Marine Lab *Exhibitions:* Hoeger-Thompson Gallery, Santa Cruz; Canyon Arts Gallery *Education:* UC-Santa Cruz

While his work is expressive, his artistic philosophy is governed by formalist concerns for essential structure and outward content. He achieves an expression of direct personal emotion through formal juxtapositions of line, meter and space. His welded metal pieces alternate between abstract expressionism and a linear lyricism. In the same way, the relationship of the yin and yang have been important elements in his work. He has been influenced by Robert Smithson, Richard Serra, David Smith, Peter Voulkos and Mark Di-Suvero.

KILIAN, ILSE TAN (Fiber Artist)
So. 1625 Hayford Rd., Spokane, WA 99204

Awards: 1st Prize, Arts and Crafts Festival, Coeur d'-Alene, ID *Collections:* City Hall, Spokane; Washington Trust Bank, Spokane *Exhibitions:* Mushroom Gallery *Education:* Kunstchule, Plauen/Vogtland, East Germany

Her work is concerned thematically with color and structurally with texture. Woven hangings are inspired by the organic forms of nature, although they are intended to be evocative rather than representational. Likewise, although modeled on external living forms, they seek to address lyrically the full range of subjective consciousness, including memory, fantasy and thought. Through this, the artist hopes to awaken in the viewer an immaterial spirituality, which sees in the abstract natural forms of her art the reflection of its self. Her method combines planning through sketching and gathering materials with a spontaneous loom technique that relies on the unconscious to produce poetic abstraction. Materials include various yarns, cotton, linen, wool and synthetic fabrics. The artist also works separately with paints.

KILLMASTER, JOHN (Painter)
2611 Davis, Boise, ID 83702

Born: 1934 *Awards:* Jurors' Award, Marietta College International Exhibition, Marietta, OH; Idaho Governor's Award for Excellence in the Arts *Collections:* FMC Corporation, Chicago; Morrison Knudsen Corporation, Boise, ID *Exhibitions:* Smithsonian Institute, Washington DC; Mussavi Art Center, NYC *Education:* Hope College; Cranbrook Academy of Art *Dealer:* Ochi Gallery, Boise, ID

He received formal training in oil and pastel figure painting and is self-taught in gouache, watercolor and casein. In the 1960s, he switched to acrylic and pursued non-objective work to develop color and compositional expertise. Early influences include the Impressionists, Surrealists and Abstract Expressionists and the Hard-

Loretta Keller, *In The Red,* 14 x 14 x 10, cast polyester resin

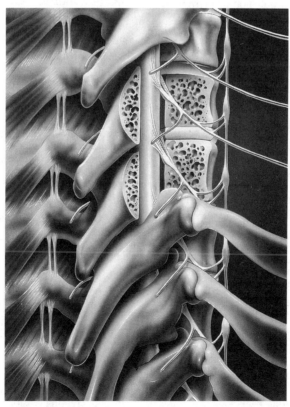

Keith Kasnot, *Medical Illustrator,* 15 x 19, gouache.
Courtesy: Intermedics, Inc.

Edge School. Recent work deals with themes such as life and disintegration, meaning and chaos, distortion and metamorphic forms. Paintings are in acrylic and oil. He also combines painting and enameling on cut-out metal to create hammered wall reliefs and sculptural work with figurative imagery. His work has led to processes in sprayed porcelain enamel, multi-colored applications and a synthesis of traditional techniques he calls "sgraffito-grisaille." Other developments of his involve the shaping and forming of light-gauge steel to create modular wall murals.

KIM, ERNIE (Ceramist)
5920 McBryde Ave., Richmond, CA 94805

Born: 1918 Awards: 2nd Place, California State Fair, Sacramento; Purchase Award, Palo Alto Art Annual Collections: Smithsonian Institute, Washington, D.C.; Everson Museum of Art, Syracuse, NY Exhibitions: Wichita Ceramics Nationals; Buenos Aires Invitational Education: Los Angeles City College

Active primarily during the 1950s and 1960s, he was inactive for some ten years as the director of the Richmond Art Center. After he retired, he had a studio built, in which he has been working since 1983. His early work shows the influence of abstract expressionists Kline, Miro, Feininger and Hoffman. Most all of the show pieces and studio pottery from this period feature extensive surface treatment, including wax resists, inlay, mishima and heavy brush and line work. Using slips and oxides, he developed a style with strong contrasting passages. In most cases, he preferred high-fire stoneware, using dull pastel and earth tones with accents of bright color. He continues to explore line and texture in clay plaques and non-objective cast bronze.

KIMBALL, CHUCK (Photographer, Printmaker)
P.O. Box 2408, Julian, CA 92036

Born: 1939 Exhibitions: La Jolla Museum of Contemporary Art; Museum of Photographic Arts, San Diego Dealer: Art Consultants West, San Diego; Pirets Gallery, La Jolla

Influenced by post-Renaissance Dutch and Flemish schools, as well as by secessionists and pictorialists in early American photography, he began serious photography in the late 1960s. His early technical training brought him work in scientific photography and his interest in figurative photography led to successes in both fashion and consumer product photography. His personal work through the 1970s and early 1980s involved abstract portrayal of the human (usually female) body. This period also marked the refinement of his interest in negative space. In 1987, he began serious work with the bromoil process. His personal style continues to follow its pictorialist beginnings with works in both silver and non-silver processes.

KING, DAVID F. (Sculptor)
500 Western Dr., Point Richmond, CA 94801

Born: 1937 Awards: 1st Prize, Kingsley Annual Art Exhibition, Sacramento Collections: Oakland Museum Exhibitions: Hank Baum Gallery, San Francisco; Crocker Art Gallery, Sacramento Education: UC-Davis Dealer: Hank Baum Gallery, San Francisco

He is known for his artistic constructions infused with a dada-esque humor and for his traditional hand tools in wood and metal, each of which he sets in its own elegant and detailed case or upon a pedestal as a piece of sculpture. Australian Hammer, for example, is a hammer with an inlaid wooden handle shaped like a boomerang and set in shallow wooden box resembling a fine cigar box. His Tooth Saw is fitted with human teeth protruding from an edge of pink gums and comes in a violin-type case. Political Tool Kit is composed of a hammer lying diagonally in a lined case, its head made of metal polished to a mirror-like finish and its handle of inlaid wood. Upon this rests a small sickle—its blade, too, of a mirror-like brilliance, its handle also of wood. Marcel Duchamp, the funk movement and the Hairy Who are influences.

KING, ROBERT (Painter)
48 Vista Del Mar, Santa Barbara, CA 93109

Born: 1953 Awards: William Dole Fund Purchase Award Collections: City of Santa Barbara Exhibitions: Brandom's, Santa Barbara; Arlington Gallery, Santa Barbara Education: UCLA

Early influences include Rivers, de Kooning and Olivera. In his training, both drawing and painting, he focused on the human figure. Early pieces feature a combination of thinly-applied oil color, and charcoal or pastel lines, which outline figures placed in an atmospheric background. He has moved from human figuration to abstracted, totemic figuration. His more recent works are increasingly tactile; the paint is applied in thick layers, with intense coloration, which creates an evocative and elemental

KING, RUTH M. (Painter)
2416 Sycamore Ct., Santa Rosa, CA 95404

Born: 1922 Awards: Best of Show, Sonoma County; Best of Show, St. Helena Wine Country Artists Exhibitions: Williams Gallery, St. Helena; Studio Gallery, Santa Rosa Education: Santa Rosa Junior College

Influenced by her knowledge of horticulture and her career as a landscape designer, she took up painting to express her feelings about nature's grandeur. She concentrates on the uses of color, light, harmony and contrast, producing happy, restful paintings that seem to invite the viewer to relax. She now paints large garden scenes, forestscapes and the everyday use of nature along busy city streets. Constantly experimenting with new supports, she has used linen, jute and various types of Masonite materials. She has also been exploring the use of pastels on these different materials.

KING, SUSAN M. (Painter)
6016 El Mio Dr., Los Angeles, CA 90042

Born: 1958 Exhibitions: California State U., Northridge Faculty Show; Rico Gallery, Los Angeles Education: USC; U. of North Carolina, Chapel Hill

In the late 1970s and 1980s, she developed an abstract expressionist style influenced by Clifford Still and Philip Guston. Her first pieces were dense compositions of oil impasto. She then began opposing open canvas and thickly painted areas. In the manner of Guston, her abstract organic forms evolved into figures. Her isolated primal forms emerge out of a rhythmic, undulating ground, devoid of normal notions of space. Her primed but apparently bare canvas provides a raw, soft quality to the work and functions as a figure as well as a ground, creating tension and confusion evocative of the tension between the individual and his or her culture and surroundings.

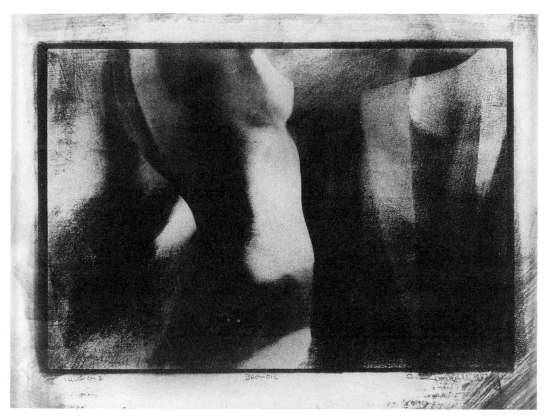

C. Kimball, *Illusions,* 6 x 9, bromoil

David Kreitzer, *The Lunch Line,* 40 x 60, watercolor

KINGSBURY, ROBERT (Sculptor)
760 Wisconsin St., San Francisco, CA 94107

Born: 1924 *Awards:* Merit Award, City of San Francisco; Design Award, NYC Art Director's Club *Collections:* City of San Francisco; Grace Cathedral, San Francisco *Exhibitions:* Pasadena Art Museum; Museum of Contemporary Crafts, NYC *Education:* U. of Michigan; Konstfackskolan, Stockholm

After receiving an abstract background in the U.S., he went to Sweden and studied a more traditional approach to sculpture under Robert Nilsson. One of his most remarkable pieces is a life-sized English thoroughbred horse carved from laminated redwood. He considers the carved redwood cathedra (bishop's seat) in San Francisco's Grace Cathedral a major work. In the early 1980s, he stopped carving wood and began sculpting in papier mache, which he uses like clay: layering it over a wire form; rasping, cutting, sanding; and finishing it with a sealer. Any of his pieces can be cast in bronze.

KINNEE, SANDY (Painter, Printmaker)
1202 N. Institute, Colorado Springs, CO 80903

Born: 1947 *Awards:* Western States Arts Foundation, Printmaker Fellowship; Pollack-Krasner Foundation Grant *Collections:* Metropolitan Museum of Art, NYC; National Collection of Fine Art *Exhibitions:* Cunningham Memorial Art Gallery, Bakersfield; Dubins Gallery, Los Angeles *Education:* U. of Michigan; Wayne State U. *Dealer:* Orion Editions, New York

He began working with shaped, hand-made paper in 1975. Combining the shaped format with screen-printing and intaglio, each "print" is uniquely inked, hand-colored and modified beyond the traditional concept of an editioned print. The work takes its influence from non-Western art, most notably from Japanese and Chinese traditions. A major series explores the forms of fans and kimonos. In these pieces, a myriad of lavish, decorative designs transform the two-dimensionality of the T-shaped kimono and the opened fan into motion and expression, while still maintaining the forms' outline and inherent flatness. While these pieces utilize a symmetrical outer form, some recent works employ a disrupted symmetry. These pieces frequently take the form of 8-foot-tall diptychs in which an element or shape that appears partially in one portion of the work reappears or is completed in another portion.

KIRBY, SHELDON (Painter, Sculptor)
4202 Norfolk Terr., San Diego, CA 92116

Born: 1924 *Awards:* State Department Fellowship to Peru *Exhibitions:* La Jolla Museum; San Diego Art Institute

As an expressionist, his early influences were the philosophical approaches of Van Gogh, Munch and the German Expressionists. His early works were paintings, but he gradually moved into the third dimension, making sculpture and multimedia work as well. He continued to work in two and three dimensions, and he developed major aquatic and abstract themes of "Marines." Later he used oil on canvas and raised line to paint images of ancient bird-man figures in his series of monumental "Talisman" paintings. He has been a teacher for more than twenty years, and he is currently working in a figurative, expressionist style.

KIRBY, THOMAS (Painter)
118 Willow St., Salinas, CA 93901

Born: 1926 *Collections:* Museum of Fine Arts, Anchorage, AK; Santa Fe Fine Arts Museum *Exhibitions:* San Francisco Museum of Art; Monterey Peninsula Museum of Art *Education:* San Francisco Art Institute *Dealer:* Gumps, San Francisco

Early in his career, he studied with Clyfford Still in San Francisco and with Mark Rothko in New York. His work, in oils and watercolors, is guided by the dictates of abstract expressionism. Although the paintings are abstracted, a recurring image is a face, its expression and appearance both complicated and expanded by the technique. Recently, he has worked most often in watercolor, using transparent, bright colors and still focusing on the image of the face. These luminous, gestural paintings are done on rag paper; the predominant colors are vivid violets and blues, which appear with white, unpainted areas. He has also created landscapes that are horizontal, as opposed to the verticality of the 'portraits'.

KIRCHNER, WILLIAM (Painter)
2602 11th Ave., Oakland, CA 94606

Born: 1945 *Awards:* Director's Award, San Francisco Art Festival *Exhibitions:* Office of the President, Stanford U.; Imago Gallery, San Francisco *Education:* Academy of Art, San Francisco; California College of Arts and Crafts

In the late 1960s and early 1970s, he found himself included in the first of a series of shows presenting a new art style called the Visionary Art Movement. At the time, he was working in oil on canvas in a hard-edged style, using intense colors and geometric patterns to explore the realm of automatic drawing and the mandala form. He spent two years creating a series of works, the "Extraterrestrial Epistemological Specimens Collection." During this time, he switched to acrylics, searching for a greater concentration of color and pattern. During the past eight years, a transformation from geometric forms toward a more lyrical response to nature prompted the flowering of a fantastic world of creatures and plant life, "The Pre-Futurist Visionary Swamp Cycle."

KIRSCH, CAROL (Painting)
1638 Huntington Dr., Ste. C, South Pasadena, CA 91030

Born: 1935 *Awards:* Purchase Award, San Jacinto Junior College *Exhibitions:* Bridge Gallery, Los Angeles City Hall; Richard Bennet Gallery, Hollywood *Education:* Cal. State-Los Angeles

The basis of her work is her interest in line and color, expressed through the medium of watercolor: the directions of lines, how they intersect and the changes they cause when combined with color form the compositional and philosophical foundations of her pieces. Working with a wide, flat brush, she mixes color on white paper in a layering technique by applying thin washes of transparent color, occasionally drawing off pigment with salt. Recent watercolor work is primarily in black and white, showing non-objective and abstract symbolic landscapes, such as the work *Road Blocks*. This piece draws its symbolism from the white lines on the highway and is related to the struggle against apartheid in South Africa.

Robert Kingsbury, *Goalie,* 15 x 17, walnut and ash. Photograph: Erik Weber

William Kirchner, *Come in the Waters Fine,* 40 x 48, acrylic. Courtesy: Martin Allen

KITTREDGE, NANCY (Painter)

c/o J.J. Brookings Gallery, 330 Commercial St., San Jose, CA 95108

Awards: Cover, Contemporary Women Artists Calendar; *Who's Who in American Art Collections:* University of Maine, Orono; Industrial Metals of the South, Inc. *Exhibitions:* San Diego Museum of Art; Laguna Beach Museum of Art *Education:* U. of Maine; U. of Miami *Dealer:* J.J. Brookings Gallery, San Jose; Joy Horwich Gallery, Chicago; Orlando Gallery, Sherman Oaks

A figurative painter, her early work was influenced by the atmosphere, people and lifestyle of New Orleans in the 1960s. Painting on masonite, she employed a palette limited to earth tones and worked with a palette knife in a post-impressionist style. In the 1970s, her colors grew brighter and more consistent with the California environment. She shifted to brushes, and her figures became increasingly expressionistic and entirely imaginary. In the mid-1980s, she progressed to large-scale canvas works of up to 8 feet. Her liberated figures in these works balloon and shrink, leap across the canvas, turn upside-down and peer from the edge of the canvas. Calmed from the transition period, the paintings have assumed a solid maturity and strength, but incorporate the powerful, rich painting and color of her previous work.

KLARIN, KARLA (Painter)

500 Ashland Ave., Santa Monica, CA 90405

Born: 1953 *Awards:* Young Talent Award, Los Angeles County Museum of Art *Collections:* Los Angeles County Museum of Art; Atlantic Richfield Corp. *Exhibitions:* Karl Bornstein Gallery, Santa Monica; Amerika Haus, West Berlin *Education:* Otis Art Institute; San Francisco Art Institute

The inspiration for her high-relief paintings is daily life, whether that be the drama of the Hollywood Bowl, the intricacy of a freeway interchange in Glendale or a still life of an artist's studio table. In the thick and loosely painted wall panels incorporating mixed-media objects and protruding planes, she chronicles the ambience of Southern California. Recent works have shifted from the somber palette and the architectural structuring of downtown Los Angeles and the pyramids of Mexico to brighter-hued vistas of the suburbs, where she has begun to introduce the figure into her landscapes.

KLEIMAN, GEORGE (Painter)

1650 Cosmo Street, Hollywood CA 90028

Born: 1946 *Collections:* Private Banking Division, Citicorp, NYC; Pepsico Inc., Purchase, NY *Exhibitions:* Van Doren Gallery, San Francisco; Mirage Gallery, Los Angeles *Education:* San Jose State U.; City College of New York *Dealer:* Suzanne Brown Gallery, Scottsdale, AZ

His formal studies in architecture and industrial design are manifest in an acute concern for space and form. Although initial paintings were figurative in nature, abstraction came naturally, and, by the late 1970s, he was producing the intensely colored, non-objective works for which he is best known. His forms, covering the full range of the color spectrum, represent energy and emotion and create a space without traditional perspective.

KLEIN, E. SUZANNE (Painter)

837 Pomona, Albany, CA 94706

Born: 1944 *Awards:* Purchase Award, Berkeley Art Center Annual Juried Show; Purchase Award, "Works of Art on Paper," Eureka *Exhibitions:* Hall of Flowers, San Francisco *Education:* Goucher College

She works in watercolors and oils, rendering both the elements of the real world and of a transcendant world. Her paintings are based on observations of life and are rendered in a suggestive, evocative style. Recently, she has been working on a series of narrative paintings of horses.

KLEIN, PAMELA HIRD (Fiber Artist)

5975 Samuel St., La Mesa, CA 92042

Born: 1953 *Collections:* Scripps Memorial Hospital, Claremont; Citibank, Orange County *Exhibitions:* A.R.T./Beasley Gallery, San Diego; Aesthetic Collection, San Diego *Education:* Pratt Institute *Dealer:* Artworks, San Diego

Having studied tapestry weaving in Sweden, she began her career using plant motifs in combination with geometric forms. Recently, she has employed a landscape image, which may be abstracted. In order to maintain clean lines in her predominantly diagonal compositions, she leaves small slits in the weave so that no color overlaps. This process has led her to experiment with open spaces that give the impression of cutouts. Weaving with yarns of cotton, wool, acrylic and silk, she uses black and white to create contrasts and accentuate the broad, flat forms created by the brightly colored yarns.

KLEINMAN, ISLE (Painter)

1132 15th St., #4, Santa Monica, CA 90403

Born: 1925 *Exhibitions:* Oranges/Sardines, Los Angeles; Ansdell Gallery, London *Education:* University of Cape Town

Her style combines broad European influences, particularly Max Beckmann and Kathe Kollwitz. Working prolifically, she paints large canvases in vibrant colors with thick impasto. Her recent woodcuts, etchings and drawings, both abstract and expressionist, refer to the suffering of humankind, and in particular, to that experienced during the Holocaust. With dark graphic lines, she depicts people who are confined in their own chaos around them, trying to break into the light. These lines contrast with an overall brightness of color and feeling that evokes her expressionist influences. Addressing the entrapment we are all conditioned to accept, there are circles surrounded by masses, which endeavor to free themselves and move upwards.

KLIMEK, CAROL ANN (Painter)

727 Garfield Ave., South Pasadena, CA 91030

Born: 1950 *Awards:* 2nd Place, Mixed Media, Sacramento Art Festival; 3rd Place, Oils, California College of Arts & Crafts *Exhibitions:* All State Building, Glendale; City College, Long Beach *Education:* Eastern Michigan U.; California College of Arts and Crafts *Dealer:* Jillian Coldiron, Los Angeles and San Francisco

She has always worked on a large scale (usually 8 by 10 feet) and emphasized texture. Her representational style features archetypal symbols, aerial views of the earth, ancient structures (contrasted with with other worldly environments), engulfing tunnels and stadiums. She uses a variety of application techniques,

Sheldon Kirby, *Marine Pieta,* 37 x 48, oil

Nancy Kittredge, *Revelation,* 36 x 48, diptych, oil on canvas. Courtesy: J.J. Brookings Gallery, San Jose, CA

Sherry Karver, *Crystal Cluster,* 36 x 52 x 1, clay

Richard Klix, *Prance,* 36 x 48, acrylic

682

George Kleiman, *untitled 3086,* 82 x 135, acrylic on canvas

Sheng-Piao Kiang, *Sunrise,* 48 x 36, mixed media

including stencil, spray gun, stucco gun, airbrush and toothbrush. Over time, her paintings have become more refined. Their contents are spiritual, and she chooses colors for emotional, rather than decorative, reasons. The main thrust of her work is to express a centralized image where all lines and shapes move toward the center and off the canvas. Because of the detail, the viewer is interested in viewing the work both from a distance and close-up.

KLINGLER, PHILLIP B. (Painter, Electronic Sound Artist)
115 W. 33rd St., San Bernardino, CA 92405

Born: 1960 *Exhibitions:* All California Biennial Exhibition, Riverside; "U.S. Out of Central America Mail Art Show," Los Angeles, Washington, D.C. *Education:* Northern Michigan U.

His paintings, influenced by Wolf Niessin, Max Beckmann, Marcel Duchamp and Jackson Pollock, are somewhat figurative, with elements of abstraction. Vividly colored human faces, exhibiting anger, boredom and shock, stare at the viewer, demanding a response. These paintings have damaged surfaces, which reveal layers of paint and refer to the complexity of the human psyche. His soundscapes are derived from electro-acoustic sound sources, which are electronically manipulated to produce harsh, noisy, industrial mediascapes. Disillusioned with the Los Angeles gallery community, he began creating and distributing his work via cassette and xeroxography. This mail-art has been traded and sold to interested artists and collectors all over the world. Pleased by the response, he finds the personal aspects of these exchanges worthwhile and satisfying.

KLIX, RICHARD (Painter)
2211 4th St., Santa Monica, CA 90405

Born: 1928 *Awards:* 1st Prize, International Art Festival, Los Angeles; Downey Museum Annual Prize *Collections:* Wiseman Collection, Europe, NYC and California; Solymer & Ditman Collections *Exhibitions:* Warner Center, Los Angeles *Education:* Yale U.

He was initially influenced by abstract expressionism, and in the mid-1950s he developed color fields of "ideographs"—impastoed lines in "Op" colors flowing spontaneously in flat patterns. After years of following the Abstract Expressionists' dictum to "paint out anything that looked like something," he began to approach realistic subject matter in the form of dream images. His more recent works utilize abstract pattern, realistic rendering and a brightly colored outline of figure. The figures themselves are transparent or only partially filled in, a technique that weds figure and ground and suggests the interconnection between man and environment.

KNOOP, JAN (Painter, Sculptor)
57 Locust Hill Rd., Cincinnati, OH 45245

Born: Awards: 1st Place, Metal Sculpture, New England Six State Competition, Brockton Art Museum, Massachusetts; 1st Place, Metal Sculpture, Cincinnati Natural History Museum *Exhibitions:* Sculpture to Wear, Los Angeles; Audubon Society Wildlife and Environmental Art Show, Los Angeles *Education:* Vassar College; Boston Museum of Fine Arts *Dealer:* Voorhees Galleries, Sarasota, FL

As a sculptor, she works with a wide variety of found objects. *Motorcycle Bug* is a comic, metallic insect constructed from motorcycle parts. Her most noted sculptures are made of dried and bleached animal bones. To effect a reincarnation of the material, she glues, pegs, wires, colors, cuts, files and draws on the bone to create pieces of austere beauty and humor. A totem pole assembled from cattle vertebrae is haunting in its mimicry of ancient human art. Another piece, formed from cattle ribs suspended from the pelvis, suggest a macabre, primitive mask. Equally innnovative is Metamorphosis I, a series of fifty paintings of animal and human forms in felt-tip and colored pencil. Each painting is completed based on elements of the previous design that have bled through the paper to the sheet below.

KNOTTER, PAUL (Painter, Video Artist)
953 11th St., Santa Monica, CA 90404

Born: 1952 *Awards:* Ford Foundation; Anna Bing Arnold Award *Collections:* Chemical Bank, NYC; Executive Life Center, Los Angeles *Exhibitions:* Newspace, Los Angeles; 49th Parallel, NYC *Education:* U. of California; Arizona State U. *Dealer:* Newspace, Los Angeles

He manipulates various media to convey complex ideas about art and contemporary culture. In his 1979 room-sized installation, *Clubhouse (Art and Leisure in the 1980s)*, he used misleading photographs, real objects and trompe l'oeil paintings as metaphors for the average citizen's perception of a consumer society. With the debris of common events, he builds up a puzzling grid of associations that forces the viewer to reconsider how the objects in the show operate in real life. His work provokes a realization about how we code the reality around us. He is also active in performance and video.

KNOWLTON, MICHAEL (Painter)
320 Calle Del Mar, Stinson Beach, CA 94970

Born: 1950 *Collections:* San Francisco Police Academy *Exhibitions:* Jeremy Stone Gallery, San Francisco; Gallery 30, San Mateo *Education:* San Francisco State College *Dealer:* Jeremy Stone Gallery, San Francisco

After studying with photo-realists Robert Bechtle and Richard McLean, he painted coastal landscapes and figures on a beach en plein air. His colors of the time approached intense purity, and his paint was full and lush. While he continues to paint from life, in 1987 he began a series of night paintings. These invented dockside landscapes were inspired by Steinbeck's novel, *Cannery Row*. Their improvised imagery is generalized, but solid enough to be believable. Using fields of muted tones and bright accents, he saturates his canvas with oil paints. He has been influence by Sargent and the Bay Area Figurative Painters.

KNUDSEN, LOIS A. (Sculptor)
14318 Carl St., Arleta, CA 91331

Exhibitions: The Egg and the Eye, Los Angeles; Museum of Science and Industry, Los Angeles *Education:* Cal. State- Los Angeles

A distinctive, naive quality marks the work of this sculptor, who works in stoneware and porcelein. Traditional ceramic techniques learned through formal studies are integrated with her own animated "pulled sculpture". The artist molds several wheel- thrown pieces into a basic form onto which she grafts humanizing elements—arms, legs, clothing. Glazes are applied sparingly in the capacity of accent only, just as are the feathers, brass poles, or wheels that complete her finished pieces. The artist gleans the majority of

Lois A. Knudsen, *Etruscan Horse,* 20 x 18, stoneware

David Kelso, *Snare,* 30 x 22, etching, aquatint.
Courtesy: Made in California

ideas for projects from animals and people in her daily life.

K.O. (Photographer)
P.O. Box 883754, San Francisco, CA 94188-3754

Born: 1950 *Awards:* Smithsonian Fellowship; CalArts Artist-in-Residence *Exhibitions:* Manuelita's Fine Arts, San Francisco; Galeria De La Raza, San Francisco *Education:* San Francisco Art Institute; UC-Berkeley

She took up photography in order to record her multi-media constructions and arrangements. The medium captivated her and she began making images of subjects as varied as the Californian lifestyles she was documenting. Working with macro and 50mm lenses, she developed a tight compositional style utilizing depth-of-field. Her later studies of street people and environmental subject matter show the influence of her formal study of film and anthropology. Her present black-and-white single-frame images and multiframe mosaics encompass a dialogue with Southeast Asia and China's southern provinces while at the same time expressing her external and internal perceptions of the Pacific Rim.

KOBIS, JEANETTE E. (Painter)
1464 Quiet Meadow Ct., San Jose, CA 95121

Born: 1926 *Awards:* Purchase Award, Richmond Museum of Art, Richmond, VA *Exhibitions:* Sun Gallery, Cupertino *Education:* Academy of Art, Chicago *Education:* Evergreen College

Her interest lies in the depiction of animal life from the naturalist's perspective; in this work, her early influences included Ernest Thompson Seton, Edwin Landseer and Charles Robert Knight. Her paintings are rendered in acrylic; her sculptures, which include both bas reliefs and freestanding pieces, are based on papier maché and finished with modeling paste and acrylic paint. Her subjects range from butterflies to elephants. Some of her works are highly realistic; others are stylized and decorative. Her later influences include the work of Robert Bateman, Bob Kuhn and David Shepherd.

KOBLICK, FREDA (Sculptor)
3535 19th St., San Francisco, CA 94110

Born: 1921 *Awards:* NEA Grant; Guggenheim Fellowship *Collections:* Art Museum, Arizona State University, Tempe; Museum of Contemporary Crafts, New York City *Exhibitions:* Crocker Museum, Sacramento, CA; Fresno Art Center, Fresno, CA *Education:* San Francisco State College; Plastic Industries Technical Institute

The first woman to graduate from the Plastics Industries Institute, she has worked with acrylic plastics as her sole artistic medium for the past 45 years. From her earliest experimental work exploring the aesthetic potential of transparent plastics, she moved to working closely with architects to create pieces that were used in a building context. She has been making freestanding acrylic sculpture since 1962. In the mid-1960s, she spent two years in England setting up and teaching in an experimental plastics group at the Royal College of Art. In 1970, she received a Guggenheim Fellowship in sculpture. She continues to work, and views the concept of plastics as having unending possibilities aesthetically, technically and expressively.

KOCOUR, RUTH ANNE (Painter)
1250 Douglas Fir Dr., Reno, NV 89511

Born: 1947 *Exhibitions:* Gallery NAGA, Boston; Sierra Nevada Museum of Art, Reno, NV *Education:* U. of Utah; U. of Colorado *Dealer:* Gallery NAGA, Boston

Her narrative paintings of figures in stylized Nevada landscapes combine fact and fantasy, exhibiting a surrealist compositional approach that juxtaposes personal and non-rational images—beautifully detailed doves float improbably above pigs; a huge paper airplane rests on the utterly flat desert floor. But unlike much modern surrealism, the pieces contain a dynamic play of psychological elements that imbue the images with lyricism and humanity. Recent developments in her work include a shift of color toward more delicate tones, which lend the pieces an even more dreamlike quality, and the use of a personalized pointillist technique. This airy pointillism contrasts with the hard edges of the flat backgrounds, reinforcing the sense of contradiction and unreality that pervade the paintings.

KOENIGSBERG, PAT (Sculptor)
96 Robin Hood Dr., San Rafael, CA 94901

Born: 1945 *Awards:* Merit Award, National Metals Exhibit, College of Marin County *Exhibitions:* San Diego Art Institute; San Francisco Museum of Modern Art Rental Gallery *Education:* Wellesley College; U. of South Carolina

Initially she focused on painting and printmaking, but in 1978 she switched to sculpture. Her first efforts consisted of primitive, childlike fantasy characters in clay and bronze. Recently, she has been constructing three-dimensional welded steel-rod sculptures, essentially drawing in space. The pieces are built from bent, curved and welded steel rods. She frequently begins by playing with them, taping the rods into different configurations before welding them into their final positions. In addition to sculpting, she has a private, part-time practice in marriage, family and child counseling.

KOHLSCHREIBER, MOLLY H. (Painter)
SVL 7524, Victorville, CA 92392

Born: 1938 *Awards:* Best of Show, High Desert Artists Annual *Collections:* Victor Valley College, Victorville; Charles County Community College, La Plata, MD *Exhibitions:* Riverside Art Museum; Watercolor West, Brea *Education:* Cal. State-Long Beach

Her paintings have always shown a Southwestern flavor. Early on, she depicted the rocky landscape of the high desert. Over the last few years, she has become enthralled with ancient, and so far indecipherable, petroglyphs and other Indian artifacts. She began collaging photographs into painting when she accidentally placed a black and white photograph of a petroglyph on a watercolor painting in progress. She liked what she saw so much that she now uses the combination to create mysterious "Photo-Glyphs" and Glyph-Scapes. She is also expressing her love of horses in a series of colorful paintings of carousel figures. She is an art instructor at Victor Valley College in California.

KOLLINGER, HARRY (Painter)
234 Elm St., #104, San Mateo, CA

Born: 1911 *Awards:* Art Achievement Award, Artists' Society International; Artist of the Year, Burlingame Art Society *Exhibitions:* McKewn Gallery, Spanishtown; San Mateo Library

Carol Kirsch, *Road Block,* 24 x 32, watercolor

Josephine Kopenhaver, *Sea Gulls— Celebration,* 19 x 24, watercolor

Impressionistic paintings of landscapes and a large variety of collages and paint-knife works make up his body of early work. More recently, he has completed a 16-inch series, his "Crystal Collection," which depicts a series of world-famous glass sculptures set against dark backgrounds of canvas or masonite. He captures reflections of light in these works using bright color and primarily large brushstrokes. His works show concern for detail and delicate line.

KOMISAR, MILTON (Sculptor)
6420 Salem St., Oakland, CA 94608

Born: 1935 *Awards:* Fulbright Fellowship; NEA Grant *Collections:* Metropolitan Life Insurance *Exhibitions:* San Francisco Museum of Modern Art; San Jose Museum of Art *Education:* UC-Berkeley; Center for Advanced Visual Studies, Massachusetts Institute of Technology

He began as a figurative painter, but in the 1960s he began making walk-in installations in the style of Segal and Kienholtz. A major transition occured in 1973, when he built light sculptures from plexiglas rods, programmed with a high-tech system of choreographed light patterns running through the rods. Over the past fifteen years, he has continued to explore the formation of visual surfaces by working with light. Changes in intensity and color are now created through software. Colors are generated through programmed combinations of red, blue and green. The architectural and organic shapes are created additively. Recently, he has begun to build permanent, modular pieces that can be reconstructed and recombined for each site.

KOO, GRACE (Painter)
311 Vista Trucha, Newport Beach, CA 92660

Born: 1921 *Awards:* Newport Beach Arts Council; Mendocino Art Center *Exhibitions:* Village Artistry, Carmel; Gallery Fair, Mendocino *Education:* UC-Irvine *Dealer:* Anna White, Mendocino

Her early works were informed by an Oriental view of cosmic unity, and although the works have become larger in size as her career has progressed, the content still explores this motif. Her collages draw on intuition and chance rather than rules and order. Those in watercolor employ rice paper that is tinted and painted. As she applies layer upon layer, the pieces achieve not only texture but an ethereal quality. She uses either primary colors or light pastels, abstract forms taking shape out of her loose, free style. Very little drawing is present; the amorphous, fluid quality arises from the tinted washes and highly textured surfaces.

KOONS, JEFF (Sculptor)
c/o Sonnabend, 420 West Broadway, New York, NY 10012

Born: 1955 *Exhibitions:* Rena Bransten Gallery, San Francisco; Daniel Weinberg Gallery, Los Angeles *Education:* Maryland Institute College of Art; School of the Art Institute of Chicago *Dealer:* Sonnabend, NYC

He reproduces or re-presents consumer goods as symbols that confront moral and social issues. In 1980, he started encasing vacuum cleaners under plexiglas boxes to represent the new and to explore self-containment, display and preservation. He turned to the idea of submersion in 1985 in a show that featured tanks in which basketballs floated in suspension, bronzes of

scuba snorkels and Nike posters of sports figures. In 1986, he created an edition of stainless steel, decorative Jim Beam decanters that were sent to the factory in Kentucky to be filled with liquor and officially sealed. Recent works include reproductions of kitsch gift items cast in steel and an inflated rabbit made in Taiwan.

KOPENHAVER, JOSEPHINE (Painter)
947 Rome Drive, Los Angeles, CA 90065

Awards: 1st Award, Los Angeles Arts *Exhibitions:* Bowers Museum, Santa Ana; San Bernardino County Museum *Education:* UC-Berkeley

Her recent body of work consists primarily of large, oil-on-canvas abstractions exploring and seeking to suggest the huge spaciousness of the sky. She also works in watercolor, which allows for suggestive and subtle structures, rather than flat assertions. In both media, she often employs collage, which is then frequently painted over, underscoring the dreamlike quality of thoughts and impressions. The works are grounded by abstract or semi-abstract structures that provide a strong vertical and horizontal line arrangement.

KOPP, J.V. (Painter)
6935 Arrowwood Ct., Modesto, CA 95355

Born: 1937 *Awards:* Award of Excellence, Franzia Gallery, Modesto *Collections:* Elena Restaurant Collection, Riverbank; B. Han Collection, Modesto *Exhibitions:* Franzia Gallery, Modesto; Pine Tree Gallery, Troy, AL *Education:* Lone Mountain College *Dealer:* Leon Boyar, NYC

The artist's formal studies included extensive training in egg tempera, watercolor, pen and ink, and pastel media. Her oil technique is the result of separate studies she made of Zurbaran and Knight. Struck by their treatment of value and shadow on the human figure, the artist added drama to her own portraits through application of a deeper, richer palette. She was fascinated by the concept of the common man as subject matter. Later, as landscapes, animals, and other subjects caught her interest, the artist gravitated toward lighter colors. Her looser, more airy style leans towards Expressionism and Impressionism.

KOS, PAUL (Sculptor)
592 Utah St., San Francisco, CA 94110

Born: 1942 *Awards:* NEA Fellowship *Collections:* San Francisco Museum of Modern Art; Fort Worth Art Museum *Exhibitions:* De Young Memorial Museum, San Francisco; Iannetti/Lanzone Gallery, San Francisco *Education:* San Francisco Art Institute

His sculptures are often conceptual pieces that, though direct and simple, address deep themes: the limits of artistic representation, the sometimes ill-defined border between functional structure and sculpture, the way in which cultural and artistic pretensions transform a functional piece. The latter ideas inform a sculpture entitled *Ramp,* an illusionistic structure in which a smoothly circular painted surface rises from the floor to the ceiling at ninety degrees. Along the way, the painted surface and the curving perspective make the climb disconcerting, even difficult. Other works rely on manipulations of textual messages; for instance, the message "the pen is darker than the pencil, but the pen runs out of ink along the way" is written in lines that shadow each other and in which, indeed, the ink script becomes lighter as the sentence nears

J.V. Kopp, *Deliberation of St. Joan,* 30 x 30, oil on canvas. Courtesy: Leon Boyar

Bernice Kussoy, *How Does Your Garden Grow?,* 36" high, welded metal

completion. Critic Kenneth Baker writes of this piece, "It is a kind of concrete poem that leads you from one sense of 'line' to another, from seeing it as writing to seeing it as drawing. Like a lot of Kos' work, it seems both frivolous and profound."

KOSTAN, J. NATASHA (Painter, Mixed Media Artist)
1234 Barrington, Los Angeles, CA 90025

Awards: Honorable Mention, Artists' Liaison, CA *Collections:* Olive View Hospital, Sylmar; Monarch Consolidated, Santa Monica *Exhibitions:* International Student Center Art Gallery, UCLA; Brand Library, Glendale *Education:* Immaculate Heart College *Dealer:* Art Source, Los Angeles

Post-impressionist and expressionist movements influenced her early paintings. During this period, she worked on developing her use of color, painting in oil and acrylic on canvas. Shortly afterward, she began creating architectural abstracts, collages with rice paper, monoprints and oil pastels. More recent works also include Byzantine calligraphy in gilded metallics. She has been deeply impressed by Diebenkorn's expression of line and Rothko's use of color.

KOSUTH, JOSEPH (Conceptual Artist)
591 Broadway, New York, NY 10012

Born: 1945 *Awards:* Cassandra Foundation Grant *Collections:* Museum of Modern Art, NYC; Whitney Museum, NYC *Exhibitions:* Leo Castelli Gallery, NYC; La Jolla Museum of Contemporary Art *Education:* Toledo Museum School of Design; Cleveland Institute of Art; School of Visual Arts, NYC; School for Social Research, NYC *Dealer:* Leo Castelli Gallery, NYC

A hard-core conceptualist, he explores the connections, relationships and analogies between visual perception and language. Early pieces are explicit investigations in which an object, its image and its verbal definition are juxtaposed. In the recent installation *Zero & Not,* he covered the walls of the entire gallery with wallpaper on which he photo-mechanically reproduced, enlarged and repeated a segment from Freud's Psychopathology of Everyday Life. The text was partially obscured by the addition of deletion bars; hence, the larger-than-life words presented were simultaneously repressed through the visual interference imposed upon them.

KOTANO, MARC (Painter)
345 Sutter St., San Francisco, CA 94108

Born: 1952 *Awards:* Society for the Encouragement of Contemporary Art, San Francisco Museum of Modern Art *Collections:* San Francisco Museum of Modern Art *Exhibitions:* San Francisco Museum of Modern Art; San Jose Institute of Contemporary Art *Education:* California College of Arts and Crafts *Dealer:* Stephen Wirtz Gallery, San Francisco

His initial canvases involved a single continuous line within a tonal color field. His gestural and painterly approach suggested the figure and often described forms in silhouette. As his style developed, his canvases became dominated by broad contours that subsequently became calligraphic, much like the early work of Paul Klee. In the earlier work, his ground had been a color field, but he eventually developed it into a worked surface reflecting his linear sensibility. Recently he has been making more painterly canvases and combining the early linear aspects with forms that he evolved from the calligraphic.

KOUZEL, MILDRED (Sculptor, Printmaker)
1048 E. Brookdale Place, Fullerton, CA 92631

Born: 1922 *Collections:* Home Savings and Loan, FL; Temple Beth Tikvah, Fullerton *Exhibitions:* Orange County Center for Contemporary Art, Santa Ana; Brand Library Galleries, Glendale *Education:* California State U. *Dealer:* Art Resource Group, Laguna Beach; Rachel Lozzi, Los Angeles

She was drawn to artists who placed figures in an environment, especially Giacometti, Manzu and Hopper. She chose wax as a sculptural medium because its freedom from armature and its responsiveness to spontaneous ideas and feelings. These sculptures are cast in bronze, treated with chemical patinas and painted in isolated areas with acrylic and oil paint. She started doing monoprints on paper as a way of exploring more images and experimenting with heightened color. As a result, sculptures became more flattened, and she used more surface drawing. The imagery and themes revolve around social and environmental observations, and the search for irony and humor. The sculptures are now abstractions or fragments of dramas. Shape continues to be the dominant element, as she continues to work with contrasting smooth and rough surfaces and areas of geometric design.

KRAMER, ALBERT J. (Painter)
3459 Meier St., Los Angeles, CA 90066

Born: 1908 *Awards:* National Watercolor Society, Los Angeles; 2nd Prize, Cleveland Museum of Art *Collections:* Hughes Aircraft *Exhibitions:* Cleveland Museum of Art; National Orange Shows, San Bernardino *Education:* Cleveland School of Art; U. of Michigan

In addition to his murals and paintings on canvas and paper, he also designs furniture, draperies, wallpaper and greeting cards. His early paintings are impressionistic works—landscapes, interiors with figures and still lifes in transparent watercolors on paper. Inspired by the so-called "naive" painters, he has since changed his style to what he terms "naive Americana." In this style, he works on both paper and canvas using acrylics or oil. He continues to paint landscapes and interiors with figures, but his subjects now include historical events and scenes from the early part of the century. He brings a bright, lively palette to his studies of a horse racing or ice skating scene; he has recently working on a series whose subject is tennis.

KRAUSE, SUE (Printmaker)
1918 Suva Circle, Costa Mesa, CA 92626

Born: 1940 *Collections:* Pepsi; Malibu Savings *Exhibitions:* Parkhurst Gallery, Costa Mesa; Haggenmakers Gallery, Laguna Beach *Education:* U. of Wisconsin

She creates delicately colored etchings and embossed watercolors of places she has seen and enjoyed. The etchings are produced by the lengthy process of cutting and marking a zinc plate, repeatedly dipping it in acid and inking, wiping and re-inking, then "pulling" a print and hand-coloring it. In these softly hued, romantic landscapes, beach scenes, Western landscapes and floral still lifes, she seeks to create warmth and joy.

KRAY, JACK (Painter, Printmaker)
3001 McKillop Rd., Oakland, CA 94602

Born: 1913 *Exhibitions:* Maxwell Art Gallery, San Francisco; Pantheon Gallery, San Francisco

Leo Krikorian, *176 BM,* 62 x 39, acrylic on canvas

Kate Krider, *Coming Apart at the Seams,* 76 x 46 x 6, cast paper, mixed media

Ilse Kilian, *Veiled Birds,* 58 x 28, weaving

691

Early work was influenced by Michelangelo, Rembrandt and Rubens. Later Rouault, Baskin and Grosz brought him up to date and inspired him, through years of drawing, painting and sculpture. More recently Degas' monoprints captured his imagination, and he brought together his disparate influences under the possibilities of the monoprint discipline. His semi-abstract prints of men and women embracing retain recognizable imagery, but change lines and colors. Outlines are simplified and violets, reds and blues are substituted for flesh tones.

KREBS, HANNES (Photographer)
P.O. Box 1629, Mendocino, CA 95460

Born: 1929 *Awards:* Grand Prix, Chile *Collections:* U.S. National Park Service; Photoguild, Mendocino *Exhibitions:* Mendocino Area Parks Association; Mendocino Art Center

He grew up in South America. His early photographs were documentations of scholastic competitions and the Chilean fishing, refining and construction industries. His extensive musical education—he was a concert pianist—allowed him to photograph the conductors and soloists of the Chilean and Argentinian National Symphony Orchestras. Due to the unavailability of color film in Chile, these early images were in black and white. Later, he concentrated on color slide and color negative expressions. He has done a complete photographic record on Chile and a large study of the National Parks of the American West. He documented the 1988-89 season of the Mendocino Music Festival.

KREBS, PATSY (Painter)
P.O. Box 446, Inverness, CA 94937

Born: 1940 *Awards:* Adolph & Esther Gottlieb Foundation Grant *Exhibitions:* Mincher/Wilcox Gallery, San Francisco; Tortue Gallery, Santa Monica *Education:* Claremont Graduate School

Serving her painting apprenticeship in New York during the 1960s, she saw a new school of abstract painting emerge from the abstract expressionism of the 1950s. This profoundly affected all of her work to come: Morris Louis, Al Held, Mark Rothko, Josef Albers and Elsworth Kelly became major inspirations for her. Her paintings from this period are shaped canvases, overlapping circles and ellipses, hinting at a deep spherical space, while remaining resolutely flat. By the late 1960s, aiming for a more personal image, she experimented with acrylic washes on canvas. Building up a density of translucent color toward the edges in a post and lintel arrangement, she achieved a radiance, while affirming the texture of the natural canvas. Eventually these explorations brought her back to flat areas of highly-charged color in a geometric format. Her recent work consists of multipanel paintings, across which large interrupted sections of a circle move, uniting the panels, revealing space in unexpected ways.

KREITZER, DAVID (Painter)
1442 12th St., Los Osos, CA 93402

Born: 1942 *Awards:* Gold Medal, San Francisco Art Directors Club *Collections:* Hirshhorn Collection, Washington DC; Santa Barbara Museum *Exhibitions:* California Polytechnic State U. Ankrum Gallery, Los Angeles; Summa Gallery, NYC *Education:* San Jose State U. *Dealer:* Summa Gallery, NYC

The artist's philosophy—that Realism mirrors reality only because it, like reality, is illusion—embodies the spirit of his painting. In a recent shift of focus, he has returned to figurative work. His approach, however, remains relatively similar to that of his landscape studies. In both alkyd and watercolor work, his technique hinges on a multitude of transparent washes laid carefully over a concise underdrawing. This produces unusual depths of color without compromising the medium's delicacy. Executed on a large scale, recent work contains much of the dramatic impact of its subject matter, the opera.

KRIDER, KATE (Mixed Media Artist)
336 "B" Lester Ave., Oakland, CA 94606

Born: 1952 *Awards:* Best of Show, College of the Siskiyous; Board of Directors, Fiberworks Center for Textile Arts *Exhibitions:* Fiberworks Gallery, Berkeley; Paper International 1989, U. of Nevada, Reno

Early in her career, she wove large-scale wall pieces in a style influenced by ikat, an ancient Japanese resist technique. She eventually took her work off the wall, and manipulated the third dimension by weaving in a wire armature. The pieces were studies that presented the abstract versus the geometric. She now uses a cast paper medium. The work is large and gestural, and her subject is exposure. For example, she exposes the back of a piece by flipping up edges and tearing and splitting the surface, revealing a hidden interior. She evokes movement by draping undulating pieces of wet paper, which harden into earth-like slabs that seem to dance and slide. "My work visually depicts transformations of spirit and internal permutations," she says, "which I express with the malleable medium of paper."

KRIKORIAN, LEO (Painting)
1001 Bridgeway, #435, Sausalito, CA 94965

Born: 1922 *Collections:* Musee du Cholet, France; Thomas Albright, San Francisco *Exhibitions:* Atelier, Paris, San Francisco; Art Expo, Los Angeles

He has long been associated with the avant-garde art scenes in San Francisco and Paris. During the 1950s, he ran The Place, a gathering spot for artists, writers, musicians and poets in San Francisco. Many observers considered The Place to be one of the primary venues for "Beat" art of all media, and it was made famous partly through the writings of Jack Kerouac, a frequent patron. Working in a proto-cubist style, his paintings evolved into color field studies. While promoting the illusion of three-dimensionality, these two-dimensional, geometric patterns always involve the the relation of the center to the edges of the design. Executed in vibrant, complementary colors of acrylic on canvas, these eye-catching works sometimes appear to float away from the surface toward the viewer. Working also in film and stained glass, he divides his time between the Bay area and Paris, exhibiting his work in the U.S. and in Europe.

KRUEGER, BRUCE W. (Sculptor)
1084 Via Roble, Lafayette, CA 94549

Born: 1955 *Awards:* Art Hero, Squiggle Gallery; Honorable Mention, California State Fair *Exhibitions:* Milwaukee Gallery, Richmond; Adventures in Art Gallery, San Francisco *Education:* California College of Arts and Crafts

In his performance art he attempts to create mass hysteria and group insanity. In pseudo-Jungian terminology, he attempts to isolate and massively amplify

Patsy Krebs, *Untitled Fan 1987,* 8 panels, 54 x 96, acrylic on canvas

Katherine Keefer, *2 Feet and Lady,* 78 x 48 x 24
(lady), ceramic with oil paint

David Kelly, *untitled,* 32 x 20, watercolor

specific feeling tone charged complexes. His small scale hypersurrealist sculptures are designed to trigger the same feeling tone charged complexes, but within a specific range of values. He has worked in nearly all sculptural media and has studied both anatomy and figure sculpture. He also makes video and performance art.

KRUSOE, SANA (Ceramist, Sculptor)
1270 N. College Ave., Rear House, Claremont, CA 91711
Born: 1946 *Collections:* Lannan Foundation, Palm Beach, FL; Follwoing Sea, Honolulu, HI *Exhibitions:* Barnsdall Municipal Gallery, Los Angeles; Long Beach Museum of Art *Education:* Occidental College; Claremont Graduate School

Her work is primarily ceramic, highly finished, large or small. Her approach is minimalist, her forms biomorphic, her colors neutral. She is partially indebted to implements and to sea and aircraft.

KUCHAR, GEORGE (Painter, Filmmaker)
3434 A, 19th St., San Francisco, CA 94110
Born: 1942 *Awards:* NEA Grant *Collections:* Museum of Modern Art, NYC *Exhibitions:* American Film Institute, Los Angeles; Pacific Film Archives

After early experimentation in 8mm film, he switched in 1965 to 16mm and began making two short films a year, including his most famous work, *Hold Me While I'm Naked*. In the early 1970s, he took a teaching position at the San Francisco Art Institute, where he continues to work. Among his influences are B-movies of the 1950s, horror comic books and television shows of the 1950s and 1960s.

KUHLMAN, WALTER E. (Painter)
27 Glen Court, Sausalito, CA 94965
Born: 1918 *Awards:* Maestro Award, Calif. Arts Council; Tiffany Foundation, NYC *Collections:* Metropolitan Museum of Art, NYC; Phillips Memorial Gallery, Washington, DC *Exhibitions:* Walker Art Center, Minneapolis; Palace of the Legion of Honor, San Francisco *Education:* Calif. School of Fine Arts, San Francisco; Academie de la Grande Chaumiere, Paris *Dealer:* Maxwell Gallery, San Francisco

His study with Clyfford Still at the California School of Fine Arts paved the way for his work as an abstract expressionist. In the early 1960s, the figure began to appear in his oils. A single, mythic figure often dominates the canvas; his work shows a Nordic theme, invoking the imagery and symbolism of Nordic mythology. Colors are generally muted grays, browns and blues. Several years ago, he began to experiment with monoprints, combining ink, pastel and watercolor. These more recent works translate the previous large, brooding oils into even more mysterious smaller spaces. Both seascapes and landscapes serve as subject matter. Major works include a series of eight studies of Beethoven done in monotype and overlayed with pastel.

KUJUNDZIC, ZELJKO (Painter, Sculptor)
P.O. Box 462, Entiat, WA 98822
Born: 1920 *Awards:* Grand, Ford Foundation; Grant, Institute of Arts & Humanities *Collections:* National Museum, Kyoto, Japan; National Museum, Geneva, Switzerland *Education:* Royal College of Art, Budapest; Academy of Fine Arts, Budapest *Dealer:* Coastal Arts League, El Granada

Born in Yugoslavia and trained in ceramics in Hungary, he has been inspired by ancient art and by the native cultures of America, Japan and Europe. At the center of his work is a concern for the human condition. In his tapestries he draws imagery from Native American culture. In his ceramic sculpture he juxtaposes negative space and positive forms, by carving through the surfaces of his hollow ceramic figures. Likewise, in paintings and murals, he carves windows of irregular shape and inlays welded or cast metal to create a unique relationship of a third dimension to the picture plain. His 16-foot tall stone sculpture, *Gate of Life* in Uniontown, Pennsylvania, is a memorial to the victims of the Nazi Holocaust.

KUMATA, CAROL (Sculptor)
424 N. Craig St., Pittsburgh, PA 15213
Born: 1949 *Awards:* NEA Fellowship *Exhibitions:* American Craft Museum, NYC; A.I.R. Gallery, NYC *Education:* U. of Wisconsin; Michigan State U. *Dealer:* A.I.R. Gallery, NYC

Her earliest small container-like pieces referred to Japanese architecture and clothing and to the artist's Japanese ancestry. Later pieces became metaphors for states of mind. Filling both the outside form and in the inside imagery of her containers with symbolism, she contrasted the two, exploring ideas of facade and reality. The pieces themselves were constructed from copper, bronze or brass sheet metal. They often included mixed media such as wood or resins or stone. Generally the metal was patinated or painted. Recent work is of steel rod and some nonferrous metals. The new work retains many of the same concerns and references. It is larger and more abstract than the earlier work but seems airy and light.

KUNC, KAREN (Printmaker, Draughtsperson)
R.R. 1, P.O. Box 71, Avoca, NE 68307
Born: 1952 *Awards:* NEA Fellowship; 1st Prize, Graphica Atlantica, Rekjavik, Iceland *Collections:* San Francisco Art Museum; Portland Art Museum *Exhibitions:* Matrix Gallery, Sacramento; Mills College Art Gallery, Oakland *Education:* Ohio State U. *Dealer:* Barbara Lorimer Fine Arts, Santa Rosa

Her first woodcuts were a series of large, colorful, vertical abstractions, with an open composition reminiscent of Oriental scrolls. She later developed a technique that enabled her to print many clear, bright colors from one block. This reductive method allows for the image to evolve as it is worked, a process more akin to painting. Using images from personal sources in a highly expressionistic and abstract manner, the large scale prints recreate qualities of light, air and movement, with hues ranging from the densely saturated to transparent auras that become part of the translucent sheet.

KURSH, STEVE (Painter, Multimedia Artist)
P.O. Box 9404, San Rafael, CA 94912
Born: 1956 *Collections:* California College of Arts and Crafts *Exhibitions:* San Francisco Art Institute; S.I.T.E., Los Angeles *Education:* California College of Arts and Crafts

After receiving his formal training in printmaking, he became interested in painting and assemblage. His exploration of multimedia and found object assemblage began one day when, in a fit of frustration, he smashed a canvas and stuck his palette through the tangled frame. Struck by the philosophical and aesthetic

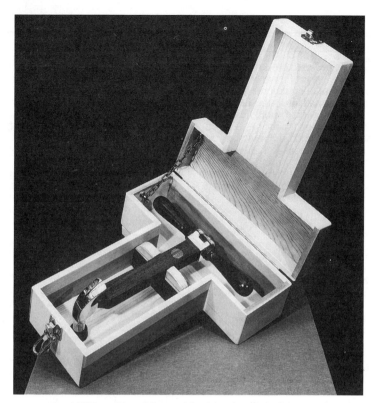

David King, *Ham Mower,* 16 x 14 x 6, wood, silver, steel

Steve Kursh, *To Be With You,* 51 x 44, polymer on wood and found objects.
Courtesy: Tom Rodrigues. Photograph: Jay Daniel

ramifications of this act, he began to produce the witty, sardonic found object assemblages for which he is best known. His pieces offer pointed commentary on consumerism, materialism, advertising, media abuse, gadget-itis and other pop culture maladies, while recognizing our perverse affection for the symbols, images and slogans that have become ingrained in our society and our collective consciousness. He is now gingerly feeling his way back into painting, but is unwilling to forego his artistic fetish for detritus. His most recent pieces are chronicles of the pop culture events, attitudes and personalities of our day.

KUSHNER, ROBERT (Sculptor)
c/o Holly Solomon Gallery, 724 Fifth Ave., New York, NY 10019

Born: 1949 *Collections:* Museum of Modern Art, NYC; Whitney Museum, NYC *Exhibitions:* Holly Solomon Gallery, NYC; Fay Gold Gallery, Atlanta *Education:* UC-San Diego *Dealer:* Holly Solomon Gallery, NYC

Early works are in the pattern of decorative art tradition, an aesthetic which came to the fore in the late 1970s in response to the restrictions of minimalism and which was determined to break the distinction between craft and high art. Recent works are bronze sculptures exhibited this year at the Holly Solomon Gallery in New York City. He has also created performances, and collaborated on costumes and set design for many theater productions in New York.

KUSSOY, BERNICE (Sculptor)
132 Ouggan Ct., Redwood City, CA 94062

Born: 1934 *Collections:* Butler Institue of Art, Youngstown, OH; Howard Lipman Foundation, NY *Exhibitions:* Suma Gallery, San Francisco; 1820 Gallery & Studios, Belmont *Education:* Cooper Union; Cleveland Institute of Art

She received a strong formal education in design and technique, and her works show a profound attraction to the human figure to express human thought. She has developed a complex style of welding using gas, arc light and other techniques, welding scrap metal in such a way as to give the illusion of warmth and movement—a crushed hunk of steel becoming a rose, a knee or a head of hair blowing in the wind. Her sculptures portray a wide range of expressions: youth and age, movement and calm, humor and solemnity, classicism and romanticism. The figures show both classical and baroque sensibilities, and the use of negative as well as positive space reveals an indebtedness to Henry Moore.

KWAN, PAUL (Collage Artist, Performance Artist)
355 15th Ave., #6, San Francisco, CA 94118

Born: 1952 *Awards:* NEA Grant; Artist-in-Residence, Intersection for the Arts, San Francisco *Collections:* Hewlett-Packard *Exhibitions:* Lumina Gallery, San Francisco; Institute of Contemporary Art, San Jose *Education:* San Francisco Art Institute; Conservatory of Music, San Francisco *Dealer:* Soker Kaseman Gallery, San Francisco

He had a rich background in music, dance, poetry, folktales and Buddhist tradition when he arrived in the U.S. in the mid-1970s. After studying western artists and filmmakers, he was prompted to explore the possibilities of combining traditional and contemporary art forms. He started working in collage, viewing it as a metaphor for understanding the fragments of his life. These pieces arise from a sense of discovery and a concern with texture, space, time and movement, expressed through the tension and interplay of color and form. Works begin as drawings or acrylic paintings and then become pasted-down cut-outs on handmade paper combined with other found objects. Often, the collages include print works and become three-dimensional. In the early 1980s, he began to create masks, puppets, films and performance art. In addition to his work with his performance group Persona Grata, he continues to work in the visual arts and has recently completed two collage-print works, *Secrets Behind Doors* and *Wild Cat Looking Her Way Out.*

KWINT-CATTOCHE, SHERRY (Painter)
Born: 1948 *Awards:* Merit Award, Crocker-Kingsley; San Jose Art League *Exhibitions:* Walnut Creek Civic Arts Center *Education:* Lone Mountain College

She uses traditional oil layering techniques to produce self-portraits with a striking realism, which obscures an underlying symbolism. A muted palette is used over an underpainting on paper rather than canvas, for a duller surface. Her work reflects a personal exploration of Jungian themes, asking the question of what is authentically human through dual and recycled images. A mask may appear on a figure, or in her hand; animal skulls are present. Compositional and often direct references to past artists are made. In one piece, a Caravaggio is directly reproduced in the background. Individual dichotomies and spiritual morality inform the images, which are for the most part female. She is concerned with representing an empowered view of woman through her own eyes, freed from male-centered eroticism. She plays with shadows and introduces contradictory light sources in order to create an internal reality that does not adhere to common laws of order.

LABAT, TONY (Installation Artist)
880 Jamestown, San Francisco, CA 94124

Born: 1951 *Awards:* NEA Grant; Englehart Award, ICA, Boston *Collections:* Centre George Pompidou, Paris; Museum of Modern Art, NYC *Exhibitions:* Museum of Contemporary Art, Los Angeles; Artspace, San Francisco *Education:* San Francisco Art Institute

His video installations deconstruct television's tradiional context and decontextualize its traditional role. His purpose is to expose the oppressive structures of the dominant culture and the transforming process of acculturation. In *Babalu*, for example, he illustrates how Desi Arnaz took a Cuban religious icon and exploited it for commercial purposes. Other works juxtapose Western language and customs with those of the Third World, and contrast true expressions of emotion with television's version of grief, joy and tragedy. He constructs installations with monitors, pieces of sculpture, furniture, found objects and directed light and shadow. His most ambitious installation took the entire top floor of the Monadnock Building in downtown San Francisco. Recreating the debris and atmosphere of a construction site, he used six monitors to address the power relationships in business and industry.

LACHOWITZ, KEITH M. (Painter)
200 Northgate Ave., Studio 8, Daly City, CA 94015

Born: 1959 *Exhibitions:* Talahassee National; Doelger Art Center *Education:* U. of Colorado, Boulder

Knox, *End of an Era,* 60 x 80, acrylic on canvas. Courtesy: American Contemplative Art Society of Tyler, TX

Zeljko Kujundzic, *The New China Doll,* 30 inches high, stoneware (ceramic)

Sandy Kinnee, *French Painted Mirror,* 16 x 38, water-color on handmade paper

His background in architecture has led him to an abstract expressionist style in his paintings. His recent work is social commentary, using backgrounds of desolate color and textural field combined with stenciled symbols and words and images in the foreground. The color fields are primarily black or red, with graphite, acrylic, newspaper and oil laid on in as many as five layers. His canvases are mounted on solid wood stretchers, allowing him the freedom to affix image elements with screws or nails or to drill and chisel the surface.

LACKEY, STEPHEN (Sculptor)
19 G Lovell Ave., San Rafael, CA

Born: 1949 *Awards:* 1st Prize, Alligator Gallery, San Francisco *Exhibitions:* Long Beach Art Association; Imago Gallery, San Francisco *Education:* U. of Stockholm, Sweden; Konstfackskolan, Stockholm

Working at his own foundry, he creates bronze sculpture that describes the transition from dead material into figures with life. Earlier work in steel and plaster gradually evolved into a cast bronze technique, using initial figures formed from sheets of wax. His occasionally abstract imagery always allows for viewers' interpretations. Recent work is figurative and is characterized by simplified human forms growing out of square sheets of metal.

LA COM, WAYNE (Painter)
16703 Alginet Pl., Encino, CA 91436

Born: 1922 *Exhibitions:* Brand Library, Glendale; Descanso Gardens, Canada *Education:* Glendale College; UCLA *Dealer:* Village Gallery, Lahaina, HI

In the early 1940s, he began his work in watercolor, painting landscapes directly from nature. During the 1950s, after studying with Rico Lebrum and Guy Maccoy, he changed media, using casein and acrylics to paint abstract landscapes and still lifes. At this time he also experimented in non-objective works involving organic forms. By the mid-1960s, he had returned to watercolor, still attracted to landscapes but now with an emphasis on light, color and space presented in recognizable forms. Painting from wet into wet to direct painting on dry paper, he has created a large body of work painted on location in Hawaii.

LACY, SUZANNE (Performance Artist, Conceptual Artist)
5212 Broadway, Oakland, CA 94618

Born: 1945 *Awards:* NEA Fellowship; McKnight Foundation Fellowship, Minneapolis *Exhibitions:* New Museum of Contemporary Art, NYC; Institute of Contemporary Art, London *Education:* UC-Santa Barbara; California Institute of the Arts

She has organized large-scale performance art events in Los Angeles, San Francisco, San Diego, Las Vegas, New Orleans, New York state and Minneapolis. Two recent events, *The Dark Madonna* and *Crystal Quilt,* involved 180 and 430 performers respectively and took over three years each to produce. Her subjects include controversial social issues— racism, violence against women, homelessness, sexism—and how the media interprets these issues. She is also a filmmaker and a videographer and was recently appointed Dean of the School of Fine Arts at the California College of Arts and Crafts. Her creative work is based on her interest in the potential of art to affect popular culture.

LA FORET LENGYEL, LAURA (Painter, Sculptor)
193 Mill St., San Rafael, CA 94901

Born: 1946 *Awards:* Merit Award, Etching, Marin Society Invitational, Anna Gardner Gallery of Artists *Collections:* Harrah's Club Tahoe; Fetzer Vineyards; Anabelle Candy Co. *Exhibitions:* Anna Gardner Gallery Invitational; Marin County Civic Center Galleries; American Zephyr Gallery, San Francisco *Education:* Mills College; Stanford U.

After exploring various styles and media, she became immersed in an intense exploration of anatomy, the human figure and portraiture. The works of Rembrandt, Rodin, Da Vinci, Rafael, Cassatt and classical Greek and Roman sculpture influenced this experimentation and discovery. Her style evolved into a modern classic realism with flowing water forms, which symbolize ideas and emotions. Her interest in the art forms of past eras led her to work in bas relief. She did extensive research on the settings, fashions and popular images of bygone societies and times. In a similar way, her painting of contemporary scenes is reminiscent of Titian, especially in her unique use of realism, light and carefully mixed colores. She has developed a distinctive modern style of portraiture in bronze and oils which incorporates spirituality and timelessness. A current series of contemporary works is concerned with the visual representation of sound and the fixed motion of musical pattern.

LAGO, SUSANA (Painter, Multimedia Artist)
6418 1/2 W. Olympic, Los Angeles, CA 90048

Awards: Ford Foundation Grant *Collections:* Los Angeles County Art Museum; Art Museum of Santa Cruz County *Exhibitions:* Roberts Gallery, Los Angeles; U. of Judaism, Los Angeles *Education:* Otis Art Institute *Dealer:* Mekler Gallery, Los Angeles

She is best known for her multimedia constructions, which combine the visual and the plastic arts with poetry. Her pieces consist of gooey, thickly painted surfaces with pieces of plexiglas, paper, found items and bits of poetry rendered in calligraphic marks. In the past, she used her art to introduce the Anglo world to Latino poetry. More recently, the poetry of Emily Dickinson has been her inspiration. This series of seventeen pieces features images of birds and bard, and such materials as Polaroid photographs, chicken wire and plastic toys.

LAKE, SHELLEY (Photographer)
967 Hammond St., Unit #4, West Hollywood, CA 90069

Born: 1954 *Awards:* 1st Place, Fine Art, AT&T Image Contest; Clio Award, Best Computer Animation *Collections:* Apple Corporation, Cupertino; Albertson International, Winter Park, FL *Exhibitions:* Natoli-Ross Gallery; Dallas Museum of Art *Education:* Rhode Island School of Design; M.I.T.

In the face of widespread computer phobia, she boldly asserts the value of modern technology as a creative partnership—one that will redefine the meaning of technology and our notions of civil intelligence. By using hyper-real, computer-generated images, she reflects the commercial media's same hyper-real treatment of familiar objects, a practice which leads to consumer penetration and the furious generation of one commercial trend after another. Her more recent

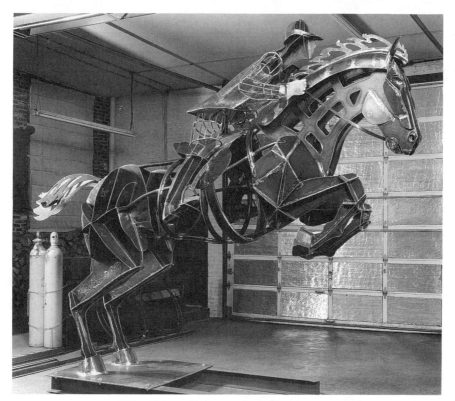

Lisa Kaslow, *The Chase,* 150 x 216 x 60, steel plates and pipe coating.
Courtesy: Rouse & Associates. Photograph: Alan Browne

Eric Lawton, *Zabriskie Point, California,* 20 x 30, cibachrome

work includes a music video, *Polly Gone,* which stars a computer-generated robot.

LAKY, GYONGY (Sculptor)
741 Filbert St., San Francisco, CA 94133

Born: 1944 *Awards:* NEA Fellowship *Collections:* San Francisco Museum of Modern Art; Oakland Museum *Exhibitions:* Oakland Museum; Musee Des Arts Decoratifs, Paris *Education:* UC-Berkeley

She works primarily with large-scale sculptures. Her Pieces work used ropes and other flexible materials in loosely arranged grid structures. These explorations often emphasized linear considerations. As her interests moved toward the possibility of distorting structure and the greater expressive use of line, she became interested in the anarchy possible in systems of organization. Her current work emphasizes casual, open structures and an improvisational arrangement of lines. Shadows assume a prominent role. While most works are executed in sticks and or wire, she has begun using bronze and other materials. In addition to stationary works, she also engages in works that are site-specific and temporary.

LAMANET, SHARI (Draughtsperson, Photographer)
1977 Green St., San Francisco, CA 94123

Born: 1949 *Awards:* Phelan Award in Photography *Exhibitions:* Cameraworks, San Francisco; Koslow/Rayl Gallery, Los Angeles *Education:* San Francisco Art Institute *Dealer:* Bruce Velick Gallery, San Francisco

Behind her work is the cubist conception of observing multiple planes in space at the same time. She diverges from the cubists by utilizing several vantage points, a technique evocative of a late 20th century sensory overload. In 1985, she began incorporating photography into her drawings. She found that photographic images allowed her to place the real world within her fantasy world of swirling vertiginous space. She has also used photo-engravings to create the same effect. The images are designed as true reflections of our time. She is a an instructor at the San Francisco Art Institute.

LAMAR, HOWARD P. (Sculptor, Painter)
967 East Ojai Ave., Ojai, CA 93023

Born: 1947 *Collections:* Merriam Webster Dictionary *Exhibitions:* New Media Gallery, Ventura College; Gift Gallery, Laguna Museum of Art *Education:* El Camino College *Dealer:* Beanie Perkins, Ventura; Barbara Glassman, Maui

His paintings and sculptures are characterized by the predominance of emotional perspective and psychological space over visual perspective and illusory three dimensions. Frustrated with the limits of two-dimensional imagery, he began to study sculpture and was greatly influenced by the works of John Cody and Brancusi. He uses a direct carving method and elements of both primitive and classical styles. Alabaster, chosen for its semi-translucent, radiant qualities, is his preferred medium. His imagery focuses on mother-child figures, and he often arranges groupings of two or three pieces and uses semi-precious stones as accents of color and shape. Influenced by Klee, Matisse, Picasso and Escher, his paintings and pen-and-ink drawings emphasize line and form, and are highlighted by bright splashes of color.

LAMB, DARLIS CAROL (Sculptor)
5515 S. Kenton Way, Englewood, CO 80111

Awards: 1st Place, American Mothers Committee, Nashville, TN; C. Lorillard Wolfe Award for Sculpture, NYC *Collections:* American Lung Association, Benson Park Sculpture Garden, Loveland, CO *Exhibitions:* Cottage Gallery, Carmel; Ferg Gallery, Castle Rock, CO *Education:* U. of Nebraska; Creighton U. *Dealer:* Machbitz Gallery, San Luis Obispo

Prior to living in Colorado, she worked as a painter and printmaker in the Midwest. She worked in oil, acrylic, batik and, especially, watercolor. Her style was rather impressionistic, and her feeling for figures derives from studies of Andrew Wyeth's paintings. She began working in clay in the mid-1970s. She felt that the gradual transition to sculpture was like coming home again, with a stong sense of place in portraying the figure. Work with Stanley Bleifield and Francisco Zuniga aided her in finding direction in the new media. She considers herself a romantic realist, compelled to depict the aesthetic and spiritually beautiful aspects of life. Inspiration for her sculptures derives from her observations of people and places and from her own imagination. Her recent work involves a sculpture depicting the four corners of the earth, *White Buffalo Woman,* a small, representational sculpture inspired by Native American themes, and a sculpture portrait of painter Nikolai Fechin.

LAMB, SHILLA ANDREWS (Painter)
P.O. Box 3, Shoreline Hwy., Little River, CA 95456

Born: 1937 *Awards:* Buckingham Scholar; Boit Prize, School of the Boston Museum of Fine Arts *Exhibitions:* N.W. Ayer Gallery, Los Angeles; Mendocino Art Center *Education:* School of the Boston Museum of Fine Arts *Dealer:* Devorzon Gallery

Her subjects are abstracted from landscapes and nature in a highly individualistic abstract style, and she is primarily interested in light and its influence. As a colorist, she works in oils on canvas and pastels on paper, with a wide palette from pale to intense shades. Her pronounced, gestural strokes sweep in wide arcs across the face of the canvas, creating spatial depth and complexity. Her formal background is in painting and sculpture, from which she has drawn a physicality of movement. Strongly stated color moves the viewer towards a center from which light radiates.

LAMBERT-POLOVY, SHIRLEY (Painter)
P.O. Box 7184, Carmel, CA 93921

Born: 1942 *Exhibitions:* Pacific Grove Art Center; Editions Ltd., San Francisco

A drastic change in lifestyle prompted her switch to the unique watercolor technique that has become her trademark. Once a studio, oil-on-canvas artist, she was forced by an illness to get out into the fresh air; at that time, she switched to abstract watercolor, painted on paper prepared in seawater. Working sometimes with a brush, and at other times, with various pouring techniques, she creates delicate, web-like paintings. The finished work, which often requires weeks to complete, is deceptively spontaneous in appearance. She also does commissioned portraiture in sepia-toned, conte crayons. By fostering an atmosphere of mutual trust, she is able to depict the more subtle, often hidden qualities, which reveal themselves in the eyes and faces of her subjects.

James A. Lawrence, 14 x 22, watercolor

Michael Lawrence, *The Boy and the Dove,* 48 x 31, oil on canvas. Ask artist? Left message on 6-1- 89

Cissi L., *Life's Journey,* 18 x 14, India ink on paper

LAMOSSE, JEANNE (Painter)
12629 Caswell Ave., #P-1, Los Angeles, CA 90066

Born: 1947 *Awards:* Adolph & Esther Gottlieb Artist Award; Hawaii State Foundation for Culture & Arts Purchase Award *Collections:* The Capital Group, Los Angeles.; Metro Goldwyn Mayer Film Co. *Exhibitions:* Brand Library Art Gallery, Glendale; Bakersfield College Art Gallery *Education:* U. of Hawaii

Over the past fifteen years, her painting has moved from expressionism to a more reductive attitude in which the total canvas surrenders to color. Her paintings explore light and color, a fascination for which she attributes to her many years spent living in the intense tropical light of Hawaii. Complicated layers of color, primarily pure hues, are laid down to produce saturated, bright color, the color field allowing for the examination of the specific light of a particular color. The result is a tangible, retinal experience. She considers her work a kind of landscape painting, and draws inspiration from nature. Her work reveals the influence of such artists as Mark Rothko and Barnett Newman.

LANCASTER, ADELINE (Painter)
6266 Killdee Ave., Long Beach, CA 90808

Born: 1905 *Exhibitions:* Long Beach Art Association; Main Library, Long Beach

Working with oil on a traditional canvas or with pastels, she paints scenes from her travels or elements of the world before her. Among her works are seventeen oil paintings of Thailand, Nepal and India. A second series celebrates the United States and includes a painting for each of the fifty states, depicting the state bird, the state flower and other images uniquely associated with the particular state. Many of her paintings are inspired by the foliage in her backyard. Before beginning a picture, she researches the history of the flower or fruit and places it in its historical context. For instance, peaches, which originate from China, are painted against a backdrop of Chinese sampans sailing on Hong Kong Bay; oranges, a fruit commonly associated with California, are set against the beige mission of San Juan Capistrano.

LANDAU, BERYL (Painter)
3290 Harrison St., San Francisco, CA 94110

Born: 1944 *Collections:* Sohio Petroleum Corp.; Bank of America, San Francisco *Exhibitions:* Bank of America Gallery, San Francisco; Los Robles Gallery, Palo Alto *Education:* San Francisco Art Institute *Dealer:* Convergence Gallery, San Francisco

Symbolic landscapes combine photographic and painterly qualities to evoke various states of mind. Bold shapes and colors close to nature make up forms, which appear abstract at close distances, but realistic from further away. While these geographical locations, vast deserts and seascapes often look familiar, they are most significant on a symbolic level. Acrylics are applied to canvases ranging from 2 to 7 feet square. The topography varies from flat, abstract planes to the sharply sculpted and dramatically shadowed.

LANDAU, MAGGIE (Painter, Sculptor)
1614 Fair Park Ave., Los Angeles, CA 90041

Born: 1946 *Awards:* Purchase Award, California Polytechnic State U. *Collections:* Roberts Art Gallery, Santa Monica *Exhibitions:* California Polytechnic State U., Pamona; Roberts Art Gallery, Santa Monica *Education:* Cal. State-Northridge; Art Center College of Design

Trained in traditional drawing and painting in oil, and influenced by the tonal subtleties of Avery, Morandi and Diebenkorn, she paints still life landscapes that read as human relationships. Her work is an exploration of the continuity between man, earth and God. In her sculpture, she has similarly transformed natural objects, such as driftwood, tree limbs and stone, into psychic states. She has recently added clay to her repertoire; the metaphysical spaces she has created of colored and manipulated natural forms are now peopled by sculpted human forms.

LANDFIELD, RONNIE (Painter)
31 Desbrosses St., New York, NY 10013

Born: 1947 *Awards:* Casssandra Foundation Grant *Collections:* Metropolitan Museum of Art, NYC; Museum of Modern Art, NYC *Exhibitions:* David Whitney Gallery, NYC; Whitney Annual for American Art *Education:* San Francisco Art Institute; Kansas City Art Institute *Dealer:* Stephen Haller, NYC; Richard Green Gallery, Los Angeles

As a graduate student, he used fluid acrylic paint and raw canvases to make paintings that had literalist undertones alluding to the abstract void. He painted various kinds of borders around the works' edges and drew his psychologically expressive colors from the natural environment. Eventually, landscape became the dominant theme in his paintings, and he contrasted the free spirit of nature with the restrictions of society. Today, nature continues as his inspiration. His materials are raw cotton duck canvas and fluid acrylic paint. "My intentions are to find form for our deepest feelings and for our need for beauty and order," he says.

LANDO, CHRISTINE M. (Painter)
2963 24th St., San Francisco, CA 94110

Born: 1952 *Awards:* Richmond Art Award *Exhibitions:* San Francisco Museum of Modern Art; Convergence Gallery, San Francisco *Education:* UC-Berkeley *Dealer:* Bennie and Sandra Merideth, Convergence Gallery, San Francisco

In the late 1960s, the works of Japanese Masters Hokusai and Hiroshige inspired her towards the humanism, elegance and clarity of imagery that would become the hallmark of her work. In the mid-1970s, she painted spontaneously with an unusual combination of gouache, oil, charcoal and acrylic. She had an anxious desire for new, more relevant values, and this led her to to study the work of the abstract expressionists. Shapes then became a subject matter, in and of themselves. She made them enlarge and contract simultaneously, through juxtapositions of black and white. Her recent paintings are interior, exterior landscapes that speak to the change and mystery of life.

LAND-WEBER, ELLEN (Photographer)
790 Park Pl., Arcata, CA 95521

Born: 1943 *Awards:* NEA Photographers Fellowship *Collections:* George Eastman House, Rochester, NY; Bibliotheque Nationale, Paris *Exhibitions:* San Francisco Museum of Modern Art; Shada Gallery, Tokyo *Education:* U. of Iowa

In the early 1970s, she became interested in the collage possibilities of color photocopy machines and pioneered work with the 3M color-in-color machine.

Ira Latour, *Barrio de Santa Cruz, Seville,* 10 x 10, photo

Beryl Landau, *California Dreaming,* 60 x 60, acrylic on canvas

She was influenced by natural history illustrations of the 18th and 19th centuries and used natural materials and contemporary photographs and illustrations to create unique transfer prints. In 1976, she began using a view camera for documentary projects. This included a commission from Seagram's Company to document U.S. county courthouses around the country. Her books include *The Passionate Collector*, a series of portraits of collectors with their collections, and *Rescuers*, a book of narratives and photographs of people who risked their lives to rescue Jews from the Holocaust.

LANDWEHR, NANCY H. (Painter, Collage Artist)
1250 Grizzly Park Blvd., Berkeley, CA 94708

Born: 1918 *Exhibitions:* Richmond Art Center; UC-Berkeley *Education:* UC-Berkeley *Dealer:* Adreinne Fish, San Francisco

Since the growth of her children, she has devoted her time to art. Many of her pieces are abstract, but often there is a dialogue between the abstract and that which it suggests in representational terms. Since the late 1980s, she has been particularly interested in painting with collage. She revels in the complete freedom of tearing, gluing, painting and inking. She applies color freely, rolling, braying and developing many different naturalistic textures.

LANGLET, RAGNHILD (Fiber Artist)
P.O. Box 508, Sausalito, CA 94966

Born: 1934 *Awards:* NEA Fellowship; California Living Treasure *Collections:* National Museum, Stockholm, Sweden; Lutheran Brotherhood, Minneapolis *Exhibitions:* Museum of American Crafts; Bank of America, San Francisco *Education:* State School of Art and Industrial Design, Stockholm, Sweden

She was born in Sweden and studied ceramics at Stockholm's State School of Industrial Design. In 1956, she came to the U.S. to teach at the Art Institute of Chicago. It was not long before she returned to the embroidering techniques of her childhood. In 1958, she began embroidery; in 1960, she accepted a position teaching textile printing at Berkeley. She used vat dyes and linen—dyeing, cutting and sewing together her pieces much as a painter would. Often her theme was turbulence in air and water. In 1980, she received an NEA Fellowship Grant and began studying the subject through hang gliding. Unfortunately this led to a crash and injury resulting in impaired vision. She is now concentrating on large-scale metal embroidery.

LANGTON, BASIL (Photographer, Mixed Media Artist)
219 S. Barrington Ave., Los Angeles, CA 90049

Born: 1912 *Awards:* NEA Awards; Guggenheim Fellowship *Collections:* Grunwald Center for Graphic Arts, Los Angeles; Henry Moore Foundation, England *Exhibitions:* Gallery 454 North, Los Angeles *Dealer:* Earl E. McGrath Gallery, Los Angeles

Major influences on his work include Bauhaus, Russian constructivism, cubism and, in particular, Picasso. As a photographer, he has documented major artists. As a printmaker, he has devised a process he calls "effacage," in which magazine photographs are effaced by using gravure tools, chemicals and other means to erase, change and transform them into a new image. The image retains fragments of the original photograph to reflect a surreal, enigmatic vision of contemporary life—a vision that is personal, private and erotic. Each effacage print is a unique transformation in scale with the first appropriated image.

LANSING, NORMAN (Painter, Ceramist)
P.O. Box 2996, Durango, CO 81302

Born: 1950 *Awards:* 1st Place, Contemorary Pottery and Best Craftsman Award, Alice and Don's Bullock's Indian Ceremonial, Santa Monica; 2nd Place, Contemporary Carving, Annual Colorado Indian Market, Whitehorse Gallery, Boulder, CO *Exhibitions:* Indian and Western Relic Show, Pasadena; American Indian Exposition, San Francisco *Education:* Ft. Lewis College; Haskell Jr. College

His early work—pen-and-ink sketching, acrylic and mixed-media paintings, murals—focused on the relation between man and nature. The symbolic traditions and spiritual motifs of the Ute people are the primary sources of his images. More recently, he has become noted for his work in sgraffito, a type of ceramics in which very delicate figures are carved through millimeter-thin layers of colored glaze applied to greenware. The vessels are then fired at extremely high heat. He is constantly experimenting with new media; he has carved ivory and designed and constructed stained-glass windows.

LAPENA, FRANK R. (Painter)
1531 42nd St., Sacramento, CA 95819

Born: 1937 *Collections:* Museum of Modern Art, NYC; Crocker Museum, Sacramento *Exhibitions:* Monterey Peninsula Museum of Art; American Indian Contemporary Arts, San Francisco *Education:* Chico State U.; San Francisco State U.

He is a Wintu Indian deeply involved in traditional Native American arts, as a singer and dancer. The spirit of native American culture and religion—the sacred circle of life—informs his acrylic on canvas paintings of sacred images. More often, he attempts to capture the essence of Native American rituals, dances and symbols. Blotting and lifting off color, layering it in translucent and transparent washes—he uses these techniques more often than straightforward application of flat, opaque paint. He is also concerned with the use of line and strong composition. He has put together a handmade book, *The World Is a Gift*, containing two essays and eight wood engravings, for Limestone Press. He has recently been working on the "Four Directions" series. These pieces are executed in a style more abstract than his previous figurative work.

LA PLANT, MIMI (Painter, Printmaker)
P.O. Box 986, Arcata, CA 95521

Born: 1943 *Awards:* Arts Slide Bank, Sacramento *Collections:* ANA Hotel, Tokyo; Bank of Southern California *Exhibitions:* Longview College, Longview, WA; Miriam Perlman Gallery, Chicago *Education:* UC-Berkeley; Humboldt State U. *Dealer:* City Gallery, Sacramento

Her first mature etchings were surrealist figure/ground compositions with a highly psycho-sexual flavor. In this series, called the "fleur de mal," she relied mainly on unconscious responses and automatic images. Her shapes were dark, tight and dangerous. In 1980, she began doing large charcoal drawings. This led to a long series of monotypes, emphasizing color and composition. Recent work has been largely acrylic paintings on paper, sometimes with added collage materials. She is interested in direct spontaneity, manipulation of

Lois A. Knudsen, *Traveling Troupe,* 22 x 19, glazed stoneware and porcelain.
Courtesy: Mr. and Mrs. Leonard Katzman

Kate Krider, *Amalgamation,* 72 x 84 x 9, cast paper, mixed media

J.V. Kopp, *Children and Goat,* 30 x 40, oil on canvas. Courtesy: Leon Boyar

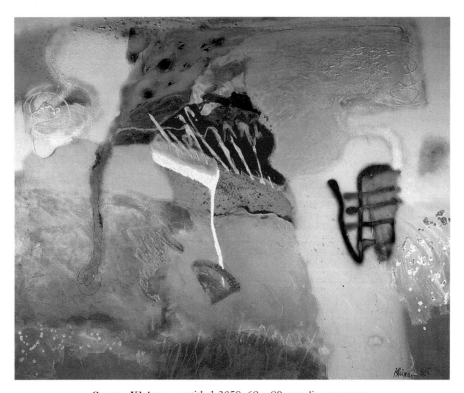

George Kleiman, *untitled 3059,* 68 x 80, acrylic on canvas

K.C. Kauffman, *Yakshi Praying,* 24 x 28, acrylic, oil crayon, oil stick

William Kirchner, *Journey Begins,* 48 x 60, acrylic. Courtesy: Martin Allen

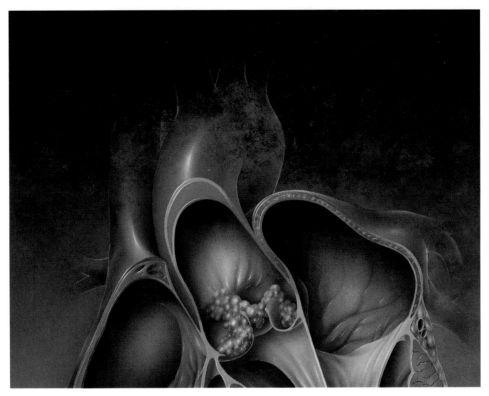

Keith Kasnot, *Medical Illustrator,* 15 x 19, gouache

Richard Klix, *Dawn,* 24 x 30, acrylic

Sheldon Kirby, *Marine,* 48 x 60, oil

John Michael Keating, *The Passenger,* 21 x 28, watercolor. Courtesy: Worley-Smith Gallery, Nevada City, CA

C. Kimball, *Pigeons in Venice,* 9 x 12, split ink bromoil

J. Natasha Kostan, *untitled,* 12 x 19, mixed media on paper

John Kapel, *Koto,* 21 x 43 x 6, bronze. Courtesy: Gallery 30, San Mateo, CA

Elaine Kennedy, *McGee Creek-August 15,* 46 x 66, acrylic. Courtesy: Mr. and Mrs. Robert Koda

Ilse Kilian, *The Comet's Tail,* 16 x 36, weaving and stitchery

David King, *Tooth Saw,* 11 x 38 x 8, steel, wood, human teeth.
Courtesy: Hank Baum Gallery, San Francisco, CA

Josephine Kopenhaver, *Vast Pacific,* 25 x 48, oil

Carol Kirsch, *Dawn,* 24 x 32, transparent watercolor.
Courtesy: Mt. San Jancinto Community College, CA

Bob Longhurst, *Loop IL,*
30 x 8 x 8, african rosewood.
Courtesy: Louis Newman Galleries

Joy Irene Lasseter, *Muse of Rameau,*
24 x 12, acrylic on canvas

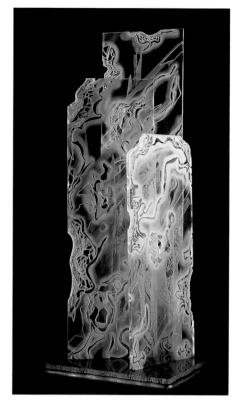

Jon Warren Lentz, *Undersea Phantasy II,*
24 x 26 x 62, sand-carved glass

Dennis Luedeman, *Matter of Scale,* 36 x 8 x 14, metal

Christine Lando, *Nightwalking I (aerial view),*
22 x 30, mixed media on paper

Stephen Lackey, *Wave,* 8 x 12 x 15, bronze.
Photograph: Jock McDonald

NanSea Love, *Mother Nature,* 30 x 40, mixed media

Frank Lapena, *Spring Spirit,* 36 x 48, acrylic

Lyle London, *Pas de Deux,* 180 x 84 x 60, bronze

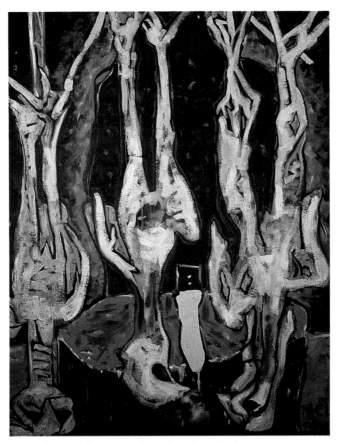

Ming C. Lowe, *The Butcher,* 75 x 57, oil on canvas

Jaye Lawrence, *Boundary with Red Line,* 60 x 28 x 8,
painted wood and cast twigs

Shirley Lutes, *K-21,* 32 x 40 x 4, cast paper pulp fiber

Pam Longobardi, *Buried Knowlege,* 84 x 70, oil on canvas with wood

Earl Linderman, *Slow Kiss,* 30 x 28, oil. Photograph: Bill McLemore

materials, interactive color and the illusion of space. Through her manipulation of materials, ideas form and become visually manifest.

LAPLANTZ, DAVID (Jeweler, Silversmith)
899 Bayside Cutoff, Bayside, California 95524

Born: 1944 *Awards:* Fulbright Grant; Honorable Mention, Ornament Magazine International Jewelry Competition *Collections:* National Museum of Modern Art, Kyoto, Japan *Exhibitions:* American Craft Museum; Downey Museum of Art *Education:* Bowling Green State U.; Cranbrook Academy of Art *Dealers:* Freehand, Los Angeles; Jett Gallery, Santa Fe, NM; J. Noblett Gallery, Sonoma

In his earlier works, he explored *champlève* enamel on fine silver. He studied under master jeweler Hal Hasselschwert, and during this period he developed raising and forging techniques to produce non-functional toys for adults. His work also included coconut shells covered with painted plates that look like armor juxtaposed with iron chain or chain mesh; the majority of these are painted black. Since then, he has progressed to limited lines of jewelry that incorporate a wide variety of materials—colored and anodized aluminum, ribbon-wire banding, lizard and other animal skins and egg-crate plex. The highly crafted works take their cue from art deco for color and style, and reveal a sense of humor and imagination, as in the brightly colored brooches inspired by his observation of tombstones.

LARSEN, HAROLD E. (Painter)
109 1/2 Victoria St., Santa Fe, NM 87501

Born: 1934 *Awards:* Festival of the Arts, Lake Buena Vista, FL; Sausalito Art Festival *Collections:* Nevada Savings and Loan; American Embassy, The Vatican *Exhibitions:* Rocky Mountain National Water Media Exhibition Traveling Show; Kentucky Watercolor Society Annual Exhibition *Education:* Michigan State U.; Kalamazoo Institute of the Arts *Dealer:* Adagio Galleries, Palm Springs; Frank Howell Gallery, La Jolla; Esther Wells Collection, Laguna Beach

He is best known for his abstract landscapes, in watercolor and mixed media, of the American Southwest. His early paintings were primarily architectural studies—historic houses, boats, docks and the like. He moved to the mountains near Santa Fe in 1980 and was struck by the vast panoramas and the watery luminescence of the atmosphere. He began to paint landscapes exclusively. To pure watercolor collage techniques he has added a variety of media: acrylic, oil glaze, handmade papers and gold and silver leaf. In addition to his landscapes, he has recently been painting masked Native American dancers and artifacts. He also has sculpted a series of pieces based on these works, in which the dancing figures move freely around one another. These pieces are done in plywood, painted in the bold primary palette of the expressionists.

LARSEN, NICOLAI (Commercial Illustrator, Painter)
2595 Alpine Rd., Menlo Park, CA 94025

Born: 1952 *Awards:* Mural Award, San Francisco Art Festival *Exhibitions:* Ames Research Center, NASA, Mountain View; Redding Museum of Art

During the mid-1970s, he developed a uniquely detailed technique for rendering nature on a cosmic scale. He uses a variety of media and techniques to create the illusion of three dimensions, including airbrush, air gun, trompe l'oeil, enamel and acrylics. Paintings feature decorative corners and a central circular area, which contains most of the painting's imagery. His palette is variable and features warm earth tones and light, cool blues and greens. He is a naturalist who cites Hudson River School artists Frederick Church and Bill Martin as primary influences.

LASSETER, JOY IRENE (Painter)
P.O. Box 21257, Oakland, CA 94620

Born: 1943 *Exhibitions:* Interfaith Peace Festival and Festival of Light, San Francisco; Gallery Sanchez, San Francisco

She is a spiritual and visionary artist who captures the essence of angels, spirits and ethereal beings from other dimensions. She began her career as a realist but soon abandoned her visible subject matter to pursue the invisible. At first, she painted abstract patterns of energy but she eventually developed ways of capturing the radiant visions she saw while meditating. Gradually ethereal forms and haunting faces emerged from her canvases. She now paints with acrylic washes on primed canvas, layering and overlapping majesty and radiance, and creating an emotional and spiritual connection between the viewer and her angelic emissaries.

LASSETTER, JAN (Painter)
322 Harrison, Oakland, CA 94607

Born: 1938 *Collections:* High Museum of Art, Atlanta; Glenn C. Janss, American Realism *Exhibitions:* Santa Barbara Museum of Art; Monterey Peninsula Museum of Art *Education:* Academy of Fine Art, Munich; Mosame Nakayama, Tokyo *Dealer:* Modernism, San Francisco

After formal training in techniques of the Old Masters and in German expressionism modeled after Emile Nolde and Osker Kokoschka, she developed an abstract expressionistic style influenced by Franz Kline. She was excited by the use of clean, vibrant color, and her first work was gestural and abstract. Gradually the images became less abstract. Starting with a large color field, she adds more and more detail, the edges no longer rough and loose but soft and controlled, the brush strokes barely visible. These landscapes, which take their images from nature, are stark and serene—devoid of human signs, but not emotion. Her recent work is primarily influenced Richard Estes' photo-realistic urban images and those of early 20th-century industrial painter Charles Sheeler. In these works, she paints her images as realistically as can be rendered and uses reflections to achieve a double image and a more interesting dimension and composition. The resulting industrial "stillscapes" have the same solitary quality of the earlier landscapes.

LASWORTH, LAURA (Painter)
1031 S. Sherbourne, Los Angeles, CA 90035

Born: 1954 *Awards:* California Institute of the Arts Scholarship; Ahmanson Foundation Scholarship *Exhibitions:* Orlando Gallery, Sherman Oaks; Muse, Los Angeles *Education:* School of the Art Institute of Chicago; California Institute of the Arts *Dealer:* Asher/Faure, Los Angeles

After exploring abstract painting, sculpture and conceptual art, she settled into figurative painting with an autobiographical series derived from early childhood memories. These small oils presented isolated details—a shattering glass, a parent's face, empty rooms and leaning walls—as chilling symbols of emotional pain and self-analysis. Later paintings depicted psychological dramas in theatrical spaces acted out by figures that were part human and part stick outlines. In 1985, she took this subject matter to a large format and switched from canvas to oil on board. She is best known for a series of unconventional portraits in which mental illness is intellectualized and ordered by exploiting the cliched language of surrealism as a formal catharsis for more intangible neurosis. Rudolf Stiener sits at a desk looking directly out of the picture plane while the great Goethenaum burns through the window. Sabina Spielrein, the Russian schizophrenic turned psychoanalyst, is abstractly portrayed floating above a piano between wall portraits of Freud and Jung. Leon Gabor, who believes he is Jesus Christ, stands beneath a swinging light bulb with letters flying around the room which quote his fanatic philosophy. A farewell is bid to Andrei Tarkovsky by angels hovering over a naked figure of a man under a white sheet. Wood panels are shaped constructions that augment the projected perspectives of the interiors in which the personalities are placed. The resulting disorientation reflects the sub-formal presence of the subconscious in which the real pursuit for meaning is forever taking place. On the pages of an open book of a painting, C.S. Lewis reminds us that "Every event which might claim to be a miracle is, in the last resort, something presented to our senses."

LATOUR, IRA (Photographer, Filmmaker)

Art Department, Cal. State-Chico, CA 95928

Born: 1919 *Awards:* Blue Ribbon, American Film Festival; Bronze Medal, International Film and Television Festival of New York *Collections:* Museum of Modern Art, NYC; San Francisco Museum of Modern Art *Exhibitions:* Monterey Peninsula Museum of Art; Alva Taylor Gallery, Chico *Education:* UC-Berkeley; Cal. State-Chico

A painter before World War II, he returned to join Ansel Adams' 1945 founding class in photography, at the San Francisco School of Fine Arts. At Adams' suggestion, he attended UC-Berkeley, and studied philosophy and aesthetics. He continued to study intermittently with Adams, Minor White and Edward Weston, who exerted a profound influence, as an artist and as a friend. He was also influenced by photojournalist Homer Page, with whom he once worked. In the mid-1950s, he accepted a teaching position at San Francisco State College, introducing German visual aesthetics (specifically Subjektive Fotografie). He resigned to work abroad as a film producer and director. Since 1968, he has been a professor of art history. He resists being categorized, but identifies most with the "Western tradition." Yet, his work reflects those earlier opposing influences: Adams and Weston on the one hand; more subjective influences from Minor White on the other; stimulated by fotoform and Dr. Otto Steinert's Subjektive Fotografie. In film, his work has tended toward the anthropological and the art historical. A recent project combines footage of flamenco by Spanish gypsies, in an amalgam of abstract and computerized imagery, with selected lines of poetry from Garcia Lorca.

LAUBSCHER, RUDOLPH (Mixed Media Artist)

3045 Hollycrest Dr., Los Angeles, CA 90068

Born: 1948 *Awards:* Cardboard Cutups Toy Contest, San Francisco Museum of Modern Art *Exhibitions:* Landscape References, Los Angeles; Fine Arts Center, UC-Irvine

First interested in rendering landscapes, he decided to try using a batik/resist method. After an initial experiment using household dyes and a bedsheet, he became intrigued by the feel of the process and the unpredictable results he obtained. Since then, he has studied fabrics, fibers and dyes. He creates bookworks and large pieces of batik fabric presented in either book form or as wall hangings. Varying his choice of materials, he uses cotton remnant prints or blends, denim, corduroy and silk. He works in bright primary colors, doing two or three sets of dyes at a time, using cookie cutters and brushes to apply the wax. He adds appliques, sticks, clasps and other objects to the batik. The book assemblages are bound with snaps, dyed wooden dowels, strings and ribbons. He feels that his work primarily belongs in people's homes rather than in museums or other institutions.

LAUDENSLAGER, JEFFERY (Sculptor)

490 Pine Needles, Del Mar, CA 92014

Born: 1946 *Collections:* Sandoz Corp., Switzerland *Exhibitions:* Merging One Gallery, Santa Monica; Carl Schlosberg Fine Arts

His work is an attempt to free himself from the perplexity of illusion. He begins with a freestanding object that is, in itself, an illusion of traditional sculpture. He implies space and volume through shapes which are actually quite flattened; and which can only be viewed effectively from one side of the sculpture. His one consistent form is a classically shaped steel pillar painted to look like stone. To his pillars, he adds solids, some of which are painted to appear transparent, or geometric elements that he has coaxed into anti-logical configurations. His pieces give the impression of a loosely assembled composition that is either floating or falling.

LAURITZEN, BRUCE (Painter)

175 Paul Dr., San Rafael, CA 94903

Born: 1934 *Awards:* Northern California Artists Annual Award; Annual All-California Award *Collections:* San Francisco Museum of Modern Art; Achenbach Collections *Exhibitions:* Palace of the Legion of Honor, San Francisco; University Museum, Berkeley *Education:* San Francisco Art Institute; California College of Arts and Crafts *Dealer:* San Francisco Museum of Modern Art Rental Gallery

In his European paintings of the early 1960s, he sublimated the figure's working posture into semi-abstract blocks of impasto color. In 1966, he returned to California and began making large, minimal, organic shapes, eventually developing a formal abstract style based on symmetrical illusion. These abstractions involved taping, rolling and spattering acrylic paint on partially primed canvases. By the later 1970s, he sought respite from intellectualism and felt a need to re-establish a connection with the tangible, He began painting large watercolors and elongated ten-foot canvases in which a single feather image symbolizes flight, freedom and transcendence. His recent series of paintings of coastal California are done in a style that merges the representational with the surreal and abstract. He uses oils, acrylics, snapped chalk lines and taped edges to create the illusion of hard edge within a soft

Ragnhild Langlet, *Breakers,* 82 x 56, fiber

Joy Irene Lasseter, *Angel of Transfiguration,*
30 x 24, acrylic on canvas

Randall Lavender, *The Tree Where Hope Was Born,* 48
x 29, oil on panel. Courtesy: Tortue Gallery Inc., Los
Angeles

textured space. Early influences include Richard Diebenkorn and Nathan Oliveira.

LAVENDER, RANDALL (Painter)
1617 E. 7th, #14, Los Angeles, CA 90021

Born: 1956 *Collections:* Frederick R. Weisman Foundation; Vanderbilt U., Nashville *Exhibitions:* Jan Turner Gallery, Los Angeles *Education:* Claremont Graduate School *Dealer:* Tortue Gallery, Santa Monica

His paintings probe the possibilities of what painting in the classical/renaissance style would be like if the mythological/Christian content were supplanted by contemporary concern over the goal of human life. His works are concerned with human content. He connects his work to the sensuous vision of Renaissance painters by using academic techniques of glazing and blending layers of semi-transparent oil on primed, shaped wood panels. In his recent work, his concerns with landscape and space have become much more explicit as has his attempt to personify such human themes as hope and inspiration.

LAWDER, DEBORAH (Painter)
904 Azalea Ave., Burlingame, CA 94010

Born: 1958 *Awards:* Artist Achievement Award, Artist Society International *Exhibitions:* Oyster Point Plaza, San Francisco; Henry Gifford Hardy Gallery, San Francisco *Education:* UCLA

She paints in accord with the method suggested by Vassily Kandinsky in *Concerning the Spiritual in Art*. In other words, she begins her canvases without preconceptions, therefore intending to create honest, spontaneous and highly emotional work. Her use of color has recently become more vivid, less tentative. Currently, her paintings feature studies of skeletal objects in blue and red oil on black gesso. She has completed a series of paintings about the tragedy of 1987 at the Concord Naval Weapons Station, when a weapons train failed to stop for anti-nuclear protestors, and Brian Willson's legs were amputated. These large-scale works measure 9 by 7 feet. Smaller pastels depicting similar subjects are 18 by 24 inches.

LAWDER, STANDISH D. (Stereoscopic Artist)
Visual Arts, B-027, U. of California-San Diego, La Jolla, CA 92093

Born: 1936 *Awards:* Guggenheim Fellowship; NEA Fellowship *Collections:* Museum of Modern Art, NYC; Cinematheque Francaise *Exhibitions:* Cooper Union, NYC *Education:* Yale U. *Dealer:* Pirate, Denver

He earned the first Art History Ph.D. in the country dealing with film as art and early on became professor of film at Yale and Harvard. In the 1960s and 1970s, he made structuralist, experimental films based on perceptual art. In 1975 he went to the University of California at San Diego to establish a media program and to do research on stereoscopic art. He has now perfected a new form of stereoscopic (three-dimensional) projected-light art. He makes his pieces using highly specialized photographic systems and presents them in a museum context through computer-controlled banks of 35mm slide projectors. He is the author of the scholarly book *The Cubist Cinema*.

LAWRENCE, JAMES A. (Painter, Photographer)
Rock Creek Ranch, Rte. 1, Box 201, Gardnerville, NV 89410

Born: 1910 *Awards:* American Artist's Professional League Award; Golden Gate International Exposition Award *Collections:* Ford Motor Co. Collection, Dearborn, MI; Mapes Hotel, Reno *Exhibitions:* Riverside Museum, NYC; Metropolitan Museum of Art, NYC *Education:* UC-Davis

At UC-Davis, he studied landscape design, but he soon turned to painting and photography. Although his early medium was watercolor, he became equally successful as a photographer, operating his own studio, in which he produced advertising and commercial photography. His watercolors of the last thirty-five years have been dominated by his love of the West— the drama of its seacoast, mountains and deserts and the town and ranch life of its people. He is an ardent sportsman and conservationist, and wildlife serves as the subject of many of his recent watercolors.

LAWRENCE, JAYE (Sculptor)
2097 Valley View Blvd., El Cajon, CA 92019

Born: 1939 *Collections:* Arizona State U.; Pacific Lutheran U., Tacoma, WA *Exhibitions:* Museum of Contemporary Crafts, San Francisco *Education:* Arizona State U. *Dealer:* Spectrum Gallery, San Diego

Early on, she combined primitive weaving techniques and folk art influences to create large-scale, organically woven sculptures made from a wide variety of natural objects. The works of Eva Hesse and Lenore Tawney were and continue to be important influences in this three-dimensional warp and weft. In her recent work, she draws more strongly on the folk art tradition. She wraps sticks and twigs in rawhide and paints them thickly with acrylics, creating brightly colored, large-scale (up to 6 feet) chair sculptures that suggest the spirit of the unknown. Often there is a framework of abstract references to the landscape or figure.

LAWRENCE, LES (Ceramist)
2097 Valley View Blvd., El Cajon, CA 92019

Born: 1940 *Awards:* Distinguished Alumni, South Plains College; Purchase Award, E.B. Crocker Museum, Sacramento *Collections:* E.B. Crocker Museum, Sacramento; Phoenix Art Museum *Exhibitions:* Museum of Contemporary Crafts; Museum of Contemporary Art, San Francisco *Education:* Southwestern St. College; Arizona St. U. *Dealers:* Alexander Gallery, Studio City; Lawrence Arts, El Cajon

Early training in commercial art led to later studies in painting, sculpture and ceramics. Paintings from this period were landscapes influenced by the light and atmospheric perspective of the panoramic views of west Texas. Continued studies in sculpture and ceramics evolved into a love of the plastic elements in sculptural pottery. The influence of both Voulkos and Rauschenberg are apparent in Lawrence's large platter forms, which include photo silkscreens of found objects. Recent work consists of sculptural vessels with surfaces reminiscent of the patterns and colors of aerial landscapes. Sometimes these narrow forms appear to be ships or boats. He often experiments with new techniques, some of which include multi-high firing with glaze, underglaze, slip, sandblasting, stainless steel and gold leaf.

LAWRENCE, MICHAEL (Painter)
239 S. Los Angeles St., Los Angeles, CA 90012

Awards: Huntington Hartford Fellow; National Society of Arts and Letters Award for Sculpture *Collections:* Bard College *Exhibitions:* Wenger Gallery,

Bruce Lauritzen, *Coastal Condos (Runner),* 38 x 50, oil

Jan Lassetter, *Dry Dock Blues,* 45 x 66, oil on canvas. Courtesy: Modernism

Los Angeles; Diane Sassone Gallery, Laguna Beach *Education:* UCLA; Bard College *Dealer:* Wenger Gallery, Los Angeles

Raised in Italy, he borrows from its cafe scenes and piazzas to populate his exuberant paintings. Incorporating elements of latter-day cubism and expressionism via Max Beckmann, the paintings portray clowns and musicians, aerial acrobats and burning hoops, bottomless cars with legs protruding beneath, horses eating carrots and women screaming. Although the material may spring from a child's world or fantasy, the figures are informed with an adult's knowledge of the world—sadness and danger lurk in the many faces. A sophisticated sense of color likewise guides the palette, which is often bright and rich, though not simply light-hearted.

LAWSON, DAVID K. (Painter, Sculptor)
P.O. Box 1028, La Quinta, CA 92253

Born: 1950 *Exhibitions:* Los Angeles Institute of Contemporary Art; Security Pacific Gallery, Los Angeles

Using primarily oils, he paints on stretched linen, rag board or artcore laminated to gatorboard. His paint application ranges from thin washes, stains or glazes to paint that is thickly applied, sometimes at high speed. He has been influenced by a variety of artists but is mostly concerned with the nature of objects. He allows his subconscious to control his work, each stroke of paint a subconscious reaction to the one that preceded it. His paintings are often almost life-size realistic nudes. His sculptures are abstracted, cartoon-like, colorful figures. After the completion of his new studio he plans to begin sculpting large figurative steel pieces.

LAWTON, ERIC (Photographer, Multimedia Artist)
2001 Wilshire Blvd., Penthouse Suite, Santa Monica, CA 90403

Born: 1947 *Awards:* Finalist, ArtQuest, Florida National Art Competition; Nominee, Art Achievement Award, Artists' Society International, San Francisco *Collections:* Bibliotheque Nationale, Paris; International Photography Museum, Oklahoma City, OK *Exhibitions:* John Nichols Gallery, Santa Paula; University Art Center, Cal. State-Northridge *Education:* UCLA; Loyola U., Los Angeles

His work evolves from years of travel: observing the people, landscapes, philosophies and fine arts of over fifty countries. He draws inspiration from ancient images and natural landscapes; he seeks to reveal the temporal and spiritual qualities of a place through an exploration of color, light, form and space. His work has progressed from Cibachrome prints to a combination of prints and other media, especially multiple-projector, computer-programmed slide montage (with music, sound, dance) and live performance in gallery, film and theatrical contexts. Seeking to reach the integral elements of a composition through a minimalist approach, he expands the context by blending and dissolving one image through another using multiple printing techniques, the superimposition of prints or overlapping slide dissolves in multimedia performances. His thesis is that by dissolving the physical form of a composition, the literal aspect of the form falls away, revealing the spiritual core which empowers the image. He has recently been working on a series of landscapes and abstractions from China, for a multiple projector show in Singapore.

LAZAROF, ELEANORE BERMAN (Painter)
718 N. Maple Dr., Beverly Hills, CA 90210

Born: 1928 *Collections:* Brooklyn Museum; Los Angeles County Museum of Art *Education:* UCLA; Leger Atelier, Paris *Dealer:* Art Options, NYC; Reece Gallery, NYC

Her work of the 1970s was primarily abstract, referring to the organic world of earth and stone shapes. From this grew another body of work in a painterly, color-field style, with brushed and scratched diagonal strokes evoking the flowing energy of air and water. In recent works, these diagonal strokes are shorter and evoke the dappled light and shade of gardens and tree forms. The overall energized surface also reveals some figuration. Her medium is largely oil on canvas; she does small-scale works in pastel and oil on paper and also editions of large-format color etchings.

LAZARUS, SHELLEY (Painter)
20327 Alerion Place, Woodland Hills, CA 91364

Born: 1936 *Awards:* 1st Prize, San Fernando Art Association; 2nd Prize, Pacific Palisades Art Association *Exhibitions:* Brentwood Art Center; Westside Health Institute Art Gallery *Education:* Syracuse U.; Otis Art Institute

She was initially inspired by the immediacy of the Impressionists, and by the luminosity of Turner's style. Her artistic goal is to bring a sense of movement and emotion, through the use of color. She works mostly in watercolor, using that medium's fluidity to capture nature in an expressive manner, rather than in a studied way. Her neo-impressionist still lifes, seascapes and landscapes depict the buildings and scenery of California and the East Coast. She prefers working on location, and has recently finished a series of landscapes and seascapes begun on Martha's Vineyard.

LEAVITT, SAM (Ceramist, Sculptor)
2651 Main St., Santa Monica, CA 90405

Born: 1946 *Exhibitions:* Del Amo Shopping Center, Torrance; Whittier Museum *Education:* School of the Art Institute of Chicago; U. of Chicago

While at the the School of the Art Institute of Chicago, he was exposed to Giacometti's sculpture. This led him to incorporate classic sculptural styles into his work, and to begin using foundry and casting procedures that have been a recurring element in his sculpture. In 1971, he moved to New York and began making surreal, slightly figurative steel drawings. He moved to California in 1972, and worked with pierced steel plates. He also took up ceramics, and made abstract aluminum sculptures that suggested the transformation of organic matter into crystal formations. In recent constructivist work, he has used bronze casting to express movement in space, to reduce detail to its most basic shape and to depict the human form in posed, formal compositions.

LEBOUTILIERE, ELAINE (Painter)
4015 E. Sierra Vista Dr., Scottsdale, AZ 85253

Collections: Los Angeles County Museum of Art

With no formal art training, she began painting when she was in her mid-twenties. Her first work was in cartooning. Using colored pencils, she produced illustrations for children's books, as well as landscapes and abstract works in acrylic, oil and watercolor. Many of her paintings are executed in the "ikebana" style,

Nelda LeVant, *Pedestals,* photographs

Jaye Lawrence, *Strata Within Bounds #2,* 76 x 24 x 21, painted wood and cast twigs

LeBoutiliere, aka Butler *The Washington Monument,* 13 x 10, watercolor

which is characterized by underpainting in acrylic and finishing in oil. Current work consists of delicate floral still lifes and is done in very deep, hot colors. She has been impressed by the works of DeGrazia and has visited him in his studio.

LECOCQ, KAREN (Sculptor)
636 1/2 W. 23rd St, Merced, CA 95340

Born: 1949 *Exhibitions:* Womanhouse, Los Angeles; Woman Art Gallery, NYC *Education:* California Institute of the Arts, Los Angeles; Cal. State-Fresno

Her early figurative painting and sculpture was influenced by George Segal. In 1971, she began studying under Miriam Schapiro and Judy Chicago, in the first feminist art program. Non-objective sculpture became her main focus. Her repeating, modular, wood-and-fabric rounded forms show the influence of Lloyd Hamerol's environmental sculptures. She now achieves an organic, biological effect, placing soft, rounded, sensual forms in a geometric or random pattern. The majority of her pieces are contained in boxes of varying sizes (from 6 to 12 square inches) and are made various media, including paper, cement, wood, gravel, fabric, sand, glass, plastics, polyester fiber and various metals.

LEE, ALDIN (Painter)
13116 Burton St., North Hollywood, CA 91605

Born: 1956 *Awards:* Scholarship, Ahmanson Foundation *Exhibitions:* California Institute of the Arts *Education:* California Institute of the Arts; U. of Illinois, Champaign-Urbana

A formal training in traditional painting led to landscapes and portraiture, influenced by Jean-August Dominique Ingres, John Constable and Rembrandt. Interest in romanticism and neo-classicism developed into a personal expressionistic style strongly informed by Eugene Delacroix. Impressionism and Baroque art has since contributed elements to large oil and acrylic media paintings, in which dramatic representation is central. Historical research has resulted in a series depicting the wedding ceremonies, hunting practices and battles of Attila's Huns. Space is carefully organized to properly display the narrative, and very little white is added in color combination, in order to achieve the highest degree of brightness. An impressionistic use of color on highly realistic figures presents an untraditional brand of realism. Recent work applies these techniques to California landscapes.

LEE, KYUNGSOO (Painter)
3053 W. Olympic Blvd., #202A, Los Angeles, CA 90006

Born: 1958 *Awards:* Exhibit of Selection by Public Subscription in Gusang, Korea *Exhibitions:* Korean Artist Association of Southern California *Education:* Sungshin Women's U., Korea

She studied fauvism, cubism and romanticism in Korea and became interested in those movements' desire for simplification and transformation. In the course of these studies, she acquired a lasting interest in the interpretation of color phenomena and the processes of color formation. Her earlier works were in oils, with large quantities of turpentine thinning some areas; in others, she scraped with a knife to create layers of different thicknesses. In these works, she sought to expose the materials of the paintings. Her later work reveals an expressionist influence. She has begun to paint on a larger scale, using oil, acrylic and gouache. Recently she painted a series of expressionistic California landscapes.

LEE, LESLIE (Ceramist)
706 S.W. Maplecrest Dr., Portland, OR 97219

Born: 1948 *Awards:* Oregon Biennial Exhibition *Collections:* Metropolitan Arts Commission, Portland; Metchosin International Summer School for the Arts, Victoria, B.C. *Exhibitions:* Carlyn Gallery, NYC; Palumbo Gallery, Carmel *Education:* Washington U., St. Louis

After receiving her degree, she was a graphic designer for several years. Working in seclusion, she developed her own style of creating figurative vessels, particularly teapots. She worked in white stoneware, experimenting with color ranges and glaze applications for "cone six electric firing." Her teapots are narrative and realistic, with subjects derived from classical mythology. Standing 10 to 14 inches high, the teapots feature fine detailing around the top and are covered with gold, silver and other glazes, which are applied and reapplied during the firing process. Recently, she has been continuing her series of clay narrations in three dimensions and on painted plates. Raku-fired work has become increasingly important to her, and she plans a series of ornamental boxes for her next project.

LEE, SUNGLEE SAKI (Painter)
1242 Harvard St., #1, Santa Monica, CA 90404

Born: 1950 *Awards:* Research Grant, UC-Santa Cruz *Collections:* Santa Monica Museum; UCLA *Exhibitions:* Claremont College, Los Angeles; Municipal Gallery, Los Angeles *Education:* UC-Santa Cruz

She is impressed with the color, movement and sounds of shamanistic rituals in her native Korea, and she identifies the role of the artist with that of the shaman. Her technique of layering images through overlapping and repetition has grown with the influence of minimalist composers such as Philip Glass. Repeated images of animals, plants and human forms dominate her fluorescently colored canvases, expressing the idea of a multidimensional reality. In a recent 6-by-6-foot painting of a man, a woman and thirty-seven porcupines, she metaphorically portrays the complexity of life and its relationships.

LEEDY, JEFF (Illustrator, Painter)
209 North St., Sausalito, CA 94965

Born: 1941 *Awards:* Gold Medal, Humor, New York Society of Illustrators *Exhibitions:* Sausalito Art Festival; Community Congregational Church, Sausolito *Education:* Syracuse U.

After fifteen years in advertising, he turned to a career in the fine arts. Now he is best known for humorous paintings and commercial illustrations. Modeling his work after that of Ronald Searle, Ralph Steadman, Jules Pfeiffer, Tomi Ungerer, Charles Bragg and Robert Osborne, he has developed a style with an impressionistic flavor. His spontaneous figures secure freely across colorful backgrounds. Working in oil pastel and acrylic, he applies color boldly. Recently, he has been working on a series of fifty psychological paintings. They feature depictions of the inner self trying somehow to cope with the outside world.

LEFKOWITZ, CAROL (Painter)
448 Clifton St., Oakland, CA 94618

Born: 1956 *Collections:* McDonald's Corporation, San Jose *Exhibitions:* Rental Gallery, San Francisco Museum of Modern Art; Solano Community College,

Sharon Lynn Lloyd, *Sacred Geometry: Chartres,*
14 x 20, watercolor, gouache

Sunglee Suki Lee, . . . *to Nietzsche,* 18 x 24, charcoal on paper

Suisun City *Education:* Kansas City Art Institute; California College of Arts & Crafts

Her early studies in sculpture and textiles are still apparent in her concern with the canvas's physicality, and in the thoughtful relationship between figures and spaces. For the last couple of years, she has painted bowls either floating in, or submerged in, water. Abstraction and realism meet in the edge between the water and the air; the shadows and reflections in the water allow for multiple levels of involvement. These oil on canvas paintings are quite large, measuring from 4 by 6 feet to 6 by 8 feet.

LEFSON, IRVING (Photographer)
3621-16 Vista Campana So., Oceanside, CA 92056

Born: 1898 *Collections:* Iverson Museum, Syracuse, NY; Heritage Museum, Sandwich, MA *Exhibitions:* Seasoned Eye II, Santa Monica; San Diego Art Institute *Education:* Cooper Union

For him, the art begins after the image is recorded on film. He uses a 35mm Nikon camera, a set of filters and four lenses: 85mm for portraiture; 135mm telephoto for distances; 55mm for close- ups and duplicating slides; and 35mm for slides. He prefers 35mm film because it compels him to simplify his composition and to make a stronger statement. He works with photo-processing chemicals, juggling, juxtaposing or intensifying color to alter space and design. He montages image over image, looking through different combinations to develop expressionistic compositions. He then etches on the slide to produce altered images of light. The resulting photographs depict a reality beyond what is visible.

LEHMER, STEPHEN K. (Photographer)
1618 W. Westgate, #5, Los Angeles, CA 90025

Born: 1946 *Collections:* Sun Valley Center, ID *Exhibitions:* Los Angeles Center of Photographic Studies; California Institute of the Arts, Valencia *Education:* California Institute of the Arts; San Francisco Art Institute

Since 1966, he has been using photography as a means of exploration, expression and self-discovery. At first, he was influenced by such diverse artists as Robert Frank, Danny Lyon and Joseph Sudek. His subjects were simple, but his conceptual and symbolic roots were deep. He then began to look at Man Ray, Duchamp, Heinecken, Kertesz and others. He found he was interested in how people can adapt to change without recognizing that a change is even taking place. He began to deal with change through repetitive images. Recent work includes sequential images of the the television and a series on the heroes of the tabloids. His colors are strong and vivid; his format is the 35mm camera.

LEIDENTHAL, WILLIAM (Painter)
2607 Waverly Dr., Los Angeles, CA 90039

Born: 1946 *Awards:* Art Quest National Exhibit Awards in Drawing *Exhibitions:* Sunnyvale Creative Arts Center; Albany Museum of Art, NY *Education:* East Carolina University, Greenville, NC

The content of his early work was influenced by Chinese landscape painters of Sung and Yuan Dynasties and Taoist ideas of man, nature and art. His style of energetic brushwork, however, resembles German expressionist and New York School painters. His background in printmaking makes its appearance in the emphasis on the drawing aspects of his painting.

Abstract works consist of an ongoing series of drawings and related intaglio prints, and oil paintings on canvas, ranging in size from 10 by 18 inches to 6 by 12 feet, which explore the creative process as a metaphor for natural evolution and geologic process. The pieces are characterized by vibrant, unusual colors, a rich and varied texture and dramatic composition, creating unique conceptual landscapes of space and light.

LEIOR, SALLY L. (Draughtsperson)
4546 Hancock Circle, Oceanside, CA 92056

Born: 1947 *Awards:* Certificate of Excellence, International Art Challenge *Exhibitions:* Safari Club Annual Convention; San Diego Wildlife Show

At the age of forty, with no formal art education, she picked up a pen, and began to create with pen and ink. She expresses her love for animals in exacting, almost photographic drawings. Her finished works have the intensity of living, breathing, contemplating animals. Her pet portraits of lop-eared bunnies, angora kittens and dogs look back at the viewer with a grace and fellowship familiar to pet owners and new parents. Her work elicits in viewers an awareness of the gift wildlife is to us, and raises one's level of awareness regarding our role in its preservation.

LEIZER, MATTHEW R. (Painter)
464 20th St., Santa Monica, CA 90402

Born: 1910 *Exhibitions:* St. Hill Art Gallery, Los Angeles; Federal Art Gallery, Los Angeles

He was trained as an architect; in 1984, he began painting full time with watercolors. He neither cares for realism nor extreme abstraction, and tries to capture nature's moods and light. He is an emotional painter who concentrates on the relationships of light and dark and the drama of color. His palette ranges from bright to muted, and he paints quickly so as not to loose brilliance. Though they may not resemble their sources, his recent landscapes, seascapes and buildings are inspired by slides from travel or sketches from life. He is mainly self-taught, but has taken workshops from Robert E. Wood and others.

LELAND, KATHERINE A. (Painter)
465 Fair Dr., #209, Costa Mesa, CA 92626

Born: 1943 *Exhibitions:* Laguna Beach Museum of Art; Los Angeles Audubon Society Wildlife and Environmental Art Show

She is primarily self-taught, although she has been influenced by Van Gogh and the Impressionists. She paints subjects from her imagination in a stylized, expressionistic manner. The paintings are pictorial, but the subjects are often fantastic—underwater scenes, views of outer space, combinations of human forms and plant parts. Much of the work is figurative, but the forms are abstracted and flattened into the picture plane. Her more recent works have been mosaic designs in oil and pastels on black canvas or paper. These works depict small creatures, highly stylized, as well as plant forms—stems, flowers, buds. The plant forms provide a framework for the designs, while the small animal creatures are arranged within that overall pattern.

LEMASTER, TED (Painter, Commercial Artist)
306 Museum Dr., Los Angeles, CA 90065

Born: 1951 *Exhibitions:* Eva Dorog Gallery, Beverly Hills; Unique Gallery, San Francisco *Education:* Arizona St. U.

Lam-Po Leong, *Grandeur,* 27 x 55, watercolor and ink on rice paper,

Leza Lidow, *Crash '87,* 40 x 59, oil. Courtesy: Carpentier Gallery, Paris

His specialty is celebrity portraiture, particularly paintings of glamorous women such as Marilyn Monroe, Diana Ross and Cher. Working in oil on panel, he paints in a realistic style, capturing not only a striking likeness, but also the essence of a celebrity's public persona. He has also painted promotional materials for ABC Television and Caesar's Palace International, as well as album covers for Motown Records.

LENHART, GERRY A. (Painter)
205 Robin Rd., Hillsborough, CA 94010

Born: 1938 *Awards:* Merit Award for Painting, San Francisco Women Artists *Collections:* Salvador Dali *Exhibitions:* West of SoHo Gallery, San Mateo; Bay Arts, San Mateo *Education:* Ohio State U.; San Francisco State U.

She received scholarships and studied art at Ohio and San Francisco State Universities and at the College of Notre Dame. Her early work was traditional and representational, but in the early 1970s, inspired by Picasso and Van Gogh, she produced a series of personal and subjective paintings and collages with fantastic and abstract themes. She now applies mud, water, silk, stones and other natural objects to 3-by-4-foot and 4-by-4-foot canvases, creating textured mystical wall hangings in blues and golds.

LENTZ, JON WARREN (Sculptor, Painter, Glass Artist)
3716 Old San Jose Rd., Soquel, CA 95073

Born: 1951 *Collections:* DeHaydu, Aptos; Rhodes, Potomac, MD; Rush, San Fransicso *Exhibitions:* Santa Cruz Art League; Open Studio, Santa Cruz *Education:* UC-Santa Cruz *Dealers:* Virgina Breier, San Francisco; Running Ridge Gallery, Ojai and Santa Fe, NM; The Art Collector, San Diego

Following nearly a decade as a commission artist, he is focusing more on exhibitions and gallery work. His work presents sand-carved glass as a medium especially suited for serious abstract intent. He has developed formats and techniques that allow him to work the visual and tactile properties of sand-carved glass to a variety of expressive ends. The pieces are deeply carved on both the sides and the edges of the glass slab, sometimes pierced. His painting are three-dimensional, either wall-mounted or displayed freestanding. His monumental sculptures began with a series of *Undersea Phantasies.* More recent sculptures, *Demoiselles* and *Aphrodite's Nightie,* are concerned with figuation and abstraction from a Picasso-influenced or minimalist vantage.

LEON, DENNIS (Painter, Sculptor)
2501 14th Ave., Oakland, CA 94606

Born: 1933 *Awards:* Guggenheim Fellowship; MacDowell Fellowship *Collections:* Oakland Museum; San Francisco Museum of Modern Art *Exhibitions:* Fuller Goldeen Gallery, San Francisco; San Jose Museum of Art *Education:* Tyler School of Art; Temple U. *Dealer:* Fuller Goldeen Gallery, San Francisco

His works prior to 1975 were studio sculptures, using material very directly. These works ranged in scale from the very small to 20 feet and were accompanied by drawings. His recent work involves landscapes. These works, done outdoors with local materials, may reach 100 feet. His new oil paintings and pastels employ the same landscape themes, into which he has lately been placing figures.

LEONG, LAM-PO (Painter)
57 Paramount Terrace, San Francisco, CA 94118

Born: 1961 *Awards:* 1st Prize, Macao Young Artist Exhibition; 3rd Prize, Chinese Painting Exhibit, Guangdong, China *Collections:* Guangzhou Fine Arts Museum, Guangzhou, China; National Museum of Arts, Beijing *Exhibitions:* Luís de Camoes Museum, Macao; Rosicrucian Egyptian Museum, San Jose *Education:* Canton Fine Arts Institute; California College of Arts and Crafts *Dealer:* Wylie Wong Asian Art, San Francisco

He is noted for figure and landscape painting that blends the contemporary and the traditional, as well as traditional Chinese calligraphy. His paintings are known for combining the compositional techniques of Chinese painting with principles of Western art—a painting of the Grand Canyon, for example, has the shifting perspective of Chinese landscapes. One early work is a hanging scroll depicting a group of ballerinas. Although mounted in a traditional Chinese manner, its content, elegant design and style resemble Art Nouveau. His recent works are dark and dreamy images of mountains and sky done in watercolor and ink on rice paper. The mountains convey a tactile sense of heaviness. The paintings are deeply rooted in the spirit of Taoist philosophy; despite their subtle blend of Oriental and Western traditions, the works maintain a distinctive cultural identity.

LERNER, SANDRA (Painter)
10 E. 18th St., New York, NY 10003

Born: 1936 *Awards:* Aldrich Museum Acquisition, NEA Museum Purchase Grant; Anne Eisner Putnam Prize, National Association of Women Artists *Collections:* Aldrich Museum of Contemporary Art, Ridgefield, CT; Kampo Museum, Fukuoka, Japan *Exhibitions:* Betty Parsons Gallery, NYC; Dubins Gallery, Los Angeles *Dealer:* Graham Gallery, NYC; Kauffman Gallery, Houston

Her works reveal the profound influence of Taoist philosophy. Divergences and complementary opposites are reconciled through a highly personal abstract expressionist style that incorporates collage, impasto, stains and calligraphic marks. Her paintings are built up layer by layer with various media: rice paper is torn and wrinkled; paint is brushed, sprayed and thrown on; and sand, gel and other materials are applied to the canvas to create multiple textures. Works include The "Tao Series" and *UJI.* Lowery Sims of the Metropolitan Museum of Art has said, "The resoundingly tangible impact of the most subtle illusive haiku conveys the sense of the impact Sandra Lerner's work may have on the viewer."

LESUEUR, DEBORAH (Sculptor, Painter)
518 S. Edison, Graton, CA 95444

Born: 1929 *Exhibitions:* Apple Blossom Fine Art Show, Sebastopol; Arts and Crafts Show, Women's Building, San Francisco *Education:* Patri School of Art, San Francisco; College of Arts and Crafts; San Francisco State U.

Drawing on ancient European images of a female deity, she uses a potter's wheel and slab and press molds to create clay sculptures of the seasons and of primeval goddesses. She often incorporates plants, using grass for hair and flowers affixed to the figure's belly as a symbol of birth. She also creates vases and plates, painted or drawn with multiple images of god-

Lyle London, *Equipoise #5,* 156 x 96 x 60, aluminum

Gerry Anne Lenhart, *She #1,* 36 x 36, acrylic

desses or of a goddess with a child. She views her work as having three important, mutually reinforcing dimensions. First, she works with ancient images of women, a heritage that has been buried by subsequent patriarchal civilization. Second, she has chosen the potter's art, which originates from the same era as the images she recreates. Third, these images of the primeval goddess, symbolizing fertility and creation, are rendered in clay, which she views as a metaphor for the origin of humanity. Taken as a whole, she believes her work helps contemporary women to make a connection with their ancient spiritual history and their position of social and religious importance.

LETTERLUND, EWA (Painter, Sculptor)
333 N. Oakhurst Dr., Beverly Hills, CA 90210

Born: 1935 *Collections:* Templari House, Rome *Exhibitions:* Gallery One, Laguna Beach; U.S. National Fine Arts Competition & International Exhibition, Tallahassee, FL *Education:* Stockholm University, Sweden

She has a background in painting, sculpting and photography; she has also worked as an illustrator on over thirty books, including *Pippi Longstocking* and other children's books. She has sculpted a figurine for True Trolls, a company that will be distributing its dolls throughout the United States. Her present painting involves working with oil and beeswax with a palette knife. Her sculpture in the Greek and Roman tradition, includes some relief work.

LE VANT, NELDA R. (Mixed Media Artist)
746 Southview Way, Woodside, CA 94062

Born: 1922 *Awards:* San Mateo County Fair; *World of Poetry Magazine* Golden Poet Award *Exhibitions:* Woodside Public Library; Redwood City Public Library *Education:* U. of Oregon, Eugene

She creates mixed-media collages using portions of photographs hand-colored with paint. Her landscapes are inspired by the scenic setting in which she lives, an appreciation of children and animals, and piano music. She has converted her home into an informal "Heritage House" museum, where she collects antiques, crafts, sheet music, furniture and embroidery. She also braids rugs.

LEVENTHAL, JACQUELINE (Photographer)
5836 Virmar Ave., Oakland, CA 94618

Awards: Rockefeller Grant *Collections:* Oakland Museum; DeYoung Museum, San Francisco *Exhibitions:* Oakland Museum; Stereo Exhibition, Sydney, Australia *Education:* UCLA

While a student at ASUC Studio, she learned traditional black- and-white photography. She began to focus on simple, single images, discovering the qualities that could make the unwanted utensils of yesteryear surreal. She progressed to the unusual and haunting, always with a sense of preciousness. In a series of masks and mannequins, she both blurred the line between animate and inanimate, and poked fun at female vanity. She has expanded to stereo photography. These pieces combine slides and photos to create surreal images of figures such as monuments and tombstones.

LEVESQUE, DAVID (Sculptor)
30273 Fremond Way, Oak Run, CA 96069

Born: 1942 *Awards:* 3rd Place, Redding Museum and Art Center *Exhibitions:* Redding Museum and Art Center *Education:* Rhode Island School of Design

His carving career began after studying model making and sculpture at the Rhode Island School of Design. An apprenticeship carving original jewelry in precious metals led him away from wood sculpture, but exposure to the works of John Rood rejuvenated his interest ten years later. Since his first piece in Douglas Fir, he has sculpted all kinds of wood in the traditional style of mallet and chisel. Figures are realistic representations of people and animals, varying in height from 10 to 18 inches tall. One recent piece, however, is slight departure. In walnut, a dragon on the back of a unicorn signifies evil's constant pressure on what is pure and good.

LEVIN, WAYNE A. (Photographer)
315 Sandalwood Dr., Dayton, OH 45405

Born: 1945 *Awards:* NEA Fellowship *Collections:* Museum of Modern Art, NYC; Society for Contemporary Photography, Kansas City, KS *Exhibitions:* Orange Coast College, Costa Mesa; Cityscape Gallery, Pasadena *Education:* San Francisco Art Institute; Pratt Institute *Dealer:* Art Lort, Honolulu

His work has been influenced by landscape photographers Minor White, Wina Bullock, Paul Capanegro and Henri Cartier Bresson. He is a documentary photographer, known for large projects completed over several years. One seven-year-long project, shot in black and white, concentrated on the relation between reality and illusion using subjects such as window displays and mirrored images. He has also documented the declining years of Kalaupapa, the leprosy settlement founded by Father Damien, in 1872, on Molokai. Compiled in a book soon to be published, these photographs were exhibited in April, 1989, as part of the 100th anniversary observation of Father Damien's death. He has recently been working on two projects. The first is a series of color photographs fusing mirrors and reflected images into natural landscapes. The second is a documentary series on the Hospice of Dayton, one of the nation's leading hospice organizations.

LEVINE, MARILYN (Sculptor)
950 61st St., Oakland, CA 94608

Born: 1935 *Awards:* Arts Award, Canada Council; NEA Fellowship *Collections:* San Francisco Museum of Modern Art; Montreal Museum of Fine Arts *Exhibitions:* Fuller Goldeen Gallery, San Francisco; Museum of Modern Art, Paris *Education:* UC-Berkeley *Dealer:* Fuller Goldeen Gallery, San Francisco; O.K. Harris Gallery, NYC

She is best known for her realistic illusionist ceramic sculpture. Her early work, however, was in painting, functional pottery and hard-edge ceramic sculpture. Recent pieces include illusionistic simulations in clay of three-dimensional leather objects. She is adept at the transformation of stoneware into convincing replicas of worn leather bags, satchels and garments. In the works, there is an emphasis on a sense of human history as told by wear and use.

LEVINE, SHERRIE (Painter, Mixed Media Artist)
c/o Mary Boone Gallery, 417 West Broadway, New York, NY 10012

Born: 1947 *Exhibitions:* Baskerville and Watson Gallery, NYC; Wadsworth Atheneum, Hartford, CT *Education:* U. of Wisconsin, Madison *Dealer:* Mary Boone Gallery, NYC

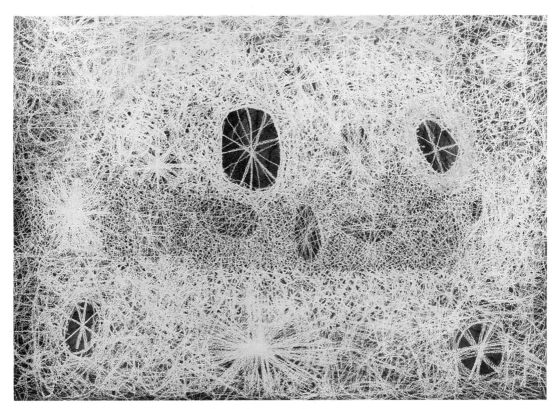

Hilda Levy, *Circular Depression Series—#13,* 20 x 29, pastel and watercolor on paper.
Courtesy: Dr. and Mrs. Marvin Rozen, State College, PA

Sharon Maney Lomanto, *I See the Light '87,* 72 x 60, oil on canvas

Around 1976, she began a series of silhouettes called "Sons and Lovers," portraits of Washington, Lincoln and Kennedy taken from coins, and subsequently cut silhouettes out of photographs found in magazines. Ideas regarding appropriation led to work that clearly exposed its origins in past art: she re-photographed work of the famous photographers Edward Weston and Eliot Porter and her new copy prints were shown at Metro Pictures. She also copied paintings by Miro, Mondrian and Malevich, among others. Says Gerald Marzorati, "she made it clear that piracy, with its overtones of infringement and lack of authorization, was the point." Recent works move in another direction: the "Gold Knot" series employs bare plywood panels in which only knots in the wood are painted gold; "Broad Stripes" are mahogany panels with vertical stripes painted in casein. In some instances, stripes have been applied to prefabricated wooden chair seats.

LEVINSON, DIANE (Ceramist)
P.O. Box 23, San Gregorio, CA 94074

Born: 1957 *Awards:* Emerging Talent Showcase Award, San Jose Art League *Exhibitions:* Art Rise Gallery, San Bruno; Gallery House, Palo Alto *Education:* San Jose State U.

After formal training in figurative sculpture, she began abstracting the figure. This work, influenced by Giacometti, Moore, Manzu and Rodin, was primarily cast in bronze. In 1979, she began working with clay, and, in 1980, after moving from New York to California, she began incorporating landscape and color. Her recent ceramic "wall" paintings began as abstractions of the coastal landscape, but became maps recording a single instant of time. Working with 30 to 50 pounds of clay, she throws the pieces on a wheel, alters them and, using slips, stains, underglazes and oxide glazes, she fires them as many as five times.

LEVY, HILDA (Multimedia Artist)
2411 Brigden Rd., Pasadena, CA 91104

Collections: Long Beach Museum of Art; Westside Jewish Center, Los Angeles *Exhibitions:* Library of Congress, Washington DC; Los Angeles Art Association *Education:* UCLA

The artist began her formal training while raising her family. From the beginning, she made a conscious decision not to emulate other artists' styles, preferring the inspiration of events, lifestyles and social patterns in her contemporary environment. In painting, she experimented with floating rectangular and linear forms as abstract expression of "ideas." Her strong, colorful patterns created calm rhythms; fleet, white lines swept in to define color fields. Sculptural concerns precipitated her recent shift to three-dimensional work, yet natural and man-made patterns and ornamentation continue to draw her interest.

LEVY, REBECCA (Painter, Sculptor)
367 N. Craft Ave., Los Angeles, CA 90048

Born: 1922 *Awards:* Best of Show, Westwood Art Association; Honorable Mention, San Bernardino Orange Show *Exhibitions:* Emerson Gallery, Encino; Long Beach Museum of Art *Education:* Immaculate Heart College; Otis Art Institute

Drawing is the basis of her visual art. She has always admired the great masters da Vinci, Michelangelo, Raphael and Rembrandt. However, she cites Lyonel Feininger as her greatest influence. For many years she has been working in oil, watercolor and acrylic painting, silkscreen and collage. She has also done countless drawings and mixed-media pieces. Recently, she has been working primarily in oil and acrylic, on a series of architectural paintings derived from her travels in Italy, Greece, Spain, Mexico and her home base, Los Angeles. Within her large body of work one finds abstracts, still lifes and landscapes on paper and canvas.

LEW, WEYMAN (Painter, Printmaker)
2810 Pacific Ave., San Francisco, CA 94115

Born: 1935 *Awards:* Merit Award, San Franciso Art Festival *Collections:* San Francisco Museum of Art; Brooklyn Museum *Exhibitions:* M. H. De Young Memorial Museum; Santa Barbara Museum of Art *Education:* UC- Berkeley; San Francisco Art Institute

The human figure has always been the central theme in his drawings and etchings, rendered in simple black line enclosing (but not completely) the figure in space. In the "psychedelic" posters of the 1960s, his full figures floated and tumbled across fields of pulsating color. In the 1970s, small areas of vivid color served as counterpoints to the white space in his drawings and hand-colored etchings. His fluid pen line is influenced by the continuous "silk thread" line in Chinese figure images and is in striking contrast to some recent painterly monotypes of ambiguous figures in empty space. The work is characterized most often by quiet, lighthearted humor.

LEWIS, NAN (Sculptor)
1221 Ocean Ave., Santa Monica, CA 90401

Born: 1924 *Awards:* 2nd Purchase Prize, All City Art Festival, Juried Show, San Diego Fine Arts Museum *Exhibitions:* Laguna Beach Museum of Art; Bowers Museum, Santa Ana

She creates abstract sculptures of the human figure and organic forms. Rodin, Brancusi and Arp were the earliest influences on her style and approach. She usually works in terra cotta, sometimes colored, although she has also sculpted in wax and has had some of her pieces cast in bronze. Her pieces are low and oblong loops with large open areas that permit light and shadow to pass through them, providing a lightness not often associated with clay forms. The undulating, natural shapes are ususally 24 by 12 inches in size. Her more recent work has grown increasingly non-representational, with an emphasis on negative space, as a result of her studies of the works of Henry Moore and Barbara Hepworth.

LEWIS, PATTY L. (Painter)
1705 East Valley Rd., Santa Barbara, CA 93108

Born: 1951 *Awards:* Best of Exhibit, Faulkner Gallery *Exhibitions:* Gallery 113, Santa Barbara; Hobar Gallery, Santa Barbara *Education:* UC-Santa Barbara

A childhood in the Orient and work in design and calligraphy have influenced her economy of line. Like Georgia O'keeffe, she is interested in the open space of the Southwestern landscape. Paintings in oil and monotypes with pastel concentrate on color and sunlight. Deep blues of the sky contrast with soft pink and lavender adobe buildings, doorways and walkways. Because of reflected light, bright areas highlight an otherwise muted canvas. Recent work experiments with inner sunlight and color in a more abstract style. Lines are stronger and more energetic than in earlier work; the curve meets the linear within simplified symbolic

Ming C. Lowe, *Buddhist Way Out,* 48 x 39, oil on canvas

Patty Look Lewis, *Doors Opening Doors,* 48 x 60, oil on canvas. Courtesy: Sarah Fargo

forms. These "landscapes of the soul" are completely devoid of figures.

LEWIS, PETER WAYNE (Painter, Printmaker)
863 Florida St., San Francisco, CA 94110

Born: 1953 *Awards:* Best in Show, Members Exhibition, San Jose Art Center *Exhibitions:* Monterey Peninsula Museum of Art; San Jose Museum of Art *Education:* San Jose State U. *Dealer:* Bruce Velick, San Francisco

His work is second- or third-generation abstract expressionism, with images drawn from his Jamaican heritage. He paints by layering figures, usually fragmented human, animal and vegetable forms, in vibrantly colored oil paint. The result is a brightly colored, textured presentation of an array of natural and abstract elements. *Down on the Nuclear Farm,* for example, is a collage of mutated faces, birds, insects and flowers. The deep green background of *Labyrinth* is full of half-formed silhouettes, foliage and animals. His work is more a result of a spontaneous combination of elements than of pre-planned design.

LEWIS, TOM (Painter)
2190 Carmel Valley Rd., Del Mar, CA 92014

Born: 1938 *Collections:* Arizona State U. *Exhibitions:* Jack Nicholas Development Corp.; About Face Exhibit, San Diego Communication Arts Group *Education:* Arizona State U.

While at Arizona State University in the late 1950s, he studied with painter Tom Harter, sculptor Ben Goo and photographer Ed Peplow. He left art in 1961 and didn't pick up a brush again until 1986. His recent large-size work bespeaks a renewed confidence and verve. He loves the immediacy of transparent watercolors, and he is intrigued by details of landscape. He renders his floral and naturalist subjects on watercolor paper from 3 by 6 to 4 by 8 feet. His style shows the influence of Turner and John Marin.

LE WITT, SOL (Sculptor, Conceptual Artist)
c/o John Weber Gallery, 1452 Greene St., New York, NY 10012

Born: 1928 *Collections:* Los Angeles County Museum of Art; Museum of Modern Art, NYC *Exhibitions:* La Jolla Museum of Art; Whitney Museum, NYC *Education:* Syracuse U. *Dealer:* John Weber Gallery, NYC

After working for architect I.M. Pei in the mid-1950s, he began making wall reliefs and then three-dimensional sculptures. With the open, modular, cubical structures of 1964, he was recognized as a minimalist. Wall drawings three years later were deliberately painted over after their exhibition, emphasizing their impermanence. A spokesman for Conceptual Art, he published several articles in the late 1960s describing the artist's concept and formulation of an idea as more important than its execution. Wood or metal open cubes in various arrangements are painted white in order to draw attention away from the display itself. The titles are significant because they bring meaning to the work by describing its premise, clarifying the abstractions of mathematics, philosophy and linguistics.

LI, EDWARD Y.W. (Painter, Printmaker)
3427B Waialae Ave., Honolulu, HI 96818

Born: 1943 *Awards:* Scholarship, Honolulu Academy of Arts; Scholarship, Cornish School of Allied Arts *Exhibitions:* El Camino Art Gallery, Torrence; Northwest Print Council Exhibition

He began his career in Hong Kong. For more than two decades, printmaking has been his primary medium. Many of his subjects, including such series as "Childhood," are autobiographical. His printmaking techniques have often been experimental and he frequently uses color to express mood and form. In his current work, drawing, printmaking and watercolor painting all overlap into a mixed-media lithography or intaglio. His finished pieces make up a logbook of his experiences. His current subjects include incidents or events that incite his emotions, curiosity or outrage. Sometimes his works are merely forms that allow his mind to assume an "alpha state."

LIANG, YEN (Multimedia Artist)
2909 Ptarmigian Dr., #2, Walnut Creek, CA 94595

Born: 1908 *Awards:* Taliesin Fellowship, Frank Lloyd Wright Foundation, Spring Green, WI *Exhibitions:* Asian Cultural Center, San Francisco; Civic Arts Gallery, Walnut Creek *Education:* Yale U.

His distinguished international artistic career spans most of this century, and includes a diverse range of media. He feels that the spirit of every branch of the arts has influenced work in all other areas. The mingling of varied careers (as a musician, architect, painter, ceramist, author and illustrator) is guided by his personal preferences, and all of his work bears an identifiable touch. He currently works in wheel-thrown clay, creating functional pieces, animals and sculpture. He also produces realistic paintings and drawings in oil, watercolor and acrylic. The sizes of these works vary from 2 by 3 inches to 5 by 6 feet; his subjects include people, landscapes and birds, especially Canadian geese.

LIASHKOV, PETER (Painter)
1052 Manzanita St., Los Angeles, CA 90029

Born: 1939 *Collections:* Capitol Group *Exhibitions:* Jan Turner Gallery, Los Angeles; Los Angeles Fine Arts Gallery *Education:* Otis Art Institute *Dealer:* Jan Turner Gallery, Los Angeles

Inspired by archaeological fragments and by Fayum Roman-Egyptian funerary portraits, he attempted in the mid-1970s to capture spiritual auras in loosely expressionistic portraits and nudes. His technique was to sandwich oil paint between two panels of glass and to reinforce the work with silicone. His recent work integrates spiritual and psychological associations and transforms them into palpable presences. He first applies acrylic and oil to smooth, sanded doorskin, then applies such textured media as powdered pigments, gels, sands and wax. Finally, he uses images of wedges, ovals and planes in contrasting degrees of opacity and transparency to activate the different colored grounds.

LIBERMAN, ALEXANDER (Sculptor)
173 E. 70th St., New York, NY 10021

Born: 1912 *Awards:* Chevalier, Legion d'Honor, France; Gold Medal for Design, Paris International Exhibition *Collections:* Museum of Modern Art, NYC; Art Institute of Chicago *Exhibitions:* Museum of Modern Art, NYC; Corcoran Gallery of Art, Washington D.C. *Education:* L'Ecole des Beaux Arts, Paris; Ecole Special d'Architecture *Dealer:* Andre Emmerich Gallery, NYC

Born in Kiev, Russia, he studied painting in Paris with Andre Lhote, then architecture with August Peret. He came to America in 1940 and began painting geometric shapes, like the circle, in a minimal style.

G. Lichtenstein, *Iridescent Dream,* 16 x 44, oil based ink on paper, Franklin Henderson Fine Art

John Lin, *Reality vs. Illusion,* 15 x 20, gouache and prismacolor

Later, during his transition to sculpture, circles appear in illusionistic space. Votives and icons are planar geometric shapes often constructed from aluminum. Experiments with assemblage in the 1960s led to a series of painted outdoor pieces made of cut boiler tanks and pipes, such as *Realms*. In 1970, huge hollow columns of steel were sliced at an angle to reveal ellipses, as in *Firmament*. Also a photographer, he often records the steps taken during construction of outdoor pieces as they are arranged and re-worked. He has published photographic essays, and has been the editorial director of Conde Nast Publications magazines for over twenty years.

LICARI, THOMAS (Photographer, Mixed Media Artist)
8336 W. 3rd St., Los Angeles, CA 90048

Born: 1949 *Exhibitions:* Pacific Design Center 1988 Design Conference; Museum of Contemporary Art, Los Angeles *Education:* USC; U. of Minnesota

In the early 1970s, he worked as a research associate at the Institute for Marine and Coastal Studies at the University of Southern California, providing photographic documentation and technical illustrations for publications of marine ecological research projects. While making the transition from science to fine art, he became interested in hand-colored photography. His first major project using this technique involved hand-coloring with oils on large 35mm black-and-white proof sheets of old cars. He enjoys transforming realistic images into surrealistic, whimsical images, recently adding paper, fabric, models, car parts, transparency films and neon to the photographs. He also builds three-dimensional sculptures of architectural images from cut, hand-colored photographs.

LICHT, HELEN ANN (Painter)
1210 Franklin Ln., Lafayette, CA 94549

Born: 1933 *Awards:* Merit Award, San Francisco Women Artists; Art in Embassies Program, State Department *Exhibitions:* Interart Gallery, San Francisco; Valley Art Center *Education:* Stanford U.; UC-Berkeley *Dealer:* Interart Gallery, San Francisco

Her pieces are reminiscent of primitive American painting. The figures are undetailed, the perspective is often slightly off and the concern seems to be with shape and the juxtaposition of color. She chooses subject matter from situations suggested to her by art history, travel and the Bible, and she has recently been doing a series based on her memories of China. In these works, she begins with a reference point and abstracts around it, painting in acrylic and using elements of mixed media and collage. Her teachers have included Joan Brown, Boyd Allen, Jay DeFeo and Lundy Siegriest. Her line drawings have been reproduced as greeting cards.

LICHTENSTEIN, GARY (Painter, Printmaker)
c/o SOMA Fine Art Press, 78 1st St., San Francisco, CA 94105

Born: 1953 *Collections:* Museum of Modern Art, NYC; Wadsworth Athenium, Hartford, CT *Exhibitions:* New York International Exhibit of Contemporary Art; Rubicon Gallery, Los Altos *Education:* San Francisco Art Institute; Antioch College West

After studying under Robert Fried at the San Francisco Art Institute and collaborating with Ken Price, Harvey Mudd and Robert Moon, he developed new and innovative serigraphic techniques that allowed him to transcend the medium's traditional boundaries. He achieves an unusual refractive effect by painting with oil based inks. His imagery has an intense and kinetic feel to it. At first, his pieces were purely abstract but he has gradually moved to a vocabulary of ethereal, cloud-like patterns with an emotional use of strong and pastel color. On viewing his work, the viewer feels that the painting has a continuing ability to change.

LICHTMAN, SHIRLEY H. (Sculptor)
6265 Elder Pl., San Diego, CA 92120

Born: 1917 *Awards:* 1st Place, Madonna Festival; 2nd Place, Downey Museum *Collections:* Jewish Community Center, San Diego; Adat Sholom Synagogue, Los Angeles *Exhibitions:* Sculptor's Guild, San Diego; Glass on Metal '87, Society of Religious Ceremonial Artists *Education:* School of the Art Institute of Chicago; Corcoran School of Fine Arts *Dealer:* Knowles Art Gallery, La Jolla

Through her art forms, she seeks to extract the spiritual qualities that are intrinsic to the physical media she chooses. She works in copper tubing and hammered copper sheets, as well as Italian glass, marble, alabaster, soapstone and hardwoods, and her pieces may be either abstract or figurative. She also creates panels incorporating vitreous enamel on copper. Inspiration is drawn from religious or ceremonial themes; some of her large architectural commissions include altars, memorials, mosaics and Menorahs. Smaller pieces may be cast bronze or carved stone.

LIDOW, LIZA (Painter)
454 Cuesta Way, Los Angeles, CA 90077

Exhibitions: Gallery Carpentier, Paris; Museum Antibes, France *Dealers:* Carpentier, Paris; Ankrum, Los Angeles

Her early large oil paintings were influenced by surrealism; she painted store mannequins with oils and mounted them on rotating lazy Susans. Her recent oils are life-sized depictions of human forms. The color scheme and style for these large canvases is similar to the work of the old Flemish Masters. She also works in black and white. Her paintings explore a variety of themes and images—the human torso; money as man's downfall; the suppression of modern woman; contemporary man's struggle to survive competition.

LIEB, REDDY (Glass Artist)
50 Dolores Terrace, San Francisco, CA 94110

Born: 1950 *Awards:* 3rd Place, San Francisco Street Glass Works *Exhibitions:* Richmond Art Center; ICB Open Studio

She has always felt a strong affinity with the work of Rene Magritte, who dealt with the illusory space that enfolds the realistic and the visible. She employs this same sense of mystery in her work with glass—a material, which is both solid and liquid. Using both realistic and abstract nature images, she carefully arranges these elements into intriguing configurations, creating a tension between the real and the illusionary. After completing an apprenticeship with Narcissus Quagliata, she became sensitized to the use of the lead line, as a beautiful descriptive element that still appears in her pieces today. She usually works from her own collages, using a sandblaster and epoxy paints to complete her glass panels. By playing a variety of bright colors against blacks, whites and grays, she makes sure that color never overwhelms the figures. Recently, she

Hal Larsen, *Kachina Returns,* 36 x 46, mixed media

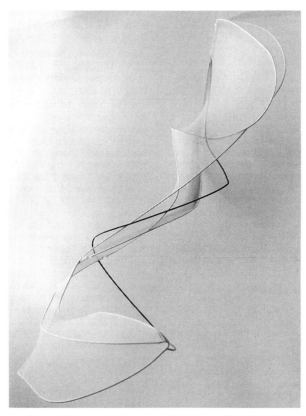

Nance Liebenson-Rex, *Ama No Gawa,* 67 x 33 x 31,
acrylic on nylon on welded steel rods

has finished a glass panel project, based on the abstract nature writings of e.e. cummings.

LIEBENSON-REX, NANCY (Sculptor, Multimedia Artist)
22014 De La Osa St., Woodland Hills, CA 91364

Born: 1957 *Awards:* Sculpture Award, Ettinger Gallery, Laguna; Millard Sheets Fellowship, Scripps Fine Arts Foundation, Claremont *Collections:* Albrecht Auditorium, Claremont Graduate School *Exhibitions:* Fresno Arts Center Museum; Bowers Museum, Santa Ana *Education:* Scripps College; Claremont Graduate School

She is best known for her three-dimensional wall sculptures, which evolved from her free form collages of torn pieces of canvas, translucent nylon, fiber materials, impasto and washes of acrylic. A chance event prompted a new development: as she removed a piece from the wall, she noticed the play of light over the nylon. She then decided to create a bas-relief structure as a frame for the collage, so light could naturally come from behind and ignite an inner glow, created by the translucent nylon and acrylic washes. This bas-relief structure soon evolved into a three-dimensional steel rod structure, with translucent nylon stretched over it. She now uses other metals, such as raw aluminum, copper wire (with a green and blue patina) and metal screens. These engaging, colorful sculptures entice the viewer to explore them from many different perspectives, as the painted metal rods jut, curve and explode from the wall, and the translucent painted sheets of nylon shimmer in the light. These contradictory elements produce structural and aesthetic tensions, and add to the sculpture's weightless, energetic, fragile character.

LIGHTBODY, JOYCE (Painter)
3433 Rambla Pacifico, Malibu, CA 90265

Born: 1954 *Awards:* NEA Grant *Exhibitions:* Los Angeles Contemporary Exhibitions; Baxter Art Gallery, Pasadena *Education:* UC-Santa Barbara

Her work is an exploration of the relationship between the systems of language and music. Lyrics are culled from the work of writers such as John Ashbery, Carolyn Forche and Alex LaGuma, as well as from newspaper editorials and word sequences of her own invention. She translates words into visual and choral patterns by coding and graphing them both tonally and rhythmically. Among her exhibits are displays of musical scores with bars of color and small writing that resemble old illustrated manuscripts of music. These scores are often exhibited at the same time they are being performed. She draws from such genres as 15th- and 16th-century part songs, rock and roll and Pygmy polyphonies.

LIGHTY, MERILEE FLETCHER (Multimedia Artist)
Kappas Marina E-5, Sausalito, CA 94965

Born: 1925 *Exhibitions:* New Masters Gallery, Carmel; Sierra Gallery, Tiburon *Education:* St. John's College, Annapolis, MD *Dealer:* Sierra Gallery, Tiburon

In the last two years, she has become increasingly interested in process paintings, using sand, glue and ink in numerous layers. She has recently been working on a Great Barrier Reef series, which consists of sculptural forms built up in handmade paper, sometimes with areas or elements of sausage casings. These works are layered, occasionally colored and sometimes

varethaned to appear wet. Some pieces are abstract, while others are representational. She constructs an armature from materials such as plasticene, cotton batting, clay and wire, and then forms sheets of wet paper over them. These forms are left to dry, then assembled and glued to the background paper. Much of her work remains pure white and is presented in plexiglas box frames with white linen backing.

LIIKALA, JOHN (Environmental and Public Artist)
410 Plateau, Santa Cruz, CA 95060

Born: 1938 *Exhibitions:* San Francisco Civic Center; Oakland Festival at the Lake *Education:* Ohio State U.

He has produced large-scale, interactive, multimedia public art forms in New York and California. In 1966, he founded the Group 212 Intermedia Workshop in Woodstock, New York; the following year, he served as a consultant on environmental art to the New York State Council on the Arts. During the 1970s, he moved to California and studied Jungian psychology, creative play and art therapy. In 1980, he established the Art Dancing Gallery in San Francisco, a center for visual and performance arts. Since then, he has continued to build life-sized collage figures for environmental installations in public spaces. He has an annual commission from the San Francisco Arts Council to create forty pieces for the summer pops festival. Either free-standing or mobile, the brightly colored, cut-out figures feature dreamlike florals and a humorous, erotic, surrealist tone. Most pieces are either silk-screened or air-brushed, and stand 5 to 14 feet tall.

LILIENTHAL, WENDY (Fiber Artist)
740 Butterfield Rd., San Anselmo, CA 94960

Awards: Award, Sausalito Art Festival; Award, Gallery Five, Tequesta, FL *Exhibitions:* P.J. Coonley, Stanford; Depot Gallery, Yountville *Education:* Parsons School of Design

In New York, she studied architecture and design, but her interests changed dramatically when she studied weaving at the Richmond Art Center in California. She experimented with loom techniques, creating colorful, abstract wall hangings that combined exotic yarns gathered in her travels. Her interests changed again when she learned the techniques of papermaking, which she added to her knowledge of weaving to create a hybrid style. She began stretching paper over warped threads, creating free-form pieces in paper with embossed designs and feathers, pods, shells and small weavings. These works have recently increased in scale; she has begun to use dyes, pigments and paints and to add elements of collage to the works. The appearance of a piece is often influenced by her travels— some pieces include gold leaf or oriental designs, and she continues to use yarns from many countries. Other works include small pieces of metal and felt-tip pens, layered and spray-painted. Most of the more recent pieces are multidimensional, some freestanding and some projecting from a wall mounting.

LIN, JOHN (Painter, Commercial Illustrator)
17738 Plummer St., Northridge, CA 91325

Born: 1955 *Exhibitions:* Cal. State-Northridge; Los Angeles Artcore *Education:* Cal. State-Northridge *Dealer:* Contemporary, Honolulu, HI

After formal training in illustration, graphic design, super-realism and surrealism, he developed his own

Frank Lapena, *Vision/Transformation,* 8 x 10, wood engraving

Earl Linderman, *Klub Twenty Grand,* 72 x 60, oil

drawing style involving gouache and prismacolor pencils. In 1985, he began studying with Marvin Harden, who trained him to use his imagination. Recently, he developed a line of greeting cards, which he calls "Art Cards." Through these cards he attempts to convey the artistic feeling in daily life. In order to make the work accessible, he uses images of reformed animal shapes and human figures. "I hope that everyone will see and feel those cards [are] different from the regular cards on the market."

LINDBERG, NORA D. (Painter)
232 Oak Ave., Galt, CA 95632

Born: 1940 *Awards:* 1st Place, Lodi Grape and Wine Show *Collections:* Nancy Dale Bivens *Exhibitions:* Jenner Art Exhibition; Montevina Wine Show, Plymouth *Education:* Sacramento City College

Interrupted by the duties of parenting, she did not paint for many years following her formal training. For the past eight years, she has painted with Rom Vila, a San Francisco Bay area artist. Painting mostly impressionistic-realist landscapes, seascapes and still lifes, on occasion she will produce an abstract piece. It is the sensuous quality of working the shape and color on canvas, be it one of gentleness or strength, that attracts her to the impressionist-abstract techniques. She finds the natural colors and movement in the clouds and seas a never-ending challenge and inspiration.

LINDERMAN, EARL (Painter)
5301 N. 69th Pl., Scottsdale, AZ 85253

Born: 1931 *Exhibitions:* C.G. Rein, Los Angeles; Vorpal Gallery, NYC *Education:* Pennsylvania St. U. *Dealers:* Vorpal Gallery, NYC; C.G. Rein, Minneapolis, Scottsdale, Los Angeles, Houston, Santa Fe and Denver

His paintings feature a handsome mustachioed character he calls "Doctor Thrill." Filled with beautiful women, as well as moody piano players, the paintings suggest Berlin in the 1930s. His nightclubs, bars and other interiors and exteriors recall art deco of the 1920s, 1930s and 1940s. In his psychological portraits, he encourages the viewer to reminisce. His works are dynamic, figurative and expressive, with dramatic, almost cinematic lighting, making the figures exaggerated but still recognizeable. He has been influenced by Matisse, Beckman and Georg Grosz. He is a professor at Arizona State University. His book, *The True and Incredible Adventures of Doctor Thrill*, was published by Paradise House Publishers in 1985.

LINTON, DAVID (Painter, Drawer)
2113 Mendonico Blvd., San Diego, CA 92199

Born: 1945 *Awards:* 1st Place, La Jolla Art Show; 1st Place, Pastel, Clairmont Art Guild *Collections:* Massachusetts Life Insurance Co. *Exhibitions:* La Jolla Art Show; Clairmont Art Guild

A native of Connecticut, he began his career at the age of twelve, and he won many awards while a student of Roy Schmidt. He now lives in San Diego and works with Californian beach and water imagery. His pastel drawings are uncommon for the medium—although not photo-realistic, they are hard, warm and vivid depictions of realistic subjects. In his drawing *Evening Shadows* of a pier, he achieves a dour and serene effect by using varying blues and subtle reds. His sun-drenched, lonely lighthouse is warm and summer-like with a pure blue sky. He is part owner of Print Produc-

tions, a company that handles reproductions of his work.

LIPOFSKY, MARVIN (Sculptor, Printmaker)
1012 Pardee St., Berkeley, CA 94710

Born: 1938 *Awards:* NEA Fellowship; Honorific Prize, International Exhibition of Contemporary Glass, Valencia, Spain *Collections:* The National Museum of Modern Art, Kyoto, Japan; Umeleckoprumyslove Museum V, Praze, Czechoslovakia *Exhibitions:* San Francisco Museum of Art; Stedelijke Museum, Amsterdam *Education:* U. of Illinois, Urbana; U. of Wisconsin, Madison

His sculpture is done in glass, with a sensual quality that derives from the material. During trips to Europe and Japan, he attempts to capture in his work the culture of a given place and his experience of it as an artist. A period spent at the Crystalex Hantich glass factory in Novy Bor, Czechoslovakia resulted in a series of sculptures molded with wood and metal materials found on the factory grounds. Each piece reflects his experience of the Czechoslovakian people and their culture — a vibrant, colorful interior in contrast to a restrained, subdued interior. *Morning Mist*, *Summer Rain* and *Pacific Sunset* reflect the environment of the Pilchuck Glass School in Washington state. Colors he applies to the glass by hand echo the changing climate of the Washington coast. Once he has extracted a body of work from an environment, he cuts, grinds and polishes in his studio to achieve the final piece. His drawings and prints are generally done in series of small, abstract watercolors that evolve from his work with glass, concentrating on color and reflection.

LIPPOLD, LARRY (Fiber Artist, Draughtsperson)
163 Staples Ave., San Francisco, CA 94112

Born: 1942 *Awards:* NEA Grant; Award, Exhibits/Projects III, Fiberworks, Berkeley *Collections:* Museum of Art, Stanford U.; Las Vegas Art Museum *Exhibitions:* Monterey Peninsula Museum of Art; Napa Valley College *Education:* San Francisco Art Institute; Cal. State-Chico

He is best known for sculptures made from rayon flock—a fiber, which, even under light pressures, crumbles to powder. He builds his pieces by setting up a hand-constructed cardboard wall. Then, using a flour sifter, a brush and a broom, he builds the floor relief, layer by layer, using different colors as he progresses. He uses the brush to shape the piece, and the broom to sweep up his mistakes and near-misses. He spends much of his work day on his hands and knees, wearing knee-pads and a protective mask. When the piece is shaped and contoured to his satisfaction, he carefully pulls away the cardboard walls, permitting the piece to stand on its own. The rolling, rippling surfaces are surprisingly sharp-edged and distinct. When the exhibit or installation is finished, the sculptures are knocked over and swept up. He also produces and exhibits his drawings on a regular basis.

LIPZIN, JANIS CRYSTAL (Multimedia Artist)
2434 Bloomfield Rd., Sebastopol, CA 95472

Awards: NEA Fellowship; Western States Regional Media Arts Fellowship *Collections:* San Francisco Art Institute; Carneqie Museum of Art, Pittsburgh *Exhibitions:* Museum of Modern Art; Centre Georges Pompidou, Paris

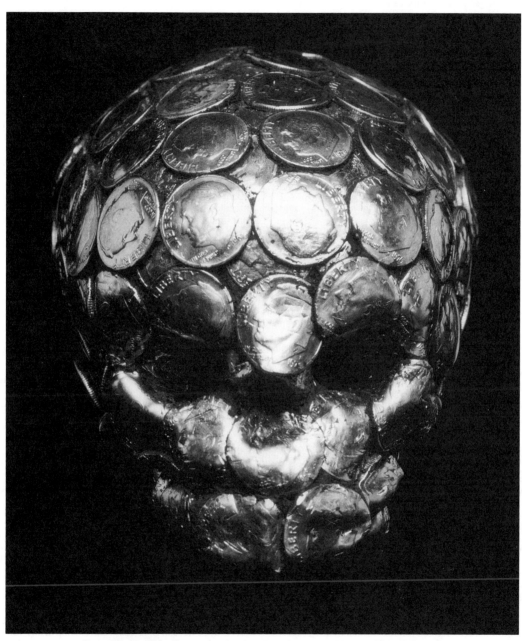

Gary Lloyd, *Baby Beam,* 4 x 3 x 4, coins. Courtesy: Earl McGrath Gallery

She is a multimedia artist who, for more than two decades, has emphasized the specific identities of her materials and revealed the workings of the processes she employs. In her film, *Government Property* she used three projectors, one of which was hand-held, to explore the tension that exists between film's function as a medium of representation and its immediate presence as a physical object. The materials of her recent work have included compressed fibers from clothes dryers, photographic emulsions and earth and archaeological artifacts. Her media have included video, film, audio recording, three-dimensional constructions and xerography.

LIU, KATHERINE CHENG (Painter, Printmaker)

2872 E. Panamint Court, Westlake Village, CA 91362

Awards: Grumbacher Award, National Society of Painters in Casein and Acrylic; Gold Medal of Honor, Allied Artists of America *Collections:* Virginia Museum, Richmond; Harrison Museum of Utah State U. *Exhibitions:* National Watercolor Society Annuals; Butler Institute of American Art *Education:* UC-Berkeley *Dealer:* Louis Newman Galleries, Los Angeles

Her watercolors deal primarily with nature and are concerned with change and balance. In 1982, she started working with monoprinting, experimenting with textural changes and spatial relationships in the printmaking medium. Today, she works with mixed media, incorporating her knowledge of water media, printmaking and collage into her works. In recent pieces, gestural areas are contrasted with highly evolved areas to form a whole with interesting textural changes. The recent "Wall Series," inspired by the observation of the aging process on actual old walls, explores transparency and textural richness.

LLOYD, FRANK (Painter)

5213 Hartwick St., Los Angeles, CA 90041

Born: 1951 *Collections:* Viacom International, Los Angeles; Nationwide Sports Publications, Beverly Hills *Exhibitions:* Venice Artwalk; Art Center College of Design, Pasadena *Education:* UC-Santa Cruz

Over the course of his artistic career, he has extracted and refined the formal themes of his work from observations of nature and his involvement with the process of painting. His style is rooted in a type of landscape-based abstraction. While most of his early work was in oil on canvas, the 1980s have seen a gradual shift to the use of acrylic on paper. By using cut-outs from his paintings and other collage techniques, he has become increasingly fascinated with intricate, high-keyed cubist constructions. In his recent work, he uses layering, branching, modular repetition and compression to build a dense network of lines. This highly colored, linear structure evokes visual experience, in which shapes emerge and disappear. Without any explicit reference to an organic subject, these works are representations of life and energy. A recent series of wooden constructions is the result of the progressive redefinition of this theme. The skeletal structure of these pieces, which measure approximately 4 by 5 feet, reveals their inner structure, suggesting abstracted natural forms.

LLOYD, GARY MARCHAL (Painter, Sculptor)

1040 N. Las Palmas, Hollywood, CA 90038

Born: 1943 *Awards:* NEA Grant; Exxon Enterprises *Collections:* Los Angeles County Museum; Museum of Contemporary Art, Los Angeles *Exhibitions:* Gallery 454 North, Los Angeles; University Art Museum, Berkeley *Education:* Otis Art Institute *Dealer:* Earl McGrath Gallery, Los Angeles

Influenced by Buckminster Fuller and by Fluxus artists Nam June Paik and Joseph Beuys, he constructed sculptural performances connecting distant locals through various electronic media such as video, telephone and facsimile machines. He combined radio transmitters and anatomical sculptures made of currency and other cultural artifacts to produce works that examine the effect of mass-media conditioning. His radio paintings and real-time sculptures are bound together by a common theme: the precariousness of human survival caused by misuse of natural and technological resources. His recent mixed-media painting and sculpture presents a series of superimposed signs ranging from images of prehistory to forebodings of destruction: an automobile and a gnarled tree trunk floating over the moon's surface suggest the interdependence of macro- and micro-universes and of man-made and natural phenomena; a painting of a mushroom cloud with a universal product code and color key suggests a relationship between conspicuous consumption and the psychological marketability of war.

LLOYD, SHARON LYNN (Painter, Mixed Media Artist)

P.O. Box 221475, Carmel, CA 93922

Born: 1951 *Awards:* Honorable Mention, Art Guild of Sonoma *Exhibitions:* Northern California Watercolor Competition, Palo Alto; Monterey Fair *Education:* UC-Berkeley

Before formal art training, she worked in the architectural and engineering fields, experiences that influenced her painting. Frequent travels through Europe further shaped her artistic approach. Relatives who were painters, and others, such as James Rosen, encouraged her to pursue fine art as a profession. At first, she employed traditional watercolor techniques. Later, she started combining watercolor with other materials to convey a layering effect in both line and shape. Stylistically, her work exhibits a systematic approach verging on pure design and pattern to explore themes ranging from cycles in nature to religious symbolism and its geometric equivalents. Music, studies of ancient civilizations and a move to the country influenced her chosen media, techniques and artistic expression. The fetishes and charms of the Native American culture, the religious symbolism of Christian culture and the rhythms and forces of nature find expression in her work as assemblages. Materials include wood, bone, shell and copper. The conjunction and juxtaposition of male and female is a current theme in her work. She explores this relationship from various perspectives and expressions, ranging from subliminal fetishistic compositions to whimsical portrayals of social events such as weddings.

LOBDELL, FRANK (Painter)

730 Cassia St., Redwood City, CA 94063

Born: 1921 *Awards:* Nealie Sullivan Award; Tamarind Fellowship *Collections:* Los Angeles County Museum of Art; Oakland Museum *Exhibitions:* Corcoran Gallery, Washington D.C.; San Francisco Museum of Art *Education:* St. Paul School of Fine Art; California

Gyongy Laky, *Stick Episode,* 90 x 75 x 6, sticks, thread, wire and paper.

School of Fine Art; Academie Grande Chaumiere, Paris *Dealer:* Oscarsson Siegeltuch & Co., NYC

A dominant figure in Bay Area art since the late 1940s, he draws from the heritage of abstract expressionism, especially from the works of Clyfford Still, creating powerful, deeply personal works that stand as a dialogue between the artist and his creation. The paintings are normally titled only by the season and year of their creation, and they reveal an agonizing process of artistic development. Evident is a preference for broad swaths, vertical lines and biomorphic shapes that verge on figurative or symbolic imagery. The palette has evolved from early somber shades to brighter colors, the works of recent decades becoming more evocative of concrete images rendered in the language of abstract expressionism. Yet despite these representational reverberations, the images defy any simple interpretation. Ultimately, the works stand on their own as rugged, highly individualistic artistic statements.

LOBELLO, PETER (Sculptor)
c/o Mary Ritter, 349 Selby Ln., Atherton, CA 94025

Born: 1936 *Collections:* Geneva Museum of Art, Switzerland; Aldrich Museum of Contemporary Art, Ridgefield, CT *Exhibitions:* Sarah Y. Rentschler Gallery, NYC; American Academy and Institute of Arts and Letter, NYC *Education:* Tulane U. School of Architecture *Dealer:* Mary L. Ritter, Atherton

He constructs sculptures employing the basic geometric shapes—the square, the triangle, the rectangle, the parallelogram—in metal or wood, both free-standing and affixed relief-like to a wall. Silver, brass, bronze, nickel and aluminum are polished mirror-like, electroplated and arranged to create variations upon the surfaces and reflective powers of the shapes. The different shapes that make up a piece are often movable or foldable, as upon hinges. Such movement within the pieces alters their fundamental shapes, their color, their relationships to one another and their reflective quality, often distorting size and form. The wall piece *Number Fifteen*, for example, folds into a diamond shape, unfolds into a square and, its hinged-triangles extended arm-like from the wall presents a multitude of reflective surfaces in silver and gray. He works in the mainstream of the 20th century's formalist tradition. A constructivist, he greatly admires Buckminster Fuller, Josef Albers and Barnett Newman.

LOCURTO, LILLA (Sculptor)
2065 E. 37th St., Los Angeles, CA 90058

Born: 1949 *Awards:* Research Grant, Southern Illinois U.; Special Projects/Multi-Arts Grant, Indiana Arts Commission *Exhibitions:* Gallery 454 North, Los Angeles; Mekler Gallery, Los Angeles *Education:* Arizona State U.; Southern Illinois U.

Beginning with drawings, she sculpts in bronze, aluminum and various resins. She has an abstract, metaphorical style that is still clear in intent and readily accessible to the viewer. Looking to nature and landscapes for subject matter, she has sculpted many pieces that deal with environmental destruction.

LODATO, PETER (Painter, Multimedia Artist)
837 Traction Ave., #103, Los Angeles, CA 90013

Born: 1946 *Awards:* NEA Grant; Award of Excellence, American Museum Association *Collections:* Seattle Art Museum; Brooklyn Museum *Exhibitions:* Burnett

Miller Gallery, Los Angeles; La Jolla Museum of Contemporary Art *Education:* Cal. State-Northridge *Dealer:* Krygier/Landu, Los Angeles

His paintings and installations are reinvestigations of visual space. Often, the viewer becomes the subject of a presentation of empty space. His choice of material varies with the project and includes oils, watercolors, drawings, sheet rock, gold leaf, plaster and wood. Influenced by the works of Bruce Nauman, his compositions also display elements of Italian Renaissance art, and Tibetan and Chinese motifs. He now works on light-related installations, particularly rooms without ceilings.

LOFLAND, MELANIE (Painter)
P.O. Box 496, Santa Cruz, CA 95061

Born: 1942 *Awards:* Celebrations and Fulfillment Award, American Foundation for the Science of Creative Intelligence, Philadelphia; Expressions of Faith Award, American Foundation for the Grand Canyon College, Arizona *Collections:* Lehigh U., Bethlehem, PA; Illuminarium Gallery, Marin *Exhibitions:* Art Museum of Santa Cruz County; Illuminarium Gallery, Marin *Dealer:* Isis Unlimited, Beverly Hills

Initially influenced by Paul Klee, cubism and the sensuality of human form, she worked acrylics directly on gessoed canvas using a wet-on-wet technique. Her harmonious stains of color are similar to those achieved with hand-dyed fabrics. Her paintings were finished with dry-brush drawing, which gave them a stained-glass effect. She has moved from a somewhat minimalist, primitive approach to a more neo-classic technique. She glazes over built-up layers of paint to give her work a deeper sense of color. She has developed a style which reflects her interests in mysticism, Shamanism and meditation. A visionary surrealist, her work is positivistic, and uses color and image to denote balance and inner peace.

LOMANTO, SHARON MANEY (Painter)
430 N. Kenter Ave., Los Angeles, CA 90049

Born: 1942 *Collections:* Silver Saddle Development, Los Angeles *Exhibitions:* Art Source Gallery, Los Angeles; Century Gallery *Education:* U. of Texas *Dealer:* Art Source Gallery, Los Angeles

Her work in the 1960s and 1970s was abstraction, influenced by the Russian avant garde of the early 20th century. Large fields of bright colors explored complementary color theory as a means of creating a dynamic of energy and spiritual tension. In the 1980s, her work has shifted to the exploration of the human figure and symbols. Her recent works, in oil on canvas, are a series of triptychs that use crosses as a repetitive image to examine male/female, birth/death themes. *We Live in Our Heads*, a recent work depicting abstract human figures with television screens for heads, is an example of her present concern with strength of line, powerful division of space and textural brush work.

LOMBARDI, STEVEN (Designer, Sculptor)
2264-146 Caminito Pajarito, San Diego, CA 92107

Born: 1954 *Awards:* Selected Designer, Artemide, Milan, Italy; Citation, American Institute of Architects, San Diego *Exhibitions:* Newport Harbor Museum, Newport Beach; Vorpal Gallery, San Francisco *Education:* New York Institute of Technology; Southern California Institute of Architecture *Dealer:* Artemide, Milan, Italy

Layla (F. Edwards), *Zikr,* 27 x 38, lithograph

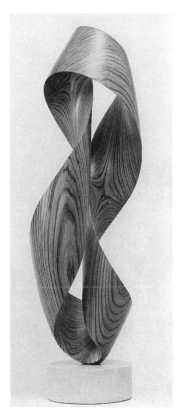

Bob Longhurst, *Loop XVII,* 30 x 11 x 8, zebrawood.
Courtesy: Louis Newman Galleries

Les Lawrence, *Fern Remembers the Backseat of that 1957 Chevy . . . That was in 1958, or was it 59 . . . or was it a 1956 Ford?* 42 x 12 x 11, fired clay and glaze.
Courtesy: Alexander Gallery

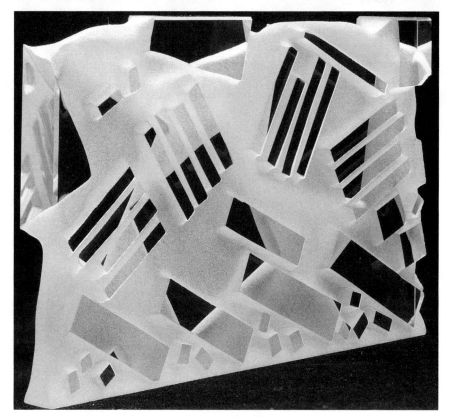

Jon Warren Lentz, *Dactyls,* 4 x 8 x 1, sand-carved glass

Pam Longobardi, *Insider Secrets: Predator and Prey,* 85 x 60,
charcoal, graphite, pastel and wire

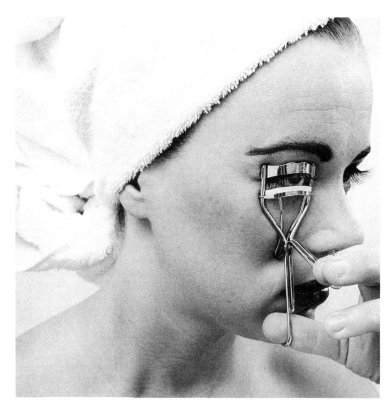

Laura S. London, *Cosmetic Ritual Series #5,* 36 x 36, black and white photo mural

Stephen Lackey, *Running,* 6 x 15 x 16, bronze. Photographer: Jock McDonald

Although he has numerous residential and commercial buildings to his credit, his main focus in recent years has been on furniture and lighting design, and on fine art. Throughout all aspects of his artwork, he is governed by a philosophy that melds a fine art aesthetic with a formal and functional design approach. He is best known for his anthropomorphized pieces: stainless steel clocks; high-tech modular seating, incorporating erector set-like elements; long-legged, gazelle-like tables; a series of robots; and light sculptures illuminated by candles. Driven by a problem-solving sensibility, he often thinks of his designs as unique sculptures, inspired by their eventual role in a larger architectural context.

LONDON, LAURA (Photographer)
327 N. Spaulding Ave., Los Angeles, CA 90036

Born: 1957 *Collections:* Sarah Spurgeon Gallery, Central Washington U. *Exhibitions:* LACPS Annual Exhibition; Los Angeles Municipal Art Gallery, Hollywood *Education:* U. of Arizona; California Institute of the Arts

Her black-and-white photomurals, usually 3 by 3 feet or larger, show diverse influences of various cinematic styles and American popular culture. During the 1970s, she produced two groups of black-and-white documentary photographs involving the relationship of people to their economic class, geographic location and social mores. By the early 1980s, she was shooting in the studio, producing a group of 16 by 20 inch gelatin silver prints that she called "Extended Portraiture." These prints are intended to compose and structure meaning through the use of cinematic lighting, symbolic objects and ordinary gesture. The resulting photographs form a kind of collective portrait/self-portrait. Her current work examines the viewer's and the culture's obsession with appearance, portraying this obsession succinctly and humorously. The dogmatism of American style is the subject of three distinct series, "Cosmetic Rituals," "American Icons & Stereotypes" and "Fashion Gesture." The images reveal the inherent contradictions of entrenched practices.

LONDON, LYLE (Sculptor)
1728 N. 81st. St., Scottsdale, AZ 85257

Born: 1947 *Collections:* R.L. Kotrozo, Inc.; Hartford Insurance Co. *Exhibitions:* G. Wayne Ashton Gallery, Los Angeles; Joslyn Center for the Arts, Torrance *Education:* Dartmouth College *Dealer:* Joy Tash Gallery, Scottsdale, AZ

He initially studied with Varujan Boghosian and various visiting artists at Dartmouth College in the late 1960s—Larry Zox, Dimitri Hadzi, Robert Indiana and Jack Zajac, among others. Zajac's style of biomorphic abstraction, in particular, has had a lasting influence on his work. After several years of carving stone and gaining practical experience in an art bronze foundry, he began working in various metals, both cast and fabricated. Earlier cast bronze pieces using a smaller scale and a more formal approach have been replaced by large-scale commissions. These larger works incorporate a greater sense of spontaneity through the use of high-tech fabrication techniques. Commissioned sculptures using water as a sculptural feature and environmental counterpoint have appeared since 1984. Recent work includes a sculpture fabricated directly from copper sheet and aluminum. Some of his aesthetic concerns are the opposition of linear to cur-

vilinear space, and in pedestal sculpture, the unification of the base with the piece. A theme of intimating the natural world rather than imitating it runs throughout his work.

LONG, JEFF (Painter)
59 Webster St., San Francisco, CA 94117

Born: 1948 *Awards:* Grant, Pollock/Krasner Foundation; Grant, Adolph and Ester Gottlieb Foundation *Collections:* San Francisco Museum of Modern Art; The Oakland Museum *Exhibitions:* San Francisco Art Institute; The Oakland Museum *Education:* California College of Arts and Crafts; Rhode Island School of Design *Dealer:* Ivory/Kimpton, San Francisco

His work attempts to synthesize ideas from the metaphorical landscape painting of Asia with the traditions of landscape painting in the West. He flattens his images and articulates them towards the abstract. Large rock formations and bodies of water are identifiable but not realistic. He crops his pictures to produce a sense of intimacy. His palette is heavy in reds, blacks and white. He is a conservationist whose exhibition at Ivory-Kimpton Gallery, "Tale of Two Rivers" included drawings and paintings of the Toulumne River and one of its tributaries, Clavey Creek. He recently began working on a group of large abstracted oils based on landscape

LONGE, BRIAN S. (Painter)
945 22nd Ave., Oakland, CA 94606

Born: 1945 *Awards:* NEA Fellowship *Collections:* Newport Harbor Art Museum, Newport Beach *Exhibitions:* Los Angeles County Art Museum; San Francisco Art Institute *Education:* UC-Irvine *Dealer:* Rena Bransten, San Francisco; Klein Gallery, Chicago

During the 1960s and 1970s, he worked on a series of abstracted landscapes. Painted on unbacked shaped canvas, they were tacked tightly to the wall, creating a dialogue between the smooth wall surface and the painted canvas field. This interest in landscape, which still prevails in his work, took a new turn in the 1980s. The landscapes themselves became more realistic, while his interest in abstraction found an answer in what he calls a "perceptual chamber," a triangular protrusion on the right of the canvas. The metaphor of the optical chamber provides a rationale for investigations of light. In 1986, the chamber paintings evolved into a series of multiplaned landscapes. Some of these involve a stack of turning landscapes, while later works were all on one plane, the shaped support creating an illusory overlap. Recent work reduces the realism and pushes for abstraction, which has found resolution in an abstracted "aerial view" perspective.

LONGHURST, BOB (Sculptor)
c/o Louis Newman Galleries, 322 N. Beverly Dr., Beverly Hills, CA 90210

Born: 1949 *Awards:* Audubon Annual Helen Eisler Memorial Award; Butler Institute of Art Friends of American Art Award *Collections:* Bank of Tokyo, NYC; American Financial Corp., Cincinnati *Exhibitions:* Louis Newman Galleries, Beverly Hills; Randall Galleries, NYC *Education:* Kent State U. *Dealer:* Louis Newman Galleries

His abstract sculptures, carved of kiln-dried exotic hardwoods, are notable for their ethereal fluidity. His "Loop Series" comprises flat twisting ribbons of wood that emphasize the spatial relationship between figure and ground; empty spaces contained by the graceful

Sharon Lynn Lloyd, *The Marriage,* 16 x 20, assemblage

Donald Louthian, *Kyoto,* 79 x 96, 8 panel folding screen, acrylic, collage

Beryl Landau, *The Real Thing,* 36 x 36, acrylic on canvas

Gerry Anne Lenhart, *Metamorphoses,* 48 x 48, acrylic and paper collage on canvas

Patty Look Lewis, *Conception,* 36 x 36, oil on canvas

Sharon Maney Lomanto, *Blue Life,* 60 x 60, oil

Jacqueline Leventhal, *A Long Way From Home,* 11 x 14, photograph

LeBoutiliere aka **Butler,** *Flowers in the Desert,* 16 x 20, oil

Lynn Lupetti, *Tales of Valor,* 24 x 30, oil. Courtesy: Edward Lohmann, owner, Lynn Lupetti Gallery

Ragnhild Langlet, *Before the Weather,* 65 x 52, fiber

Lorraine Judd Lubner, *untitled #12,* 70 x 91, acrylic on canvas

Ira Latour, *Oskar Kokoschka, Salzburg,* 11 x 14, Kodachrome.
Courtesy: San Francisco Museum of Modern Art

Bruce Lauritzen, *Cliff Dwellers II (Coastal Series)* 38 x 50, oil

Hal Larsen, *Horned One and Zia Koshare,* 36 x 46, mixed media

Gilbert Sanchez Lujan *a.k.a.* Magu, *Our Family Car,* mixed media.
Courtesy: Magu Studios, Santa Monica. Photographer: Tom Vinetz

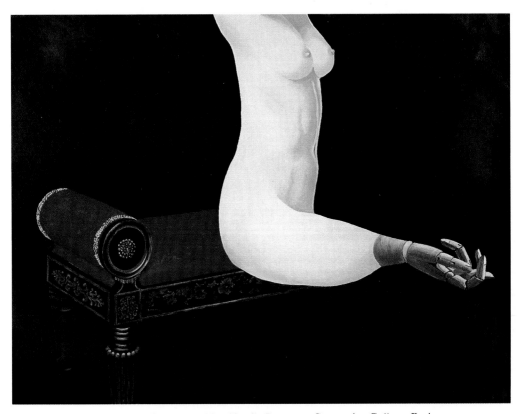

Leza Lidow, *Temptress,* 30 x 40, oil. Courtesy: Carpentier Gallery, Paris

Gyongy Laky, *Fast Road Home,* 50 x 135 x 6, sticks, cloth, plastic and wire.
Photograph: R. Banish and L. Black

Nelda LeVant, *Win One for the Gipper,* photograph

James A. Lawrence, *First Snow,* 13 x 19, watercolor

G. Lichtenstein, *Sky's Moment,* 40 x 60, oil-based ink on paper.
Courtesy: Franklin Henderson Fine Art, San Francisco

Cissi L., *Three Women,* 39 x 58, oil on canvas

Eric Lawton, *Gatehouse, Cayucos, California,* 20 x 24, cibachrome

Layla (F. Edwards), *Green Book,* 28 x 34, pastels, inks

Hilda Levy, *Floral Rebirth,* 34 x 36 x 23, sculpture, wood and jewelry

Nance Liebenson-Rex, *Cry Out Beyond the Edge of Dreams,* 29 x 51 x 24, acrylic on nylon on welded steel rods with copper

John Lin, *New Image Greeting Card,* 15 x 20, gouache and prismacolor

Diana Lovett, *Bronze Level,* 21 x 36, handmade paper

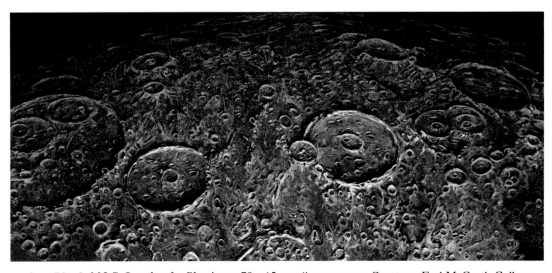

Gary Lloyd, *M.I.C. Searches for Plantinum,* 78 x 15, acrylic on canvas. Courtesy: Earl McGrath Gallery

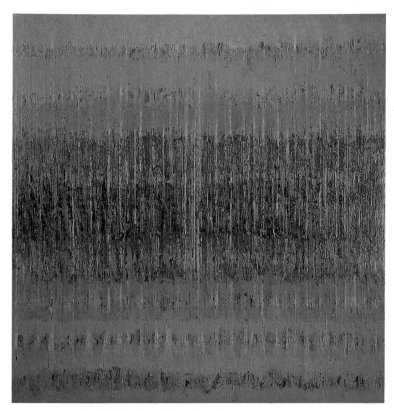

Zach Ma, *Out of the Blue,* 69 x 69, oil on canvas

Barbara Macdonald, *The Quest,* 14 x 10 x 2, mixed media

Gwen Manfrin, *Dripping Marbles,* 21 x 27, pastel

John D. Marchant, *Wild Coffee,* 48 x 48, acrylic. Courtesy: Dimitrios Serifimedes

loops of wood are negative elements as important to the composition as the positive. The pieces have a fragility and seem to follow a musical lyricism. Pieces wrought from the hardest woods have an airy lightness. He sees his work as a reinterpretation of natural forms: dried, twisted leaves, the shape of stones worn away through centuries of erosion. Recently, he has begun working with marble and granite.

LONGOBARDI, PAM (Painter, Printmaker)
3620 Topside Rd., Knoxville, TN 37920

Born: 1958 *Awards:* Premier Award, Taller Galeria, Fort Cadaques, Spain; 1st Place, Printmaking, Art-Quest, Long Beach *Collections:* North Miami Museum of Art; Pratt Graphics Center, NYC *Exhibitions:* Matrix Gallery, Sacramento; Rental Gallery, San Francisco Museum of Modern Art *Education:* U. of Georgia; Montana State U. *Dealer:* Kyle Belding Gallery, Denver; Carlton Cobb Gallery, Atlanta

Her formative experiences include extensive underwater diving, a job as a firefighter in Wyoming and paleontologic work in Montana's Northern Tier. These confrontations with nature led her to consider establishing parallels between natural forces and objects in the physical world and the emotional forces of our lives. The recurring, transformational imagery in her work—the iceberg, the eroded butte, the bird—are combined with depictions of natural forces. The surfaces of her works are "toothy," and she incorporates sculptural elements and raised areas of paint into her compositions. She uses charcoal and graphite with much erasure, manipulated oils on canvas and highly worked lithographs that also display a distinct physical presence. Much of her recent work deals with the sense of individual and collective responsibility as an emotional state. Her concern is with people's individual actions and collective interactions along with natural and unnatural forces, and with the powers of control, fate and chance.

LOOMIS, ROBERT (Painter, Commercial Illustrator)
1487 Parrott Dr., San Mateo, CA 94402

Born: 1915 *Collections:* Public Library, San Mateo *Exhibitions:* P-Art-A Gallery, San Francisco

He began his art career as a poster artist for a printing company in Columbus, Ohio. After working as an illustrator and a layout artist, he moved to Los Angeles and became a record jacket designer for Capitol Records. Recent abstract work is based on right brain/left brain experiments, including realistic drawings rendered from upside-down subjects. These experiments considerably freed his abstract expression and influenced even his more realistic work. Commissioned by the San Mateo City Council, he painted a series of over forty works memorializing the city's changing scenery, its streets, parks, buildings and residents. He has also been working on a series of paintings of Golden Gate Park.

LOPINA, LOUISE CAROL (Painter)
7 Calle Agua, San Clemente, CA 92672

Born: 1936 *Awards:* Clayton Bruckner Memorial Award, National Nature Exhibition *Collections:* Cincinnati Natural History Museum; Miami Bank of Ohio *Exhibitions:* Adler Gallery, NYC; Grand Central Galleries, NYC *Education:* School of the Art Institute of Chicago *Dealer:* G & R Gallery of Wildlife Art, Buffalo, NY

Her paintings invariably are studies of animals that lend each of the creatures depicted a personality of its own; even in a herd of buffalo, no two will look the same. Her oils utilize rich and full-colored earth tones, and her watercolors are transparent and fluid. Design elements in her paintings are inspired by the abstract artist Franz Kline, yet she works in a painterly fashion in the spirit of Bruno Liljefors and Arthur Tate, whose paintings influenced the artist in their depiction of "feelings and behavior of animals, more than detail for detail's sake."

LOPPNOW, DUANE (Sculptor)
772 Casiano Dr., Santa Barbara, CA 93105

Born: 1933 *Collections:* General Mills Corporate Collection, Minneapolis; Bank of America *Education:* U. of Oregon *Dealer:* Maxwell Gallery, San Francisco

A sculptor with a background in engineering and architecture, he designs, casts and welds large-scale, abstract metal pieces for a variety of architectural settings. The pieces express his private philosophy while still leaving the viewer to his or her own interpretation. The lines and planes of his sculpture "work" from any point of view; and his surfaces may be either textured or smooth, either painted or left exposed to the elements. Some works are bold and massive, while others show the quiet strength and delicate precision reminiscent of Japanese calligraphy. He owns and manages his own foundry, and his work reveals a mastery of metals: It is high technology applied to art.

LORIAUX, MAURICE (Painter)
P.O. Box 4605, Santa Fe, NM 87502

He is best known for his work in the interior design and iconography of churches. His art teachers, Ada Robinson and Laura Requa, heavily influenced his style and approach. His paintings are characterized by deft knife work, heavy impasto and deep brushstrokes. Although most of his current work consists of mountainscapes, landscapes and portraits, he also designs stained glass for churches.

LOU, RICHARD A. (Photographer)
1368 14th St., Imperial Beach, CA 92032

Born: 1959 *Awards:* Poems, The New Best Chicano Literature, Cultural de la Raza, San Diego *Exhibitions:* Sushi Gallery, San Diego; Centro Cultural de la Raza, San Diego *Education:* Clemson University; Cal. State-Fullerton

What distinguishes his socially provocative "Inner City Portraits" from most street photography is the subjects, according to critic Hilliard Harper. They are not real. The images look like the usual inner-city stereotypes: a Skid Row bum in torn t-shirt, sitting on the pavement, legs splayed, pants rolled up to the knees; a gang member haranguing the photographer. However, the artist has created these images. To them he adds, in diptych format, a page including typed biographical data—name, date of birth, sex, marital status, education—and a statement by each subject, made during the portrait session. But the people caught by the camera are reflections of the photographer. Each image is a self-portrait of the artist, playing the role of an inner-city denizen. The subjects' comments are the artist's thoughts.

LOUIE, REAGAN (Photographer)
1210 Rose St., Berkeley, CA 94702

Born: 1951 *Awards:* Guggenheim Fellowship; NEA Fellowship *Collections:* Museum of Modern Art, NYC

Exhibitions: Museum of Modern Art, NYC; San Francisco Camerawork *Education:* Yale U.; UCLA

His portraiture is as much an exploration and search through his own background as it is a documentation of the communities he uses as subjects. Since 1978, he has been photographing Asian communities throughout California, and since 1980 he has made more than half a dozen trips to the People's Republic of China. In China, he improvised street portraits of men, finding in them a provisional signpost in his search for his now forgotten homeland. His essay, "One Journey to China," was published along with a portfolio of his photographs in *Aperture*, No. 106. He is Instructor in Photography at the San Francisco Art Institute.

LOUTHIAN, DONALD (Painter)
888 Creek Dr., Menlo Park, CA 94025

Born: 1929 *Awards:* U.S.A. Purchase Award, Missouri Art Museum; 1st Place, Palo Alto Arts Festival *Collections:* Kalamazoo Institute of Arts; Henry Ford, II *Exhibitions:* Rhode Island School of Design; Gallery Fair, Mendocino *Education:* U. of Kansas *Dealer:* Running Ridge Gallery, Ojai & Santa Fe, NM

Two years with the army in Japan left a strong Oriental influence on his work. Early wet-on-wet, small-scale, semi-abstract watercolors and gouaches were influenced by Japanese Sumi ink paintings and the works of Lyonel Feininger and Mark Tobey. After studying in Mexico and moving to California, he began to produce larger scale acrylic paintings in new and brighter colors. Texture was important in the collage and acrylic work of this time. He uses Western materials in an Oriental folding screen format. Working with acrylic and collage on wood or stretched canvas, he creates environmental size four-to-eight-panel screens. His subject matter continues to be inspired by the Western landscape.

LOVE, NAN (Painter, Computer Artist)
P.O. Box 451, Santa Rosa, CA

Born: 1949 *Awards:* 1st Prize, Painting, Visionary Art Show, San Francisco; Best in Show, Russian River Woman's Art Show, Santa Rosa *Exhibitions:* Hatley-Martin Gallery, San Francisco; Rosicrucian Museum, San Jose *Education:* Cal. State-Hayward

Her art plays on the delicate edge between living in a dream world and creating a new reality. Influenced by the Italian Renaissance and the art of China, she has worked in isolation since 1979. In her previous style, she mixed watercolor with gouache, and glazes with acrylics to give her paintings the look of oils. Often she added gold leaf, enamels, rhinestones, semiprecious stones and specialty papers for special effects. She pasted layers of matte board onto the work for three-dimensionality and pressed grooves into unpainted board for an embossed look. Since 1986 she has used highly sophisticated software (Lumena 8 and Lumena 16) and an IBM AT computer to intensify her already complexly detailed work. She draws all of her images by hand on the computer, and the machine's high resolution distinguishes her work as photo-realistic.

LOVE, NANNETTE (Painter, Printmaker)
1160 Pine St., #4, San Francisco, CA 94109

Born: 1958 *Awards:* Robert Howe Fletcher Cup; Cornelia McKay Award *Exhibitions:* Club Nine Art Motel, San Francisco; Goodman Gallery, San Francisco

Education: San Francisco Art Institute; Herron School of Art

While her early work is abstract expressionist, she claims a broad range of influences, including modern painters Morris and de Kooning, the Impressionists and painters of the Italian Renaissance. This period saw tar and enamel painted on large billboard paper, powdered graphite and turpentine used on printmaking paper and acrylics applied on unprimed canvas to create large "watercolor" color fields. Recent work finds her integrating the figure into her pieces. Black-and-white etchings and large oil paintings have a primitive look, while featuring modern figures. She continues to think of her work as a "snap shot" of an emotion, an instant of time, a feeling or flashback to a moment or situation.

LOVETT, DIANA (Paper Artist)
20 Rio Vista, #B, Oakland, CA 94611

Born: 1955 *Exhibitions:* Uncle Gaylord's, Oakland; Gallery in the Vineyards, St. Helena *Education:* Ohio U.; Arizona State U. *Dealer:* Art Concepts, Walnut Creek

Initial work was in experimental fiber arts, with an emphasis on color and texture. Moving from tapestry to surface design techniques such as blueprinting, color xerography and photographic techniques coupled with weaving, the artist chose to pursue paper-making to counter the overwhelming time demands of fiber work. Her work is nonrepresentational, based upon designs again emphasizing color and texture. Large, abstract pieces are executed in the Japanese method learned during her artistic training, which requires hand-layering with multiple colors one sheet at a time to create unique works. After the wet pulp has been colored, textured and dried, the artist manually highlights and outlines the design with acrylic or pencil. This medium has enabled her to utilize her experience in fiber art as well to work with the peculiar aesthetics of paper art.

LOWE, MING C. (Painter)
73-985 Catalina Way, Palm Desert, CA 92260

Born: 1945 *Exhibitions:* Ming C. Lowe Gallery, Palm Desert; College of the Desert, Palm Desert

Though she lives isolated in the desert, she fills her neo-expressionist paintings with powerful avant-garde images. In the early 1980s, she did a series dealing with pop culture and rock and roll music. In 1984, she exhibited raw paintings on the imminence of war among the superpowers. Death was the subject of her recent exhibition, "New Work." She executed this series of large-scale oil paintings in black and illuminated her canvases with glowing colors. Symbolic paintings like *Death and Dominoes* and *Diamond Heart* were inspired by the Buddhist funeral of her friend, blues musician Paul Butterfield. Other pieces such as *Portrait of Garry Gilmore* and *Final Moments* are self explanatory.

LOWRY, JANICE (Assemblage Artist)
6308 Gregory, Whittier, CA 90601

Born: 1946 *Exhibitions:* Venice Art Walk; Santa Barbara Art Forum *Education:* Art Center College of Design *Dealer:* ArtSpace, Los Angeles

Working within constructed wooden frames that stand for houses, she creates three-dimensional assemblages depicting the joys and woes of modern domestic life. Recurrent items include small, cut-out fish, animals,

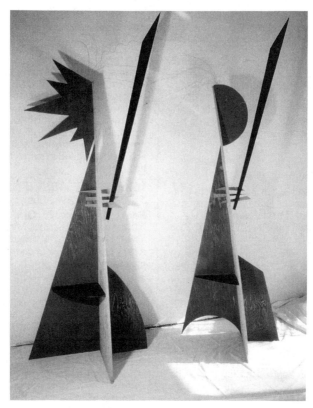

Steven Lombardi, *Warriors,* 72 x 24 x 18, painted plywood and powder coated aluminum

Christine Lando, *Nightwalking XII (Remember the Swimming Pool Dream),* 30 x 22, mixed media on paper.
Courtesy: Convergence Gallery, San Francisco, CA

dolls, ladders, pottery and charms, as well as more personal imagery, such as a wreath of gum wrappers in her grandfather's favorite flavor. The quirky tableaux contain an open narrative, allowing viewers to draw their own conclusions about the scene. She views her works as metaphors for the self, and draws on her own journal of daily life as the source of the objects, themes and composition of each piece.

LOWRY, LINDA (Painter)
704 Spruce St., Apt. B, Boulder, CO 80302

Born: 1956 *Awards:* Finalist, Art in Public Places *Collections:* Mountain Bell, Denver *Exhibitions:* Artquest, Los Angeles; Chicago Art Expo *Education:* U. of Colorado *Dealer:* Jan Cicero Gallery, Chicago; Kyle Belding Gallery, Denver

She is concerned with interiors as an expression of individuality and humanity, and her paintings portray various man-made living environments. These large paintings, with their focused viewpoints, open composition and cropped objects, create a sense of immediacy, and place the viewer inside the rooms depicted. The style is realistic, the brush strokes are simple and descriptive, and the vibrant palette creates a graphic impact. Windows evoke contrasts in value, color, shape and mood; the cool light of the outdoors emphasizes the dark, warm light of the interiors. The architectural verticals and horizontals of the rooms contrast with the organic shapes of the landscape.

LOYNACHAN, RALPH (Painter)
116 1/2 South Catalina St., Los Angeles, CA 90004

Born: 1955 *Exhibitions:* Los Angeles Municipal Art Gallery; Los Angeles City College Art Gallery *Education:* USC; San Jose State U.

The structural elements developed in his work result from an expressive need to appropriate from his surroundings. Evocative of psychological landscapes, his large, collaged mixed media paintings reflect an automatic visual journal. Objects of daily use are recycled over a background of acrylic paint and charcoal: a rubber plug for a navel, flowered fabric, the skin of a black umbrella, news photos, linoleum, broken mirrors, wallpaper. These syllables of visual information alternately fuse together and fracture the picture plane to function as an analogy for the position and relocation of figurative elements within our "disposable society." Robert Rauschenberg's use of layered imagery and language to communicate his socio-cultural perspective was an encouraging model in the development of Loynachan's technique. His pieces are autobiographical tableaux that often reflect his off-the-wall humor. They are personalized in the act of sorting through the abundance of assimilated material, but they do not express elements of his own life so much as they record his responses to the world. The intimacy of such cultural referents creates an excavated sense of the viewer's own history as well.

LUBNER, LORRAINE JUDD (Painter, Collage Artist)
916 Stonehill Ln., Los Angeles, CA 90049

Born: 1931 *Awards:* Honorable Mention, Laguna Beach Invitational *Collections:* ARCO; IBM *Exhibitions:* Ben Uri Gallery, London; Art Space, Los Angeles *Education:* UCLA *Dealer:* Art Space, Los Angeles

An abstract expressionist, she constructs emotional passages of color. Her acrylic work is painterly and intuitive; rough geometric figures and spaces sit in landscapes of aggressively charged or somber color. She layers her surface with a "particularizing" ground color, preparing her canvass for the pigment she wants to see in the final painting. Using collage to structure a unified, non-figurative image, she layers colors and shapes, censoring and changing her amalgam of ephemerae, painting and textures, until she has achieved a "veiled surface" that both reveals and hides her method.

LUCAS, ELIZABETH (Calligrapher)
518 Monrovia Ave., Long Beach, CA 90814

Born: 1936 *Awards:* Graphic Design Award, New York Society of Scribes/Master Eagle Gallery *Exhibitions:* Long Beach Museum of Art; Senior Eye Gallery, Long Beach *Education:* Whittier College

She paints pictures with words and letter forms, florals and abstract designs in ink, gouache and watercolor with pen and brush. She is owner of a company that sells greeting cards on which her own work appears, and she also teaches calligraphy and bookbinding, administers a university program in calligraphy and is active in the professional societies of her art. She is the author of *Calligraphy, The Art of Beautiful Writing, Italic Letterforms*. Although she was trained by masters in an ancient art demanding discipline and control, her designs are intensely personal and issue from the heart.

LUCERO, HARKIN, JR. (Sculptor)
4401 San Leandro Blvd., Oakland, CA 94601

Born: 1950 *Collections:* Banco Central of Spain, San Francisco; Bank of Portugal, San Francisco *Exhibitions:* American Indian Center, San Francisco; Two Trans-America Center, San Francisco *Dealer:* Sun Bronze, NYC

A native of Pueblo, Colorado, he draws inspiration from the ancient Indian cultures of both Americas for his sculptures in marble and bronze. His work explores the religious themes that often imbue primitive and tribal art: reverence of God, the individual's relationship to God and the divine nature of each person. One example of his work is the *Oracle of Four Winds*. It is composed of three faces: each bronzed visage is carved in relief from its own vase-shaped base and rests one atop the other, totem-like. He does almost all his work by traditional hand techniques, carving the marble for subsequent casting in bronze with hammer and steel point, eschewing the pneumatic tools of modern techniques. He has sculpted in granite, wood, clay and plaster and has painted in oil as well. In addition, he has executed numerous bronze logos by commission for governmental agencies and commercial businesses.

LUCEY, JACK (Painter)
84 Crestwood Dr., San Rafael, CA 94901

Born: 1929 *Awards:* Safety Award, State of California; De Young Museum Award, San Francisco *Collections:* Standard Oil Company, San Francisco; Pacific Orient Lines, San Francisco *Exhibitions:* California Museum of Science and Industry, Los Angeles; Frank Lloyd Wright Civic Center, San Raphael *Education:* Academy of Art College; San Francisco State U.

After receiving formal training, with emphasis on figurative and illustrative art, and exploring the challenge of art for the print media, he developed a realistic, representative style that incorporates some impressionist elements. He has been particularly in-

Lorraine Judd Lubner, *untitled #11,* 78 x 91, acrylic on canvas

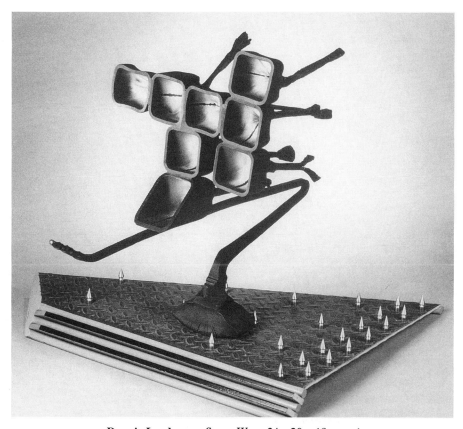

Dennis Luedeman, *Space Wars,* 24 x 30 x 18, metal

Shilla Lamb, *Mac Kerricher, Park Series Screen #2,* 84 x 120, oil on canvas. Courtesy: De Vorzon Gallery

Gilbert Sanchez Lujan *a.k.a.* Magu, *Procession,* 132 x 120 x 120, mixed media.
Courtesy: Los Angeles County Museum of Art

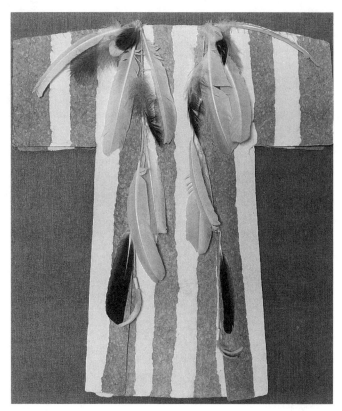

Shirley Lutes, *K-13,* 31 x 40 x 4, cast paper pulp fiber

Donald Louthian, *Spring Rain,* 56 x 48, acrylic on canvas

fluenced by Lautrec's figure drawing and design proportions, and by Van Gogh's use of color and form. His subject is the agricultural landscape, especially scenes that depict the interaction of human efforts, modern mechanization and the land and sky. He uses a variety of media, each for a different effect: pen and ink drawings to render detail; watercolor for softness with accuracy; acrylics for brilliant color reproduction; and oil for expressive freedom. He has also produced works focusing on aircraft, especially antique, World War I-era airplanes.

LUEDMAN, DENNIS (Sculptor)
1673 8th St., Oakland, CA 94607

Born: 1954 *Awards:* Ford Foundation Grant; Sterling Silver Design Competition *Exhibitions:* Academy of Art Collage, San Francisco; Art and Architectural Design, Baltimore *Education:* U. of Washington, Seattle; Rochester Institute of Technology *Dealer:* Hatley/Martin Art Gallery, San Francisco

Formal training in jewelry and silversmithing design and fabrication, as well as sculpture, allowed him to develop a wide variety of techniques that act as a vocabulary of form, rather than as mere tools of process. In graduate school, he began working in a more formal, less functional format; an introduction to heavy machines gave his work a clean, hard-edged look. After he lost access to these machines on his move to California, the fabricated geometric forms lost such tight patterns and surfaces. Experimentation with blacksmithing has substituted more fluid, amorphic elements. Some pieces may be interpreted as furniture; others have an almost organic, sci-fi creature look. *Whether Vain*, for instance, has a honeycomb of steel spikes that flow together like tentacles or a mane. The underside of each is touched with a drop of red paint, suggesting blood. More recent work incorporated massive columnar forms with a wide variety of surface applications and textural details.

LUJAN, GILBERT SANCHEZ (Sculptor)
210 Bicknell Ave., Santa Monica, CA 90405

Born: 1940 *Exhibitions:* Los Angeles County Museum of Art; La Jolla Art Museum *Education:* UC-Irvine; Cal. State-Long Beach

During his student years, he developed the concern with Meso-American roots that has since been the crux of his art. His work is informed by a whimsical sense of humor and his folk style is a celebration of his dual background in Chicano and Southern Californian culture. Early in his career, he transformed cultural motifs such as custom cars, graffiti and Southern Californian landscapes into sculpture, paintings and drawings. Recently, his work has expanded to include such larger projects as car sculptures, and the Santa Monica-related sculpture, *Surf Flame Job*. His work is included in the book, *Hispanic Art in the U.S.A., 30 Painters and Sculptors*.

LUNDEBERG, HELEN (Painter)
8307 W. Third St., Los Angeles, CA 90048

Born: 1908 *Awards:* Outstanding Achievements in the Visual Arts, Women's Caucus of Art *Collections:* Los Angeles County Museum of Art; San Francisco Museum of Modern Art *Exhibitions:* Laguna Art Museum; Los Angeles County Museum of Art *Dealer:* Tobey C. Moss Gallery, Los Angeles

She studied with artist Lorser Feitelson in the early 1930s, and each exhibited a symbiotic influence on the other in terms of iconography and subject matter. The two explored modernism and "post-surrealism" in the 1930s; Lundeberg's works of this period attempted to reconcile the subconscious, dreamlike imagery of surrealism with a classical, rational figuration. Her seminal *Double Portrait of the Artist in Time* depicts a child contemplating a flower next to a clock whose hands are at 2:15; in the background, a portrait of an older woman contemplating a similar flower hangs on a wall; and the young girl casts the shadow of an adult. The concepts she deals with here recall Dali and Magritte; she uses identifiable obects, human figuration and a more logical (though not purely logical) composition to convey intellectual content. Later work is associated with the "hard-edge" school, incorporating flat, unmodulated areas and abstract shapes and color fields to suggest landscapes, still lifes and architectonics. Her abstract paintings have never been "non-objective"; both figurative and abstract work abounds with imagery and metaphors associated with the female form. She remains, as always, concerned with formal as well as subjective values.

LUNDGREN, CISSI (Painter, Fiber Artist)
P.O. Box 485, Solvang, CA 93463

Born: 1920 *Exhibitions:* Hart House, Toronto *Education:* College of Art, Stockholm; Otte Skold Art School

As a young artist in Stockholm, she studied with Otte Skold and Edwin Ollers. Looking to the works of Kai Fjell, Georges Braque and Edvard Munch, she began eliminating detail and creating simplified abstract forms. During the 1940s, 1950s and 1960s, she lived and worked in Norway, England and Canada, and in 1973 she moved to California. Presently, she continues to paint abstract forms, often incorporating symbolism in the pursuit of balance and harmony. She uses a palette knife to apply oils to stretched canvas. Aside from painting, she has produced mosaics in stone (up to 9 by 30 feet) and large, abstract, stitched textile works.

LUNDY, GAY D. (Painter)
280 Woodridge Rd., Hillsborough, CA 94010

Born: 1934 *Awards:* Foster City Art League; Peninsula Art Association *Exhibitions:* San Mateo County Fair; Foster City *Education:* San Francisco State University

After studying under Alexander Nepote, among others, at San Francisco State University, she began to develop a whimsical style in pen-and-ink drawings, as well as a realistic style. Many of the pen-and-ink drawings sold at this time, and some were sold as lithographed reproductions. Study continued under L. Busta and S. Houlton. Through the years, she has developed skill in watercolor children's art, oils and acrylics, on a commissioned basis. She has recently been focusing on children's watercolors and oil still lifes.

LUPETTI, LYNN (Painter, Lithographer)
P.O. Box 5776, Carmel, CA 93921

Born: 1938 *Collections:* Smithsonian Institution, Washington D.C.; Barbara Bush, Washington D.C. *Exhibitions:* Lynn Lupetti Gallery *Education:* San Jose State U.

Formally trained in commercial art and technical illustration, she worked in both advertising and textbook illustrating before beginning her fine art career. She is an admirer Vermeer, Renoir, da Vinci and Fra Angelico, as well as Alma-Tadema and Bourguereau. In

NanSea Love, *Rainbow Warrior,* 20 x 30, computer painted

Lynn Lupetti, *The Prince,* 24 x 30, oil. Courtesy: Edward Lohman, Owner, Lynn Lupetti Gallery

some of her colorful figurative oil paintings, children interact with costumed fantasy characters ("the magic people"); in others, beautiful nudes sit in front of verdant impressionistic landscapes. She draws on the techniques of the Old Masters, and combines impressionism, realism and ultra-realism. "The magical, wonderful diversity of humanity is the object of my devotion."

LUTES, SHIRLEY (Multimedia Artist)
11 Coalmine View, Portola Valley, CA 94025

Born: 1921 *Awards:* 3rd Prize, Bay Area Arts and Crafts Guild; First Women In Design International, San Francisco *Exhibitions:* Calif. Crafts Museum, San Francisco; Interart Gallery, San Francisco *Education:* San Jose State U.; Pacific Art League, Palo Alto *Dealer:* Interart Gallery, San Francisco

She concentrates on depicting the power of womanhood abstractly through sculptures that are primarily achieved in wood. Brancusi and Modigliani have been strong influences. In 1974, she became interested in relief printmaking, creating embossments both as stop-action images and as symbols emphasizing light and shadow. These concerns later developed into more sensual three- dimensional pieces of paper sculpture. By 1981, handmade paper had become her medium, and she returned to the figure by exploring the garment as a symbol of collaboration between East and West. She casts paper pulp with embedded materials, using a vacuum table or the hand method and sometimes adding hand-dyed fabric and color pulp. She then folds the piece and embosses it on an etching press and subsequently laminates it in a multimedia process. Among her works are paper kimono sculptures in white, off-white and natural colors, which she sometimes decorates with feathers or cord.

LYKE, LINDA (Printmaker, Paper Artist)
569 Lotus St., Los Angeles, CA 90065

Born: 1944 *Awards:* Purchase Award, La Grange National Exhibition; Purchase Award, Alabama Works on Paper *Collections:* Cleveland Museum of Art; Security Pacific Bank, Los Angeles *Exhibitions:* Ettinger Gallery, Art Institute of Southern California; Lang Gallery, Scripps College, Claremont *Education:* Kent State U. *Dealer:* Rental Gallery, Los Angeles County Museum of Art; Art Source, Los Angeles

In her work, she is completely involved with every step of the printmaking process. She makes her own paper from cotton paper pulp, often dyeing it or embossing yarn into the surface. She works with an acetate sheet, applying various colors, and then printing the designs on the paper. Her works are expressive, abstract and brightly, boldly colored. Her imagery includes landscape, ancient architectural forms, hieroglyphic characters and other works of art, e.g., images of urns or pottery. She is conversant with the fundamental signs and symbols that communicate meaning on many different levels of consciousness; thus, although the forms are abstracted, most of them are recognizable and very accessible to the viewer. She also creates pieces from painted cast paper.

LYNN, ELAINE (Painter)
16720 E. Clinton Ave., Sanger, CA 93657

Born: 1930 *Awards:* Joyce Aiken Purchase Award, Cal. State-Fresno *Collections:* Cal. State-Fresno Art Museum *Exhibitions:* Fresno Art Museum; Phoebe Conley Gallery, Cal. State-Fresno *Education:* Cal.

State-Fresno; Art Students League *Dealers:* Plum's Gallery, Fresno; Fig Tree Gallery, Fresno

She has been deeply influenced by the West's flat open spaces. Her earlier watercolor and acrylic work showed plowed or irrigated fields that stretched unendingly beyond the canvas. In other works, she combined the illusion of images such as rocks or puddles of water with a concern for the medium's material reality, its flat surface, brushstrokes, canvas and paint. Her recent work is about enclosed spaces—the white wall and content within versus outside walls and content without. Though none of the work is non-objective, she paints in a abstract style. Her triptychs and paintings range from 4 by 12 to 5 by 7 feet.

LYTTLE, R.B. (Printmaker)
P.O. Box 403, Point Reyes Station, CA 94956

Born: 1927 *Awards:* 2nd Place, Graphics, Northwest Arizona Fine Arts Association; Honorable Mention, Marin County Fair *Exhibitions:* Logan Franklin Show, San Rafael; Fairfax Library *Education:* UC-Berkeley

After teaching himself woodcut and line cut printing, he became interested in printmaking. Since 1980, he has worked with a drypoint needle on zinc plates to create black-and-white prints. Influenced by modern sculpture and German expressionism, he often renders images of the grotesque, as well as birds and animals. He describes himself as an impulsive artist who continues to learn about himself through his work.

MA, HAMIL (Painter)
521 Joyner, Ridgecrest, CA 93555

Born: 1949 *Awards:* Honorable Mention, San Bernardino Museum *Collections:* Home Savings *Exhibitions:* Maturango Museum; San Bernardino Museum *Education:* Otis Art Institute, Los Angeles *Dealer:* Bonnie Hall, Santa Monica

He is a wilderness artist who paints in watercolor. He grew up in Hong Kong, where he started painting at the age of eight. In 1959, he emigrated to the U.S., and studied at the Otis Art Institute. From 1980 to 1985, he painted in the high Sierra Nevada Mountains. Traveling through the wilderness and doing sketches on location, he finished the work in the studio. He is currently more interested in secluded desert areas. His pieces have become larger and more colorful, approaching a hyper-realism. He recently began watercolors of the Mojave and Colorado Deserts.

MA, ZACH (Painter)
1053 S. Mayfair, Daly City, CA 94015

Born: 1951 *Exhibitions:* San Francisco Museum of Modern Art, Rental Gallery; Emanuel Walter Gallery, San Francisco *Education:* San Francisco Art Institute *Dealer:* Art Directions, San Francisco

Initially attracted to abstract expressionism and field color painting, he did a series of monochromatic oils early in his career. For a year at a time, he painted in each of blue, red, black and, for two years, in white. His repetition of color and image gave each piece the feel of a cultural artifact. His interest in Duchamp and objects eventually led him to include depth in his painting. His recent, large work is much more image-oriented. In pieces such as *Button Up*, he makes use of everyday objects. His media include assemblages, accumulations and multimedia paintings involving oil, enamel, acrylic, crayon and other materials. He is also a Tai Chi instructor.

Geer Morton, *Still Life for Joan,* 28 x 28, acrylic on canvas

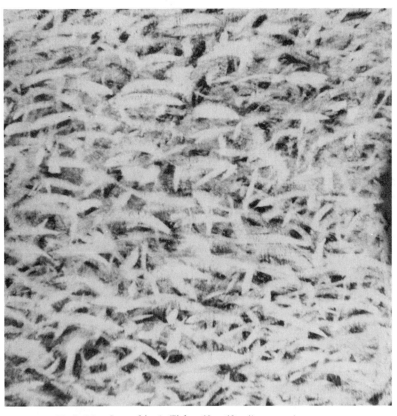

Zach Ma, *Something's Fishy,* 69 x 69, oil, enamel on canvas

MCALISTER, MICHAEL (Collage Artist)
1001 Broadway, Apt. D, San Diego, CA 92101

Born: 1952 *Awards:* 1st Prize, Chapman College Exhibition, "Emerging Artists Series," Riverside Art Museum *Collections:* Chapman College, Orange *Exhibitions:* Los Angeles Design Center; Overreact Gallery, Long Beach *Education:* United States International U.; Cal. State-Long Beach

In his work, certain media are manipulated to function in unusual ways, so that their traditional characteristics are disguised. For example, colored pencil may be used on colored Xerox reproductions so that the two elements blend to look more like a flat painting than collage. Visual metaphors confront modern problems, such as when mythical imagery is used to represent disease and famine. In *Daring To Be More*, stereotypically glamorous, overtly sexual faceless women are overlaid on a background splashed orgasmically with patterned color. Earlier pieces are usually bright and kinetic, reminiscent of 1960s psychedelic art. Specific influences include Max Ernst and the Surrealists, as well as Chicago artists Ed Paschke, Jim Nutt and Karl Wirsum. Of late, he has shifted to black-and-white collages with charcoal and film negatives. These are larger and less detailed, constituting a high-contrast play on the concept of shadows. Images may be cut out and pasted onto another piece of paper.

MACARAY, LAWRENCE RICHARD (Painter, Printmaker, Collage Artist)
628 Buttonwood St., Anaheim, CA 92805

Born: 1921 *Awards:* Downey Museum of Art; Southern California Exposition Prize, Del Mar *Collections:* Bowers Museum, Santa Ana; San Bernardino County Museum of Art *Exhibitions:* Los Angeles County Museum of Art; Long Beach Museum of Art *Education:* Whittier College; Cal. State-Long Beach

He takes a multimedia approach to his art by using direct oil painting, photography, etching, drawing and collage techniques. The different media are so carefully tailored into the finished piece that only the closest scrutiny reveals where one medium ends and another begins. The works juxtapose representational images—often from several cultural sources and in varying styles—to create personal, eclectic visions and narratives. Tricks of perspective, visual puns, surprising repetitions of motifs and other examples of the artist's humor and playfulness abound in his compositions.

MACARTHUR, WILLIAM C. (Painter, Multimedia Artist)
5801 River Oak Way, Carmichael, CA 95608

Born: 1915 *Awards:* 1st Place Purchase Prize, California State Fair, Sacramento; Full Color Reproduction, "Prize-Winning Art/Book 7," Allied Publication, Inc. *Collections:* Crocker Art Museum, Sacramento; California College of Arts and Crafts, Oakland *Exhibitions:* ArtWorks, Fair Oaks; Comara Gallery, Los Angeles *Education:* Washington State U.; California College of Arts and Crafts *Dealer:* Djurovich Gallery, Sacramento

His work gained recognition in the 1960s, when he was known for his hard-edged technique and geometric abstractionist style. His recent works are mixed-media paintings constructed from gunny sacks, rocks, rice paper and other materials.

MACAULAY, THOMAS (Installation Artist)
5510 S. Scarff Rd., New Carlisle, OH 45344

Born: 1946 *Awards:* Guggenheim Fellowship; Asian Cultural Council Fellowship *Exhibitions:* O.K. Harris, NYC; Twining Gallery, NYC *Education:* St. Olaf College; U. of Iowa

He creates architectural installations that are designed for and integrate aspects of the space in which they appear, creating visual distortions and altered perceptions as viewers walk through them. By revealing the nature of illusion, fixed in our very way of perceiving, he demonstrates the limitations and inaccuracies of our point of view and how that point of view or conceptual framework alters what we see. In 1983, he began exploring the format of the circle.

MCAULIFFE, CLAIRE S. (Painter)
25435 Avenida Cappella, Valencia, CA 91355

Born: 1936 *Exhibitions:* Zola Gallery, West Hollywood; Newport Harbor Art Museum, Newport Beach *Education:* California Institute of the Arts

Influenced by the works of Kandinsky, Cezanne, Gauguin, Matisse, Helen Frankenthaler and Milton Avery, she creates glowing landscapes in brilliant colors. Her works are intensely personal and metaphorical, and evoke many different moods of the land and sky. She derives her imagery from an interplay of experience and imagination. She works with untreated canvas, first using an understain, then thickly applying bright, primary colors to create the images.

MCBRIDE, DIANE BOLHAGEN (Printmaker)
3761 Wasatch Ave., Los Angeles, CA 90066

Born: 1947 *Collections:* Pallas Galleries, London *Exhibitions:* Queens Museum, NY; Sea Gallery Group, Venice; *Education:* Academy of Fine Arts, Ghent, Belgium; *Dealer:* Anne Goodman, Marina Del Rey

Influenced by the technique of her teacher Ruth Leaf, the works combine painting with monoprints, linoleum cuts and etchings that stress linear detail in final prints. Small areas of grays, blues and browns are applied *à la poupée*, evoking and underscoring the texture of her landscape subjects. She develops two to three strata in each print, interpreting the site in a representational style. Non-specific figures intensify the sense of life, celebration and vibrancy created by this layering. Recent work explores the plant and animal life of California with increasing specificity and directness. She works exclusively on paper.

MCBROOM, TERRI (Printmaker)
139 N. Ann St., Ventura, CA 93001

Born: 1956 *Awards:* Santa Barbara Art Association; Purchase Award, Ventura College *Collections:* Ventura College *Exhibitions:* Gallery 113, Santa Barbara; Ventura County Historical Museum *Education:* UC-Santa Barbara

She began her career as a ceramist, with the formal study of china painting; she turned to printmaking as a more flexible medium. Influenced by the philosophy of Japanese artists, she works with natural subject matter, suggesting what is not there through her composition and flat design. Symbolism also plays a large part in developing the shapes and lines used to portray an image. Stones represent power or tranquillity, and water is used to suggest purity and cleansing. Recently, her work has moved to more figurative interpretations,

Jack McLarty, *Night-time, Kahneeta,* acrylic.
Courtesy: The Image Gallery, Portland, OR

Lee McCormick, *Peaceful Dream,* 22 x 28, pen and ink

in subdued grays and reds. Often, she leaves an area vacant to stimulate the viewer's imagination.

MCCAFFERTY, JAY DAVID (Painter, Video Artist)

1017 Beacon St., San Pedro, CA 90731

Born: 1948 *Awards:* NEA Grant; New Talent Award, Los Angeles County Museum of Art *Collections:* Los Angeles County Museum of Art; Long Beach Museum of Art *Exhibitions:* Long Beach Museum of Art; Cirrus Gallery, Los Angeles *Education:* UC-Irvine *Dealer:* Cirrus Gallery, Los Angeles

Although primarily known for his "solar burn" paintings, his work encompasses a variety of fields including video, photography and painting. "Solar burn" paintings are perforated wall pieces created by focusing points of sunlight on paper through a magnifying glass until the spot ignites and singes a hole in the material. He devised the process in the mid-1970s, lining up row upon row of charred holes in gridded abstractions. Within these narrow parameters, he has found a surprising variety of visual effects and expressive possibilities. The holes range from tiny pinpricks and slots to smoky-whiskered mouths and gaping fissures. Later work is brightly painted, but still tightly regulated like his earlier work, blending the opposites of freedom and structure. He has also been exploring the possibilities of video as a creative medium.

MCCARTNEY, SHERYL (Painter)

211 12th Ave., Santa Cruz, CA 95062

Born: 1954 *Awards:* Jean Myer Grant for the Study of Painting, Los Angeles School of Art and Design; Scholarship Awards, Laguna Beach School of Art And Design *Collections:* Sarah Wilson Collection, Mesa, AZ; The Gallery of Fine Art, Santa Cruz *Exhibitions:* Los Angeles International Art Exposition, NYC; Rosicrucian Egyptian Museum, San Jose *Dealer:* Carolyn Toder, Santa Cruz; Ed Aceto, Bothell, WA

A "Visionary" painter, she has been influenced by her instructor Robert Wood, and by the technique and imagination of Fredrick Church. She paints both abstractly and realistically. Her dramatic imagery ranges from scenes inspired by the Orient to those taken from ancient South America. At times, her colors are subtle and compellingly elusive; other times, she makes use of a dramatic, high contrast. In her glazed acrylic painting, she evokes a wide variety moods.

MCCLAIN, MALCOLM (Painter, Multimedia Artist)

2980 Somerset Pl., San Marino, CA 91108

Born: 1923 *Exhibitions:* Los Angeles Harbor College; Fine Arts Gallery, Calif. State U., Los Angeles *Education:* Pomona College

Peter Voulkos, Paul Soldner and John Mason were the main influences on his early career. He has worked in both plastic and visual media, and his works often combine both genres. "Postcards" is a series of painted ceramic scenes of the Los Angeles area. A newer series of drawings and paintings on paper and canvas, present California landscapes with familiar settings in a colorful style that varies from realist to abstract. Besides his career as an active artist, he also writes extensively about the art world and is a contributing editor to *ArtWeek.* He has also published articles in *American Crafts, American Ceramics, Images & Issues* and *Visions* magazines.

MCCLAY, ROBERT (Commercial Illustrator, Painter)

79 Santa Elena, Daly City, CA 94015

Born: 1932 *Awards:* James D. Phelan Art Awards Exhibition, Palace of Legion of Honor, San Francisco *Exhibitions:* Lone Wolf Gallery, San Francisco *Education:* San Francisco St. U.

Bosch, Bruegel and the Surrealists, as well as popular illustrators N.C. Wyeth and Maxfield Parrish all influenced his early work. Subsequent experiments with collage and acrylics led to a style featuring multiple viewpoints and a layering of images. Over the years, he has also developed his skills as a portrait painter, working in both oils and acrylics. By combining the fantasy and realism of his landscapes and cityscapes with portraiture, he has developed his own trademark genre, the "personal fantasy portrait." Current work in oil recreates abbeys and other European Gothic structures. These paintings in stone grays, browns and other muted colors are drawn from his memories of recent travels through France, Italy, Spain and Greece.

MCCLEARY, DAN (Painter)

2521 W. 4th St., Los Angeles, CA 90057

Born: 1952 *Collections:* Metropolitan Museum of Art, NYC; Los Angeles County Museum *Exhibitions:* Tatischeff Gallery, NYC; Gallery Paule Anglim, San Francisco *Dealer:* Krygier/Landau Contemporary Art, Santa Monica

His early paintings were taken from movie stills, but as he progressed, his work came more strongly under the influence of late 19th-century French painters such as Degas and Manet; he gave up creating secondary works of art derived from other works of art and started painting directly from his experience of life and the world. He does oil paintings on canvas, and his pastel drawings are usually figurative. Working with commonplace moments, he freezes them in time, thereby lifting them out of their temporal flow and investing them with a special tenderness. Although his subjects sometimes stare directly at the artist/viewer as if offended by the act of voyeurism, his work is basically optimistic, functioning as a appreciation of each human's individuality.

MCCOLLUM, MIKE (Painter, Printmaker)

1920 Union St., Oakland, CA 94608

Born: 1939 *Awards:* NEA Grant *Exhibitions:* Wenninger Gallery, Boston; Lawrence Gallery, Portland *Education:* UC-Berkeley *Dealer:* Magnolia Editions, Oakland

Generally speaking, his work deals with the placement of the figure in a landscape. He pays special attention to the surfaces of his paintings and prints, because he believes that they are just as important as the figure being recorded. Working in oil on medium-sized canvases, he uses intense colors that are not necessarily realistic or descriptive of the subject. He has a gestural, immediate style, heavily influenced by Peter Voulkos and other abstract expressionist artists.

MCCORMICK, KATHLEEN (Painter)

812 Stagecoach Rd., Trinidad, CA 95570

Born: 1949 *Collections;* Humboldt State U. *Exhibitions:* Silverlining; Foyer Gallery, Humboldt State U.

She is an abstract artist whose colorful, non-representational work at times contains landscape influences. Intuition is the cornerstone of her process. After

Jerry McGrath, *The Nubian,* 24 x 19, type C.
Courtesy: Jan Kesner Gallery, Los Angeles, CA

Sheryl McCartney, *Over There,* 33 x 41, acrylic

priming the canvas with rabbit-skin glue or latex house paint, she applies washes with brushes. She then applies layers of oil paint using a brush and palette knife to work wet on wet or wet on dry, whichever is required by the painting. Her surface is thick and her colors are vivid. She has been influenced by Larry Thomas, Marie Thiebault, Hans Hoffman and Elmer Bischoff.

MCCORMICK, LEE (Painter, Mixed Media Artist)
1200 Roosevelt St., Richmond, CA 94801

Born: 1959 *Exhibitions:* Smoking Cessation Project, Richmond; Designs Concepts International, Berkeley *Education:* East Bay Skills Center

He is best known for the stippling, or dotting, technique he uses for the shading in his portraits of entertainers, political and sports figures and other celebrities. His media are quite varied and include watercolor, charcoal, pen and ink, crayons, enamels, pastels, oils, acrylics and liquid metals. He also uses other substances such as fingernail polish, lipstick, shoe polish, model paints and colored chalk to add texture and distinctive detail. Besides portraits, he also paints birds, flowers, plants, animals and landscapes. Quite often he works from photographs and strives to capture the subject in a vividly realistic style.

MCCORMICK, PAM (Sculptor)
97 Wooster St., New York, NY 10012

Born: 1948 *Awards:* NEA Award; Audubon Naturalist Society Award *Collections:* Lockport Museum, NY *Exhibitions:* San Jose Institute of Contemporary Art; Stanford U. *Education:* San Jose State U.; Stanford U.

In the early 1970s, she created walk-through works in orchards and playgrounds in San Jose, on the sand at Laguna Beach and in San Francisco's Golden Gate Park. She worked with musicians at Stanford to create a sound environment, using a computer to create wind sound that harmonized with the sounds in eucalyptus trees. After moving to New York in 1980, she created her first floating sculpture, inspired by the reflections and movement of the wind over water. She continues to work on sculpture that takes its form from the wind and that literally or figuratively reflects the environment in which it is situated. Her recent work includes solar and water-driven electrical fountains, floating works and ice gliders. Although her primary interest is in outdoor public art, she also works in watercolor, draws with a Macintosh computer and makes small, linear, welded sculpture.

MCCOY, LANI (Photographer)
7796 Lookout Dr., La Jolla, CA 92037

Born: 1946 *Collections:* Anthenaeum, La Jolla *Exhibitions:* 39th Annual International Exhibition of Photography, Del Mar; Anthenaeum Music & Arts Library, La Jolla

The artist's photographs capture fleeting moments of spiritual connection that occur between people of vastly dissimilar cultures. Her fascination with the mystical undercurrents and the stark, simplistic beauty that marks Asian life has taken her through Sikkim, China, Thailand and India. A project entitled "The Eyes of Tibet" lead her on a grueling trek through the harsh environment of central and western Tibet. Her portraits convey the warmth and cheerful serenity of this seldom-photographed people. Her spontaneous compositions convey sometimes startling confronta-

tions, but the open curiosity in the eyes of the subjects draw the viewer in just as it captured the admiration of the artist.

MCCULLOCH, CREWS (Painter)
127 Regent St., Alameda, CA 94501

Born: 1950 *Awards:* Governor's Design Conference; National Scholastic Art Award *Exhibitions:* Susan Carr and Associates, San Francisco; Valerie Miller & Associates *Education:* Humboldt State U.; U. of Kentucky *Dealer:* Valerie Miller & Associates; Patricia Blume, San Francisco

After formal traing in drawing and design, he apprenticed with a metal sculptor, and worked in printmaking and ceramics before settling on painting as his chosen medium. His large, dreamlike watercolors are akin to the works of painter/printmaker Joseph Raffael but have a surreal edge. He rubs powdered pigment into the canvas before painting thickly with oils. The resulting raised surface gives his work the feeling of an archeological dig. His art expresses the experience of growing up on a Kentucky farm. His images are recognizable but non-realistic. Large florals and other subjects are completed in conservative hooker's green, prussia blue, cerulean blue, vermillion and van dyke brown.

MACDIARMID, SANDRA PHIPPS (Mixed Media Artist)
6505 Trinidad St., San Jose, CA 95120

Born: 1937 *Awards:* Mary Hill Memorial Award, National Pastel Society of America, NY *Collections:* American Tobacco Co., Richmond, VA; Silicone Graphics, San Jose

She thinks of herself as a contemporary realist and colorist, and is involved simultaneously in three different artistic endeavors. Her abstract paintings attempt to follow the principles of oriental design. Rendered in multilayered glazes with collage effects, these paintings owe their appearance to her work with a series of kimonos. She folds and shapes rag paper collages into kimonos, then applies metallic threads and acrylics. Her painterly landscapes are realistic interpretations of intriguing natural settings. Throughout the body of her work, she considers the rendering of light her main theme.

MACDONALD, BARBARA (Sculptor)
P.O. Box 701, Woodacre, CA 94973

Born: 1925 *Exhibitions:* Galeria Mesa, Mesa, AZ; Crocker-Kingsley Annual Competitive Exhibition, Crocker Art Museum, Sacramento *Education:* Cal. State U.-Long Beach

She began as a painter of color-saturated landscapes, still lifes and figures. After 1964, she lost interest in color. While working with raw umber on wet rice paper during a period of experimentation, she discovered form and turned to carved sculpture. She used stone and wood materials and also produced works cast in bronze. Both Jean Arp and Henry Moore influenced her work, and she is at ease with figuration and abstraction. In 1972, she wrote a masters thesis on environmental sculpture. In 1980, the influences of Conner, Cornell and Herms led her to work in assemblage and collage. She made small environments, often in box format. Today she exposes the folly of society's darker and lighter sides through mixed-media works of nature's and man's cast-offs.

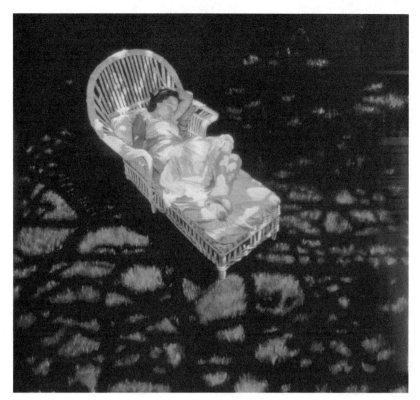

David Martin, *Dappled Siesta,* 78 x 78, oil on linen

Barbara Macdonald, *Down to the Sea in Ships,* 12 x 12 x 4, mixed media

MCDONALD, GUIYERMO (Painter)
Rt. 5, Box 5464, Albuquerque, NM 87123

Born: 1928 *Awards:* Scholarship to France, Scholarship U.S.A.; Honorific Mention, Bicentennial American Exhibition, Paris *Collections:* U. of New Mexico; English Church, Lima *Exhibitions:* Albuquerque Museum; Museum of Contemporary Art, Lima, Peru *Education:* Escuela Nacional de Bellas Artes, Lima, Peru; U. of New Mexico

He was born and educated in Peru, and his early influences were Cezanne, Van Gogh and Gauguin. He developed a coloristic style that fit somewhere among the styles of Byzantine, primitive and Egyptian art. His early subjects were religious, and in 1948, he painted 29 10- by-4 1/2-foot murals of "The Jesuit Martyrs" for a Catholic Church in Lima, Peru. Later, he painted the 14 stations of the cross for Lima's English Church. Since living in Albuquerque, he has moved toward a more expressionistic style and landscape as a subject matter. He has painted three large murals in this country, one at the University of New Mexico and the other two in private residences.

MCDONALD, KAREN M. (Draughtsperson)
25 Montgomery St., Los Gatos, CA 95030

Born: 1956 *Awards:* Roth Mott Internship *Collections:* Baltimore Gas and Electric, San Francisco; IBM, Charlotte, NC *Exhibitions:* Melody Gallery, Santa Fe; L'Agrifoglio Gallery, Milan *Education:* San Francisco Art Institute *Dealer:* Barbara Anderson Gallery, Berkeley

Using dreams, fears and personal experience as sources for subject matter, the artist's works tend to have the intensity of life-long emotional convictions. She works with chalk on canvas; a recent series being "Couples In Bed," which deals with a variety of levels of relationship and accompanying perceptions of space and shape. In *Big Red Man*, for instance, the male of a couple is distanced from his female bedfellow by color, size and orientation—he is large, red and facing away from his small, pale companion. The colors are rich, blended, bright pastels, which, in combination with the underlying sandpaper, create the illusion of velvet. Her use of color and her freedom of subject matter recalls Gaughan, and the works evoke the openness and color of the Southwest, where she was raised.

MCETHCHIN, STAN (Sculptor)
70 Wayside Rd., Paradise, CA 95969

Born: 1924 *Exhibitions:* Paradise Art Center; Sierra West Annual Show *Education:* San Mateo College; UC-Berkeley *Dealer:* Scott Schulman, Chico

Always fascinated with the forms and shapes metal could take, he took welding classes at San Mateo College, and metal sculpture at Berkeley. A mechanical engineer for the last fifty years, he works entirely from recycled materials. His sculpture inclines toward the humorous and decorative: a pair of dice, one perched on top of the other; a giant, old-fashioned bicycle, made out of plumbing material; an Indian with quiver and bow, fashioned from an old refrigerator and other materials; a flock of birds flying in formation above a large rock. He also makes Japanese-style bridges and abstract sculptures.

MCGEE, LOUISE MARIE (Painter, Draughtsperson)
1061 Angelus Ave., San Diego, CA 92114

Born: 1947 *Exhibitions:* Ashanti, La Jolla; Afro-American Museum, Los Angeles *Dealer:* PAC, San Diego *Education:* San Diego City College

Her drawings and paintings derive from her knowledge of black history in America and her desire to transmit this knowledge to others. Through the years she has collected photographs of Blacks from the te 19th century and early 20th century which inspire much of her work. She also paints historical portraits of Jesse Jackson and Martin Luther King, Jr., as well as other works which feature the contributions of Black Americans to mainstream American culture.

MCGEE, WINSTON (Painter)
1710 Smith Dr., Turlock, CA 95380

Born: 1924 *Awards:* Fulbright Grant, Paris, France; Gold Medal for Artistic Activity, Academie Italia delle Arti, Milan *Collections:* Palace of the Legion of Honor, San Francisco; British Museum, London *Exhibitions:* California State U., Stanislaus, Turlock; Fresno Arts Center *Education:* U. of Missouri *Dealer:* Abanté Fine Art Gallery, Portland, OR

While working in Paris, he discovered the tenets of the French school, which he combined with the approach and style of the New York abstract expressionists. He achieves the liveliness and powerful composition of his paintings through the use of broad color application and sure drawing. He makes inventive variations in loose, spontaneous brushstrokes over a tightly conceived structure. He develops the figurative and natural subjects of his works in series, each phase moving toward abstract essentials of the motif. Open forms and masses interact with voids in large, simple rhythms. His unique manner of seeing and shaping images gives a heightened sense of emotion and stability. Recently, the scale of his work has been greatly enlarged for outdoor pieces and public works. He created the mural *California Wall*, by incising, building up and glazing ceramic tiles. He has also created a series of prints that exhibit the painterly color and style that is his trademark. Recently he has been working on series of abstract paintings of women in symbolic forms.

MCGINNIS, DONNA (Painter, Draughtsperson)
351 Devon Dr., San Rafael, CA 94903

Born: 1940 *Awards:* College of the Mainland Purchase Award, Texas City, TX; 1st Place, San Mateo County, San Francisco Bay Arts *Collections:* California Palace of the Legion of Honor Museum, San Francisco; Transamerica Corp., San Francisco *Exhibitions:* Dubins Gallery, Los Angeles; Oakland Museum *Education:* Washington State U., Pullman *Dealer:* Dubins Gallery, Los Angeles

Influenced by her father's black-and-white photographs, she explores the structure and meaning of commonplace objects with a graphite pencil. Ordinary objects, such as a fence or a vice, are rendered meticulously and take on an heroic, almost menacing air. Design elements of volume, shape, form, texture and light and dark become subjects in her drawings of cyclone fences. Delicate vegetables are depicted in new ways. She has begun to use prismacolor pencils, oil paint and pastels. In a recent series of pastel drawings

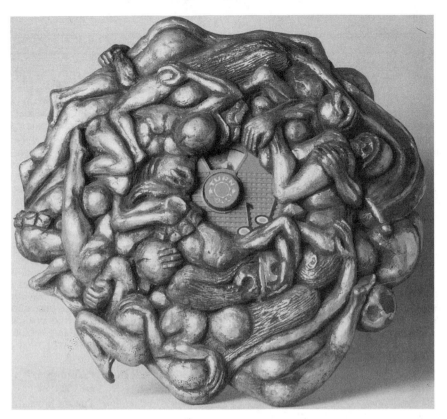

E. Mathews, *Rondel,* 18-inch diameter, epoxy, steel, wood (music box)

D.A. McIver, *Big Slash,* 66 x 60, mixed media on canvas

of boxes, she studies the effects of light and dark shadows.

MCGOVERN, BRIAN JAMES (Painter)
1161 Western Ave., Petaluma, CA 94952

Born: 1955 *Awards:* Best of Show, Baycon, San Jose Convention Center; Distinguished Leadership Award, American Biographical Institute, Wilmington, DE *Exhibitions:* Collins Art Gallery, San Francisco; Lucy Stern Theater, Palo Alto *Education:* Northridge U. *Dealer:* Artist Studio, Petaluma

His early work is characterized by a highly realistic technique reminiscent of Rubens and of landscape artists Church and Moran. These paintings are narrative in tone and are best described as "High Fantasy" or "Cosmic-Romantic." They feature surrealistic colors, flora and fauna. Recent paintings in acrylic are more humanistic, concentrating on the human form, psychological concepts and alegorical fUUms. He describes this work as "visionary surrealism," that is, a realistic approach to mystical ideas. Elements of social and classical surrealism are also apparent in these paintings.

MCGOWAN, TEXIE R. (Painter)
2661 Adrian St., Napa, CA 94558

Born: 1927 *Awards:* Signature Award, Society of Western Artists; Semi-finalist, *Artists* Magazine Floral Competition *Exhibitions:* Guala Art Center; National League of American Pen Women, Souverain Winery, Geyserville *Education:* California College of Arts & Crafts *Dealer:* Oberon Gallery, Napa

Although influenced by color field painting and other abstract styles, she has continued to paint more realistic, figurative works. About fifteen years ago, she developed an interest in watercolors, using them to paint landscapes and other figurative subjects, in an impressionistic realist style. The images in her current paintings comprise a small part of their overall design, which includes a shallow depth of field and a good amount of white area. Occasionally, the composition demands acrylics or collage elements. The paintings are usually 20 by 30 inches in size, although they are occasionally larger.

MCGRATH, JERRY (Photographer)
2314 Blackfoot Ave., Placentia, CA 92670

Born: 1954 *Awards:* Ilford Corp., Cash Award; Brea Gallery, Cash Award *Collections:* Coca-Cola Corp., Atlanta *Exhibitions:* Orange Coast College, U. Art Gallery, Costa Mesa; Irvine Valley College *Dealer:* Jan Kesner, Los Angeles

He is best known for full color Cibachrome prints of assembled still lifes. This work evolved from a previous fascination with the dramatic lighting techniques and narrative visual styles of Fellini and Hitchcock, and the suprematist and futurist art movements. Since the mid-1980s, his work has focused upon mythological and archetypal themes and figures, particularly the Adam and Eve creation myth. In the past, he worked with color transparencies on Cibachrome or type C paper. More recently, however, his work has combined painting and photography. He has produced a series of photo-paintings executed on rag that has first been applied with gesso. This series addresses the theme of humanity's struggle against its own creations.

MACGREGOR, GREG (Photographer)
6481 Colby St., Oakland, CA 94618

Born: 1941 *Collections:* Museum of Modern Art, NYC; San Francisco Museum of Modern Art *Exhibitions:* San Francisco Museum of Modern Art *Education:* San Francisco State U. *Dealer:* O.K. Harris, NYC

Originally trained as a physicist, he ventured into art school in 1970 and was strongly influenced by the surrealist photographer Jerry Uelsmann. Early work brought together technology and surrealism in the publication *Deus Ex Machina*, a black-and-white photographic book with images of an industrial society and its machines invading personal psychic space. The next major body of work was "Oddities in the Western Landscape," an exhibition which depicted surreal interactions of people and space. His focus continues to be on technology as a source for art; interests include large, hand-colored, surreal landscapes of a post-industrial society, perhaps in decay; black-and-white images of minor and major explosions conceived for the camera, but usually misdirected in their destructive force to create nonsense; and large color photographs of earth-moving and highway-construction equipment reduced to the scale of Tonka toys.

MCGREW, BRUCE (Painter)
P.O. Box 160, Oracle, AZ 85623

Born: 1937 *Exhibitions:* Tucson Museum of Art, AZ; Annex Gallery, Santa Rosa *Dealers:* William Sawyer Gallery, San Francisco; Davis Gallery, Tucson

While studying art in the 1960s, he was influenced by the abstract expressionist movement and the themes and motifs of Mexican art. His paintings take two basic forms. The first, usually oil on large surfaces, utilize the human figure, drawing from European and Central American traditions. These paintings revolve around metamorphosis as presented by classic mythology and Biblical stories. Figures change form, seemingly at will; a goat, for example, slides out from a human skin. The other type of painting comprises watercolor landscapes painted from sketches of his travels through Britain, Italy, the Southwest, Mexico, Hawaii and the eastern seaboard. These landscapes are also full of movement and change. Although these works refer to the poetic, they are fully visual, with an emphasis on form and light.

MC INTOSH, HARRISON (Ceramist)
4206 Via Padova, Claremont, CA 91711

Born: 1914 *Awards:* Fellow, American Crafts Council; Panelist, NEA *Collections:* Los Angeles County Museum of Art; Musee National de la ceramiue, Paris; Smithsonian Institute, Washington, DC *Exhibitions:* Los Angeles County Museum of Art; Tokyo Metropolitan Museum, Japan *Education:* USC; Claremont Graduate School *Dealer:* Louis Newman Galleries, Beverly Hills

His first ceramics teachers were Glenn Lukens, Richard Petterson and Marguerite Wildenhain. He was also influenced by the tenets of the Bauhaus School of Design, the mid-century Swedish school of ceramics and by elements of nature. He has preferred to work within the more sophisticated, purified concepts of ceramic design rather than with the more spontaneous abstract expressionism. He creates works exhibiting a total mastery of his materials and techniques using stoneware clay enhanced with brushed, carved or incesed designs, and a controlled oxidation

Janet Mackaig, *When does CATTLE become COW,*
30 x 22, Xerox on Arches

Gwen Manfrin, *Canes,* 20 x 25, pastel

firing. While known for his traditional vessels, he has also created a variety of floating cosmic forms set off in arrangements with wood, metal and mirrored surfaces. These pieces depict moons or planets reflected on clear lakes, pure weightless forms in space and the suggestion of speed in an object mounted on a downward-sloping, chromed surface.

MCIVER, D. ANGUS (Painter, Sculptor)
3025 Exposition Pl., #A, Los Angeles, CA 90018
Born: 1948 *Education:* UCLA

His work spans two and three dimensions. Some of his expressionistic paintings are traditional figurative/landscape studies, while others are abstractions with grid/colorist concerns. In one black-and-white series, he juxtaposed black and white painted bars with bars of charred raw canvas. His surfaces have developed into three-dimensional reliefs. What began as angular projections on a surface are now forms in relief and free-standing sculpture. His subjects are often paired figures, and he has recently been incorporating vacu-forming processes for a set of bronze reliefs.

MACKAIG, JANET (Mixed Media Artist)
23821 Salvador Bay, Laguna Niguel, CA 92677
Born: 1931 *Awards:* 2nd Place, Angel's Gate Cultural Center, San Pedro *Collections:* Citicorp Bank, San Francisco *Exhibitions:* Barbican Center, London; L.A. Artcore Gallery *Education:* Cal. State-Los Angeles

During the 1970s, she used photo-emulsion and photo-silkscreen to create political images on canvas. She photographed the trash left behind by Pasadena's Rose Parade and Chicago's 1968 Democratic Convention. Her vivid and political acrylic paintings of the era were influenced by Robert Rauschenberg and showed a fascination with experimental works. During the 1980s, influenced by Cy Twombly and Antonio Tapies, she began to emphasize animal and landscape painting over abstract printmaking. Large canvases, soft colors, marks of all descriptions made with paint, graphite, colored pencils, wax and anything else she might find typify the work. She layers the media, scraping and polishing the canvas. In her handmade books, she combines monoprint and xerox prints with poetry.

MACKEY, JENNIFER (Fiber Artist)
P.O. Box 469, Scotia, CA 95565
Born: 1955 *Exhibitions:* California State Fair, Humboldt; Society of Arts and Crafts, Boston *Education:* Aegean School of Fine Arts, Paros, Greece

The sophisticated silk and linen garments she creates for women have an international flavor that recalls her studies abroad. Traditional garment designs from several cultures, including Greece and France, are combined in fluid, diaphanous patterns for separates that are as timeless as they are flattering. The artist's use of abstract surface design elevates the clothing to the status of wearable art. Colors are often bright, without being glaring. A subtle non-color such as gray will be used as a backdrop for vivid brush-strokes of azure and gold. Her separates are cut to please a contemporary, fashion-wise market. Designs such as the circle skirt, the trapeze top, and the long-sleeve hooded tunic are future classics.

MCKINNE, ELIZABETH (Painter)
337 Tenth Ave., #3, San Francisco, CA 94118
Born: 1953 *Collections:* Paine Webber, Inc., NYC *Exhibitions:* Janet Steinberg Gallery, San Francisco;

Hanes Art Center Gallery, Chapel Hill, NC *Education:* U. of Colorado, Boulder; U. of North Carolina, Chapel Hill *Dealer:* Iannetti-Lancone Gallery, San Francisco

Her earliest works are abstract; they take their lead from her interest in mark-making and movement (in school she was a student of dance as well as art). Since 1978, images of everyday objects have appeared in her work. Working with a combination of pencil drawing, watercolor and gouache on paper, she places images of shoes, bowls, vases and flowers in fields of flecks, smears of color and contrasting lines. The overall effect is somewhat humorous, though, the artist claims, simply as an unintended by-product. In 1983, she began including oil and charcoal among her media. She painted many triptychs and diptychs; she produced large and small scale sooty charcoal and charcoal/gouache works on paper. Recent pieces have become more abstract once again. Nonetheless, natural forms, their application in the design of man-made objects and motifs and, ultimately, their relationship to the human form, remain her source of imagery. The newer work is darker in both appearance and meaning, but still often possesses the sense of play found in the earlier pieces.

MACKO, NANCY (Painter, Printmaker)
Studio #21, 1252 N. Padua Ave., Upland, CA 91786
Born: 1950 *Awards:* Jean and Arthur Studio Art Faculty Award, Scripps College; Sabbatical Research Fellowship to China, Scripps College *Collections:* Security Pacific Corporation, Los Angeles *Exhibitions:* Double Rocking G Gallery, Los Angeles; Wignall Museum, Chaffey College, Rancho Cucamonga *Education:* UC-Berkeley *Dealer:* Double Rocking G Gallery, Los Angeles; Iannetti-Lanzone Gallery, San Francisco

Her recent paintings are an expression and investigation of the idea of boundaries: physical, as in multiple horizons; metaphysical, referring to multiple levels of awareness; and personal, in terms of limits, edges and interaction. She has a strong interest in color and abstraction. She uses thick applications of acrylics on canvas, and a bold, gestural sweep to express the idea of change and transformation. Underlying her work is the theme of water, which she uses to express deep emotion. She has recently been working on a large body of abstract landscapes, using a combination of strong, direct colors and muted washes. She is currently Professor of Art at Scripps College and the Claremont Graduate School.

MCLARTY, JACK (Painter, Printmaker)
1809 N.E. 70th St., Portland, OR 97213
Born: 1919 *Awards:* Mural, Public Auditorium, Portland *Collections:* British Museum, London; Library of Congress, Washington D.C. *Exhibitions:* Portland Art Museum; Smithsonian Institution, Washington D.C. *Education:* Museum Art School, Portland; American Artists' School, NYC *Dealer:* Image Gallery, Portland

Like Hieronymus Bosch's images of society beset with war, famine and social decay, his work mixes playful fantasy with a fundamentally dark vision of where the world is heading. Populated by giant babies, colorful robots and fantastic toys and buildings, his recent paintings erupt with visionary dismay at the state of human society. Influences include the Mexican muralists Diego Rivera and Jose Clemente Orozco, Max Beckmann, surrealism and folk art from around

Peter Mayor, *Cypher (Maquette),* 20 x 13 x 20, aluminum

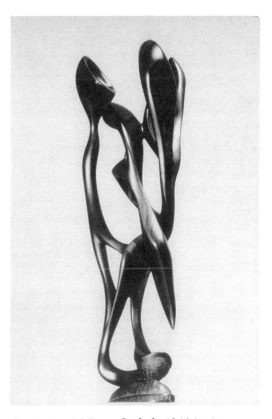

Georganna Pearce Malloff, *East Meets West,* 32 x 73, woodblock print

Barrington McLean, *Sankofa,* 19 high, ebony

the globe. Although he painted in oil for twenty years, he now works in acrylics. He uses a raw canvas soaked with a single ground color (usually in the middle range of value and color) and tries for color and expression in the low-intense range.

MCLEAN, BARRINGTON (Painter, Sculptor)
2565 F. Mission St., Santa Cruz, CA 95060

Born: 1938 *Exhibitions:* Contemporary Museum of Art, Panama *Education:* California College of Arts and Crafts; San Jose State U.

Cezanne, Pollock and Miro were early influences, as was Kandinsky, whose philosophy served the artist as a philosophical point of departure. An early breakthrough was a group of shaped canvases done in an abstract expressionist manner with stains and embellished with oils. Today, he makes Makonde-influenced sculpture. He begins with hardwood, which he carves. He then makes a mold and casts in bronze via the lost wax process. Except for the pouring of the bronze, the artist is involved in the total process from the mold-making wax pattern to the chasing and finishing of each piece. He has recently been negotiating an exclusive on a memorial bust of Dr. Martin Luther King, Jr.

MCLEAN, CANDACE C. (Painter, Collage Artist)
4701 36th Ave. North, St. Petersburg, FL 33713

Born: 1953 *Collections:* Modesto Tobacco & Candy; Raymond James, Inc. *Exhibitions:* Creative Design Gallery, Marco Island; Art Rages Gallery, Clearwater, FL *Dealer:* Shar/Decor, Largo, FL

Working in watercolor, she began her early studies in a photo-realistic style. Her subject matter was nature, especially flowers and butterflies. Inspired by Georgia O'Keeffe's strong colors and abstract style, she began combining her own expression of nature in the abstract with her early experimentation in three-dimensional art. Inspired by the natural movement of life and growth, she painted flowers that refused to be bound by the perimeter of the mat and butterflies that took flight past traditional boundaries. She then began sculpting out of paper. Progressing from sculpted watercolors, she moved into multi-material collage, combining her painted abstract designs with foils, fibers, glitter and other materials.

MCLEAN, RICHARD (Painter)
5840 Heron Dr., Oakland, CA 94618

Born: 1934 *Awards:* NEA Grant *Collections:* Whitney Museum of American Art, NYC; Guggenheim Museum, NYC *Exhibitions:* Documenta 5, Kassel, West Germany; Whitney Museum of American Art, NYC *Education:* California College of Arts and Crafts; Mills College *Dealer:* O.K. Harris, NYC

During the 1950s, influenced by Richard Diebenkorn, Nathan Oliveira and the New York school, he vacillated in his abstract expressionist oil painting between non-objective and figurative images. Inspired by Kurt Schwitters, he also worked in collage from the late 1950s until the early 1960s. By 1968, disenchanted with abstraction, his work became firmly rooted in what came to be called photo-realism. He has been painting images of horses for twenty years. He regards his subject and its showground and stall environment as a still-life arrangement. His imagery is taken from his own slides. Recently he has been interested in how the horse functions in a rural landscape. Painting in both

oil and watercolor, he traces the canvas in pencil via slide projection, then applies a thin layer of paint in iconographical increments, finishing each section over a period of two or three months.

MCMILLIN, MELISSA BODINE (Painter)
201 Ocean Avenue, 503B, Santa Monica, California 90402

Awards: Honorable Mention, Painting, California State Fair,

Her figurative paintings begin with loose charcoal sketches applied directly to unprimed canvas. Working with live models, the artist intuitively selects a pose and proceeds to rough out the figures. She fleshes out the drawing with oil paints in rich, emotive hues inspired by her admiration for the work of Paul Cezanne and Vincent Van Gogh. Her colorist tendencies are given even greater freedom in the abstract works that she also creates. Even in realistic works, the artist relies heavily on her emotional response to subject matter. Color's unique ability to dramatize and conduct mood continues to fascinate her.

MCMILLAN, STEPHEN (Printmaker)
2719 San Mateo St., Richmond, CA 94804

Born: 1949 *Collections:* Brooklyn Museum; Achenbach Print Collections, San Francisco *Exhibitions:* Pacific Grove Art Center; Kala Institute Gallery, Berkeley *Education:* University of California, Santa Cruz

His artistic vision was profoundly influenced by the Bay area landscape as well as by the energy of Van Gogh's swirling colors, the vivid imagery of Escher and the play of light and shadow in the photographs of Ansel Adams. After exploring many techniques and styles, he has settled on aquatint etchings of landscapes based on his own photographs. Recent work has featured three plate aquatints with color overlays in reds, yellows, blues and blacks. He works by using acid-resistant paints, then dipping copper plates in acid. The recurring natural imagery of his work encourages the viewer to look carefully at the world and to preserve the beauty of nature.

MCMURTRY, PATRICK (Painter, Sculptor)
5 Old Hill Ranch Rd., Glen Ellen, CA 95442

In the late 1960s, after the impact of the psychedelic movement, he began seeking ways to integrate deep personal experience in his art. Oil painting became a very important tool in that process of self-realization. As this process continued, the work of Max Ernst provided him an entrance into "automatism," a phrase coined by Andre Breton. The method, comparable to automatic writings, allows chance and the subconscious to work on a piece, so that its effects go beyond the limits of the artist's intentions. Today his work includes sculpture as well. In both media, each piece is guided by its own pulse, sometimes sublime, sometimes grotesque.

MCNEILL, RALPH S. (Painter)
88 Belcrest Ave., Daly City, CA 94015

Born: 1929 *Awards:* Silver Medal, Richmond Art Annual; Purchase Award, San Francisco Art Festival *Collections:* San Francisco Museum of Modern Art; San Francisco Art Commission *Exhibitions:* Claudia Chapline Gallery, Stinson Beach; Nanny Goat Hill

Richard McLean, *Western Tableau with Italian Chairs,* 50 x 86, oil on canvas. Courtesy: Stephen Alpert. Photographer: D. James Dee

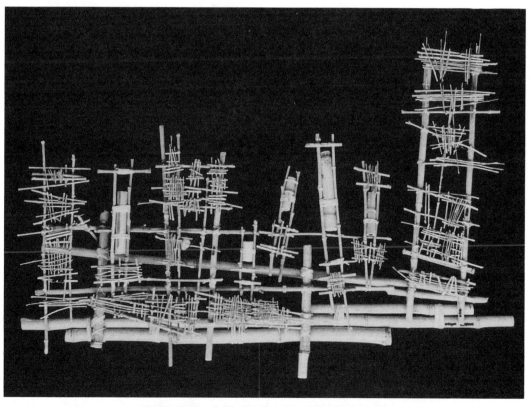

Judith Mills, *Spirit Catcher,* 24 x 36, mixed media

Gallery, San Francisco *Education:* Academy of Art, San Francisco; San Francisco Art Institute

Following formal training in academic drawing and painting, he developed a naturalistic style of oil painting, with which he has explored time and the possibility of extending time into painting. Recently, he has been working in watercolor, exploring the connection between Japanese prints and cubism. Fractionalized figures in surrealistic situations are rendered in low-key, moderately saturated colors. This work is influenced by the works of Kuniyoshi and Juan Gris (his favorite cubist artist).

MCROBERTS, SHERYL (Sculptor)
1319 Lewis, Laramie, WY 82070

Born: 1950 *Awards:* Purchase Award, Missoula Museum of the Arts; University of Wyoming Foundation Grant *Collections:* Missoula Museum of the Arts, Missoula, MT; Doane College, Crete, NE *Exhibitions:* Humboldt State U., Arcat; Lone Wolf Gallery, San Francisco *Education:* Indiana U.; St. Cloud State U.

Since moving to Nebraska, her work has centered on landscapes. Inspired the by the act of stroking the land involved in contour farming, she responded to the curvilinear forms of the earth as his subject matter. The sweep of space and sky which she encountered in Wyoming added features of speed and energy to her work. The idea of velocity began to enter into her visual vocabulary, and she explored the idea of visual perception at eighty mph. Her sculptures are applied with very dry, black and white gouache. More recent sculptures are oil painted. Greatly thinned, her applications underscore the dry, arid feeling of the high, western desert.

MADDOCK, PAM (Draughtsperson, Painter)
1035 Hacienda Ave., Davis, CA 95616

Born: 1948 *Awards:* Purchase Award, Crocker Kingsley, Crocker Art Museum, Sacramento *Collections:* Crocker Art Museum, Sacramento *Exhibitions:* Jennifer Pauls Gallery, Sacramento; Northern California Artists Drawing Show, M.U. Gallery, Davis *Education:* Washington State U. *Dealer:* City Gallery, Sacramento

Her formal training was in sculpture and printmaking. She then became interested in giving three-dimensional form to the images in the prints. She then turned to painting. Iconic forms replaced the literal physicality of the earlier sculptural works. The figure has grown more overt in her works, and her on-going concern with texture has evolved into increasingly gestural patterns. In large-scale graphite drawings, she uses a conceptual process of working away from an initially established figure through retracings, modifications and cancellations to wrest the form toward flux rather than out of it. Additionally, she uses small oil sketches in counterpoint to the scale of the larger work.

MAGIN, LUIS FLORES C. (Ceramist, Painter)
340 S. Normandie, #311, Los Angeles, CA 90020

Born: 1931 *Collections:* Security Pacific Bank, Los Angeles *Exhibitions:* Limited Editions Gallery, Beverly Hills; UCLA *Education:* U. of Buenos Aires, Argentina *Dealer:* Magin Studios, Los Angeles

In his student years, he studied at Vincente Forte's Plastic Studio in Buenos Aires. Pre-Columbian art has been his greatest influence. This influence lends a sense of antiquity about his works, especially those involving gold leaf. Though some contain figures, many are abstract evocations of ancient scenes. The works are painterly reliefs over Oleo margarine and watercolor. The medium is metallic colored oil paint and since 1976 he has employed gold, copper and silver leaf. More recently he has looked to the Mayan indians for inspiration. He has exhibited widely in South America, Central America and in the 1980s, California.

MAGNUS, MICHAEL (Painter, Sculptor)
Hermosa Beach, CA 90254

Exhibitions: Village Gallery, Redondo Beach; Long Beach Museum of Art

His work has taken two directions. As an impressionist landscape artist, he uses a vibrant brushstroke and a spectrum of subtle colors to capture the locale and ambience of southern California. He also constructs brightly colored, neon sculptures, which are mounted on a background of complimentary colors to achieve a sculpted effect.

MAJDRAKOFF, IVAN (Painter, Assemblage Artist)
13088 Broadway Terrace, Oakland, CA 94611

Born: 1927 *Collections:* Cranbrook Museum, Bloomfield Hills, MI; Minnesota Art Institute, Minneapolis *Exhibitions:* San Francisco Museum of Art; Museum of Modern Art, NYC

While still in school, he focused on black-and-white abstract and expressionist drawing. Influenced by Picasso and Klee, his color work was highly structured and occasionally organically abstract. He is now particularly interested in working with acrylic on canvas. His dense, colorful paintings are visually complex, yet accessible. He intermixes a variety of optical systems, including an unusual technique, which features an extruded line that defines forms. In addition, he has been working with non-narrative assemblages, and adhering objects to canvases and painting over them. These works synthesize his sense of fantasy and interest in assemblage.

MAKI, ROBERT (Sculptor)
8 Florentia St., Seattle WA 98109

Born: 1938 *Awards:* NEA Fellowship *Collections:* National Museum of America Art; Stanford University *Exhibitions:* Seattle Art Museum; Richards Hines Gallery, Seattle *Education:* Western Washington U.; U. of Washington *Dealer:* Laura Russo, Portland

This artist is often incorrectly labeled a minimalist. For the more than twenty years his work has involved illusionary structures and situations lending perceptual ambiguity to both interior and large-scale outdoor concepts. The concept of "fragment" is the key to interpreting the sculptures' integral role in creating a symbiotic relationship between viewer, object and space. He explores the pentagon shape, in both its non-coplanar and convex forms—an exploration based on the structural theory derived from the works of Bernini, Schwitters and Brancusi. He has recently been executing a monumental public installation in red granite with seven components up to 50 feet wide. Another monumental piece is comprised of a 60-foot waterwall and 24-foot stone arch as part of his collaboration on the design of Westlake Park. Drawings have also been an important part of his work, and he has recently been adding color to them as they expand on sculptural objects as images.

Ron S. Moore, *Waiting for Wings,* 60 x 18 x 52, wood, acrylic

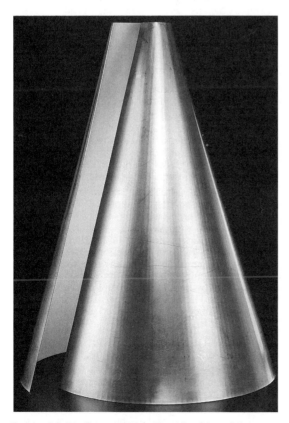

Robert Maki, *Canary 1986,* 48 x 40 x 34, stainless steel with yellow interior. Courtesy: Laura Russo

Jennifer Mackey, *Hooded Silk Jumpsuit,* hand-screened and painted silk. Courtesy: Mark Guerra and Jacque

MALAN-NICELY, MELINNA (Ceramist)
5620 61st Dr., N.E., Marysville, WA 98270

Born: 1958 *Exhibitions:* Arts Council Gallery, Everett, WA; Eloise Pickard Smith Gallery, UC-Santa Cruz

Trained as a studio potter by Al Johnson, she has pursued functional ceramics alongside more experimental slab works. Her unusual, organic vase forms and wall hangings are constructed from white stoneware and feature bright underglazed slip decoration applied by brush, spray or a combination of the two. She works primarily in functional pottery thrown on the wheel. Exhibiting a Japanese influence in form and decoration, her pieces display refined forms with smooth surfaces and carefully rendered detail. The decoration resembles Sumi brush painting and features a hand-painted iris motif with simple bands of color. She often uses a pale green transparent glaze to soften the white body.

MALLOFF, GEORGANNA PEARCE (Painter, Sculptor)
P.O. Box 113, Caspar, CA 95420

Born: 1936 *Awards:* Canada Council Grant; Artist in Residence, Johnson Atelier *Collections:* California College of Arts and Crafts; Harbour Front Contemporary Art Gallery *Exhibitions:* Mendocino County Museum; Banff Centre For the Arts, Canada *Education:* Scripps College; U. of Michigan *Dealer:* Stary Sheets Gallery, Gualala

During the 1960s and 1970s, she created sculpture gardens in the redwood forests of British Columbia. Influenced by Brancusi, Arp and French surrealism, her forms progressed from ceramic to metal and then to wood. In 1976, she created the first "Cosmic Maypole" for the U.N. Conference On Habitat. During the same period she studied marble carving in Italy and Yugoslavia. In her impressionistic, prismacolor pencil drawings of the era, she depicted vertical totemic forms in colors as lucid, transparent and healing as those in stained glass. She has recently been working figuratively in marble, stone and wood. Her bas reliefs in stained wood depict goddesses and boddhisattvas. She has recently completed a series of fantasy animal kingdoms in acrylics and a series of autobiographical dream paintings in oils.

MANFRIN, GWEN (Painter)
47 Rheem Blvd., Orinda, CA 94563

Born: 1956 *Awards:* 1st Place, Professional Photography; C.C. County Fair *Exhibitions:* Banaker Gallery; Civic Arts Gallery, Walnut Creek *Education:* UCLA

After she graduated from college, her first paintings were figures painted in oil. The influence of Vermeer was apparent in her crisp lines and strong clarity of image. In 1979, she took a sabbatical from painting and began infrared filming to create surrealistic effects and chiarascuro darkroom manipulations. When she returned to painting and pastel in the mid-1980s, her work showed the influence of the photographic process. Hard edges and a more representational style represent a break from her previous impressionistic mode. She also uses chalk pastel to create crisp, slick surrealistic still lifes of reflective surfaces.

MANN, JEFFRY (Woodworker)
P.O. Box 3420, Aspen, CO 81612

Born: 1955 *Collections:* Ethan Allen Museum, Danbury, CT *Exhibitions:* Hokin-Kaufman Gallery, Chicago; Contemporary Craftsman Gallery, Santa Fe, NM *Dealer:* Hokin-Kaufman Gallery, Chicago

After graduating from high school, he went to work as a carpenter. At an important juncture in his career, he took a woodworking workshop with a notable wood craftsman, Sam Maloof. After sale of one the chairs that he made in the workshop, and he began working solely from his own designs. Creating mainly rocking chairs, he works with fine woods and designs his chairs with precision. A trademark of his style is exposed joinery. His work first attracts attention visually because of its beauty, but he also works carefully to make the chairs, when sat in and rocked, kinesthetically pleasing. Careful attention is especially given to the back, in which he always likes to provide a strong fulcrum to support the lower back and the seat.

MARALDO, USHANNA (Painter)
P.O. Box 5188, Santa Barbara, CA 93108

Awards: 1st Prize, National Drawing Exhibition, San Francisco Museum of Modern Art; Outstanding Achievement, I.A.C., NYC *Collections:* Trump Tower, NYC; Warner Brothers, Hollywood *Exhibitions:* San Francisco Museum of Modern Art; Oakland Art Museum *Dealer:* The Annex Gallery, San Diego

Her visual concerns focus on an exploration of man's present and potential living spaces. Her tools are natural structures, geometric forms of stellar configurations, and cultural artifacts. In her "Humana" series, she shows man's confrontation with life and the subsequent freedom he gains by mastering himself and his ideas. The images of her "Cities of Light" and "Cosmic Calculus" series—pulsating, vibrant imagined landscapes, depict a synthesis of natural forms, architectural structures and elements of energy as evident in music, dance, cultural signs and scientific advances. She employes mixed media, watercolor and acrylics on paper and canvas.

MARC, JAMES (Painter)
P.O. Box 5132, Larkspur Landing Sta., Larkspur, CA 94939

Born: 1949 *Awards:* Award of Merit, California State Fair; Honorable Mention, Los Angeles West, Semi-Annual Art Show *Exhibitions:* Northwind Gallery, Mill Valley; Kentlent Gallery, Tiburon *Education:* San Francisco Art Institute; College of Marin

He is a semi-abstract realist whose work has surrealist overtones. For the first 25 years of his career, he painted in oils. The overwhelming fumes from oil paint eventually took a physical toll on his body and he switched to acrylics in the early 1980s. He has recently been following two main directions. He paints his multi-layered semi-abstract canvases with a thick modeling paste medium. His naturalistic skyscapes are characterized by thinned paint, long perspectives and vast distances. He feels that the most important thing any painter can do is develop a deep understanding of what creating is.

MARCHANT, JOHN D. (Painter)
4103 Emerald St., Oakland, CA 94609

Born: 1953 *Awards:* 3rd Prize, A.A.O. Gallery, NYC; Honors in Etching, San Francisco Art Institute *Exhibitions:* Brickling Galleries; Landell Galleries *Education:* San Francisco Art Institute

He began as a printmaker, but has recently concentrated on works in acrylic on canvas. His work is figurative and situational, often exploring slightly un-

M. Maye, *Life's Pathways Meander,* 14 x 10, pastel

John D. Marchant, *Cowries,* 16 x 20, colored pencils. Courtesy: Dimitrios Serifimedes

conventional and humorous subjects. A recent series depicting empty lawn chairs conveys a sense of possibility and opening, as well as the structuralism of human experience. Deep pastels underscore the emotional content of the paintings without referring directly to them—suggesting the unspoken communications in personal interactions.

MARCHESCHI, CORK (Sculptor)
192 Connecticut St., San Francisco, CA 94107

Born: 1945 *Collections:* Kunstmuseum, Dusseldorf; Ashi Shimbune, Tokyo *Exhibitions:* National Gallery, West Berlin; Van Abbe Museum, Eindhoven, Holland *Education:* California College of Arts and Crafts *Dealer:* Nerlino McGear, NYC

He began working with electrical light in 1959, using small Christmas tree bulbs behind glass bottles filled with colored water. He expanded his technique in the 1960s, using neon tubes and nichrome wire to achieve more elaborate effects. His influences came more from poetry, jazz and blues than from any visual source. He collaborated with Alan Watts during this period. His work since the 1970s has consisted of simple geometric compositions made of neon tubes. These pieces are sometimes open to the air, sometimes wholly or partially screened by translucent glass or plastic. They are usually flat compositions, wall-mounted. His range of effects in this prosaic medium is great; his neon is capable of many intensities and variations of color; the optical effects created with generated light are powerful.

MARCHIORI, CARLO (Painter, Ceramist)
357 Frederick St., San Francisco, CA 94117

Born: 1937 *Awards:* Academy Award Nominee for Animation; International Broadcast Award, Hollywood Radio and TV Society *Exhibitions:* Golden Nugget Casino, Las Vegas; Nordstrom's, San Francisco *Education:* Istituto D'Arte, Venice; Istituto D'Arte, Padua

After a successful career as an illustrator and film animator, he moved to San Francisco in 1979 and began making murals. He drew on his European background for their creation, particularly 17th and 18th century Italian painting. His murals are traditional and realistic; full of emotion and expression, they display a concern with the human soul. Trompe l'oeil and academic mannerism are evident in his work and some of his pieces bear a similarity to the Pompeiian frescoes. His medium is acrylic on canvas and his large projects are usually completed in sections and assembled later on the location wall.

MARCSISIN, ELIZABETH (Painter)
196 B Santa Barbara Ave., Daly City, CA 94014

Born: 1934 *Exhibitions:* Pyramid Gallery, NYC; Gallery House, Palo Alto *Education:* San Francisco U.; California College of Arts And Crafts

During the latter part of her formal training, she was influenced by David Park, Elmer Bischoff and Richard Diebenkorn. At that time, her oils-on-canvas paintings of the figure featured a spontaneous, expressionistic style. Between 1975 and 1986, she stained dream symbols, figures and simplified geometric forms onto an unprimed canvas using acrylics and a pastel-colored palette. Recently influenced by the imaginative works of Paul Klee, she continues to paint figures and dream images. In one fanciful piece, a woman and man dance in space. She has returned to a more spontaneous, expressionistic style, and usually works with acrylic on paper.

MARCUS, IRVING (Painter)
601 Shangri Lane, Sacramento, CA 95825

Born: 1929 *Exhibitions:* San Francisco Art Institute; Memorial Union Art Gallery, UC-Davis *Education:* U. of Iowa; U. of Minnesota

Using unnaturally vivid colors combined with forms that define the edge of figuration, he depicts everyday human activity with cynically primitive renderings. The interactions of his figures are almost novel-like in both complexity and accessibility. His current work uses an increasingly narrative compositional style that is both situationally absurd and rigorously patterned. His recent work, done in oil pastel on paper as well as oil paint on canvas, creates invented figures that explore directly and expressively the underlying themes of his more realistic pieces of the 1970s. Of the recent series, Christopher French has written, "His acid colors, tightly meshed within the confines of particular forms, reinvent human images as an act of revenge and rebirth. Appearing in configurations that are at once more horrible and more intimate than their media sources, they produce doubt. They are singular in stubborn insistence on the conflagration, conjunction and inversion of what is unthinkingly taken as fact."

MARCUS, JIM (Miniaturist)
P.O. Box 919, Bolinas, CA 94924

Born: 1943 *Awards:* Academy of Honors, International Miniature Artists *Collections:* Miniature Museum of Kansas City; Angels Attic, Santa Barbara *Exhibitions:* National Geographic Society; Miniature Museum of Kansas City *Education:* California Institute of the Arts

He works primarily on miniature reproductions of Victorian San Francisco row houses, using unstained hardwoods of various hues as well as fabrics and stained glass to reproduce period homes in meticulous detail. He thinks of these works as sculpture about houses, the fine-arts qualities of which are counterpointed in separate and more purely sculptural work. The artist received training in woodcarving in Japan, then began producing miniatures in limited editions. Their striking attention to detail is key to the changes in perception effected by their disruptions of conventional scale and point of reference. Materials such as faded velvet are used unconventionally to simulate aged metal roofs, thus heightening the effect of disquieting juxtaposition within the trompe l'oeil context. Interiors likewise make use of decontextualized elements such as kimono silk, which form their own logic in environs of displaced scale.

MARGON, SARITHA (Painter, Multimedia Artist)
434 N. Ontare Rd., Santa Barbara, CA 93105

Born: 1933 *Awards:* 1st Place, Painting, Southern California Fair, Del Mar *Exhibitions:* Southern California Figurative Art, Los Angeles; Pacific Coastline Drawing Show, Salem, OR *Education:* Jepson Art School; Otis Art Institute *Dealer:* Delphine Gallery, Santa Barbara

Her style has been influenced by her teachers William Brice, Howard Warshaw, Rico Lebrun and Hans Hoffman; she has always maintained her interests in Spanish and pre-Columbian art, the folk art of Mexico and the drawings of Van Gogh. Recent relief paintings refer to the inner, psychological realm. In these pieces,

M.E. Martinez, *Cockfighting,* 48 x 53, oil on canvas

Lynn Pollock Marsh, *Transformation: Djed Pillar,* 24 x 18, pencil and wash

Jim Marcus, *The Cadoza Residence,* 48 x 22 x 38, hardwoods

figures and objects tangle and disentangle themselves, alternately trapped and escaping. She cites the works of de Kooning, especially his latest "ribbon" paintings, and the works of Jasper Johns as particularly significant to her later work.

MAREE, WENDY (Painter, Sculptor)
P.O. Box 2421, Lake Arrowhead, CA 90069

Born: 1938 *Awards:* 1st Place, Watercolor and Pastel, Windsor Arts Festival; San Bernardino County Museum *Collections:* H.R.H. Prince Feisal, Saudi Arabia; Gena Rowlands *Exhibitions:* Phyllis Morris Gallery; Lake Arrowhead Library, Blue Jay *Education:* Windsor Maindenhead College

Known throughout the world for her oil and acrylic paintings, she began winning awards as a youth in Windsor, England. Study with Vascow Lazzlow provided her with a traditional foundation in realism and particularly informed her use of color. Technical maturity and the influence of Matisse and Picasso later led her in more abstract directions, though she continues to explore all forms of representation. Since the 1960s, her images have been defined more with shadow than with color as she has experimented with minimalist forms for their capacity to transform under the eye of the beholder. She appreciates interpretations of her work that are at odds with her intent because of the visual experience's personal nature, yet insists that the significance of a piece depends upon the presence of meaning. In recent acrylics, bold, dark angles and curves intersect on a white background. Bright splashes of color add a note of unexpected vibrancy and reflect the intensifying effect of the California sun. A simplicity of style and childlike qualities often evoke a sense of memory; flat imagery appears to freeze movement as though under glass. Always striving for economy of dialogue, she has nonetheless taken a very traditional approach towards her bronze sculptures. Maintaining that one cannot learn to run until the art of walking has been perfected, she has concentrated on lyrical, narrative forms to begin work in the medium. In *Enfance*, she has noted the deforestation controversy in Europe by depicting a young woman seated on a naked tree trunk, holding the last leaves and flowers. Attracted to bronze's stability, she is also interested in working with stone.

MARI, DAWN (Painter)
6000 W. Sunset Blvd., #203, Los Angeles, CA 90028

Born: 1954 *Collections:* Bay Banks, MA *Exhibitions:* Corner Gallery, NYC; Grafin Gallery, Pasadena *Education:* Syracuse U. School of Art

At first, she painted the countryside and farm lands of her rural New York upbringing. In college, she studied advertising and design and later had a successful commercial career in Boston. In 1988, she moved to Los Angeles where she has been successful at portraying special corporate messages and themes for corporate collections. She now paints abstracted landscapes, waterfalls, cityscapes and dolphins. Her media include acrylics on canvas, watercolors, pastel, monoprints, limited editions and poster art prints. All of the work shows the influence her early years in the country had on her sense of color and emotion. She now does the majority of her paintings on commission.

MARIE-ROSE, HENRI (Sculptor)
205 Missouri St., San Francisco, CA 94107

Born: 1922 *Awards:* 2nd Prize, American Trust Company Prize, San Francisco; Bank of America Prize, 75th Annual Painting and Sculpture Exhibition of S.F.A.A., San Francisco *Collections:* City of San Francisco; San Francisco Museum of Modern Art *Exhibitions:* San Francisco Art Festival; California State Fair *Education:* Ecole des Arts et Metiers, Martinique

The artist grew up determined to master the skills of the artisans who sold their wares daily along the main streets of his Carribean homeland, Martinique. After he completed formal training, three one-man shows brought to light his considerable talent for sculpture, an avenue that allowed him to utilize his diverse skills to create award-winning welded steel and brass pieces. He draws from stories, beliefs and theories that have fascinated him over the past forty years. Biblical tales, ancient Greek mythology, and social issues inspire and lend titles to his work. In his oil paintings, the artist draws heavily on the sensual, vivid colors and forms of his tropical birthplace.

MARINI, MONICA (Painter, Printmaker)
2716 Russell St., Berkeley, CA 94701

Born: 1941 *Awards:* 2nd Prize in Painting, Bienal Femimundo *Collections:* California Progressive Asset Management, San Francisco *Exhibitions:* Hourian Gallery, Oakland; National Salon of Painting, Argentina *Education:* National School of Fine Arts, Buenos Aires

While still living in Argentina, she was influenced by the work of the neo-expressionist Argentine, Romulo Maccio. Her early, semi-abstract representations of human figures melt into areas of color. These soon gave way to entirely abstract compositions. In 1974, she moved to California where printmaking became her main form of expression. She adds dimension to her graphics by combining collage with lithography. Color of countless intensities is also important. Among her subjects are the strength of women, strong nude bodies and repetitions of hands and arms. Her recent work is based on movements of the sun.

MARINOFF, ELAINE (Painter)
14974 Corona Del Mar, Pacific Palisades, CA 90272

Born: 1934 *Collections:* Robert Troy, Atlanta; Mr. and Mrs. Lester Weinstein, Los Angeles *Exhibitions:* Heritage Gallery, Los Angeles; Criteria Inc., Denver *Education:* UCLA *Dealer:* Hilda Chen, Waterfront Gallery, San Francisco

Her figurative serigraphs and oils on canvas evoke sensuality; her primary concerns are for light and the linear movement of form in space. The surfaces of her larger-than-large paintings are softly patined and luminous, enhancing both the mystery of her figures and the intertwined lines of her composition. Her newer work is pigmented, with wax worked in thickly to increase the paint's textural quality. The power and force of the human body in motion is the predominant theme, which she represents directly through the depth and vitality of her technique. Her narrative work celebrates lustful sensuality and expresses private musings and *joie de vivre*.

MARIONI, PAUL (Glass Artist)
4136 Meridian Ave. N., Seattle, WA 98103

Born: 1941 *Awards:* NEA Fellowship and Building Arts Grant *Collections:* American Crafts Museum,

Jim Marcus, *Mower,* 9 x 23 x 13, hardwoods and found objects

Wendy Maree, *Enfance,* 11 x 6 x 5, bronze. Courtesy: June Allyson

M.E. Martinez, *Arrangement with Plant Cuttings,*
19 x 20, wax and dry pigments on handmade paper

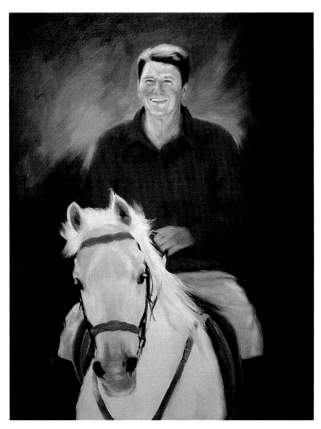

Pat Massié, *The President on His Horse,* 30 x 24, oil

Barry Masteller, *Tangent,* 68 x 80, diptych, acrylic on canvas

John Maxon, *Favor,* 60 x 84, oil on linen

Therese May, *Sugar Bowl,* 84 x 84, stitched fabric, acrylic paint

M. Maye, *Fish Story,* 21 x 27, pastel

Igor Medvedev/Mead, *Costa del Sol,* 40 x 54, gouache

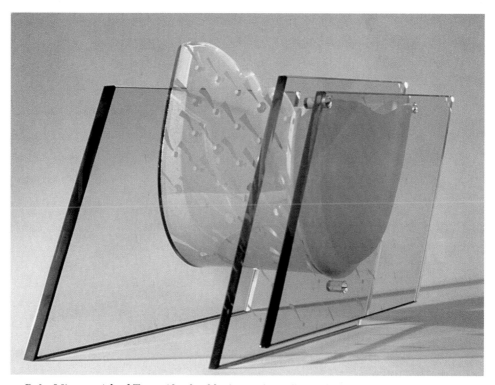

Babs Miyano, *Ark of Tears,* 13 x 9 x 20, slumped, sandblasted and plate glass construction

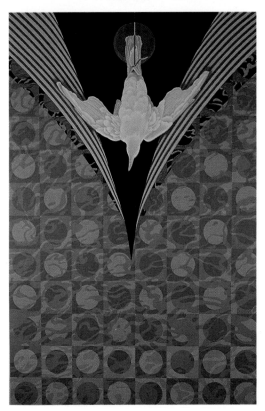

Hideo Muranaka, *Split,* 64 x 42, acrylic on paper

D.T. Murphy, *Gone Fishin',* 24 x 36,
acrylic and sand on masonite

Yvonne Cole Meo, *Flowering
(Transformative Phase),* 30 x 80, oil on canvas

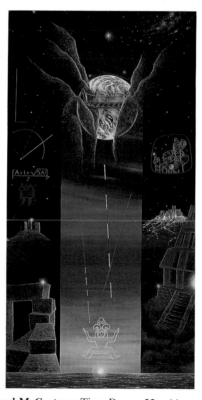

Sheryl McCartney, *Time Dance,* 22 x 44, acrylic

Evid Moore, *Creation,* 60 x 36, acrylic on canvas

Judy Mulford, *I'm 50 and I'm Glad, I Think,* 9 x 13,
clay, pine needles, raffia, dye, paint, beads

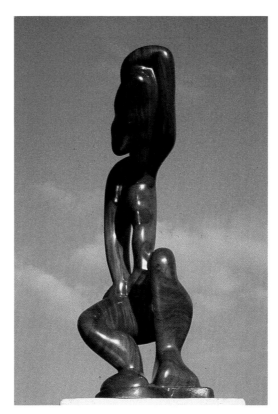

Barrington McLean, *untitled,* 48 high, Palo Chino wood

Jennifer Mackey, *Spring Hand-Screened Silks,*
hand-printed and painted silk.
Courtesy: Mark Guerra and Jacque Wendler

Lani McCoy, *The Welcoming Party,* 16 x 20, photograph

Moxzer, *untitled,* 9 x 12, enamel on wood

Susan Moss, *Green River,* 50 x 38, oil on paper.
Courtesy: Cynthia McLaren, Los Angeles, CA (Ruth Bachofner Gallery)

Lee McCormick, *Fresh Air,* 30 x 40, pastels and felt tip pens

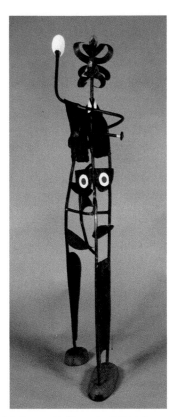

E. Mathews, *Suffragette,* 54" high, copper

Melissa Bodine McMillin, *Sadness,* 48 x 36, oil/charcoal on canvas

Jack McLarty, *Baby, Baby Look What You...,* acrylic.
Courtesy: The Image Gallery, Portland, OR

Daniel J. Miller, *My Bird in Space,* 240 x 48 x 12, stainless steel

Ron S. Moore, *You-Hoo,* 77 x 57 x 29, bronze

Claire Stebbins McAuliffe, *Yosemite,* 80 x 55, acrylic and pastels on canvas

Nina Medici, *Self,* 16 x 20, acrylic

Richard Moquin, *Frammento del Sole,* 42 x 36 x 8, painted marble

Jeffry Mann, *Rocking Chair G.10,* 24 x 46 x 46, Western quilted maple & E. I. Rosewood. Courtesy: Joanne Lyon Gallery, Inc., Aspen CO

Jerry McGrath, *Jean Paul Are You Sure?,* 24 x 20, cibachrome. Courtesy: Jan Kesner Gallery, Los Angeles, CA

NYC *Exhibitions:* Dorothy Weiss Gallery, San Francisco; Walter White Gallery, Carmel *Education:* U. of Cincinnati *Dealers:* Walter White Gallery, Santa Monica; Traver Sutton, Seattle

He has been influenced by absurdist philosophy and art's concern with illusion and reality. In his glass art, he strives to capture and manipulate light. He works in both large and small scale. His larger, commissioned works are architectural in intent and made from cast glass for public spaces and private homes. His smaller fine-art pieces concern the surrealist expression of the human spirit.

MARIONI, TOM (Sculptor)
693 Mission, #805, San Francisco, CA 94105

Born: 1937 *Awards:* Guggenheim Fellowship; NEA Grant *Collections:* Oakland Museum *Exhibitions:* Galeria Foksal Warsaw, Modern Art Gallery, Vienna; Eaton Show Gallery *Education:* Cincinatti Art Academy

Inspired by such artists as Marcel Duchamp and John Cage, he continues to work in the field of conceptual art. Found objects are appropriated not to represent themselves, but as metaphor. These objects are arranged in installations and tableaux, and are frequently under yellow light, giving the work a warm atmosphere. The pieces are set with lights in a manner to cast shadows and create a mood for the work.

MARSDEN, GUY (Sculptor, Mixed Media Artist)
2022 Aco Blvd., Santa Monica, CA 90405

Born: 1955 *Collections:* Los Angeles Center for Psychotherapy *Exhibitions:* Center for Neon Art, Phoenix; Museum of Neon Art, Los Angeles *Education:* Maryland Institute, College of Art

His evolution as an artist paralleled his growing engineering skills. As a result, his work represents a lifetime of synthesizing art and technology. His sculptures are all-electronic, containing controlled kinetic light systems ranging from color CRT's to miniature light-emitting diodes to large glass "lightning globes." He creates his pieces from hand-blown Pyrex, wood and translucent acrylics. Currently, he works on larger sculptures, extending the plasma/high voltage/neon art form. One recent work, *Dodeca Rockola*, not only expands this genre, but also incorporates complex new concepts in physics.

MARSH, LYNN POLLOCK (Sculptor, Draughtsperson)
804 Bryant St., Palo Alto, CA 94301

Born: 1938 *Awards:* Fessenden Foundation Grant, San Diego *Collections:* City of Palo Alto *Exhibitions:* San Francisco Art Dealers' Association; City Museum, San Mateo *Dealer:* Warner Roberts, Palo Alto

With the intention of creating a personal iconography of the archetypal feminine in sculptural form, she has, during the last fifteen years, produced nearly a thousand drawings and sculptures of the female form. Beginning with the figure, she has created a totemic abstract world of fleshy, bony personages, fused interlocking shapes and ambiguously sensual, suggestive forms. She has been influenced by Gaston Lachaise, Ann Morency, Henri Matisse and Henry Moore.

MARSHALL, GAYLE (Painter, Sculptor)
441 Kanekapolei, Honolulu, HI 96815

Born: 1945 *Awards:* 1st Place, Ocean City, NJ Boardwalk Show; Featured Artist, Magnum, P.I. *Collections:* Atlantic City Chamber of Commerce *Exhibitions:* Honolulu Academy of Art; Hawaii Watercolor Society *Education:* U. of Georgia; U. of Hawaii *Dealer:* Bakkus, Honolulu

In the 1960s, studies in design and architecture led her to the field of architectural renderings and paintings of old buildings. Her interest in fabrics, pattern and beads developed from a desire to produce more functional works in the 1970s into designs of "art-wearables" and fiber and clay fantasy figures. Her recent paintings are primarily in acrylic, with a combination of thick and thin washes. She draws the imagery of her paintings from Hawaiian myths and petroglyphs, Asian fabric patterns and tropical floral patterns which she develops from stencils. Her loose, brilliantly colored brushstrokes combine realism and stencil stylization of the figure and abstraction in the surrounding patterns.

MARSHALL, MAUREEN G. (Painter)
55 Biltmore Estates, Phoenix, AZ 85016

Born: 1921 *Collections:* British Consul General, Seville; Pakistan Consulate, San Francisco *Exhibitions:* San Francisco Museum of Modern Art; San Francisco Art Commission *Education:* UC-Berkeley

Her interest in a non-traditional approach to the human face and figure was stimulated by the compositional patterns developed by the impressionists, particularly Van Gogh, Cezanne and Matisse. For the last several years, she has been creating works in a paper collage medium. Working with Italian, English and Japanese papers, she creates collage portraits of figures once considered to be idols of their own and subsequent times. These are rendered in sepia tones, from rose beige to dark brown. They include complete landscape backgrounds, and vary in size from 22 by 26 inches to 4 by 6 feet. She has also painted many trompe l'oeil screens and cupboards. Though she lives in isolation from current art trends and fashions, her art nevertheless expresses a deep involvement with humanity and the feelings of the individual.

MARTENS, DANIEL P. (Painter)
1700 Golden Gate, #5, Los Angeles, CA 90018

Born: 1935 *Awards:* Art Quest Finalist *Exhibitions:* Whittier Museum; Hillcrest Museum

When he first entered art school, he was a figurative painter. He came under the influence of the San Francisco Bay Area abstract figurative painters. His present work is metaphysical or mystical, a synthesis of the primative and the contemporary. A combinations of fur, sticks, stones, feathers and bones reflect the 20th century's exploration of form and color. Most of the works are wall hangings, some are three-dimensional and by free-standing. He is currently working in a bas relief style. The works are inspired by primitive cultures and by the materials themselves.

MARTIN, BILL (Painter)
P.O. Box 511, Albion, CA 95410

Born: 1943 *Awards:* Grant, Tiffany Foundation *Collections:* Oakland Museum; Neue Gallerie der Stadt, Aachen, W. Germany *Exhibitions:* Oakland Museum; San Francisco Museum of Modern Art *Education:* San Francisco Art Institute *Dealer:* Joseph Chowning Gallery, San Francisco

His early work as a California Visionary reflected an imaginative and fantastic concept of life in the future. In the mid-1970s, he began to balance the earlier fantastic views with pure and incisive interpretations of the landscapes of Marin County. Canvases are often circular and framed in wood, so that the viewer has the sensation of looking through a telescope or peephole. *Autumn* is a circular view in oil, 55 inches in diameter, of a group of trees with people lounging in the grass next to a winding brook. *Sunbeams* is a circular canvas, smaller in diameter, depicting convincing shafts of light through trees.

MARTIN, DAVID A. (Painter)
2348 Loma Vista Pl., Los Angeles, CA 90039

Born: 1951 *Awards:* Circle Gallery Award, *American Artist* Magazine; Stacey Foundation Grant *Exhibitions:* Los Angeles County Museum, Sales and Rental Gallery; Mirage Editions, 11th St. Gallery, Los Angeles

With a romantic sensibility, he has combined elements of the turn-of-the-century American painting with a painterly style and a vision based on personal observation. His quiet subjects are familiar and natural, but he shifts and alters elements and spaces to achieve satisfactory designs. His images of pink hacienda-style houses are washed in contrasts of violets and oranges, and accentuated by an occasional verdant cypress. His figurative works lie in comfortable repose, dappled with a spattering of light. His lawns are marked by bright bursts of statuary, molten fuschia, bouganville and wisteria. His media are pastels and oils.

MARTIN, GEORGE (Architectural Metalworker)
1708 Berkeley St., Santa Monica, CA 90404

Born: 1923 *Awards:* NEA Grant *Exhibitions:* Renwick Galleries, Smithsonian Institution, Washington, D.C.; Museum of Contemporary Crafts, NYC

A Ph.D. in industrial metallurgy, he worked in the aerospace industry and taught metallurgical engineering at UCLA, before opening Creative Metal Crafts in 1972. Working in iron, steel, brass, copper and titanium, he uses both traditional craft methods—blacksmithing, repousse—and modern manufacturing techniques, such as laser cutting and plasma welding, to achieve his aesthetic and functional designs. Commissioned to create gates, railings and furniture, he creates his pieces as sight specific responses to aesthetic problems. His inventive furniture is a combination of metal, leather and wood, such as a rocking chair that rocks in four, instead of two, dimensions.

MARTIN, LEMORA (Ceramist)
5507 College Ave., #11, Oakland, CA 94618

Awards: Toonibs Prize, UC-Berkeley; Scott Kelm Prize, W.C.C.A.C. *Exhibitions:* C.A.C., Walnut Creek; Pro Arts *Education:* UC-Berkeley

Influenced by Frida Kahlo and Spanish surrealist painter Remedios Varo, she is a symbolist who explores her own psyche. She dramatizes her internal conflicts and processes by arranging scenery and human and animal figures in small, clay environments. Formally trained as a sculptor and inspired by folk and primitive art, she has worked in clay for the last sixteen years. She constructs her small narrative pieces from porcelain and white stoneware, adorning them with stains, china paints and low-fire glazes.

MARTIN, SUSAN (Sculptor, Mixed Media Artist)
560 Walnut Ave., Vacaville, CA 95688

Born: 1948 *Awards:* Pollock/Krasner Foundation Award, NYC *Exhibitions:* U. of California Fine Arts Gallery, Irvine; Fiberworks Gallery, Berkeley *Education:* California College of Arts and Crafts

Her earlier work, influenced by textile art and primitive sculpture, consisted of abstract forms in thread, wire, hardware cloth and cardboard. Recent abstract sculptures in concrete and plaster are informed by the concept of the knee, a cylindrical bent form. She also constructs and groups sculptures of spheres and cubes into arrangements suggesting mundane objects or situations, as, for example, a game board, a circle of trees or a fence. Sculptures are usually 8 feet in height and 10 to 12 feet in diameter. She cites Lee Bontecou, Carl Andre, Jackie Winsor, Richard Serra and Robert Smithson as major influences on her recent work.

MARTINEZ, MARIA ELENA (Painter)
7706 McHenry Ave., Modesto, CA 95356

Born: 1944 *Exhibitions:* Riverside Art Museum; Southern Exposure Gallery, San Francisco *Education:* Los Angeles City College; U. of Oregon, Eugene *Dealer:* Ariel Gallery, NYC

While she paints in the pure medium of oils, her imagery projects itself as collage. Her canvas takes form from various angles, and its various parts unite to create movement. Regardless of subject, her images are brilliant, multicolored contrasts of warm and cool hues. She combines real scenes and objects with imaginary ones, in painting that is non-realistic. Some of her subjects have dealt with social problems and with man's oneness with the earth. She has been influenced by Magritte, Munch and the subtle, serene surrealism of Georgia O'keeffe. She is currently painting still lifes and florals, on the handmade paper she creates using various fibers.

MARY-GEORGE (Painter)
9126 Olin St., Los Angeles, CA 90034

Born: 1942 *Awards:* Fellowship, Virginia Museum of Fine Art; Fuji Fine Arts Award, Fuji Art Museum, Japan *Collections:* Fuji Fine Art Museum, Japan *Exhibitions:* The Front Porch/Human Arts Gallery, Venice; Mary-George Gallery, Los Angeles *Education:* Virginia Commonwealth U. *Dealer:* Zeneta Kertisz, Venice

Heavily influenced by Van Gogh and de Kooning in her earlier years, she developed an explosive, gestural style of landscape painting. By using loose, vivid colors in acrylic to suggest her subject matter, she bridged the gap between abstraction and realism with a lyrical, free-flowing style. In the early 1980s, she became interested in the Japanese sumi school of painting, and began what has continued to be an ongoing search: to capture the essence of the subject and crystallize it on the two-dimensional surface. Exploration of the quality of line on paper and its direct connection to the life condition of the artist became an area of investigation and expression. Her recent work is influenced by David Hockney, and features the introduction of the figure into the landscape arena. While maintaining her stylistic commitment to the sumi style, her use of line has become more free and expressive.

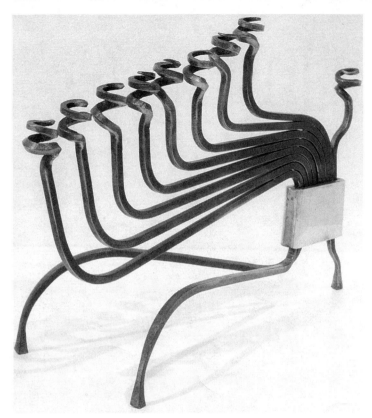

George Martin, steel. Photographer: Mac L. Olds

Melinna Malan-Nicely, *Margaret,* 12 inches diameter,
white stoneware with underglaze, pencil

Nancy Macko, *Winter Cycle,* 48 x 72, acrylic on canvas. Courtesy: Ianetti-Lanzone Gallery, Inc.

Daniel J. Miller, *Wall, Arch and Post,* 84 x 180 x 96, stainless steel

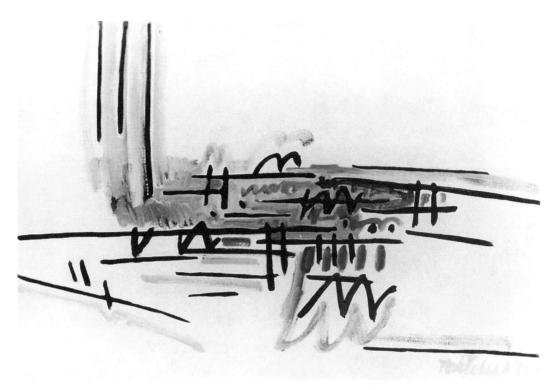

Bill Mitchell, *Sonata #1,* 24 x 36, acrylics

Tegwin Matenaer, *Dancing Shadows,* 11 x 14, silver gelatin print

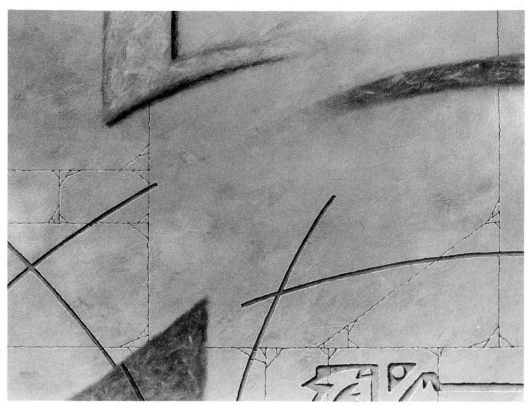

Barry Masteller, *Wall Painting IV,* 22 x 30, acrylic on paper. Courtesy: J.W. Robinson Co., Beverly Hills, CA

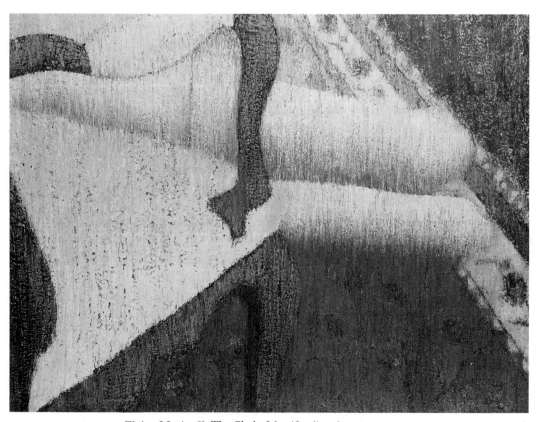

Elaine Marinoff, *The Chair,* 36 x 48, oil and wax on canvas

John Maxon, *Crossover,* 48 x 72, oil on linen

Charles Miltenberger, *Laura,* 52 x 72, oil on canvas

MASLOW, GENE (Painter, Sculptor)
407 Mermaid, Laguna Beach, CA 92651

Born: 1925 *Exhibitions:* Museum of Modern Art, NYC; Los Angeles County Museum *Education:* Otis Parson's Art Institute, Los Angeles *Dealer:* Art Source/Nancy Ryan, NYC; Collector's Object Gallery, Laguna Beach

He studied India's culture and art (he spent the years between 1965 and 1973 living in India), while pursuing the practice of Integral Yoga; as a result, he developed conceptions of integrating the long-standing contradiction between a two- or three-dimensional approach to art. He now employs a synthesis of both dimensions in plexiglas construction sculpture, oil paintings, drawings and montage litho printmaking. In this new work, he brings an abstract-expressionist's two-dimensional conception of equal tensions across the picture plane into the more three-dimensional reality of figurative expressionism and iconographic symbols. At one time a member of the influential action-painting movement, in the 1980s, he has been instrumental in introducing a "new-consciousness-art" into the art world.

MASON, YURI (Painter, Draughtsperson)
45 Alhambra Ct., Portola Valley, CA 94025

Born: 1920 *Exhibitions:* San Francisco Museum of Modern Art; Stanford U. *Education:* Boston Museum of Fine Art

His early study of the human form was the basis of his current abstract expressionist ideas. From 1955 to 1973, he made canvas studies based on nuclear particle physics. During the late 1970s, he used acrylics to explore the possibilities of color fields. His reaction to human emotions, moments of revelation and the inconsistencies of life, underlie his recent canvases. He is now deeply concerned with the threat of nuclear war, environmental pollution and moral issues. His art is intended to express and communicate to the world his own life experience. Influences include Masaccio, Da Vinci, Cranach, Durer, Grunewald, Cezanne, Matisse, Van Gogh and Munch.

MASSIE, ELIZABETH K. (Painter, Paper Artist)
1311 Berkeley St., Santa Monica, CA 90404

Born: 1944 *Collections:* Downey Museum of Art; IBM Corp., Orange; *Exhibitions:* Art Collector Gallery, San Diego; Suzanne Brown Gallery, Scottsdale, AZ *Education:* UC-Berkeley

Her bas-relief paper wall sculptures emerge from an extensive background in both the traditional arts and in contemporary paper art techniques. This background includes the study of painting and sculpture, in Europe; archaeological artifacts, textiles and fibers, in South America; and advanced printmaking and papermaking techniques, in the U.S. The latter included work in vacuum forming processes, embossment and general construction. She is best known for a series of stacked chromatic paper sculptures. They are constructed from thousands of torn-and-cut paper shards arranged in horizontal or vertical stacks. She handcolors the papers with tints, natural and photo-sensitive dyes, glazes and gel media, then affixes them to the primed linen canvas base with silicone cement. When a work is completed, she encloses it in a completely transparent plexiglas box. These works in undulating shadows and hues function as metaphors for experience and memory. Recently, she has been painting mixed-media abstracts on linen canvas—meditations, which unfold in an extension of textural, linear and color saturation sand layers.

MASSIE, PAT (Painter)
3330 Chenu Ave., Sacramento, CA 95821

Born: 1947 *Awards:* Ribbon Award, *Artist* Magazine, London; *Exhibitions:* Montana Institute of Art; Centre International D'Art Contemporain, Paris *Education:* Alexander School of Painting, San Diego

Her work in oil on linen canvas is inspired by both American and French Impressionists. Light, color and form rather than subject matter are her dominant concerns. Seeking color that vibrates and glows yet maintains a transparency, she develops the work through thin layers, with the final application always wet on wet. Expressive brush strokes and light-filled, pastel colors produce vivid yet delicate works, evoking a sense of motion and energy in scenes that are otherwise tranquil. Her current subjects are landscapes and waterscapes in pinks, mauves and warm greens, marking a change from her previous use of dark greens and blues; soft edges furthermore increasingly replace the hard lines common in her earlier work.

MASTELLER, BARRY (Painter)
P.O. Box 920, Pacific Grove, CA 93950

Born: 1945 *Collections:* Syntex Corp., Palo Alto; Security Pacific Bank, Los Angeles *Exhibitions:* Ankrum Gallery, Los Angeles; San Jose Museum of Art *Dealer:* J.J. Brookings, San Jose

Influenced by Cezanne and by the art of the Middle Ages, he developed a series of "intuitive abstract portraits" during the 1960s. In 1971, he became interested in Duchamp, the surrealists and the abstract expressionists, and in the way the subconscious and dreams are transformed into art. In the late 1970s, constructivism played an increasing role, while his sometimes humorous acrylic and watercolor paintings of the era were surrealist. Since 1982, constructivism, surrealism and abstraction have been his main concerns, his principle subjects being architectural—walls and structures. He uses acrylics to paint on canvas, paper and constructions, giving the works a painterly feel. His underpainting shows through a brushed overcolor, and his vibrant, lively surfaces are reminiscent of old wall-painting or architectural abstraction.

MASTERSON, JULIE (Photographer)
855 Old Mill Rd., San Marino, CA 91108

Born: 1940 *Awards:* 1st & 2nd Prizes, Los Angeles Photography Center *Collections:* W.W. Henry Co.; Hill, Betts, & Nash *Exhibitions:* Site Gallery; Larchmont Gallery, Los Angeles; Pacific Asia Museum, Pasadena *Education:* Stanford U. *Dealer:* Contemporary Art Consultants, Pasadena

After studying with Ansel Adams, Paul Caponigro, Eliott Porter, Richard Misrach, Robert Glenn Ketchum and others, she adapted the zone system for black-and-white photography to color photographs. Her cibachrome prints of landscapes and flowers show the influence of Richard Misrach's palette and Georgia O'Keeffe's composition. She has recently completing a portfolio of still life biographies. One such biography comprises a series of twenty platinum prints, which detail the particulars of the subject's life, collected over her ninety-three years; taken together, they amount to a life portrait. The artist also continues to work with landscape.

Dawn Mari, *Crystal,* 24 x 36, 6 color litho process

Wendy Maree, *The Aristocrat,* 60 x 40, acrylic on canvas

Pat Massié, *Santa Maria Degli Scalzi of Venice,* 30 x 20, oil

MATEESCU, PATRICIU (Sculptor, Ceramist)
58 Woodland Wy., Dayton, NJ 08810

Born: 1927 *Awards:* Gold Medal, International Ceramic Show, Faenza, Italy; Diplome d'Honneur, Biennial of Ceramics, Vallauris, France *Collections:* Musees Royaux d'Art et d'Histoire, Bruxelles; Musee de l'Ariana, Geneve *Exhibitions:* Galleria Maray, Englewood, NJ; Downey Museum of Art *Education:* Fine Arts Academy, Bucharest, Rumania

Before fleeing the political oppression of Socialist Rumania in 1979, he fled the artistic constraints of socio-realism by deconstructing and sectioning the sphere to form abstract geometric and organic pieces. He pushed the limits of accepted media by executing his monumental sculptures out of porcelain or polyester mixed with fiberglass, materials previously used only in industry. After he moved to the United States, his sculptures took on an increasingly organic aspect, which is complemented by the simplicity of their geometric spirit. For example, in his sculpture *Crazy Love Flowers*, which is exhibited at UCLA, huge, twisted slabs of polyester and fiberglass appear to grow out of the concrete and reach toward the sun. His investigation into the use of the sphere has changed in his most recent work. Instead of merely abstracting parts of the sphere, he seeks a more dramatic effect by destroying symmetry altogether. "From time to time, I play with unique pieces which are simple joy without mathematics."

MATENAER, MRS. TEGWIN A.
(Photographer, Graphic Artist)
P.O. Box 2538, Redding, CA 96099

Born: 1947 *Awards:* Best of Photography Annual, Photographer's Forum *Exhibitions:* Redding New Works Gallery, Redding; Shasta County Arts Council, Redding *Education:* Cal. State-Fresno

The influences of Monet and Van Gogh, and formal training in drawing, painting and Native American art history are the foundations for her interpretation of figurative and landscape themes. In photography, her use of light in the natural environment has been influenced by Ansel Adams; her form and content, by Eliot Porter and Ernest Haas. She uses graphic, photographic and mixed media to interpret the world around her, juxtaposing various images of issues confronting the environment and society, while following Fritz Scholder and William F. Reese in their encouragement: "go with your gesture!"

MATHERS, JAMES (Painter)
11316 Massachusetts Ave., Los Angeles, CA 90025

Born: 1964 *Collections:* Uwe Anderson, Hollywood *Exhibitions:* Turske and Whitney Gallery, Los Angeles; Studio Marconi, Milan *Dealer:* Turske and Whitney Gallery, Los Angeles

His oil paintings depict a relationship between the human organism and biological disaster. He uses the body as a metaphor for the conflict between man and the environment. Early work mimicked cells, human tissue and scenes from biology books. Later he brought a landscape feel to his large canvases of viscera, bone marrow and bodily processes. He paints impatiently on a large canvas laying on five or six levels of color. With tools he has made himself he gouges out figures and shapes. Strangely convoluted shapes emerge as figures only from a distance. His simplicity

of technique helps people to recognize the dialectic he portrays.

MATHEWS, ELDEN C. (Painter, Sculptor)
4337 E. Burns St., Tucson, AZ 85711

Collections: Univ. of Arizona Sports Center *Exhibitions:* Milwaukee Art Museum; Oshkosh Art Museum *Education:* U. of Wisconsin

At first, he allied abstract expressionism with a philosophical interest in Zen. He employed a free and open approach to all media, with influences from Rodin and Henry Moore. He now moves between the figure and abstraction, sculpting in wood, stone, steel and plastic. In his sculpture, he allows his medium to dictate the eventual form of the work. Likewise, the patterns on his white canvases often set the stage for his creative concepts. His painting media include encaustic, tissue paper, oil, acrylic and plastics. He has recently become interested in doing large commissioned sculptures for private and public places and has completed a large welded-steel commission for a gallery in Holland.

MATTHEWS, SUSAN (Painter)
2512 Regent St., Berkeley, CA 94704

Born: 1954 *Exhibitions:* Berkeley Art Center; Gallery 44, Oakland *Education:* UC-Berkeley; San Francisco State U.

Her work is in series format, involving subjects, such as vases and flowers, dogs and buildings. She works on a fairly large scale, using enamel and acrylic. She simplifies her subjects, using them symbolically to address emotional issues which cross all boundaries. Considering them all self-portraits, the paintings of the "Dog" and "Building" series are done from local Oakland subject matter. The dogs, painted in a style that is both emotional and awkward, refer to themes such as entrapment, rape and crossroads. In "Buildings," the subjects are stripped of their graffiti and decay and reduced to planes of light and dark; the claustrophobia of urban starkness contrasts with the infinity of the skies.

MATTSON, DONNA C. (Painter)
5443 S.E. 40th, Portland, OR 97202

Born: 1951 *Awards:* Outstanding Artist of the Year, Women's Century Club, Nampa, ID *Collections:* William Temple House, Portland; Captain Billy Bang's Pub, Portland *Exhibitions:* Northern Idaho College; Touring Exhibition, U. of Oregon Visual Arts Resources *Education:* U. of Idaho *Dealer:* White Bird Gallery, Cannon Beach, OR

She uses her extensive travel experiences as the basis for her realistic works, making several sketches as the idea for a painting takes shape. While traveling in Italy, she became familiar with the work of Gatuso, an influence still apparent in her work. She was trained in oil painting, but has recently switched to acrylics because of their quick-drying quality. This permits her to paint more quickly, adding movement and "sketchiness" to the completed works.

MAURICE, ANNE MULDER (Ceramist)
20 Eagle Rock Rd., Mill Valley, CA 94941

Born: 1951 *Awards:* 1st Place, David Lloyd Kreger Prize, Washington D.C.; 1st Place, William Barber Sculpture Prize, Washington D.C. *Exhibitions:* American Ceramic National, Downey Museum, Los Angeles; Elaine Potter Galler, San Francisco *Education:* Michigan State U.; George Washington U.

William E. Mayfield, *Dream Weaver,* 19 x 19, oil on canvas

Therese May, *Stripped-Fish,* 29 x 29, stitched fabric, acrylic

She has always had a fascination with kites and with the feelings of fluidity and soaring this form evokes. Her work expresses these emotions through the use of oriental imagery. All of her brightly colored wall sculptures are centered with a sun or moon motif, and emphasize movement, shape, color and pattern. They are created by incorporating fiber into the clay body, to achieve lightweight, thinly-rolled slabs. She then applies underglazes, stains and glazes to the structures. After firing, the pieces are assembled and mounted, using the wall as an additional design element. She selects her palette in terms of the meanings and feelings evoked and associated with various colors. The cultural and social awakening of China in the 1980s played a predominant role in her work. More recently, though, she has been recording her surroundings and the natural forces in her environment.

MAX, PETER (Painter, Printmaker)
37 W. 65th St., New York, NY 10023

Born: 1937 *Awards:* Official Artist, Constitutional Bicentennial Celebration; Grammy Award *Collections:* Museum of Modern Art, NYC; Corcoran Gallery, Washington, D.C. *Exhibitions:* M.H. De Young Memorial Museum, San Francisco; Newport Harbor Art Museum *Education:* Art Students League; Pratt Institute *Dealer:* Peter Max Enterprises, NYC; Stephen Gill Gallery, NYC

He was born in Berlin and spent his early years in China, South Africa, Israel and Paris before settling in the United States in 1953. During the mid-1960s, he gained recognition as the primary protagonist of psychedelic art. Combining random and improvisational imagery, he painted posters for airlines, television, libraries and musicians, and for moon shots, eventually branching out to product design for clocks, sheets, pillows and dinnerware. The exotic and eclectic images were referred to by some as composites of art nouveau, pop and op. Beginning in the the 1970s, his art became "super-optimistic, looking with great foresight towards a super-civilization, highly technologically oriented." His recent work, such as *The Better World*, reflects that optimism, combined with environmental and humanitarian concerns. Other recent work includes the "American Pop" series, which probes that movement and the artist's role in it, and "Ladies of the Eighties," studies and profiles of the female form. The newer work is in a looser, more painterly "neo- fauve" style.

MAXON, JOHN (Painter, Printmaker)
2080 Chanticleer Ave., Santa Cruz, CA 95062

Born: 1947 *Collections:* Koll Corporation, Livermore; Vesti Corporation, Boston *Exhibitions:* Erikson and Elins Fine Arts, San Francisco; Allrich Gallery, San Francisco; Young Gallery, San Jose *Education:* San Jose State U.; UC-Davis *Dealer:* Allen Harleen, San Francisco; Wayne Shoshana, Los Angeles

He creates abstract, panoramic landscapes, chiefly oil paintings and monotypes. Helen Frankenthaler has influenced his style, executed by employing washes and solvents to give shape to the forms, which are then worked by traditional methods of painting. His work is moving toward what he calls "implied realism," a domain between realism and abstraction wherein feeling, evoked through of color, takes precedence over content. He also plans to work his paintings into shaped aluminum forms in order to explore three-dimensionality.

MAY, THERESE (Fiber Artist)
651 N. 4th St., San Jose, CA 95112

Born: 1943 *Exhibitions:* Quilt National, American Craft Museum, NYC; San Jose Institute of Contemporary Art *Education:* U. of Wisconsin; San Jose State U. *Dealer:* Great American Gallery, Atlanta

She creates hand-sewn quilts, using pieces of fabric, appliques and acrylic paint. Trained as a painter, she took up quilting in the early 1960s, when her children were small. For many years, she alternated between quilting and painting, until she found a way to combine these two interests. She works from her own hand-drawn designs; her imagery includes geometric shapes, flowers and fantasy plants and animals. Once the quilt is assembled, she uses it as a canvas, applying finishing touches in acrylic paint. The expressionist influences of her early years are still evident in the quilts' intricate designs, patterns and imagery. She believes that the quilts themselves, as well as her role as a quiltmaker, present the viewer with a non-traditional view of the domestic arts. The quilts have been exhibited throughout the U.S. and are featured in a new book, *America's Glorious Quilts*, edited by Dennis Duke and Deborah Hardy.

MAYE, MARGARET (Painter)
318 Jessie Ave., Sacramento, CA 95838

Born: 1917 *Awards:* Best of Show, Northern California Artists; Special Purchase and Honorable Awards, City Gallery, Kobe, Japan *Exhibitions:* Himovitz Gallery, Sacramento; Judah Magnes Museum, Berkeley *Dealer:* Himovitz Gallery, Sacramento

Inspired to pursue a career in art by Placerville artist James Estey, she initially painted still lifes and large, realistic landscapes in acrylic. She then began experimenting with a more expressionistic style, progressing to pastels and developing a unique, figurative style in drawings on sandpaper. Many of these compositions are primitive and mythological, in a manner reminiscent of Chagall. She uses bright colors and creates dreamlike and, at times, haunting images. Figurative human and animal figures, some with elongated and curving limbs, occupy her canvases—floating, playing and dancing in story-like settings. In *Fish Story*, human characters cavort with ducks, dogs, fish and turtles on a yellow, blue and purple background. Her concerns range from feminism to spirituality in her exuberant exploration of human nature.

MAYFIELD, WILLIAM E. (Painter, Mixed Media Artist)
744 Niagara, San Francisco, CA 94112

Born: 1949 *Exhibitions:* Oconie County Club; Black Man's Art Gallery *Education:* San Francisco City College; San Francisco State U.

After formal training in graphic design, he was influenced by the styles of Salvador Dali and Dewey Crupler and later by the works of Davide and Frederic Remington. His fantastic/surrealistic style employs aggressive colors, mixing the rich fullnes of acrylics with the softer approach of oils. The rich skies and shadows of the work create an illusion of a three-dimensional dream, recalling much of Dali's work. His paintings combine studious research, sheer chance and subconscious impulses. Also a sculptor, his mixed-media pieces combine cast ceramics with wood.

Hiroki Morinoue, *Sky Piece,* 26 inches high, laminated masonite. Photographer: The Art Loft

Igor Medvedev/Mead, *Lydia,* life size, carrera marble

MAYNE, JOHN (Sculptor)
1630 26th Ave., San Francisco, CA 94122

Born: 1946 *Awards:* Exhibition Award, Art Commission Festival, San Francisco *Collections:* New Orleans Museum of Art *Exhibitions:* One Market Plaza, San Francisco; McKenna Auditorium, San Francisco *Education:* Louisiana State U.

After many years of painting the figure from life, he started applying objects to the canvas. Influenced by Rauschenberg, Larry Rivers, Haitian primitive artists and the voodoo tradition of New Orleans, he continued to experiment until these assemblages evolved into full, three-dimensional figures made from found objects. He uses objects and contemporary binding substances (latex, epoxy, etc.) to construct classically conceived figures. These narrative pieces are presented in installation form, usually accompanied by sound and light enhancement.

MAYOR, PETER (Sculptor)
3608 Maplewood Ave., Los Angeles, CA 90066

Born: 1948 *Collections:* UCLA Permanent Collection *Exhibitions:* Cross Creek Gallery, Malibu; L.A. O Zone *Education:* Brooks Art Institute, Santa Barbara

His early explorations in bronze show the influence of the naturalistic abstractions of Jean Arp and Henry Moore. In 1977, his work became more structural, reflecting his early concerns and training as an architect. Working with the manipulation of planes through space, he has created a language of form by which both formalistic and a personal iconography might be expressed. Using folded as well as interlocking planes of metal, he has created a body of work which deals with issues of balance, tension and interrelationships while exploring the act of creativity itself, creating not aesthetic objects but philosophic statements that "dance the dance of geometry."

MAZZELLI, ROSLYN (Sculptor)
1433 Van Dyke Ave., San Francisco, CA 94124

Born: 1941 *Awards:* Art in Public Buildings, California Arts Council *Collections:* Chapman College, Los Angeles; Bramlea Pacific Corp., Oakland *Exhibitions:* San Francisco Arts Commission Sculpture Festival *Education:* San Jose State U.

She works in aluminum, producing large, abstract sculptures for outdoor public installations. Grounded in natural forms, the works evoke a sense of movement and dance through the interplay of brightly colored auto enamels and open, delicate constructions. Described as star- or sun-like, the sculptures express an energetic relationship with the installation site and the viewer. Dynamic optical curves are created by using straight tubing, drawing on the influence of Naum Gabo's early works.

MEADOW, E.K. (Painter)
1734 Brockton Ave., No. 208, Los Angeles, CA 90025

Born: 1927 *Awards:* Hopwood Award for Poetry, U. of Michigan *Exhibitions:* Orlando Gallery, Sherman Oaks; Pence Gallery, Davis *Education:* U. of Arizona, Tucson *Dealer:* Orlando Gallery, Sherman Oaks

In the 1960s, she embraced figurative abstract expressionism while studying with disciples of Hans Hoffman at the University of Arizona. She moved to Northern California and the funk influence of Arneson, De Forest and Wylie there led her to experiment with metaphorical assemblages and to several years' involvement with highway imagery and sprayed automobile lacquers on steel. In the 1970s, she returned to oil on canvas and began pursuing the traditional and formal aspects of realistic landscape paintings. She moved to Southern California in the early 1980s, and her romantic photo-realist paintings feature local landscapes, especially as viewed from inside an automobile on the road.

MEDEIROS, DIANA R. (Painter, Draughtsperson)
164-A Linda St., San Francisco, CA 94110

Born: 1952 *Exhibitions:* Jeremy Stone Gallery, San Francisco; Gallery Sanchez

She was born in Germany and spent her childhood in several different cities in Europe, Japan and the U.S. Her oil paintings are completed in stages. She uses a jar with Japan Dryer mixed in turpentine to hasten the drying process; when the painting is completely finished and dry, she applies a varnish finish to preserve it. She also enjoys working with poster paint, on either thick paper or illustration board. For her drawing, she uses wax colored pencils because of the ease with which colors can be blended. Ebony pencil and various inks are also frequently used. Subject matter includes people, nature and images from her imagination. Recently, she has been experimenting with performance art staged in front of scenes she has painted.

MEDICI, NINA LADIMA (Painter)
900 S. Serrano Ave., #604, Los Angeles, CA 90006

Born: 1954 *Exhibitions:* Cotton Exchange Show, L.A.C.E. Exhibition, Los Angeles; Edwards of Ireland, La Jolla

Simplified form and clear color in her work reveal the influence of Paul Klee, the Impressionists, Oriental Art and Southwestern light. After extensive experimentation and research, acrylics became her medium of choice for their speed and versatility. Seeking a means of bridging the gap between the tangible (object) and intangible (experience), she studied surrealist and Renaissance art, including the writings of Magritte and Da Vinci. Using numerous thin layers of pure color and gel medium, she builds rich, subtle color upon a toned ground.

MEDVEDEV/MEAD, IGOR (Painter, Sculptor)
420 Roosevelt Way, San Francisco, CA 94114

Born: 1931 *Exhibitions:* Palace of the Legion of Honor, San Francisco; Hanson Gallery, La Jolla *Dealer:* Hanson Gallery, Mill Valley

He was in Europe, and his study there led to an extensive knowledge of traditional painting and sculpting techniques. He works in many media. His original technique of "dimensional art" used in his "Anima" series involves encasing a low relief behind a transparent screen and then painting in the background to visually fuse the two planes. The resulting illusion of three-dimensionality in two dimensions creates the mysterious effect of something precious partially obscured behind a veil. Thus he expressed the feminine aspects of his own soul, or "anima". Later paintings utilize a technique originally developed by Titian and the Flemish painters of the 16th century. An underpainting is made with water-based casein paint, then successive layers of oil glaze and casein are applied. The images themselves are "lyrical" in their atmosphere of space and tranquillity and represent an

E.K. Meadow, *Camper-back on Little Santa Monica Blvd.,* 36 x 54, oil on canvas. Courtesy: Orlando Gallery. Photographer: Susan Einstein

Lani McCoy, *Hat for All Seasons,* 16 x 20, photography

Martin Mondrus, *Waterfall,* 12 x 18 charcoal

831

inner landscape more than any specific locale. The recent "Costa del Sol" collection chronicles his impressions of southern Spain in this way, with alternate washes of translucent and opaque watercolor and gouache in geometric patterns of pure color contrasts.

MEDWEDEFF, JULIE (Painter)
400 S. Hauser, #6K, Los Angeles, CA 90036

Born: 1959 *Exhibitions:* Fine Arts Gallery, U. of California, Irvine; Burbank Creative Arts Center *Education:* UC-Irvine; Santa Ana College

The issues of fear, violence towards women and the materialistic superficiality of suburban American culture underlie her mixed-media paintings and works on paper. In *Woman and Eagle*, for example, a giant eagle and devilish woman in a blue dress face the viewer. Both look dazed, rather than triumphant, as we are accustomed to seeing them portrayed in patriotic, symbolic contexts. In contrast to these stereotypical figures, a smaller, unclothed male figure serves as a symbol of innocence. *Red Painting with Two Women*, an acrylic collage on canvas that is built up from a ground of red and green Christmas wrapping, features two women: transparent, non-corporeal, with stiff gestures and eyes that are either closed or blocked off, they have no contact with one another or the environment. By dealing with the surface commonalties of middle class, suburban life, she exposes the underlying mores, values and peculiarities. This literal approach, with its irony, provides some comic relief to what might otherwise be only grim.

MEISTRICH, DONNA (Multimedia Artist)
P.O. Box 4433, San Rafael, CA 94913

Born: 1954 *Exhibitions:* Sonoma Arts Gallery, San Francisco; Freehand Gallery, Los Angeles *Education:* Academy of Art, San Francisco

She has explored the possibilities of acrylics, watercolor, oils, photography and sculpture, in a search for a medium which allows her the greatest amount of emotional expression. Her work, in all media, is known for its gentle humor. In one sculpture, for example, people stand on each others' shoulders stretched toward a box just slightly out of reach. Made of Fimo, much of her jewelry features happy, smiling faces with springs and antique glass jewels. She enjoys working with bright, vibrant colors. In addition, she has been planning a short film, utilizing claymation—a technique in which clay figures are posed, filmed, then reposed in a way which simulates real movement.

MELNICK, MYRON J. (Sculptor)
1366 Garfield St., #601, Denver, CO 80206

Born: 1953 *Collections:* Pepsi Cola International, NYC *Exhibitions:* Shoshana Wayne Gallery, Los Angeles; Editions Limited, San Francisco *Education:* U. of Colorado, Boulder; U. of Minnesota, Minneapolis

He is an abstract visual artist, whose large and visually complex work reveals a concern with architecture, archaeology and modern art. He began working in clay and explored that medium for over a decade. Developing a fascination with painting, he used pigments on large clay surfaces. As this work grew, he found clay confining; he sought the more versatile material he eventually found in paper. He colors his cast paper sculptures with the same dry pigments he used on clay, applying them directly to the paper's surface, giving the work the appearance of stone, peeling paint or archaeological artifacts. He employs numerous textures

and utilizes industrial objects to achieve a rich relief surface in these paper works. He recently published several monoprint editions centered on the same themes.

MELTZER, HAL (Painter)
1308 Factory Place, 2A, Los Angeles, CA 90013

Born: 1954 *Collections:* Bank of America, San Francisco; Sparkasse, West Berlin *Exhibitions:* Fun Gallery West, San Francisco; Berlin Museum *Education:* Stanford University; Otis Parsons Art Institute

Memories from early childhood of Disney and Dali can be seen as elements that have evolved in his work. Influenced by Pollock, Sam Francis, the surreal landscapes of Yves Tanguy and automatism, his early works offer the combined effect of automatic and abstract surreal landscapes. Leaving California for New York, his experience of the pop surrealism at the Fun Gallery and Kenny Scharf provided yet another forum for surrealist work. After 1983, Berlin became his second home. For the past four years, he has been working on "The Berlin Paintings," a series of landscapes about life in Berlin today, contrasted with the often bleak and colorless aesthetic of East Berlin and behind the Iron Curtain in general. His paintings are characterized by fluorescent acrylics, a great deal of line work in India ink and an occasional use of gold leaf.

MENDENHALL, JACK (Painter)
5824 Florence Terrace, Oakland, CA 94611

Born: 1937 *Awards:* Purchase Award, Butler Institute of American Art *Collections:* Oakland Museum; University Art Museum, Berkeley *Exhibitions:* Oakland Museum; O.K. Harris Gallery, NYC *Education:* California College of Arts and Crafts *Dealer:* O.K. Harris Gallery, NYC

A realist painter working in both oil and watercolor, he utilizes a refined brush technique to capture the world of the contemporary nouveau riche that comprises the subject matter of his paintings. Using images from popular magazines, and occasionally professional models, he paints the opulent interiors that are the trademark of his work. The result is a reflection of the American fantasy rendered in meticulously realistic style. Paintings of mirror-clad interiors tend toward the abstract, as the complexities of reflected realities become blurred upon the canvas. In these works, formal concerns are perceived under the rubric of realism. Influences include 17th-century genre paintings, pop art and minimalism, as well as such artists as Vermeer, Ingres, Matisse, Diebenkorn, Mondrian and Thiebaud.

MEO, YVONNE COLE (Painter, Sculptor)
P.O. Box 6146, Altadena, CA 91001

Born: 1928 *Awards:* James D. Parks Special Award, National Conference of Artists *Collections:* Archives, Oakland Museum; Museum of African-American Art, Los Angeles *Exhibitions:* Museum of Science and Industry, Los Angeles; Arroyo Gallery, Los Angeles *Education:* Cal. State-Los Angeles; UCLA; Union Institute, Cincinnati

Her profound interest in ecology and in the psychological, philosophical and creative realms of human activity has been the inspiration for her work. She began interpreting images of space travel in oils on canvas and in assemblages and mixed-media pieces, exploring themes of space and psychology. Her recent works have progressed from cosmic paintings in which

Evid Moore, *Ojo de Dios,* 22 x 17, acrylic on paper

Yvonne Cole Meo, *Barren Devastation (Apocalyptic Phase),*
40 x 30, oil on canvas

brilliant colors give the illusion of the explosive forces in universe to work concerned with the preservation of the Earth's ecology. The images emerge from her deep feelings and respect for the Baobab Tree and its meaning and value in its native Africa. The branches of the Baobab appear anthropomorphic and digital, and thus she combines images of the human body with the tree's form to produce imagery recalling the apocalyptic and transfromative phases of the Baobab's Life Cycle.

MERCHANT, LAURENT (Ceramist)
240 2nd St. E., Sonoma, CA 95476

Born: 1958 Exhibitions: San Francisco Arts Commission; Sonoma Arts Guild Dealer: Kersting Gallery, Sausalito

In 1973, he began his training as an apprentice under the leading French ceramists Pierre Mestre and Nanou La Chiez-Rey. His early influences included traditional French pottery and Japanese and Korean porcelains. After moving to Los Angeles in 1976, he began experimenting with large-scale ceramic sculpture. In 1980, he opened his own studio in Sonoma. During the last two years, he has combined his interest in large-scale ceramics with color, and he is now producing "paintings urns." At first, these were hard-edged, designed works with motifs reminiscent of art deco and art nouveau. Recently they have been more spontaneous, textured and random. Using underglazes, blending and multiple firings, he gives the pieces depth and a sense of age.

MEREDITH, ANN (Photographer)
460 40th St., Oakland, CA 94609

Born: 1948 Awards: 1st Prize, Alameda County Fine Arts Exhibition; Finalist, Cable Car Awards Collections: Hercules Corporation, Berkeley; U. of California, Berkeley Exhibitions: Somar Gallery, San Francisco; California History Center and Foundation, Cupertino Education: UC- Berkeley; California College of Arts and Crafts

Known internationally for her black-and-white portraits, she has chronicled every aspect of women's culture in photography and oral history for the last seventeen years. Her collections reveal moments of transition and affirmation, the obstacles perpetuated and denied by mainstream male culture, the silent battles and personal victories shared by women. Don't Call Me Honey recognizes the sacrifices working women must make and the perseverance they must demonstrate daily in both traditional and non-traditional jobs. Dykes and Their Dogs presents lesbians from a viewpoint free of insulting generalizations. By displaying their unique definition while noting their similarities to everyone else, she invites the viewer into their individual realities. Her most recent project depicts the strength with which the "hidden population" of the AIDS epidemic lives with the disease, alone, on the street or at home with family and friends. The formal use of large-scale images bordered in black helps to convey the emotional drama experienced by these women.

MERIANS, HANNA (Painting)
319 Fourth St., Sausalito, CA 94965

Born: 1925 Collections: Bibliotheque National, Paris; Magnes Museum, Berkeley Exhibitions: American Zephyr Gallery, San Francisco; Palos Verdes Art Cen-

ter, Palos Verdes Education: San Francisco Art Institute

She has worked with printmakers in Switzerland, painted the landscapes and people of Africa and studied batik with native masters in Indonesia. Much of her present work consists of semi-abstract, highly imaginative pen-and-ink drawings and watercolors reminiscent of Chagall, with whom she shares a common ethnic and cultural heritage. She is also developing a series of completely abstract three-dimensional constructions using prints on heavy, handmade paper, which she shapes and combines with other materials. These works are frequently inspired by the movement of dancers, birds, water, clouds and other natural forms.

MERJANIAN, GRACE (Painter)
18701 Deodar St., Fountain Valley, CA 92708

Born: 1924 Awards: Artist of the Year 1983 & 1984 Exhibitions: Mariners Gallery, Dana Point; Costa Mesa Art Gallery, Santa Ana Education: San Bernardino Valley College

After raising a family, she took an oil painting class in 1974. Her love for painting grew as she painted and she found herself in several classes a week. After developing a realistic style using a glaze technique, she experimented with watercolor and gouache, applying some of her oil techniques to the newer media as well. First splashing on transparent watercolors, then putting darks on the paper, she produces bright vibrant color in a realistic style, adding transparent watercolor as a glaze. Her attraction to watercolor lies in part in the accidental forms that are created as she splashes the paint on, which she can then follow and develop. Her work continues to be realistic, with the creation of a sense of depth one of her fundamental fascinations. Her landscapes are executed in watercolor and gouache; for her floral images, she returns to oil.

MERKEN, BETTY (Painter)
900 N. Citrus Ave., Los Angeles, CA 90038

Born: 1947 Collections: Drexel Burnham Lambert, Beverly Hills; ANA Hotel, Tokyo Exhibitions: Kouros Gallery, NYC; Orange County Center For Contemporary Art, Santa Ana Education: U. of Washington, Seattle Dealer: Ruth Bachofner Gallery, Santa Monica

A former Seattle artist and textile designer, she relocated in Los Angeles in the early 1980s, to develop her career as a painter, full time. Always interested in the lyrical and dynamic aspects of line, color and pattern, her work expresses a deep emotionality, and reflects an articulate involvement with intuition and perception. She considers herself a romantic artist, and her large oil on canvas paintings—with their evocative linear elements and patterns, filtering through color field areas—resonate with poetic overtones.

MERRILL, TODD (Photographer)
1029 Carolina St., San Francisco, CA 94107

Born: 1956 Awards: Award of Excellence, California Works, California State Fair; Visiting Artist, East Germany Collections: Bibliotheque Nationale, Paris; Fotografie Forum, Frankfurt Exhibitions: Studio 666, Paris; Fotografic Centrum, Stockholm Education: San Francisco Art Institute Dealer: Carol-Marc Lauvriller, Paris

His early work was an attempt to describe individuals with archetypal symbolism following the prototypes of C.G. Jung. Painted backdrops were used, with subjects

L. Merchant, *Family Portrait,* biological-ceramic.
Courtesy: Kersting Gallery

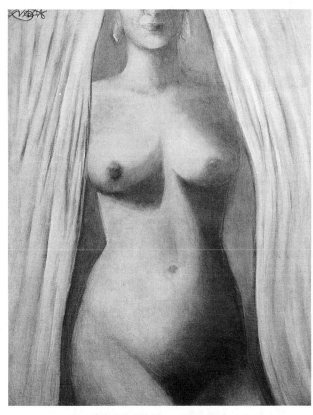

Nina Medici, *Window,* 24 x 30, acrylic

integrated into the picture and sometimes painted themselves. As the "politics of communication" became less clear to him because of the seeming ambiguity of a strictly symbolic language, photographic realism became more critical to the works, and he began to place greater emphasis on description. He substituted real life objects for the previous archetypal signs, creating a forum for investigating culture (especially American) and people based on the type of objects they acquire and how they are arranged. All his work is done in color with an 8 x 10 view camera.

MESQUITA, ROSALYN E. (Painter, Mixed Media Artist)
13426 Vanowen, Van Nuys, CA 91405

Born: 1945 *Awards:* Ford Foundation; UC-Irvine Honorium Arts Award *Collections:* State of New Mexico *Exhibitions:* Art Store, Los Angeles; Cal. State-Northridge *Education:* UC-Irvine *Dealer:* Alan Shaw, NYC

Her work primarily concerns surfaces and the tactile sensation a particular texture can generate. First influenced the Process Art of Dorotea Rockburn, she paints autonomous topographical surfaces in the form of landscapes and other geological features. She applies thin layers of acrylic and spray paint, creating a transparent effect. Her color key is low, similar to that found in nature. She generally chooses the rectangular format for its suggestion of horizontal movement, and the entire surrounding edge of the work is somewhat irregular, complementing the textural qualities of the organic surface in the interior space.

METZGER, MILES (Sculptor)
P.O. Box 444, Angels Camp, CA 95222

Born: 1950 *Awards:* Mayors Purchase Award, Beverly Hills Affair in the Garden *Exhibitions:* Maui Marine Art Expo; Miles Metzger Fine Arts Gallery *Education:* Denver U.; Instituto Del Arte, San Miguil de Allende, Mexico

In 1974, he began working with steatite (soap stone). Early pieces in the medium were smaller limited-edition, hand-carved sculptures. After co-inventing the "klinemetz" saw, he was able to quarry monument-sized stones. His sculpture progressed to large, one-of-a-kind pieces, depicting various forms of marine and wildlife, as well as figurative representational works. He has recently been working on a series of stone sculptures, in which human and animal forms are integrated.

METZLER, DOUGLAS (Painter)
10829 Westminster Ave., Los Angeles, CA 90034

Born: 1947 *Awards:* Award of Merit, Bibliotheque Nationale, Paris *Collections:* Security Pacific Bank, Los Angeles *Exhibitions:* Rosamond Felson Gallery, Los Angeles; Gallery at the Plaza, Los Angeles *Education:* School of Visual Arts, NYC

For ten years he explored the physical problem of giving energy to photographs. Influenced by Newman, Marden and Kelly, he began using acrylics to paint on his own photographs in a figure ground style: the photograph being the figure and the color-field being the ground. Influenced largely by pre-perspective 14th Century European painting, he adhered these painted photographs to wood panels and framed them directly within the context of the work. He has since added perspective to his figures, while leaving a flat atmospheric ground. His subjects are narrative; he paints in acrylic; and he frames his mystical social statements in post-lintel wood.

MEYER, DEANNIE (Painter)
1731 Gregory Way, Bremerton, WA 98310

Born: 1938 *Awards:* Seattle Gold Key Award *Exhibitions:* North Valley Art League, Redding; Jane Belden's Gallery, Weaverville

After her formal training, she became interested in portrait work and character studies. Her friend and mentor, the late Frank Adams, encouraged her further study and research in a semi-realistic, semi-impressionist technique. She has experimented on various types of stretched materials (from cotton canvas to stretched silk) and with various techniques (from drybrush to wet-on-wet applications in oil, watercolor and pastels). Recently, she has been working in a photo-realistic style, using a drybrush technique in oil on stretched silk. Painting from a limited palette of soft colors, she has been working on portraits and floral still lifes.

MEYER, ELMER F. (Painter)
5929 Van Keppel Rd., Forestville, CA 95436

Born: 1910 *Awards:* Society of Western Artists; Santa Rosa Art Guild *Exhibitions:* American Watercolor Society, NYC; Southwestern Watercolor Society *Collections:* Santa Rosa City Hall *Education:* California School of Fine Arts *Dealer:* Branscomb Gallery, Bodega Bay

He has worked as a graphic artist, art director and lithographer for forty-two years, but he has always separated his commercial expertise from his development as a fine artist. Painting outdoors in Northern California offers him rich scenic material for his keen perception. While observing nature, he does not copy but rather rearranges the given to arrive at more forceful pictorial concepts. Human figures are drawn directly from life and are integrated into the landscape in order to enhance his statement. He studied privately with Millard Sheets and is the author of the book, *Watercolor Painting on Location.*

MEZIAT, CARLOS KOELER (Painter, Performance Artist)
6823 Romaine Dr., Los Angeles, CA 90038

Born: 1954 *Exhibitions:* Hraeus Studio/Gallery, Los Angeles; Venice Biennale *Dealer:* Hraeus Studio/Gallery, Los Angeles

His works range from small figurative sculptures to huge canvases and large installations of found and other industrial-oriented objects. He began his career in Rio de Janeiro as a dancer and choreographer of classical ballet and opera. He also worked in contemporary dance, film and video before coming to Los Angeles.

MICHEL, MARGARET (Sculptor)
640 Park Court, Santa Clara, CA 95050

Born: 1955 *Exhibitions:* Katia Lacoste Gallery, San Jose; Rosecrucian Museum, San Jose *Education:* Ecole du Louvre, Paris

Departing from an academic background in art, she incorporates elements from diverse art traditions: the suggestive quality of Chinese brush painting, the physical attitudes of Indian sculpture, the eroded fragmentation of Greek classical bronzes and the figure study photographs of Edward Muybridge. She delves into the interior of the form, taking into account the

Jeffry Mann, *Rocking Chair K.6,* 24 x 46 x 46, walnut, ebony, maple, leather. Courtesy: Joanne Lyon Gallery, Inc., Aspen, CO

Grace Merjanian, *Raccoon Territory,* 30 x 21, watercolor and gouache

abstract quality of the shapes, convex and concave, in relation to the negative space that surrounds them. The fragmented figures are presented in a space that frames the form and invites viewers to contemplate the figures' references to inner psychological states.

MICKELSEN, STEVEN (Sculptor)
9005 Balsa St., Rancho Cucamonga, CA 91730

Born: 1943 *Exhibitions:* Trails West Gallery, Laguna Beach; Upland Wings, Upland *Education:* Cal. State-Long Beach

Influenced by the renaissance sculptors Lorenzo Ghiberti and Michelangelo and the western sculptors Gutzon, Solon, Lincoln Borglum and James Earle Fraser, he attempts to achieve perfection in the sculptural representation of horses. A native of Utah he spent his youth on trail rides and roundups. Western themes dominate his work. In graduate school, he sculpted a 12-foot equestrian statue and diorama. His present work is a series of small bronze pieces on the famous cowboys, the Wild Bunch. He continues to work on the representation of the surface quality and the anatomy of the horse.

MIHAYLOVICH, ALEXANDER (Painter)
1235 Brockton Ave., #304, W. Los Angeles, CA 90025

Born: 1958 *Awards:* American Bicentennial World Youth Awards Exhibition *Exhibitions:* Museum of Science & Industry, Los Angeles; Griffith Park Observatory, Los Angeles; Jugoart Gallery, Belgrade *Education:* Santa Monica City College *Dealer:* Earl McGrath, Gallery 454, W. Hollywood

A self-taught painter, he created images of the moon, planets and stars in his early work. This changed when he visited several archaeological sites in Yugoslavia during the late 1970s and early 1980s. He was intensely affected by the survival of the human spirit through works of art that had been buried for centuries. He began to ponder the fate of individual artistic expression and spirituality in the face of modern, high-tech society. These concerns have led him to his works on carefully prepared surfaces of wood, canvas and tin. He uses acyrlics and oil glazes to create images of classical and Renaissance sculpture with architectural elements placed in lush settings. These realistic paintings appear to be archaeological artifacts themselves, with depictions of cracked walls and ghostly human figures in wooden and metal frames, adorned with Latin phrases in classical characters. The frame materials serve as abstract representations of the harsh realities of modern life.

MIKHAILAS, MARIA (Painter, Sulptor)
1219 7th Ave., San Francisco, CA 94122

Born: 1949 *Exhibitions:* Rosecrucian Museum, San Jose; San Francisco Arts Commission Gallery *Dealer:* Radiance Productions, San Francisco

The works of this Bay Area oil painter are illuminated by a flowing, emotional use of color. She pours, feathers and strokes paint onto primed, untempered masonite, bringing to the work a fluidity and mystery by contrasting rich, luminescent color with deep, oceanic darkness. She achieves the color by applying multiple layers of washes and glazes. Her images of feminine symbols and women are increasingly realistic. Having recently studied sculpture with Harriet Moore, she has taken her incandescently-lit pieces into three dimensions, creating painted color assemblages.

Turner, Leonardo da Vinci, William Blake and Albert Ryder have had the most influence on her recent work.

MILLER, ALICE K. (Painter, Paper Sculptor)
2065 Edinburg Ave., Cardiff, CA 92007

Born: 1958 *Dealer:* Art Works, San Diego

Design is an important element in both her figurative and abstract work. Shapes, reflections and negative spaces characterize her tightly rendered watercolors of landscapes, vegetables or still lifes. Her landscape-influenced abstractions are freely painted and spontaneous. She paints these multimedia works on linen, silk, canvas or rice paper and uses such materials as string, glitter, iridescents and gold leaf to create rich textures and elaborate designs of. Her current abstracts are growing more detailed and more design oriented. She also spends a great deal of time exploring paper sculpture using a variety of unusual materials to create greater depth and alluring textures. She has had formal training in graphic design and fine art.

MILLER, DANIEL J. (Sculptor)
3081 La Jolla St., #E, Anaheim, CA 92806

Born: 1947 *Awards:* California Art in Public Places Competition *Exhibitions:* Design Center of Los Angeles; Orange County Center for Contemporary Art *Education:* Cal. State-Fullerton *Dealer:* James Lodge, Irvine

His work consists of architectural-sized metal sculptures fabricated from stainless steel, aluminum or occasionally other media. Using standard fabrication techniques, he takes sheets of metal and cuts, bends and then welds them into the desired form. He denies any political or social comment in his work, doing "each piece simply for the beauty of the form itself." *Twist and Slide,* a playfully bent 14-foot-long metal ribbon, and *My Bird in Space,* a delicately curved, 20-foot-tall free-standing sculpture in stainless steel, typify his work. He has recently been working on smaller abstract pieces using stainless steel and stone and composing an edition of small work between large commissions. He serves on several public art committees and is dedicated to expanding the opportunities for public art displays.

MILLER, JUDITH (Painter)
c/o Hank Baum Gallery, P.O. Box 26689, San Francisco, CA 94126

Born: 1939 *Exhibitions:* Seipp Gallery, Palo Alto; Pacific Grove Art Center *Education:* San Jose State U.; San Francisco Art Institute *Dealer:* Hank Baum Gallery, San Francisco

She has led a varied life, from her childhood on a cattle ranch to the life of a young housewife and mother in the Silicon Valley. Her media include oil on canvas, drawings in mixed media and monotypes. She creates intuitively by layering, scraping, working and playing until the combined elements take on their final form. In monotypes, she uses different viscosities of ink and transfer drawings to build layers of form, color and space. The content of her work is non-linear and non-narrative, an articulation of the dialectic between an industrial economy and an information economy, between spiritual re-awakening and hyper-materialism, between global economics and political nationalism, and between the hope for peace and the threat of imminent destruction.

Charlene Modena, *Totem—Sea Rafts,* 14 x 14 x 10, bird quills, mixed media, handmade paper, bronze.
Photographer: Lee Fatheree

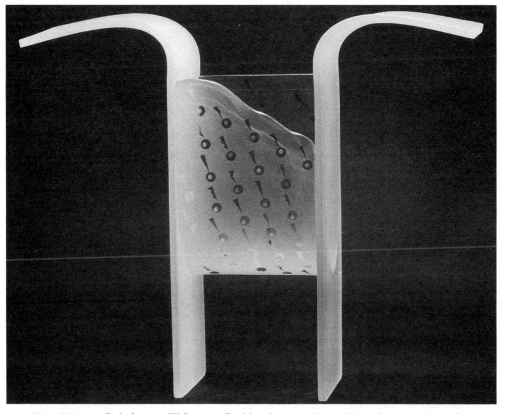

Babs Miyano, *Raindancers Welcome,* 17 x 22 x 6, slumped, sandblasted glass construction

MILLER, KAY (Painter)
1255 18th St., #2, Boulder, CO 80302

Born: 1946 *Awards:* NEA *Collections:* New Museum of Contemporary Art, NYC; U. of Iowa *Exhibitions:* Corcoran Biennial of American Painting, Washington DC; Gorman Museum, UC-Davis *Education:* U. of Houston; U. of Texas *Dealers:* Foxley/Leach Gallery, Washington, DC; Cydney Payton Gallery, Denver

She has always been interested in instilling spirit into the images of her work. Her painting is a metaphorical journey and a process of self-understanding and her work is replete with symbols of the metaphysics of existence. She applies paint thickly, building up forms in relief that hover between the visual and the tactile, referring to the physical while pointing to the spiritual.

MILLER, MARCIA (Printmaker)
16930 Sheldon Rd., Los Gatos, CA 95030

Born: 1950 *Awards:* Annual Bay Area Woman's Graphic Art Competition *Exhibitions:* Print San Jose Traveling Exhibitions; Citadel Print Center *Education:* Purdue U. *Dealer:* Janet Greenly, Saratoga

Her floral etchings have been influenced by Chinese landscape artists' concepts of space and beauty. She discovered etching after training in painting and drawing. When she moved to California from the Midwest, she began working with color. She uses from one to eleven plates to make images of agapanthus, irises, geraniums and water lilies. She frequently wipes the image intaglio, à la poupée. In addition, she stencils and rolls additional applications of color on the surface of the plates before arranging them on the press bed with additional collagraph paper plates. Her crisp images emerge as embossed paper molds of her plates. The white of the paper acts as an active space and contrasts with her rich aquatints and raised color lines.

MILLER, MELINDA (Painter)
4901 Tara Terrace, Culver City, CA 90250

Born: 1944 *Exhibitions:* Art Space, Los Angeles; Whittier College

She works in oils, and cites Matisse, de Kooning and Pollock as her major influences. In the tradition of abstract expressionism, the work is void of concrete images, the impact generated instead via monochromatic color fields accented by controlled paint incidents, or areas of heavily impastoed paint with lines drawn through. She says of the work: "Each painting is a carefully formed world of its own, consisting of color and line interactions and incidents of paint handling, which create an optical richness and emotional content."

MILLER, WENDY FRANKLUND (Painter, Mixed Media Artist)
W. 204 Euclid, Spokane, WA 99205

Born: 1943 *Collections:* Illinois Bell, Chicago; Washington Trust Bank, Spokane *Exhibitions:* Mendecino Art Center; Gallery II, Washington State U., Pullman, WA *Education:* Eastern Washington U.; Banff Center, Alberta, Canada *Dealer:* Miriam Perlman, Chicago

During the 1960s and 1970s, she worked primarily with oils and acrylics in both a figurative and non-figurative vein, until she began making images in other media—mainly dyed, handmade paper pulp. Since the early 1980s, her large pieces of handmade paper have been primarily abstract, as she explores themes that range from personal to social. Recently, the series "Witness" probes the plight of the aged in an increasingly figurative style. Another development is the inclusion of handmade paper, wood and plexiglas sculptures in her installations. Influenced by her background as a painter, her use of color is emotional and symbolic, in intense magentas, yellows and blues.

MILLER-KUSZ, BETSIE (Painter, Muralist)
33 Gladys St., San Francisco, CA 94110

Born: 1945 *Awards:* Grant, California Arts Council *Collections:* Hastings College of Law Library, San Francisco *Exhibitions:* Sociedad Mexicana de Artes Plasticas, Mexico City; Cowell Gallery, San Francisco *Education:* Purdue U. *Dealer:* Jeff Nathanson, San Francisco

Her early works were strongly influenced by the hard-edged geometric paintings of the 1960s in NYC. After moving to San Francisco her forms became progressively looser, the space of her paintings more expansive. Her abstract works of the late 1970s and early 1980s used undulating elements moving into great pictorial space. After repeated exposure to the cultures, light and structure of Mexican art, her forms evolved into figures which she arranged in a compositional layout of intersecting planes. She works on an unprimed canvas and uses a very active brushstroke. She has also used shaped canvases on interlocking planes to create the illusion of three dimensions against the reality of two dimensions.

MILLS, JUDITH (Painter, Mixed Media Artist)
822 Hartzell St., Pacific Palisades, CA 90272

Born: 1938 *Exhibitions:* Los Angeles County Art Museum Rental Gallery; Long Beach Art Association

Primarily self-taught, she has been drawn to the mythological and primitive in art as a result of her extensive travels in Mexico and the Southwest. Her acrylic on paper works were influenced by the use of color in the works of Picasso and Diego Rivera. She also works in mixed media and has created a series of bamboo spirit catchers. Influenced by Klee, she paints with oil and India ink on wood.

MILTENBERGER, CHARLES (Painter)
P.O. Box 1548, Capitola, CA 95010

Born: 1950 *Awards:* Winner, American Artist National Competition; 1st Prize, Blatch Museum of Fine Arts, Melbourne, FL *Exhibitions:* Santa Cruz Picture Framing and Gallery; Marianne Partlow Gallery, Olympia, WA *Education:* California State U., Northridge *Dealer:* Marianne Partlow Gallery, Olympia, WA

His early realistic style was influenced by the works of the Old Masters. After moving to California, his palette lightened, and he renewed an interest in color. He prepares ninety percent of his own canvases, treating raw canvas with rabbit skin glue and lead primer. He has preferred streaky gray tempera imprimatur with blue, violet, orange and a range of light colors to black or earth tones. He considers himself a photo-realist and works from photographs of landscapes, family members and friends.

MINER, ALISON (Painter)
1280 Temple Terrace, Laguna Beach, CA 92651

Born: 1949 *Exhibitions:* Laguna Beach Festival of Art; Glaeria Uno, Puerto Vallarta, Mexico *Dealer:* Knowles Gallery, Los Angeles

William Minschew, *Stassis/Dynamics,* 26 x 23 x 6, bronze, marble.
Photograph: Richard and Juanita Delaney

Azad Moore, *Day is Done for the Cowboy,* 18 x 24, oil on canvas

Her paintings in oil and acrylic feature the landscapes and people of Mexico, Spain and Italy, all seen through the mind's eye. Her naive, primitive style is reminiscent of Rousseau and Goya. Balancing realistic and fantastic images, she paints in various shades of blue, often decorating her work with gold leaf and silvery sprinkles. She depicts the world as a wonderfully alive matrix, from which life evolves into diverse and complex forms.

MINICK, ROGER (Photographer)
732 Kentucky St., Vallejo, CA 94590

Born: 1944 *Awards:* Guggenheim Fellowship; NEA Grant *Collections:* Museum of Modern Art, NYC; San Francisco Museum of Modern Art *Exhibitions:* Los Angeles County Museum of Art; Centre Georges Pompidou, Paris *Education:* UC-Berkeley

His photography is characterized by the exploration of the relationship between man and the environment and by a concentration on American culture. He has toured the United States, making series of photographs of the inhabitants of each region of the country—visitors to the U.S. National Parks, immigrant workers, patrons of Southern California shopping malls. He seeks to capture with precision and character the flavor of the nation's diverse regions in photographs that are rich in color and detail. He has also created a series of urban landscapes taken from a moving automobile in Southern California.

MINSCHEW, WILLIAM E. (Painter, Sculptor)
13083 Tollhouse Rd., Clovis, CA 93612

Born: 1937 *Awards:* Fulbright Scholarship, Rome; National Sculpture Award, NEA *Collections:* Dunavant Corporation; Cal. State-Fresno *Exhibitions:* Chancellor's Distiguished Artists, California State University; Zantman Gallery, Palm Desert *Education:* U. of North Carolina *Dealer:* Zantman Gallery, Palm Desert

The underlying concepts of his works are architectonic, reflecting his undergraduate training in architecture. Throughout his career he has explored and integrated various media, such as cement and foam core, ceramic clay, stainless steel and acrylic plastic and marble and bronze. He has recently been exploring a system of cement over foam core to create large-scale works with low weight. He continuously focuses on containing potential energy masses in the path of their direction, preserving the moment between static and kinetic, as in his recent series of marble and bronze pieces. Forms frozen at the apex of angles or the rim of containers reveal a classical grounding and refer directly and formally to architectural themes. Works also include lacquered bronze castings from computer-generated map surfaces, and large-scale sculpture for architecture. His efforts are being expanded by a study of Japanese techniques.

MINZA, LINDA M. (Sculptor)
P.O. Box 494, Rough & Ready, CA 95975

Born: 1954 *Awards:* Honorable Mention, Lake County Fair; Honorable Mention, California State Fair *Exhibitions:* Jay Twigg Law Office, Upper Lake; Books of Harmony, Nevada City

Much of her inspiration comes from science fiction and the art of special effects experts; but she primarily draws upon the details offered in nature. Moving around the country, collecting seeds, pits and rocks, she glues them onto a framework, to which she will also inlay precious and semi-precious rocks and stones. Wood is carved; gold in its natural forms, crystals or diamonds are inset. *Punk Dragon*, a dragon created from such materials, won Honorable Mention at the Lake County Fair in 1975. At this point, she takes inspiration from all the people who bring her treasures they find, hoping they'll see them in her next project.

MISKULIN, JAN (Painter)
1441 Wentworth Ave., Sacramento, CA 95822

Born: 1928 *Awards:* 1st Award & Gold Medal, California State Fair; Grumbacher Award *Collections:* Fi-Tech Corporation; 1st Western Title Insurance Co. *Exhibitions:* Depot Gallery, Napa Valley, Yountville; Garden Silks Gallery, Sacramento *Education:* Stanford U.; U. of Guadalajara *Dealer:* Garden Silks Gallery, Sacramento

Influenced by oriental calligraphy at an early age, she studied sumi brushwork with Chiura Obata at Berkeley. She admires Maurice Logan of the California School of Watercolor, and has been drawn throughout her entire career to the looseness and fluidity of the medium. She is primarily a landscape artist, and the vignette-style watercolor work of Andrew Wyeth inspired her to master the use of white paper and negative space. This quality has become a trademark in her paintings, along with meaningful brushwork and a strong contrast of values. Her works emphasize interpretive feelings and spiritual vitality.

MISRACH, RICHARD (Photographer)
1420 45th St., Emeryville, CA 94608

Born: 1949 *Awards:* Guggenheim Fellowship; NEA Fellowship *Collections:* Museum of Modern Art, NYC; Metropolitan Museum of Art, NYC *Exhibitions:* University Art Museum, Berkeley; Oakland Museum *Education:* UC-Berkeley *Dealer:* Fotomann, Inc., NYC

His series "Scenes from the American Desert," years in the making, concerns the desert as place and metaphor. The effect of human presence in the desert is an important part of his imagery. He captures stillness through the depiction of boats with patterns of reflections on still waters or images of railroad tracks stretching across the land. His desert world is plagued by stark, dramatic disasters, such as fires and floods, an environment fragile yet unyielding in the face of natural power and human encroachment.

MITCHELL, WILLIAM (Painter, Sculptor)
3506 Gay Way, Riverside, CA 92504

Born: 1927 *Exhibitions:* Los Angeles Century Gallery; Los Angeles Municipal Gallery *Education:* Claremont College *Dealer:* Gilbert Gallery, Riverside

Both paintings and sculptures are an outgrowth of earlier hard-edge painting based on calligraphy of the Russian alphabet. He has since expanded on that theme to include Greek and Chinese characters as a foundation for simple shapes and forms. A black-and-white palette is used in both media. Sculptures are done in clay and wood, with some welded metal and bronze casting; paintings are in acrylic. Strongly influenced by the power and simplicity of early primitive art, he seeks precision, balance and simplicity. He is also impressed by Henry Moore's use of natural forms to create anthropomorphic sculpture. His work contains metaphors that make powerful statements with great economy of design, thus requesting contemplation rather than an immediate fascination.

Bill Mitchell, *untitled,* 14" high, clay with low-fire glaze

Jim Morphesis, *Mambo,* 81 x 126, oil and mixed media on wood panel.
Courtesy: Tortue Gallery. Photograph: Brian Forrest

MIYANO, BABS (Glass Artist)
47-532 Pulama Rd., Kaneohe, HI 96744

Born: 1956 *Awards:* Acquisition Award, Hawaii State Foundation on Culture and Arts *Exhibitions:* Crossings France-Hawaii, Paris, Cannes; Japanese-American Craft Invitational, Morikami Museum, Del Ray Beach, FL *Education:* U. of Hawaii; California College of Arts and Crafts

Influenced by pop art in the 1970s, she created visual puns in glass using various hot, warm and cold glass techniques. Since 1981, she has been producing more formal and abstract work, creating constructions that are characterized by an elegant clarity of form, and cleanness of line. In *Raindancer's Welcome*, a slumped glass panel, softened by heat and bent into a controlled curve, is supported by two pristinely cut and curved, glass uprights. Other works show an influence of oriental aesthetics, where she combines glass with metal, fiber or stone.

MIYASAKI, GEORGE (Painter, Printmaker)
2844 Forest Ave., Berkeley, CA 94705

Born: 1935 *Awards:* NEA Fellowship; Guggenheim Fellowship *Collections:* Museum of Modern Art, NYC; San Francisco Museum of Modern Art *Exhibitions:* San Francisco Museum of Modern Art; La Jolla Museum of Art *Education:* California College of Arts and Crafts *Dealer:* Stephen Wirtz Gallery, San Francisco

His main influences were Nathan Oliveira in printmaking and Richard Diebenkorn in painting. His work started in an abstract expressionist style, shifting in the mid-1960s with his geometric and photo-transfer series. From there, spray images dominated his paintings and prints until the mid-1970s. The next period was marked by a combination of geometric concerns with soft colors superimposed on a grid pattern. Up to this period, he was known primarily as a printmaker, but his emphasis since the late 1970s has been on painting. He works on paper and canvas in a mixed media technique, using layers of laminates, paper and paints on all surfaces, including the large paintings on the canvas. He prefers the additive and subtractive options that the play of paper and paint allows—the counterpunctual, expressive play of surfaces becoming the major focus of the image.

MODENA, CHARLENE (Sculptor)
P.O. Box 230, Star Rte., Muir Beach, CA 94965

Born: 1942 *Collections:* Butler Museum, Youngstown, OH; Xerox Corporation, Mexico City *Exhibitions:* California Craft Museum, San Francisco; Gallery Tomasz Schulz, Poland *Education:* San Francisco State University

Intrigued by mixed media, she follows an abstract textural approach with some shamanistic-figurative influences. Between 1965 and 1975, metal was her medium, and she enjoyed exploring the "opposites" of iron and gold. This interest in opposites expanded, and for five years she investigated the contrasting of metal and hand-made paper. Since then she has been mixing a variety of materials, including sticks, beach glass, bird quills and beach rocks with metal and hand-made paper. Recently, she has been working on a series of environmental installations: 130 small (2-by-30-inch) woven gold and bird-quill rafts, thirty-five bronze ladders 5 inches high, nine 3-foot shaman staffs and seven small boats (10 inches in length) will be placed at the ocean shore at different times in the year to be washed away with the tide. "For so many years I have used objects from the sea," she says, "that now I am returning them in the form of my art."

MODESTY (Painter, Sculptor)
2393 Mission St., #1, San Francisco, CA 94110

Born: 1959 *Awards:* 1st Place, Young Artists Exhibition, San Francisco Art Institute *Exhibitions:* Media Gallery, San Francisco; Gregory Ghent Gallery, San Francisco *Education:* San Francisco Art Institute *Dealer:* Media Gallery, San Francisco

Described by some as "21st-century art," his flourescent landscapes are post-apocalyptic urban environments containing hints of past human existance. His sculptures are expressions of his concerns in altered perspective and synthetic colors. He has extracted elements from the work of Picasso and Miro and combined them with his academic background as the basis for his recent work. While some representational images are provided for viewers as references and connections, the work maintains an aura of science fiction. Recently, he has been working on a series of scenes of National Parks, depicting water falls and trees at Lake Tahoe.

MOEN, DAVID (Painter, Sculptor)
3448 Hollydale Dr., Los Angeles, CA 90039

Born: 1949 *Awards:* Best of Show, San Diego Art Institute Annual National Competition; Foothills II Award, North American Sculpture Exhibition, Foothills Art Center, Golden, CO *Collections:* Lucy Adelman; Jacqueline & Roger Evans *Exhibitions:* Artspace Gallery, Los Angeles; Cal. State-Los Angeles *Education:* Chouinard Art Institute, Los Angeles

He takes his aesthetic bearing both from "primitive" art and from early 20th-century modernism, notably surrealism and constructivism. To these influences he adds the explosive opening created by abstract expressionism in its radical gestural treatment of paint. In his early series of terra cotta sculptures and tableaus, figurative forms emerge from torn, stretched and compacted masses of clay. Painting dominates his current work, in which two themes recur: death and generation. He explores these themes in paintings of forms reminiscent of walls, windows, doors and architectural structures—images that create a theatrical, ritualistic space occupied by a highly abstracted figure. The spaces reveal the influence of De Chirico, and the figures might suggest a prone corpse, a woman's breast or other generative forms.

MOLLOHAN, KATHLEEN (Fiber Artist)
703 Breckenridge, Helena, MT 59601

Born: 1937 *Awards:* 1st Place, Art in the Mountain Time Zone, Denver *Collections:* I.B.M., Helena, MT; The Great American Bank, San Diego *Education:* U. of Colorado; Elkhorn Mountain Weaving School *Dealer:* The Aesthetics Collection, San Diego

She was originally an oil painter, but the dreamworld paintings of Marc Chagall led her to search for ways of conveying poetry and lyricism that were neither abstract nor representational. She chose fiber, and with tapestries she portrays an inner world of dreams and fantasies. Her fragmented images seem to float in a horizonless medium. She achieves this dreamlike senesation by manipulating an undulating twill—her own weaving technique, involving a combination of traditional (Aubusson) flat tapestry techniques and a

Keith Monaghan, *Homage 3-85,* 36 x 30, acrylic on canvas
Courtesy: William Sawyer Gallery

Crews McCulloch, *untitled,* 22 x 18, pencil

four harness loom-controlled textural wave. Her current tapestries involve non-representational, symbolic landscapes.

MONAGHAN, KEITH (Painter)
N. E. 1705 Lower Dr., Pullman, WA 99163

Born: 1921 *Awards:* Washington State U. Distinguished Service Award; Washington Governor's Invitational *Collections:* Seattle Art Museum; Saudi Royal Family *Exhibitions:* William Sawyer Gallery, San Francisco; Seattle and Tacoma Art Museums *Education:* UC-Berkeley *Dealer:* William Sawyer, San Francisco

In one of his characteristic works, a young woman sits before a mirror that reflects the Palouse hills behinds her. Like the hills, she is awash in a lemon-yellow light and striped with green. Another piece features a harvest crew in lavenders and blues resting against a porch rail during a lunch break. Despite the use of colors and the bold, sensuous shapes of people at home in a Western landscape, these compositions are reassuringly familiar. In many of his recent canvases, the artist pays tribute to the Old Masters—a painting of a sheriff sitting at a saloon poker table with his buddies is deliberately reminiscent of Caravaggio's 16th-century work, *The Calling of Saint Matthew.* In his paintings, he resists the temptation to copy or parody, achieving a distinct quality of his own.

MONDROS, MARTIN (Painter, Printmaker)
929 Ocancha Dr., Los Angeles, CA 90065

Born: 1925 *Awards:* 1st Prize, Painting, Pasadena Society of Artists; 2nd Prize, Westwood Center of the Arts Open Watermedia Exhibition *Collections:* Skirball Museum, U. of Southern California, Los Angeles *Exhibitions:* Glendale Community College; San Bernardino County Museum *Education:* Claremont Graduate School

His early work consisted of family portraits and urban landscapes of his native Los Angeles. He was influenced by a variety of divergent artistic styles and approaches, including those of Velazquez and Van Gogh. In the early 1960s, he branched out to intaglio printmaking. Working in an expressive realist style, his oils, watercolors and etchings have revolved around subjects of great personal interest to him. He has also created large indoor murals using a modified oil technique he developed for just such projects. A recent mural, entitled *The Knight's Path,* features images and themes from classical mythology and his own imagination, which deal with war and peace.

MONROE, JOE (Painter)
4121 Wilshire Blvd., #514, Los Angeles, CA 90010

Born: 1959 *Collections:* Joan Rivers, Hollywood; Dudley Moore, Hollywood *Exhibitions:* Steiner Gallery, Miami; Patton/Duvall Gallery, Los Angeles *Education:* Illinois State U., Normal *Dealer:* Patton/Duvall, Los Angeles

Entranced by color during his student days, he found his early work in graphics unfulfilling. After leaving the commercial field, he fused his fascination with color with his experience in graphics, adding modern details to his idols Matisse, Magritte and Klee. His surreal work has progressed into a modern fantasy of worlds beyond our reality. Starting with watercolors on paper, he now paints with acrylic on canvas. His variety of pure colors shocks the viewer; his format and size are larger than life. He has recently painted a fresh series of brightly playful landscapes, from the country near Los Olivos. Joe's art became a way of life, he began working in pen and ink and watercolor. In these media he developed his draftsmanships and sense of color. His work is often personal and autobiographical. Recently, he completed a series of pastel transfer monotypes that incorporated written elements from journals. His palette for these recent landscapes and figures is made up of summer and spring colors. Currently he is working on a folio of etchings to be called "The Honeymoon Suite," as well as a new series of monotypes and paintings.

MONTGOMERY, JOHN A. (Draughtsperson)
4175 Mill St., Fortuna, CA 95540

Born: 1944 *Awards:* Artists Society International Art Achievement Award Program; Best of Show, Annual Fallkirk Exhibition, Marin County *Exhibitions:* Quay Gallery, San Francisco; Ink People Alternate Gallery, Eureka *Education:* UCLA; U. of Southern California *Dealer:* Mill Creek Gallery, Fortuna

He began formal art training when he was twelve years old. His early portraiture and renderings of human skulls were influenced by trompe l'oeil techniques. He is now best known for large-scale (3-by-4-foot or 4-by-5-foot) drawings that combine realistically rendered portraits or objects with elements of geometric abstraction. Working with colored pencils, he occasionally adds touches of ink, pastels, oil and oil pastels. He prefers bright primary colors and enjoys working with the interplay of light and shadow, form and color. His style is often technically tedious, requiring more than one month to complete a single work. With a surgical practice to manage, he enjoys the creative process as much as the final product.

MONTOYA, CINDY (Painter)
4188 Gibraltar Dr., Fremont, CA 94536

Born: 1967 *Awards:* 1st Place, Acrylic, Pleasanton County Fair *Exhibitions:* Art and Wine Festival, Fremont; Niles Art Gallery, Fremont

Her strength is composition, and she favors abstract florals with an abundance of movement. She has studied with Dorita De'Ovalle, progressing from early, small canvases to large murals up to 10 feet long, often painted in homes. Although she works well with all media—watercolor, acrylic, oil, pastel, charcoal and pencil—she prefers watercolor because of its challenging nature.

MOORE, AZAD (Painter, Photographer)
1078 W. Celeste, Fresno, CA 93711

Born: 1919 *Awards:* 1st Place in Oil Painting, Armenian General Benevolent Union, Fresno *Exhibitions:* Fresno District Fair; Armenian General Benevolent Union, Fresno

A late bloomer, she was sixty-six when she won her first ribbons at the Fresno District Fair. Influenced by Norman Rockwell and Linda McCoy, she is a Sunday painter who makes oil paintings of scenes and people from photographs. Besides paintings, she creates "Grand Ladies of the Past" out of bottles she drapes with cloth, material and lace and then sprays with bronze or copper paint. She recently completed a small statue of Martha Washington.

MOORE, ELANIE A. (Painter)
P. O. Box 1462 Idyllwild, CA 92349

Born: 1940 *Awards:* L.S.B. Leakey Foundation *Exhibitions:* Salon Internacional Xerox, Panama City; San

John A. Montgomery, *Richard Shaw II,* 40 x 32, pencil
Courtesy: Mill Creek Gallery

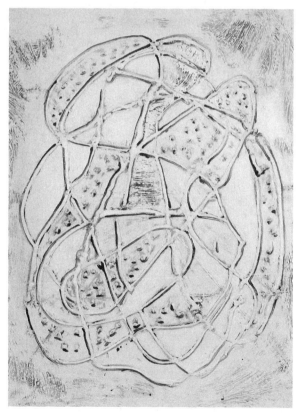

Saritha Margon, *Web II,* 52 x 44, oil, mixed media
Courtesy: Delphine Gallery

Jacinto College *Education:* Art Center College of Design

The rich, intensely focused and cohesive art of aboriginal murals in Baja California provoked her to re-evaluate the human relationship to both art and nature. While her work maintained its previous formalism through the use of taped straight lines and edges, she began to add a human figure in aboriginal form, representing the human archetype. Painted in multiple layers of translucent acrylic on top of sand, rocks and sticks that adhere to stretched canvas, the 6- to 10-foot panels confront the viewer with an imagery of dreams and universal symbols. Her present work explores the modern connection between man and his created environment, as opposed to the natural, pre-existing environment in which the aborigines found themselves. The straight lines traversing the canvas symbolize modern structures and ideas. The writing of Lucy Lippard, as well as studies of A. R. Penke and Matt Mullican, have influenced her exploration of these images that are at once ethereal in their grace and symbolic nature and concretely grounded in the shared past of human perception.

MOORE, EVID (Painter)
P.O. Box 42735, Los Angeles, CA 90050

Born: 1951 *Exhibitions:* Eye of the Vortex Bookcenter, Sedona, AZ; Mystic Moments, Cottonwood, AZ *Education:* UC-Santa Barbara; Los Angeles City College

After exploring many techniques and styles, she has chosen acrylic on paper as her medium of choice. She worked realistically for many years until she felt confident enough to paint strictly from her imagination. This direction was encouraged in several art classes, including one in animation which taught her about layering, transparencies, reflections and the continuous stream of images which make up a single piece of art. By the mid-1980s, her painting was completely driven by the conscious manipulation of subconscious energies and images. As such, paintings from this period vary widely in content and style. She arrived at her current idiom when she took up a traveling lifestyle. She has also started to paint realistically again, inspired by the beautiful Western landscapes which surround her.

MOORE, HARRIET (Painter, Sculptor)
717 14th Ave., San Francisco, CA 94118

Born: 1920 *Awards:* 1st Prize, Graphics, Plainfield Art Association; 1st Prize, Sculpture, Penn. State U. *Collections:* U. of Calif. Medical Center *Exhibitions:* Vorpal Gallery, San Francisco; City Lights Inc., San Francisco *Education:* Bennington College; Art Students League *Dealer:* Vorpal Gallery, San Francisco

Trained in the abstract and avant-garde traditions of the early 20th century, she turned from what she felt to be the sterility and amnesia of these art forms to painting within the tradition of narrative, myth, dream and fantasy. Besides sculptured portraiture of private individuals and historic persons, she is also drawn to create figures of animals—rhinos, cats, owls or fish that are carved in stone, and, when drawn in pen, are sometimes transformed into mythical beasts—harpies, centaurs and dragons. Her main inspiration and vehicle of expression is Dante's *Divine Comedy.* Exploring themes and images that range from the dark, diabolic, grotesque and monstrous scenes of the *Inferno* to the sublime, celestial, ineffable experiences of

the *Paradiso*, she has thus far created twenty 9-by-4-foot mural panels in charcoal, crayon and oil paint, and fifteen sculptures of varying size in stone, wood, terra-cotta and bronze.

MOORE, INA MAY (Painter)
5718 N. 10th Ave., Phoenix, AZ 85013

Born: 1920 *Awards:* Grunbacher Medal, Scottsdale, AZ; Best of Show, Watercolor Association of Arizona *Collections:* Valley National Bank, Phoenix, AZ; Thunderbird Bank, Tempe, AZ *Education:* U. of Arizona; Arizona State U. *Dealers:* El Mundo Magico, Sedona, AZ; Bob Nation, Prescott, AZ

Having worked with many media, including oils, sculpture and clay, she decided to devote herself to transparent watercolor. John Dewey and the French Impressionists led the way for her through artistic discovery and growth over the years. She paints out of love, both for the process and its result. She enjoys working with the luminosity and color, the spontaneity of watercolor, and the challenges the medium presents. Her style varies from realistic to experimental, depending on her response to the subject. She works in a wet on wet technique, sometimes using other materials and techniques, such as spraying through Kleenex, to achieve special textural and visual effects. Her pieces are usually 30 by 40 inches in size and rendered in a varied palette.

MOORE, JENNIFER (Fiber Artist)
4515 Auhay Dr., Santa Barbara, CA 93110

Born: 1955 *Awards:* Best of Show, Southern California Handweavers Conference, Los Angeles; Juror's Award, Celebration of Weaving V, Youngstown, OH *Exhibitions:* Downey Museum of Art, Los Angeles; International Gallery, San Diego *Education:* Lewis & Clark College, Portland

She was formally trained as a biological illustrator, and her penchant for creating subtly undulating color patterns led her to explore the technique of double-weave pick-up for her abstract geometric designs. Two layers of fabric are woven simultaneously and exchanged at selected points to create complex patterns that evidence her interests in mathematics, architecture and music. Done primarily in cotton with the occasional addition of silks and metallics, her designs are woven into panels ranging in size from 12 by 12 inches to 4 by 6 feet. The panels are stretched over boards and framed.

MOORE, RONALD S. (Painter, Sculptor)
3802 Happy Valley Rd., Lafayette, CA 94549

Born: 1950 *Awards:* Scholarship, Calif. College of Arts and Crafts, Oakland *Exhibitions:* Viridian Gallery, NYC; Galerie Bateau Lavoir, Oakland *Education:* Calif. College of Arts and Crafts; Diablo Valley College *Dealer:* Thaler-Rolph Associates, Carmel

His early sculptures were small whimsical wooden machines. Searching for something more personal, he began to construct crude male figures, also out of wood. As his forms became smoother and more detailed he switched to bronze, and though the medium was heavier the work was still lighthearted in nature. The forms are now primarily female and range in size from maquettes to life size. His realistic, oil-on-canvas landscape and figurative paintings also reflect a lighthearted mood. He describes his pictures as whimsically oriented.

Maureen Marshall, *Idols,* 22 x 27, collage

Jean Moore-Woods, *Coptic Cristo-Black Jesus,* 20 x 16, oils.
Courtesy: Cleo Brown

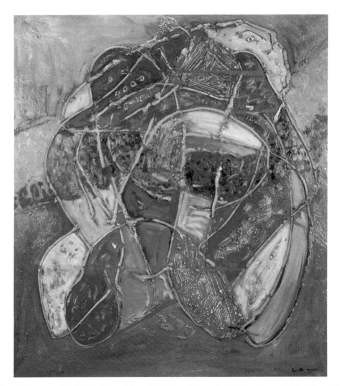

Saritha Margon, *Web II,* 52 x 44, mixed media, oils. Courtesy: Delphine Gallery

Charles Miltenberger, *untitled,* 79 x 90, oil on canvas

L. Merchant, *Terra-Cotta Memories,* 24 x 24, ceramic.
Courtesy: Kersting Gallery

Janet Mackaig, *Ladders of Fire,* 48 x 56, acrylic and pencil on canvas

Elaine Marinoff, *Love Birds,* 48 x 48, oil and wax on canvas

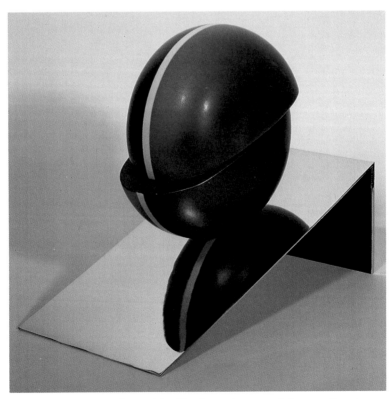

Harrison McIntosh, *Racer,* 16 x 13 x 9, stoneware and chrome. Courtesy:
Louis Newman Galleries, Beverly Hills. Photograph: Schenck and Schenck

Dawn Mari, *Peaceful Reflections,* 40 x 40, acrylic on canvas

Melinna Malan-Nicely, *Place Setting (Iris Pattern),* white stoneware with underglaze

Geer Morton, *Still Life with Red Checkered Tablecloth,* 32 x 38, acrylic on canvas

William Minschew, *Artist's studio "Volterra" with sculpture "Vector Passim",* bronze. Photograph: Mark Citret

Azad Moore, *Perpetual Splash,* 18 x 24, oil on canvas

Elizabeth Marcsisin, *The Journey #2,* 15 x 17, acrylic

Gloria Moses, *Everglades,* 36 x 24, oil

David Martin, *Stanley Sunset,* 33 x 41, pastel

Hiroki Morinoue, *Evening Wave,* 36 x 48, watercolor on paper. Photograph: The Art Loft

Judith Mills, *Supernatural 2,* 30 x 22, acrylic on paper

Henri Marie-Rose, *Hermit Crab,* 24 x 35 x 32, copper, bronze, granite

Grace Merjanian, *Hidden Canyon,* 23 x 29, watercolor and gouache

D.A. McIver, *Couples,* 21 x 21, bronze relief

Martin Mondrus, *Sierra Cliffs,* 38 x 52, oil

Patricia A. Murray, *Support Group,* 40 x 54 oil

Jim Morphesis, *Skull and Red Door,* 72 x 80, oil and mixed media
on wood panel. Courtesy: Jake and Ruth Bloom

Crews McCulloch, *Swimming,* 41 x 25, watercolor, acrylic

Robert Maki, *Five Point Romanesque Star,* 36 x 138 x 108, painted steel.
Courtesy: Laura Russo Gallery, Portland, OR

Tegwin Matenaer, *With the Rainbow Cloud,* 8 x 10 & 11 x 14, cibachrome photo print

Peter Max, *Mondrian Ladies IV,* 36 x 48, acrylics on canvas. Courtesy: Hanson Galleries, Beverly Hills, CA

William E. Mayfield, *The Rogue,* 24 x 36, acrylic on canvas Courtesy: Susan Taniguchi

Elanie Moore, *Balance and Integration—Tribute to Lucy Lippard,* 96 x 240, acrylic

Marge Mount, *Study for Persphone I,* 36 x 48, pastels on paper

Teresa Muñoz, *As It Was in the Beginning,* 30 x 96, collagraph print

MOORE-WOODS, JEAN (Painter)
405 Serrano Dr., Apt. 5C, San Francisco, CA 94132

Born: 1947 *Exhibitions:* The San Francisco African-American Historical and Cultural Society; California Legislature/Capitol Building Cafeteria, Sacramento; *Education:* San Francisco State U.; Morgan State U.

With bold form and a striking intensity of color symmetry, she blends African simplicity and utilitarianism with Western European and Afro-American aesthetics and symmetrical appeal. She executes her oil portraits, pictures of animals, outdoor scenes and still lifes in a wide range of greens, browns, blues and earth tones. One painting is a profile of an African woman; in another, she depicts the Golden Gate Bridge under a full moon. She has been influenced by Leroy Neiman, Toulouse-Lautrec, Gauguin, Erte, Jacob Lawrence and Henry Tanner.

MOQUIN, RICHARD (Sculptor)
132 Woodland Ave., San Rafael, CA 94901

Born: 1934 *Awards:* Oakland Museum Award for Sculpture *Collections:* Oakland Museum; Saks Fifth Avenue *Exhibitions:* Gallery Paule Anglim, San Francisco; Michael Dunev Gallery, San Francisco *Education:* San Francisco State U.

Abstract expressionist influences are evident in his geometric sculptures and wall installations. He also constructs large, allegorical clay figurative pieces and smaller landscape "sites" consist of multiple units of clay assembled on tableaux. Recent work in Carrera, Italy has influenced his latest constructions made of slabs of the famous marble. These pieces portray what he calls "fragments" of air, water and the human figure.

MORALES-DENNEY, ELIZABETH (Commercial Illustrator, Painter)
P.O. Box 676, Inverness, CA 94937

Born: 1950 *Exhibitions:* Wrubel Gallery, The Nature Company, Berkeley; Oakland Museum of Art *Education:* State U. of New York, Binghamton; San Francisco State U.

She combines her science background with her art talent to create scientific illustrations and educational material for textbooks, children's books, museums and exhibits. As a science illustrator, she strives to render accurately archeological artifacts, maps, diagrams and other materials, to promote the storage and communication of scientific information. Most of her fine arts work has a botanical theme. She works in pen and ink, watercolor, gouache and pencil. These works are more fanciful and stylized than her other, more objective work.

MORAN, DOUG (Painter, Sculptor)
1058 E. 1st St., Santa Ana, CA 92701

Born: 1949 *Collections:* National Collection of Fine Arts, Smithsonian Institution, Washington D.C.; Metropolitan Museum of Art, Miami *Exhibitions:* Works Gallery, Long Beach; Claremont Graduate School Gallery *Education:* Western Michigan U. *Dealer:* Works Gallery, Long Beach

In 1975, he began a ten year body of work referred to as wallscape paintings. His sources were more personal than art historical—the influences of abstract artists, such as Kelly, Albers, Held and Johns were carried beyond the appearance of cool, literal minimalism. These works operate at the interface of art and architecture, and intentionally engage a major dilemma concerning the artist's heritage and habitat. In 1979, he articulated an actual architectural facade, as a staged painting for the Standard Concrete Materials Building in Santa Ana. Recent concerns are manifest in a work titled *Vintner's Pause*, a 32-ton concrete, granite and stainless steel construction. Pivoting in an 8-foot-deep pit, counterbalanced by a 40,000 lb. steel "shack", the entire form sways with the wind. The piece is a salute to the agricultural history of a rapidly growing community. The work marks a growth in the concerns of the artist toward a regional, rather than personal, awareness of environment as "place."

MORAN, JOE (Printmaker, Painter)
5095 N. "F" St., San Bernardino, CA 92407

Born: 1935 *Collections:* Los Angeles Municipal Art Gallery *Exhibitions:* Paul Villasenor Gallery, San Bernardino; Cerritos College, Norwalk *Education:* UC-Riverside; Claremont College

After he studied in the mid-1960s and early 1970s, with David Lawrence, James Strombotne, Paul Gardner Darrow and Roland Reiss, his pieces became vehicles of social commentary. The images of these works are three-dimensional, placed on layers of glass. In the late 1970s, calaveras, or skulls, became the central image as a symbol of social decay. Using a collage approach, they appear in a book format with written commentaries. He continues to use the 110 page book format as his main means of expression. Each page contains images, puns, ideas and written criticism. The individual pages are art in their own right which then become an art book. The books, of which he has produced 28, can be exhibited, so that a viewer may thumb through them. In addition, he takes ideas from each volume and creates separate pieces of art via printmaking, collage or assemblage.

MORANDI, TOM (Sculptor)
33058 S.E. Peoria Rd., Corvallis, OR 97333

Born: 1943 *Collections:* Capitol Building, Portland OR; Portland State U. *Exhibitions:* Squibb Museum, Princeton, NJ; Pence Gallery, San Francisco *Education:* U. of Ohio; Indiana U. *Dealer:* John Pence, San Francisco

He moved west from Pittsburgh in the 1960s. While his work maintains the strong mechanical ethic associated with that industrial center, it has also assumed a grace and balance that is more closely allied with the West Coast. He works mainly in cast and fabricated metal and relies heavily on contemporary industrial processes and equipment. Known primarily for his large commissioned sculpture, he has recently begun work on a series of human scale pieces. He explores the possibilities of combining lifesized sections of the human figure with geometric forms, using pseudo-mechanical components as transitional devices.

MOREHOUSE, MICHELLE O. (Ceramist, Mixed Media Artist)
585 Salmon Creek Rd., Bodega, CA 94922

Born: 1950 *Awards:* Ceramics Invitational; California Museum of Art; Luther Burbank Center, Santa Rosa; Honorable Mention, Marin Civic Center Exhibition of the Arts, San Rafael *Exhibitions:* Oberon Art Gallery, Napa; David Cole Gallery, Inverness *Education:* San Francisco Art Institute; Sonoma St. U.

Her work in lithography, etching and photo cyanotypes featured floral and animal forms. Utilizing these same images in her clay expressions, she creates complex assemblages with clear narrative content. Progressing from these personal images in clay to homages to other artists such as Freda Kahlo, Mark Rothko and Edward Hopper, she has begun to combine painting and iconography in three dimensions. Recently, she has incorporated found objects in her assemblages, particularly drawn from sites in rural America and Mexico. Her colors are very emotional and primal, with strong sexual overtones.

MOREHOUSE, WILLIAM (Painter)
P.O. Box 210, Bodega, CA 94922

Born: 1929 *Collections:* Whitney Museum, NYC; San Francisco Museum of Modern Art *Exhibitions:* Guggenheim Museum, NYC; San Francisco Museum of Modern Art *Education:* San Francisco Art Institute; San Francisco State U. *Dealer:* J.J. Brookings Gallery, San Jose

A former student of Clyfford Still and Mark Rothko, he initially worked in a non-objective style until the 1960s, when he began to include references to landscapes and objects. In paint, pastels, lithographs and drawings, his method is serial and thematic. The "New York Subway" series evolved during the late 1970s as an exploration of subterranean spaces and associated structures. Recent work, described by one critic as "numinous" abstraction, focuses on the theme of duality and is spiritual in nature. Suggestions of figuration have been appearing in his work since 1986.

MORETTI, ANTHONY H. (Painter, Sculptor)
45 Cole Ave., Williamstown, MA 01267

Born: 1944 *Awards:* Massachusetts Arts Lottery Grant *Collections:* The Oakland Museum; Mills College Art Gallery, Oakland *Exhibitions:* Richard L. Nelson Gallery, UC-Davis; Berkshire Artisans Gallery, Pittsfield, MA *Education:* California College of Arts and Crafts; California Institute of the Arts

His initial paintings were playful and conceptual, consisting of row upon row of little daubs of color. Gradually the brushstroke—the formal focus of his work—began to lengthen, and the whole scale of his paintings increased. His present work is linear, describing space and volume. He continues to work in oil on linen; the surfaces of his paintings continue to be colorful, conceptual, layered and very active. He has also recently been working on a series of welded steel sculptures, which are painted in a highly expressionistic style.

MORI, MARYLN (Painter)
P.O. Box 3455, Saratoga, CA 95070

Born: 1939 *Exhibitions:* Montalvo Center for the Arts; Los Gatos Museum *Education:* San Jose State U.

After courses at a community college she began painting large fruits and vegetables, changing and magnifying them into lively abstractions. Making use of the opaqueness and transparency inherent in the combination of acrylic and canvas, she developed a spontaneous watercolor technique. Living for a time in Japan influenced her sense of space. Recent paintings are increasingly abstract—fruits and vegetables fill large canvases and are no longer representational. Feline images and human figures have also appeared and the colors are strong. Her oil pastels on white paper are in strong primary colors. "My metaphor will continue to be fruits and vegetables."

MORINOUE, HIROKI (Painter, Printmaker)
P.O. Box 153 Holualoa, HI 96725

Born: 1947 *Awards:* Hama Ten Governor's Award, Yokohama, Japan; 1st Prize, Suisai Renmei Ten, Tokyo *Collections:* Honolulu Academy of Arts; Contemporary Arts Center of Hawaii *Exhibitions:* Contemporary Museum of Hawaii; Kabutoya Galleries, Tokyo and Nagoya *Education:* California College of Arts and Crafts

He makes mixed-media paintings, prints, ceramics and sculpture. His early, realistic work in watercolor and in oil consisted of landscapes, studies of rock formations and portraits. In the late 1970s, impatient with painting objects in nature and influenced by his studies in Japan, he began to paint patterns and surface textures with wide areas of color gradations. He scored the surface of the paper with a variety of tools for a deeper absorption of color. More recently, he has made incisions in the paper with a razor-like tool, thus creating a sort of embossed or relief effect. Of late, he uses simple geometric patterns for the form of his paintings, which allows him to concentrate on the interaction of color in his three-hued system.

MORITA, JOHN TAKAMI (Printmaker)
1640 Ahini St., Honolulu, HI 96819

Born: 1943 *Awards:* NEA Fellowship *Collections:* San Francisco Museum of Modern Art; Honolulu Academy of Arts *Exhibitions:* Alternative Museum, NYC; Intergrafik, West Germany *Education:* San Francisco State U.; San Francisco Art Institute *Dealer:* Gallery EAS, Honolulu

In the early 1970s, he became dissatisfied with the limitations of photography, which he felt did not allow for an expressionist search into the meaning of human experience. Experimenting with different techniques, be began etching with the dry-point technique directly onto the metal plate of a previously etched photographic image. Eventually, in the early 1980s, he began combining four plates together in larger pieces, measuring upwards from 36 by 48 inches in size. These pieces took as subjects images of his ancestors and family and combined them with images of the Ware family of San Francisco. Although these works already have a sociological focus, recently his works have grown patently political, some of them dealing with the suffering in the Middle East.

MORPHESIS, JAMES (Painter)
339 East 22nd St. New York, NY 10010

Born: 1948 *Awards:* Louis Comfort Tiffany Foundations Grant; Young Talent Award, Los Angeles County Museum of Art *Collections:* Los Angeles County Museum of Art; San Francisco Museum of Modern Art *Exhibitions:* Museum of Modern Art, NYC *Education:* California Institute of the Arts; Tyler School of the Arts *Dealer:* Freidus/Ordover Gallery, NYC; Tortue Gallery, Los Angeles

He uses the images of the crucifix, the fall of Icarus from the heavens and the punishment of Prometheus as representations of both man's greatest achievements and the price man has paid for knowledge. In his paintings, gestural strokes of oil and magna are worked into and over heavily collaged surfaces. His desire is to have the painting process more than cover mortal limitations. His assemblages incorporate religious iconography and suggest his attempts at a dialogue with the past.

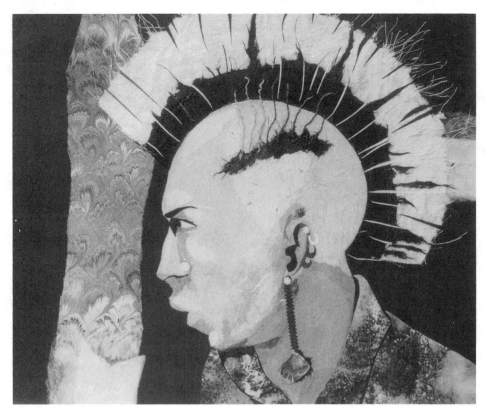

Maureen Marshall, *Kings Road Punk,* 22 x 26, collage

Jean Moore-Woods, *Winter Over Still Water,* 16 x 20, oils. Courtesy: Cleo Brown

Harrison McIntosh, *Bowl,* 7 x 12, stoneware. Courtesy: Louis Newman Galleries, Beverly Hills, CA.
Photographer: Schenck and Schenck

Richard Moquin, *Fragment of California Smoke,* 55 x 29 x 8, painted marble

Elizabeth Marcsisin, *The Beginning,* 16 x 20, acrylic on canvas

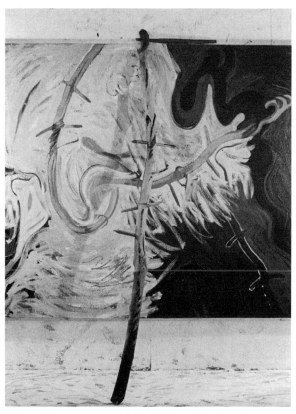

William Morehouse, *untitled 1986,* 80 x 80 x 24, oil on canvas
and wood. Courtesy: J.J. Bookings Gallery, San Jose,CA

MORRIS, CARL (Painter)
919 N.W. Skyline Blvd., Portland, OR 97229

Born: 1911 *Awards:* Retrospective Exhibit, Ford Foundation; Anne Bremer Memorial Prize, San Francisco Museum of Modern Art *Collections:* Guggenheim Museum, NYC; Metropolitan Museum of Art, NYC *Exhibitions:* Seattle Art Museum; Kraushaar Galleries, NYC *Education:* Art Institute of Chicago *Dealer:* Kraushaar Galleries, NYC

His quiet, abstract paintings are infused with a spirituality that is drawn from nature. He has been influenced by art of the Far East, particularly the abstract qualities revealed in ancient Indian, Chinese and Japanese art. In the *New York Times*, Devree has said, "His color is tonal and subtle; he captures the mood of transition while objects as such are still discernible. This is lyric abstraction at its most suggestive, with a hidden music all its own. The slow effect of time in a world of massive forms makes itself felt in Morris' rugged poetry." He works in acrylics on canvas, Belgian linens and rice paper.

MORRIS, MARI (Fiber Artist)
536 W. Loma Alta, Altadena, CA 91001

Born: 1944 *Collections:* Bellview Hospital, NYC *Exhibitions:* Brockman Gallery, Los Angeles; Del Mano Gallery, Pasadena *Education:* UC-Berkeley; Pratt U. *Dealer:* Brockman Gallery, Los Angeles

She employs a combination of Oriental, African, Bolivian and Native American images and techniques in her own tapestries and fiber sculptures. Her diverse training includes four- and eight-harness weaving with Kaye Sekimachi, Aubusson tapestry weaving with Michelle Lester and Japanese Kasuri with Yoshika Wada. She prefers primitive imagery because it is organic and helps her to develop an expressive language in fiber art. Besides the more obvious aesthetic considerations of her work, weaving also holds a more profound and spiritual meaning for her. She was inspired by an anthropological thesis on the Dogon people of Africa, who think of the warp as male and the weft as female. For them, and for her, weaving is the creation of the web of life.

MORROW, ALLAN (Painter)
c/o Rogue Gallery, 3804 Ray St., San Diego, CA 92104

Born: 1950 *Awards:* Calif.-Hawaii Biennial, San Diego Museum of Art *Collections:* Institute of Contemporary Arts, Korea; National Gallery of Modern Art, Portugal *Exhibitions:* Berkeley Art Center; San Diego Art Institute *Education:* San Diego State U. *Dealer:* Rogue Gallery, San Diego

The path that led to his current fascination with roads, highways and streets, began with his interest in Wayne Thiebaud's use of color and shadow and Monet's "Waterlilies," series, which he views as an influential source of abstract expressionist landscapes. Using Mark Tobey's style of rhythmic calligraphy on a large, colored background, he flattens the plane and uses patterned gestural brush work and shadows, removing the horizon line to create an aerial perspective. He subsequently began juxtaposing a realist interpretation of a palm tree or street sign to the aerial views. In some pieces, he has gone one step further, adding a third dimension. In *Desert Table,* he has painted a simple desert scene of cactus, rocks, sand and deserted black asphalt roadways on the top of a table and continued it on a canvas that forms the backdrop. The canvas at the back of the piece can be removed.

MORSBERGER, PHILIP (Painter)
562 Cragmont Ave., Berkeley, CA 94708

Born: 1933 *Collections:* Ashmolean Museum, Oxford, England; Butler Institute of American Art, Youngstown Ohio *Exhibitions:* Rochester Memorial Art Gallery, NY; Morley Gallery, London *Education:* Carnegie Tech; Oxford University *Dealer:* Rena Bransten Gallery, San Francisco

Each decade since 1950s has marked a new period of focus. In the 1950s, he was exposed to abstract expressionism at Carnegie Tech, and then traditional figuration at Oxford. He painted the figure through the 1960s. In the 1970s, he re-examined aspects of abstract expressionism. In the 1980s, he has been working to reconcile the two, handling the figures expressionistically, with a humorous edge. *The Unicorn's Garden* is a work from a recent series of narrative montage compositions, which, he says, is something of a cross between a Renaissance tapestry and the Sunday comics.

MORTON, GEER (Painter)
P.O. Box 425, Hopland, CA 95449

Born: 1935 *Collections:* Gulf Oil, Houston; Capital Group, Los Angeles *Exhibitions:* A.M. Sachs, New York; Dubin Gallery, Los Angeles *Education:* San Francisco Art Institute; San Francisco State College *Dealer:* Twining Gallery, NYC; Tarbox Gallery, San Diego; Young Gallery, Saratoga

He was born in the country, and his work reflects an ongoing love for land, light and color. In the 1960s, he attended the San Francisco Art Institute and studied with Diebenkorn and Bischoff. While there, he fell under the spell of his teachers' broad-brush realism, a technique that facilitates a fast, emotional and economical attack on the subject. He now works in acrylic on canvas, painting what he sees when he sees it. He still paints with an easel, and he is committed to direct artist-subject contact. His love of the look of land, flowers, faces and bare arms and backs keeps him working to push the limits of our perception of art and nature.

MOSES, EDWARD (Painter)
1233 Palms Blvd., Venice, CA 90291

Born: 1926 *Awards:* NEA Grant; Guggenheim Fellowship *Collections:* Art Institute of Chicago; Museum of Contemporary Art, Los Angeles *Exhibitions:* White Art Gallery, UCLA; L.A. Louver Gallery *Education:* UCLA *Dealer:* L.A. Louver Gallery

As a color-field abstract painter, he held his first major New York show in 1969. In the 1970s, diagonal and near-horizontal stripes were a recurring motif in various media including acrylic and plastic resin (Hagamatama, for example), pigment or rhoplex, on diverse surfaces ranging from canvas to laminated tissue paper. In 1979, his work departed from recognizable images as the canvases became large monochromatic expanses. He has also made lithographs.

MOSES, GLORIA (Painter, Printmaker)
2307 Bagley Ave., Los Angeles, CA 90034

Born: 1940 *Collections:* Purchase Award, Springfield Bank of Missouri; UCLA Hospital *Exhibitions:* Community College of Jewish Studies, Los Angeles; Palm Springs Museum, Palm Springs *Dealer:* Los Angeles

Gloria Moses, *Taos Scene #1,* 24 x 36, oil

Judy Mulford, *Back from Africa,* 19 x 7, clay, pine needles, nails, bark, waxed linen, wax, dye

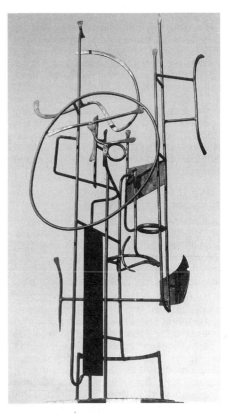

Henri Marie-Rose, *Moon Over San Francisco,* 72 x 38 x 21, iron, bronze. Photographer: George Posner

Art Museum Rental Gallery; Orlando Gallery, Los Angeles; Wittengberg Gallery, St. Louis

She is influenced by abstract expressionism and impressionism and by the art of Pollock, de Kooning, Winslow Homer, Van Gogh and Hopper. Her subject matter includes landscapes and the human figure, and her work is characterized by the use of three to four colors on the brush simultaneously and by the technique of using a loaded brush on the canvas. She is currently working with large and small oil paintings in glazes and impasto, employing rich blues and greens and floral reds, golds and purples. Her watercolors portray landscapes of flowers, trees and mountains, and city scenes with figures. The prints she creates are highly personal and expressionistic and vary from figuration to landscape and from monochromatic to four-color/four-plate etchings.

MOSHER, MIKE (Painter, Computer Graphics Artist)
2561 Mardell Way, Mountain View, CA 94043

Born: 1955 *Collections:* Gerald Ford Presidential Library, Ann Arbor, MI; Weilbauer Collection, Quito, Ecuador *Exhibitions:* Southern Exposure Gallery, San Francisco; Euphrat Gallery, De Anza College, Cupertino *Education:* San Francisco State U.; Dartmouth College

After painting or organizing over a dozen neighborhood murals for the San Francisco Art Commission during the late 1970s and early 1980s, he began to adapt his figurative style to computer paint systems. The use of the computer enabled him to focus more on the content of the image rather than its physical rendering. His colorful, figurative works feature groups of human figures, usually adolescents, in which the boundaries between figures are somewhat broken down. The works have a photo-cubist feel, reminiscent of silk-screen printing. His "Daniel Webster" series was inspired by portraits in the collection of Dartmouth College. Using computer imaging, he manipulated the portrait by rearranging and resizing the surface planes of the figure's face. Recent works consist of schematic motifs from semiconductor and digital electronics, incorporating autobiographical material, and presented in comic book-style drawings and computer images.

MOSS, SUSAN (Painter)
4767 York Blvd., Los Angeles, CA 90042

Born: 1944 *Awards:* Who's Who in American Art *Collections:* Los Angeles County Museum *Exhibitions:* Albright-Knox Gallery, Buffalo; Ruth Bachofner Gallery, Santa Monica *Education:* U. of Nevada, Reno; Otis Art Institute *Dealer:* Ruth Bachofner Gallery, Santa Monica; Boritzer/Gray Gallery, Santa Monica

In the early 1970s, she painted pure, color-field light spaces. This work evolved into internal landscapes of pure color and emotion. She now emphasizes powerful strokes and intense color. Her concept of automatism plays a large part in her spontaneous landscapes of the subconscious. In the "Black Forest" series she explored her relationship to her own ancestral drama, including the struggles of her grandparents in wartime Germany. Her recent work involves oil on linen, oil on paper and crayon on large sheets of rag paper, specifically designed for the artist. First she stains her surface; then smears, brushes and strokes it in an emotion-filled, gestural technique.

MOTHERWELL, ROBERT (Painter)
909 North St., Greenwich, CT 06830

Born: 1915 *Awards:* Belgian Art Critics Prize, Brussels; Gold Medal, Pennsylvania Academy of the Fine Arts *Collections:* Museum of Modern Art, NYC; Metropolitan Museum of Art, NYC *Exhibitions:* Museum of Modern Art, NYC; Whitney Museum of American Art, NYC *Education:* Stanford U.; Columbia U. *Dealer:* M. Knoedler, NYC

Combining interests in art, philosophy and psychoanalysis while doing graduate work in the 1930s, he traveled to Europe and became fascinated with the exiled Surrealists and with French symbolist poetry. He exhibited with the Surrealists in New York in 1942, but shortly afterward helped form the New York abstract expressionist movement. He has always made paintings along with collages, and in the last two decades has made several hundred prints. Committed to an abstract vocabulary, he conveyed meaning from the artist's unconscious mind, guided by instinct modified by reason. He is known for paintings which cover entire walls such as *Elegy for the Spanish Republic, No. 34.*

MOTT, BONNIE (Painter)
2628 5th St., Santa Monica, CA 90405

Born: 1951 *Awards:* Anna Bing Arnold Art Council Award *Exhibitions:* San Francisco State U.; Oregon State U. *Education:* UCLA

Trained in the modernist tradition and influenced by the art and philosophy of India, she has always worked primarily from the unconscious, letting her intuitive impulses create a dialogue between herself and a piece. Her paintings are constructed from unstretched, sewn-together pieces of canvas and sculpted with high relief forms. Encrusted with richly colored oil pigment, the works possess a shimmering vibration of intense energy and subtle images of openings and lush, verdant growth existing simultaneously with disintegration.

MOTTISHAW, BARRIE (Painter)
8012 Waring Ave., Los Angeles, CA

Born: 1945 *Exhibitions:* Koplin Gallery, Los Angeles; G. W. Einstein Gallery, NYC *Education:* Antioch College; Claremont College Graduate School *Dealer:* Koplin Gallery, Los Angeles

Her watercolor landscapes contrast idealized panoramas with the contributions of modern society within them. The muted lines of mountain ranges, rivers, bluffs and trees are interrupted by geometrical freeway overpasses, electrical towers and water tanks. She bagan working in nature while living primitively on an island in Canada. Her work is a direct, contemporary extension of 18th- and 19th-century landscape painting; she makes a preservationist statement against urban blight with an appeal to the conservative tradition of watercolor itself. Recent work focuses on old bridges over the Los Angeles River and coastal mountain views in long, horizontal format.

MOUNT, MARGE (Painter)
Born: 1938 *Awards:* Carnegie Grant; California Arts Council Grant *Collections:* Stanford U.; Bay View Savings, Petaluma *Exhibitions:* Art Trails, Sonoma County; The Mill Gallery, Petaluma *Education:* San Francisco Art Institute; Stanford U. *Dealer:* Sarah Hylton, Santa Rosa

Claire Stebbins McAuliffe, *Southern California Landscape #8,* 78 x 60,
acrylic on canvas. Courtesy: Jeanette Gadt

Susan Moss, *Voyage South,* 72 x 60, oil on canvas.
Courtesy: DJMC (Ruth Bachofner Gallery), Los Angeles, CA

After an intensive training at the San Francisco Art Institute under Julius Halofsky, she pursued a Master's degree at Stanford University, where she studied with Frank Lobdell and Nathan Oliveira. Making extensive uses of pastels, she frequently depicts cloudscapes infused with the symbolic significance of Greek mythology, combining a nature-lover's devotion to realism with the subjective abstraction of an artist striving to express moral and ethical issues in allegorical works. Her works use colors boldly to convey an intensity that is brilliant rather than realistic, in keeping with the hyper-real tenor of her subject matter and thematic concerns.

MOXZER-HARRIS, JIENO (Painter)
1711 Q St. #5, Sacramento, CA 95614

Born: 1913 *Exhibitions:* California State Capitol Building, Sacramento; Weatherstone Coffee House, Sacramento *Education:* Traphagen School of Fashion

Influenced throughout his life by Picasso, Erte, Abrey Beardsley, Klee, Cocteau, Incan Primitive Art and Margaret Mead, he works with symbolic and mystical images in a variety of media. Somewhat abstract in form, his plaster masks are cast from selected human faces, then altered to affect allegory. They are painted with tempera and watercolor, then decorated by copper and white wire, junk jewelry, string, twigs, leaves and Spanish moss, feathers and any other kind of natural and found objects. Handcarved wood plaques are painted with vivid enamel, acrylic and house-paint colors, and reflect the movement of American Indian ritual. He was trained as a professional actor and dancer; thus, rhythm and grace figure prominently. Commedia del arte clowns, harlequins and troubadours carry ancient instruments; pen-and-ink, pastel, wash and tempera drawings contain draped royal personas suggesting cult figures.

MUGNAINI, JOSEPH (Painter, Printmaker)
4226 Canyon Crest Rd., Altadena, CA 91001

Born: 1912 *Awards:* 1st Prize, Lithographs, Library of Congress Pennell Collection, Washington, DC; Academy Award Nomination *Collections:* Los Angeles County Museum of Art; Smithsonian Institution, Washington DC *Exhibitions:* Pasadena Art Museum; UC-Santa Cruz *Education:* Otis Art Institute *Dealer:* Heritage Gallery, Los Angeles

His work includes paintings, etchings, lithographs, book illustrations and film sets. Although his images are relatively representational, their design is based upon the principles of abstract spatial organization. This characteristic makes the work especially suited to the fantasy and science fiction genre, and many of his illustrations have accompanied such classics as the works of Ray Bradbury, special editions of *Ben Hur*, *Time Machine* and *War of the Worlds*. He is currently working on large-scale, figurative paintings in oil and acrylic; the art direction and set design for an upcoming science fiction film; another of many college art texts; and an instructional television series. In his work, he seeks to express intangible factors "beyond the frontiers of reality."

MULFORD, JUDY (Fiber Artist, Mixed Media Artist)
2098 Mandeville Cyn. Rd., Los Angeles, CA 90049

Born: 1938 *Exhibitions:* Downey Museum of Art; Del Mano Gallery, Brentwood *Education:* Cal. State-Northridge

She is an artist, lecturer, teacher and weaver who has done textile research throughout Micronesia and Mexico. Originally a weaver and painter, she now creates three-dimensional basket/containers, using clay and pine needles as her basic materials. Her pieces reflect the influences of her international travels and contact with other cultures. Having progressed into making vessels that incorporate personal imagery, she writes and paints on her vessels and sculpts female images that portray a storyboard of her life's progression. Her "soul containers" are made of clay and pine needles, and require months of planning. They are heavy, somber, tedious and repetitious. She also makes handmade-paper "cloud/spirit" baskets that are the complete opposite: fragrant, colorful, light, airy and spontaneous.

MULLICAN, LEE (Painter, Ceramist)
c/o Herbert Palmer Gallery, 802 N. La Cienega Blvd., Los Angeles, CA 90069

Born: 1919 *Awards:* Guggenheim Fellowship; Tamarind Fellowship *Collections:* Museum of Modern Art, NYC; San Francisco Museum of Modern Art *Exhibitions:* Los Angeles County Museum of Art; L.A.C.E. *Education:* Kansas City Art Institute *Dealer:* Herbert Palmer, Los Angeles

His abstract works crackle with repeated small geometric designs and flashes of color. Images are drawn from Native American and pre-Columbian sources, and his art has much to do with themes and motifs found in the collective unconscious discussed by Jung and his followers. His works are characterized by a deeply rendered surface, and he often uses a knife to work on a painting's surface. His recent artworks have encompassed a variety of materials and techniques, including large color fields with sign and symbol overlays, bronze and ceramic sculpture and computer graphics work transferred to prints.

MULLICAN, MATT (Mixed Media Artist)
c/o Michael Klein, Inc., 611 Broadway, 308, New York, NY 10012

Born: 1951 *Exhibitions:* Michael Klein, NYC; Dallas Museum of Art *Education:* California Institute of the Arts *Dealer:* Michael Klein, Inc., NYC

In 1987, he was invited by the Goldie Paley Gallery at Moore College of Art in Philadelphia to create nine major works for public spaces. His works in stone, glass, textile, canvas and paper were intended to "deflate the seriousness embedded in symbols, to blend the universal with the everyday." A performance in the 1970s consisted of having himself hypnotized on stage and verbally transcribing his journey through his personal history. Later, when semiology began to become a serious interest, he created fake reproduced art. This was followed by making worthless objects from which he created rubbings. His works incorporate symbols which look like universal signs.

MUNOZ, TERESA (Printmaker)
8136 Holy Cross Pl., Los Angeles, CA 90045

Born: 1945 *Collections:* Johnson Manfredi & Thorpe; U. of Mexico, Del Chopo *Exhibitions:* Malone Gallery, Los Angeles; Los Angeles Printmaking Society, Brand Library Galleries, Glendale *Education:* Cal. State-Long Beach

The artist's early interest in sculpture remains evident in her printmaking. Her concern with movement and with creating a sense of roundness and depth are hold-

Melissa Bodine McMillin, *Bag Lady,* 36 x 24, charcoal/oil

Moxzer, *Labyrinth,* 9 x 12, enamel on wood

overs from her initial abstract organic sculptures. Study of Rodin's work precipitated a heightened interest in surface activity and negative space, but printmaking began to demand more attention, and after college the artist pursued this medium to the exclusion of others. The kinetic, high-key quality of her early prints derives much from her admiration for Kandinsky and Klee. Later, as the collagraph process drew her interest, explorations by Clare Romano and John Ross convinced her to alter and refine her technique. The artist continues to develop new inking and printing techniques in hopes of achieving a unique clairity and richness of print.

MUNRO, ALAN A. (Painter, Multimedia Artist)
2858 N.W. Monterey Place, Corvallis, OR 97330

Born: 1930 *Collections:* Wichita Art Museum; Portland Art Museum *Exhibitions:* Harcourts Contemporary, San Francisco; Moorpark Community College *Education:* Wichita State U.

During graduate school, he discovered the work of the abstract expressionists and developed a more individual style that includes some surrealist influences. He works on large surfaces, usually from 2 by 3 feet to 6 feet square, of either canvas or 300 lb. De Arches paper. Bright primary colors in acrylic appear in boldly composed areas bounded and controlled by darker blues, black and white. Colors are variably applied, thin in some areas, impastoed in others. This variation in color and texture creates the impression of change and opposition. His artistic philosophy is summarized in a hand-written note pinned to the wall of his studio: "A fragile balance between stability and order."

MURANAKA, HIDEO (Painter)
179 Oak St., #W, San Francisco, CA 94102

Born: 1946 *Awards:* Honorable Mention, F.A.I. 20th Annual Juried Exhibition, San Bernadino County Museum, Redlands; 1st Prize, International Art Exhibition, Museo Hosio, Capranica-Viterbo, Italy *Education:* Tokyo National U. of Fine Arts and Music *Dealer:* Collectors Gallery, Oakland Museum Association

Since about twenty years ago, fresco has been the primary influence and inspiration of his work. He attempts to translate traditional Japanese painting styles through the creation of a fresco surface in his paintings, which are done in acrylic on rice paper or masonite. Most often, he works in extremely close-keyed tones, creating silhouette figures that dissolve into their deceptively void backgrounds. In *In a Corner of My Studio,* for example, a doll is foregrounded on a dull gray background. Closer examination, however, reveals a shadowed but active middle ground and background. His work invites the eye to linger and to concentrate more deeply in order to appreciate and understand the image.

MURPHY, DENNIS THOMAS (Painter, Sculptor)
1907 B Oak St., San Francisco, CA 94117

Born: 1949 *Awards:* Fred Gellert Foundation Grant; ASI Achievement Award *Collections:* French Hospital, San Francisco *Exhibitions:* Gallery 3220, San Francisco; Haight-Ashbury Cultural Arts Center, San Francisco *Education:* New York University

He was involved primarily in stone carvings during the 1960s and 1970s, his work was abstract in form. While attending medical school, he became fascinated with the human form and apprenticed with a master sculptor in New York, studying Renaissance techniques of stone carving, bronze casting, human anatomy and design. His work is intended as an exploration of humanity beneath the layers of ego, as expressed by the simplicity of his forms. Light and playful, his sculpture reflects connection to the earth, both in his choice of clay medium and in its content. His paintings expose the various levels of reality embodied by layers of paint. Sand and other materials also give texture to the paintings and result in a unique surface that creates soft, irregular colors.

MURRAY, PATRICIA A. (Painter, Mixed Media Artist)
1270 Monterey Blvd., San Francisco, CA 94127

Born: 1939 *Exhibitions:* Shorebirds, Tiburon; San Francisco Women's Art Gallery, San Francisco *Education:* Washington U.

She has a background of ten years work in the mental health field, and her art carries psychological or personal overtones. Working in oils and in watercolors, she attempts to achieve as much visual representation as possible with a minimum of colors (usually browns and blues) and formal elements. Drawing on her own psyche and experiences, her works strive to simplify or amplify the person, place, object or idea. These representations, once very abstract, have become more figurative over time.

MURRILL, GWYNN (Sculptor)
29012 Crest Pl., Agoura, CA 91301

Born: 1942 *Awards:* Guggenheim Fellowship; Prix Di Rome *Collections:* Los Angeles County Museum of Art; Security Pacific Bank, Los Angeles *Education:* UCLA *Dealer:* Asher/Faure, Los Angeles

He began as a painter. His first sculpted works were large lions, animals and giraffes, made from pieces of laminated construction-site wood glued together and shaped with a large disk sander. Though he still considered himself a painter at the time, he continued with sculpture because he liked the physical labor and the three-dimensional form. After he made a few pieces in wood, he began looking at sculpture from Africa, pre-Columbian Mexico, Egypt, Greece and Renaissance Europe. He continued making animals in wood until 1984 when he received an NEA grant. Since receiving the grant, he has worked exclusively with bronze.

MYERS, GIFFORD (Sculptor)
1267 Boston St., Altadena, CA 91001

Born: 1948 *Awards:* Young Talent Award, Los Angeles County Museum of Art; NEA Fellowship *Collections:* Los Angeles County Museum of Art *Exhibitions:* Los Angeles County Museum of Art; Los Angeles Municipal Art Gallery *Education:* UC-Berkeley; UC-Irvine *Dealer:* John Berggruen Gallery, San Francisco

Styles ranging from international-style modernism to postmodernist kitsch reveal his background in architecture. "Real Estart" is a series of wall-mounted miniature sculptures approximately 3 1/2 inches across. Constructed of materials such as bronze and ceramic, the pieces are glazed and then painted with acrylic. Both Hockney and Ruscha are strong influences as windows of urban and suburban houses, often opening on to swimming pools, reflect scenes that appear to be part of the same space the viewer occupies. Pieces often reverberate with social and political im-

Peter Max, *Crimson Lady,* 41 x 28, acrylic on paper. Hanson Galleries, Beverly Hills, CA

Hideo Muranaka, *Moment,* 32 x 24, pencil, ink on paper

D.T. Murphy, *Dance for Joy,* 9 x 17, woodcut

Patricia A. Murray, *Fenced,* 56 x 39, oil

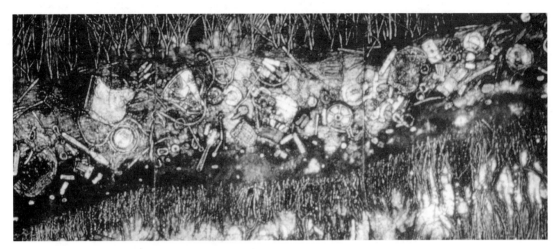

Teresa Muñoz, *Stroll on Blue Monday,* 30 x 72, collagraph print

Barry M. Nakasone, *Third Parent,* 20 x 18 x 12, metal, clay, cement

plications, evoked in a tongue-in-cheek manner. *Hedge/Wedge/Hold Out* (7 1/4 by 4 3/4 by 2 1/2 inches) refers to the confrontation between the private and corporate world: A tiny house made from one-dollar and five-dollar bills is wedged between two looming black skyscrapers. The soaring real estate market is the subject of *Imminent/Eminent Domain* (3 by 5 by 2 1/4 inches) in which a boarded-up red brick building marked for demolition sits next to a similar building whose windows reflect a modern high-rise.

MYERS, JEAN (Architectural Glass Artist)
P.O. Box AG, South Lake Tahoe, CA 95705

Born: 1928 *Awards:* Honorable Mention, Modern Liturgy Visual Arts Award; Craftsman Award, AIA Central Valley Chapter, Sacramento *Collections:* St. James Episcopal Church, San Francisco; Cherokee Memorial Park, Lodi *Exhibitions:* Sutter General Hospital, Sacramento; Christ the King Catholic Community Church, Las Vegas *Education:* UC-Berkeley; Stanford U.

Although she had been a watercolorist for fifteen years, she turned to glass art when she studied at the San Francisco Art Institute with Narcissus Quagliatta. In the mid-1970s, she also studied with Ludwig Schaffrath, master designer of the German contemporary glass movement. She works primarily in leaded, blown glass, designing and executing works that enhance the architecture into which they are set. Her work is most often commissioned for hospitals, churches, chapels and private residences. Images are both abstract and figurative, though abstracted from realism. Recently she has branched out to work in etched glass, wall painting, bas relief, mosaics and carved brick. Her brick bas reliefs are rough and earthy in stark contrast to the elegant, smooth glass windows and dividers.

Judi Campanaro, *Eagle Medicine,* 18 x 24, oil. Courtesy: Eagle Medicine

Marge Mount, *Demeter IV,* 36 x 48, oil on canvas

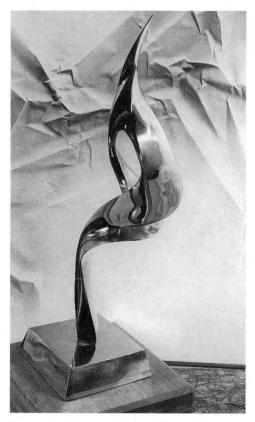

Leonardo Nierman, *Flame of Hope,* 12 feet, bronze.
Courtesy: University of Central Florida

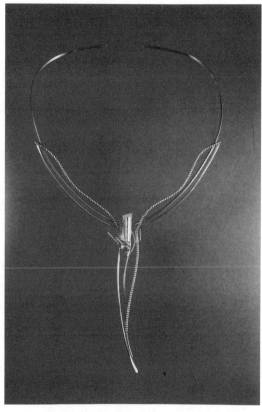

Dawn Nakanishi, *Flotation,* 4 x 4, sterling brooch,
formed and fabricated

Elanie Moore, *Grid/Checkerboard-Base Seven,* 42 x 66, acrylic

Bob Nugent, *Jardim, Suica VII,* 30 x 20, pastel on paper. Courtesy: Roy Boyd Gallery

Keiko Nelson, *Winter,* 72 x 84, paper sculpture. Photograph: Gary Sinick

Catherine Norman-Pitman, *Conspiracy,* 16 x 20, acrylic on masonite

Jackie Nach, *Message of Matter I,* 22 x 30, mixed media on Arches paper

NACH, JACKIE (Multimedia Artist)
1574 Roybury Dr., Los Angeles, CA 90035

Born: 1945 *Exhibitions:* Brentwood Art Center; S.I.T.E. Gallery, Santa Monica *Education:* Johannesburg School of Art, South Africa; UCLA

A successful graphic artist for ten years in her native South Africa, the artist eventually came to study fine art in the U.S. in 1973. She gravitated toward printmaking and photo-etching, experimenting with layers of translucent color. Her studies of the post-Impressionists inspired a concern for fractured light and its interaction with color. A humanitarian by nature, the artist strives to make her work express the common bond that she feels exists between all men. Her utilization of elemental symbols over which color is layered and blended in expressive, gestural swatches points to her search for man's collective consciousness.

NADALINI, LOUIS E. (Painter)
1726 15th Ave. #10, Seattle, WA 98122

Born: 1927 *Awards:* James Phelon Award, Palace of the Legion of Honor, San Francisco; Merit of Art, Salon Internationale Diplome D'Honneur, France *Collections:* Oakland Art Museum; UC-Berkeley *Exhibitions:* San Francisco Museum of Modern Art; Oakland Art Museum *Education:* Art Students League; San Francisco Art Institute *Dealer:* La Galerie Mouffe, Paris, France

Portraits, landscapes, figuration and abstraction make up the broad range of his concerns, dealt with in an equally broad range of media including oil, acrylic, brush and pen, ink and watercolor. In all cases, the artist fixes his attention on what he sees with the "mind's eye"—an unconscious selection that rearranges what he has seen and felt in people and nature. He composes paintings in which one recognizes the figures but not the background, at least not on a literal level; these paintings sidestep representation to arrive at an image that speaks to the unconscious, the effect of such an image being to communicate from the artist's unconscious to that of the viewers.

NADLER, HARRY (Painter)
4820 Guadalupe Terr., N.W., Albuquerque, NM 87107

Born: 1930 *Awards:* Fulbright Grant *Collections:* Guggenheim Museum, NYC; U. of California *Exhibitions:* Albuquerque Museum; University Art Museum, U. of New Mexico, Albuquerque *Education:* UCLA *Dealer:* Shippee Gallery, NYC

His abstract style has been influenced by the geometric orientation of Mondrian, and by the interplay of color and form of Matisse. An early interest in combining geometric structures with biomorphic forms has evolved in a geometric direction, as shown in his experiments with "magic squares" and "golden sections." He paints with handmade tempera paints on oriental rice paper, mounted on canvas. Although he is intellectual in his approach to art, his works display deep emotion.

NAGAKURA, SCOTT (Painter)
1745 N. Orange Dr., #230, Hollywood, CA 90028

Born: 1938 *Awards:* Critic Prize, Paris; Premio D'-Onore, Venice *Exhibitions:* Matsuya Ginza, Tokyo *Education:* Tokyo U. of Arts; Accademia Di Belle Arti Di Roma, Italy

In Tokyo and Rome, he studied painting in pastel and drawing in charcoal, pencil and watercolor. For over twenty years, he devoted himself to pastel painting and used a soft, colorful and free touch to express the nuance, shade and profundity of music. His images, situated between the concrete and the abstract, bore the influence of Odilon Redon, Botticelli, Giorgione and Dufy. When he moved to California from Tokyo it was "to turn over a new leaf." He abandoned his old style and began to paint and sketch the houses, landscapes and landmarks of Hollywood and Beverly Hills. Currently, his aim is to create an original style by mixing the classical with the modern, refined and light.

NAGLER, STEVEN (Performance Artist)
525 W. 12th St., Claremont, CA 91711

Born: 1950 *Awards:* NEA Grant; LACE Interdisciplinary Grant, NEA and Rockefeller Foundation *Exhibitions:* MAG Gallery, Santa Monica; Santa Monica Arts Commission *Education:* Claremont College

He trained as a ceramist in the early 1970s; he found his way into performance art by the late 1970s. A founding member of the performance ensemble HANGERS, he and other visual artists, actors, dancers and musicians performed throughout Southern California in the late 1970s and early 1980s. He studied with minimalist choreographer Rudy Perez and, as a result, began creating movement-based performance works. In 1984, he formed SHRIMPS in collaboration with choreographer Pamela Casey, installation artist Gail Youngquist and composer Michael Monteleone. The ensemble of large men and petite women explores issues of power, domination and sexual stereotypes by exploiting size, scale and gender. Typically, SHRIMPS performs rhythmic movement patterns on specifically designed platforms that serve as big drums. Performers are cast according to size and special ability, eschewing the dance tradition of casting only trained dancers to execute movement.

NAKANISHI, DAWN E. (Jeweler, Metalsmith)
P.O. Box 610043, Redwood City, CA 94061

Born: 1957 *Awards:* Finalist, International Art Competition, Los Angeles; Craftsperson of the Year, Oakland Museum *Exhibitions:* National Ornamental Metal Museum, Memphis; Mission Cultural Center, San Francisco *Education:* San Diego State U.; San Jose State U. *Dealer:* Paul/Luster Gallery, San Francisco

Trained in both metalsmithing and jewelry and inspired by Japanese craft and nature, she formed metal sheet and wire into fluid and sensual essences of natural forms. She abstracts leaves, shells and tropical flowers into pure sculpture. Nature continues to inspire her as she continues to use metalsmithing processes to fabricate jewelry and small sculpture. Her sterling silver and copper jewelry and objects are dynamic in composition, yet intimate enough to wear on the body. She has also explored the use of different surface treatments with patinas and acid etching.

NAKANO, YUZO (Painter, Printmaker)
1060 Heinz St., Berkeley, CA 94710

Born: 1942 *Awards:* Artist-in-Residence Grant, California Art Council; Small Project Award, Inter Arts, Marin, CA *Collections:* Achenbach Foundation, San Francisco; Art Institute of Chicago *Exhibitions:* Triton Museum; Kala Institute, Berkeley *Education:* Atelier 17, Paris; Contemporary Institute of Art,

Anthony Natsoulas, *This is Not a Game,* life-size, bronze, acrylic, urethane paint, glass. Courtesy: City of Sacramento

Sandra Grassi Nelipovich, *Band in a Balloon,* 25 x 31, batik on silk

Tokyo *Dealers:* Kala Institute, Berkeley; Vorpal Gallery, San Francisco

He studied oil painting in Japan and printmaking in Paris under S.W. Hayter. Although influenced by Hayter's theory of color and space, he preferred to explore his subconscious inner world through black-and-white images made in traditional aquatint and etching techniques. His growing interest in the material world, in physical phenomena and in the latest theories of space and time culminated in 1980 with two books of sequential images entitled "Evolution of Light," which reflected his concept of the natural world. Immediately thereafter, his imagination engaged in the possibilities of abstract concepts, he began to paint again, according to an "abstract system," in an accumulation of repeated marks or discontinuous lines of color. He calls these line paintings "Light Sculptures." They are meant to construct a tangible space and to serve as "scores" to his experimental musical compositions, which he makes on an electronic Midi system. He has also explored his artistic concerns in multi-media performance works, such as his *Noh One Knows.*

NAKASHIMA, JANICE (Painter)
281 Audubon Circle, Sacramento, CA 95831

Born: 1949 *Exhibitions:* Crocker-Kingsley Annual, Crocker Art Museum, Sacramento; The Galleria, Sacramento *Education:* Claremont College

Drawing her artistic vision from the works of the Abstract Expressionists, she has explored different ways of making tangible the important, intangible aspects of her life. During the 1970s, she sought ways to express her feelings in abstract form, using inks on paper, rendered semi-transparent with rhoplex. She then drew on this paper, creating layered images. Light passed through the drawings as they hung, highlighting the layered forms, and communicating her thoughts on the passage of time and the different qualities of memory. She now uses more color—especially muted purple, black and blue—than in the past, and has begun to work with more land- and waterscape imagery.

NAKASONE, BARRY M. (Sculptor)
748 Lukepane Ave., Honolulu, HI 96816

Born: 1954 *Awards:* Japanese Chamber of Commerce Award *Collections:* Academy of Arts; State Foundation of Culture and the Arts *Exhibitions:* Wing Luke Memorial Museum, Seattle; Academy of Arts, Honolulu *Education:* U. of Hawaii, Manoa *Dealer:* Gallery EAS, Honolulu

Japanese historical themes and forms contrast with such modern materials as cement and metal. In graduate school, he used primitive and oriental firing techniques. Later, he began sculpting in a mixed media of fiber and clay. In his present work, he has moved towards a recognition of his Japanese heritage. Some pieces resemble such traditional icons as Kimono dolls. He combines these traditional forms with industrial materials such as metal, cement and clay. The pieces are unglazed, using primitive firing techniques such as raku and flash firings. He has been greatly influenced by Jay Kavipil, Suzanne Wolf, David Kuraoka and Wayne Higby.

NAKAYOSHI, TAKESHI (Printmaker)
1718 Anza St., San Francisco, CA 94118

Born: 1952 *Collections:* Mills College *Exhibitions:* Voyage Gallery, Japantown, San Francisco; Dot Gallery, Kyoto, Japan *Education:* San Francisco Art Institute *Dealer:* Walton-Gilbert Gallery, San Francisco

His style is influenced by the impressionists, cubists, and constructivists and by Kurt Schwitters and Mercel Janco. He splashes color on wet watercolor paper to create condensation effects and color dispersions. These works, called "viol," try to express the joy of Nirvana. Returning to printmaking, he created his own technique, "multiple monoprinting." Unlike other printmaking processes, no press is involved. Instead, he prefers to work with stencils, colors and the texture and chemistry of the paper. Always searching for new abstract, spiritual symbols, he is studying Mayan, Olmec and Polynesian geometries.

NANESSENCE (Painter, Photographer)
P.O. Box 2408 Julian, CA 92036

Born: 1943 *Awards:* Purchase Awards, Small Images *Exhibitions:* Museum of Photographic Arts; Ariel Gallery, NYC *Education:* Swarthmore College; Parsons School of Design, NYC

She brings a hands-on, emotional dynamic to photography and often all but obscures the medium with a variety of techniques. In some works she creates abstract shapes through a more or less controlled shredding of gelatinous negatives. For others, she paints on prints with inks and oils, making images that appear to be abstract canvasses. Only upon close inspection can the viewer recognize the original photographic image of a body, shadow or social gathering. Believing that the essence of art in the '80s is in its very incompleteness, she finds that perfection is no longer attainable by modern culture. This belief is the impetus for her work. Her most recent interests include publishing a grassroots hometown newspaper and documenting persons in the arts who could not otherwise afford a quality photographic record.

NATSOULAS, ANTHONY (Sculptor)
2207 Park Ave., Chico, CA 95926

Born: 1959 *Awards:* Fellowship, Skowhegan School of Painting and Sculpture; Tiffany Foundation Nominee *Collections:* Byron Meyer; Daniel Jacobs *Exhibitions:* Rena Bransten Gallery, San Francisco; San Francisco Art Commission Gallery *Education:* UC-Davis *Dealer:* Rena Bransten, San Francisco

He studied with Bob Arneson and began his career by using objects around him as models to explore the different aspects of clay and glazes. Growing dissatisfied with making objects to place on pedestals, he progressed to working with the full figure, soon developing life-sized figures that literally stand on their own two feet. The figures assume lively, dynamic expressions in many different postures and are intended to express the personal limitations and restrictions of the American middle-class. The pieces are brightly colored, and their interaction with the issues they address evokes humor. For example, in the piece *I Hate What I Don't Understand,* a 6 1/2-foot man stands on a 4 1/2-foot head, symbolizing his confusion.

NAUMAN, BRUCE (Sculptor)
c/o Leo Castelli Gallery, 420 W. Broadway, New York, NY 10012

Born: 1941 *Awards:* NEA Fellowship; Aspen Institute for Humanistics Studies Grant *Collections:* Whitney Museum, NYC; Los Angeles County Museum of Art

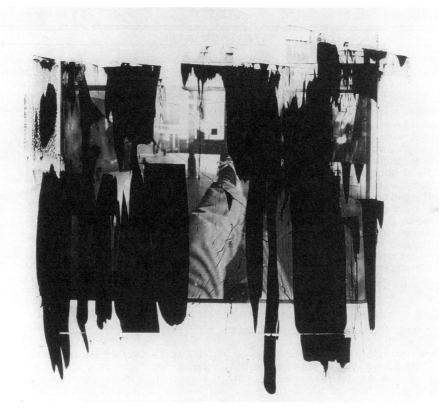

Nanessence, *Inked Artwalk,* 30 x 34, inks over silver print

Patricia Georgiana Norman, *Lilith's Domain: Nammu—The Mother Who Gave Birth to Heaven and Earth,* 46 x 52, oil on canvas

Exhibitions: Museum of Modern Art, NYC; Whitney Museum, NYC *Education:* U. of Wisconsin; UC-Davis *Dealer:* Leo Castelli Gallery, NYC; Gemini G.E.L., Los Angeles

In the late 1960s, he gained recognition with multimedia presentations in such media as neon, rubber, fiberglass, sound, video and even holography. Slogans in neon played with language and mocked advertising gimmicks. Pieces made of rubber and fiberglass were bent, folded and hung, emphasizing the objects' properties rather than the objects themselves. He has made casts of his own body in fiberglass, clay and neon, during taped or live performances in an attempt to probe self-awareness. At times, the audience members were asked to participate in video performances in order to expand their own self-awareness. Language, inner meaning and experience continue to be important in the sculptures and various other presentations.

NELIPOVICH, SANDRA GRASSI (Batik Artist)
5922 Calle Cedro, Anaheim, CA 92807

Born: 1939 *Awards:* Honorary Diploma, Accademia Universale, Alessandro Magno, Prato, Italy *Collections:* McDonald's Corporate Headquarters, Oakbrook, IL *Exhibitions:* Whittier Museum; Lawry's California Center, Los Angeles *Education:* U. of Illinois; School of the Art Institute of Chicago

A former Illinois art teacher, she is influenced by the naivete of children's art as well as by the Yugoslavian primitives. In the 1970s she moved to California, and her batik has since evolved from simple forms and figures to intricate themes often involving many dye baths and waxings. She creates fanciful, humorous themes that are at once primitive and detailed in a varying array of colors. In one piece people sit in an old-fashioned wagon and play musical instruments. In another, children, bakers and prostitutes combine in a cheerful Parisian street scene. "Art can be fun and optimistic and still make a statement," she says.

NELSON, EDITH MACFARLANE (Painter)
Star Route Box 170, Twisp, WA 98856

Born: 1908 *Awards:* Purchase Prize, Washington Federated Women's Club *Exhibitions:* Brewster High School; Leavenworth High School *Education:* U. of Washington

Her career began in the late 1920s, when she studied landscape and portraiture under the influence of post-impressionism. A career as a high school art teacher left some time to execute large expressionist-inspired canvases. These combined elements of formal composition, sketched in advance, with a bold freedom of execution. A move to a more remote area of the state necessitated a shift into more conventional genre subjects, due in part to the conservative tastes of the rural populace. The regional style met with local approval and resulted in several mural commissions for public facilities, while more adventurous works remained stored in the artist's studio.

NELSON, EILEEN (Painter, Sculptor)
7 Regent Ct., Novato, CA 94947

Born: 1940 *Exhibitions:* San Francisco African-American Historical and Cultural Society; Crown Zellerbach Gallery, San Francisco *Education:* Illinois Institute of Technology, Chicago; American Academy of Art

This sculptor works in mixed media, creating pieces that may be free-standing or wall hangings. Recent works are sculptural and use the motion of the air for movement. Prior to these, she worked on a series of hanging bas reliefs. The works are lightweight and colorful, composed of interconnected parts and designed to make the space they fill come alive with color and motion. One series of hangings depicts the people, life, and colors of Novato, California. The pieces, made from canvas and wire, are bendable and intended to be touched and moved. A muralist as well, she has depicted the 1906 San Francisco earthquake for a competition concerning the history of the city.

NELSON, KEIKO (Painter, Printmaker)
9 Arlington Lane, Kensington, CA 94707

Born: 1948 *Awards:* United Nations Poster Contest; International Contemporary Paper Art Chicago *Collections:* City of Chicago; Cairo Opera House, Egypt *Exhibitions:* Gallery of Tokyo, Japan; Institute for Design and Experimental Art, Sacramento *Education:* International Art Institute, Japan; Staatliche Hochschule fur Bilden und Kunst, Hamburg, West Germany *Dealer:* Miriam Perlman, Chicago

Her work evokes the ancient traditions of her native Japan. She began as a child in Kyoto with formal studies in the classical arts of tea and flower arranging. She explored the traditional folk arts of Indonesia and Thailand, whose influence can be seen in her strongly emotional use of form and color. Later studies in Europe and the United States were also influential. Her pieces are a melange of East and West. Typical are her cast paper and mixed-media kimonos. She enriches the austere geometric shapes of the traditional Japanese garment with a rich emotional eccentricity that is both modern in its expression and ancient in its natural elements.

NELSON, LOLA (Painter, Wood Carver)
4049 E. Michigan, Fresno, CA 93703

Born: 1944 *Awards:* S.W.A. Signature Award, Society of Western Artists; 1st Prize, Reedley Fiesta Art Show, Reedley *Exhibitions:* Annual Hall of Flowers, San Francisco; Wilson's Galleries, Fresno *Dealer:* Carolyn Hecker, Fresno

Influenced by old masters such as Rembrandt and by Remington, she began painting in a traditional style while in high school; she began showing her paintings in 1983. Her subjects typically include realistic landscapes, wildlife, farm equipment, portraits and florals. She uses underpainting and glazes to give subjects the sense of being illuminated from behind. In the watercolor, *Abandoned Memories*, she depicted an old tractor in front of a barn. Wood is another of her media, in which she produces carvings of small animals. Working from her own photographs or in pleine air, she has recently painted a series of purple, pink and orange underpaintings for oil landscapes from the Mt. Whitney, California area. She is equally versatile in watercolor, oils and pastels.

NERI, MANUEL (Sculptor)
251 Post St., San Francisco, CA 94108

Born: 1930 *Awards:* NEA Fellowship; Guggenheim Fellowship *Collections:* San Francisco Museum of Modern Art; Oakland Museum *Exhibitions:* Corcoran Gallery, Washington, DC; San Francisco Museum of Modern Art *Education:* California School of Fine Arts

Mildred Nordman, *Busy Corner,* 50 x 40, oil

Lola Nelson, *Rustin' Out,* 18 x 24, oil

Dealer: John Berggruen Gallery, San Francisco; Charles Cowles Gallery, NYC

A class with ceramist Peter Voulkos turned him away from the study of engineering to the serious pursuit of an art career. After a number of abstract expressionist paintings and funk art pieces, he turned to the figure. Bright enamel paint was applied in places to these early figural plaster sculptures in order to enhance texture and contrast; the figures were left mostly white. Later, interested in the effects of light and shadow, he discontinued the use of color in favor of the plain white plaster figures depicting gestural movement. Bronze casts have been made of some of the pieces, the bronze reworked and then painted. Recent marble sculptures are treated similarly to earlier works in plaster. He works with stone in his studio in Carrera, Italy, and is a professor of art at the University of California at Davis.

NEUHAUSER, PAIGE (Painter)
P.O. Box 684, Santa Barbara, CA 93102

Born: 1957 *Collections:* Tsukamoto Steel; The Grill, Montecito, CA *Exhibitions:* Faulkner Gallery *Education:* Louisiana State U.

During her college years, she worked primarily in pencil, developing a photo-realist style. Her interest in light, dark and shadow led her to experiment with black and white photography. Similarly, she found that watercolors allowed her to render light and dark in a realistic manner. Later she turned to dry pastels, preferring to work in a realist style shaded by Impressionist influences. The larger paintings are executed in acrylics, and the smaller pieces are often night scenes in which she focuses on the interplay between shadow and color.

NEVINS, ELEANOR S. (Painter, Printmaker)
4478 N. College Ave., Fresno, CA 93704

Born: 1903 *Awards:* 1st Place, Society of Western Artists Show, Fresno *Exhibitions:* Artists Guild of America; Delegant Gallery *Education:* UC-Berkeley

As a child, she painted scenes of the family ranch. Later, she studied at the University of California at Berkeley and taught high school and adult education classes for more than twenty years. Her subjects include still lifes, landscapes, animal paintings—especially of horses she has known—and portraits, which she does on commission. She paints alla prima, first blocking out her shapes with charcoal and then trying to capture her subject in one layer of paint. Some call her style impressionistic. Her palette is limited and her brush is bristled. She has also painted with pastels. She is a member of the Society of Western Artists.

NEWBORG, CAROL (Sculptor)
2021 S. Alameda #8, Los Angeles, CA 90058

Born: 1954 *Awards:* Pollock-Krasner Grant *Collections:* Skirball Museum; Los Angeles Jewish Museum *Exhibitions:* Junior Art Center, Barnsdall Park, Los Angeles; USC Fisher Gallery *Education:* UC-Berkeley

Her early sculptures were a series of "Sanctuary" installations comprising hand-formed clay cylinders. These site-specific installations were designed to create meditative, spiritual spaces. More recent installations are based on archaeological and architectural Mayan imagery.

NEWCOMB, GREER (Painter)
1319 Tasso St., Palo Alto, CA 94301

Born: 1907 *Exhibitions:* Ojai Art Center, Ojai, CA; Stanford Art Gallery *Education:* Detroit Society Art & Crafts; Cranbrook Art Academy, Bloomfield, MI

She has completed series on elves, fairies and salamanders and has made thirteen paintings of the Grand Canyon. Other paintings in oils and acrylics are post-impressionist seascapes and tree studies. She has recently been illustrating and writing a monograph on trees of significance in the Old and New Worlds. In *Konmbaoum Tree*, one of the paintings she will use in the book, she depicts the symbolic Tibetan tree that has a different sanskrit letter on each leaf. These trees, painted in oils, acrylics and Sumii (a type of Chinese ink) are now in private hands but will be collected for the book. She is a poet, and her work has been published widely.

NEWELL, ED (Painter)
13855 Manakee Ave., Clearlake, CA 95422

Born: 1929 *Awards:* 1st Prize, 21st Annual Society of Western Artists; Watercolor Award, DeYoung Museum, San Francisco *Exhibitions:* Periwinkle Gallery, Pacifica; Maggon's West, Clearlake

Although he took classes with Elliot O'Hara, he is mostly self-taught. Now that he is retired from shipyard work, he devotes himself to watercolor painting. Inspired by all of creation, he creates landscapes of the Clearlake area. Striving for spontaneity and fresh, clean brushwork, he works to make technique automatic—freeing the mind to explore color relationships and textures. He cites Winslow Homer, John Singer Sargent, Charles Burchfield and Andrew Wyeth as his favorite painters, and believes that art and painting contain the seeds of salvation.

NEWICK, BOB (Painter)
125 Greendale Drive, Los Gatos, CA 95030

Born: 1927 *Awards:* Midwest Watercolor Society Merit Award *Exhibitions:* Los Gatos Museum; Fellowship Gallery *Education:* Chicago Academy of Fine Art

He works with very large brushes to explore a vocabulary of shapes. Beginning with a traditional subject, he deconstructs its shapes into unrelated forms that still maintain a cohesive movement, energy and sense of place. He has worked with a wide spectral palette, but presently is concentrating on works in gray tones. Previously, he worked in oils, woodblock, and metal embossing while a commercial artist.

NEWMARK, SHEILA MEYER (Painter, Printmaker)
125 N. Orange Dr., Los Angeles, CA 90036

Born: 1940 *Awards:* 1st Place, La Mirada Festival of Arts; Best of Show, Women's Caucus for Art/Los Angeles *Collections:* Security Pacific National Bank; Bank of America *Exhibitions:* Conejo Valley Art Museum, Thousand Oaks; Barbican Gallery, London *Education:* USC; Parsons School of Design

Paintings, monotypes and hand-worked woodcuts using intense, saturated color and bold shapes make up the current body of work of this artist. Drawing from the landscape, architecture and people in her surroundings, the information is translated into large abstractions which contrast strong brush strokes with areas of flat color and rich texture. The woodcuts range in size from twenty by thirty inches to four feet by eight, and appear more like paintings than prints. Using the vocabulary of abstract expressionism, especially as found in the work of Helen Frankenthaler, the

Paige Neuhauser, *Windows, Nice,* 17 x 23, Dry Pastel. Courtesy: Karel deVeer

Ed Newell, *Pacific Mood,* 20 x 22, watercolor

works stress the importance of color and shape contrasts.

NEWTON, LORNA S. (Painter)
649 C. Street, Lemoore, CA 93245

Born: 1955 *Awards:* Powell Award in Watercolor, Kings County Art League *Exhibitions:* Artisans Gallery; The Muse Gallery *Education:* Austin State U., Nacogdoches, TX

She has been influenced by the colors of Mark Adams, the colors and patterns of Paul Gauguin, and the perspectives of O'Keeffe and the Japanese watercolorists. She paints with watercolor and works in series. Among her subjects are flowers, koi ponds, swans, peacocks, and classical poses of women with a nouveau and deco feel. She begins her work by transferring her subject matter to a sheet of washing paper. She then masks it down and floods the surface with watercolor dye, producing stains much like those of watered satin. She layers colors into the background using a negative painting technique to produce the plant, lace, root, or scroll shapes found in wallpaper. When the background is complete she works on the main subject, bringing it forward in thin glazes of color.

NEWTON, RICHARD (Performance Artist)
620 N. Cherokee Ave., Los Angeles, CA 90004

Born: 1948 *Exhibitions:* Documenta 6, Kassel, W. Germany; Spazio Zero, Rome; Los Angeles Theater Center *Education:* Univ. of California

In structuring his work, he sets up a presentation in which the audience has no time-frame in which to gauge its viewing. There is no implied beginning, middle or end. Each audience member comes forward voluntarily to engage the artwork and departs when through. Work is then carried forward not as a fact but as a series of perceptions and remembrances of how things were. The act of affecting the viewer has now become more important, more valuable, than the object of art that made the interaction possible. These social relationships of object to maker to beholder are chosen to explicate his work as an artist.

NICHOLSON, PAUL (Painter)
13660 Green Valley Rd., Sebastopol, CA 95472

Born: 1945 *Exhibitions:* Bridge of Beauty, San Francisco; Festival of Space Music and Art, Palo Alto, CA

Dali, Miro and Magritte are early influences on his style. By the late 1970s, he evolved canvases of highly detailed, psychological landscapes and studies of the female form. His large abstractions of the 1980s invite comparisons with the work of Kandinsky; in addition, the works allude to three dimensionality. Although the work is abstract, he draws the viewer to a central point in the canvas. His current "Energy" series involves layering and glazing. He paints with oil in colors ranging from the vibrant to the muted.

NIELSEN, ELINORE ANN (Painter, Printmaker)
P.O. Box 2281, Berkeley, CA 94702

Born: 1938 *Collections:* American University, Cairo *Exhibitions:* Mill Valley Library Art Gallery; American Cultural Center Gallery, Cairo *Education:* School of the Art Institute of Chicago; UC-Berkeley

Drawing over etchings and lithographs with prismacolor pencils comprise earlier works. The pencil strokes over etchings created tactile illusions of interwoven threads in three-dimensional frames. Drawing over lithographs created free-floating images of intense color in an atmospheric luminosity of silver. Recently, she created a series entitled "Four-Part Inventions in Silver" by first printing electronic circuit boards on an etching press and then drawing with oil-base colored pencils over the inked impressions. The four vertical panels resemble miniature Oriental screens of metallic luster overlaid with expressionistic calligraphy and impressionistic imagery. As educator as well as artist, her experiences include teaching and consulting in California, serving on the faculties at the University of Illinois and the Colegio de Guatemala, and working as artist for archaeological excavations in Egypt.

NIELSEN, MARGARET (Painter)
5106 Franklin Ave., Los Angeles, CA 90027

Born: 1948 *Awards:* NEA Fellowship; Beaubourg Foundation Fellowship, Paris *Collections:* Madison Art Center, Madison, WI; City of Los Angeles *Exhibitions:* Corcoran Gallery, Washington, DC; Santa Barbara Museum of Art *Education:* Calif. Institute of the Arts, Valencia, CA *Dealer:* Asher/Faure Gallery, Los Angeles

From 1970 through the early '80s, she employed inanimate objects such as ladders, post cards and hats in small-scale oil paintings to suggest human interaction and psychological drama. Her work has since evolved into an ongoing narrative of what appears to be a hunting trip. Depictions of nocturnal drama in dreamlike wilderness settings convey a continued concern with the infusion of archetypal content. Her images create a dramatic, ritualistic atmosphere—for example, rivers of turquoise snakes and red-orange fish struggling to reach a campfire. Sizes range from 4 by 5 feet to 8 by 10 feet; all of her work is done in meticulous detail with a very small brush. She chiefly uses transparent colors in an oil glazing technique that results in intense portrayals of a natural world gone out of control.

NIERMAN, LEONARDO (Painter, Sculptor)
Reforma 16-b, San Augel, Mexico 20 D.F.

Born: 1932 *Awards:* Winner, International Sculpture Competition, Central Florida Univ.; Palm D'Or, Beaux Arts, Monaco *Collections:* Art Institute of Chicago; Boston Museum of Fine Arts *Exhibitions:* Museum of Science and Industry, Los Angeles; Upstairs Gallery, Beverly Hills *Dealer:* Merrill Chase, Chicago

Although at first impression his work is abstract, the elements are inspired by the forces of nature—wind, fire, meteors, lightning, space, underwater eruptions, the instant of the creation of the universe. Also underlying the the final abstract forms are images of dreams and eternity. *Peace and Flame* are bronze sculptures that twist and flow flame-like, their sharp curving edges creating movement and defining space. His painting *Form in Suspension* recalls the sculptural concern with space while presenting a multitude of straight and curved lines intersecting in a violent explosion in the center of the canvas, geometric shapes flying off from the point of intersection. "A great deal of my speculations have been motivated by the forms of wings, flames, storms, birds and crystal worlds, all of them somehow interrelated by the use of music as a constant obsession during the creative process," he says.

NININGER, SUSAN (Mixed Media Artist)
P.O. Box 15841, Los Angeles, CA 90015

Judy North, *It Furthers One to Cross the Great Waters,* 144 x 72, acrylic on canvas. Photograph: Mel Schockner

Richard Newton, *The Former Miss Barstow with Every Tom, Dick and Harry in a Doll's House,* 3-act play. Photo: Eric Engler

Born: 1952 *Awards:* NEA Fellowship; Western States Arts Foundation Artists Fellowship *Exhibitions:* Los Angeles County Museum of Art; Los Angeles Institute of Contemporary Art *Education:* Rhode Island School of Design; U. of New Mexico; U. of Washington

Inspired by Antonio Gaudi's sculptural approach to architecture, she applied architectural thinking to designing for the human body. Pursuing costume as an art form, she began to incorporate learned techniques in ceramics and fabrics, and eventually other materials such as wood, cast paper and metals, toward the development of images for her sculptural costumes that are are passionate and intense. Her works of "Costume Sculpture" are pieces that vary in size from a series of little girls' bathing suits to larger kimono forms, each piece implying a story or emotional fantasy intended to stimulate the viewer's imagination. Her recent garments include a series of warrior costumes. *Clown Warrior,* comprises of a parasol hat, reeds, paper, fabrics and metal studs. This costume is part of a San Francisco based choreographer's repetoire. *Royal Warrior* is made of printed cotton, velveteen, fur, dice, seed pods, broken mirrors and metal lions' paws, with a piece of sculptural armor attached at one shoulder. This is intended as a static image exploring shape and texture in juxtoposition to the human body. Both works employ materials as physical metaphors for psychological armor suggesting symbols of our behavior.

NISHIDA, YOSHIHIRO YOUKEE (Painter)
263 W. El Redetto Dr., Monterey Park, CA 91754

Born: 1946 *Collections:* Cranbrook Museum, Bloomfield, MI *Exhibitions:* Design Center of Los Angeles; Brand Library Art Galleries, Glendale *Education:* Cranbrook Academy of Art

For seven years, this artist studied the technical aspects of printmaking, paying particular attention to lithography. Weary of searching for techniques, he began in 1980 to paint on old lithographic plates, thus beginning his work as a mixed-media artist. He paints on any surface he has at hand, laying down shapes and patterns until struck by an idea. The work is organic, spontaneous and marked by exuberant color and gesture. His finished pieces are abstract, and their primitive qualities sometimes suggest Mayan art, although the artist has not studied Mayan art or culture.

NOCITO, JAMES M. (Painter)
3549 Arnold Ave., San Diego, CA 92104

Born: 1960 *Awards:* Certificate of Merit, Metro Art International Exhibition; Pennsylvania Governor's School for the Arts Scholarship *Exhibitions:* Art 54 Gallery, New York; La Jolla Museum of Art *Education:* Carnegie Mellon U.; Columbia U. *Dealer:* Art Directions Inc., San Diego

While studying with Justin Schorr at Columbia, he became interested in collage. Using a form of calligraphy that he developed into a personal language, he collaged symbols on rice paper, creating large tomb-like pieces. He drew from varied artistic disciplines, ranging from courtroom sketching to set design, and his collages became more intricate. He combines elements from his drawings, woodcuts, paintings and photographs with images from medieval and Renaissance art, and then prints and hand-paints the pieces. In addition to the collages, he has recently completed a series of gouache-and-ink paintings and continues to design collages for Exoticards, an internationally distributed greeting card company.

NODELMAN, NANCY (Mixed Media Artist)
108 Hacienda Dr., Tiburon, CA 94920

Born: 1937 *Awards:* San Francisco Artists' Co-op; Marin Society of Artists *Collections:* Bank of America, San Francisco *Exhibitions:* Falkirk Cultural Center, San Rafael; College of Marin *Education:* Ohio State U.; San Francisco Art Institute

She is impelled by an artistic sensibility that wishes to restructure and revise both the content and the intent of objects, materials and images. Though she is essentially self-taught, her early collages and assemblages of found objects indicated a "Japanese" sensibility. Classes enabled her to integrate printmaking into her wall-hung work, and she has developed processes that make paper appear metallic, wood-like or clay-like. She has increasingly been inspired by tribal and ancient forms. As her occasionally freestanding work has developed dimension, she has become more influenced by the diverging sculptural styles of Isamu Noguchi, John Chamberlain and David Nash.

NORDMAN, MILDRED (Painter)
225 Chilverton St., Santa Cruz, CA 95062

Born: 1904 *Awards:* Best Painting, Association of Honolulu Artists *Exhibitions:* Santa Cruz Art League; Montalvo Art Gallery, Saratoga, CA *Education:* U. of Iowa

She works with a palette knife, quickly using large quantities of paint. Her paintings of trees and the sea are executed with a full palette, particularly yellow and the other primaries. She has recently restored some 17th century paintings.

NORIEGA, RAMSES (Painter)
6753 Radio Dr., San Diego, CA

Born: 1944 *Awards:* Recognition Banquet, Hispanic Society of the Arts *Exhibitions:* La Casa de Arte, La Jolla; Anuska Gallery, San Diego *Education:* UCLA

His art is concerned with the social, political and economic forces that imperil the Chicano community in this country, and which assail many poor nations around the world. After experimenting with a variety of styles and techniques, he developed his own somewhat expressionist-surrealist style, well-suited to rendering the social criticism and psychological elements that form the basis of his work. Using watercolor or acrylic, he builds thin, transparent fields of color, then breaks them up with pen and ink forms. His work has a nervous appearance, as though the images were in motion, or had been drawn over a bumpy surface. His palette includes a range of cool and warm colors. He cites Borges, Rembrandt and Van Gogh as major influences.

NORMAN, DARRELL M. (Paper/Fiber Artist)
7715 Boulder Ridge Trail, Shingletown, CA 96088

Born: 1950 *Awards:* 3rd Prize, Mixed Media, California State Fair, Sacramento *Collections:* U. of Dubuque, Iowa *Exhibitions:* Nichols Gallery, Mendocino; Redding Museum *Education:* U. of Iowa

After university courses in textiles and art, she concentrated on weaving, spinning and dyeing. In 1979, she became interested in handmade paper, and studied with internationally known papermaker, Bob Nugent. Responding to the spontaneity of paper, but wishing to retain the tactile and textural qualities of

Nancy Nodelman, *Close to Open,* 16 x 24, mixed media. Courtesy: M. Crnich, San Francisco

Kristina Rice Nugent, *Triangle Trees,* 24 x 40, oil on linen

fiber, she began incorporating fibers into handmade paper. During this period, work developed from three-dimensional assemblage to two-dimensional collage. The materials included handmade paper of abaca, flax, linen and sisal, felt, silk fibers, angora goat hair and bamboo. In 1986, she produced a series of heavily textured handmade paper garments. Recently, she has become interested in cast paper as a medium for three-dimensional form. These pieces utilize a variety of techniques and materials, including metallic threads and fiber, shibori dyed silk fabrics and woven handmade paper.

NORMAN, PATRICIA GEORGIANA (Painter, Printmaker)
2205 Westmont Dr., Alhambra, CA 91803

Born: 1930 *Exhibitions:* Brand XVII, Glendale; Chaffey Community Art Association Juried Show, Ontario *Education:* California State U.

While she continues to print etchings and monotypes, her painting has moved from watercolor to oil. She also creates artist books. Three arenas—psychology, feminism and mythology—converge in her work. She begins by "doodling," releasing free-floating images from her imagination. These images are then developed in an expressionistic style, influenced by Gorky, Tobey and Motherwell, that balances line with color wash and barely delineated form. She paints on canvases from 36 by 40 inches to 46 by 52 inches in size, occasionally creating diptychs. Images are glimpsed underneath the whitewashed passages and stand in relation to the viewer much like a memory, an elusive thought or a fragment from a myth.

NORMAN, TYLER (Painter)
Route 1, Box 108, Taylor, TX 76574

Born: 1925 *Collections:* Bishop Petroleum, Houston; Kilroy Co. of Texas, Houston *Exhibitions:* Southwestern Watercolor Society; Rocky Mountain National Water Media Show *Education:* Houston Museum of Fine Arts School; U. of Houston *Dealer:* The Alley Gallery, Galveston, TX

Her images of robed figures and tropical landscapes reflect the diverse cultures she experienced while traveling in India, Nepal and China. Her media include oil, pastel and watercolor, and she applies paint in layers of thin washes. She renders her pieces in an impressionistic, semi-abstract manner influenced by Millard Sheets, and her subjects range from portraits to creative paintings of scenery and nudes. She has exhibited widely and has recently been working on series of nudes and landscapes. "I yearn to capture the individual quality of beauty that is found in every man, woman and child; that vision of nature which surrounds them and makes their world whole," she says.

NORMAN-PITMAN, CATHERINE (Painter)
P.O. Box 8529, Universal City, CA 91608

Born: 1954 *Awards:* 1st Place, Acrylic Painting, Creative Arts Center, Burbank; 2nd Place, Acrylic Painting, Nepenthe Mundi Society, Omaha, NE *Collections:* Matel Corp., CA; Keneth Fine Food & Spirits, NJ *Exhibitions:* Limited Edition Gallery, Beverly Hills; A. Beck Gallery, Sherman Oaks *Education:* Los Angeles Valley College

A self-taught artist, she began in 1979 to paint the world as if seen through louvered windows. Typically, her subject is the figure, with architecture as a structuring element. In her treatment of the human form,

she departs from structure to show strength of emotion. In the foreground of *Hollywood Boulevard*, an older woman stands near a star on the street; in the background, there is a marquee with a poster of a dancer. In another painting, a realistically-painted boy stands in front of a black, white and gray brick wall. She paints with acrylics on textured masonite tempered with gesso, and makes her hard edged forms vibrate, by juxtaposing flat color with blended, lighter values or contrasting colors. Recently, she has worked with acrylics on paper as well as pastel on paper to further her ideas with the Through the Louvres style.

NORRIS, KARALEE (Enamel Artist)
6655 Palo Verde, Twenty-Nine Palms, CA 92277

Born: 1957 *Awards:* 1st Place, California Midwinter Show *Exhibitions:* Glass on Metal Exhibition, San Diego *Education:* San Diego State U.

She studied oil painting at college until she discovered the technique of enameling on metal, which she studied under JoAnne Tanzer. She was greatly intrigued by the combination of disciplines in this technique, which involves potter's glass ground with oxides of color and fixed to steel or copper in a process of fifty or more firings. Her favorite stylistic device is the splintering of recognizable forms into patterns of shape and color. Her recent work is on a large scale of 8 by 10 feet or greater. These works, in the style of three-dimensional landscape, are pieced together with smaller forms. She uses sawed copper shapes settled into a mahogany background that follows the design. Enameling is still an important component of these works, which sometimes use a projected photographic image as the beginning of the design.

NORRIS, TREVOR (Painter)
2415 S, Santa Fe Ave. #8, Los Angeles, CA 90058

Born: 1948 *Awards:* Purchase Award, Santa Barbara Arts Council *Collections:* Santa Barbara Arts Council; Fisher Gallery, U. of Southern California *Exhibitions:* Pierce College, Thousand Oaks; Barnsdau Park Municipal Art Gallery *Education:* Central School of Art, London; UC-Santa Barbara *Dealer:* Jan Baum Gallery, Los Angeles

His style varies from figurative to abstract depictions of images ranging from views of buildings, cars and tracks to geometric figures, abstract patterns and non-objective forms. His trademark works are painted enamel aerial cityscapes and landscapes on aluminum and steel. Executed in bold colors, these works are influenced by American abstract expressionism, pop art, and California "surface" works. He developed more recent paintings from previous study in ceramics and from an affinity with high gloss, reflective surfaces and glazes. He often sands down the paintings to obtain a faded, timeworn or decayed appearance.

NORTH, JUDY (Painter, Glass Artist)
3 Tamarack, San Geronimo, CA 94963

Born: 1937 *Awards:* Tiffany Foundation *Exhibitions:* San Francisco Museum of Modern Art; Fuller- Goldeen Gallery, San Francisco *Education:* Otis Art Institute; San Francisco Art Institute

After completing her formal training, she began a search for her own identity. For many years, she painted large-scale watercolors of a psychological nature. Her paintings, which were full of color, imagery and wet washes, were attempts at revealing her feelings; they were navigations of her observations and

E.K. Meadow, *Eleventh Street, Santa Monica II,* 36 x 60, oil on canvas. Courtesy: Orlando Gallery.
Photograph: Susan Einstein

George Martin, *Gate,* 216 x 72, forged steel, gold leaf

Richard McLean, *Zoffany, with Eddie Delahoussaye Up,* 38 x 55, oil on canvas. Courtesy:
Mr. Anthony Speelman. Photograph: Whiteline

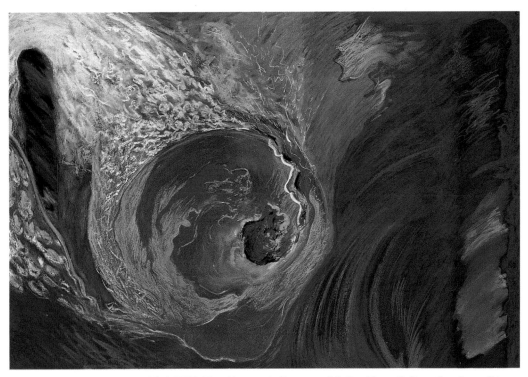

William Morehouse, *untitled 1987,* 30 x 44, pastel. Courtesy: J.J. Bookings Gallery, San Jose, CA

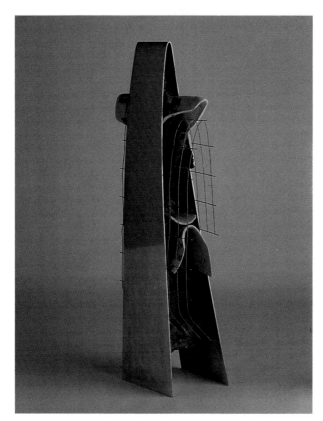

Barry M. Nakasone, *Hinamatsuri,*
49 x 18, metal, clay, cement

Nancy Nodelman, *Found and Lost II,*
36 x 24, mixed media

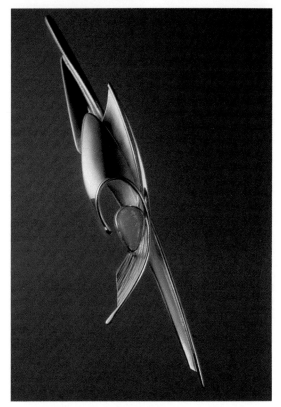

Dawn Nakanishi, *Brooch,* 6 x 2, sterling, opal

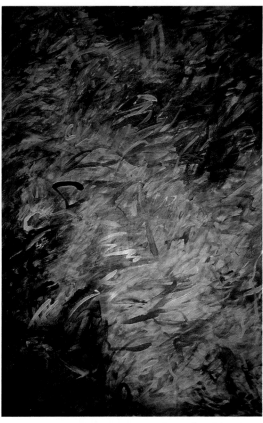

Patricia Georgiana Norman, *Sacred Spring: II,*
43 x 30, acrylic on rag paper

Keiko Nelson, *Spring,* 72 x 84, paper sculpture

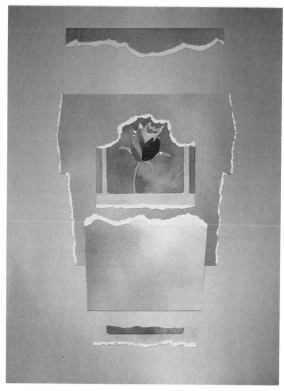

Tyler Norman, *Out of Qom,* 30 x 22, watercolor

Leonardo Nierman, *Prism,* 48 x 36, acrylic on masonite

Jackie Nach, *Ariel,* 30 x 40, oil and gold leaf on canvas.
Photographer: William Nettles

902

Judy North, *I Give You a Golden Thread,* 69 x 52,
mixed media on paper. Photograph: Mel Schockner

Edith Nelson, *Nespelem Heritage,* 16 x 20, oil

Youkee Nishida, *Painted Panel Series L- 4,*
57 x 40 x 1, mixed media on panel

Anthony Natsoulas, *Facing It,* 71 x 34 x 36, clay, glaze, canvas, oil.
Courtesy: Ross Turk. Acrylic painting by Martin Camerata

Nanessence, *Shadowed Paper Roll,* 30 x 34, oils over silver print

Mildred Nordman, *Turbulence,* 45 x 55, oil.
Courtesy: Santa Cruz Gallery and Museum, Santa Cruz, CA

Catherine Norman-Pitman, *We See Things Differently,* 16 x 20, acrylic on masonite

Sandra Grassi Nelipovich, *Nymphs, Satyrs and Fanciful Friends,* 30 x 25, batik on silk.
Courtesy: Mr. and Mrs. Robert Dobkin

Kristina Rice Nugent, *Light Passage,* 36 x 48, oil on linen

Lola Nelson, *Abandoned Memories,* 18 x 24, watercolor

Paige Neuhauser, *El Avenida, Barcelona,* 19 x 29, Dry Pastel

Ed Newell, *The Dam,* 15 x 22, watercolor

Richard Newton, *The Man Who Could Eat Glass,* performance art. Photo: Eric Engler

Ken Orrett, *Fallen Fire,* 66 x 39, oil, joint compound on wood. Photograph: Thomas Burke Photograph

Robert Ortlieb, *Illuminata,* 30" high, red and green alabaster
on black Belgian marble. Courtesy: Miranda Galleries,
Newport Beach and Laguna, CA

J.J. Oling, *Mahali Pa Maji (The Watering Place),*
40 x 30, oil on canvas

Philip Orlando, *As American as Apple Pie,* book sculpture, 12 x 10,
mixed media. Courtesy: Orlando Gallery

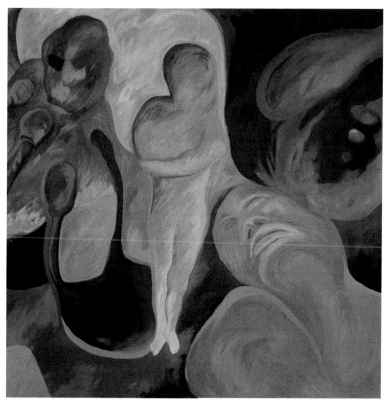

Graciela Ovejero, *Tip,* 48 x 48, acrylic

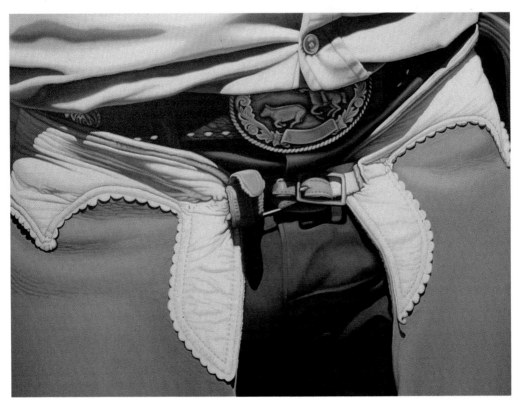

Maxine Olson, *Cowpoke,* 36 x 48, oil

Jilla Parhami, *Story of Freedom and Oppression,* 72 x 48, acrylic color, sand, prismacolor and cotton on canvas. Courtesy: Paul Davis

reflections of the times in which she lived. She has continued with the same themes, but she now paints on gessoed paper with a mixed media of watercolor, gold and silver leaf, oil stick, lacquer and acrylic.

NUGENT, BOB (Painter)
Art Dept., Sonoma State University, Rohnert Park, CA 94938

Born: 1947 *Awards:* Fulbright Foundation; National Endowment for the Arts *Collections:* Museum of Art, Sao Paulo; Philadelphia Museum of Art *Exhibitions:* Smithsonian Institute; Museum of Modern Art *Education:* UC-Santa Barbara *Dealer:* Roy Boyd Gallery, Santa Monica

Working in pastel on hand- and custom-made paper and in oil on canvas, he has shifted radically from his previous concerns. Until recently, a limited palette of white and earth tones and relief surfaces defined the parameters of his work, integrating poetic texts as a counterpoint to the paper media. Both alien and nostalgic, these pieces evoked an archaeological relationship, as though they were artifacts discovered from an unknown world. Now emphasizing color and abstract representations on flat surfaces, his most current series is of gardens in Brazil. Seemingly ordinary vegetables and plants take on an otherworldly appearance. Typical is *Suica XXXIV*. In this piece, a Chinese cabbage emanates an almost sacred light from its white tips, rising from rich, black earth in a deep green and blue background. The expressionistic style of this work further underscores its emotional familiarity and striking presence. No longer reveries, his works bring to the viewer a dazzling array of colors and dynamic lines that provoke attention and confront the natural environment. Of this series, Robert MacDonald has written, "They pulsate in imitation of the rhythms and tones of Brazilian music and life . . . dazzling impressions of an evanescent present."

NUGENT, KRISTINA RICE (Painter)
Mira Costa College, One Barnard Dr., Oceanside, CA 92056

Awards: Grumbacher Medal for Creative Use of Color; Award of Excellence, Western Federation of Watercolor *Collections:* U. of Seattle; U. of California *Exhibitions:* Albuquerque Museum; Crocker Art Museum, Sacramento *Education:* UC-Davis; UC-Santa Barbara

She studied printmaking and drawing at the University of California at Santa Barbara and concentrated on color and the surreal as a graduate student at UC-Davis. She returned to a figurative style as her work matured, drawing and painting with oils and becoming nationally known for her boldly colored, spontaneous watercolors. She now paints strong simplifications of the landscape form. She rejects conventional solutions to painterly problems and instead concentrates on the abstract, stressing color and color interaction and investigating the landscape subject in a personal way.

NUNN, TOM (Sound Sculpture, Original Musical Instruments)
3016 25th St., San Francisco, CA 94110

Born: 1946 *Exhibitions:* San Francisco Arts Commission Gallery; Sonic Arts Gallery, San Diego

With degrees in music composition, in 1975 he began an extensive personal study of non-traditional improvisation. He developed an assortment of sculptural musical instruments using common, inexpensive materials such as plywood, combs, nails, springs, threaded steel rods, stainless steel sheets, bronze brazing rods, and toy balloons. His instruments resemble living creatures and are designed specifically for improvisation, having elements of non-linearity and ambiguity. In performance, they are electronically amplified using contact microphones and digital processors.

NUTZLE, FUTZIE (Cartoonist, Illustrator)
P.O. Box 325, Aromas, CA 95004

Born: 1942 *Awards:* College Journalism Awards *Collections:* Oakland Museum; Museum of Modern Art, NYC *Exhibitions:* Santa Barbara Museum of Art; USSR-Bay Area Cartoon Exchange *Education:* Cleveland Institute of Art; Ohio State U.

Sparsely executed yet poignant cartoons have appeared in numerous magazines and newspapers throughout the United States, including *Rolling Stone* and the San Francisco Chronicle. Although he has worked in oils, acrylics, pastels, etchings, and lithographs, the primary medium for his cartoons has been pen and ink drawing. He has illustrated a variety of books, posters, and catalogues and has authored and illustrated three books of cartoons, including *The Modern Loafer*. Subject matter is often satirical, commenting on social issues through puns or absurdity. The world of the conscious and subconscious is expressed in a style that has been compared to Edward Lear.

NYIRI, JOE (Sculptor)
3525 Albatross St., San Diego, CA 92103

Born: 1937 *Awards:* 1st Award in Sculpture, San Diego Museum of Art; Sculptural Commission, San Diego Public Schools Collections; Stephens College, MO; Anchorage Museum of Art *Exhibitions:* Art Beasley Gallery, San Diego; San Diego Museum of Art *Education:* U. of Wisconsin *Dealer:* Art Collector Gallery, San Diego

While at the University of Wisconsin, he was influenced by the American sculptor David Smith. Early works were welded-steel abstractions employing brazed brass, copper and bronze surfaces and depicting ancient Viking themes. Some pieces were partially figurative, others totally abstract. In 1972, he created a series based on cities and states. These seven- and eight-foot pieces were made out of aluminum and steel and were welded or bolted together. Since 1980, he has concentrated on images of the altar and of sanctuary, expressing their mythological, religious and historical associations. He currently works in aluminum, steel and mixed media using both painted and natural surfaces.

OAKES, BAILE (Sculptor)
586 Mateo St., Los Angeles, CA 90013

Born: 1951 *Awards:* NEA Building Arts Grant *Collections:* City of Santa Monica; County of Santa Barbara *Exhibitions:* World Expo, Brisbane, Australia; Long Beach Art Museum *Education:* Rochester Institute of Technology

He has been influenced by classical conceptions of divine symmetry and modern architectural concepts of space. His sculptures are spaces with which people can interact and become a part of. One piece, *Gestation III*, is an homage to birth and regeneration. Made of cedar, it is large enough to enter and sit in. A vertical slit is oriented to the setting sun of the winter solstice.

Another piece was a sculptural courtyard designed for the State Beach at Gubbinoda. This work suggests spaces and defines areas with long walls and curved seating areas. He views his artistic search in life as finding the visual relationships that strike the peaceful chord within all.

O'BANION, NANCE (Mixed Media Artist)
251 Post St., 4th Fl., San Francisco, CA 94108

Born: 1949 *Awards:* NEA Fellowship; Arthur Jacobsen Memorial Award for Excellence in the Arts *Collections:* City and County of San Francisco; Musée des Arts Decoratifs, Lausanne, Switzerland *Exhibitions:* The Allrich Gallery, San Francisco; American Craft Museum, NYC *Education:* UC- Berkeley *Dealer:* The Allrich Gallery, San Francisco

She creates fiber art by pressing abaca fibers into sheets and then crumpling, air-brushing, dyeing and painting them. Color is applied by using screens, and the paper is then set on a painted bamboo or rattan structure. By adding telephone wires to the construct, she provides strong yet almost ephemeral color and a humorous reference to communication. Colors range from intense reds and blues to more subdued tones of black, white and gray and to pastel colors. Some pieces use natural colors such as forest green and variations on brown with gold and silver accents. She also paints on 4-by-4-feet sheets of handmade paper with oil pastel, applying thousands of strokes to create a symphony of color. She achieves a three-dimensional effect in these flat works by placing sheets of paper with cut-out squares over the colored background.

OBENCHAIN, RICHARD F. (Painter)
9441 Ben Way, Cazadero, CA 95421

Born: 1944 *Awards:* Hughes Aircraft Corporation; Bob Hope Cultural Center, Palm Desert *Exhibitions:* AIA Gallery, Santa Clara; Monterey Peninsula Museum of Art *Education:* U. of Kansas *Dealer:* A Gallery, Palm Desert

His formal training as an architect is especially apparent in his meticulous composition and concern for spatial development. Working in oil on canvas and watercolor on paper, his technique reflects his admiration for 19th-century American painters such as Frederick Church, William Chase and John Singer Sargent. He prefers a highly saturated palette and a large canvas, usually 8 by 4 or 8 by 6 feet. He paints large figurative landscapes in series, focusing on specific geographic sites. These include the topography of Death Valley and the palm canyons of the southern California desert. Plants are also featured as important images, as in his two series on this topic, a banyan series and a palm series, which both reflect his fascination with nature. In contrast to modern abstract trends, his paintings depict deep, three-dimensional space and intricate, figurative composition. Color, structure and a painterly approach are his primary considerations.

O'BRIEN, JOHN S. (Painter, Ceramist)
2753 Angell Ave., San Diego, CA 92122

Born: 1934 *Awards:* Juror's Purchase Award, 25th Annual Faculty/Staff Art Exhibit, UC-San Diego *Collections:* Chancellor's Complex, UC-San Diego; Creighton U. Medical School, Omaha, NE *Exhibitions:* Perspectives Gallery, San Diego; Macy's (Bullock's) Gallery; *Education:* Creighton U.

His early work was chiefly influenced by Monet and by Pissaro's use of color. He subsequently developed a more individual, realistic style reminiscent of American Realists Charles Burchfield and Edward Hopper. Since 1980, he has painted a large number of watercolors using wet-on-wet and dry brush techniques. The three-dimensional modeling of forms by light is conveyed through the use of vibrant colors and precise composition. Eschewing the purely decorative, he is primarily interested in recording his most intimate reactions to a subject, as it appears and when he likes it most. His goal is to express his love of American culture and landscape, capturing the ethos of a given scene.

OCHOA, VICTOR OROZCO (Muralist)
P.O.Box 8251, San Diego, CA 92116

Born: 1948 *Awards:* California Arts Commission Artist in Residence; Visual Arts Fellowship, Combined Arts and Education Council of San Diego *Exhibitions:* Centro Cultural de la Raza, San Diego; La Jolla Museum of Contemporary Art *Education:* San Diego State U.; San Diego City College

He is a muralist of international reputation, and his works continue the tradition of Rivera and Orozco in their political and cultural orientation. He is a founding member of San Diego's Border Art Workshop/Taller de Arte Fronterizo (BAW/TAF) and the Centro Cultural de la Raza, and his murals are done for and about the Chicano community. He has completed more than twenty-seven projects, and his current four-part installation depicts San Diego before the arrival of the Europeans, as well as the direction the multiethnic community is taking—reflected in the schools upon whose walls he is painting. As a member of BAW/TAF, he was part of the "Border Realities" series, which used performance, conceptual pieces and installations to redefine the concept of the "discovery of America" and the "border as war zone."

O'CONNOR, CASEY (Painter)
1488 Howard #B, San Francisco, CA 94103

Born: 1962 *Awards:* Sobel Scholarship *Exhibitions:* Media, San Francisco; Architects and Heroes, San Francisco *Education:* San Francisco Art Institute; Orange Coast College

He is best known for his abstract paintings on found objects such as discarded panels of masonite, doors, and old window shades. His recent works feature his total obsession with cups. These images, more like portraits than still lifes, resemble prints or symbols found on stamps. He also paints objects with dramatic design elements, such as targets and aerial perspectives of common objects. His limited palette includes muted maroons, browns, and grays. He has also painted 10-by-40-foot murals in San Francisco's financial district. Mixing colors on the wall, he applies the latex paint with drippy, fat brushstrokes. He paints to express his desire to be connected to his art, and via his art, to the viewer and general community.

ODA, MAYUMI (Painter, Printmaker)
P.O. Box 310, Star Rte., Sausalito, CA 94965

Born: 1941 *Collections:* Museum of Modern Art, NYC; Museum of Fine Arts, Boston *Exhibitions:* Tucson Art Museum; Mills College, Oakland *Education:* Tokyo U. of Fine Art

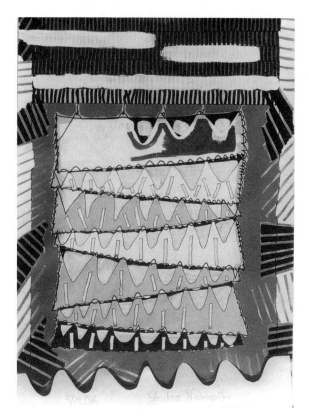

Youkee Nishida, *5/19/86,* 35 x 26, mixed media

Graciela Ovejero, *Along the River Banks,* 48 x 36, acrylic

She works in a style and imagery that recalls Japanese Ukiyo-e, impressing screenprinted ink on soft, absorbent Japanese paper to create a lush, textured surface, the visual effect enhanced by her use of metallic-colored inks. Her sensual, spiritual images can be traced to such diverse sources as Greek mythology and Japanese tradition. The works are dominated by goddesses or goddess-like feminine forms that swim or dive gracefully through the sea, an expression of the eternal and a celebration of the figure that is reminiscent of Matisse. Over time, her female forms have become more realistic and less stylized, and their undersea and pastoral environments more detailed.

ODZA, THEODORE (Sculptor)
P. O. Box 41, Inverness, CA 94937

Born: 1915 *Collections:* Oakland Art Museum; U. of California Art Museum, Berkeley *Exhibitions:* Palo Alto Cultural Center; Montalvo Center for the Arts, Saratoga *Education:* UC-Berkeley *Dealer:* Gallery Route 1, Pt. Reyes Station

One of his influences is Stankiewicz, but unlike Stankiewicz, who used recognized products of industry, Odza's fragments are anonymous pieces of steel that have survived exposure to stress— heat, explosion or impact—and are unrecognizable individually. His oeuvre is completely abstract. Employing an electric-arc- welding technique, he assembles pieces that range from ten inches to ten feet in height. The surfaces are treated with a combination of phosphoric acid and leather dyes, which leaves a rich, crusty, subtly colored surface but does not totally obscure the steel look. *Fold and Return*, a piece that embodies his recent interest in high relief, features minimally attached torn and embattled metal that stands out from a serene background.

O'FINN, DONALD ZEDALAN (Painter)
2437 Peralta Apt. E, Oakland, CA 94607

Born: 1957 *Exhibitions:* Lab Gallery, San Francisco; Art Society International, San Francisco *Education:* San Francisco Art Institute *Dealer:* Ariel Gallery, NYC; Museum of Modern Art Rental Gallery, San Francisco; Joseph Chowning Gallery, San Francisco

During his initial years, he worked to reconcile the influence of Bay Area figurative painters with his search for an idiosyncratic style appropriate to his range of abilities. He felt the need to mediate between realism versus an expressionist style. In 1984, he found the resolution of this conflict, painting detailed, surrealist erotic themes. One such painting features a nightgown-clad, six-armed, hermaphroditic bride under a halo. The creature is dancing and breastfeeding a child wrapped in a serpent; above her, a priest descends a spiral staircase. Other experimentation has taken up interiors, still lifes and nudes on torn masonite with scarred or dense surfaces. Themes of decay, time, and change are the result of the influence of Duchamp and Bruce Conner.

OGAWA, MIHOKO (Stained Glass Artist)
86-660 Lualualei Hmstd. Rd., Waianae, HI 96792

Born: 1915 *Collections:* Buddhist Temple, East Los Angeles *Exhibitions:* Art Festival, Laguna Beach; Exhibition of Stained Glass Association of Hawaii

Her father was the renowned Japanese glass artist Sanchi Ogawa. She spent many hours at his side, watching him compose the designs for the windows and murals he built throughout the country. After much of this work was destroyed in World War II, she dedicated herself to reworking his designs, bringing them to life once again. Her work represents the fusion of Oriental and Occidental art—Eastern themes and motifs executed with Western technology. The designs are filled with traditional Japanese art motifs such as flowers, plants, animals, and fish. Her current project is a medium-sized piece that features a pool of water, water lillies, and carp. She hopes to write a book about her father's life and work.

OGINZ, RICHARD (Sculptor)
1849 Lemoyne St., Los Angeles, CA 90026

Born: 1944 *Awards:* Ford Foundation Grant; Young Talent Award, Los Angeles County Museum of Art *Collections:* Los Angeles County Museum of Art; Arts Council of Great Britain *Exhibitions:* Long Beach Museum of Art; Gallery of Functional Art, Venice, CA *Education:* Temple U.; U. of Wisconsin, Madison

During an eight-year stay in Great Britain, he developed a great interest in the relationships between the figure, landscape and scale. This interest has remained the central issue of his work. The friendship and instruction of sculptor Hubert Dalwood also greatly influenced his artistic approach. He sculpts in a wide range of materials including wood, cement and metal. The connection of the human form to the man-made landscape is the theme of recent work. In one series, for example, a white plaster cast head, sitting inside a small house, forlornly peers through a window. Another untitled work features a nude man and woman on a construction site, embracing in the midst of scaffolding. He also draws and constructs functional tables.

OHASHI, KUNIO (Neon Artist, Sculptor)
7712 Gloria Ave., #4, Van Nuys, CA 90027

Born: 1925 *Exhibitions:* Museum of Neon Art; White's Old Town Gallery *Education:* Los Angeles City College

After a formal art education, he studied neon design and glass bending. His recent work involves a combination of sculpted neon and natural objects such as wood, rocks or clay. His pieces often involve human or nature images. In *Heart of Neon*, two reaching arms offer a swirling piece of glowing circular yellow. In *Sequoia*, a small shaft of blue-white light illuminates a craggy piece of driftwood and a dead branch of a tree. *Waterfall* is a high-tech interpretation of the falling-water theme with vertical and curved lines of light representing water falling over real rocks and rough, jagged, glowing glass representing the turbulent waters below.

OHIRA, MINORU (Sculptor)
1194 N. Chester Ave., Pasadena, CA 91104

Born: 1950 *Awards:* 2nd Prize, First Monumental Sculpture Competition, Tokyo; Lorser Feitelson Foundation Award, Los Angeles *Collections:* Honolulu Academy of Art; Long Beach Museum of Art *Exhibitions:* Space Gallery, Los Angeles; Don Soker Gallery, San Francisco *Education:* Tokyo National Institute of Arts *Dealer:* Space Gallery, Los Angeles

He was trained in his native Japan and then in Mexico City, where he resided for several years, and he is now a resident of Los Angeles. His work shows the influence of diverse cultures— particularly the primitive cultures of Mexico. Using found scraps of wood, he

Mary Lovelace O'Neal, *Hamman—Morrocan Bath House,* 83 x 139, mixed media on canvas.
Photograph: Lewis Watts

Minoru Ohira, *Barco de Maya,* 49 x 105 x 7, wood, slate. Courtesy: Space Gallery

constructs elaborate, three-dimensional works. Small wooden pieces daubed with lavender-gray and pink that thrust forward from the wall are held in frameworks of tied branches painted black or black and red. Other works are loosely based on the architecture of Mexican pueblos as if seen from a low aerial view. These works, constructed of wood, slate and shards of glass bound with twine, cannot be categorized culturally. He also makes works on paper, usually with Chinese brush and ink in one color; many of the abstract forms in these works echo his sculptural pieces.

OKAMURA, ARTHUR (Painter, Sculptor)
P.O. Box 367, Bolinas, CA 94924

Born: 1932 *Awards:* National Society of Arts and Letters; San Francisco Arts Commission *Collections:* Art Institute of Chicago; Whitney Museum, NYC *Exhibitions:* California Palace of the Legion of Honor, San Francisco; Ruth Braunstein Gallery, San Francisco *Education:* School of the Art Institute of Chicago *Dealer:* Ruth Braunstein, San Francisco and Los Angeles

From the age of fifteen until he was twenty-seven, he worked in a commercial silk-screen studio, where he received his first instruction in graphic design and layout. He turned to painting while attending the Art Institute of Chicago, and his first works in that medium demonstrated abstract, surrealist inclinations that gradually grew into a kind of abstract/realist mode. He has recently been painting tropical fish in water with oils and watercolors and making papier maché sculptures of fish and water. He is also using scratch board to illustrate an original book of magic tricks. His other media include prints, movies, and video art.

OKELBERRY, ELLEN (Painter)
937 Westhaven Dr., Trinidad, CA 95570

Born: 1932 *Collections:* St. John's Episcopal Church, Freeport, IL; Fiene Construction Office Complex, Batavia, IL *Exhibitions:* California Watercolor and Drawing Survey; Tomaso's, Eureka *Education:* California College of Arts and Crafts; Northern Illinois U.

In the 1950s, she painted impressionist and abstract expressionist canvases in oils. She then went to Europe and painted landscapes in a realistic style, heavy with palette knife and scumbling. She continued with landscapes and in the 1960s she added figures into her scenes, a move which represented a new connection with the universe. As the decade progressed, she became interested in Chinese calligraphy, studied clay sculpture and pottery and began teaching at a community college in Illinois. In the early 1980s, she moved to the San Francisco Bay area and began studying Old Master techniques. Her former loyalty to realism gave way to a flowing abstraction of nature, where inner light relates to outer light. She is now greatly influenced by O'Keeffe, Wyeth, Turner, Rembrandt and ancient and modern painting techniques.

OKI, PEGGY (Painter, Commercial Illustrator)
5966 Via Real #3, Carpinteria, CA 93013

Born: 1956 *Collections:* Bank of Montecito *Exhibitions:* The Coffee Grinder, Carpinteria; Doubletree Hotel, Ventura *Education:* Santa Barbara City College; UC- Santa Barbara

Her scientific training in environmental biology and animal behavior is apparent in her choice and treatment of subjects. They include flowers in bloom, graceful grasshoppers, exotic birds, dolphins at play and other marine life. A surfing enthusiast, she likens painting to the excitement of immersion in the power of the ocean. Recently she has focused on the endangered species of the world as the subjects of her paintings in hopes of inspiring the viewer to respect the planet's many vulnerable environments and life forms. Her portrayals of wildlife are photo-realistically rendered to capture the expressions of her subjects as they would be seen in their own environments.

OLING, J.J. (Painter)
1017 Faysmith Ave., Torrance, CA 90503

Born: 1921 *Awards:* Certificate of Excellence, Graphics Gallery, Strathmore Paper Company *Collections:* Ronald and Nancy Reagan; Kenya Travel Consulate, Los Angeles *Exhibitions:* De Mille Gallery, Laguna; Tarbox Gallery, San Diego

His first oil painting was done on the side of his World War II B-24 Liberator, the "Little Warrior" now featured in advertisements for the "Air War Over Europe" video tapes. He continued to combine art and aviation while working as a flight engineer and pilot for a major commercial airline. Many of his cartoons, illustrations and drawings were published throughout the 1950s and 1960s. He now produces realistic paintings of Asian and African wildlife. His extensive travels in Africa, the Middle East, the Orient and the Americas have provided him with the knowledge and photographs he uses as the basis for his work. Each wildlife painting begins with the element he considers the most crucial—to capture the expression of the animal's eyes. His recent paintings include a series of elephant studies.

OLIVARES, CLARE (Painter)
848 Stannage Ave. #7, Albany, CA 94706

Born: 1951 *Awards:* Premium Award, Oil Painting, Cal Expo *Exhibitions:* Bay Arts, San Mateo County Arts Council; Chico Art Center, Chico *Education:* UC-Berkeley; Mills College

One of her first art teachers greatly influenced her artistic approach, which emphasizes the qualities of the surface, figure- ground relationships, simple color formations, and referential symbolism. Working primarily in acylics, she explored the varieties of light and color, producing paintings which often consisted of a floating or frontally placed object on a modulated color field. She progressed from acrylics to oils to mixed media and on to a process of painting on rag paper and primed canvas. The thicker, more textural painted surfaces display a better developed sense of color. Referential or narrative landscapes influenced by the Bay area Tantric school have replaced the simple figure on a ground. These vibrantly colored paintings also contain symbolic figurative elements placed in unusual settings.

OLIVEIRA, NATHAN (Painter, Sculptor)
785 Santa Maria Ave., Stanford, CA 94305

Born: 1928 *Awards:* Guggenheim Fellowship; Tamarind Fellowship *Collections:* Museum of Modern Art, NYC; San Francisco Museum of Modern Art *Exhibitions:* Oakland Museum; Whitney Museum, NYC *Education:* California College of Arts and Crafts *Dealer:* Charles Cowles Gallery, NYC

A key artist in the Bay Area Figurative School that emerged in northern California in the 1950s, he is

Robert Ortlieb, *The Muses,* 39 inches high, bronze on black Belgian marble. Courtesy: Miranda Galleries, Newport Beach and Laguna, CA

J.J. Oling, *Punda Malia (Zebra),* 40 x 30, oil on canvas

known for large, gestural paintings of solitary figures depicted against empty backgrounds in an abstract expressionist style. He turned to sculpture in 1982, translating powerful gestures into stylized manipulations of the body's proportions. Central to his work is a humanistic vision that focuses on the figure, which is portrayed as a generalized image and a symbolic presence rather than an individual form. He seeks to uncover deeply hidden truths about spirituality and the human condition, and he uses masked and costumed figures to reveal the ambiguity of identity in contemporary life.

OLLMAN, ARTHUR L. (Photographer)
4310 Goldfinch, San Diego, CA 92101

Born: 1947 *Awards:* NEA Artists Fellowship; Beyond War Peace Award *Collections:* Museum of Modern Art, NYC; Centre Georges Pompidou, Paris; *Exhibitions:* Whitney Biennial; Centre Georges Pompidou, Paris *Education:* U. of Wisconsin; Lone Mountain College *Dealer:* Ursala Gropper, Sausalito

After ten years of experimentation with black and white in long exposures, he began experimenting with over-saturation and shadow colors in 1976. He captured the taboos and dangers of the nocturnal, urban environment in bizarre scenes of California cities. Recently, he has developed a cinematic quality to his work. People in opulent settings move during the long exposure. This creates a soft ghosting or total transparency which he uses as a metaphor for the passage of time and for the nervous mannerisms of the inhabitants of these types of spaces. He produces images twenty by twenty-four inches.

OLSEN, DORIS (Painter)
17364 Overland Trail, Sonora, CA 95370

Born: 1931 *Awards:* 1st Prize, Still Life Miniature Painters, Sculptors and Engravers Show, Washington, D.C. *Exhibitions:* Sonora 1987; Sonora 1988 *Education:* Art Students League; Academy of Art, San Francisco *Dealers:* Glory Hole Gallery, Sonora; Country Gallery, Jamestown

Working in oil, watercolor and acrylic, she developed her style by using soft-edged images and clear, bright colors. She works by developing the painting's negative space, then creating the image. Recent work includes limited editions prints on one hundred percent archival rag paper. This series, "Country Flowers and Historical Houses," also includes a short history on both the country and city Victorian houses. She also is exploring leaf pattern arrangements on canvas. These works are rendered in acrylic with airbrush, using soft pastels to create an illusory, shadowy appearance.

OLSEN, FREDERICK L. (Ceramist)
Box 205 PC, Mt. Center, CA 92361

Born: 1938 *Awards:* NEA Grant *Collections:* Gallery of New S. Wales, Australia; Palm Springs Desert Museum *Exhibitions:* Elaine Horwitch Gallery, Palm Springs; Lang Gallery, Pomona *Education:* U. of Redland; UCLA *Dealer:* Elaine Horwitch Gallery

His ceramic education began at USC, under Carlton Ball. He continued to study for two and a half years with Japanese master potters Tomimoto Kenkichi and Kondo Yuzo and spent five years working as a potter around the world, after which he returned to California to build his own home and studio. His work has evolved from functional tableware and off-center decorative vessels, which provided enough income to

make a living in the isolated town of Pinyon Crest, but his present clay sculpture captures the shapes of his high desert environment. He molds supple desert colors and forms into surreal images where each piece becomes its own stage and play.

OLSEN, POMM (Painter)
4865 Hartwick St., Eagle Rock, CA

Born: 1954 *Awards:* Watercolor West *Collections:* 20th Century Fox, Los Angeles; Hart Shock, Los Angeles *Exhibitions:* Brand Library; Celebrity Center International *Education:* Cal. State-Humboldt; Faculty des Lettres and Ecole des Beaux Arts, Aix-en-Provence, France

She is a watercolorist whose pieces have a distinctive old world charm. Her timeless subjects include European buildings, children at play on beaches, lonely lighthouses in the night, and hidden corners of town. Her teacher, Scott Moore, brought her to the watercolor medium. Her French-American heritage has been an important element of her diverse imagery. Her works are characterized by a mysterious interplay of light and shadow and interior and exterior. Within each piece is her trademark, the "elusive apple." She has been featured in *American Artist Magazine.* Having mastered watercolor, she feels that she can produce any effect she wants.

OLSON, MAXINE (Painter, Draughtsperson)
1555 Lincoln St., Kingsburg, CA 93631

Born: 1931 *Exhibitions:* William Sawyer Gallery, San Francisco; Palm Museum, Palm Springs *Education:* Cal. State U.-Fresno; Otis Art Institute

She is a photo-realist who paints images of people in social interactions. Often, she depicts the male groin, in a comment on the stigma attached to women looking at men. She begins with a projected photographic subject, then applies thin layers of oil paint, building up a highly realistic surface. Recently she has been combining photographs of various subjects to create a more multi-dimensional effect. Her work has been included in *Sex: Female, Occupation: Artist* by N. Treadwell, and in the catalogue *The West As Art,* published by the Palm Springs Desert Museum. She has been influenced by Audrey Flack, Kacere and Alfred Leslie.

OMATA, KAY (Painting)
1781 Sunset Ave., Santa Monica, CA 90405

Born: 1953 *Exhibitions:* Art Institute of Southern California, Laguna Beach; Art and Architecture Exhibition of Art, Los Angeles County Museum *Education:* Cal. State-Fresno; Cal. State-Long Beach *Dealer:* Merging One Gallery, Santa Monica; Valerie Miller Gallery, Palm Desert

Inspired by the works of Arshile Gorky, she developed an individual, abstract expressionist style focusing on the tension between emotion and cognition. Because she paints every day, her works are like a diary, recording her states of mind in layer upon colorful layer on the canvas. Each layer responds to the ones beneath, so that the paintings take on an organic quality. Executed in dark colors, the paintings often begin with a monoprint and sometimes incorporate collage elements into their abstract design.

O'NEAL, MARY LOVELACE (Painter, Printmaker)
440 Haddon Rd., #2, Oakland, CA 94606

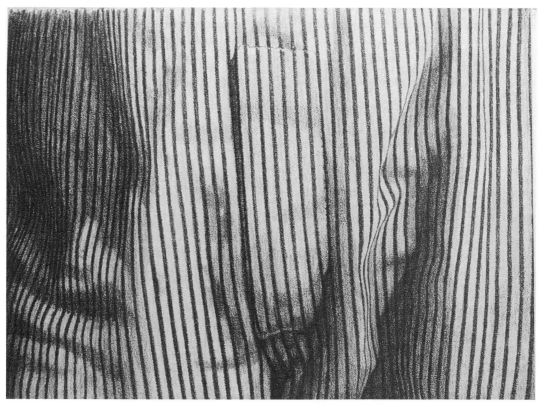

Maxine Olson, *Coveralls,* 22 x 33, pencil

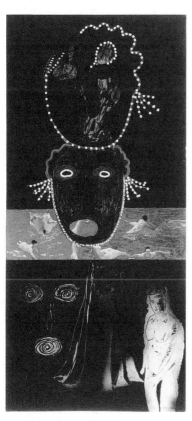

Philip Orlando, *Swimmer,* 37 x 21, mixed media. Courtesy: Orlando Gallery

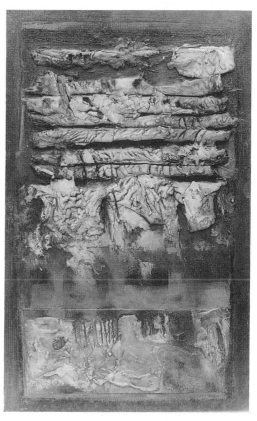

Ken Orrett, *Little Grief,* 7 x 11, oil, modeling paste, paper on wood. Photograph: Thomas Burke

Collections: San Francisco Museum of Modern Art; Oakland Museum *Exhibitions:* Jeremy Stone Gallery, San Francisco; Rolando Castellon Gallery *Education:* Columbia U.

She is known for her entirely conceptual and non-realist paintings. Early in her career, she was influenced by the works of de Kooning and Klein; later she used the principles of composition in Stella's work as the basis for her own. These minimalist abstractions were executed in black (and other limited colors) and glitter. She concentrates on a painterly approach and on paint handling. Color is a special interest, and she works to balance hot and cool colors, often using an intermediary. Still affected by a trip several years ago to Morocco, she has been working on a series of paintings based on the country's people, society and art.

O'NEILL, JENNIFER J. (Painter)
3841 Redding Ave., Sacramento, CA

Born: 1952 *Awards:* Award of Excellence, Sacramento Works *Exhibitions:* Rara Avis Gallery, Sacramento; Accurate Art Gallery, Sacramento *Education:* Cal. State-Sacramento

After formal training in New York and California, and experimentation with different media, she began to work exclusively with watercolor. Influenced by African artists, Native American artists and ancient artists associated with goddess worship, her work has evolved into symbolic narratives derived from nature and primitive forms. Limiting her palette to the three or four colors she mixes together to create shades, she paints bold expanses of color on large sheets of rag paper. She has a strong sense of design and her work usually includes masked human figures, flowers and animals symbolic of the Jungian collective consciousness.

ORLANDO, PHILIP (Painter, Performance Artist)
14553 Ventura Blvd., Sherman Oaks, CA

Born: 1930 *Exhibitions:* Irvine Art Center; Orlando Gallery *Education:* UCLA Extension

His paintings, drawings and books are part conceptual art, part found objects and part personal diary. Sometimes he collages together old books with hand-colored photos and other elements. He paints humorous designs over the books, which completely obscure the existing text. His imagery involves his dance experiences, his present environment and his fantasies about the future. He founded the Orlando Dance Studio in 1953 and the Orlando Gallery in 1958. Recently, he has been involved with performance art, creating such works as *Help! I'm In Seattle.* His current interests include design, color, shapes, forms and choreography of works of art.

ORNITZ, ELLEN (Painter, Ceramist)
921 W. Koch, Bozeman, MT 59715

Born: 1951 *Awards:* Purchase Award, American Ceramic National IV *Collections:* UC-Santa Cruz *Exhibitions:* Maude Kerns Art Center, Eugene, OR; International Gallery, San Diego *Education:* UC-Santa Cruz; Indiana U.

Her ceramic sculptures reflect a preoccupation with narrative imagery. Dreamlike images from mythology, literary archetypes and observations of natural phenomena also contribute to her work. These images of visual and emotional power are drawn, photographed and painted in preparation for sculpture. As the sculpture takes form, these initial conceptions give way, and the piece assumes a life of its own. Painting dominated her college years, and this influence is evident in the surface treatments of her sculptures. The clay is carved, underglazed, airbrushed, stenciled, glazed and overglazed. After firing, the surfaces are accentuated with acrylic and enamel paint. Media such as wood, glass and wire may be added. The desired image dictates the choice of materials. A recent series explores the relations of people to one another within their environment. Archetypal elements of fire and water play an important role in this interaction. Her sculptures are theatrical, setting the stage for a symbolic event. The work is designed to elicit a response—the viewer participates by pondering the significance of the scenario. Achieving this intrigue is crucial to the success of these sculptures.

OROSCO, JUANISHI (Painter, Printmaker)
5538 Bradford Dr., Sacramento, CA 95820

Born: 1945 *Awards:* Letter of Commendation, U.S. House of Representatives *Collections:* U. of California, Santa Barbara; Harvard U., Cambridge, MA *Exhibitions:* San Francisco Museum of Modern Art; Los Angeles County Museum of Art *Education:* Cal. State-Sacramento *Dealer:* Gina Montoya, Sacramento

The primary influences on his artistic development were the major artists of the Mexican mural movement. This reflects not only a concern with technical skill, but also an interest in art as an instrument of consciousness-raising. Along with Jose Montoya and Esteban Villa, he founded Centro de Artistas Chicanos, a cultural arts center dedicated to teaching art throughout the Chicano community. Much of his work is involved in the design, supervision and execution of public murals. His individual artistic efforts consist of paintings and silkscreen prints. He paints in acrylic and automotive paint using, airbrush and air-gun techniques. He is mainly concerned with how color and form combine to create a luminosity and transparency on canvas. His prints feature figurative and abstract forms based on Southwestern and Meso-American icons and symbols. He is also exploring ways of working with these same techniques on ceramic tile pieces ranging from 4 by 4 feet to wall size.

ORR, ERIC (Painter, Sculptor)
1725 W. Washington Blvd., Venice, CA 90291

Born: 1939 *Awards:* NEA Grant *Collections:* The Panza Collection, Milan, Italy *Exhibitions:* Los Angeles County Museum of Art; The Works Gallery, Long Beach *Education:* UC-Berkeley

He has worked in a variety of materials rendering inner states of being. His work, until the early 1980s, was dominated by the use of shamanistic materials and forms. Substances included lead, gold, meteorite dust, ground lion's tooth, dust from the Great Pyramid in Egypt, human blood (his own) and fragments and dust from pulverized human skull. His more recent paintings are patterned after Japanese Mu painting. This style is characterized by monochromatic color fields which appear to float within the framed border. *Myriad Oceans of Time, Other Side of Blue #6* and *Without Blue #3* are all rendered in blue and, typical of the style, fade to darkness at the edges, giving the paintings an ethereal, transcendent quality. Many of his sculptures incorporate fire as a design element. *Prime Matter* was constructed from an upright girder

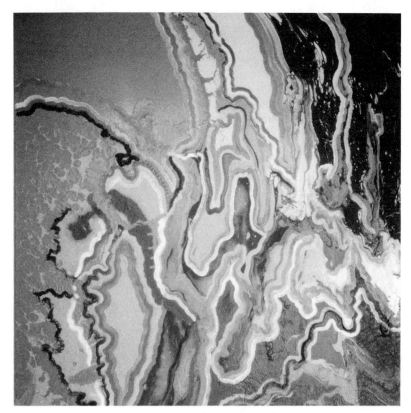

A. Gregg Pader, *Somewhere Between the Sands of Time I,* 36 x 36, mixed media

Carlos Raul Perez, *The Chairs,* 48 x 72, oil on canvas. Courtesy: Schwartz Cierlak Gallery

fitted with gas and water nozzles. When activated, the sculpture produces a pillar of fire within a misty cloud.

ORRETT, KENNETH C. (Painter)
P.O. Box 98, Boulder Creek, CA 95006

Born: 1921 *Exhibitions:* Los Angeles Art Association; Phelan Award Show, San Francisco Museum of Modern Art *Education:* Calif. Art Institute; UC-Berkeley

The early part of his career was primarily given over to teaching. Since his retirement, he has pursued fine art painting. He works with oil and modeling paste in a range of format sizes. Works progress from color fields suggesting landscape and light to final paintings influenced by formal and structural considerations. Working with the aesthetic/symbolic challenge of composition, he strives to create paintings which speak to inner thoughts and emotions. He uses meditation and music to prepare for creative work and cites Cezanne and Picasso as major influences.

ORTLIEB, ROBERT (Sculptor)
11111 Jerry Ln., Garden Grove, CA 92640

Born: 1925 *Collections:* Palm Springs Desert Museum; Miranda Galleries, Newport Beach and Laguna *Exhibitions:* Palm Springs Desert Museum; Creative Galleries, NYC *Education:* USC

Sculptures in wood, plexiglas, bronze and marble balance between emotional, intellectual and spiritual forces. Forms range from robust twists and thrusts of life-filled shapes in movement and from poetic evocations to abstract figures of raw power and majesty. He begins carving without preparatory sketches or plans, preferring to work directly. The form within the material is brought out, often through incarving, so that shapes emerge from inner forms.

OSATO, SONO (Mixed Media Artist)
3604 Richmond Blvd., Oakland, CA 94611

Born: 1960 *Awards:* Djerassi Foundation Artist in Residence *Exhibitions:* New Art Gallery, San Francisco; San Francisco Arts Commission Gallery *Education:* California College of Arts and Crafts; Arizona State U.

Due to its diversity, her work defies simple categorization. In painting and in sculpture, her pieces are more concerned with their own construction than with allusions to the world outside. Unlike much California art, her works are dark and refer to inner space rather than expansive, light landscapes. Her paintings tend to exude a dense physical presence because of her practice of mixing aspalt, beeswax, sand and marble dust with the paint. She builds thick, textured surfaces that are sometimes echoed by bulges built beneath the canvases. Her sculptural work is an outgrowth of her painting, often featuring found objects or natural, unconventional materials set in unusual combinations. In one piece, for example, she built a bed of earth surrounded by lengths of lumber, presenting the gallery floor in the form of a deadend footbridge. Another work is constructed from lumber and canvas, covered with asphalt. Additional materials she has used include tar and other substances usually associated with industrial construction and manufacturing.

OUTCAULT, WILLIAM H. (Sculptor)
2065 E. 37th St., Los Angeles, CA 90058

Born: 1949 *Awards:* Research Grant, Southern Illinois U.; Grant, Indiana Arts Commission *Exhibitions:* Gallery 454 North, Los Angeles; Mount St. Mary's College, Los Angeles *Education:* Mankato State U.; Southern Illinois U.

Influenced by Gorky, his work deals with the themes of danger and random violence. In attempting to convey the existential dread as well as the paradoxical whimsy of modern life, he uses plant-like forms as metaphors for the organic qualities of violence. Through these images, he addresses the dichotomies of strength and vulnerability, vulgarity and elegance, lyricism and danger. Beginning with cardboard and wax, he casts his pieces in metal, bronze and aluminum, making pieces that are six to eight feet high. Often made with found objects, his current work is tighter and more refined than the linear, lyrical pieces he made earlier in his career.

OVEJERO, GRACIELA (Painter)
P.O. Box 449, San Diego, CA 92112

Born: 1956 *Collections:* Provincial Museum of Tucuman, Argentina *Exhibitions:* Installation Gallery, San Diego; Galeria de la Ciudad, Tijuana, Mexico *Education:* National U., Tucuman, Argentina *Dealer:* Hamid Dayani, San Diego

Her early figurative work was influenced by Spilimbergo, Berni and Maccio, and especially by Bacon's treatment of space and Goya's dark period. Searching for a contemporary humanist style, she combined figures as planes among planes with carefully balanced colors and tones. The resulting neo-cubist style soon evolved into a more organic, fluent idiom. She works in bright acrylics on stretched and loose canvas of life-size or larger proportions, focusing on social commentary and inner psychological struggles, which often results in grotesque imagery reminiscent of Edvard Munch. These expressionistic, figurative works feature contrasting colors that move through the composition's space and forms.

PACKARD, EMMY LOU (Painter, Printmaker)
3352 18th St. #3, San Francisco, CA 94110

Born: 1914 *Collections:* Oakland Museum of Art; Pushkin Museum, Moscow *Exhibitions:* San Francisco Museum of Art; F.J. Michaels Gallery, San Francisco *Education:* UC-Berkeley *Dealers:* Oakland Museum Rental Gallery; F.J. Michaels, San Francisco

She has had a varied and distinguished artistic career. She cites the single most important influence in her life as Diego Rivera, with whom she studied in 1928. In 1940 she helped him to paint a mural during that year's Golden Gate International Exposition. Now living in the San Francisco Bay Area, she is well known as a muralist in her own right, having supervised and executed several public murals. She currently works in hand printed wood and linoleum block cuts. Other media have included oil, watercolor and acrylic painting, as well as drawing and sculpture. She has recently written a book about Rivera's San Francisco frescos.

PADER, A. GREGG (Painter)
148 Zinnia Circle., Vallejo, CA 94591

Born: 1946 *Collections:* Lawrence D. Trevett, San Francisco; Allen Wall, Benicia *Exhibitions:* Ariel Gallery, NYC; Leonard's Artspace Gallery, Modesto *Education:* San Francisco State U.

The artist's "instant imaging" painting technique was developed in response to Jackson Pollock's drip art. The unique simultaneous application of color is done from atop a ladder, which the artist places above a supine canvass. Holding a board, to which he has at-

Maija Woof Peeples, *Let Me Call You Sweethare,* 8 x 11, ink on paper

Emmy Lou Packard, *Frederick Douglass,* 30 x 40, linocut. Photograph: Don Beatty

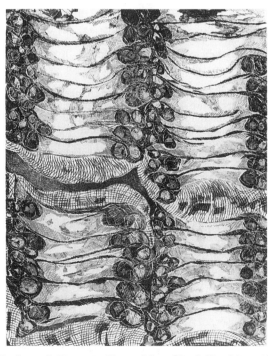

Barbara G. Parsons, *Nature Morte No. 1,* 22 x 30, etching

tached twelve cans filled at random with paint, the artist lets spill the different colors, relying on gravity and chance for their placement. The resulting "master image" is the inspiration for whatever additions he makes with brush. This image is finally effected by changes that occur during the drying process. In his pouring method, layers of paint are built up on the canvass. As the top layers dry, they crack, revealing valleys of contrasting color. The artist is continually fascinated by this phenomenon, and believes the finished painting to be a joint effort by man and nature.

PADULA, FRED DAVID (Filmmaker, Photographer)
47 Shell Rd., Mill Valley, CA 94941

Born: 1937 *Awards:* 1st Place, San Francisco International Film Festival; Recognition Award, New York Film Festival *Collections:* San Francisco Museum of Art; George Eastman House, Rochester *Exhibitions:* San Francisco Museum of Modern Art; Kalamazoo Institute of the Arts *Education:* San Francisco State U. *Dealer:* Canyon Cinema, San Francisco

After studying music, his early work was in abstract color photography. During the mid-1960s, he began making films. He began to fly small planes in the early 1970s, experimenting with abstract aerial photography. His still photos are entirely abstract and at the same time symbolic; often they suggest images such as faces. He has worked in 2 1/4, 4 x 5, and 35mm formats. using 35mm for aerial work. He also composes electronic music, which he employs in his motion pictures. The films and music address themes and theme variation: he repeats scenes rhythmically or hypnotically. The same or similar subjects are shown in variable light, seasons, position and perspective.

PAIK, YOUNHEE (Painter)
30 Jordan Ave., San Francisco, CA 94118

Born: 1945 *Awards:* 29th San Francisco Art Festival *Exhibitions:* San Jose Museum; April Riddle Gallery, Los Angeles *Education:* Seoul National U., Korea; San Francisco Art Institute *Dealer:* Allrich Gallery, San Francisco

Over time, her Oriental background changed her aesthetic perspective from human-centered thought to nature-oriented understanding. Human figures disappeared as large flows of clouds and water appeared on her canvases. This more imaginative atmosphere is expressed through oil paint poured and splashed on the painting's surface and molded with swiftly brushed calligraphic strokes. This technique produces a dynamic, wind-swept effect, as though the color and shapes themselves are in motion. Her paintings often have a real-world referent, but this is only a starting point for more abstract yet clear and evocative images. In *One Day I'll See*, cloud-covered blue panels open up, permitting a glimpse of the starry sky beyond.

PALMER, JUDITH (Printmaker)
2040 Arroyo Dr., Riverside, CA 92506

Born: 1934 *Awards:* Galleries Elect Purchase Award, Venice, CA; Juror Award, National Works on Paper, Dulin Gallery of Art, Knoxville, TN *Collections:* Riverside Art Museum; California State Polytechnic U. *Exhibitions:* Barbican Center, London; All California Biennial, Riverside *Education:* UC-Berkeley; Claremont Graduate School *Dealer:* AQL Fine Arts, Fullerton; Valerie Miller, Los Angeles

She seeks to express the importance of language as a sign system, in which form and meaning are an integral unit. Working with and exploring the content inherent in line and texture, she uses photo-etching techniques to capture found language from streets, walls and discarded waste paper. She transfers these photo images onto zinc plates and combines them with the more rigid and contrived language of etching. The result is a dialectic between her language and the more general language of art, between energy and containment, between the spontaneous and the contrived. Her work shows an affinity with Paul Wunderlich, Jackson Pollock, Cy Twombly and Richard Diebenkorn.

PALMER-ALLEN, LYDIA (Painter)
2951 35th Ave., Sacramento, CA 95828

Born: 1937 *Awards:* Latham Foundation Human Education and Peace Poster Competition; Honorable Mention, Roseville Arts Center *Exhibitions:* Roseville Arts Center; Artists Gallery, Sacramento *Education:* Sacramento City College

She works in a unique, strongly impressionistic style, integrating a forceful freedom of vibrant color with a constant underlying rhythmic movement. The works, often punctuated by animated figuration, culminate in celebrations of linear and color harmony. A child prodigy who left art for twenty-five years, she has been influenced by Darryl Forney, Fred Dalkey and David Currey, her teachers at Sacramento City College. She paints in all media but concentrates on watercolors.

PAOLI, DAMON (Sculptor)
499 Alabama St., #328, San Francisco, CA 94110

Born: 1949 *Awards:* Nomination for Best Set Design, San Francisco Theater Awards *Exhibitions:* Southern Exposure Gallery, San Francisco; Pine Branch, San Francisco *Education:* San Jose State U.

In the early part of his career, he was concerned to a great extent with drawing and was strongly influenced by Paul Klee. Following his studies at San Jose State, his drawing took on a more conceptual format. Operational and functional elements became more important, and composition was left simply to occur as it might. His first installation piece was a kind of industrial water reservoir. His work since 1978 shows a fascination with synthetic materials and how to use them to describe natural subjects. The materials he uses in his pieces include synthetic netting, clear polyethylene, fake wood veneer paneling, and styrofoam. Among the subjects he has dealt with are ponds, pine branches and the interior of a castle; in his works, the finished pieces say as much about the materials as they do about the subject.

PARHAMI, JILLA (Painter)
5232 Winnetka Ave., Woodland Hills, CA 91364

Born: 1951 *Awards:* Gold Medal, National Museum of Art, Iran *Exhibitions:* UCLA *Education:* Calif. State U., Northridge; Farah Pahlavi U., Iran

Although she received an academic traditional training as a student in Iran, her early style was surrealist and influenced by Persian miniature painting. When she moved from Iran to the U.S. in 1979, she began looking at Hundertwasser's work as well as primitive and children's art. Her fantasy paintings then became more abstract and symbolic. In 1982 she began creating three-dimensional surfaces over which she painted. Her ideas of interactive arts have recently led to commissions for work on aluminum. These pieces can be

David Elmer Pearce, *White Peonies,* 24 x 30, oil on canvas

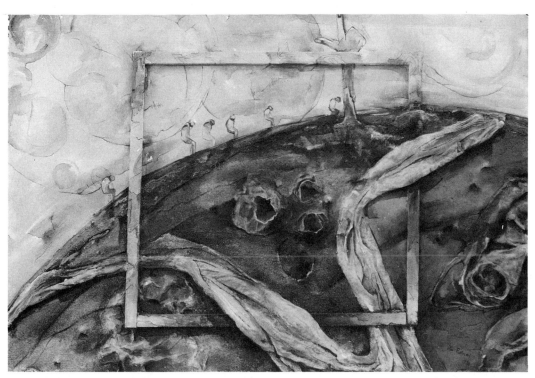

Jilla Parhami, *Can Man Control Time and Earth? Side 2,* 72 x 48, mixed media on aluminum.
Courtesy: Paul Davis

as large as 20 by 8 feet. Her current influences include Jackson Pollock, Jean Fautrier, and Tapies, influences that existed earlier, but which are now more prominent. She believes that art should be an organic part of architecture and interior design.

PARFIT, ERIC G. (Painter)
603 Las Perlas Dr., Santa Barbara, CA 93111

Born: 1909 *Awards:* Society of Graphic Artists, London; Santa Barbara Art Association *Exhibitions:* Los Olivos Gallery; Gallery 113, Santa Barbara *Education:* Cambridge U.

Applying the back lighting techniques of an experienced motion picture cameraman to landscape painting gives his work a vibrant and brilliant effect. He uses only primary colors and, from them, mixes all his shades, adding an occasional burnt sienna. He uses a course, natural sponge for his oak and eucalyptus trees. His colorful landscapes reflect a contact with Rowland Hilder and Heaton Cooper, the popular English landscape painters. He executes these paintings in a conservative and realistic, yet transparent, style. One series of mountain scenes, "Mountain Majesties," was done at Glacier National Park in Montana.

PARKER, LAURA (Photographer)
25027 Peachland Ave., #257, Newhall, CA 91321

Born: 1959 *Awards:* Pasadena Centennial Purchase Award *Collections:* Pasadena Public Library *Exhibitions:* Los Angeles Municipal Art Gallery; Dinnerware Artists Co-op *Education:* California Institute of the Arts

Her interest in poetic association and personal myth led her to produce a series of photographic triptychs in addition to more narrative work in which she used herself as model. Through juxtaposition, toning and vignetting, she endeavors to transcend the more commonplace nature of the photographic medium. Current work explores the synthesis between artificial and natural. House-shaped icons framing black-and-white xeroxes of historical heads are floated in color landscapes that vary from the bucolic to the burnt-out. Pigment is sometimes applied to the surroundings to heighten the entire scene's surreal effect.

PARKER, LAURA L. (Painter, Glass Artist)
557 Southgate Rd., Sacramento, CA 95815

Born: 1961 *Exhibitions:* Zitos Restaurant, Sacramento, CA; Nicole's Restaurant, Sacramento *Education:* Sacramento State U.

After formal training in photo-realism, she developed a looser, more impressionistic style of painting that has carried into the free-form style of her glass sculptures. Primary influences have been Laddie John Dill and Manuel Neri. Her paintings are executed in bold strokes with watercolor sticks over watercolor washes. Glass sculptures have been transformed from a polished, high-tech look to pate-de-verre, where the form invokes rhythm and balance in a primitive, archetypal manner. Her recent series of glass sculptures evolved from molds she made from the human body: She placed glass sheets on the molds and both were then fired in a kiln, resulting in delicate, curving abstractions.

PARKER, LEROY W. (Painter, Ceramist)
40 Meek Pl., Lafayette, CA

Born: 1941 *Collections:* Oakland Museum; City of Sacramento *Exhibitions:* Slant Gallery, Sacramento;

Harcourt's Contemporary, San Francisco *Education:* California College of Arts and Crafts; San Jose State U. *Dealer:* San Francisco Museum of Modern Art; Fort Mason, San Francisco

A colorful marbleized imagery characterizes his work in several media. He has produced hundreds of large abstract watercolors, in addition to ceramic vases and eight-foot-tall columns tht are colorful and abstract. He also fabricates hand-made paper work from natural fibers which he cooks, bleaches, blends and colors. Tirelessly, he has created permanent installations in concrete and ceramics, as well as worked with marbleized fabrics. His work is rich in color and form. The artist describes the work as esthetically 'hot.'He has been influenced by Picasso's wide use of media as well as the imagery and technique of Monet, Degas, and the Impressionists.

PARKER, WILMA (Painter)
222 Clara Street, San Francisco, CA 94107

Born: 1941 *Collections:* Palm Springs Desert Museum; de Saisset Museum *Exhibitions:* National Air & Space Museum, Washington, DC; Lisa Dubins Gallery, Los Angeles *Education:* School of the Art Institute of Chicago; Rhode Island School of Design *Dealer:* Dubins Gallery, Los Angeles

Her subject matter until recently was largely botanical, and her works interpreted multiple-exposure photographs of foliage through oil or pencil on canvas or paper. Her technique of creating a flat, transparent-like color expanded photorealistic renderings into hyper-real worlds that invite exploration of memory and interior space. The structuralism of the previous work, combined with her concern for form and space, has lead to the current series of works on architecture, which include interiors, cityscapes and buildings reflected in other buildings. These works are rendered in a reductive manner on dark-grounded linen. She has also been working in acrylic and oils on paper, and on a series of plexiglas constructions.

PARSONS, BARBARA GALUSZKA
(Printmaker)
3650 Loval Valley Rd., Sonoma, CA 95476

Collections: Oxford University, England; Kala Institute *Exhibitions:* Victoria and Albert Museum, London; Printmakers Council of Great Britain, London *Education:* Oxford U., England

She has recently been favoring viscosity work over more traditional English techniques because of its superior capacity for layering colors in a print. Her present abstract images are inspired by the ordered negative/positive space of Chinese characters and the tensile movement suggested in their expression. The prints provide a non-representational vocabulary to explore the role of language and symbol in a representational and humanistic context, and the similarity of this role for the speaker, the writer and the draughtsman. Her exploration of color in these pieces further develops the relationship of the printing plate to its two-dimensional product, achieving a clarity of hue and an infusion of light that is nearly tangible.

PASCHKE-IRVIN, CHRIS (Calligrapher)
2753 Bechelli Ln., Redding, CA 96002

Born: 1951 *Exhibitions:* Foundation for the Arts of Peace, San Francisco; CFA Gallery, Redding

With extensive training in manuscript study and letter analysis, and an interest in English heraldry and the

Carl Provder, *True Nature,* 23 x 30, mixed media on Arches paper

Wilma Parker, *Oleanders,* 40 x 64, oil on canvas. Courtesy: Dubins Gallery, Los Angeles, CA

Irish *Book of Kells*, she attempts to depict the written word as an art form. Rudolph Koch and contemporaries such as Frederick Neuebauer and Karlgeorg Hoefer, as well as the German Expressionists have inspired her recent free form calligraphic works. The study of the planes of lettering and their dimensional relationship to the exterior environment are key elements in her work, highlighted by innovative frame designs and unique modes of presentation. She brings the two-dimensional written word into a third dimension by hand carving letterforms into ragboard. Gouache, ink, pencil, assorted ragboards and handmade papers all interrelate to create a three-dimensional experience, featuring the calligraphic letter form as the subject of fine art.

PASHGIAN, HELEN (Painter, Sculptor)
731 S. Grand Ave., Pasadena, CA 91105

Awards: NEA Grant *Collections:* Andrew Dickson White Museum of Art, Cornell U. *Exhibitions:* Hotel de Ville Museum, Paris; Security Pacific Bank, Los Angeles *Education:* Pomona College *Dealers:* Works Gallery, Long Beach; Modernism, San Francisco

Visually provocative, intellectually rewarding and technically innovative, her work is first of light, then color and gesture. These are not really painting in the traditional sense but framed strata of color, with light imprisoned in the material itself. What appear to be smooth-surfaced, highly organized gestural systems are carefully controlled layers of molded, dyed epoxy embedded in a sandwich of gessoed canvas backing and clear, mat automotive surfacings. Between these are two float overlapping sheets of epoxy whose pleated, folded, notched and ridged sections either occur intact or are broken into repetitive patterns. Over them trail passages of brightly colored epoxy, creating bursts of energy and spontaneity.

PASKEWITZ, BILL (Painter)
2464 "B" North Glassell St., Orange, CA 92665

Born: 1953 *Awards:* Anna E. Meltzer Award *Exhibitions:* West Coast Gallery, Newport Beach; Laguna Art Museum *Education:* Cooper Union, NYC *Dealer:* The Underground Gallery, Newport Beach

His continued interest is in producing images that challenge one's perception. His early work featured disoriented and ambiguous use of space to achieve the effect, combining the artificial and the real, high abstraction and decoration, illusion and allusion. His current works, done in acrylic on large canvases, are abstractions with elements from still lifes, landscapes and figures. Working with an intense palette, he creates images that dissolve into a mass of brushstrokes or into another image. They become rearranged, inverted and juxtaposed in the process of painting and viewing. Only the movement of the overall composition echoes the viewer's original perception of the image.

PATERSON, RUDI (Painter)
5 York St., London W.I. England

Born: 1939 *Awards:* Grolla D'Ora Art Exhibition, Venice *Collections:* Gallery Art Naieve, Melbourne, Australia; Roy Miles Fine Art Gallery, London *Exhibitions:* Air Jamaica Art Exhibitions, London; Carmichael Fine Art

Born in Jamaica, he trained at the Royal Academy of Dramatic art and had a successful acting career. Entirely self taught, he took to painting while convalesc-ing from a serious neck injury in 1969. His works evoke the vivid colors and natural beauty of the Caribbean. His series "Reflections" featured scenes of tree lined rivers, local architecture, and tropical birds and flowers.

PATRICK, ALICE (Painter, T-Shirt Artist)
941 W. 75th St., Los Angeles, CA 90044

Born: 1940 *Collections:* Stevie Wonder *Exhibitions:* California Museum of Science and Industry, Los Angeles; Barnsdall Gallery, Los Angeles *Education:* Otis Art Institute; Los Angeles City College *Dealer:* Aliceland, Los Angeles

She has been influenced by Charles White, Van Gogh and David Mosely. After formal training in oil painting, she began to work from photographs, using a palette knife and mixing paint directly on the canvas. Her subjects are normally black women in the work force. She first gained renown for *Women Do Get Weary*, a charcoal pen on wet paper drawing depicting four seated tired- looking black women. She has recently been doing a brightly colored series on male sports figures. In a recent limited edition series of oils, "Tanya," a little black girl in formal dress sits at a piano.

PATTERSON, KAREN M. (Painter)
1903 Temple #119, Signal Hill, CA

Born: 1955 *Collections:* Wells Fargo Bank, San Francisco *Exhibitions:* Lawrence Ross Gallery, Beverly Hills; Somerset Gallery, Palm Springs *Education:* San Francisco State U.; El Camino College *Dealer:* Dyansen Gallery, Beverly Hills, New York, Boston, San Diego

Although the post-impressionist style of pointillism comes to mind first with regard to her work, she considers herself primarily a colorist, although loosely influenced by the work of Seurat, Cross, and Sisley. Her watercolor work in particular differs from the calculated oils of the post-impressionist masters by its coloring and design. In her work one finds paintings of figures and still lifes, but she prefers to paint local landscapes. Covering the entire surface of the paper in an intricate process of overlay and inlay of pigment, she takes care to preserve the intensity and integrity of the color. In order to do this, some of her larger, 30-by-40-inch paintings have taken up to six months to complete.

PATTERSON, PATRICIA (Painter)
467 La Costa Ave., Leucadia, CA 92024

Born: 1943 *Collections:* John Muir College, UC-San Diego; Northern Trust Bank, Chicago *Exhibitions:* Los Angeles County Museum of Art; University Art Gallery, UC- Riverside *Education:* Parsons School of Design *Dealer:* Newspace, Los Angeles

For more than twenty years, she has painted the people, animals and landscapes of Inishmore, one of Ireland's remote Arin Islands. Her first paintings, made after a trip there in the early 1960s, emphasize loosely painted figures with an overt style. By the mid-1970s, the paintings were larger and much more focused on the subjects, which are rendered in an understated, realist style. She also adds wooden picture frames, which she paints as well, to lend a homemade, cozy feeling to the presentation. In addition, she has created an installation with facsimile tables, chairs, fireplace, window, floor and walls, with two paintings of scenes that hang in the installation space.

Zaro Piliguian, *Inner Empressions,* 18 x 24, oil

Lydia Palmer-Allen, *Counterpoint,* 24 x 18, watercolor

PATTERSON, ROBERTA (Photographer)
668 Ramona St., Palo Alto, CA

Born: 1958 *Awards:* 1st Place, Screenprinting, Pacific Art League Membership Competition, Palo Alto *Exhibitions:* Pacific Art League Membership Competition, Palo Alto; Triton Museum, Santa Clara *Education:* Doane College

Her work is focused on alternative processes in photography, particularly the possibilities presented by cyanotype and Van Dyke printing techniques. The latter produces a range of deep, indigo blues; the former affords an almost endless range of browns. Combining the processes yields mustard yellows and green hues. She develops the photographic images on monotypes and screenprints. She enjoys stretching technique to the limit, combining processes to recreate the psychological mood present when the photograph was snapped. She strives to create strong images—ones that will provoke a response, whether positive or negative.

PAUL, DOROTHY SHORT (Painter)
71 San Marino Dr., San Rafael, CA 94901

Born: 1920 *Awards:* 1st Place in Watercolor, Hoosier Salon; Purchase Prize, South Carolina State Fair *Exhibitons:* Marin Arts Guild; Gualala Art Association *Education:* Cranbrook Academy of Art; O'Hara Watercolor School

She is concerned with texture, light, and shadow. Though her hero is Winslow Homer, her liberal use of dry brush, controlled approach, and her choice of neutral colors cause her style to resemble that of Andrew Wyeth more closely. Working from preliminary sketches and photographs, she develops a mood and concentrates on composition and design in her paintings. Often she incorporates figures and other subjects from her imagination as well as from material she has collected. She is currently painting a series of Spanish and Italian scenes. She is coauthor with Phoebe Flory and Eliot O'Hara of "Portraits in the Making" and "Watercolor Portraiture."

PAULINE, MARK (Machine Performance Artist)
1458-C San Bruno Ave., San Francisco, CA 94110

Born: 1953 *Awards:* NEA Interarts Grant *Exhibitions:* Shea Stadium, NYC; New Langton Arts, San Francisco *Education:* Eckerd College

In 1979, he founded Survival Research Laboratories (SRL), an organization dedicated to exploiting the potential of science and industry for creating a new medium of expression. The central feature of SRL's unique idiom is the machine performance, which is a theatrical presentation consisting of a series of ritualized interactions between machines, robots, and special effects devices, with humans present only in the context of operators or audience. SRL works with complex technologies and can create and control enormous and potentially dangerous public presentations in a safe, effective manner.

PAULSON, M. (Painter)
391-A Arkansas, San Francisco, CA 94107

Born: 1953 *Exhibitions:* John Pence Gallery, San Francisco *Education:* U. of Washington, Seattle

His work is strongly narrative, reflecting a keen interest and formal training in theater, from both a practical and academic standpoint. The pieces include a central, representational image surrounded by a frame depicting related figures or symbols which tell a story about the central image. He works in two primary media: cut paper collage and oil on wood panel. The cut paper work is characterized by brightly colored, cartoon-like images from memories of the 1950s and 1960s. Joy is the central emotion communicated, but the work is not sentimental. The oil on wood panels retain the color sense of the cut paper but are more serious in nature. One series from 1989 comprises thirteen paintings illustrating the Norse myth "The Death of Balder."

PAVA, ESTHER (Painter)
2318 Hastings Dr., Belmont, CA 94002

Born: 1921 *Awards:* 2nd Prize, Thirty and One Artists Beaux Arts Festival; 2nd Prize, Burlingame Art Society Show *Exhibitions:* Society of Western Artists, Walnut Creek; Burlingame Recreation Dept. *Education:* Rhode Island School of Design; San Francisco State U.

Though she enjoys abstraction and a looser style, her early experience as a commercial artist left a stamp of realism on her painting. Subject matter includes landscapes, still lives and abstraction. Her admiration for Monet and Renoir led her to studied with Henry Hensche—an experience which is reflected in her vibrant use of oils, and her love for the subtleties of color. She recently became fascinated by the versatility of watercolors. Since she began experimenting with that medium, her canvases have shown an increasing looseness and freedom.

PAYSON, HUONG N. (Painter)
2419 N. Val Vista Dr., Mesa, AZ 85203

Born: 1943 *Collections:* Macalester College, St. Paul, MN *Exhibitions:* Unicorn Oriental Gallery, Scottsdale, AZ; International Porcelain Art Teachers, Los Angeles *Education:* Macalester College

Her admiration of Robert Bateman and Andrew Wyeth led her to use acrylic and oil to paint wildlife and people. Her keen observation of nature and her drive for perfection result in her work's super-realism. Now she prefers painting on porcelain. It is an exacting art, calling for proficiency in several media. The pigments are mineral oxides of various metals such as gold, iron, chromium and cobalt. After each thin layer is applied, the piece is fired to the precise temperature needed to melt the paint into the glaze. Each layer is translucent, permitting the viewer to see through the outer layers to the inner ones. By this process, she is able to achieve a jewel-like quality in her work. Her portraits reveal a neo-realistic clarity that seems to pierce her subjects' souls.

PEARCE, DAVID ELMER (Painter)
155 Nieto Ave., Long Beach, CA 90803

Born: 1937 *Awards:* Gold Key Awards, National Scholastic Art Competition, Pittsburgh *Collections:* El Pueblo Museum, Colorado Historical Society *Exhibitions:* Fine Arts Center, Taos, NM; Gilpin County Art Museum, Colorado *Education:* U. of Southern Colorado *Dealer:* Metcalf Gallery, South Pasadena, CA

He achieved early success as an abstract expressionist and has moved on to painting a variety of styles and subjects: hard-line abstractions of the Southwest landscape; classically realistic landscapes; the seashore in a more contemporary style; and period, academic

Bruce Pierce A.W.S., *Grand Canyon Picture,* 32 x 39, egg tempera

Sara Petty, *Meshes,* 5 x 7, prisma (animation drawing). Courtesy: Ms. Elfriede Fishinger

florals. He has recently been developing a series of historical paintings of the Southwest. Although he is largely self-taught, he has studied with William Hartley and Paul Ihrig and has been influenced by the Dutch and Flemish Masters.

PEARCE, PATRICIA A. (Mixed Media Artist)
1580 Tarrytown, San Mateo, CA 94402

Born: 1948 *Awards:* Grand Prize, 3rd Biennial Exhibition of Prints, Wakayama, Japan; Grant, Peninsula Community Foundation *Collections:* Nieman Marcus, San Francisco; Wells Fargo, San Francisco *Exhibitions:* Montalvo, Calif. Center for the Arts; Pacific Prints, Palo Alto *Education:* San Francisco State U.; UC-Irvine *Dealer:* Miller/Brown, San Francisco

Her early work on paper explored images of garments using various printmaking techniques. She began to work mainly in collagraph and monotype prints creating singular images of kimonos in Her subtly shifting, subdued pieces are constructed in a three step process. The scaffolding for the fabric image is made from a silk organza collagraph place. She adds a monotype to the collagraph print to layer veils of ink one over another to create the illusion of layers of fabric, and then hand alters the image to heighten the illusion of reality and add new elements.

PEEBLES, GENE (Painting)
866 41st Ave., San Francisco, CA 94121

Born: 1953 *Collections:* Bank of America, San Francisco; Colby College Museum of Art, Waterville, ME *Exhibitions:* San Jose Institute of Contemporary Art; William Sawyer Gallery, San Francisco *Education:* U. of Illinois

Early American painters of the Hudson River school, notably Albert Bierstadt, Frederick Church and Thomas Cole, have strongly influenced his style. He adapted their realistically lush, painterly style to skyscapes rendered in a more contemporary realistic style that, because of the subject matter, often borders on abstraction. Working in oil and pastel, he blends and combines colors into each other to achieve a softly hued, undulating painting of the sky and clouds. His paintings, which precisely capture all manner of skies and clouds, are dominated by white and by shades of blue. He says that his work is most successful when he can obtain a sense of motion ranging from stillness to raging thunder, feeling the clouds roll across the sky in constant change.

PEEPLES, MAIJA WOOF (Painter)
2586 King Richard Drive, El Dorado Hills, CA 95630

Born: 1942 *Awards:* Calif. Society of Etchers; Calif. State Fair Art Show *Collections:* Cincinnati Art Museum; Mathews Art Center, Tempe, AZ *Exhibitions:* La Jolla Art Musuem; Crocker Art Musuem, Sacramento *Education:* UC-Davis *Dealer:* Candy Store Gallery, Folsom

She studied at the university level with William T. Wiley and Robert Arneson. Under the influence of Edward Hicks, Henri Rousseau and the Etruscan tomb paintings of Cerveteri, she developed her "Beastie"-style of drawing to create paintings, ceramics, etchings and multimedia works bearing such titles as *Beast Haystacks*, *Let Me Call You Sweethare* and *Life Is Just A Bowl Of Terriers*. Rainbows of birds, penguin-filled mountains and rivers, parrot philodendrons and crocodile palms are among the images that figure in her large and boldly colored oil paintings. She is sometimes grouped with the funk school of painters, owing to her work's naive and comic effect.

PENDARVIS, PATRICE (Painter, Multimedia Artist)
727 Albian, San Diego, CA 92106

Born: 1956 *Awards:* 1st Place, Southern California Expo, National Society of Arts and Letters; 1st Place, Woman's Show, Art Kauai, Kauai Society of Artists *Collections:* IBM; Hawaii State Foundation on Culture and the Arts *Exhibitions:* Cabrillo Art Center, San Diego; Gallerie Bianca, Santa Barbara

She has been painting since she was 7 years old, and is almost entirely self-taught. In recent years, her technique has evolved from traditional watercolor on paper to watercolor-collage. Using twelve different kinds of rice paper, she tears small pieces and glues them to 300 lb. paper, watching as the design emerges. She uses the various textures for different elements, such as water, clouds, flowers, trees and rocks. When the glue has dried, she carefully paints each piece, creating a nearly three-dimensional, watercolor Hawaiian landscape. Nature is her inspiration, and she works from a palette of "true colors" to render for others the beauty of her adopted tropical home. Recently, she has been using the same technique for murals and triptychs, some of which reach ten feet in length.

PENGELLY, ROBERT (Painter)
P.O. Box 189454, Sacramento, CA 95818

Born: 1949 *Awards:* Philip Conrad Travel Award-Florence *Collections:* Sacramento Metropolitan Arts Commission *Exhibitions:* Himovitz-Jenson Gallery, Sacramento; J.F. Kennedy Library, Vallejo *Education:* London Art School *Dealer:* Iannetti Lanzone Gallery, San Francisco; Michael Himovitz Gallery, Sacramento

His early works were Hopper-influenced watercolors and oils. In the mid 1970s he began to investigate less representational ways of conveying emotional content, which resulted in abstract expressionist/cubist fragmentation. Since emigrating to the U.S. in 1984 he has returned to realism and concentrated on watercolor, developing a controlled and structured approach to the recognizable. For example, foliage, influenced by the neatly trimmed gardens and shrubbery of domestic America, has become especially potent as elements and devices. His primary themes are Victorian architecture with solitary figures, either human or animal. With his work increasing in scale, he continues to refine both his technique and formal organization of imagery.

PENIDO, MARCUS A. (Painter)
14055 Tahiti Way, #107, Marina Del Rey, CA 90242

Born: 1953 *Exhibitions:* Beverly Hills Sutitier Gallery, Santa Monica; Mark Reuben Gallery, San Francisco

At the age of thirteen, he started painting with oils in the classic realist tradition. Works by Calder introduced him to the world of modern art, and for twelve years, he worked first with gouache on paper, and then acrylics on canvas, to produce abstract expressionist paintings. These paintings are characterized by a tension between free forms and geometric shapes. During the last eight years, four of which have been in California, he has returned to oil painting in a figurative style. His recent output takes the city of Los Angeles as its subject: the day-by-day lives of its people, their dreams versus their reality.

Jeanette Pincus, *Weavers—Antigua–Guatamala,* 22 x 30, watercolor

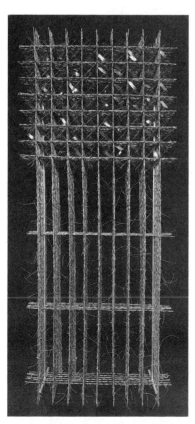

Ellen Phillips, *Segment—Wall of the Past,* 84 x 36 x 24, wire and transparencies. Photographer: Gerald M. Williams

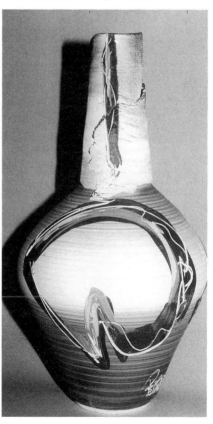

Brad Pettigrew, *untitled,* 28 x 12, ceramic. Courtesy: John Thomas Gallery

PENNEL, RYAN (Photographer, Sculptor)
4832 Lotus, San Diego, CA 92107

Born: 1958 *Exhibitions:* San Diego Urban Nude; Art Walk Show, San Diego *Education:* San Diego State U.

Influenced by Duane Michals, he combined text with two- dimensional images of nudes—*Lunch Nude, Gay Men at Beach*—in his "San Diego Urban Nude" project. At San Diego's outdoor Art Walk, he photographed two nude models, mounted the photographs on a thirty-two-by-forty-inch collage and then placed the nude models in front of the piece. In sculpture, his influences include the geometric qualities of cubism; in his photography surrealism has been important, as have the teachings of Pasha Turley and Imogen Cunningham. He has recently been combining the photographic image with glass sculpture.

PENNINGTON, DAVID (Painter)
P.O. Box 846, Bisbee, AZ 85603

Born: 1952 *Collections:* Prudential Life Insurance, New York; Valley National Bank of America, Tucson *Exhibitions:* 33d Annual National Juried Exhibition, San Diego Art Institute; 1987 Phoenix Biennial, Phoenix Art Museum *Dealer:* Art Space, Los Angeles

Influenced by tantric abstraction, surrealism, painterly expressionism and iconicity, his work falls into two categories. The first of these consists of geometric, analytic abstractions constructed of paint segments which display random drips and splashes of color on a vertical shaped support. While the segments build and materialize an image, the painterly "incidents" begin to dematerialize and create atmosphere. The second is traditionally framed collages, repositories of items of a transitory and recycled nature. Narratives are implied through a juxtaposition of materials and imagery, including linoleum, paint-by-numbers pictures, fabric and religious books.

PEPPER, SASHA (Painter)
1222 Cole St., San Francisco, CA 94117

Born: 1942 *Awards:* Honorable Mention, Gallery House Juried Exhibition, Palo Alto; Exhibition Award, Gallery Imago, San Francisco *Exhibitions:* Southern Exposure Gallery, San Francisco; SOMAR Gallery, San Francisco *Education:* UC- Berkeley

She studied with Elmer Bischoff at Berkeley in the early 1970s, and was strongly influenced by the Bay area figurative school and the early Abstract Expressionists in their methods of handling paint and imagery. Her early abstract works in oil, on canvas or paper, were characterized by organic forms, tightly interwoven in a narrow space—a style reminiscent of early de Kooning. For a brief period in the early 1980s, she worked with acrylic on unprimed canvas, using washes, staining and drip techniques. These paintings featured landscape imagery modeled from the California hills. Influenced by contemporary European expressionist painters, she has returned to oil paint and figurative imagery. She prefers the viscosity and texture of oils, their rich color, the medium's potential for working and reworking and the possibilities of combining drawing into the paint with charcoal and oil sticks. Painting from gestural drawings, she creates figures which exist either in abstract space or in more definite landscapes. The spatial relations among the figures, and their fragmentary gestures, symbolize different areas of human experience.

PEREZ, CARLOS RAUL (Painter)
3000 Stanford Ave., Marina Del Rey, CA 90292

Born: 1953 *Exhibitions:* Orlando Gallery, Sherman Oaks; Schwartz-Cierlak Gallery, Santa Monica, CA *Dealer:* Schwartz-Cierlak Gallery, Santa Monica

After apprenticing with Los Angeles photographer Norman Frimkess, he worked at the Elson-Alexandre Studio as a portrait photographer. In 1973 he began teaching himself to paint, with a special interest in realism. Initially, he used his photography as the foundation for commissioned portrait painting; later photographic studies of people became the focal point of his work. He broadened his art by experimenting with paints, textures, and new perspectives. His most recent work has taken on a mystical realism, which can be seen in works such as *The Chairs*, an oil on canvas in which eight different chairs are lined up horizontally, appearing to sit on the surface of a body of water, the horizon of water blending imperceptibly with that of the sky. He still considers photographic studies of people, however, to be his greatest source of inspiration.

PEREZ, VINCENT (Painter, Printmaker)
1279 Weber St., Alameda, CA 94501

Born: 1938 *Awards:* Grant, American Institute of Graphic Artists; 4th Annual Gertrude B. Murphy Gold Award *Collections:* San Francisco Museum of Modern Art; Oakland Museum *Exhibitions:* Palo Alto Cultural Center; Oakland Museum *Education:* Pratt Institute; California College of Arts and Crafts

His illustrative science fiction and fantasy work is in a variety of media, including woodcuts, drawings and acrylic and oil paintings. His science fiction paintings have been reproduced in calendars, and he has done covers for *Time* magazine and other national publications. He has also done post-production art for George Lucas' "Indiana Jones and the Temple of Doom" and Disney's "The Scheme of Things." Recent work includes a series of woodcut prints for Potlatch Corporation and anatomical drawings for publication in textbooks and advertising purposes.

PERLMAN, JOAN (Painter, Draughtsperson)
P.O. Box 884394, San Francisco, CA 94188

Born: 1954 *Awards:* NEA Fellowship; MacDowell Residency Grant *Collections:* Achenbach Foundation, Fine Arts Museums of San Francisco *Exhibitions:* San Francisco Museum of Modern Art; Judah L. Magnes Museum, Berkeley *Education:* San Francisco Art Institute; California College of Arts and Crafts *Dealer:* John Berggruen Gallery, San Francisco

From 1979 through 1985, her richly layered works were oil paintings, monotypes or a mixed media of pastel and collage. Working both abstractly and representationally, and with an emphasis on light and dark, her images were derived from Middle Eastern architecture and the architecture of other cultures. Her recent work is about boundary, containment, force and conflict. Using urban, industrial structures as her source and the formal elements of light, mass and weight, she contrasts a geometry of man made forms with the "powerful void" of nature, to create a strong sense of opposites interacting and to address the relationship of nature and technology. Her media are oil paint on wood or canvas, and large pastel/charcoal drawings.

Bruce Pollack, *Boundaries Vaguely Defined,* 30 x 26, resin. Courtesy: K. Stalinger

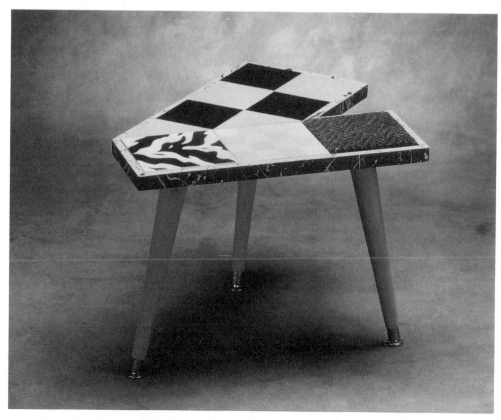

Michael J. Pickard, *Study Table #3,* 16 x 18 x 18 ceramic tile, carpet tile, painted wood

PETERS, EVELYN (Painter)
406 N. Lake Dr., Granite Shoals, TX 78654

Born: 1927 *Awards:* 1st & Purchase Prizes, Great American Art Competition *Collections:* Agricultural Hall f Fame, Bonner Springs, KS; Museum of Great American Art, Webster, TX *Exhibitions:* Golub Gallery, Steamboat Springs, CO; Museum of Art of the American Southwest, Houston

She paints animals, traditional western scenes, houses blanketed in snow, and other images of nostalgic Americana. Her early influences were Sidney Lawrence's traditional realism and the more exploratory styles of Edward Betts and Al Brouillette. Through formal study with Frank Covino, Margaret Kessler and Bob Wygant, she developed a detailed individual style involving acrylic, alkyd and oil. Today, she shows a concern with light and achieves a painterly realism through a combination of controlled brushwork and techniques of glazing, scumbling, spattering, sgraffiti, spongework and stippling. She is also an official Coast Guard artist.

PETERS, MARY ANN (Painter)
71 Columbia, 4th Fl., Seattle, WA 98104

Born: 1949 *Collections:* Seattle Art Museum; Hughes Corporate Headquarters, Los Angeles *Exhibitions:* Los Angeles Municiple Gallery; Richmond Art Center *Dealer:* Linda Farris, Seattle

Her work is a marriage of historical architectural forms and a modernist sensibility. Through misplaced timeworn images, she suggests history, heritage and a sense of place. Her symbolic references are cross-cultural, and draw meaning from myths and mankind's archeological past. Her evocative, sensitively colored works have been informed by the work of Kandinsky, Malevich and Mondrian. Her recent frescos implicitly refer to the past, but she is also beginning to use such three-dimensional materials as wood, slate and cement. Her symbolic images remain, but they are now more literal and defined.

PETERS, URSULA (Mail Artist, Poster Artist)
8 Balboa Ave., San Rafael, CA 94901

Born: 1934 *Awards:* 1st Award, Dimensions '80, Livermore *Collections:* Einhod Museum, Israel; Museum of Modern Art, Los Angeles *Exhibitions:* Rysunku Gallery, Poznan, Poland; Mission Cultural Center, San Francisco *Dealer:* Little Bear Productions, San Rafael

Disgusted with the international art scene, she has sought to promote political awareness and a new humanism through book art, mail art, performances, political posters, and international simultaneous art events. She has been inspired by Klaus Steack of West Germany and she accompanies her huge silk-screen posters with offset prints in book-sized and postcard editions. Her private works are white pencil drawings on black paper that are alternately melancholy and ecstatic, often completed under the influence of the best perfume, alcohol, music, and cigarettes. She is establishing an alternative print workshop with silk-screens and offset machines.

PETTIGREW, BRAD (Ceramist)
8101 Holder St., Buena Park, CA 90620

Born: 1949 *Collections:* Gibraltor Savings and Loan; 7-Up Corporation *Exhibitions:* D. Genaro Galleries, Santa Monica; Village Artistry, Carmel; Del Mano Galleries, Pasadena

In the late 1960s, he took inspiration from the work of Carlton Ball and Peter Voulkos. At the time, he threw large pieces, which he incised with expressionistic drawings and glazed in soft muted colors from the cone ten range. The paintings of Franz Kline and Mark Rothko and ceramics of Don Reitz are more recent influences, while he continues to use a combination of porcelain and stoneware, throwing and handbuilding his pieces. He achieves an incised sgraffito effect and a wet/dry look by painting and airbrushing ceramic stains and englobes. He has a wide palette and he uses a complete range of colors from black to pastels.

PETTY, SARA (Animator)
1803 Mission St., #12, Santa Cruz, CA 95060

Born: 1947 *Awards:* Grant, American Film Institute; 1st Place, International Animation Festival, Ottawa *Exhibitions:* Los Angeles County Museum of Art; Short Film Showcase, NYC *Education:* Texas Tech U., Lubbock; UCLA

After studying painting in her native Texas, she moved to Los Angeles to study with Lorser Feitelson, a California Hard-Edge painter she admired. In 1975, interested in the Futurists and time arts, she began exploring the possibilities animated pastel drawings. Her first film, *Shadrac,* was followed by *Furies,* an intense, highly-textured study of abstraction set in motion, which featured two dynamic cat forms that turned to abstract shapes, while maintaining a feline motion. In her recent film, *Picture Window,* dynamic movement has given way to a more contemplative, painterly approach. With intricate drawings in pastel, charcoal and prism, she depicts cyclic metamorphoses of abstract forms, as well as the movement of light through windows and ephemeral transparencies.

PFAFF, JUDY (Sculptor, Conceptual Artist)
c/o Holly Solomon Gallery, 724 Fifth Ave., New York, NY 10019

Born: 1946 *Collections:* Albright-Knox Art Gallery, Buffalo *Exhibitions:* Holly Solomon Gallery, NYC *Education:* Yale U.; Washington U., St. Louis *Dealer:* Holly Solomon Gallery, NYC

She is most well known for large, energetic, visually charged, abstract installations assembled with a wide variety of materials such as wire, wood and cloth. Her two-dimensional works also make use of unusual materials, such as contact paper on mylar, some appearing as condensed, flattened versions of the installations. Recently, she has been creating wall sculptures with a still life theme. As in her other works, underneath a surface of charged energy of seeming chaos, lies a disciplined and succinct, if complex, order.

PFEIFFER, PAUL M. (Painting)
1035 Sutter St., San Francisco, CA 94109

Born: 1966 *Awards:* San Francisco Art Institute Printmaking Award *Exhibitions:* San Francisco Art Institute; City Hall of San Francisco *Education:* San Francisco Art Institute

Trained as a printmaker, his early work was very flat, the product of a personal system of organizing visual imagery. He was inspired by the Old Masters and American realist painters and switched to painting in oil and acrylic. Working in a figurative, narrative style, his dream-like paintings have an almost surreal appearance. He works by contrasting vivid colors with more subtle shadings, creating an engaging interplay between light and shadow, figure and ground.

Virginia Pochmann, *No. 131 White Iris,* 22 x 30, watercolor. Courtesy: Dianne Hanson

Audri Phillips, *So Real,* 36 x 48, oils

PHILL, DANIEL (Painter)
P.O. Box 11763, San Francisco, CA 94101

Born: 1955 *Awards:* Stanford Fellowship; Household Finance Corporation Painting Award, International Exhibition and Calendar, Chicago *Collections:* Koret Foundation, San Francisco; Nordstrom *Exhibitions:* San Francisco Arts Commission Gallery; San Francisco Art Institute *Dealers:* John Pence Gallery, San Francisco; Wade Gallery, Los Angeles

Artists from his native Pacific Northwest—Mark Tobey, Morris Graves and Kenneth Callahan—were early influences. In the late 1970s, he painted with acrylic on canvas employing an oil technique and explored action painting, dynamic surfaces, implied motion, abstract expressionism and automatism. Later, working with Nathan Oliveira and Frank Lobdell, he further developed his own style of abstraction—loose, gestural, thickly painted biomorphic shapes in vast environments—working primarily in oil on canvas and in acrylic on paper. At this stage, Diebenkorn, Park, Motherwell and Matta influenced his work. At present, his style is more refined and more geometric, the surfaces sparser by active and heavily layered. He achieves a variety of textures by the juxtaposition of these dense opaque areas and transparent areas.

PHILLIPS, AUDRI (Painter)

Born: 1953 *Awards:* 3rd Prize, Art Contest, Pasadena *Collections:* Wavefront Technology Company, Santa Barbara; Channel Islands Orthopedic Medical Group, Oxnard *Exhibitions:* Burbage Theatre Gallery, Los Angeles *Education:* Carnegie-Mellon U.

The artist weaves a narrative quality through her large oil paintings to comment on social and metaphysical issues. Often tempered with a large dose of humor, the people and objects of her compositions are given equal importance. While these elements are rendered in realistic style, their surroundings might just as easily be a series of open, floating, geometric planes as a car, or a living room. Ordinary objects like can openers and hair dryers become interesting under the artist's whimsical treatment. They move, jump and fly of their own accord, sometimes under the very noses of their blasé human owners.

PHILLIPS, ELLEN (Sculptor)
9463 Mesa Vista, La Mesa, CA 92041

Born: 1929 *Awards:* Artist Guild Exhibition Award, San Diego Museum of Art; Meritorious Performance and Professional Promise Award, San Diego State U. *Collections:* Alexandria Museum of Art, Alexandria *Exhibitions:* Spectrum Gallery, San Diego; San Diego State U. Master Gallery *Education:* San Diego State U.; Cornell U.

Coming out of a craft background in fiber and clay, she began sculpting with handmade paper, producing couched and vacuum- formed reliefs of wet-torn and molded paper, as well as free- standing layered grid forms. The larger pieces include steel armatures in combinations of paper and fiberglass, hardware cloth and transparencies. The forms are non-objective or abstract, the work influenced by the repetition, binding, layering, and chance and impermanence in the work of Eva Hess. The artist's interest in Jungian psychology continues to inform her work, the pieces' passages and barriers approximating the threshold between the conscious and the unconscious. She continues to use uncommon sculptural materials, such as

bonded sand, barbed wire, inscribed transparencies and chain-link fencing, in these confrontational pieces.

PHILLIPS, JIM L. (Graphic Artist)
1410 Webster, Studio 1406, Santa Cruz, CA 95062

Born: 1944 *Awards:* 1st Place, Monterey Naval Post-Graduate School Religious Art Show *Exhibitions:* Cabrillo College; Pacific Garden Mall, Santa Cruz *Education:* California College of Arts and Crafts, Oakland

As an underground graphic artist, his first cartoon series was published in *Surfing Illustrated Magazine* in 1963. While attending the California College of Arts and Crafts in the mid- 1960s, he painted murals for lodgings and psychedelic cars, refrigerators and surfboards. He also did surrealist and abstract expressionist religious paintings influenced by Bosch and Disney. From the late 1960s to the early 1980s, he freelanced in a variety of areas, including advertising, rock posters and T- shirts. As art director of Santa Cruz Skateboards Inc., he currently turns out wild skate graphics for the new wave pop culture of the skateboard world.

PICHETTE, MARY (Painter)
22213 Moneta, Carson, CA 90745

Born: 1931 *Awards:* 1st Prize, San Pedro Art Association *Exhibitions:* Palos Verdes Commercial Art Association; San Pedro Art Association

While at college, this artist was influenced by Monet, Van Gogh, and Gauguin. Rapidly painted portraits on a color primed surface with no preliminary studies are typical of the early works. Color and pattern were important concerns in these works as was the hint of the mysterious. After college in the early 1950s came a hiatus from painting that lasted until 1984, when the French Impressionist exhibit, "A Day in the Country," provided inspiration to pick up the brush again. This artist feels that it is necessary to feel oneself part of the landscapes or related to the portrait subject. The media for recent works are oil and pastel.

PICKARD, MICHAEL JOSEPH (Ceramicist)
1478 Paseo del Mar, San Pedro, CA 90731

Born: 1959 *Awards:* Ceramic Award, Palos Verdes High School; Bank of America Art Achievement Award *Collections:* Thousand Oaks Public Library *Exhibitions:* San Luis Obispo Student Art Exhibit; San Luis Obispo County Pottery Show *Education:* Cal. Polytechnic, San Luis Obispo

His original ceramic pieces were traditional, functional pottery. In 1985, he began experimenting with low-fire ceramics and direct ceramic silk-screening onto tile. In 1986, he started working for a Los Angeles architect, incorporating architectural and design influences into his work. He also began to further explore the graphic design possibilities of silk-screening onto ceramic tiles. His recent work is diverse. Sometimes he plans his pieces, sometimes they are spontaneous. Both his art and his attitude have been influenced by Memphis designers, his love for surfing, his job, his travels. He is currently designing dinnerware sets, tile furniture, and lighting fixtures.

PICKFORD, ROLLIN (Painter)
930 E. Sierra Madre, Fresno, CA 93704

Born: 1912 *Awards:* 1st Prize, Watercolor USA; Best of Show, All-California Invitational *Collections:* Springfield Art Museum, MO; State of California *Ex-*

Grace Purpura, *Russian Girl, Leningrad, 1987,* 8 x 10,
photocolor and black and white

Carole Pierce, *Courtyard,* 20 x 24, monoprint

hibitions: Octagon Museum, Santa Cruz; Stanford U. *Education:* Stanford U. *Dealer:* Fresno Arts Center

The oils and acrylics are large—done on 6-by-8-foot canvas—and the wet acrylic is often poured on in a fashion reminiscent of Morris Louis and Paul Jenkins. The watercolors are considerably smaller, usually 22 by 30 inches. Over time, his work has covered a range of styles: abstract design; representational landscapes in the tradition of Derain and Cezanne; watercolor abstractions of nature; and large, non-objective canvases of the "poured" pieces. The palette too changes, varying from muted monochromatics to high-key colors. Recent paintings, primarily oils and watercolors, explore the relationship of figure to landscape.

PIEKUNKA, THOMAS L. (Painter, Mixed Media Artist)
1984 N. Main St. #401, Los Angeles, CA 90031

Born: 1961 *Exhibitions:* Southern California Contemporary Art Gallery; Loyola Marymount University Gallery *Education:* Art Center College of Design; Loyola Marymount U.

He was initially influenced by cubism and surrealism, although he was also intrigued by constructivist works and diorama (three-dimensional miniature scenes with painted model figures and background). Challenged by combining divergent forms and ideas, his early works consisted of multi-dimensional, mixed media pieces which displayed both representational and cubist elements. More recently, he has looked to the works of Frank Stella and Elizabeth Murray for inspiration. *Left and Right* is the first in a series of works investigating conflicts between idealistic hopes and cynical realities. The juxtaposition of abstract expressionist and representational styles echoes this conflict. Portraying the extremes of life—beauty and ugliness, war and peace, good and evil, right and wrong.

PIERCE, BRUCE (Painter)
2019 Navy St., Santa Monica, CA 90405

Born: 1937 *Exhibitions:* Department of Culture, Hamburg, West Germany; Beverly Hills City Hall *Education:* Art Center College of Design *Dealer:* Carol Sheff, Los Angeles

His paintings are characterized by the tension between technology and nature, and thematically, his works focus on the humane resolution of this conflict. His images are combinations of European still-life and American landscape art. One painting, for example, features a toaster set in front of the Grand Canyon. In another, he places a flea-market building in a denuded Valley of a Thousand Oaks. In his recent work, he has preferred egg tempera, a painting technique dating back to 12th-century European art. Although this is a slow process, the addition of egg to raw pigment results in a painting that appears to radiate light.

PIERCE, CAROLE (Painter, Printmaker)
105 Upper Rd., P.O. Box 1032, Ross, CA 94957

Born: 1949 *Awards:* Material Award, North American Print Exhibition; Award For Excellence, National Academy of Design, NYC *Collections:* Harvard U.; Torbourni Beacci Hotel, Florence *Exhibitions:* Boston Printmakers Exhibition; De Cordova Museum *Education:* Southern Methodist U.; San Francisco Art Institute

Influenced by El Greco, Mark Rothko and Joan Mitchell, she has tried to attain the mystical and dreamlike light and open spaces of her native Texas.

During art school, she experimented with large areas of color wash on primed and unprimed canvas. In recent years, her large oil paintings (up to 9 by 8 feet) in subdued siennas, yellows, blues and greens have become abstract and more geometric in structure. She applies layer upon layer of color, producing a pulsating light on the canvas. Black-and-white prints of space, doorways and windows have a more figurative quality suggesting color even in their colorlessness.

PIETERS, EDWARD M. (Paper Artist)
7980 D Sevan Court, San Diego, CA 92123

Born: 1939 *Collections:* Fullerton Museum, Fullerton; Laguna Museum of Art, Laguna Beach *Exhibitions:* Circle Gallery, Los Angeles; San Diego Museum of Art *Education:* Wayne State U.; San Diego State U. *Dealer:* La Jolla Fine Art, La Jolla

He began his artistic career as a sculptor of welded steel, but is best known now for his paper sculptures. His restless works depict natural movement such as water falling in waves or wind blowing through the grass. Working in both wet pulp and dry paper, he folds, tears, shapes, molds and builds forms quickly and intuitively. Although nature is his inspiration, his works address the spritual, and he takes his cue from Huxley's belief that creating art is a spiritual experience. He has also worked to adapt or develop technology appropriate to the medium, for example, transforming paper into porcelain forms and developing a porcess for casting paper forms in bronze.

PIJOAN, IRENE (Painter)
23 Garretson Ave., Rodeo, CA 94572

Born: 1953 *Awards:* NEA Fellowship *Collections:* Guggenheim Museum, NYC; Oakland Museum *Exhibitions:* Guggenheim Museum, NYC; Quay Gallery, San Francisco *Education:* UC-Davis *Dealer:* Rena Bransten Gallery, San Francisco

Her work has always dealt with the interior, spiritual struggles of humankind through the depiction of human figures. In the early 1980s, influenced by ancient Greco-Roman painting, she began building up figures in encaustic relief on small painted panels. The intimate iconography of the wax pieces developed into sculpture created out of plaster and wax and attached to large canvases that were painted but designed to stand on the floor and become part of the ordinary living environment. A series of large rectangular paintings on wood followed. In these pieces, she made her personal spiritual concerns more obvious and attempted to make them more generalized. Recently she has painted on sections of concrete taken from demolished buildings in order to deal with the place of spiritual concerns in the sterile environment of contemporary suburbia.

PILIGUIAN, ZAROUHI (Painter, Collage Artist)
828 Morris Place, Montebello, CA 90640

Born: 1933 *Collections:* Association Culturelle Armenian, Salle a Aharonian, Montreal *Exhibitions:* Armenian Cultural Center, Montebello; A.G.B.U. Art Gallery, Los Angeles

Born in Alexandria, Egypt, she grew up in a mixed cultural atmosphere, suffused with Armenian, European and Egyptian influences—a mixture of Western and Near Eastern sensibilities which is evident in her work. After many years of study, her style evolved from expressionism to fauvism, and she began

Tom Piekunka, *Left and Right,* 72 x 66, mixed media

Deanna Pini, *Dragon Boxes,* 8 x 5, 6 x 4, ceramic, mixed media

painting large spaces with bright oil and watercolors. She still felt the need to diversify, and believed that collage could provide a new outlet for her imagination. Using colored ink and tissue paper, she adds a number of transparent layers to an underpainted canvas, using acrylic for retouching, and a final varnish wash. She prefers working with people, especially children, and still life subjects. Her highly expressive and accessible works display a strong sense of form and sensitive treatment of light, color and the human figure.

PINCUS, JEANETTE C. (Painter)
5378 B Sosiega, Laguna Hills, CA 92653

Born: 1909 *Exhibitions:* Klutznick Hall, Washington, D.C.; Union League Club, Chicago *Collections:* Combined Insurance of America; Allstate Insurance *Exhibitions:* Denver Museum; Haggermaker Gallery, Laguna Beach *Education:* Art Institute of Chicago *Dealer:* Studio, Laguna Hills

Early florals were painted with wet on wet colors. Eliminating whites, she used oil on masonite covered thickly with gesso, giving her pieces a soft, misty feeling. Her current colorful work has been influenced by travel. She often presents vigorous market scenes using various brush strokes and sharp lights and dark shapes. People talking with one another is a common theme in her work, displaying a concern with peace and communication. Her paintings force the effect of movement and suggest many people in light and shadow.

PINI, DEANNA (Ceramist)
1339 Mission Ridge Rd., Santa Barbara, CA 93103

Born: 1946 *Awards:* UC-Santa Barbara Research Grant *Exhibitions:* Clay House, Santa Monica; Del Mano Galleries *Education:* UC-Santa Barbara; San Jose State U.

After researching ancient saggar and smoked ceramics, she combined her own ongoing sense of experimentation with a variety of traditions to create non-utilitarian ceramics. In her work, the clay is like a skin, which allows the form to move and at times becomes eggshell thin. The work has color, but instead of glazing it, she allows the clay to touch the fire and burns organic materials. Her earlier work was in art and environmental design involving young children. Her training in ceramics was primarily utilitarian and was augmented by a visit to Europe's ceramic industries. Her interest in ancient ceramic techniques began in 1977.

PINKERTON, CLAYTON (Painter)
P.O. Box 77, Amador City, CA 95601

Born: 1931 *Awards:* Fulbright Grant; James D. Phelan Award in Painting *Collections:* Illinois Bell; De Young Memorial Museum, San Francisco *Exhibitions:* Whitney Museum, NYC; Museum of Modern Art, NYC *Education:* California College of Arts and Crafts; U. of Paris *Dealer:* Michael Himovitz Gallery, Sacramento

Following a decade in which he created lyrical works evocative of the scope and range of landscape, he began in the late 1950s to focus on the human form and the human condition. Works of this period explore personal values and attitudes and focus on such themes as isolation/interaction and separation/relation. Reaction to the Vietnam War led to his withdrawal from the art world, which caused him completely to re-evaluate and re-examine art. Subsequent works in

the early 1980s, such as those exhibited in "Art Bridge" in Kobe, Japan and "The Human Form" in Mesa, Arizona, combine the elements of an often ironic and satiric humor with the concerns of his earlier works.

PINKHAM, JULIA (Textile Painter)
305 S. Kalorama St., Ventura, CA 93001

Born: 1957 *Exhibitions:* Special Olympics Benefit, Camarillo; Buyers Market of American Crafts, Valley Forge, PA

She is a textile painter who creates brightly colored textile wall pieces, floorcloths, pillows and three-panel screens. Her images reveal the influence of her extensive travels in Mexico. Often, she combines geometric patterns and hieroglyphics with idealized nature scenes of cartoon-like birds, butterflies and lizards. To make these functional pieces, she brushes textile pigments and acrylics onto raw canvas and cotton fabrics, which she later turns into pillows or screens. When working on floor pieces, she seals her works with poly-varnish. "I am drawn to everyday objects that remind me of the natural world and its beauty," she says.

PIRIE, GAYLE D. (Painter)
1888 Golden Gate Ave. #36, San Francisco, CA 94115

Born: 1963 *Exhibitions:* Limn, San Francisco; Zuni, San Francisco *Dealer:* Saxon Lee Gallery, Los Angeles

When she began painting seven years ago, she was intrigued by the painterly and literal urban and suburban landscapes of Bischoff, Hopper, and Diebenkorn. She tries to capture the clarity of the Bay area's northern light by using such subject matter as stucco walls, post-World War II homes in Oakland, strange steps, and topiary sculpture. Working from her own photographs, she paints with oil on linen and canvas. Her compositions have recently focused on the juxtaposition of shubbery and various kinds of Bay area architecture, and she has completed a series of paintings based on the gardens of Italy and France. Although she paints representationally, she incorporates a somewhat incongruous sense of space, spirit, and tension in every painting.

PITT, LILLIAN (Ceramist)
11528 S.E. Lincoln St., Portland, OR 97214

Born: 1943 *Awards:* Purchase Award, Metropolitan Art Commission, Portland; City of Gresham Purchase Award, OR *Collections:* Indian Arts and Crafts Board, Washington, D.C.; Museum of the Plains Indian, Browning, MT *Education:* Mt. Hood Community College *Dealer:* Quintana's Gallery, Palm Springs

She began to work in raku primarily for the brilliant rainbow luster and spontaneous crackle of the material, suiting her intent to portray the Indian legends of her childhood. Borrowing freely from these oral traditions, she created masks with whistling mouths, feathers, buckskin and shells. She presently fires in a kiln of Japanese design, using an 8th-century Korean method of wood firing. She has begun to work with deeper, three-dimensional shapes and designing in incising shadow to capture the mystery of current within the kiln during the 10-day enclosure period. Her work is an expression of her appreciation for her heritage as a Warm Springs-Yakima Indian.

PITTMAN, LARI (Painter)
c/o Rosamund Felsen Gallery, 669 N. La Cienega Blvd., Los Angeles, CA 90069

David Elmer Pearce, *Fleming Floral,* 30 x 24, oil on canvas

John Pugh, *Colonnade,* 204 x 204, acrylic paint

Dorothy Provis, *Circles,* 72 x 16,
synthetic fur and wood construction

Jeanette Pincus, *Jennie – Tonga,* 22 x 30, watercolor

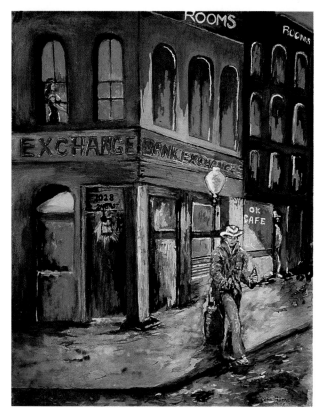

Lydia Palmer-Allen, *Bank Exchange-Old Sac,* 19 x 15 goauche

Bruce Pollack, *Mild, Cosmic Paranoia,* 72 x 72, acrylic on canvas.
Courtesy: K. Stalinger

947

Grace Purpura, *Laundromat,* 60 x 60, oil on canvas

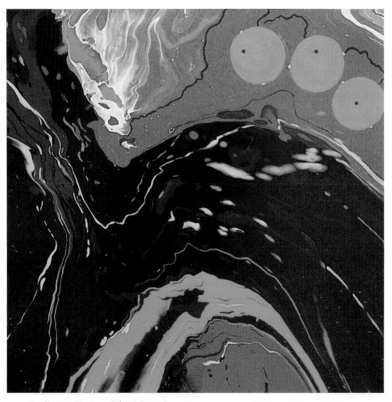

A. Gregg Pader, *The Mysterious Appearance of Three Green Spheres,*
36 x 36, mixed media

Evelyn Peters, *Night Winds,* 16 x 20, acrylic

Maija Woof Peeples, *I'm Stork on You,* 41 x 46, oil on canvas

Carole Pierce, *untitled,* 84 x 96, oil

Robert Privitt, *Gate I,* 84 x 83 x 26, welded and painted steel

Joe Price, *Egg Series III: Barbed Wire,* 5 x 7, 46 screen serigraph.
Courtesy: Gallery 30, San Mateo, CA

Sara Petty, *Picture Window,* 5 x 7, prisma (animation drawing). Courtesy: Dr. William Moritz

Virginia Pochmann, *No. 173 Cactus Flower,* 22 x 30, watercolor

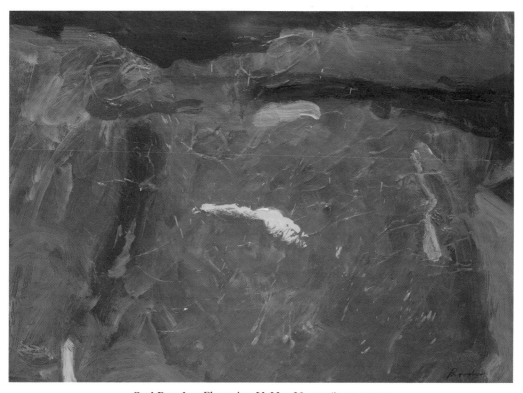

Carl Provder, *Floatation V,* 22 x 30, acrylic on paper

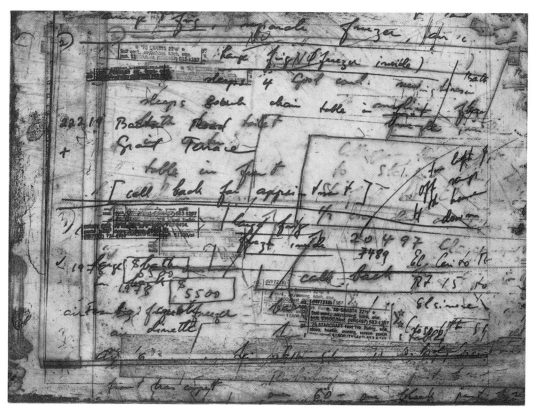

Judith Palmer, *Romoland—red/green,* 18 x 24, photoetching. Photograph: Eleanor Bell

Barron Postmus, *Along the Little Big Horn,* 24 x 48, oil. Courtesy: Gallery Americana, Carmel CA

Emmy Lou Packard, *California,* 48 x 1020, concrete. Courtesy: University of California Student Center. Architect: Vernon Demars. Photograph: Don Beatty

Wilma Parker, *Golden Blue,* 42 x 68, acrylic and oil on canvas. Courtesy: Dubins Gallery, Los Angeles, CA

Michael J. Pickard, *Cups and Saucers, Series #3,* 3 x 5 x 5, earthenware

Bruce Pierce A.W.S., *Canyon View,* 24 x 36, egg tempera

Zaro Piliguian, *Composition,* 24 x 30, mixed media collage

Deanna Pini, *Cat Box II (A Sociological Commentary),* 17 x 20 x 8, ceramic, mixed media

Clayton Pinkerton, *Saturday,* 30 x 44, mixed media. Courtesy: Michael Himovitz Gallery

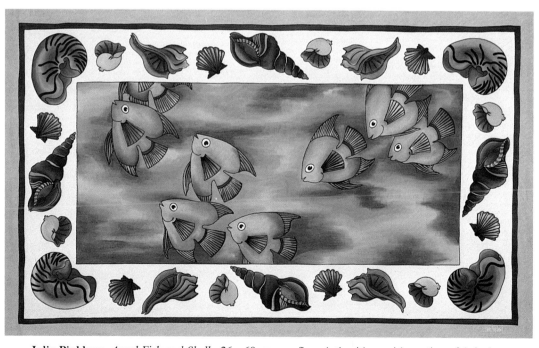

Julia Pinkham, *Angel Fish and Shells,* 36 x 60, canvas floorcloth with varnish coatings, fabric dyes

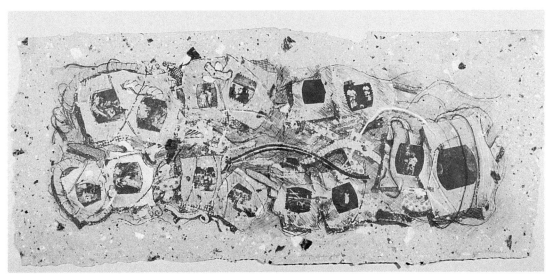

Joan E. Popovich, *Silent of Free Play,* 28 x 60, lithograph and aquarelle on handmaking paper. Courtesy: California Polytechnical University, Pomona, CA

Robert Richards, *Pink Fish Ball Machine,*
48 x 18 x 12, ceramic sculpture with glass.
Courtesy: Viewpoint Gallery, Carmel, CA.
Photograph: J. David Gray

Bruce Rod, *Moisture,* 55 x 25 x 24, wood, oil.
Courtesy: Peter and Eileen Norton

Shahrokh Rezvani, *Mystical Equalibrium VI,*
65 x 45, acrylic on canvas

Somers Randolph, 40 x 24 x 14, alabaster

Helen J. Rumpel, *Melusina Attracting Neptune's Sun,* 39 x 16, creative stitchery.
Courtesy: Baker Fine Art Gallery, Lubbock, Texas

Born: 1952 *Awards:* Art Matters Grant; NEA Fellowship *Exhibitions:* Rosamund Felsen Gallery, Los Angeles; Museum of Contemporary Art, Los Angeles *Education:* UCLA; California Institute of Arts *Dealer:* Rosamund Felsen Gallery, Los Angeles

The paintings, on mahogany or paper, are relentlessly overpopulated with pop-culture icons, abstract organic biomorphs, strangely skewed cities, identifiable or unknown swirling geometric shapes and lines, and text. The images draw from surrealism and Oriental calligraphy, but owe perhaps their greatest inspiration to the cartoons of Disney and especially Chuck Jones. Perhaps as important as the visual imagery are the works' titles: political commentary on American society such as *Manifest Destiny, The Gold Standard* and *The United States of America;* poetic incantations of an ideal future reality such as *Where suffering and redemption will sprout from the same vine (7344 A.D.)* and *Where the soul intact will shed its scabs (8624 A.D.);* and haiku-like aphorisms: *At an old age, how sweet to die in the arms of one's love* and *The scent of a flower, for a moment, makes eternity bearable.* In the latter, the juxtaposition of simple haikus with elaborate, frenzied paintings is neither cynical nor ironic; rather, the titles condemn through their very gentleness the chaotic complexity of the modern age, a complexity which the excess of imagery expresses.

PLOEGER, JOHN (Painter, Draughtsperson)
c/o Hank Baum Gallery, P.O. Box 26689, San Francisco, CA 94126

Born: 1943 *Exhibitions:* Graphics Gallery, San Francisco; Hank Baum Gallery, San Francisco *Education:* California College of Arts and Crafts; UC-Berkeley *Dealer:* Hank Baum Gallery, San Francisco

While in school, he became convinced that realism was an effective emotional and intellectual direction for his work. His acrylic-on-canvas paintings feature mundane bits of life presented in extreme close-up or in an abruptly cropped and enlarged style. He like to combine images in a well-defined space, permitting each painting to develop its own artistic logic as it progresses. He also draws using extremely hard pencils to create works of astonishing realism. His works reveal special attention to realistic highlights and shadows, as well as almost surrealist touches, such as the fading in and out of images. In some instances, the drawings feature repeated images, such as fences, that evolve into geometric abstractions. He also plays with a layering of images, so that some elements behave as expected spatially while others are ambiguous or appear to exist outside the pictorial space.

POCHMANN, VIRGINIA (Painter)
235 Oak Rd., Danville, CA 94526

Born: 1938 *Awards:* Louisiana Watercolor Society Purchase Award; West Texas Watercolor Society Award *Collections:* City of Sunnyvale; Millard Sheets *Exhibitions:* Fireside Gallery, Carmel, CA; Bernard Galleries, Walnut Creek, CA *Education:* U. of Wisconsin *Dealers:* Bernard Galleries, Walnut Creek

Her works are based entirely on natural subjects, with an almost exclusive concentration on flowers in close-up. The paintings range in tone from large areas of brilliant white to deep, nearly pure black backgrounds. Her use of tonal contrast and her exploration of shadows within the subjects communicates a strength of form; her highly realistic watercolor renderings underscore the natural vibrancy and lively intensity of her subject matter.

PODMORE, AMY (Sculptor)
408 1/2 S. Minnesota Ave., St. Peter, MN 56082

Born: 1960 *Exhibitions:* Pence Gallery, Davis; Schaefer Gallery, St. Peter, MN *Education:* UC-Davis *Dealer:* Dorothy Weiss, San Francisco

Her early work was influenced by narrative religious paintings and sculptures she saw in Italy, particularly the works of Giotto and Masaccio. She wanted to capture the passion and unwavering self-assuredness that made those paintings so evocative and personal. Her realistic, figurative sculptures were constructed primarily in clay and usually depicted a confrontation between two figures. Her present work is still figurative, while she strives to confront the viewer. She has increased the scale to life-size or larger, and often incorporates winged images, wind, sound, water and gravity into these pieces in order to intensify the initial visual impression. Media include cement, steel, copper, rocks and found objects. She now wants her work to be less related to art history and more evocative of the viewer's own creation of a personal history with the individual piece.

POETHIG, JOHANNA (Muralist, Performance Artist)
1951 Oak St. #4, San Francisco, CA 94117

Born: 1956 *Awards:* Artist-in-Residence, California Arts Council; Cash Award and Commission for Mural, Mayor's Office of Community Development, San Francisco *Exhibitions:* Gallery Space, San Francisco; Harvey Milk Recreation Center Building, San Francisco *Education:* UC-Santa Cruz

After formal training in figurative and portrait painting in oil, she began to be more interested in abstract expressionism. Her work was influenced by that of Kandinsky and the contemporary German expressionist painters. Her interest in public, community and political art, as well as large scale environmental, site-specific art, prompted her to begin painting murals. The great Mexican muralists, Rivera, Orozco and Camerena, and the national mural movement were her inspirations. At this point, she switched to acrylic paints, and her style became bigger and looser in style. During this time, she painted a mural memorializing the late Harvey Milk, one celebrating the Philippine Revolution and many others with a political or social theme. She paints on large pieces of stretched or unstretched canvas with an immediate, expressionistic application of acrylic paint. Water, swimming pools, floating, diving and primates are her main subjects. These large works, usually 10 by 12 feet, are indoor murals. This work has been transferred to mosaic and tile. She also works as a community artist and performance artist, concentrating on installations, costumes, songwriting, video and film and slide displays.

POLLACK, BRUCE (Multimedia Artist)
527 Third St., San Francisco, CA 94107

Born: 1954 *Awards:* 1st Prize, San Diego Art Institute *Exhibitions:* Force Nordstrom Gallery, San Francisco; Art Commission Gallery, San Francisco *Education:* San Francisco Art Institute

Philosophy, physics and spiritual beliefs motivate the artist to paint and sculpt abstract images. His conviction of the "responsibility" of an artist to educate his fellow man inspires him to seek symbols and images with which to teach and communicate. Recent work is based on contemporary discoveries in quantum physics. Time, synchronicity and the transformation of matter are expressed through his heavy impasto, acrylic paintings. His palette is vibrant, the color fields explosive— reminiscent of storms. In his fiberglass and resin sculptures, the artist simultaneously explores his favorite concepts and takes a good-natured poke at conceptual art.

POLOS, IRIS STEPHANIE (Painter, Draughtsperson)
5801 Broadway, Oakland, CA 94618

Born: 1947 *Collections:* Oakland Museum *Exhibitions:* Art for Art's Sake, San Francisco; Lawson Galleries, San Francisco *Education:* California College of Arts & Crafts *Dealer:* Force Nordstrom Gallery, San Francisco

Working throughout the 1970s on large acrylic paintings and small-scale prismacolor pencil drawings and watercolors, her transitional pieces were two large works, one a 100-foot collage and the other a watercolor series made up of several sheets of watercolor paper that could be read as self-contained abstractions or as units of the larger wholes. Recent work has been in large scale, including mixed-media wall constructions, casein paintings and drawings on Color-aid, a silk-screened paper. Figurative themes work their way from abstractions in an agressive, expressionistic manner, giving these images a visionary authenticity as vehicles for emotional communication. The sentimentality of maternal scenes is undercut using confrontational depictions of cupids, bones and other appendages, as well as striking color combinations.

POMODORO, ARNALDO (Sculptor)
345 Sutter St., San Francisco, CA 94108

Born: 1926 *Collections:* Museum of Modern Art, NYC; Hirshhorn Museum & Sculpture Garden, Washington, DC *Exhibitions:* Forte di Belvedere, Florence, Italy; Columbus Art Museum *Dealer:* Stephen Wirtz, San Francisco

Critics often associate his geometric forms and exposed interiors of great complexity with the world of technology. However, the artist sees his work as evidence of the intellect and as a concentration on the more visceral aspects of life. His early interests were in set designing and jewelry miniatures. Later he made a type of relief sculpture that was strongly influenced by the imagery and calligraphy of Paul Klee. In Brancusi, he found a means of clarifying his dualistic imagery. In 1960, he came to America, where he was inspired by the country's vastness to make the large, geometric bronze sculptures which characterize his work today.

PONTY, DENI (Painter)
2616 Medlow Ave., Los Angeles, CA 90065

Born: 1948 *Exhibitions:* Otis Art Institute of Parsons School of Design, Los Angeles; Ivey Gallery, Los Angeles *Education:* Netherlands College of International Relations; U. of Oregon *Dealer:* Koslow Rayl Gallery, Los Angeles

His traditional training quickly gave way to more abstract expression in the 1960s. He subsequently returned to a neo- realist style, grounded in Old Master technique and influenced by the principles of modernism. Using vibrant, dramatic colors and compositions, he creates scenes which feature figures and settings in a narrative context. He has also produced a series of overtly erotic paintings. Working in oil on vellum, these paintings of voluptuous artist's models in moments of repose are more subjective than his other work and combine close attention to anatomical detail with the quietness and simplicity of ordinary moments of everyday life.

POOLER, FRANK (Painter, Sculptor)
2801 Engel Dr., Los Alamitos, CA 90720

Born: 1926 *Awards:* American Scandinavian Foundation; Order of St. Olaf Medal, King of Norway *Exhibitions:* Okada Association, Long Beach; Unitarian Society, Long Beach *Education:* St. Olaf Collage; U. of Iowa *Dealer:* Ariel Gallery, NYC

He is totally self-taught in art, with an obvious Chinese and Australian/Aboriginal influence. He works in paper collage, which tends toward realism. His watercolors and acrylics are expressionistic, and his sculptural work takes form in aluminum wire, fabric and clay. Whimsy permeates his unique series of out- of-frame works depicting sporting events and submarines. He has a strong belief in the joy of creating, and utilizes a wide variety of materials.

POPOVAC, GWYNN (Painter, Draughtsperson)
17270 Robin Ridge, Sonora, CA 95370

Born: 1948 *Exhibitions:* Four Winds Gallery, Sonora; Mountain Matters, Sonora *Education:* UCLA

Impressed early on by the illustrators of the early 19th Century, she began combining ink, watercolor, and colored pencils to illustrate her dreams in a detailed decorative style. She brings a graphic style to her works on canvas, laying down threads of oil paint and filling areas with a variety of stroked in patterns. Her paintings are dreamscapes of merging and emerging images, phantasmagorias where viewers are surprised by their own discoveries. Since 1986 she has been working on a series of mask drawings, using these bilaterally symmetrical compositions of gemstones, feathers, sea shells and insect wings to experiment with means of producing effects of iridescence, transparency, and metallic patinas.

POPOVICH-KUTSCHER, JOAN (Painter, Printmaker)
2014 Primrose Way, Pomona, CA 91766

Born: 1951 *Awards:* Chines Association Painting Scholarship; Grant, California Arts Council *Collections:* Union Gallery, Cal. State-Pomona *Exhibitions:* The Print Club, Philadelphia; Gallery 57, Fullerton *Education:* California Institute of the Arts; Cal. State-Fullerton

She is a deaf artist. Her work reflects the anger and pain of being mistakenly placed in a mental hospital as a child. Her primary medium is etching. She uses the rope symbology of an Alpha Beta game card to communicate the fear and darkness of that early period in her life. Her cluttered, messy-looking, but deeply psychological, images resemble the interior of the old state mental hospital. Printing on handmade paper adds a narrative quality to her work. She gains the correct emotional quality by carefully controlling color combinations. Her recent three-dimensional pieces convey her past frustrations while communicating the freedom she felt on leaving the mental hospital.

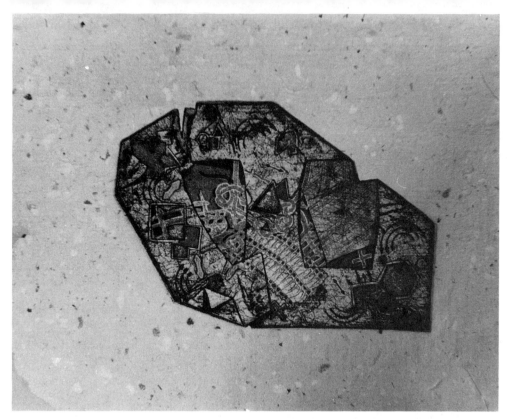

Joan E. Popovich, *Emotions of Art,* 15 x 17, etching and Aquarelle on handmade paper

Clayton Pinkerton, *Telling Mrs. T. About Her Property,* 30 x 44, mixed media.
Courtesy: Himovitz/Saloman Gallery

POPPE, DEAN M. (Painter)
Studio 204, 710 13th St., San Diego, CA

Born: 1947 *Exhibitions:* Bowers Museum, Santa Ana; Mt. San Jacinto Juried Open, San Jacinto *Education:* UC- Irvine

Inspired by the works of Wayne Thiebaud, his first paintings were large canvases, covered with formal grids modeled in relief, and overpainted in a vigorous, almost expressionistic style. This interest in the conflict between the formal and the informal evolved into his next works, which were large, visual fields of crumpled paper, overlaid with grids. Eventually, he deleted the grids, switched from acrylics to oils and painted crumpled paper on shaped canvases. More recently he has returned to a rectangular format. He now uses the vivid glazes of the grisaille technique to finish his pieces. Thematically, the conflict between two- and three-dimensional images has replaced his involvement with formal composition and elements.

POPPLETON, ERIC (Photographer)
1755 Correa Way, Los Angeles, CA 90049

Born: 1959 *Collections:* Indianapolis State Museum; Muncie Art Gallery, IN *Exhibitions:* California Institute of the Arts *Education:* Ball State U.; California Institute of the Arts *Dealer:* Margaret Romoro, Los Angeles

His interest in photography began when he was a junior in college. Since then, he has developed a documentary style of photography, in both black and white and color, which is often presented an installation, with accompanying materials and media. Two of these projects, "Main Street Portraits" and "Lee and Larry Rains," focus on plain, everyday people and their lives. His other work includes commercial/corporate photography and a documentary of a charity bicycle trip. He works in 35mm and 4 x 5 formats. He cites Irving Penn, Richard Avedon, August Sander, Robert Frank and Diane Arbus as influences.

PORCELLA, YVONNE (Quiltmaker)
3619 Shoemake Ave., Modesto, CA 95351

Born: 1936 *Collections:* Oakland Museum; Fairfield Processing Corp. *Exhibitions:* McHenry Museum, Modesto; American Craft Museum, NYC *Education:* U. of San Francisco *Dealer:* Great American Gallery, Atlanta

She has worked in the fiber arts for more than twenty years and is known for her bold geometric quilts, which sometimes combine painted panels of people and animals, stenciled words and embedded metallic objects. She is also known for her kimono designs, which frequently incorporate quiltmaking techniques. Incorporating two different styles and palettes, her work varies from brightly colored rainbow and checkerboard patterns using the strip technique with bold contrasts of black, white and red cotton, to pale, ethereal constructions in hand-painted and dyed silk. She has authored several books related to quilting techniques, as well as *A Colorful Book*, concerning design.

PORCHIA (Painter, Sculptor)
9953 West Wanda Dr., Beverly Hills, CA 90210

Born: 1955 *Collections:* Equity Realty Corp., Century City *Exhibitions:* Adamson Gallery, Brentwood; Santa Monica Fine Arts Studio *Education:* UCLA

Inspired by fauvism's vivid colors and free treatment of form, she creates paintings and sculptures that have strong, bold colors, forms and shapes. Her cut-outs are created in the manner of Matisse: she paints large pieces of paper a variety of intense colors, cutting out the shapes and symbols that portray a particular setting and mood. Her desert-inspired sculptures are first designed in clay—sometimes, incorporating found objects and different textured tools. She makes her own latex molds for each piece, then casts it, in either bronze or hydrocal cement. She patinates the cement pieces with acids and acrylic paint.

POST, GEORGE (Painter)
327 Cumberland St., San Francisco, CA 94114

Born: 1906 *Awards:* Member, American Watercolor Society *Collections:* Metropolitan Museum of Art, NYC; San Francisco Museum of Modern Art *Exhibitions:* San Diego Watercolor Society; College of Holy Names, Oakland *Dealer:* Kerwin Galleries, Burlingame

After early studies at the San Francisco Art Institute, he began painting watercolor landscapes in a style influenced by Stanley Wood and John Marin. Over the years, he has come to be associated with the California Watercolor style. His landscapes are usually divided into three or four large interlocking areas derived from fundamental geometric shapes. Within these shapes, the work is usually quite detailed. The details work to draw the viewer into the painting, and then the larger, simple geometric design can exert its influence over the viewer's sensibility. He has taught at Stanford University and San Jose State, among other academies of higher education, and his work has appeared in *American Artist* and *Fortune*.

POSTMUS, BARRON (Painter)
7251 Bernadine Ave., West Hills, CA 91307

Born: 1937 *Awards:* 1st Place, Landscape, 1988 National Wildlife Show, Kansas City; Merit Award, 1988 National Western & Wildlife, Minneapolis *Collections:* Sears Corporate Tower, Chicago; W.R. Snodgrass Co., Los Angeles *Exhibitions:* Gallery Americana, Carmel; Waterhouse Gallery, Santa Barbara *Education:* Los Angeles Art Center College

Beginning as a technical illustrator in the aerospace industry, he later worked as a commercial illustrator and designer, providing him with a disciplined background and meticulous technique. Carefully selecting locale and blending rich detail and light, he works to achieve a sense of romantic nostalgia in his landscapes, often populated by old woodframed houses or abandoned farm machinery. Working in oil on a small to medium scale, the pieces combine sentimentality with an intense attention to detail. Many of his pieces have been rendered as limited edition prints.

POTTER, GEORGE KENNETH (Painter, Sculptor)
7000 Fair Oaks Blvd. #35, Carmichael, CA 95608

Born: 1926 *Collections:* City of San Francisco *Exhibitions:* Northwind, Mill Valley; NutTree, Vacaville *Education:* San Francisco State U.; Academie Frochot, Paris; Academy of Art, San Francisco *Dealer:* Provenance, Tahoe City; A Gallery, Palm Desert

Most often painting cityscapes and natucials in watercolor, he has designed and executed murals, sculpture, glassworks, and prints. His watercolors are of high impact color, full of action and movement, compressing space in both realistic and abstract form. Many works are concerned with deep space or atmospheric

Joe Price, *Iris in Brown Bottles,* 24 x 18, 90 screen serigraph.
Courtesy: Gallery 30, San Mateo, CA

Barron Postmus, *First Flowers,* 18 x 14, oil.
Courtesy: Gallery Americana, Carmel, CA

qualities, and often they express playful or humorous sentiments. The ongoing themes in the work, whatever the medium, deal with the relationship of mankind to the environment, sometimes rebelling against the dehumanization of society, at other times outlining history or looking forward optimistically, even joyfully.

POULSON, LORY (Mixed Media Artist)
5846 Vallejo, Emeryville, CA 94608

Born: 1951 *Awards:* Future Masters, Los Angeles Jr. Chamber of Commerce *Collections:* Flanagan Typography, Berkeley; Arthur Herman, Benicia *Exhibitions:* Los Angeles Municipal Art Gallery; Los Medanos College, Pittsburgh, CA *Education:* California Institute of the Arts; San Francisco Art Institute

Her early charcoal drawings and oil paintings featured the human form, both life-size and larger than life. In the 1960s, she began to deconstruct the figure, introducing geometric shapes and using plaster and clay to isolate segments of the torso. This led ultimately to a period of total abstraction and formalist study of shape, color and paint. Now she has returned to figuration, working in monotype with pastel overlays and drawings. The immediacy and flexibility of monotype has allowed her to incorporate painterly handling and precision drawing in these large-scale symbolic faces which are distanced and symbolic.

POWELL, MARILYN JOAN (Painter)
7619 Flora Avenue, Maplewood, MO 63143

Born: 1946 *Awards:* 2nd Place, California Works; Honorable Mention, Laumier Sculpture Park *Collections:* Good Earth, San Francisco; Down by the Station, Kirkwood, MO *Exhibitions:* Sun Gallery, Hayward; California State Fair *Education:* U. of Missouri *Dealer:* Leah Levy, Berkeley

Formally trained in graphic design, she executes her fine art work both realistically and abstractly. Influences range from Paul Klee and Mark Rothko to Georgia O'Keeffe and Mary Cassatt. Current works are small and in pen and ink, graphite and watercolor on cloth and paper. Her subjects are traditional still-life objects, such as eyeglasses and fruit, and Midwestern stores and train stations. Color is central to these studies, and she carries them out with a deliberateness that sacrifices spontaneity for a concern with form. She is also inspired by watching children's first experiences with the visual arts, music and nature, and she closely watches the development of fiber arts in the United States.

PRAZEN, RICHARD J. (Sculptor)
2037 W. Lindsay Dr., Taylorsville, UT 84107

Born: 1953 *Awards:* Best in Program, Lincoln Welding Society *Collections:* Anheuser-Busch; Triangle Distributing *Exhibitions:* Denver Museum of Natural History; Sierra Gallery, San Francisco

His subject matter continues to be birds, particularly birds of prey; he has concentrated on depicting eagles, which he considers to be one of God's noblest creatures. His pieces are welded, displaying extraordinary detail reminiscent of bronze castings. His work is, however, based on more traditional blacksmith's techniques.

PREGILL, PHILIP (Painter)
Box 1367, Alpine, CA 92001

Born: 1944 *Exhibitions:* Orange County Art Association National Juried Competition, Fullerton; Long Beach Art Association Juried Competition *Education:* U. of Oregon

The artist expresses his fascination with the interrelation of indoor and outdoor environments around the Mediterranean. Interior and exterior are separated by simple doorways and windows, allowing a constant view and movement between the two. In a recent exhibit, five large, square oil paintings hung in a row on one wall like five wide-open windows or doorways demonstrated this interest. The paintings are of a cool, blue, obscuring light. Through the grayed-down tint of greenish-blue that fills the view, landscape features such as a horizon, sky and trees are just barely discernible. In two of the works, a dark figure emerges from the brushy layers of paint, hesitant and awkward. He is painted in black with no shine, like a black hole, a negative space.

PRESTINI, JAMES (Sculptor)
2324 Blake St., Berkeley, CA 94704

Born: 1908 *Awards:* Plaque, National Woodturning Conference; The Berkeley Award, UC-Berkeley *Collections:* Museum of Modern Art, NYC; Musée des Arts Decoratifs de Montreal *Exhibitions:* Oakland Museum; Art Institute of Chicago *Education:* Yale U.; Institute of Design, Ill. Inst. of Technology *Dealer:* Creators Equity Foundation, Berkeley

He pioneered the art of woodturning, establishing the turned wooden bowl as an object not only of utility but of aesthetic value. Influenced by the Bauhaus School and by Oriental art, he created hundreds of highly-controlled, delicate vessels. He has experimented with the possibilities of laminating by the use different grains, a variety of woods, curved cuts and stacked lamination. He has worked with and been influenced by Laszlo Moholy-Nagy and, in Chicago, architect Ludwig Mies van der Rohe. His sculptures have been exhibited around the world, in diverse locations from Guatemala to Yugoslavia. Special projects include formulating a program in woodworking, metal working, plastics, printing, ceramics, textiles, photography and cinematography for the National Institute of Design in Ahmedabad, India.

PRESTON, ASTRID (Painter)
920 Centinela Ave., Santa Monica, CA 90403

Born: 1945 *Awards:* NEA Fellowship *Exhibitions:* Krygier/Landau Contemporary Art, Los Angeles; Patty Aande Gallery, San Diego *Education:* UCLA *Dealer:* Krygier/Landau, Los Angeles

In the 1970s, she made parallel line drawings, worked on clay-coated paper and used shadow drawings to explore the human body. By 1979, she had begun using an enamel medium on shaped aluminum to paint the Southern California landscape. As the work progressed, her focus became the house, and by 1983 the landscapes were dark—showing roads and shadows or houses at night. Landscape continues to be her subject, and in her recent psychologically charged oil paintings, she blends northern light with California sunshine and explores light in its stages of clarity, shifts from day to night and movements from foreground to background.

PRICE, JOE (Printmaker)
2031 Belle Monti, Belmont, CA 94002

Born: 1935 *Awards:* Lessing J. Rosenwald Prize; Louis Lozowick Memorial Award *Collections:* San Francisco Museum of Modern Art; National Gallery of

John Pugh, *Taylor Hall Mural,* 288 x 432, acrylic paint

Julia Pinkham, *Hummingbirds and Christmas Cactus,* 60 x 36, canvas floorcloth with varnish coatings, fabric dyes

Robert Privitt, *Fire Shrine,* 63 x 40 x 36, welded and painted steel

American Art, Washington, D.C. *Exhibitions:* Associated American Artists Gallery, NYC; Triton Museum of Art, Santa Clara *Education:* Northwestern U.; Stanford U. *Dealer:* Associated American Artists, NYC; Jane Haslem, Washington, DC

His serigraphs—prints made with silkscreen—are often mistaken for watercolors because of their vitality. Trained as a realist, he gave up that style to work abstractly. When he returned to representational subject matter in 1973, his interest in abstraction remained in the compositional space. He is concerned with the relation of space to the subject, with the effect of the quality of light on, in, and around the subject, and with shadow play. He attempts to make subject matter function as a foil for color and for the darks and lights within compositional space.

PRICE, KENNETH (Printmaker, Ceramist)
c/o Tally Richards Gallery, 2 Ledoux St., Taos, NM 87571

Born: 1935 *Awards:* Tamarind Fellowship *Collections:* Los Angeles County Museum of Art *Exhibitions:* Whitney Museum, NYC; Museum of Modern Art, NYC *Education:* Otis Art Institute; Chouinard Art Institute *Dealer:* Gemini G.E.L., Los Angeles; Tally Richards Gallery, Taos, NM

In reaction to the large-scale art of the 1950s and 1960s, he has become a principal figure in the renaissance of clay in fine art, making small-scale ceramic sculptures. Early ceramic cups were often decorated with animals and other motifs, defying artistic interpretation because of their seeming simplicity and blandness. The cups were followed by biomorphic shapes in earth tones. Recent miniature work in polychrome glaze and paint is abstract, utilizing geometric forms.

PRIVITT, ROBERT (Sculptor)
2161 Ruskin Ave., Thousand Oaks, CA 91350

Born: 1938 *Awards:* National Sculpture Award; Art in the Embassies Program, U.S. Dept. of State *Collections:* Oklahoma Arts Council, Oklahoma City; Indiana U., Bloomington *Exhibitions:* Arizona Distinguished Artists' Exhibition; National Drawing and Small Sculpture Show *Education:* U. of Tulsa; Indiana U.

After studying under Alexandre Hogue, he found his experiences as a journeyman ironworker and welder strongly influenced his understanding of the architectonics of structure. His early steel pieces were industrial components he arc-welded together. He received a HEW grant to work with Hispanic children in New Mexico, and there became intrigued with color's power to change space and mood. His present humanly-scaled constructivist work reflects his formalist concerns with physical and psychological balance. He welds painted steel, using color to balance the decontextualized, illogical shapes he joins together.

PROVDER, CARL (Painter)
1416 Elva Terrace, Encinitas, CA 92024

Born: 1933 *Awards:* 1st Prize, Southern California Expo; 1st Prize, San Diego Art Institute *Collections:* Hyundai Motor America; Harcourt, Brace, Jovanovich *Exhibitions:* Riverside Museum; Knowles Gallery *Education:* Pratt Institute; Columbia U.

After an art school training that emphasized design, he progressed from an abstract style to one of abstract expressionism, spontaneously responding to the painterly surfaces that developed. The works are grounded in cubist spatial concepts and employ low-key colors combined with an accented color note. Presently his work explores textural effects in acrylic and mixed media abstractions. These seductive textures and colors seem to appear from unconscious, emotional explosions arising from shifts in awareness. Influenced by his study of Zen, his use of form is lyrical and his colors natural, within a framework of non-intellectual exploration. His influences include Tapies, Frankenthaler and Motherwell.

PROVENZANO, SAMUEL PAUL (Painter)
293 8th St., San Francisco, CA 94103

Born: 1923 *Awards:* Rochester Finger Lakes, Syracuse U. *Collections:* San Francisco Museum of Modern Art; Oakland Museum *Exhibitions:* Oakland Museum *Education:* Syracuse U.; Academy of Fine Arts, Florence, Italy; Hans Hofmann School, NYC *Dealer:* Frances Joslin Associates, The Show Place, San Francisco

This painter has worked in both figuration and abstraction. In the 1970s, he produced the "Flip" series—fruits and vegetables in mixed media on paper. Another major series in black, gestural calligraphy explores the compositional possibilities from his signature, and Army serial number. In these works, the lines make their way over a subtly marbled white surface amid bursts of vivid reds, yellows and blues. His paintings have integrity and a personality of their own.

PROVIS, DOROTHY (Construction Artist)
123 E. Beutel Rd., Port Washington, WI 53074

Born: 1926 *Collections: The Racine Journal*, Racine, WI; International Minerals & Chemical Corporation, Boston *Exhibitions:* Ventura College; Fresno City College *Dealer:* Fridholm Fine Arts, Asheville, NC

For more than twenty years, she has been constructing freestanding sculptures in fur, and more recently, in other materials as well. The innovative idea occurred to her while attending the University of Wisconsin during the mid-1960s. Many artists from diverse fields have influenced this work. The architecture of Mies van der Rohe prompted an appreciation of abstraction's often obscured content. The structuralist philosophies of Charles Biederman and the color theories of Josef Albers deepened her understanding of form and color. The most profound influence on her work has been Eli Bornstein's artistic statements on space and color. Her reductionist philosophy keeps the forms bold, concrete and highly symbolic. In the past, pieces tended to take one of four forms: stripe, square, triton and totem. She constructs a wooden armature and covers it with fur and metallic or rope knitting. This outer sculptural skin expresses the ideas of comfort, warmth and primitive, sensual pleasure. She has conceived work on a monumental scale, but space and construction considerations have limited her recent pieces to ten feet in height.

PUGH, JOHN (Painter)
P.O. Box 964, Los Gatos, CA 95031

Born: 1957 *Awards:* Public Places Project, Sacramento *Exhibitions:* Los Gatos Honda, Los Gatos; Michael Layne and Associates, Los Gatos *Education:* Cal. State-Chico

During his studies, he followed a natural transition from realism through surrealism, abstraction and visionary fantasy, ultimately finding his expression as a

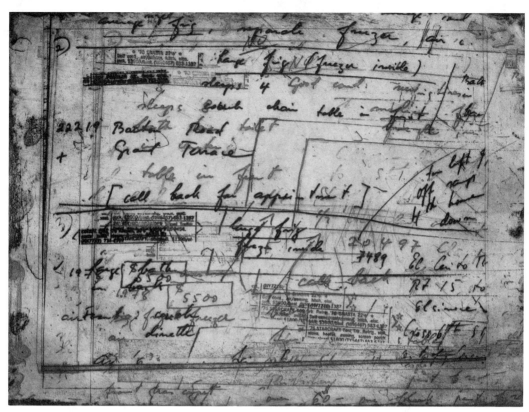

Judith Palmer, *Romoland—red/green,* 18 x 24, photoetching. Photograph: Eleanor Bell

Dorothy Provis, *Pagoda,* 74 x 16 x 16, synthetic fur and wood construction

muralist. His mural style developed from traditional two-dimensional representation to the illusionary perspective of the Renaissance; he then refined his technique by adding a dimension of timelessness into the *trompe l'oeil* style, depicting elements of the architectural past in a present-day context. This juxtaposition of past and present not only "tricks the eye" but also stimulates the mind of the viewer. In a deeper sense, his work expresses the continuity of artistic expression from antiquity to the present. He not only incorporates his *trompe l'oeil* murals into existing structures but has taken part in the design of several buildings. This marriage of architectural and artistic elements greatly enhances the illusionary aspect of his work by combining both real and imaginary space into one complementary creation.

PULS, LUCY (Sculptor)
345 Sutter St., San Francisco, CA 94108

Born: 1955 *Exhibitions:* Sculpture Center, NYC; E.M. Donahue Gallery, NYC *Education:* U. of Wisconsin, Madison; Rhode Island School of Design *Dealer:* Stephen Wirtz Gallery, San Francisco

She is best known for her sculptures made of fiberglass, corrugated metal, and machine bolts. Although the pieces vaguely echo natural forms, they seem more akin to architectural and industrial forms.

PURPURA, GRACE (Painter, Photographer)
290 Challenger Ave., San Jose, CA

Born: 1929 *Awards:* Fulbright Grant; International Photo Finalist, *Life* Magazine *Collections:* University of Colorado; Casa de la Cultura, Livorno, Italy *Exhibitions:* Denver Museum of Art; University of Santa Clara *Education:* SUNY, Brooklyn; Cal. State-San Jose

Her painting and photography utilizes deeply introspective images that draw from a sense of intuition. The figures in a landscape have a spiritual relationship with their environment, and the entire scene is often pervaded by a dream aura. Born in Brooklyn, she was exposed to modern painting at an early age. Her study with Mark Rothko, Jimmy Ernst and Ad Reinhardt led to experimentation with abstract expressionism while she lived in Italy. After becoming interested in photography as another way of seeing, she studied filmmaking with Jean Renoir and Cavalconti at UCLA. Her interest in alternate belief systems has motivated extensive travel throughout the world.

PUSKAS, CHRISTINE (Painter)
3782 Mission St., San Francisco, CA 94110

Born: 1958 *Collections:* San Francisco Museum of Modern Art *Exhibitions:* San Francisco Museum of Modern Art; Oakland Museum *Education:* School of the Museum of Fine Arts, Boston; San Francisco City College

Realism, Asian art and ethnic themes are characteristic of her work. She prefers large, figurative works but also exhibits smaller, more detailed pieces with accompanying urban histories. Subject matter includes scenes from everyday life—for example, people going about their daily business in her neighborhood. She also does realistic renderings of human anatomy and of people juxtaposed with scenes from nature. Paintings are in oil and mural paint, while drawings are executed in graphite and prisma pencil as well as oil pastels. Concepts include a 160-foot-wide, 15-foot-high sundial with a fountain and waterfall proposed for the northeast slope of Twin Peaks in San Francisco.

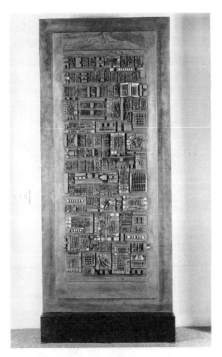

Arnaldo Pomodoro, *Tavola della Memoria II* (artist proof, edition of 2), 94 x 40 x 10.5. Courtesy: Museo Italo-Americano. Photograph: Ed Beyeler.

Evelyn Peters, *The Prairie Peddler,* 24 x 36, alkyd. Courtesy: Mr. and Mrs. L.J. Huff, Ft. Worth, TX

Ron Robertson, *The Third Wave,* 26 x 20, assemblage. Courtesy: Astra Gallery, Santa Barbara, CA

QUADT, CAROLYN (Painter)
P.O. Box 2939, Seal Beach, CA 90740

Born: 1942 *Collections:* Visual and Performing Arts Gallery; P.E. O'Hair Co. *Exhibitions:* Claremont West Gallery; Cerritos Art Fair *Education:* Scripps College; Claremont Graduate School

Early works show the influence of artists Stella, Mondrian and Albers. Trained with an emphasis in hard-edged geometric forms, she first worked with a bristle brush and later abandoned it for an airbrush. Compositions at this time are basic in form and design, relying on bright, bold colors (usually secondary hues) for their dynamism. While recent works continue to explore geometric designs and bold contrasting colors, many are more representational, using a softer, although often defined, edge to render abstract landscapes, which might include cloud formations, trees and other flora. A free-flowing "watercolor effect" is achieved with acrylics applied with large, soft brushes. Many pieces are painted on multiple canvases, which can be hung separately or as a group. These pieces can be seen to continue the tradition of Louis, Pollock and O'Keeffe.

QUAGLIATA, NARCISSUS (Glazier)
1535 5th St., Oakland, CA 94607

Born: 1942 *Awards:* NEA Fellowship *Collections:* Metropolitan Museum of Art, NYC; Corning Museum, Corning, NY *Exhibitions:* Esther Saks Gallery, Chicago; Oakland Museum *Education:* San Francisco Art Institute

Born in Italy, where he studied with Giorgio de Chirico, he immigrated to United States in the 1960s and continued his art studies at the San Francisco Art Institute, where Richard Diebenkorn was one of his painting instructors. He began working in glass shortly after finishing his education and has continued in the medium ever since. His work was profoundly influenced by the pop art movement of the 1960s and its successors in the 1970s, in particular Peter Max, who especially influenced his use of color. Some of his work, such as *Treasures In the Mediterranean*, is also reminiscent of the "T-shirt" and poster art of the 1970s. He is the author of the book *Stained Glass from Mind to Light* and has twice received NEA Fellowships.

RABINOWITZ, SHERRIE (Video Artist)
700 Cedar St., Santa Monica, CA 90405

Born: 1950 *Awards:* NEA Fellowship; American Film Institute Fellowship *Collections:* Museum of Modern Art, NYC; Long Beach Museum of Art *Exhibitions:* Museum of Contemporary Art, Los Angeles; Museum of Modern Art, NYC *Education:* UC-Berkeley

While a student of architecture and environmental design, she helped create Optic Nerve, one of the early video groups in San Francisco. She soon began to meld architecture and video work, which led her to view media in terms more of environment than of programming. Since 1975, she has collaborated with video artist Kit Galloway under the name of Mobile Image to develop alternative structures for video as an interactive communication form. They have used a wide range of technologies, including satellites, video and computers. The *Satellite Arts Project: 'A Space With No Geographical Boundaries'* was produced in collaboration with NASA. In this satellite image/dance performance, NASA's Goddard Space Flight Center in Maryland and the Educational TV Center in California were electronically composited into a single image that was displayed on monitors at each location, where live performances were taking place.

RADCLIFFE, ANDREW (Painter, Printmaker)
P.O. Box 170658, San Francisco, CA 94117

Born: 1963 *Collections:* Dow Jones Corporation, NYC; Chemical Bank, NYC *Exhibitions:* Nancy Hoffman Gallery, NYC; Achenbach Foundation, San Francisco Fine Arts Museum *Education:* Pratt Institute; San Francisco Art Institute *Dealer:* Contemporary Realist Gallery, San Francisco; Nancy Hoffman, NYC

His early oil-on-canvas work is strongly rooted in the figurative tradition. These dramatic paintings feature carefully posed and lit characters set in seascapes, mountainscapes or urban settings. Of these works, his bright paintings of bathers brought him early recognition.

RADDATZ, KEITH (Painter)
2121 Dartmouth, Palo Alto, CA 94306

Born: 1944 *Awards:* Purchase Award, Bradley National Competition *Exhibitions:* Art Institute of Chicago; Arts Council of San Mateo County *Education:* Layton School of Art; U. of Wisconsin, Milwaukee

He has a strong background in figuration and an interest in the form and content of imagery. His early influences were diverse, and his early work included both realism and expressionism. His experiences as an art conservation technician gave him the opportunity to study the techniques of the various schools. He is currently following two paths. In one, he loosely brushes acrylic paint onto toned papers, creating landscapes or cloud studies based on direct observation, memory and imagination. In the other, he renders highly realistic forms and textures with oil on panels, drawing together elements of portraits, still lifes and landscapes to create unified pictorial statements.

RADEKA, LYNN M. (Photographer)
9391 Mayrene Dr., Garden Grove, CA 92641

Born: 1951 *Awards:* Honorable Mention, Los Angeles Times *Collections:* Agfa-Gaevaert, Chicago; Dean Hesketh Co., Anaheim *Exhibitions:* Mills House Gallery; Koslow/Rayl Fine Art Gallery, Los Angeles *Education:* Cypress College *Dealer:* Koslow/Rayl Fine Art, Los Angeles

After studying with Ansel Adams, Wynn Bullock, Al Weber and Henry Gilpin, he found his subjects in nature and in the small towns of the American West and Canada. Death Valley, the canyons of Utah and serene picket fences are some of his fascinations. As early as 1975, he studied the principles of film manipulation and black-and-white contrast masking. And while he uses various procedures in the printing and processing stages of his work, his images never aim to go beyond a feeling of reality. Rather, they impart a real sense of the intense and the unusual. For example, recent images have conveyed a feeling of peace and quiet, a response to the visual relationships found in nature and the quaint port towns of Washington's Puget Sound. He is currently producing a series of fine-art duotone posters for several Western National Parks.

Larry R. Rankin, *Seagull,* 6" model, polished bronze
Courtesy: Sheldon Swope Art Museum, Terre Haute, IN

Keith Raddatz, *Mackford Prarie Mauve Cow Study,* 13 x 15, acrylic and pencil

973

RADZAT, MARILYN K. (Painter, Assemblage Artist)
1000 Freestone Ranch Rd., Bodega, CA 94922
Born: 1945 *Exhibitions:* Projects Gallery, San Raphael; Illuminarium Gallery, Conte Madera

After twenty-five years of exploring many different media, she realized her passion was creating the figure form with clay and fabric as a canvas, upon which to incorporate the exciting combination of oil paint, fabric, design and collage work. She has recently been working with porcelain clay. The face, hands and feet of the figures are hand-built, fired and painted with oils and gold leaf, then finished with a wax overlay. She handstitches the bodies, using raw silk fabric with a wire armature. Her collage materials include antique velvets and laces, authentic turn-of-the-century Navaho rugs, Indian bone needles, Chinese silver boxes and "other treasures." Recent work includes a series of figures depicting the Seven Virtues.

RAE, LINDA (Sculptor)
1514 Juanita Ct., Napa, CA 94558
Born: 1947 *Awards:* Honors Award, National League of American PEN Women, San Francisco *Exhibitions:* 14 Sculptors Gallery, NYC; International Show, Golden, CO *Education:* UC-Berkeley; Cal. State-San Luis Obispo

Influenced by Zuniga, she deals almost exclusively with the female figure. Beginning with line drawings and working without models, she strives for simplicity. Her clay and bronze cast solitary, abstract women are engendered with power, tension and incipient movement. Figures are distorted and re-proportioned: heads are small, thighs are massive, feet are sturdy wedges and arms are either very long and attenuated or solidly muscled. Her present, large "spirit beings" were inspired by Native American culture. She is also working in cement media, creating life-size female forms that suggest power and energy.

RAE, SAM (Painter)
36282 Ennis Rd., Squaw Valley, CA 93675
Born: 1944 *Award:* Rudolph M. Gans Memorial Award *Exhibitions:* William Saroyan Theatre, Fresno; Lyford Cay Gallery, Nassau, Bahamas *Education:* Edinburgh College, Scotland *Dealers:* Allards Gallery, Fresno; Visions Gallery, Reedley

His early work was both atmospheric and impressionistic, utilising layers of dense and transparent paint brushed and scraped to create a complex surface. Subsequent work has convinced him that each medium is best suited to a different subject. He endeavors, therefore, to become proficient in all of them, and as he works with each, he notices differences in all the others. For example, his recent work in watercolor has substantially lightened his work in oils. He concentrates on composition, striving to give each work a solid formal foundation and a sense of movement. He often works from photographs, using a broad palette to render realistic yet subjective views of the world around him. Environmental subjects, such as Yosemite Park and endangered animals, are featured in his recent work.

RAFFAEL, JOSEPH (Painter, Printmaker)
c/o Nancy Hoffman Gallery, 429 W. Broadway, New York, NY 10012
Born: 1933 *Awards:* Tiffany Foundation Fellowship; Fulbright Award *Collections:* Metropolitan Museum of Art, NYC; Smithsonian Institution, Washington DC *Exhibitions:* Whitney Museum, NYC; San Francisco Museum of Modern Art *Education:* Cooper Union; Yale U. School of Art *Dealer:* Nancy Hoffman Gallery, NYC

Photo-realistic paintings of the 1960s were depictions of nature taken from photographs: animals, ponds and foliage. Large-scale close-ups of animal faces, such as *Lizard's Head,* and human faces such as *African Lady* were sensuous replications reflecting a deep concern for nature, for "observing fertile and fantastic things that have within them the power to erupt, like Vesuvius." This interest in nature's mystical qualities made his approach quite different from that of other photo-realists. His media changed from oil to watercolor, pastel and lithography, as renditions of natural phenomena became less photographic and more impressionistic—for example, as in the watercolor entitled *Luxembourg Gardens: Memory.* He says, "I like to think I paint feeling. I am interested in spirit as expressed in nature, the invisible made visible."

RAGAN, CONNIE (Painter, Printmaker)
2605 S.W. 99th St., Oklahoma City, OK 73159
Born: 1951 *Collections:* Heard Museum, Phoenix; Gilcrease Museum, Tulsa *Exhibitions:* Finnish Film Institute, Helsinki; Smithsonian Institution, Washington DC *Education:* U. of Oklahoma *Dealer:* Adagio Galleries, Palm Springs

Inspired by home, family and motherhood, she presents her female subjects in a holistic manner. She uses conceptual and physical layering to bring a sense of spatial, temporal and cultural depth to her work. Influenced by the artists of the Southwest, she works in an uncluttered manner. Her palette is full of grays, magentas, blacks, reds and pinks. In the watercolor *Silent Invitation*, she depicts a woman walking through layers of trees in shades of blue and grey. In another piece, she portrays a woman flying through the sky and dreaming above rocks and trees. Her primary medium is watercolor.

RAJNUS, S. (Painter)
HC 62, P.O. Box 68, Malin, OR 97632
Born: 1940 *Awards:* Best of Show, Governor's Invitational, Salem, OR *Collections:* Oregon State University, Corvallis *Exhibitions:* Wild Wings Gallery, Portland & San Francisco; National Wildlife Fine Art Show, Kansas City, MO

Having painted professionally for many years, the artist credits education in art and science, in particular, biology, for laying the foundation for the portrayal of the "subject of life." A one-time teacher, the artist now paints full-time, usually using oils or watercolor as the medium of choice. Subjects vary from landscapes and flora and fauna to close-up still lifes. Fundamentally a realist, the artist works with a limited palette of six or seven colors, choosing to create a illusory surface wherein the viewer perceives details that are themselves only suggested.

RAMOS, ANTHONY D. (Video Artist, Performance Artist)
1225 Linda Rosa Ave., Los Angeles, CA 90041
Born: 1944 *Awards:* NEA Fellowship; Rockefellor Foundation Fellowship *Collections:* Whitney Museum, NYC *Exhibitions:* Centre Georges Pompidou, Paris; Whitney Museum, NYC *Education:* California In-

Andrea Rogers, *Uncle Slim Becomes a Souvenir,* 30 x 40, acrylic on canvas. Photographer: Kiana Decker

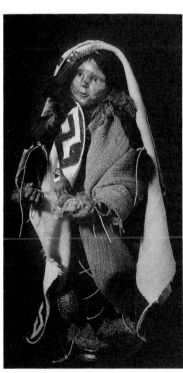

Marilyn Radzat, *Willow Basket,* 42" tall, porcelain and fabric. Courtesy: Mr. and Mrs. Robertson, San Francisco, CA Photograph: A. Zidek

Somers Randolph, *untitled,* 12 x 9 x 9, alabaster. Photograph: Jennifer Durham

stitute of the Arts *Dealer:* Electronics Arts Intermix, NYC

His first works were experimentations with early black-and-white reel video systems and attempts at using art as a focal point for Eastern and Western philosophies. In the 1970s, he traveled through Africa and the Middle East, and in 1980 he moved to Paris, using the city as a base for the performances and video installations that he mounted throughout Europe. Today, he uses a multimonitor configuration to mix dadaist images with homages to earlier artists. He especially emphasizes the role of women in history and society, including ancient female-oriented religions. He also focuses on the relationships between contemporary physics and ancient religions.

RAMOS, MELVIN JOHN (Painter)
5941 Ocean View Dr., Oakland, CA 94618

Born: 1935 *Award:* NEA Fellowship *Collections:* Museum of Modern Art, NYC; Guggenheim Museum, NYC *Exhibitions:* James Corcoran Gallery, Santa Monica; Oakland Museum *Education:* Cal. State-Sacramento *Dealer:* Louis K. Meisel Gallery, NYC

After he studied with Wayne Thiebaud in the 1950s, his early works focused on the female figure in a precise and straightforward manner. In the early 1960s, he turned to pop art paintings of comic-strip heroes, borrowing and inventing characters to comment on the mass-media images in energetic, distorted compositions. Later he became known for "pin-up" girls accompanied by exotic animals, as in *Aardvark. Chiquita* was a picture of a peeled banana with a woman inside. In the 1980s, his attention has turned to the iconography of the California landscape, and recently, he has returned to investigations of the human figure.

RAMSAY (Painter)
Ramsay Galleries, 119 Merchant St., Honolulu, HI 96813

Born: 1947 *Awards:* National Scholastic Gold Key; Award of Excellence, National League of American PEN Women *Collections:* Plaza Hotel, NYC; P.P.G. Industries *Exhibitions:* Waldorf Astoria Hotel, NYC; Capitol Rotunda, Washington, DC *Education:* Carnegie Mellon U. *Dealer:* Ramsay Galleries, Honolulu; Three Rivers Gallery, Pittsburgh

At the age of ten, she used a two-pronged brush and India ink to translate landscapes into monochromatic lines. She has excelled in many different media, but has continued throughout her career to create in pen and ink. Her landscapes have evolved into images of built environments such as hotels and historic streets. Working on commission, she draws without drafting aids. The intense detail of her architectural renditions requires hundreds of hours of location work, and the unforgiving nature of the ink medium continues to challenge the artist intellectually and graphically. She runs her own galleries in Honolulu.

RANDOLPH, SOMERS (Sculptor)
32 W. Anapamu, #211, Santa Barbara, CA 93101

Born: 1956 *Collections:* Ford Motor Company; General Motors Corporation *Exhibitions:* Artists Society International, San Francisco; Los Angeles Art Expo *Education:* Princeton U.

A whittler since childhood, he carves freeform alabaster sculptures known for their daring engineer-ing and sensuous curves. He cites Hepworth, Arp, Brancusi and Rivera as the major influences on his style and approach. Sculpting in Borego Desert alabaster, as well as in bronze and wood, he often sandblasts one side to produce textual contrast. He models some sculptures after the Moebius strip, producing very open forms, about 2-to-3-feet tall.

RANES, CHRIS (Painter, Printmaker)
3973 Bibbits Dr., Palo Alto, CA 94303

Collections: De Saisset, Santa Clara; Hewlett-Packard Corporation, Palo Alto *Exhibitions:* Ivory/Klimpton Gallery, San Francisco; Hilles Art Gallery, Harvard U., Cambridge, MA *Education:* Pratt Institute; U. of Santa Clara *Dealer:* J.J. Brookings Gallery, San Jose; J. Noblett, Sonoma; Galerie Suisse de Paris

Born in Warsaw, raised in Paris and trained by Hans Hoffman, Josef Albers, James Brooks and Jimmy and Max Ernst in New York, she makes oil paintings and lithographs of strong, expressionistic images and of Oriental color and delicacy of brushwork. She works in series, on canvas or paper—often handmade—sketching directly in oil so as to produce the effect of a print. Her palette consists of a wide range of colors, cool and warm. For the foundation for her works, she often uses authentic autoradiograms from biological research, upon which she applies paint thickly and in layers cut deep by linear, calligraphic strokes and swirls.

RANKIN, LARRY R. (Sculptor)
633 E. Pedregosa St., Santa Barbara, CA 93110

Born: 1949 *Awards:* 1st Place, Sculpture, Affaire in the Garden, Beverly Hills *Collections:* Guadalajara Jalisco Fine Arts Center, Mexico *Exhibitions:* Arpel Gallery, Santa Barbara; Gold Coast Art, Oxnard *Education:* Northern Arizona U.

After learning to work in cast bronze, he moved on to master welded metal, and stone- and wood-carving. His sculptures are powerfully-designed, non-objective forms. They are characterized by smooth, polished surfaces and the generous use of negative space as a design element. Subjects include human figures, organic forms, numbers, man-made objects, machines and completely imaginary shapes. His works convey his love of family, sense of humor and expert knowledge of his art. His pieces vary in size from 6 inches to 7 feet. He is especially well-known for the four-ton sandstone sculpture *Brotherhood*, which he co-created with Mexican sculptor Martin Gonzalez.

RANSTROM, ALMITA (Assemblage Artist)
6086 Marcella Way, Buena Park, CA 90620

Born: 1930 *Exhibitions:* Gallery 318, Los Angeles; Santa Barbara Contemporary Arts Forum *Education:* Cal. State-Fullerton

Fulfilling a lifelong ambition, she returned to school in the late 1970s. While there, she discovered that her talent for combining and transforming found materials had a name— assemblage—and that it had a place in the contemporary art world. Inspired by Joseph Cornell, she began making collage boxes. Later, she incorporated full-sized furniture and architectural objects. The ideas and motifs of magic, both generically and personally, are of special importance. She has created a whole group of assemblage projects that, in one way or another, are reflections of this interest. Her magic wands, for example, are made from mulberry branches 2 to 8 feet long; she finishes them with pastels, paints and carvings and a variety of found objects, such as

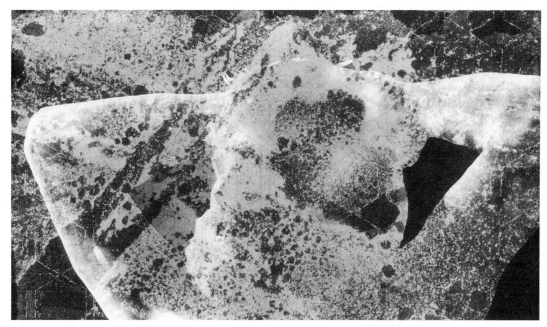

S.L. Rieman, *Bill,* 22 x 30, watercolor on paper. Courtesy: Dr. David Tonnemacher

Ramsay, *Memories Under the Monkeypod,* 8 x 16, ink. Courtesy: Ramsay Galeries, Honolulu

dragon beads, buttons, bells, pipes, broken glass, jewelry and leaves treated with metallic paints. Recent projects include *Wizard* (the personification of a wizard constructed with chairs, cloaks and rainbows) and *A Case for Magic*, with magic wands and other objects arranged to make an open violin case into an altar.

RAPHAEL, VICTOR (Painter)
328 N. Irving Blvd., Los Angeles, CA 90004

Born: 1950 *Awards:* 1st Prize, "Union Artist" Show, Calif. Museum of Science and Industry, Los Angeles *Collections:* Mr. and Mrs. Leonard Vernon, Los Angeles; David C. Ruttenberg, Chicago *Exhibitions:* Richard Green Gallery, Los Angeles; Los Angeles County Museum of Art Rental Gallery *Education:* UCLA *Dealer:* Richard Green Gallery, Los Angeles

He enjoys the challenge of working in painting, photography and video, frequently combining these media in an effort to create solutions to formal and intuitive problems in artmaking. Man Ray, Pollock and Mondrian have been strong influences. His painting balances a logical structure with an intuitive energy to create color-field abstractions in oil, pastel, acrylic and enamel. Colors include copper, black, white, gold and blue. In his current photography, he uses the Polaroid photo, to which he adds surface paint and other materials such as gold leaf. These series of "small paintings" employ both abstract and figurative imagery in a synthesis of the ancient past and the future. One group of Polaroids depicts galactic landscapes with pictographs, creatures of ancient origin and universal symbols such as orbs, circles and spheres.

RATCLIFF, MARY C. (Sculptor)
630 Nelson St., Berkeley, CA 94707

Born: 1942 *Exhibitions:* Crown Zellerbach Gallery, San Francisco; Sonoma State University *Education:* Rhode Island School of Design

After formal training, she moved to New York City where she was involved with the first video collective, Videofreex. In 1973, she came to San Francisco, where she began a series of wind sculptures using Lumar, mylar and Tyvek ribbon. She went on to create indoor sculptures using satin, rayon and mylar ribbon, either tied to suspended hoop forms or arranged in subtly colored wall hangings. Recently, she has explored activation of interior sculptures through collaboration with dancers and musicians and has begun working with neon on a series of illuminated hoops arranged on poles in a procession.

RATTEY, HARVEY (Sculptor)
1460 Bear Canyon Rd., Bozeman, MT 59715

Born: 1938 *Awards:* Gold Medal, Western Artist of America *Collections:* Congressman Ron Marlenee, MT; Senator John Melcher, MT *Exhibitions:* Nat'l Trail of Tears, Telaquah, OK; Squash Blossom Gallery, Palm Desert

He is a former rancher and part Assiniboine (Native American). His work shows a deep sensitivity and concern for the history, future and honor of the Indian people. He depicts wildlife, the rodeo and Indian life and customs in bronze miniature sculptures. He has been a full time sculptor since 1971. His formal training includes a Hines-Zemsky class with Robert Bateman and the Zahourek, Anatomiken workshop.

RAVARRA, PATRICIA (Sculptor)
1045 Leavenworth St., #5, San Francisco, CA 94109

Born: 1947 *Awards:* Fulbright Grant *Exhibitions:* International Triennale, Lodz, Poland; United States Information Agency *Education:* San Francisco State U.

Trained in painting, drawing and sculpture, she studied the textile arts at university and tapestry design with Magdalena Abakanowicz in Poland, who emphasized the relationship between textile works and architecture, and the creation of works of art appropriate to the public place in which they are to be displayed. She dyes nylon fiber, such as fishing line, with brilliant color and weaves large panels using the ancient technique of card-weaving. These pieces may either be hung on a wall or set freestanding. The woven works, though solid and sturdy, are transparent and translucent and express her fascination with the interplay of light and color. The imagery is abstract.

RAZ, SYLVIA (Sculptor)
1112 Norman Place, Los Angeles, CA 90049

Born: 1949 *Exhibitions:* Art Institute of Southern California, Laguna Beach; University of Judaism, Los Angeles *Dealer:* Los Angeles Art Association

Being of South American origin, she was greatly influenced by the art of the native cultures and the Latino-American masters. Her subject matter has revolved around the figure (both human and animal), motherhood, instinct, temptation, pain and passion. She has worked mainly in carved stone, with an accent on the dynamic relationship between artist and nature. Trying to find an escape from the limitations of stone, she began working in wood. These new pieces also offer another dimension missing from her other work—color. She strives to capture in her sculptures the pathetic, ridiculous and sublime aspects of life.

REAGAN, GERTRUDE MYRRH (Painter)
967 Moreno Ave., Palo Alto, CA 94303

Born: 1936 *Awards:* 2nd Place, Watercolor, 3rd Place, Sculpture, Pacific Art League *Collections:* Smithsonian Institution, Washington DC; Lane Publishing, Menlo Park *Exhibitions:* Richmond Art Center; Lawrence Hall of Science, Berkeley *Education:* Stanford U.

She acquired her love of land formations, maps and diagramming ideas from early exposure to geology and *Scientific American*. Themes in her work also include cosmology, physics, biology, perception and patterns generated by nature, mathematics and computers. Scientists in her family inspired these themes, and Gyorgy Kepes' book, *The New Landscapes*, crystallized them. From the late 1950s to the early 1970s, she expressed these ideas in relief prints. From then until now, she has worked in batik and shibori—Japanese wrinkle-resist dyeing and spray-painting processes on cloth and paper. Shibori involves forming thin paper into three-dimensional forms before spray-painting them in subdued colors. The chief theme of these paintings is the earth as seen from space. Some of her fabricated "satellite views" exist in computer enhanced versions. She continues to diagram ideas in paintings and computer animations. Her most recent concerns are patterns of geology as well as the human condition, the latter influenced by Kaethe Kollwitz and Goya.

Victor Raphael, *Infant Planet,* 4 x 4, acrylic on polaroid

Manika Aia Rogers, *Who Cares,* 36 x 36, oil

RECTOR, MARGE (Painter)
25 San Carlos, Sausalito, CA 94965

Born: 1929 *Awards:* Texas Painting and Sculpture Exhibit, Dallas; Cash Award, Humble Oil and Refining Co. *Collections:* McDermott-Smyser Collection, Dallas; *Exhibitions:* Butler Institute of American Art, Youngstown, OH; New Mexico International Art Show *Education:* Texas Technical College

She paints hard-edge abstractions with acrylic on primed canvas. In her early paintings, she used a variety of techniques to create flatly painted areas where viewer movement resulted in movement in the painting. Among these techniques were: negative and positive image reversal; optical image completion; optical vibrations and after image; implied movement in a "captured form" series; and apparent movement in a series of spaced double-canvas paintings with holes cut in the top layer. More recently, she has introduced color in a meaningful way. In her current paintings, she begins with a free flow of paint in various dilutions and goes back to create hard-edge, solid color images.

REED, CARL (Sculptor)
1530 Alamo Ave., Colorado Springs, CO 80907

Born: 1944 *Awards:* Hand Hollow Fellowship; Merit Award, Great Plains Sculpture *Exhibitions:* Sheldon Memorial Gallery, Lincoln, NE *Collections:* City of Aurora, CO; U. of Wisconsin *Education:* Dartmouth College; Pratt Institute *Dealer:* Ruth Bachofer, Santa Monica

He displays the methods by which his large, abstract sculptures are created, inviting the viewer to participate in their construction. This idea springs from the massive barns and antique ships of his New England boyhood. He was deeply impressed by the way the carefully placed construction details reduced their size and impassivity to a human scale. His primary goal is to harmonize forms and substances in a manner that allows the pieces to speak for themselves. This has led him to combine materials that are substantially different in character, such as steel, concrete and wood. He believes that outdoor sculpture is constantly altered as one views it during different times of day and the changing seasons. Strong relationships can also be established between a piece and its surrounding environment, including nearby architecture. He tries to address these issues in his work by incorporating open forms, which visually capture negative space, and by curving contours, which often create a lively interplay with architectural forms.

REED, NATALIE (Sculptor, Painter)
P.O. Box 96, Carmel, CA 93921

Born: 1931 *Collections:* Monterey Beach Hotel; Mt. Kenya Safari Club, Africa *Exhibitions:* Santa Catalina Gallery, Monterey; Fireside Gallery, Carmel *Education:* U. of Miami; U. of the Americas, Mexico

As a young student at the Art Institute of Chicago, she was greatly impressed by the works of Marc Chagall and Salvador Dali. She also felt an artistic connection with O'Keeffe's experiments in form and color, Kandinsky's use of music in his imagery and Monet's studies in light. After her travels in Europe and the Orient—making films of the museums, cathedrals, chateaux, temples and ruins—she went to Africa, where she was enthralled by the movements of animals in the wild. She painted a series of murals and created sculptures, characterized by the choreography of natural rhythms, colors and textural relationships. Her two-dimensional work demanded three-dimensional expression, and led to bronze studies of animals and dancers in motion. Her work is most often noted for its "arresting aliveness."

REEVES, DANIEL (Video Artist)
c/o Capp Street Project, 65 Capp St., San Francisco, CA 94103

Awards: NEA Fellowship; NEA Grant *Exhibitions:* Pacific Film Archive, UC-Berkeley; Capp Street Project

His video works reverberate with implicit and explicit spirituality. *Ganapati: A Spirit in the Bush* combines aphorisms and poetic text with a dense flow of images of elephants in the wild and suffering at the hands of man. The video stands as both a powerful indictment of the mistreatment of animals and as a document of our dissociation from the natural world—and media's role in that dissociation. His recent installation in conjunction with Capp Street Project took place in an abandoned chapel. He combines rows of buddhas, rat traps and wind chimes made from wine goblets and hammers with video images constantly projected on a screen that wraps around the layout. The videos manipulate space through use of slow-motion and time-lapse photography, while their recorded sounds meld with the chimes. Critic Christine Tamblyn writes, "Synthesizing ancient cosmological symbolism with contemporary technological formats, Reeves effectively [utilizes] the electronic evanescence of video to convey ephemeral states of spiritual transcendence."

REGISTER, GENE A. (Painter)
6321 Fairlane Dr., Oakland, CA 94611

Born: 1929 *Awards:* 1st Place, Ft. Lauderdale Guild, FL; 1st Place, Del Ray Beach Art Association *Collections:* Fanny's Restaurant, Evanston, IL *Exhibitions:* Gallery 113, Faulkner Gallery, Santa Barbara; Montecito Fine Arts Gallery *Education:* American Academy of Art *Dealer:* Robert Bailey, Montecito

After formal training in commercial art and illustration, he worked in advertising for several years. Then he taught art at the American Academy of Art for twelve years, developing his technique, and exploring different styles and media. Moving to Florida in the late 1960s, he modified his palette to incorporate more pastels. He worked entirely in acrylics—which he applied in layers—and glazes of drybrush. Gradually he shifted to oils and to combinations of oils and acrylics. By the mid-1970s, he was moving from a sharply focused style to more spontaneous work in watercolor. In recent work, he creates abstract forms in watercolor or graphite—later developing them realistically, by pushing subject matter to the abstract with more watercolor or oil.

REHFELD (Painter)
1508 Seetwood Dr., Daly City, CA 94015

Born: 1954 *Collections:* Rehfeld International Museum and Art Gallery *Exhibitions:* Daly City Community Center; UC-Santa Barbara Art Museum *Education:* College of San Mateo; UC-Santa Barbara

He is an avant gardist for whom color plays the cohesive role. Into his unique style, he has incorporated such fundamental elements as light and dark contrasts, positive and negative spatial compositions and innovative new criteria. He lays paint on in a thick impasto, often with a drawing implement, or squeezes

Ron Russell, *Celestra* 36 x 48, lacquer on glass. Americana Gallery, Carmel, CA

Gene A. Register, *Maine Bounty,* 24 x 30, oil

paint directly from the tube. His collage-like work is normally abstract with geometric elements. In other works, dancing figures appear, and in this work his limited palette expands to include brighter blues and yellows while his paint application becomes flatter.

REICHMAN, FRED (Painter)
1235 Stanyan St., San Francisco, CA 94117

Born: 1925 *Awards:* Purchase Award, San Francisco Art Festival; Award of Merit, Art Festival of the City & County of San Francisco *Collections:* San Francisco Museum of Modern Art; Oakland Museum *Exhibitions:* Gallery Paule Anglim, San Francisco; Smith Anderson Gallery, Palo Alto *Education:* UC-Berkeley; San Francisco Art Institute *Dealer:* Iannetti/Lanzone Gallery, San Francisco; Mekler Gallery, Los Angeles

He apprenticed as an animated cartoonist in Hollywood before beginning formal art training at Berkeley. His early influences include Klee, Cézanne, Miro, Matisse, Bonnard, Clayton Price, Morris Graves and Max Weber. He progressed from imagined nature themes to nature images based on observation, and after discovering the work of Jules Pascin, he abruptly changed from thick impasto, palette knife and glazes to thinly built-up layers of paint and matte surfaces, working with alkyd colors that permit more translucency and fluidity. His paintings are large, gentle meditations infused with the energy and meaning of negative space and the silences of Oriental art. Color as an expression of light plays an important role in the works—large luminous fields of color are sparsely populated by everyday objects—a cat, a stone, a flower—that are imbued with a transcendental, Zen-like power and significance, standing at the same time as concrete, functional objects and as symbols of the artistic symbiosis of physicality and spirituality that informs all his work.

REID, CHARIE (Painter)
2679 15th Ave., Carmel, CA 93923

Born: 1955 *Exhibitions:* Hoyt Gallery, San Francisco; Carol Lawrence Gallery, Beverly Hills *Education:* Pennsylvania State U.

She was trained academically in the trompe l'oeil techniques of the Old Masters. Her earlier work was humorous and surreal. Images of Christ in a sports car and Einstein happily driving an Indy style racer were two of her most successful prints. Today, she paints gentle statements about personal development, the magic of life and the beauty of nature. Her subjects include polished crystals, musical instruments and tasseled tapestries. She compliments all of these with delicate lace and intricate silver backgrounds or surreal sunsets and starlit skies. She is noted for her detail work, as well as for her fine eye for color and composition.

REILLY, JACK (Painter)
12720 Washington Blvd., 2nd Fl. Los Angeles, CA 90066

Born: 1950 *Awards:* NEA Artist Residency/Exhibition Touring Grant; Best of Show, Bellair National Exhibition *Collections:* Oakland Museum; Fresno Metropolitan Museum *Exhibitions:* Stella Polaris Gallery, Los Angeles; Mission Gallery, NYC *Education:* Florida State U. *Dealer:* Merging One Gallery, Santa Monica

Extreme opposing forces at work typify the essence of his paintings. Works have always demonstrated a responsibility to art history in the particular issues and stylistic tendencies he chooses to explore. During recent years, a clear-cut and logical development has taken place. From stark illusionism dealing with pictorial space to the multilayered, shaped canvases, artistic options such as movement/stillness, thin/thick, color/neutrality and edge/amorphic have been prevalent in his paintings. Recent pieces incorporate built-in sound that he composes and records for specific pieces.

REILLY, LORRAINE ALMEIDA (Painter)
P.O. Box 355, Point Reyes, CA 94956

Born: 1936 *Exhibitions:* Oakland Museum; Richmond Art Center *Education:* San Francisco Art Institute *Dealer:* Gallery Route One, Pt. Reyes

During her formal training, she discovered that images in her paintings were often recognized by others as archetypal visions. The mystery of these spontaneous images led her to explore psychology and mythology and to employ unconscious phenomena in her art as a source of wisdom and truth. She has explored many media, probably best known for her small works in acrylic glazes and iridescent pigments. More recently, after several series of symmetrical images in a variety of media—enamels, acrylics, dyes, silk, plastic, leather and canvas—she began a collection of black-and-white drawings in charcoal called "Charges." In these works, she creates illusions of space, form, light and darkness by means of luminous organic forms.

REILLY, MICHAEL W. (Painter, Commercial Illustrator)
4871 Regents Park Ln., Fremont, CA 94538

Born: 1952 *Awards:* 1st, 2nd, & Honorable Mention Ribbons, San Mateo County Fair *Collections:* The Golden Path *Exhibitions:* Collins Gallery, San Francisco; Western Regional Science Fiction and Fantasy Convention, Oakland Museum of Art

After completing formal art training, he began developing animation skills. His pieces of the era showed the influence of the Disney artists of the 1940s, 1950s, and 1960s. He worked in the Silicon Valley as a graphic artist, and used three-dimensional effects to create animation for video arcade games. He also illustrated promotional pieces for the high-tech industry. Today, his work is characterized by intense concentration on detail and use of color. He now blends worlds of fantasy and science fiction to create a surrealistic effect. He uses an airbrush and his media include watercolor, acrylic, gouache and oil.

REIMER, EMILY A. (Painter)
1969 Kentucky St., Redwood City, CA 94061

Born: 1914 *Exhibitions:* Peninsula Art Association, Belmont; Pacific Art League, Palo Alto

Primarily an abstract painter, she says she works with ideas born from her subconscious, translating them to color on canvas. Beginning with blots of color in acrylic, she often turns the canvas from side to side until she sees intuitively how the composition can work as a whole. Influenced by such artists as Van Gogh, Picasso and Kandinski, she prefers a vibrant palette, the paintings characterized by numerous brilliant circles of color against a pink background. *Grey Abstract* features similar moments of color, only here they are set within a grey field.

Chris Ranes, *Nucleotides IX,* 30 x 23, mixed media, oil on paper

Shahrokh Rezvani, *Mystical Equalibrium VII,* 41 x 30, mixed media

REIMHOLZ, LYNN FALCON (Multimedia Artist)
810 Grenada Ln., Plum Island, Foster City, CA 94404

Born: 1927 *Awards:* Best of Show, Portland State U.; 1st Place, Pasadena Invitational *Exhibitions:* Kansas Regents Center, Kansas City, MO; Portland State U., Oregon *Education:* Portland State U.; Kansas City Art Institute

The artist's desire to avoid being identified with any one specific style allows her to pursue the direction of the work itself. While Matisse and Picasso were among her first sources of inspiration, studies of the New York school of the 1950s encouraged the experimental side of her nature. A recent project relating to the Vietnam Memorial employs large, styrofoam maquettes as models for bas-relief work on canvas. Although the maquettes alone can be considered finished art, the subsequent abstracted, collage-oriented pieces express more immediately her reoccurring theme of "the void."

RENAKER, DAVID (Painter)
1931 Anza St., San Francisco, CA 94118

Born: 1940 *Collections:* Pomona College *Exhibitions:* ASI Gallery, San Francisco; Hall of Flowers, Golden Gate Park, San Francisco *Dealer:* Gregory Ghent, San Francisco

His earliest works were allegories. More recently, he has attempted to banish ideologies from his paintings, but never completely. He enjoys toying with the viewer's perceptions, playing with perspective as he forces three-dimensional volumes onto two-dimensional surfaces and manages to make opaque pigments look like translucent sources of light. He finds these tricks and buffooneries sufficient reason for making art.

REYNOLDS, ROBERT (Painting)
958 Skyline Dr., San Luis Obispo, CA 93401

Born: 1936 *Awards:* Top Award, California Survey of Drawing & Watercolor, Humboldt *Exhibitions:* Hutchins Gallery, Cambria; C.L. Clark Galleries, Bakersfield *Education:* Art Center College of Design; California Polytechnic U. *Dealer:* Hutchins Gallery, Cambria

Influenced by the English watercolor school of painting and by the works of American artists Winslow Homer, John Singer Sargent and Maxfield Parrish, he is dedicated to landscape painting. Working in a representational style, his watercolor paintings convey his interest and deep feeling for the subject. Patterns of nature are interwoven into strong compositions that seem to glow with the interplay of light, shadow and color. He has a refined technique which captures color and light by overlapping combinations of thin layers of paint, heightening the luminous, atmospheric quality of his paintings. He has recently been engaged in two projects. He has been working on a series of paintings which depict the four seasons in the High Sierra mountains, scheduled for several solo exhibitions; in addition, he has recently completed a stamp design commissioned by the U.S. Postal Service commemorating the Hearst Castle's historical landmark status. The design will be used on postcards in the Postal Service's "Historic Preservation" series. He is a professor of art at Cal-Poly in San Luis Obispo.

REZVANI, SHAHROKH (Painter, Printer)
8721E Piccadilly Rd., Scottsdale, AZ 85251

Born: 1943 *Awards:* Who's Who in International Art, Lausanne, Switzerland *Collections:* Palace of the Legion of Honor, San Francisco; Detriot Institute of Art *Exhibitions:* Gallery West, Los Angeles; Basel International, Switzerland *Education:* Ball State U.; Wayne State U. *Dealer:* The Wright Gallery, Dallas

His interest in experimenting with different printmaking techniques prompted his enrollment at Wayne State University. There he concentrated on multiple-plate/color-viscosity intaglio and the monotype process, but more importantly, he discovered *cliché verre* under the tutelage of Aris Koutroulis. His works in this medium exhibit an angular, mathematical clarity and differ from his abstract work in intaglio, handmade paper collage and monotype, which either feature organic-looking forms or contrast surface patterns and textures. In his *cliché verre*, he attempts to create effects not possible in his inked prints, exploring the appearance of textures and the illusion of geometric objects floating in an eerie, airless space. On one level, the shapes appear to be scientific and camera-made images of a magnified crystallized substance. On another level, the crisp shapes, tones and spatial illusion reveal the artist's hand.

RHOADS, NEIL (Fiber Artist)
2036 22nd St., #2, San Francisco, CA 94107

Born: 1949 *Awards:* Artist's Grant Program, National Wool Bureau, NYC *Collections:* I. Magnin & Co., Santa Clara *Exhibitions:* Out of Hand Gallery, San Francisco; Ruby O'Burke Gallery, San Francisco *Education:* O'More School of Design

He has worked in several media including oil on canvas, furniture and textile design, ceramics, and fiber art. In all of these media, the relationship of the material to the hand, and the relationship of color to the psyche have been his driving interests. Presently he works in clay and fiber, celebrating the complex relationships between man's physical and spiritual bodies. He expresses the dynamic force fields and aura of the human body in the juxtaposition of color and the rhythm of line and shape in his fiber works. With vivid colors and engaging geometric designs, his art portrays the subtle but essential energies of existence.

RICE, LELAND DAVID (Photographer)
P.O. Box 4100, Inglewood, CA 90309

Born: 1940 *Awards:* NEA Grant; Guggenheim Photography Fellowship *Education:* Arizona State U., Tempe; Chouinard Art Institute; San Francisco State College

Influential on his work were Jack Welpott, Don Worth, Oliver Gagliani and Paul Caponigro, all of whom he encountered during his years of formative education. His large-format images in black and white and color are abstracted, minimalist and surreal—for instance, presenting furniture in an unoccupied interior that nevertheless reveals the presence of people, or producing a series of portraits by using unoccupied chairs. He has also created a series of stark interiors, bare of any accouterments.

RICE, RAYMOND (Painter, Mosaic Artist)
P.O. Box 703, Mendocino, CA 95460

Born: 1916 *Awards:* San Francisco Poetry and Film Festival *Collections:* California Institute of the Arts, Valencia; Lewis & Clark U., Portland, OR *Exhibitions:*

S. Rajnus, *Eventide,* 22 x 30, mixed media

Robert Reynolds, *Sierra Snow Patterns,* 22 x 30, watercolor

Bay Window Gallery, Mendocino; Palace of the Legion of Honor, San Francisco *Education:* Chicago Academy of Fine Arts; Art Students League

He has had a varied artistic career with roots in traditional painting, drawing and sculpture. In the mid-1960s, he began making films based on his paintings. These 2- to 20-minute films were produced using animation techniques. He has also worked extensively in mosaic and illustration. Recent work consists of abstract images or rows of faces rendered in oil and pen and ink on long, wooden strips. These are suspended from the ceiling, kept whole or segmented and tied together with cord or with brass or copper links. To these images, he has added coins, artifacts, beads and other materials that augment the dominant design. These pieces are slightly filmic and derive from previous filmmaking experiences.

RICH, ANDREA (Printmaker)
706 Western Dr., Santa Cruz, CA 95060

Born: 1954 *Exhibitions:* Cultural Council of Santa Cruz; Wilshire Ebell Art Salon, Los Angeles

Her wildlife prints reflect a concern for endangered species in the shadow of man's destructive treatment of the environment. She is primarily influenced by the Japanese ukiyo-e prints for their tight composition, elegant lines and delicate use of pattern, though she also appreciates the strong emotional impact of expressionists Munch and Kellowitz through the use of bold lines and color. She is attracted to the enormous range of expression possible in such a simple medium, yet she still uses very traditional methods of production. The key or line blocks are cut in cherry; four to six pine or plywood blocks are made for the color prints. She uses oil-base lithographic inks and often pulls the prints entirely by hand.

RICH, MICHAEL (Painter)
1516 Westerly Terrace, Los Angeles, CA 90026

Born: 1945 *Exhibitions:* Dream Masters Gallery; Artistic Endeavors, Simi Valley *Education:* Art Center College of Design

He believes in a total rejection of the tenets of modern art. Influenced by Theodore Lukits, he draws inspiration from non-interpretive art from the turn of the century. He is primarily interested in the realistic depiction of the human form in a recognizable setting. Working with bold, untempered brushstrokes, he believes that the work of art arises from analytical reasoning, rather than involved rendering.

RICHARDS, BRUCE (Painter)
508 N. Belmont Ave., Los Angeles, CA 90026

Born: 1948 *Awards:* NEA Fellowship *Collections:* San Francisco Museum of Modern Art; La Jolla Museum of Modern Art *Exhibitions:* Laguna Beach Museum of Art; Cirrus Gallery, Los Angeles *Education:* UC-Irvine

He studied with Robert Irwin; his early paintings were concerned with the minimal/conceptual styles of the late 1960s. These paintings incorporate the painting's "history" as part of the intended presentation. The "objectness," i.e. the canvas support, paint layering, etc. of the painting was an integral part of the image. Recent images began in 1978, with a conscious attempt to record personal situations, rather than recent art history. The images chosen are metaphorical, and the title of each is the introduction to the work's narrative. *First Thanksgiving* is a tiny painting of grains of corn, meticulously rendered in oils on linen. *Formal Couple*, an oil on two panels, features a bow tie and three buttons in the first, and a string of pearls in the other. Ultimately, however, the humor of such paintings as *Formal Couple* is a temporary detour from the artist's more pensive meditations on life, death, love and history. Chairs that measure our daily arrivals and departures, clocks that measure our time on earth and skulls that serve as reminders of death are the central symbols of his aesthetic vision.

RICHARDS, ROBERT (Sculptor)
741 2nd St. East, Sonoma, CA 95476

Born: 1937 *Awards:* Purchase Award, Richmond Art Center; San Francisco Art Commission *Collections:* Smithsonian Institution, Washington DC; Richmond Art Center *Exhibitions:* New American Sculpture, U.S. State Department; UC-Berkeley; UC-Davis; Cal. State U.-San Jose *Education:* San Jose State U.; California College of Arts & Crafts *Dealers:* Viewpoint Gallery, Carmel; Vorpal Gallery, San Francisco

Starting first as a painter and printmaker with study and studio in England, he changed his pursuit to ceramic sculpture after graduate work in the early 1970s at the California College of Arts and Crafts, and with Robert Arneson at UC-Davis. He developed a style of illusionistic landscape and object study using themes based on the American West. Clay sculptures are brightly painted in watercolor style with works approaching 6 feet in height. He translates three-dimensional forms into two dimensions and two-dimensional forms into three, wherein natural environments and man-made objects coincide.

RICHARDSON, HARRY S. (Sculptor)
10060 Old Redwood Hwy., Penngrove, CA 94951

Born: 1928 *Collections:* Youngstown Museum, OH *Exhibitions:* Branscomb Gallery, Bodega; Maxwell Galleries, San Francisco *Education:* Cleveland Institute of Art *Dealer:* Sculpture House, Carmel

Since 1956, he has operated his own gallery to market his own work. While he has geared himself toward monumental works, he produces an array of smaller pieces, including jewelry, knives and gemstone carvings to manage expenses. Birds, animals and people are his subjects, each captured in a stylized but emotional stance, one where something expected or unexpected portends to happen. In these pieces, he frequently combines several materials, from metal to stone to glass. His objective is to fashion works which appear to defy gravity. He has developed his own techniques for shaping difficult materials such as the hard gemstones for his small sculpture and jewelry, and hard steels for his knives.

RICHARDSON, SAM (Sculptor)
4121 Sequoyah Rd., Oakland CA 94605

Born: 1934 *Collections:* M.H. de Young Memorial Museum, San Francisco; Smithsonian Institution, Washington, DC *Exhibitions:* Museum of Modern Art, NYC; Whitney Museum, NYC *Education:* California College of Arts and Crafts *Dealer:* Martha Jackson Gallery, NYC; Fuller-Goldeen Gallery, San Francisco

An interest in landscape brought him to the use of formal elements from images of his native California. The content of his large constructions and installations is determined largely by the arrangement of forms. Light, heat and activity on the desert are explored when wood, cloth, rope and paper are integrated by

Natalie Reed, *Young Zebra with Bird—A Conversation,* 7 x 12, bronze

Robert Richards, *Navajo Loom Bed,* 18 x 18 x 15, ceramic sculpture.
Courtesy: Vorpal Gallery, San Francisco, CA

the effects of shadow, color, line and texture in the tent-like *Desert Image: Wedges/Area 5*. Pieces in series draw cumulative meanings as he seeks to express mankind's "universal relationship with the land—not to tell a story but to suggest a familiar experience, an illusion that will lead one to ponder rather than know."

RICHEN, JOHN MATTHEW (Sculptor)
34940 NE Wilsonville Rd., Newberg, OR 97132

Born: 1943 *Collections:* U.S. National Bank of Oregon; First National Bank, Seattle *Exhibitions:* La Shayne Gallery, Montreal; C.G. Rein Galleries, Los Angeles *Education:* Oregon State U.; U. of Washington *Dealer:* C.G. Rein Galleries, Los Angeles, Santa Fe, Minneapolis, Scottsdale

Two drawing and sculpture classes were enough to convince him to change his career path from architecture to sculpture. He works by drawing an idea, then making a pattern from this drawing. Sometimes he draws the pattern directly on the sheet metal. After the metal is cut, he uses grinders, torches and inserts to create the finished steel-and-bronze sculpture. He is known for the light-reflecting areas that are ground into the pieces. These are added as part of the overall design and highlighted by lights positioned around the sculpture. He has recently been using special air equipment to complete a commission in granite.

RICHMAN, GERRY (Painter, Sculptor)
234 Lower Walden Rd., Carmel Highlands, CA 93923

Born: 1931 *Awards:* Award of Merit, California Expo; 1st Place, Monterey Fair *Collections:* President Ronald Reagan; Michael Landon *Exhibitions:* Monterey Museum Biennial; Pacific Grove Art Center *Education:* Otis Art Institute, Los Angeles; UC-Santa Cruz

He is comfortable with both figuration and abstraction. In the 1960s and 1970s, he made decorative sculpture. By 1981, his work began to reflect the influences of the Hoffman School, i.e., formal plasticity and ideated tactility. He rejected perspective and deep space, opting instead for a flat modern approach involving bright colors and geometric forms. He then played with cubism before turning to a classical direction in his drawing. Influenced by Japanese art, he drew large figures composed of tonal scrumblings with colored pencils. Since 1984, his work reflects the subjective search for inner realities through the painting process.

RIEDELL, CHRISTINE (Photographer)
6001 N. Arlington Blvd., San Pablo, CA 94806

Born: 1946 *Awards:* James D. Phelan Award in Printmaking; California Arts Council Grant, Artists in the Schools *Collections:* The Oakland Museum *Exhibitions:* Mandeville Gallery, Whittier College; Chabot College Art Gallery, Hayward *Education:* San Francisco State U.

Her early work in photography was influenced by the mystical, transformative view of nature expressed in the works of Wynn Bullock and Todd Walker. While experimenting with the many techniques she had learned during her studies of the history of photography, she invented a unique way of using gum bichromate, layering the images on the ground. She continued to work with alternative processes until the mid-1980s. She then re-examined her style and adopted a more straightforward, documentary, black- and-white approach. This was an attempt to eliminate extraneous information from the composition. Using a large-format camera and plus-x film, recently she has been working on a project which documents the history and terrain of the Great Basin.

RIEMAN, STEVE (Painter)
1188 Tahoe Ave., Yucca Valley, CA 92284

Born: 1942 *Awards:* Certificate of Merit for Watercolor, National Academy of Design *Collections:* Redlands Community Hospital *Exhibitions:* Riverside Art Center and Museum; Salmagundi Club, NYC *Education:* Art Center College of Design *Dealer:* Himmerdinger, Palm Desert

Trained in product design, he is a free-lance designer, who has been producing fine art since 1980. His work reflects a preoccupation with the delicate balance between the natural and artificial world. Using atomization, he paints over and around the various natural and artificial objects he renders on watercolor paper. Between paint applications, he allows the desert winds to move the mask objects. By assembling the real components of the landscape and imitating nature's processes—deposition and erosion—he produces paintings that are at once texturally realistic and abstract in design.

RIIS, BETTY (Painter)
7422 Girard Ave., La Jolla, CA 92037

Born: 1924 *Collections:* Aerospace Museum, San Diego; U.S. Coast Guard Museum *Exhibitions:* San Diego Art Institute; Salmagundi Club, NYC *Education:* Hunter College; USC *Dealer:* Knowles Gallery, La Jolla

Influenced by Joaquin Sorolla and Mary Cassatt, she has always been fascinated by the figure. She is the society portrait painter of La Jolla, California, thriving on the challenge of pleasing her clients with her oils on canvas. Group compositions and environmental portraits are her specialty. One painting, *Girls in White,* is based on Sargent's full-length panels. She has the facility of capturing the personality as well as the likeness of her subjects. She has recently been working on costume party paintings, which will be part of her series on people at parties.

RING, AL (Painter, Printmaker)
721 De Haro St., San Francisco, CA 94107

Born: 1934 *Awards:* Ford Foundation Grant *Collections:* Kaufman & Broad *Exhibitions:* Natsoulas Novelozo Gallery, Davis; Smith Anderson Gallery, Palo Alto *Dealer:* Smith Anderson Gallery, Palo Alto

Muted colors and a feeling of quiet reserve typified his early work, which had been influenced by Matisse, Balthus and the Bay Area Figurative Painters. A gradual move to abstract images in the late 1960s allowed more freedom to develop an individual vocabulary, which sought to take full advantage of the sensuous elasticity of paint. He builds the painted surface in several layers, rendering free-flowing, ribbon-like forms in rich, clear, bright colors. The freshness of the space is underscored by the vibrant movement of his forms. Their dancing feeling has pushed the work into three or more panels of canvas and to shaped canvases, in order that they may be fully contained. His paintings convey a feeling of comfort and the joyous experience of living.

Betty Riis, *The Hare Bros.,* 24 x 36, oil Courtesy: Knowles Gallery, La Jolla, CA

John Richen, *Eagle,* 40" tall, steel and bronze

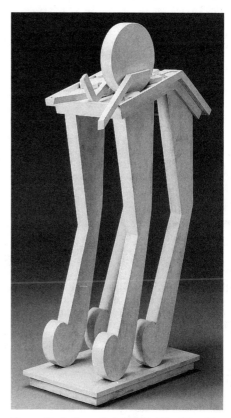

Bruce Rod, *Sans Color Shift,* 54 x 26 x 15, wood, oil

RINKE, KLAUS (Painter, Sculptor)
P.O. Box 2099, Venice, CA 90294

Born: 1939 *Collections:* Tate Gallery, London; National Gallery of Berlin, W. Germany *Exhibitions:* Centre Pompidou, Paris; Museum of Modern Art, NYC *Education:* Folkwang School, Essen *Dealer:* James Corcoran, Santa Monica

A painter and sculptor influenced by the forms and forces in nature, he creates works that explore elements found therein. Early sculptures concern themselves with the formal qualities of water, the pieces combining water and sculpted steel. A series of drawings that examine the relationships between time, space and distance followed. The images are abstract; some are linear. Over time, abstractions of human form became the focus of his attention; he spent two years on a graphite series of human forms. He continues to draw, sculpt and paint. The paintings are done in acrylic and oil on canvases in sizes ranging from 3 by 4 feet to 10 by 15 feet.

RISEMBERG, RICHARD (Photographer)
205 N. Ridgewood Pl., Los Angeles, CA 90004

Born: 1953 *Exhibitions:* Gallerie Telloor, Alkmaar, Holland; West Los Angeles City Hall Gallery, Los Angeles Department of Cultural Affairs

Originally trained as a writer, he became disenchanted with the indirectness of words and the commercialism of the literary world. He stumbled upon photography while experimenting with a variety of visual arts. His early works were influenced by Weston and Adams, but this changed as he realized he was more interested in light than design, in emotion rather than formalism. After he viewed published collections of the works of Josef Sudek and Linda Butler, he decided that he would rather invoke feelings of community, mortality and solidarity than expressions of awe or intellectual discussion. Recently he has been using large-format cameras to capture small corners of light and occasional intimate scenes of urban life. He does not practice manipulation of the negative or image, since he feels that this would be an imposition of his own ego rather than a step towards a faithful, sensitive and perceptive reproduction of reality. He describes his images as akin to haiku—photographs which can be understood and appreciated at a pre-verbal level of consciousness.

RITCHEY, RIK (Painting)
667 11th St., Oakland, CA 94607

Born: 1953 *Exhibitions:* Pascal de Saarthe Gallery, San Francisco; Smith Anderson Gallery, Palo Alto *Education:* Mills College *Dealer:* Pascal de Saarthe Gallery, San Francisco

After painting in a representational manner, he experimented with differing degrees of abstraction before returning to landscape paintings in the mid-1980s. These landscapes evolved into a format of extremely elongated vertical paintings on carved wood panels that explore the neutral ground between painting and sculpture. The narrow, limited perspective of these landscapes, inhabited by a single attenuated rod-like object and often bathed in eerie light, creates the illusion of depth, confronting the traditional concept of landscape and forcing the viewer rethink the ideas of perception and space. Critic Kenneth Baker says, "To the eye, the landscape is the opposite of a panorama: spatially deep but constricted, like a peek through a door that is barely open." He continues to experiment with a metaphoric use of materials in a pictorial rendering.

RIVERA, JUDITH (Pastel Artist)
691 C. Stonehouse Dr., Napa, CA 94558

Born: 1945 *Collections:* Napa Valley Heritage Society *Exhibitions:* Oberon Gallery, Napa; William Gallery, St. Helena *Education:* Concordia U. *Dealer:* Oberon Gallery, Napa

Through fantasy images of dreams and ideas, she conveys universal emotions capable of a definite healing power. Her colors are based on a basic four-square grid of geometric line and mass compositions. He begins by making a charcoal or ink sketch on 100% rag paper. With pure-colored soft pastels, she then draws areas of color, adding detail and darker colors in layers. Finally, she adds a fixative, a process that enables her to add a certain amount of color spontaneously. She began her career as a painter, working representationally in oils. When her instructors pushed her to work more intellectually, she found that approach unsatisfying.

ROBERSON, PAMELA (Photographer)
6267 Robin Hood Way, Oakland, CA 94611

Born: 1948 *Awards:* Artist in Residency, Yosemite National Park *Collections:* Bibliotheque Nationale, Paris *Exhibitions:* California Academy of Science, San Francisco; Oakland Museum *Education:* UC-Berkeley *Dealer:* The Weston Gallery, Carmel; J. J. Brookings, San Jose

After studying art history in Paris, she taught herself photography and traveled throughout the Middle East as a freelance editorial photographer. Later, her first major series of fine art photographs, "Dunescape", featured landscapes of the Southwest using evocative, sensual colors. The completion of this series marked a brief shift to working with view cameras on murals of monumental size. Returning to a small format, her most recent series depicts environmental nudes. Set in surreal landscapes, such as granite gorges, lava beds and slot canyons, the nude forms are integrated into the landscape. Sometimes a strobe light is added to enhance the colors of the afterglow of a sunset. The work seeks to probe the line between what is familiar and what is representation.

ROBERTS, JACK (Painter)
888 Research Dr., #111, Palm Springs, CA 92262

Born: 1940 *Awards:* Cash Award, Midwest Biennial, Joslyn Art Museum, Omaha, NE *Collections:* IBM, San Jose; Irvine Corp., Newport Beach *Exhibitions:* Barbara De Vorzon Gallery, Los Angeles; Elaine Sternberg Gallery, Chicago *Education:* U of Nebraska, Omaha *Dealer:* Retrospective Gallery, La Jolla

After graduating from the University of Nebraska, he painted representational cityscapes and landscapes. This work was followed: first, by a series of abstract expressionist paintings; then, by geometric minimalist constructions using vinyl acrylic lacquer on aluminum. Following the mainstream of contemporary American art style, he moved to Denver in the 1970s. He returned to abstract expressionism, re-exploring the large canvas with confidence and experience, finding success as an "action field colorist." In 1987, he established a winter studio in Palm Springs; Los Angeles imagery now dominates his attention. In recent work, he takes the urban scene as his subject.

Lynn Falcon Reimholz, *Memorial #15,* 60 x 72, acrylic on canvas

Daphne Rockwell, *Rosa,* 10 x 8 x 8, bronze

ROBERTS, MICHELE (Painter, Printmaker)
135 Wadsworth Ave., Santa Monica, CA 90405

Born: 1954 *Awards:* Juror's Award, Works on Paper Exhibition, San Marcos, TX *Collections:* Times Mirror Co., NYC; Michael Crichton, Los Angeles *Exhibitions:* Laforet Museum, Tokyo, Japan; B-1 Gallery, Santa Monica *Education:* UC-Santa Cruz *Dealer:* Robert Berman, Santa Monica

In her figurative paintings and monoprints, she draws heavily from sources as widespread as folk art's patterned boarders, Franz Marc's expressionistic animals and Keith Haring's pictographic images. Effervescent and extroverted, her pieces give shape to inner stories and visions. Her work is simplified but not simple—a combination of personal expression, social didacticism and visual embellishment. She fills her psycho-social canvases with bold primary colors, mixing traditional painting techniques with cartooning. She often uses more than one panel and juxtaposes both obscure and straightforward titles with haunting, biting, whimsical imagery. She has recently been working on a series of monoprints.

ROBERTSON, RONALD G. (Painter, Assemblage Artist)
420 Miramonte Dr., Santa Barbara, CA 93109

Born: 1927 *Awards:* Research Grant, UC-Santa Barbara *Collections:* Korn Collection, Tokyo *Exhibitions:* Santa Barbara Museum of Art; Contemporary Arts Forum, Santa Barbara *Education:* Academie Andre Lhote, Paris; Black Mountain College, NC *Dealer:* Arpel Gallery, Santa Barbara

After formal art training, he worked as an automotive stylist, an illustrator, a teacher and an author (*Contemporary Printmaking in Japan*). He incorporates objects of all kinds—household junk, things combed from the beach, found objects, wood, paper, modeling materials—with sculpture, model-making, painting, collage and printmaking to create large, three-dimensional paintings and assemlage. Emphasizing the effects of color and texture, his works are united by a symbolism of surfaces affected by time and change and by a transformation of materials that suggests meanings below the surface. In his recent marine series, he manipulates corrosion to suggest the evolution of time and the ocean's effect on the subject matter.

ROBERTSON, VICKI (Painter)
618 N. Fortuna Blve., Fortuna, CA 95540

Awards: 1st Prize, Amateur, Ventura College *Exhibitions:* Ventura College Gallery; Old Town Gallery, Eureka

She is an impressionist painter with formal training in music and architectural engineering. Early in her career, she made jewelry, fabric, wood sculpture and rugs. Later, she studied with James Faber, whose master was Monet, and looked to the work of Van Gogh, Renoir and Monet for inspiration. She became an accomplished draftsman and colorist and worked in watercolor, encaustic, pastel, oil and ceramics. She now paints exclusively with acrylics on wood or canvas. She starts on a dark, primed surface and achieves and image that glows like a landscape seen through the facets of a diamond, "not unlike those masters of Paris 100 years ago," she says.

ROBINSON, HILDA C. (Draughtsperson)
2664 Francisco Way, El Cerrito, CA 94530

Awards: Best of Show and Purchase Prize, Museum of Science and Industry, Chicago *Exhibitions:* Berkeley Art Center; Portola Valley Arts & Crafts Show *Education:* UC-Berkeley

Having studied the classical techniques of representation and perspective, she finds her more recent work has been influenced by Impressionists such as Bonnard, Daumier and Toulouse-Lautrec. She draws with oil pastels, creating rich, vibrantly colored drawings which feature scenes of everyday life. In these drawings, she combines secular and religious influences into a new vision of Blacks in America. Recent works comprise a series of studies of the contemporary, workaday lives of Black women. Exhibiting German expressionist tendencies in color and neo-expressionist gestures in form, the three-dimensional collage works—in which the use of color is important—are a marked departure from her characteristic style. These pieces, however, continue to examine everyday life in scenes drawn from the memory, imagination and experience of the artist.

ROBINSON, SHARON (Textile Artist)
1750 Donner Dr., Santa Rosa, CA 95404

Born: 1938 *Collections:* California Polytechnic State U., San Luis Obispo *Exhibitions:* Herbst Theatre, San Francisco; Fashion Institute of Technology, NYC *Education:* California College of Arts and Crafts

A child of World War II and the Depression, she chose fiber as her medium because it was inexpensive. Her garments always relate to other cultures and times. She often adapts a pattern from an old costume and makes it her own, creating textures through the repetition of circles or lines and rich colors. Her coiled baskets are shiny, high-tech forms. She has recently worked on a series of dyed red and black baskets sewn from pine needles. All her pieces are characterized by a meticulous attention to color, texture and form.

ROBINSON, SUE ANN (Book Artist)
1129 Gaviota Ave., Long Beach, CA 90813

Born: 1946 *Awards:* Artist's Residency, Visual Studies Workshop *Exhibitions:* Irvine Fine Arts Center; Texas Woman's U., Denton *Education:* Columbia U.; U. of New Hampshire, Durham

She alters books, and makes offset printed paper constructions as well. In a special project for the 1984 Olympic Games, she took an old history book, added chapters about women and minorities and decorated the pages with collage, ribbons and tickets. Her recent *Traces of Ritual*, is an altered high school yearbook. Her paper constructions are participatory: the viewer may leave them in their flat printed form, or choose to assemble them into a geometric form. *Blue Silk Silo*, an 11-by-17-inch print, can be assembled into an 11-by-8-by-6-inch structure. Humor and themes of travel are often important to her. In her current book, *Chisolm Hours*, she explores the myth of the American cowboy.

ROCK, BONNIE (Collage Artist)
3000 Country Club Dr., Costa Mesa, CA 92626

Born: 1941 *Exhibitions:* U. of Delaware Biennial, Newark; Laguna Art Museum *Education:* Ball State U.

Marilyn Radzat, *Rise of the Firebird,* 36" tall, clay and mixed
media. Courtesy: Isis Rising Gallery, San Francisco, CA.
Photograph: A. Zidek

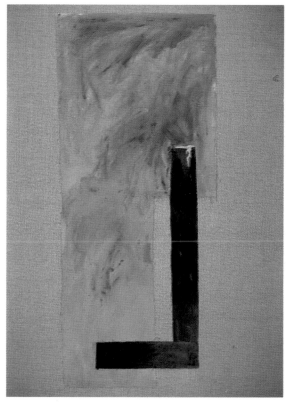

Lynn Falcon Reimholz, *Viet Nam #5,* 31 x 71, acrylic on canvas

Andrea Rogers, *101 Things to Do,* 30 x 22, prismacolor.
Photographer: Kiana Decker

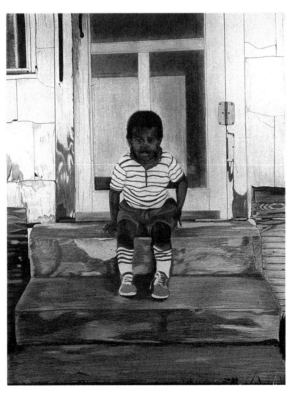

Manika Aia Rogers, *Dessie's Nephew,* 44 x 30, multimedia

Linda Rae, *Private Reflections,* 16 x 10 x 13, bronze

Ofer Rotem, *2nd Destiny Call,* 48 x 36, mixed media on masonite

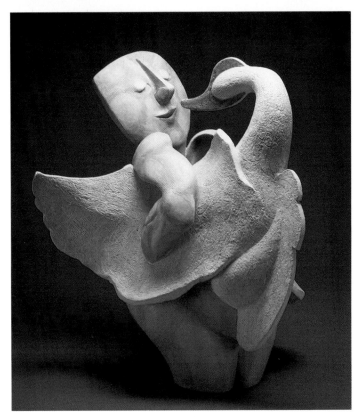

Jerry Rothman, *Leda And,* 26" high, ceramic

Larry R. Rankin, *Together,* 30 x 25 x 12, alabaster.
Courtesy: Mr. and Mrs. Howard Larson

Gene A. Register, *Red, White and Gold,* 24 x 30, oil

Roy Rydell, *Still Life #53,* 20 x 16, acrylic. Courtesy: W. & L. Trabing Collection

Robert Reynolds, *Symphony Suite: Interlude,* 35 x 24, watercolor

Bonnie Rock, *Strangled Cry,* 14 x 18, mixed media collage

Mary Jane Root, *Splash,* 73 x 61 x 2, oil and acrylic.
Courtesy: Michael Himovitz Gallery

Victor Raphael, *Rocket,* 4 x 3, gold leaf on polaroid

Dorothy Rossi, *Familia Reflected,* 46 x 48, oil on canvas

S. Rajnus, *Morning Gloria,* 22 x 22, watercolor

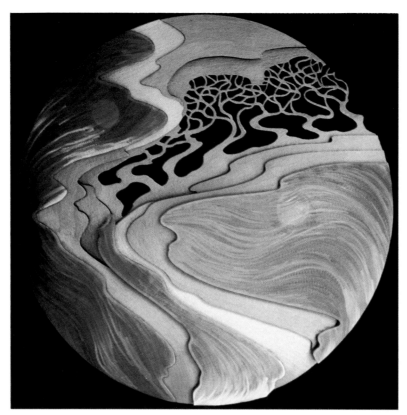

John Richen, *Winter River,* 39" diameter, steel and bronze

Natalie Reed, *Lace Against Strength—Big Sur,* 36 x 36, oil

Andrea Rich, *Golden Eagle,* 13 x 13, woodcut

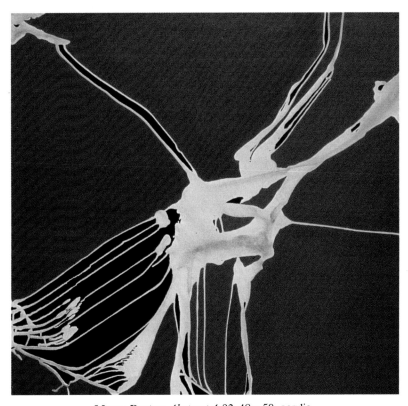

Marge Rector, *Abstract 4-82,* 48 x 50, acrylic

Ron Robertson, *The Wave Machine,* 24 x 21, assemblage.
Courtesy: Collection of Ian Morrison, AMD Inc.

Edytha Ryan, *Rattlesnake,* 12 x 12 x 18, steatite

Andrew Radcliffe, *Seascape with Bathers, 1987,* 72 x 88, oil on canvas

Jill Rosoff, *Poppies at Giverny,* 29 x 21, watercolor

Gerald Richman, *Sam's Porch,* 36 x 48, oil on canvas. Collection of Stu and Sara Cerato

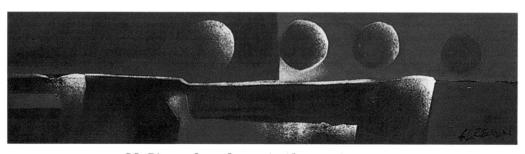

S.L. Rieman, *Lunar Images,* 4 x 15, watercolor on paper

Tom Rose, *Big Mind on Fire,* 50 x 75, cibachrome photograph

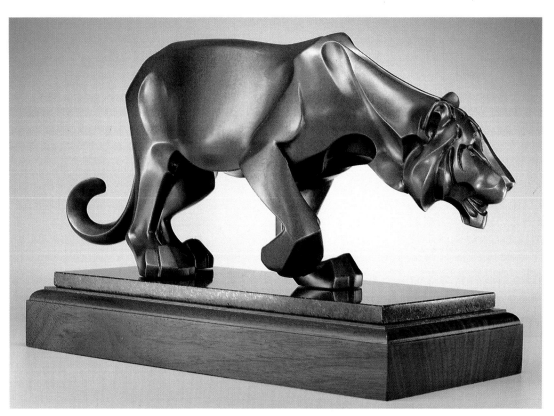

Rosetta, *Tiger,* 8 x 14 x 6, bronze. Courtesy: Runyan-Fischer Foundries, Sand City, CA.
Photograph: Mel Schockner

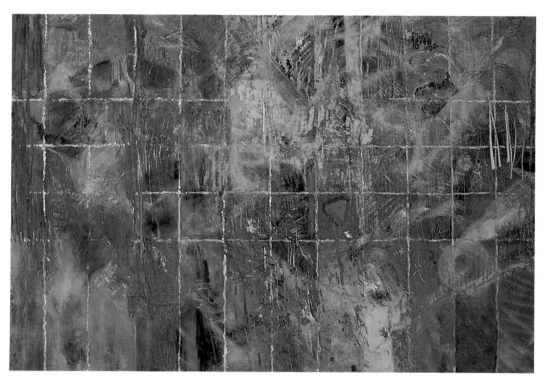

Nancy Russell, *Pyramid of the Trees,* 48 x 72, oil and wax on canvas

Keith Raddatz, *Silent Soliloquy-Timeless Stones,* 4 x 7, oil on museum board

Ramsay, *Old British Consulate,* 8 x 23, ink. Courtesy: Ramsay Galleries, Honolulu

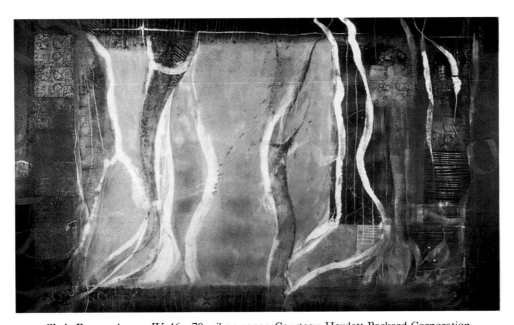

Chris Ranes, *Aegean IV,* 46 x 70, oil on paper. Courtesy: Hewlett Packard Corporation

In the early 1980s, she studied experimental painting with Donna Sharkey. She became influenced by Joseph Cornell's intimately private art in boxes, and began creating her own intimate tableaus, on the theme of sorrow in human relationships. She assembles small and miniature (5 by 7 inches to 1 1/2 by 2 inches) mixed-media collages, from multiple layers of photo fragments, gold-leaf fibers, bits of costume jewelry, acrylic paint and scraps of paper from the 1930s and 1940s. In her miniature handmade books of graveyard art (one of which is titled *Ici repose*), she used photos of artist's tombstones as a basis for a one-of-a-kind, mixed-media collage. All of the grave sites are photographed in European cemeteries.

ROCKWELL, DAPHNE (Sculptor)
107 Papermill Creek, Novato, CA 94949

Born: 1919 *Awards:* The Burgess Insurance Award, North American Sculpture Exhibition, Golden, CO *Exhibitions:* San Francisco Arts Commission Exhibition of Sculpture; Marin Society of Artists Open Fine Arts Exhibition *Education:* Mills College; College of Marin; Escuela Nacional de Pintura y Escultura, La Esmeralda, Mexico

She was born in Mexico. Her portrait sculpture has been influenced by the powerful imagery of Mexican Pre-Columbian art, her studies with Franciso Zuniga and the dynamic Mexican art movements of the 1940s and 1950s. In Marin County, where she now resides, she enjoys the continual challenge of capturing in bronze the portraits of California's diverse ethnic population. Her many commissioned portraits and figures aim to express clarity and simplicity in bronze.

ROD, BRUCE (Sculptor)
2020 N. Main, #220, Los Angeles, CA 90031

Born: 1947 *Awards:* Artist in Residence Grant, Roswell Museum and Art Center, NM; Visual Arts Fellowship in Sculpture, Arizona Commission on the Arts *Collections:* Springfield Art Museum, MS; Roswell Art Museum, NM *Education:* Moorhead State U.; U. of Wisconsin, Madison *Dealers:* Simard/Halm Gallery, Los Angeles; Ivory/Kimpton Gallery, San Francisco

As a student, he used unpainted wood as his primary sculptural medium. He also painted a series of large flat canvases, often depicting animals in unusual situations. His recent painted sculptures are strongly influenced by a minimalist tradition of space definition and object arrangement. These pieces contain references to folk and arts and craft traditions, and at the same time, emphasize the artist's individuality and eccentricity of compositions. His recent series of Asian-influenced wall pieces have a strong graphic quality. They are very contemporary looking, and, in an understated way, they suggest the recognizable objects that their very structure defeats.

RODGER, BETTY (Painter, Sculptor)
Star Rte. 42, #3190, Mountain Springs, NV 89124

Born: 1957 *Collections:* Davis, Johnson, Mongul, and Colombatto, Inc., Los Angeles *Exhibitions:* The Works Gallery, Long Beach *Education:* U. of Hawaii; Otis Institute *Dealer:* The Works Gallery, Long Beach

She considers herself a visionary artist. She creates images which communicate a sense of peace and unity to the viewer. She believes that the symbols she uses help to create a link between the individual subconscious and the universal spiritual realm. Her paintings feature abstract images of floating with a backdrop of sea, sky or cosmological space. She works on Masonite panels treated with twenty to thirty coats of gesso. She blends her own paint of raw pigment mixed with gum binder, keeping the colors intense in a somewhat watery consistency. Her limited palette features red, blue and yellow in conjunction with black, white or gold leaf. Sprayed onto the prepared surface, the paint's application produces a feathery soft, atmospheric appearance. She also sculpts pieces out of lightweight polyurethane foam. Prepared with gesso and painted in black, white or gold leaf, the sculptures are often suspended from the ceiling. In exhibitions, she often combines sculptures and paintings to create a coordinated environment.

RODINI-HARTMAN, ARLINE (Painter, Printmaker)
235 Water St., Point Richmond, CA 94801

Born: 1936 *Awards:* 2nd Prize, California State Fair *Exhibitions:* California State Fair; Oakland Museum *Education:* UC-Berkeley

Continuing in the plastic space tradition of Hans Hoffman, Franz Kline, Willem de Kooning and Mark Rothko, her early paintings, prints and sculptures were abstract with hints of figures and landscapes. She was particularly drawn to old, broken-down buildings. Rauschenberg influenced her to go beyond the canvas and to use fabric in her painting. She made collage paintings, using old-paint rags in an abstract and occasionally geometric ways. Her welded-steel sculptures of the time were melted, linear, rhythmic, sometimes allegorical forms in space. The quick and spontaneous linear quality of her recent wood-block prints suggests representational figurative and landscape forms.

ROGERS, ANDREA (Printmaker)
8401 E. Crestwood Way., Scottsdale, AZ 85253

Born: 1947 *Awards:* Grant, Alpha Delta Kappa, Kansas City, MO *Collections:* Melvin Hellwitz; O'Connor, Cavanaugh, Anderson, Westover, Kinningworth and Beshears, PA *Exhibitions:* Kerr Cultural Center, Scottsdale, AZ; Rotunda Gallery, U. of Arizona *Education:* Northern Arizona U. *Dealer:* Canyons Gallery, Palm Springs

Influenced by printmakers of the past, particularly Toulouse Lautrec and the satirists (Goya, Daumier, etc.), her work also involves painting (acrylic) and drawing (mixed-media). Her intaglio work encompasses all techniques: line etch, aquatint, flat bite, etc. Her previous work was based on contemporary womankind and included pieces like *Barbie Dreams of Genie*, a mixed-media comment on housework and expectations for women. Since 1985 she has satirized "Western Art." "Having grown up in Arizona I know what has happened to the Old West," she says. Her drawings, paintings and etchings, such as *Ghost of The Golden West*, *Uncle Slim Becomes a Souvenir* and *The Outlaws*, all depict horse and cow skulls in various poses. Recent work is spiritual and lyrical in theme. Paintings such as *DayBreak*, and *Tree of Divine Knowledge* are influenced by the Baha'i faith and represent man's return to God, his maker. She recently began a suite of fifteen etchings, with hand decorated frames, portraying a mermaid and her companions on a spiritual quest.

ROGERS, ART (Photographer)
P.O. Box 777, Point Reyes, CA 94956

Born: 1948 *Awards:* Guggenheim Fellowship; SECA Recipient, San Francisco Museum of Modern Art *Collections:* San Francisco Museum of Art; Center for Creative Photography, U. of Arizona, Tucson *Exhibitions:* San Francisco Museum of Modern Art; Focus Gallery, San Francisco *Education:* San Francisco Art Institute

A commercially successful San Francisco photographer, he moved to Point Reyes, California in 1971 to pursue more personal work. His documentation of the area in the black-and-white "Point Reyes Family Album" has been printed in the local weekly newspaper, *The Point Reyes Light,* for fourteen of the last seventeen years. His early pictures were taken with a 35mm camera. Most of his images are now made with a Pentax 6-by-7, and he is currently working on a series of contact prints made from an 11-by-14-inch view camera. He prefers Afga Portriga for skin tones and likes the stability of Cibachromes. He exposes and develops film using the principles of a modified zone system. He continues to work commercially in the Point Reyes area.

ROGERS, MANIKA AIA (Painter, Draughtsperson)
Summer Storms Knoll, 14415 Clymar Ave., Compton CA 90220

Born: 1959 *Awards:* Bank of America Achievement in Community Art Award; Ahmasnson Foundation Scholarship *Exhibitions:* Lindhurst Gallery, USC *Education:* Marymount Palos Berdes College; USC

With the exploratory theories and techniques she learned from contemporary masters in college, she was able to enhance her style and cultivate her ideas in order to communicate non- verbally, through color and design. She uses combinations of prismacolors, gouache, conte, transparent watercolor and charcoal to enliven her oil and acrylic paintings. With this wide range of colors, she interprets nature's environmental landscapes and other atmospheric attitudes. As she captures the perfect and imperfect balance of nature at any specific moment, she reveals universal physical and non-physical conditions—social and personal attitudes, emotions and expectations. *Dessie's Nephew*, for example, is not an urban child, but a country boy, comfortable with his life style and environment: his family, the purity of the atmosphere and the free reign given his imagination.

ROKEACH, BARRIE (Photographer)
499 Vermont Ave., Berkeley, CA 94707

Born: 1947 *Collections:* Oakland Museum of Natural History; Bank of America, San Francisco *Exhibitions:* Syntex Gallery, Palo Alto; Municipal Art Gallery, Los Angeles *Education:* UC-Berkeley *Dealer:* Mark Levinson, San Francisco

He is best known for abstract aerial photographs. He shoots in color and in black and white, using classical photographic techniques. Prints are enlarged to emphasize the formal or geometric visual qualities of natural and civilized land. In this way, he challenges the viewer's conventional notions of landscape.

ROLDAN, JOHANNA RUDJEN (Painter)
40 Forest Grove Dr., Daly City, CA 94015

Born: 1963 *Exhibitions:* Annual Spring Show, San Francisco Art Institute; Diego Rivera Gallery, San Francisco *Education:* San Francisco Art Institute

Her work has been influenced by Leon Kossof, Lucien Freud and Max Beckman. Working in oil paint on canvas, she starts with a thick layer of residue from solvent/brush cleaner. She carves figures and images by moving around, scraping off and adding more sludge, as well as fresh oil paint and hot wax. The sculptural, bas relief appearance is the result of generations of paint combined with chalk dust and sand. Her works are characterized by the presence of distorted human figures or parts of figures, especially hands and feet. Sometimes figures appear blindfolded with clothing or in the process of removing their bandages and blindfolds. Naked men, women and children appear in different groups, some playing in a tree or sharing masks or in the process of departing. All figures are bald and appear quite vulnerable; all express a touching tenderness and expressive pathos, communicating a longing for a sense of family and community.

ROLL-PREISSLER, AUDREY (Painter, Multimedia Artist)
P.O. Box 7532, Jackson, WY 83001

Born: 1932 *Awards:* Wyoming Governor's Award *Collections:* UNICEF, NYC; Ford Motor Company Executive Art Collection, Dearborn, MI *Exhibitions:* Palm Springs Museum; Whitney Gallery of Contemporary Western Art, Cody, WY *Dealer:* Inkfish Gallery, Denver; Main Trail Gallery, Jackson, WY

She is best known for her satiric, figurative plywood cut-outs. Her art is the result of a keen observation of urban and rural life. Executed in vibrant swirls of acrylic, her works are spirited and broad-brushed in style. The cut-out motif is used as a shaped picture plane that combines satirical humor and artful lines and colors. Starting from small drawings and paintings, the work progresses to jig-sawing. The cut-outs poke fun at convention and pomposity wherever she finds it.

ROLOFF, JOHN (Sculptor)
2020 Livingston St., Oakland, CA 94606

Born: 1947 *Awards:* Award, Guggenheim Foundation; NEA Fellowship *Collections:* San Francisco Museum of Modern Art; Oakland Museum *Exhibitions:* Whitney Museum, NYC; San Francisco Museum of Modern Art *Education:* UC-Davis; Cal. State-Humboldt *Dealer:* Fuller Goldeen Gallery, San Francisco

His early works are primarily clay objects that emphasize landscape and process—geology studies in college naturally allied with his ceramic interests. The ship as a symbol of personal voyage and transformation has been a recurring theme in his art. Recently, he has done "site" works of fired ceramic structures. Incorporated within the fired elements are living plants trained over shaped trellises. The images are often ship forms, although floral and botanical images may occur. In these later works, his interests in process, landscape and nature are operating on a larger scale.

Rachel Rosenthal, *L.O.W. in Gaia,* performance. Photographer: Jan Deen

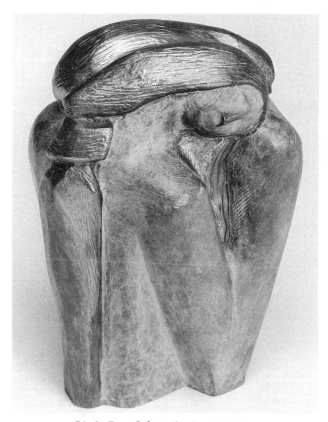

Linda Rae, *Solace,* 6 x 4 x 4, bronze

ROMANO, MIRIAM ALBA (Painter, Draughtsperson)
1054 E. Terrace Dr., Hanford, CA 93230

Born: 1950 *Exhibitions:* College of the Sequoias Theatre Gallery, Visalia; Metropolitan Museum, Fresno *Education:* U. of Rosario, Argentina

After formal training in expressionist painting, she developed an individual figurative expressionistic style influenced by Escher's work. In her "Mnemonic" collection, she used pen and ink to wrangle with questions of art as a reaction to memory. In 1981, she became interested in surrealist form and continued to execute her work in pen and ink and oil paints. She then began to focus on the expression of contemporary subjects using glazes and layering. In her recent "political surrealist" work, she brings surrealist writings and collage effects together into complex detailed compositions.

ROOT, MARY JANE (Painter)
P.O. Box 277151, Sacramento, CA 95826

Born: 1938 *Awards:* Nominated for Woman of Achievement Award, California Federation of Business and Professional Women's Clubs *Exhibitions:* Himovitz/Salomon Gallery, Sacramento; Lincoln Plaza Gallery, Sacramento *Education:* Cal. State-Sacramento; San Jose State University *Dealer:* Michael Himovitz, Sacramento

After exploring various forms of realism, including portraiture and small easel painting, she began in 1978 to explore the styles of the Surrealists and Abstract Expressionists, including Miro and Jackson Pollock. Eventually, she developed an unconscious method of painting large color fields using acrylic on large canvases. Recently, she has begun to convey natural geographic and geophysical phenomena with oil, acrylic and texture paste. The works are heavily laden with textural outbursts of color, and the separated canvases she uses add a linear as well as sculptural dimension. The pieces emit dignity and power.

ROSE, ARLETTE (GOSIESKI) (Folk Artist)
Box 370, Englewood, CO 80151

Born: 1941 *Awards:* White House Easter Celebration *Collections:* Denver Art Museum; Craft and Folk Art Museum, Los Angeles *Exhibitions:* Saks Gallery, Denver; Gilman Galleries, Chicago *Education:* Art Center College of Design; L'Ecole de Dessin Applique a la Mode, Paris

Although she recently began painting with oils, she is best known for her fabric work, which she calls "applique tapestry." She is a pioneer in rediscovering the traditional skill of applique (a form of quilting): using as many as 450 different fabrics for one tapestry, she designs intricate forms of collage by juxtaposing, overlapping and assembling cut forms; the final work is secured with a web of stitchery, not glue. In this way, she has foregone the use of shade, shadow and line and has instead developed textural and pattern integrations. She draws inspiration from Grant Wood, Currier & Ives, Grandma Moses, Modigliani and Mary Cassatt.

ROSE, TOM (Painter)
4053 Harlan St., #310, Emeryville, CA 94608

Born: 1960 *Awards:* Honorable Mention, Los Angeles County Museum; Honorable Mention, Pacific Grove Art Center *Exhibitions:* Gallerie Michael, Beverly Hills; Riskin Sinow, San Francisco, Los Angeles

Education: UCLA; UC-Berkeley *Dealer:* Gallerie Michael, Beverly Hills

An initial interest in surrealist artists Dali, Miro and Max Ernst contributed to wild, lugubrious landscapes populated with imaginary creatures. A later push into a more concrete, abstract vision along Kandinsky's lines developed conceptual focus, when he began working in mixed media. Photographic and textural collage added new dimensions to his use of minute detail to create presence and volume. Symbols of nature, architecture and art history have also brought a philosophical intensity to his work, as fragments of collage that serve to bridge style and content within a strongly implied narrative. This has allowed him to organize and codify both meaning and formal surface relationships into a comprehensive whole. Recent work uses Cibachrome color photography to create composite and montage reinterpretations and to focus on and exploit key areas of his paintings. A 6-inch square of painted detail, for example, may be expanded into an image 6-feet-square. Some work is reproduced onto stained glass-like transparency material, thus removing it from the canvas and into the realm of photography and light.

ROSEN, JAMES MAHLON (Painter)
513 Benton St., Santa Rosa, CA 95404

Born: 1933 *Awards:* NEH Grant; Artist in Residence, Ferrara, Italy *Collections:* Museum of Modern Art, NYC; Victoria and Albert Museum, London *Exhibitions:* Betty Parsons Gallery, NYC; San Diego Museum of Art *Education:* Cooper Union; Cranbrook Institute of Art; Wayne State U.

His oil and watercolor paintings draw from minimalism for many of their techniques, developing a kind of minimalist, sometimes almost subliminalist, impressionism hovering on the threshold of vision. His paintings allow the viewer to reconstruct for themselves the forms and associations—psychological, historical, cultural, spiritual—that he has distilled within the work. Very often, themes of his paintings are taken from other art—for example, "after Grunewald and Goya".

ROSENFELD, HOWARD (Photographer)
746 S. Plymouth Blvd., Los Angeles, CA 90005

Born: 1932 *Awards:* La Mirada Festival of Art, La Mirada, CA; Honorable Mention, Annual Juried Show, San Diego Art Institute *Collections:* U.S. State Department; Northrop Corporation *Exhibitions:* New York U.; Museum of Science and Industry, Los Angeles *Education:* Illinois Institute of Technology *Dealer:* Ruth Bachofner, Los Angeles; Barbara Tamerin, NYC

He studied art with Paul Weighart and visual training/art history with Walter Peterhans; at the Institute of Design, he studied photography with Harry Callahan and Aaron Siskind. Influences include the work of Edward Weston, Paul Strand and others from the "Sharp-Image" school. He has worked in formats of all sizes and in both black-and-white and color, exploring the abstract and linear subjects found particularly in the urban landscape. His recent work is in a medium-sized format and primarily in color. An essentially romantic and abstract view of the universe informs his photos, and his range of subjects has expanded to include rural and natural landscapes. His exposure techniques block in colors strongly. A series entitled "Geometrix" responds to the image's linear and geometric character: He captures subjects at such

Gloria Ross, *Andromeda #I,* 24 x 30, mixed media, Courtesy: Select Art, Dallas, TX

Andrea Rich, *Fox,* 6 x 11, woodcut

Bonnie Rock, *The She in He,* 4 x 5, mixed media collage

close range that the original image disappears, the remaining geometry merely hinting at what was.

ROSENTHAL, RACHEL (Performance Artist)
2847 S. Robertson, Los Angeles, CA 90034

Born: 1926 *Awards:* Vesta Award; Obie Award *Exhibitions:* Los Angeles Festival; Documenta 8, Los Angeles

Influenced by Antonin Artaud's theories, as well as by the work of John Cage and Merce Cunningham, she was director and performer of Los Angeles' Instant Theatre for ten years. From 1975 to 1981, her performance pieces were strongly autobiographical. Since 1981, she has dealt more forcefully with issues, such as the environment, nuclear proliferation, animal rights, toxic waste, aging and sexism. Nevertheless, her work remains theatrical and entertaining. She reaches her audience on many levels; text, compositional strategies, audio-visual support and the use of multiple personae all figure into her performance work.

ROSENWASSER, SY (Sculptor)
1260 15th St., No. 1212, Santa Monica, CA 90404

Born: 1925 *Exhibitions:* Los Angeles Art Expo; Shidoni Bronze Gallery, Tesuque, NM

His work in sculpture reflects the relationship of basic masses to life forms. The use of bone structure as the underpinning for the stability of organic shapes reflects his admiration for the figures of Henry Moore. He currently works with large environmental pieces. These are covered with a transparent brown- gold or blue-green patina which is warm and invites the viewer's touch.

ROSETTA (Sculptor)
P.O. Box 467, Woodacre, CA 94973

Born: 1945 *Awards:* Chilmark Award, National Sculpture Society *Collections:* Roar Foundation, Los Angeles *Exhibitions:* North American Sculpture Exhibition; National Sculpture Society, NYC *Education:* U. of Delaware; Art Center College of Design *Dealer:* Runyon-Fischer Foundries

She moved from early pencil portraiture to producing clay busts, out of desire to translate the "grace and flow of line into the three-dimensional." After initially working toward realistic sculpture, she refined her style to reflect ideal images, gaining power through simplification. This evolution occurred largely as a result of her years spent as a graphic designer. She later moved to bronze as the medium for her works, for its permanence. Recently, she has focused on small sculptures of great cats, capturing the monumental power of the animals on a small scale.

ROSOFF, JILL (Painter)
35189 Beach Rd., Capistrano Beach, CA 92624

Born: 1956 *Collections:* Guenoc Winery, Middletown; Fidelity Federal Savings and Loan, Los Angeles *Exhibitions:* Paramount Studios, Los Angeles; Allen Edwards, Beverly Hills *Education:* UC-Berkeley *Dealer:* Hank Baum Gallery, San Francisco; The Business of Art, Los Angeles

She studied with Joan Brown and Elmer Bischoff, concentrating on figurative painting; she worked primarily with oils, and experimented with other media, until she settled on watercolor as her medium of choice. These early paintings were devoted to developing technique, and exploring the possibilities of color. After a long series of small, intimate still lifes, she has moved into larger formats, usually 22-by-30-inches or 40-by-60-inches. Her subjects include bright floral studies, studies of space and architectural detail and transitions from light to shadow. Her naturalistic paintings display an adept color sense, which is communicated through a variety of techniques including patterning, washes and layering.

ROSS, CHERESE (Painter)
P.O. Box 674, Paso Robles, CA 93446

Born: 1951 *Awards:* 3rd Place, Painting, San Luis Obispo County Fair *Collections:* Dr. Martin Luther King Hospital, Los Angeles *Exhibitions:* Art a la Carte, Los Angeles; A.S.I., San Francisco *Education:* UCLA

She began her career by painting abstracts and landscapes, and later she studied art and design at U.C.L.A. before taking a break to begin a family. Today, she paints brightly colored watercolor landscapes and sometimes experiments with gouache and oil paints. She has also been known to paint geometric abstractions. Recent work includes Wild West scenes that were executed on the windows of several local banks during the Paso Robles State Fair. She has been influenced by Lautrec, O'Keeffe, Gauguin and the Impressionists.

ROSS, GLORIA (Painter)
2408 Rockbrook Ct., Plano, TX 75074

Born: 1943 *Awards:* Cash Award, Visions of Ourselves *Collections:* Greater Northern Telecom, Richardson, TX; Environmental Protection Agency, Washington, D.C. *Exhibitions:* Zaner Gallery, Rochester, NY; San Jacinto Gallery, Dallas *Dealer:* Select Art, Dallas

With formal training in sculpture, she developed an individual expressive sculptural style influenced by the work of Henry Moore and primitive African sculpture. Her current works are predominately large-scale paintings and monoprints with themes ranging from expressive, archaic imagery to sophisticated color studies. The latter combine simple geometric forms with large areas of radiating color that often seem to float in an atmospheric ground of shifting hue and value. These combinations of rich and subtle colors juxtaposed with geometric forms create a sense of depth and provide the viewer with an opportunity to experience color on a sensuous and physical level. Her influences also include Bonnard, Rothko and Diebenkorn.

ROSSI, DOROTHY M. (Painter)
831-45th Ave., San Francisco, CA 94121

Born: 1932 *Exhibitions:* Underglass Gallery; San Francisco Women Artist *Education:* Art Students League *Dealer:* San Francisco Women Artist

She began studying art at the age of twelve and was greatly influenced during the early part of her education by the abstract movement. In the course of her development as an artist, she has experimented with many different expressions and styles. Her primary concern is with the psyche of the dream world, and her paintings clearly reflect her strong interest in the occult, the psychology of dreams and mythology. In her work, she attempts to capture that which links the day world with dream consciousness by reanimating dream images against psychological and mythological backgrounds. She has produced also produced prints and sculpture.

Jill Rosoff, *Up from the Street, Firenze,* 22 x 30, watercolor

Dorothy Rossi, *Refirmament of Venus,* 46 x 65, oil on canvas

ROTEM, OFER (Painter)
3868 Coolidge Ave., Oakland, CA 94602

Born: 1953 *Awards:* Scholarship, Israel-American Cultural Foundation *Collections:* Indigo Research Inc., Rehovot, Israel; Hasneh Insurance Co., Tel Aviv *Exhibitions:* Minx Gallery, San Francisco; Lawson Galleries, San Francisco *Education:* Bezalel Academy of Art and Design, Jerusalem

In 1968, he began painting abstractly: he dripped, spilled and splashed paint on canvas or plywood, occasionally incorporating found objects or figurative drawings into the work. Since 1973, he has employed various techniques to make figurative, drawings and paintings. Currently, he sprays, brushes and occasionally drips paint on canvas or masonite. His images are figures, mostly women. They are at once sensual and spiritual and, because of his minimal use of illusionistic space and light, they seem to exist more on the surface of the painting than in it. Working with layers of paint and texture, he achieves a sense of real depth and tactile energy. Of contemporary painters, he admires Francis Bacon, Lucian Freud and Hans Belmer.

ROTER, JOSEPH (Painter)
848 Descanso Way, San Rafael, CA 94903

Born: 1931 *Collections:* American Ergonomics, Sausalito *Exhibitions:* Laguna Honda Hospital, San Francisco; Hillside Manor Convalescent Hospital, San Rafael *Education:* School of Visual Arts, NYC

A professional commercial graphic artist and fine art painter, and the owner of his own commercial graphic and fine art service, he has invented "Rainbow Art™," a new method of visualization which promotes and encourages mental and physical well being. He also makes "Corporate Theme Art™," which consists of custom geometric or free form paintings and graphics that businesses use to promote corporate identity. These works are made in shaped, interlocking adjustable units which can be rearranged at the owner's discretion. Roter's colors are luminous and iridescent, in acrylic, oil, casein and pastel.

ROTH, MARY K. (Photographer)
2440 S. Barrington Ave., #113, W. Los Angeles, CA 90064

Born: 1954 *Awards:* Merit Award, Art Quest; Purchase Award, Galleries Elect *Collections:* U. of Wisconsin, Eau Claire *Exhibitions:* Galleries Elect, NYC; Site Gallery, W. Los Angeles City Hall *Education:* U. of Illinois, Champaign/Urbana

Early photos were a tool in graphic design. After moving to California in 1976, she began exploring landscapes and pop images. Influenced by Warhol, Sandy Skoglund, William Wegman and the Surrealists, her early 16-by-20-inch black-and-white prints were painted over with oils. As her work progressed, colors became more intense. This technique of handpainting the print allows her to take natural images, such as animals or landscapes, and make them surreal. Programmatic pop architecture of California has been another source of subject matter. She has recently been working on a series of Southwestern landscapes.

ROTHMAN, JERRY (Ceramicist)
20442 Sun Valley Dr., Laguna Beach, CA 92651

Born: 1933 *Awards:* NEA Fellowship *Collections:* Victoria and Albert Museum, London; Museum of Modern Art, Tokyo, Japan *Exhibitions:* Municipal Art Gallery, Los Angeles; Los Angeles County Museum of Art *Education:* Los Angeles City College; Los Angeles County Art Institute *Dealer:* Louis Newman, Beverly Hills

The term "Bauhaus-Baroque," coined by the artist, expresses the tension between intellectual formalism and the organic extravagance implicit in his work with ceramics. His art education at Los Angeles City College introduced him to both the conventions of classic art and quasi-bauhaus beliefs which undermined them, and two years in Japan as a sculptural designer contributed greatly to the urgent sensuality that has since characterized his style. He later experimented with unusually large dimensions for clay, overcoming many of the medium's limitations by developing a shrink-free clay which allowed him to strengthen forms with metal. Always challenging assumptions about ceramics, he maintains that the "inherent quality" of a material is limited by only what an artist can visualize and extract. Even his bicentennial soup tureens reject their own purist forms with indulgent ornaments that recall an extreme sense of the baroque. And his more recent series of lidded vessels assault stylistic orthodoxy with their suggestive imagery.

ROTHSTEIN, MARJORIE HOPE (Sculptor)
1155 N. La Cienega Blvd., Los Angeles, CA 90048

Born: 1952 *Awards:* 1st Prizes, Mixed Media and Sculpture, Juried Exhibition, Great Neck Public Library, NY *Collections:* GTE, Los Angeles; Twentieth Century Fox Studios, Los Angeles *Exhibitions:* Couturier Gallery, Los Angeles; Pacific Design Center, Los Angeles *Education:* Boston U.; New York U.

She is best known for organic, rounded, biomorphic sculptures in stone, metal and fiberglass. After years of training in fine arts and design, she became passionate about monumental art and the need to incorporate it within an architectural context. With the use of color as a major factor in more recent puzzle shapes, she is re-examining different materials, including resin, cast paper and paint. She prefers jewel-toned surfaces, which appear to have been evolving for centuries, emanating from a metallic undertone. She strongly believes that appropriately designed art helps keep people alive and well in a corporate environment.

ROWELL, JANICE (Ceramist, Jeweler)
P.O. Box 876, Pacifica, CA 94044

Born: 1950 *Collections:* Arizona State University Art Museum *Exhibitions:* Arizona State University Art Museum; Long Beach Museum of Art

Among the first in the country to raku porcelain rather than stoneware, she became known for her open and bottle-neck vases, onto which are fired patterns of earth tones such as bronze, rust and deep green. Using a natural fiber brush, she adds effects of smoke and resin to the surfaces. In recent years, she has also begun work on a series of small sculptures of women on acrylic altarpieces. Frequently the sculptures come in groups of three, in which the figures represent concepts of id, ego and superego or work, rest and dance. The pieces may be thrown, cast and hand-fabricated. In addition to the sculptures and vessels, she creates jewelry using acrylic clay.

ROYAL, REBECCA (Painter)
10330 Bodega Highway, Sebastopol, CA 95472

Born: 1945 *Collections:* Music Library, Western Washington U.; Children's Hospital, Los Angeles *Ex-*

Jack Reilly, *Counter Point,* 52 x 64, acrylic and mixed media on layered shaped canvases.
Courtesy: Merging One Gallery, Santa Monica

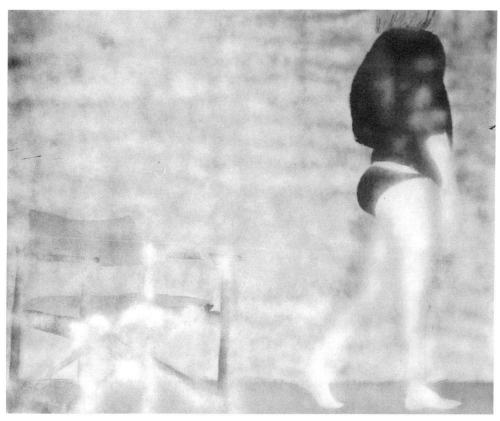

Ofer Rotem, *Failure Fallout,* 48 x 60, mixed media on masonite

Marge Rector, *Abstract 75-6,* 40 x 40, acrylic

Jerry Rothman, *Coming Out #2,* 38" high, ceramic

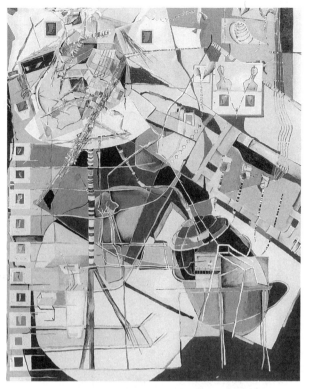

Tom Rose, *Familiar Mutations,* 50 x 40, acrylic on canvas

Mary Jane Root, *Halley's Comet,* 49 x 61 x 2, oil and acrylic.
Courtesy: Michael Himovitz Gallery

Gerald Richman, *Beginnings,* 48 x 72, oil on canvas with tape

Cheresé Ross, *Fragile Ride on Road from Past,* 12 x 18, watercolor

Andrew Radcliffe, *Cityscape,* 28 x 36, oil on canvas

Nancy Russell, *Cosmic Harmonies,* 36 x 72, oil on canvas

hibitions: Mill Gallery; Artrails West, Sebastopal *Education:* Cal. State-San Pedro; Western Washington U.

She has been influenced by the works of surrealist, abstract and experimental artists, and has therefore developed several modes of artistic expression. In one, she juxtaposes representations of psychological states with recognizable objects in rooms or fields. These large-scale works are characterized by dense groupings of figures and a thinly painted surface. Or, working in a slightly different idiom, she uses folded pieces of paper as design elements in purely abstract paintings. She works with a brush and palette knife using a muted palette, which includes flesh, okra, yellow, crimson, green and violet. In recent work, which synthesizes ideas from psychology and mythology, she paints exclusively with brushes to create the illusion of deep space accented with touches of color.

ROYLANCE, LYNN (Painter, Sculptor)
Rt. 9, P.O. Box 70, Santa Fe, NM 87505

Born: 1943 *Collections:* MGM, Los Angeles; Executive Life Insurance, Los Angeles *Exhibitions:* Oranges/Sardines Gallery, Los Angeles; LAART Gallery, NYC *Education:* California Institute of the Arts

After graduating from the California Institute of the Arts, he became interested in the subtleties of feeling that could be evoked by the use of light. Influenced by the work of Monet, Robert Irwin, Jules Olitski and Keith Sonnier, he began working with neon light cast in polyester resin. Placed in the corner of a room, a piece creates an entire light environment; as a wall or floor installation, it produces a more focused color. Recent work is "concerned with the layers that make up reality." To this end, he uses a variety of materials—wood, pigmented plaster, metal, paint, stone, glass—to produce works ranging from the simple house form to paintings and wall sculptures. In all of these, there is a layering of materials and then a scraping or grinding of selected areas to expose abstract patterns in the layers beneath. The intent is to involve the viewer in the layers and patterns that constitute the whole.

RUBIN, DOROTHY M. (Painter)
1170 Sterling Ave., Berkeley, CA 94708

Born: 1927 *Exhibitions:* Jadah Magnes Museum; UC-Berkeley

She is a self-taught artist with no formal art training. She considers herself a colorist and most of her figurative paintings convey messages related to religion, politics or science. She applies heavy layers of acrylic medium to the canvas with palette knife or sometimes with brush. Her work shows a concern with the processes and her brushstrokes can be seen clearly on the canvas. Her recent series, "Places of Power," is a Freudian study of Abraham's tomb. She is also producing abstractions of the bubble chamber.

RUIZ, DANIEL (Painter)
7352 Vista del Monte, #6, Van Nuys, CA 91405

Born: 1961 *Collections:* Cedar-Sinai Medical Center, Los Angeles *Exhibitions:* Otis/Parsons Rampart Building, Los Angeles; Villa Montezuma, San Diego *Education:* Otis Art Institute

In his early work, he used charcoal on paper, rubbing some areas away and drawing on top of them. The combinations of lines and shapes in these works are echoed in later compositions. Working in charcoal and

pastel on 26-by-40-inch paper, he first sketches the figures and backgrounds, then colors them with pastels. This technique is used in his recent "Street Scene" series, which features large abstract figures and architectural backgrounds. With the repeated shapes and lines, the works have the appearance of a puzzle that was crudely put together. He cites abstract expressionist Willem de Kooning and the Ocean Park paintings of Richard Diebenkorn as major influences.

RUMOHR, LOIS E. (Painter, Sculptor)
240 Renoak Way, Arcadia CA 91006

Born: 1922 *Awards:* Death Valley Invitational Art Show; Cowgirl Hall of Fame, Hereford, TX *Collections:* Art Center College of Design; Death Valley Museum *Exhibitions:* Death Valley Invitational; Raeburn House Gallery, Palm Springs *Education:* Art Center College of Design

Her exploration of the reservation areas in the 1970s inspired her work as a sculptor and painter. Bronzes and pastel and pencil drawings depict the Indian cultures and pioneer figures of early California. These are based on an extensive study of anatomy, armature, patina, mold making and the lost wax process, and are influenced by her appreciation of the work of Malvina Hoffman. The lifelike Apache, Navajo and Pueblo Indian bronzes derive from experience and have a deeply personal authenticity. Her drawings detail the more spiritual elements of American Indian culture and a historical presentation of the American West. Photo-realistic renderings of figures and portraits range in value from very light to very dark in a single piece, capturing the intensity of light and of the way of life in the Old West. These western studies, such as *Old Crump*, are drawn from in-depth research on historical materials, rather than more romantic interpretations. Her original works are modeled in crystalline wax and cast in bronze, then given a chemical patina.

RUMPEL, HELEN J. (Fiber Artist)
320 Cadiz Rd., Santa Fe, NM 87501

Born: 1937 *Collections:* Kresge Art Museum; Sheldon Museum, Lincoln, NE *Exhibitions:* Art Institute of Chicago; Spaso House, American Embassy, Moscow *Education:* Stephens College; U. of Wisconsin *Dealer:* Baker Fine Art Gallery, Lubbock, TX

She is a contemporary fine art stitchery artist and a symbolic expressionist. She began embroidering when her two sons were young, making toys and decorating clothes. She went on to study extensively stitchery under Danish and English tutors. She has since traveled widely in Yugoslavia, Greece, Turkey and the Soviet Union where she assimilated techniques and discovered new imagery. Her current imagery is a mixture of Byzantine and New Mexican influence. Her pieces have a mystical enchantment about them and are rich in color and texture. Her 1988 exhibit, "Images and Ikons" at the American embassy in Moscow was timed to coincide with the millenium of the Russian acceptance of Byzantine religion and art. To her, needle expressions are messages in symbols of love.

RUNSTADLER, KURT (Sculptor)
4625 Ravenwood Ave., Sacramento, CA 95821

Born: 1955 *Awards:* Best of Show, Beverly Hills Affair *Collections:* Corning Museum; Saks Fifth Ave. *Exhibitions:* David Bernstein Gallery; Holsten Gallery, Ft. Lauderdale

Helen J. Rumpel, *Kachina's Two,* 20 x 18, creative stitchery.
Courtesy: Baker Fine Art Gallery, Lubbock, Texas

Edytha Ryan, *Whale Pair,* 29 x 18 x 12, serpentine. Courtesy: The Nature Company, Berkeley, CA

He and his wife, Marsha, create three-dimensional paintings in glass. First introduced to the medium in 1976, they were fascinated by its inherent qualities of light, transparency and fragility. At first, they made stained-glass pieces, but their self-taught approach enabled them to evolve and to draw freely from inner resources. They now often create geometric abstractions, working in a constructivist manner and using materials such as clear float glass and other commercially available tints. Their "Wires" was a series of newspaper-like pieces done in industrial glass and a wire grid. Their goal is to expand the vocabulary of glass.

RUNSTADLER, MARSHA (Sculptor)
4625 Ravenwood Ave., Sacramento, CA 95821

Born: 1948 *Awards:* Best of Show, Beverly Hills Affair *Collections:* Corning Museum; Saks Fifth Ave. *Exhibitions:* David Bernstein Gallery; Holsten Gallery, Ft. Lauderdale

[See Rundstadler, Kurt]

RUSCHA, EDWARD JOSEPH (Painter, Conceptual Artist)
1024 3/4 N. Western Ave., Hollywood, CA 90029

Born: 1937 *Awards:* NEA Grant; Guggenheim Fellowship *Collections:* Museum of Modern Art, NYC; Los Angeles County Museum of Art *Exhibitions:* Whitney Museum, NYC; San Francisco Museum of Modern Art *Education:* Chouinard Art Institute *Dealer:* Leo Castelli Gallery, NYC

Early pop paintings are hyper-realistic depictions of garages—some on fire—and other buildings. A humorous series describes proper word and name usage. *Every Building on the Sunset Strip* was just that, in a montage showing both sides of the street. He is known for books of photographs of ordinary things, such as *Twenty-six Gasoline Stations* and *Real Estate Opportunities,* in which typography and pictures are combined to make a cohesive whole. Text is eliminated. They are simply reproduced snapshots; the books do not "house a collection of art photographs—they are technical data like industrial photography."

RUSSEL, NANCY (Painter)
1567 Meadow Circle, Carpinterie, CA 93013

Born: 1933 *Exhibitions:* Orange County Center for Contemporary Art; College of Creative Studies, UC-Santa Barbara *Education:* UC-Santa Barbara

In 1982, she became interested in Bonnard's use of color and began exploring encaustic. At the same time, she made a series of paintings based on masterworks of Degas, Whistler, Chase and others. In this series, called "Directional Forces," she explored the formal qualities of masterworks by making fractured copies that emphasized directional forces. Presently, she builds beautiful, textured surfaces by juxtaposing brilliant and subtle colors. Themes of time and continuous creation are implied by screens of abstraction with partially emergent figures. She works with oil on canvases ranging from 4 by 6 to 5 by 6 feet. Her paintings are combinations of spontaneous energy and formal decision.

RUSSELL, RON (Painter)
P.O. Box 1351, Sonoma, CA 95476

Born: 1938 *Awards:* Arizona Art Festival; Best of Show *Collections:* Smithsonian Institute, Washington D.C.; Omni Publishing *Exhibitions:* Oklahoma Art Festival; Utah Art Festival *Dealer:* Gallery Americana, Carmel

He is a visionary artist who paints cosmic scenes that have never been seen by the human eye. Works such as *Magester II* and *Celestia* are haunting and colorful evocations of the space frontier. He paints with raw pigment and lacquer on the back side of tempered glass plates. He layers the media and bakes on each of his fifteen coats with infrared light. This method prevents oxidation and gives the work a depth difficult to achieve on a traditional canvas. Among his influences are his father, artist Clive Bradshaw Cushing and the French beatnik painter Robert LaVigne. He has recently been working on smaller variations of the same themes.

RUTH, SHEILA (Painter)
2323 E. Olympic Blvd., Los Angeles, CA 90021

Born: 1951 *Awards:* California Arts Council Grant; Los Angeles Cultural Affairs Department Exchange Artist *Collections:* Long Beach Museum of Art; Screen Actors Guild *Exhibitions:* Los Angeles City Hall Gallery; Molly Barnes Gallery, Los Angeles *Education:* U. of Minnesota; International College

Initially a painter, she began in the early 1970s to work in video and photography as a means of making politically and socially relevant art that could reach a mass audience. She later made collages of drawings and her photographs as slice-of-life, social commentary pieces. One such work, *I'll Take L.A. Over New York . . . (and Vise Versa),* was widely distributed as a poster. In an effort to make a personal statement that communicates on a universal level, she returned to painting, moving from the linguistic form of the collages to more abstract, metaphorical expression. For several years she painted large, black-on-black images of anthurium flowers, and her recent imagery is purely biomorphic abstraction. The shapes take on figurative reference and continue her interest in the interplay of male/female energies and the duality of the tension created by simultaneous opposition and resolution.

RUTLEDGE, REUBEN (Painter, Photographer)
325 E. William St. #11, San Jose, CA 95112

Born: 1955 *Exhibitions:* Monterey Peninsula Museum of Art; San Jose Museum of Art *Education:* San Jose State U.

His initial style developed from the "Brucke" artists, particularly Kircher. He studied the works of Heidegger, Jaspers and Merleau-Ponty. From paintings, he moved to site-specific installations based on Heidegger's description of the Greek Temple. Because of the need for economy and space and the drive to reach a bigger audience, his recent work has turned toward photography. His concern for the immediacy of the image and its manipulation is a more direct attempt to capture the existential symbolism of the subject or setting.

RYAN, EDYTHA (Sculptor)
2501 Lafayette Dr., Davis, CA 95616

Born: 1942 *Awards:* Commission, California Dept. of Education *Collections:* RAS Corp., Sacramento *Exhibitions:* Southwest Sculpture, Scottsdale, AZ *Education:* UC-Davis

While working with sculptors Manuel Neri and Ralph Johnson at UC-Davis, she focused almost exclusively on the figure. These early expressionistic pieces were executed in wire, gauze and wax. In 1985, she began

Roy Rydell, *Aerial Hedge and Protecting Arbor,* 18 x 25, ink, watercolor

Harry S. Richardson, *Kingfishers,* 8 x 14, gemstone

carving naturalistic animals in stone. These pieces reflect her current interest in art expressed as craft. Underscoring her preference for direct imagery, she places a strong emphasis on the formal qualities of these sculptures.

RYDELL, ROY (Painter)
201 Pine Flat Rd., Santa Cruz, CA 95060

Born: 1915 *Awards:* County of Santa Cruz; Santa Cruz County Preservation Society *Exhibitions:* Villa Montalvo, Saratoga; Art Museum of Santa Cruz County *Education:* USC; UC-Berkeley

An active, licensed landscape architect in semi-retirement since 1980, he lays a sense of whimsy atop a strong sense of order. His early, brilliantly colored symbolic oil paintings were influenced by surrealism and German expressionism. Later, he produced a large body of acrylic still life paintings of fabrics combined with other objects. His current choice of subject matter reflects a playful affection for objects. The home, gardens, animals and flowers are depicted as still lifes. Working from a sketchbook, and using a full palette of brilliant but tasteful colors, he paints with acrylics and produces ink drawings with watercolor washes.

RYMER, ILONA (Painter)
P.O. Box 822, 4126 Casey Ave., Santa Ynez, CA, 93460

Born: 1921 *Awards:* Affiliate Award, Laguna Beach Art Association *Collections:* Presidential Collection 1982 (Reagan) *Exhibitions:* Valley Arts Gallery, Los Olivos; Mary Livingston Gallery, Santa Ana *Education:* Cal. State-Long Beach; Phoenix Art Institute, NY

Her early work was representational; study with Rex Brandt, George Post and Robert E. Woods led to a more fluid wet-into-wet watercolor technique. She admired the Impressionists, and patterned her work after Toulouse-Lautrec and Degas. Many drawings emphasized line, and were sparse in color. As the art editor of the magazine, *Arabian Connection*, she designed the format and covers, and contributed articles. Tiring of purely representational painting, she has tried to create greater movement and a more meaningful use of light, by fracturing the form, and embellishing shapes with no fewer than thirty to forty values of color. These softly colored acrylics are an attempt toward a representational cubism.

SAAR, BETYE (Assemblage Artist, Collage Artist)
8074 Willow Glen Rd., Los Angeles, CA 90046

Born: 1926 *Awards:* NEA Award; Purchase Award, California State College, Los Angeles *Collections:* Los Angeles County Museum of Art; University Museum, Berkeley *Exhibitions:* San Francisco Museum of Modern Art; Whitney Museum, NYC *Education:* UCLA; USC *Dealer:* Monique Knowlton, NYC

Her assemblages and collages, reminiscent of Joseph Cornell's box constructions, draw heavily from African and African-American heritages and from voodoo, mystical and occult imagery. Snakes, tarot cards and stars and moons populate the constructions, along with feathers, sequins, buttons, gold foil, strips of ribbons and other collected objects. Her work of the 1970s contained powerful political and social criticism and parody, especially of minority stereotypes: *The Liberation of Aunt Jemima* features the black "mammy" as a revolutionary, wielding a gun and hand grenade. Her

work of the 1980s, while often still politically and socially concerned, has taken on a meaning at once more personal and more universal—reflections on childhood, love, beauty, aging and mortality.

SAAR, DOROTHY (Painter)
915 Madison, Monterey, CA 93940

Born: 1925 *Exhibitions:* Gallery Americana, Carmel; Cottage Gallery I, Carmel *Education:* Iowa Wesleyan; U. of Illinois

She paints florals, landscapes and figures in oils. Her work is characterized by challenging compositions and panoramic colors. Her florals go beyond the traditional vase of flowers on a table; they are green house arrays, or masses of blooms in a sun room. Her palette is wide and her colors are harmonious. A New York publisher has reproduced an edition of twenty-six of her serigraphs and prints. Her work has has been featured in *Architectural Digest*, and she has been selected by the U.S. State Department for its program "American Art in Foreign Embassy Residences." She works mainly on commission, and her paintings have been exhibited in Canada, Australia and Europe.

SAARNI, BETTY J. (Painter)
1434 Grizzley Peak Blvd., Berkeley, CA 94708

Born: 1925 *Awards:* Gretzer Award, East Bay Watercolor Competition *Collections:* Phoenix Art Museum, AZ *Exhibitions:* Watercolor West Exhibition, CA; Art Space Gallery, Sacramento *Education:* UC-Berkeley; California College of Arts and Crafts

She attempts, in her watercolor landscapes, to convey her response to environmental and atmospheric conditions surrounding her subject. Convinced that the medium of watercolor is impressionistic, she studied impressionist techniques under the tutelage of Frank Webb and Robert Wood. Working wet and loosely on either coated or uncoated paper, she encourages the natural bleed and transparency of the paint. She is often happily surprised by the resulting color-mix. A long-time admirer of stained glass, she works toward the same brilliance of hue in her painting. That light and its impact on color continues to fascinate her is evident in the delicate luminosity of her recent studies, and her adroit utilization of the underlying paper's whiteness.

SACHS, MORRIS (Sculptor)
733 31st Ave. San Francisco, CA 94121

Born: 1923 *Collections:* Public Health Collection, Public Health Center #5, San Francisco; International Institute *Exhibitions:* Sunnydale Arts Center; San Francisco Art Festival *Education:* State U. of New York; San Francisco State U.

A figurative hardwood sculptor, he creates sensual female figures between three and five feet tall. His influences include temple sculpture from India as well as German expressionist sculptors, particularly Ernst Barlach. His pieces are often dancing figures, but with the appearance of being solid rather than willowy. One example of his work is a satirical statue of a plump ballerina, dedicated to George Balanchine, who caused controversy in the American ballet by his favoritism of thin and anorexic women. The artist works almost exclusively in exotic hardwoods, including those from South America, Africa and Indonesia. He primarily uses hand tools rather than automated lathes or drills. The highly textured pieces are not painted; instead, he covers them with a fine shellac or

Rosetta, *The Lion,* 5 x 11 x 6, bronze. Courtesy: Runyan-Fischer Foundries, Sand City, CA.
Photograph: Mel Schockner

Mikki Staton, *The Murran,* 26 x 18, walnut burl, tung oil finish.
Courtesy: Edward S. Curtis Gallery, San Anselmo, CA

a thin layer of varnish to emphasize the beauty of the natural wood grain.

SADBERRY, HARVEY (Painter)
1923 Hyde St., San Francisco, CA 94109

Born: 1945 *Exhibitions:* National Museum of Modern Art, Lisbon, Portugal; Downey Museum of Art, Los Angeles *Education:* San Francisco Art Institute

In the 1970s, he received formal training in abstract expressionism and minimalism. Between 1982 and 1987, he was concerned with pure rhythm, and, inspired by mythological allusions, he used thick, glossy, dense black pigment in an acrylic gel medium to paint small canvases with titles like *Mass for the Celebration of the 553rd Anniversary of the Death of Joan of Arc*. In his recent, brilliantly colored abstract landscapes, he manipulates superimposed painterly images, abandons flatness and allows space to fluctuate in paintings that are reminiscent of an earlier innocent style.

SADLE, AMY A. (Printmaker)
2918 14th St., Columbus, NE 68601

Born: 1940 *Awards:* Best of Show, San Diego Print Club National *Collections:* Statue of Liberty Museum *Exhibitions:* Kansas U.; San Diego Print Club *Education:* U. of Rhode Island; U of Iowa *Dealer:* The Collector, San Diego

After working many years as an oil painter, she began studying printmaking under Fritz Eichenburg. Simple, direct woodcuts were an early fascination and she still works to push the medium beyond its normal bounds, challenging the old rules of inking and printing. Her woodcuts are figurative; she uses unorthodox color methods, distorted perspectives, disassociated objects and mixed media. Often she juxtaposes two images, giving her work the look of a double exposure. She continues painting, completing brightly colored oils and watercolors. In addition to her painting, she is also president of Impact Inc., a non profit organization that sponsors the work of female Nebraska artists.

SAFER, CAROL STAR (Painter, Sculptor)
504 Laurel St., Santa Cruz, CA 95060

Born: 1925 *Collections:* National Air and Space Museum, Smithsonian Institution, Washington, DC; Cosmonaut Museum, Moscow *Exhibitions:* Ames Research Center, Moffett Field; California Museum of Science and Industry, Los Angeles *Education:* Cornell U.

The theme of a large amount of her work is outer space—the Earth, the Moon, the planets, solar flares, nebulae—viewed from the perspective of space. She views her paintings as educational as well as artistic. Some of the recent work is sculptural, as in her depictions of the lunar surface, which are displayed on pedestals and table tops. The paintings range in size from 18 by 24 inches to 4 by 8 feet. Because of the health hazard of her medium, clear casting resin, she has returned to her early work in Chinese brushstroke and Japanese sumi painting. She has recently been working on a book on Zen monks.

SAINE, RONALD J. (Painter)
524 W. 52nd. St., Los Angeles, CA 90037

Born: 1950 *Exhibitions:* Afro-American Art Museum, Los Angeles; Charles White Art Festival, Pasadena *Education:* Los Angeles Trade Technical College; West Los Angeles College *Dealer:* Artist Extraordinaire, Los Angeles

In his childhood paintings, he depicted faces and people from his imagination. He began working from newspaper ads and once in art school, he was influenced by the great masters Da Vinci, Rembrandt and Michelangelo for their earthy palettes and dramatic lighting. Since leaving school, his appreciation has expanded to include contemporaries Barnes, Rockwell and Warhol, among others. A figure painter for many years now, he has worked on large canvases, mostly "super close-ups," though some are of multitudes in motion. His colors are vibrant and seldom muted, with points of high contrast. In all instances, whether the characters be of renown or fictitious, he strives to portray life in its most striking reality.

SAINT JAMES, SYNTHIA (Painter)
P.O. Box 27683, Los Angeles, CA 90027

Born: 1949 *Awards:* Prix de Paris; Prix du Centenair *Collections:* Richard Pryor; Disney Studios *Exhibitions:* Musee des Duncan, Paris; Pacific Design Center *Dealer:* Wanda Wallace Associates, Los Angeles; Am Wheeler, NYC; Art International, Atlanta

Self-taught, she began her work in abstracts and landscapes. The most evident influence is that of impressionism, particularly in her earlier paintings and in those exhibited in France. She then progressed to a series on wild and domestic animals. Her works also reflect her extensive travels, include journeys to Martinique, Tahiti and Hawaii, and her paintings are informed by the cultures and peoples of the Caribbean, South Pacific, Asia and Native America. Paintings, primarily oil on canvas, incorporate the contrast of pure, flat areas of color, as well as minute brush strokes. She has recently begun an Oriental series, drawing from Tibetan culture. *Tibetan Women* depicts two figures with mixed planes of pure, light-filled color and close detail, combining the sensibility of her earlier abstract works with her precise interpretations of exotic cultures. Other subjects that she treats include a series on "The Many Colors of the American Indian" and Tibet.

ST. JOHN, TERRY (Painter)
2736 Shasta Rd., Berkeley, CA 94708

Born: 1934 *Awards:* James D. Phelan Award; Contemporary Southern Artists Award *Collections:* Mills College, Oakland; City of San Francisco *Exhibitions:* Sheldon Memorial Art Galleries, UC-Santa Cruz; Notre Dame College *Education:* California School of Fine Art; California College of Arts and Crafts *Dealer:* Victor Fischer, San Francisco

During the mid-1970s, he learned the intricacies of plein air painting by traveling with Louis and Lundy Siegriest. He combined outdoor techniques with the figurative painting he learned from James Weeks, creating small, post-impressionist landscapes of painterly figuration. In his series of Santa Cruz canvases, he laid on ultramarine blue primer, which he covered with broadly shaped buildings of pure reds and greens and a gray sky. He continues to paint in the open, often moving between studio and location work, reworking the painting until it is completed. He has recently been combining abstraction and figurative detail in a series of intensely colorful small paintings.

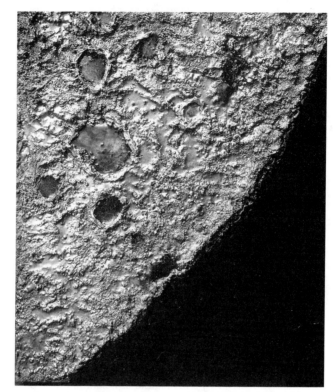

Carol Ann Safer, *Lunar Landscape,* 48 x 60, resins and mixed media. Photographer: Bill White

Virginia St. John, *Kelly,* 30 x 36, pastel

ST. JOHN, VIRGINIA (Painter, Printmaker)
8855 Atlanta Avenue, Suite 188, Huntington Beach, CA 92646

Born: 1948 *Exhibitions:* Walt Disney Studios Gallery, Laguna Beach; Barbizon Art Centre, London *Education:* Iowa State U.; Art Center College of Design *Dealer:* Gallerie Patou, Laguna Beach

She was born into a family of artists, and soon learned how to render emotion and mood, winning her first national award at age seven. In earlier work as a portraitist, she preferred acrylics, and an oil glaze technique. Recently, she has had two concentrations: pastels and printmaking (stone lithography, woodcuts and etching). Applying chalk pastels in gestural strokes, rather than in the traditional blending technique, she creates spontaneous, expressive, realistic images in vibrant colors. Her prints are characterized by the same fluid line and attention to detail. She also occasionally works in mixed-media, incorporating photocollage in her etching. Technically masterful, she is best known for the sensuality and deeply emotional content of her work.

SAKATA, KEIKO (Painter)
2042 Corinth Ave., Los Angeles, CA 90025

Born: 1933 *Collections:* Executive Life Insurance Co., Los Angeles *Exhibitions:* Gild Hall Gallery, Southhampton, NY; Art Rental Gallery, Los Angeles County Museum of Art *Education:* UCLA

Interested in exploring the optically elusive relationship between "positive" and "negative" space in painting, she has shifted her initial emphasis on figurative forms to that of abstract patterns. In her "shojie" series, a number of paintings with white-unpainted areas edged by minimally colored areas, abstract patterns are created when one stares at the painting for a period of time, sometimes creating the illusion of three-dimensional depth. In the "satellite" series, several triangular canvases are used instead of a single square canvas. Arrangement of these canvases produces varying interactions between the positive and the negative spaces, as well as altering the illusory effects.

SAKIMURA, ETSUKO (Ceramist, Mixed Media Artist)
P.O. Box 1019 L, El Cerrito, CA 94530

Born: 1946 *Awards:* Expert's Choice Award, 1st Art Achievement Awards, ASI; Purchase Award, Baulines Craftsman's Guild/Macy's of California *Collections:* Sacramento LRT/Arts Commission; Saks Fifth Avenue, Boca Raton *Exhibitions:* Del Mano Gallery, Los Angeles; Elaine Potter Gallery, San Francisco *Education:* San Francisco St. U.

During formal training in textiles, she was strongly influenced by the works of Abacanowycz and Eva Hesse. In 1980, while studying ceramics under David Kuraoka, she realized that textiles were too limiting. She began exploring slab construction techniques that allowed her to express the flowing motion of fabric through the static medium of clay. Soon she began exploring the technical possibilities of other media, such as bronze and glass, with the objective of capturing the fluidity of fabric in an expression of dance-like movement. Choosing processes that are inherently unpredictable—such as pate de verre glass, pit-firing ceramics and multi-patinating metals—she never begins a particular sculpture with the result already in mind. She follows Hesse's directive, allowing the process to express itself, rather than manipulating the process to produce predictable results. She brings a textile artist's multimedia approach to her work, attaching such items as stone, shell, thread and paper onto the final piece. Her recent work involves capturing the motion of dance in ceramic, bronze and glass kimono figures. Recent work also includes a series of ceramic tiles, which are pit-fired or raku-fired and feature pieces of fabric, mother-of-pearl, thread and hand-carved floral and leaf patterns.

SALANS, SALLY (Painter, Photographer)
45 26th Ave., San Francisco, CA 94121

Born: 1927 *Awards:* Merit Award, Photography, San Francisco Women Artists *Collections:* Mrs. Joan Carroll, San Francisco *Exhibitions:* Marshall Myers Gallery, San Francisco; San Francisco Women Artists Gallery *Education:* Lone Mountain College, San Francisco

Early in her career, she did commercial window decoration and freelance illustration before moving into fine art. Her paintings are done primarily in transparent watercolors and oils, ranging from semi-abstract florals and landscapes to works of total abstraction. She is a self-taught photographer and sees her move to photography, which is her primary focus now, as a natural transition from painting. Black-and-white portraits of children and "situational" scenes predominate her photographic work. One such scene comprises a baby viewed by three adults making faces; another depicts children dancing on the beach. She works to create a state of mind that is at once serious and lighthearted and an effect that allows a subsequent release of built-up emotion.

SALEM, DONNA KARIO (Sculptor)
544 Mateo St., Los Angeles, CA 90013

Born: 1931 *Awards:* Art in Public Places Award, San Diego County *Exhibitions:* Merging One Gallery, Santa Monica; Madrona Gallery, San Pedro *Education:* Barnard College; Columbia U.; UCLA

Abstract in its elements, and representational in configuration, her figurative constructions are made of welded bronze and aluminum on a human scale. Each sculpture, assembled from crisply defined hard-edged parts, seeks to capture a moment in time that reflects the emotional, psychological or political force which is its inspiration. The pieces incorporate humor and satire, expressing narrative and commentary simultaneously.

SALEMI, MICHAEL SIEGEL (Draughtsperson)
1040 34th St., #1, Sacramento, CA 95816

Born: 1961 *Collections:* I.D.T. Corporation, Chicago *Exhibitions:* Nevada County National Bank Building, Grass Valley; Karen Long Gallery, Long Beach *Education:* Southern Illinois U., Carbondale *Dealer:* Worley/Smith Gallery, Nevada City

His early influences leaned toward the highly refined surrealists (Rene Magritte, Salvador Dali and M.C. Escher). He later abandoned two-dimensional work to concentrate on rough-cast, bronze and aluminum sculptures; these were influenced by the mood and subject matter of Ed Kienholz, and the casting techniques used by Reuben Nakian and Ernest Trova. After leaving school, he became interested in combining aspects of his earlier surrealistic drawing and his

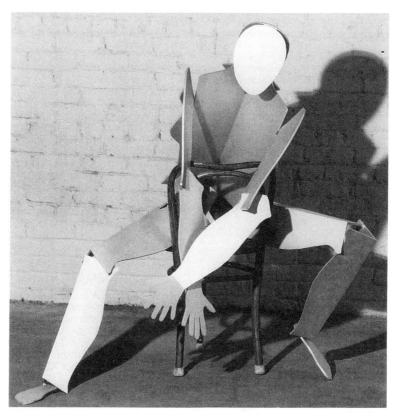

Donna Kario Salem, *Pausing for a Backward Glance,* 49 x 52 x 25, aluminum

George Stillman, *Pearl St.,* 28 x 28, egg tempera. Courtesy: Gallery Imago, San Francisco

knowledge of sculptural form and space. The figures in his drawings could easily be transformed into many sculptural media; however, by using surrealist techniques, he creates ambiguous space and proportions that cannot be achieved in sculpture. In his drawings, he tries to achieve a light, translucent quality through hard-lined figures and perspective—thus emphasizing the mix of two- and three-dimensional qualities. He has also ventured back into sculpture, creating abstract pieces using found items, such as plastic pads, wood construction materials and carpet padding.

SALINGER, JOAN (Photographer, Computer Graphic Artist)

c/o Fine Arts Dept., Orange Coast College, 2701 Fairview Dr., Costa Mesa, CA 92626

Born: 1951 *Awards:* Michigan Council for the Arts; C.S. Mott Foundation *Exhibitions:* B.C. Space Gallery, Laguna Beach; Saint Mary's College *Collections:* New Orleans Museum of Art; Kresge-Kmart Collection *Education:* U. of Michigan; Cranbrook Academy of Art

Her work has always been experimental and autobiographical. Early on, she made abstract, lushly colorful photographs and photograms of fabrics. When she moved to California, she began to work more playfully, contrasting a straight photograph with a manipulated painterly photogrammed field to which she added humorous or gestural scribbles of rock and roll. She then began using computers, combining hand-colored plotterworks with hand-colored or found photographs. Later, she scanned color photographs into the computer and experimented with mixing imagery, concept, process and media. She is currently working on an AST 286 AT with Targa 32-color board, using a high resolution Howtek color scanner to digitize photographs and a Matrix PCR to output to film at 2000 or 4000 lines. Her software is Lumena by Time Arts. She is an instructor at Orange Coast College in Costa Mesa, California.

SALMOIRAGHI, FRANCO (Photographer)

P.O. Box 61708 Manoa Station, Honolulu, HI 96839

Born: 1942 *Collections:* Contemporary Arts Center, HI; Honolulu Academy of Arts *Exhibitions:* Stones Gallery, Kauai, HI; Gallery EAS, Honolulu *Education:* Ohio U.; Southern Illinois U.

His photographs create a childlike sense of living in a metaphysical world. His work includes documentary, fine art, personal and commercial photography. His black-and-white personal work is closely associated with the sense of spiritual power he derives from living in Hawaii. He has documented the Hawaiian people, attempting to preserve a history and pride in the people's spiritual relationship to the land. His photographs of the aina (land) have been an attempt connect the photographic image to the islands' spiritual power. His commercial work includes editorial and stock photography for books and magazines published in Hawaii and internationally.

SALLE, DAVID (Painter)

c/o Mary Boone Gallery, 417 W. Broadway, New York, NY 10012

Born: 1952 *Awards:* CAPS Grant *Collections:* Whitney Museum, NYC; Basel Kunstmuseum *Exhibitions:* Larry Gagosian Gallery, Los Angeles; Leo Castelli Gallery, NYC *Education:* California Institute of the Arts *Dealer:* Mary Boone Gallery, NYC

He operates in a new figurative vein as part of the European and American conceptual painting movement, which ranges from total abstraction to a combination of abstraction and figuration. Images are taken from high and low culture, many of them appropriated. Mixed-media diptychs and triptychs combine drawing, painting, sculpture and photography to present strong figures, often nudes who appear to be viewing interacting figures. Women are usually depicted on their backs or kneeling, often without clothes—their faces are seldom seen. The works suggest endlessly shifting perspectives with ambiguous messages. He has deliberately incorporated the rhetoric and art conversations of the 1980s to make ironic commentaries and has said he would like to think of his work as "totally promiscuous and omnivorous."

SALSKA, JOANNA (Painter)

2306 McGee Ave., Berkeley, CA 94703

Born: 1951 *Awards:* Gold Medal, Pen and Brush, NYC; Merit Award, Golden Gate Weavers, Berkeley *Collections:* Southland Corp. Collection *Exhibitions:* Fiberworks Center for the Textile Arts, Berkeley; Pro-Arts, Oakland *Education:* Academy of Fine Arts, Warsaw, Poland *Dealer:* Allrich Gallery, San Francisco

Her most vivid inspirations occur while her eyes are closed. Choosing to look to the landscape of the mind, of imagined scents and colors, she transposes a mental world, one unlike the physical universe, whose essence, she says, will never be captured, to paper and in so doing strengthens it. Working with paints and clippings, she is "like a sorcerer" commanding and calling forth forces and yet awed by her discoveries. In some instances the paintings are taken a step further and rendered as tapestries. In contrast to the source of inspiration, the treatment is flat, in the basic European tradition. The works are characterized by bright pinks and oranges with contrasting dark blues.

SALTOS, ELIZABETH (Sculptor)

1045 17th St., San Francisco, CA 94107

Born: 1948 *Awards:* NEA Fellowship *Collections:* AT&T, San Francisco; Kaiser Permanente Medical Center, Oakland *Exhibitions:* Fort Mason Foundation, San Francisco; Dana Reich Gallery, San Francisco *Education:* Southern Conn. State U., New Haven; U. of Texas, Arlington *Dealer:* Judith Litvich, San Francisco

Her early work employed black, white, red, blue and yellow and horizontal, vertical and diagonal lines. This format governed *Prism, Conversion and Summation*, a 112-foot-long prism with an overlay of red, blue and yellow. Her work derives from silkscreen techniques, which are used to create large-scale geometric sculptures that are both site-specific and site-adjusted. She is currently exploring color, texture and three-dimensionality, primarily using galvanized sheet metal and adhering to straight line geometry. She has started to bend and fold the metal to create an "origami" of industrial material in conjunction with transparent color that incorporates the interaction of light. She achieves varying textures by sanding and scratching the metal.

SANDER, JEROME (Painter)

750 N. Occidental, Los Angeles, CA 90026

Born: 1949 *Exhibitions:* California State U.; Art Center College of Design *Education:* U. of North

Magda Santonastasio, *Central American Fragments,* 8 x 6, etching line.
Courtesy: Tuhuana Press, San Diego, CA

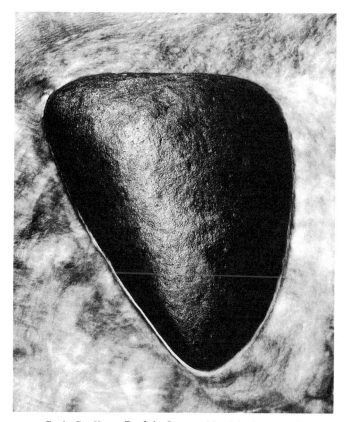

Craig Scoffone, *Rock in Stream,* 11 x 14, photograph

Carolina; UC-Santa Barbara *Dealer:* Orlando Gallery, Sherman Oaks

His early paintings and drawings treated a variety of subjects, including still life, figuration, landscapes and interiors. The instinctive and tactile traditions of European painting, as practiced by Titian, Caravaggio, Velazquez, Goya and Monet, were primary influences. The study of Cezanne and Picasso sparked his exploration of abstraction. After moving to Los Angeles in the early 1980s, he began to paint oil paintings of sculptural figures, often nude, whose direct iconic presentation suggested a state of mind or consciousness. This progressed to more naturalistic, narrative paintings, involving single and multiple male-female couples, whose interaction suggested emotional and psychological drama. Besides these pieces, he is also known for his watercolor floral paintings. Playing with the relative position of the blossoms against a solid color background, he paints these brightly colored works in a hybrid abstract-realist style.

SANDERS, KEITH (Painter)
39865 Cedar Blvd., #331, Newark, CA 94560

Born: 1934 *Awards:* Award of Merit, San Diego Watercolor Society; Livermore Art League Open Spring Show *Exhibitions:* National Watercolor Society Member's Show, La Brea; San Diego Watercolor Society International Exhibition *Education:* Art Center College of Design; Trinity U. *Dealer:* Suzanne Fraser, Saratoga

He has been working with watercolor since he was in high school. During his school years, he was impressed by the works of Kandinsky, the "Blaue Reiter" group, Mondrian, Dufy, Chagall, Rouault and, especially, John Marin. By the late 1960s, he was beginning to work in the wash-over-wash style that has become his trademark. By using as many as fifteen washes of varying colors, he is able to achieve a luminous, glowing surface that reveals smooth, transparent planes of soft color and form. His "Bridge Series" paintings—a metaphor for his own artistic development— formed a transition between his boldly colored, semi-figurative work and the more muted, non-objective paintings of recent years. His recent paintings are inspired by the colors and landscape of the desert Southwest. He has been painting in acrylics, using his standard watercolor technique. The pale washes of blue gray, yellow ochre and sienna capture the broad, warm features of this primitive landscape.

SANFORD, GEORGIA L. (Painter)
2027 Swazey St., San Luis Obispo, CA 93401

Born: 1930 *Awards:* 4th Prize, San Luis Obispo County Fair; 1st Prize, Santa Maria Valley Art Association *Exhibitions:* San Luis Obispo; Annex Gallery, Morro Bay *Education:* U. of Denver

She uses the formal elements of painting as a means to the end of expressing ideas and emotions; the nude figure is an essential element in the construction of the mythic realities that she conjures. After she carefully studies the figure and the various elements within the landscape of the painting, she renders the paintings realistically in oil and egg tempera. Precise draftsmanship and muted color are used to strengthen the symbolism. Themes of aging, witchcraft, worshipers, dancers and crucifixions symbolize psychological events, dreams and visions tending towards the mystical and the surreal.

SANGER, MICAH (Painter)
P.O. Box 500, Oregon House, CA 95962

Born: 1950 *Collections:* E.F. Hutton, NY *Exhibitions:* Goethe Academy Museum, Renaissance; Landfall Gallery, Carmel *Education:* Clemson U.; U. of Santa Barbara; Cal. State-Chico

For some thirteen years, he was attracted realism's subtle interractions of color and light. At the same time, he studied music and architecture and began to be influenced by the abstract elements in Oriental art and that of Vassily Kandinsky. Eventually the paintings became large, abstract "fields of energy," comprising a variety of media. Influenced by photographs from space and by CAT scans of the human body—design elements from science and electronic engineering—the large abstracts have a unique presence. The canvases are sometimes 12 feet in length, often first primed in gold pigment, then layered with other color washes with subtle shades of iridescent hues woven through.

SAN JUAN, CLYDE (Painter, Commercial Illustrator)
55 Bluecoat Dr., Irvine, CA 92720

Born: 1957 *Exhibitions:* Cypress College of Fine Arts; Parsons Brinckerhoff Quade & Douglas; Terry Houseworth, Illustration & Design Group

Throughout his books, paintings and drawings, there is a continuing emphasis on the environment and a commitment to the environment's place in the processes of living. His first book, *The Continuing Flight of Icarus* (1984), was a mostly figurative anthology of his early pen-and-ink drawings. He is an avid backpacker, spending weeks at a time on "Lone Wolf sojourns." This is reflected in the lack of figures in his 1987 exhibit, "Evocative Lands." His 1988 "Heart on Land" exhibit featured an excerpt from a planned series of "chapters." The first chapter, "Conversations in Fading Light," is part of a series of hand-crafted boxes containing images, photographs, maps or found objects. He has recently been working on the next chapter, "Maps."

SAN SOUCI, DANIEL (Commercial Illustrator, Painter)
694 Calmar Ave., Oakland, CA 94610

Born: 1948 *Awards:* Best Illustrated Books of 1978, New York Times; Gold Medallion Award, Christian Booksellers Association *Collections:* Orange County Library; Doubleday & Co., Inc., NYC *Exhibitions:* Scott Gallery, Orinda; Piedmont Decorators Showcase *Education:* California College of Arts and Crafts *Dealer:* Jane Feder, NYC

After his formal schooling, he traveled through the western U.S. executing paintings on location. Since the mid-1970s, he has illustrated over thirty books and numerous book jackets, including the C.S. Lewis *Chronicles of Narnia* series. As an illustrator of books, he feels it important to spend time painting outside of the studio. His large landscapes, influenced by the work of Edward Hopper, feature light brushwork with expressive, natural colors. Unlike the tightly rendered illustrations, these watercolor paintings are more freeform and spontaneous in both rendition and spirit.

Clyde San Juan, *Some night when it's a full moon . . . the de Chirico panorama,* 11 x 14, mixed media

Vern Swansen, *Epsilon,* 12 x 16, ink-pen drawing

SANTIAGO, SUSAN (Painter, Draughtsperson)

1178 N. Topanga, P.O. Box 650, Topanga Canyon, CA 90290

Born: 1949 *Exhibitions:* Bank of American, Sherman Oaks; Century Gallery, Sylmar *Education:* New York U.; Cal. State-Los Angeles *Dealer:* Orlando Gallery, Sherman Oaks

After her formal training and a move to California from the East Coast, she found both her style and her approach changed dramatically. Influenced by the warm hues of the California landscape and the ideas of the post-modern movement, her work lightened considerably, and became more free and open in the rendition of space. The imagery in many of these paintings was a combination of architectural forms and of figures and motifs drawn from classical mythology. Her recent works are more figurative, centered primarily on the human figure. She works with pastel pencils on black paper, filling the foreground with the subject and leaving the background a void. She prefers working with subjects she knows, and strives to capture that individual's interior world of hopes, fears and ideas. This work is influenced by Lucian Freud, Alice Neil and Balthus.

SANTONASTASIO, MAGDA (Painter, Printmaker)

4228 Mars Way, La Mesa, CA 92041

Born: 1937 *Awards:* National Art Award of Costa Rica; Gold Medal, Watercolor Annual Contest, Costa Rica *Collections:* Fine Arts Museum of San Francisco; West Berlin Library, Germany *Exhibitions:* Love Library, San Diego State U.; Iturralde Gallery, La Jolla *Education:* U. of Costa Rica

Influenced by Emil Nolde and other German Expressionists, her watercolor paintings display a free, liberal use of color and artful composition. Her unrestrained style represents a break with traditional Costa Rican watercolor art, which has emphasized broad brushstrokes and delicate coloration. Subject matter consists of natural forms, particularly landscapes and flowers. Her prints are characterized by fine lines and delicate detail. For the last several years, she has worked on zinc plates in a style inspired by pre-Columbian fabrics. These pieces are richly textured and often include bits of writing and treatment with aquatint.

SANTORE, ROBERT B. (Painter, Printmaker)

900 E. 1st, #310, Los Angeles, CA 90012

Born: 1961 *Collections:* San Jose Museum of Art; T.R.W. Permanent Collection *Exhibitions:* Los Angeles Municipal Art Gallery; Diane Nelson Gallery, Laguna Beach *Dealer:* The Portfolios, Beverly Hills

Language was the underlying theme of his early work. In his early pieces, he would first inscribe a complex system of symbols in the undertexture of his canvas. Over this surface he then applied layers of transparent medium, achieving a stained glass like surface. Finally he painted characteristic circular shapes with semi-thick, dark pigments. He maintains his interest in language and expressionism, and has started to combine those concerns with High Renaissance painting and pop art imagery and tradition. He paints these billboard sized pieces on irregularly shaped canvases using a mixed media of oil, encaustic, solvent transfer, gold leaf, silk-screen and collage. The works often convey political or satirical themes.

SAPIEN, DARRYL (Painter, Performance Artist)

4333 Balboa St., San Francisco, CA 94121

Born: 1950 *Awards:* NEA Fellowship *Collections:* Guggenheim Museum, NYC; San Francisco Museum of Modern Art *Exhibitions:* Southern Exposure Gallery, San Francisco; Center for Visual Arts, Oakland *Education:* San Francisco Art Institute

In the early 1970s, while still attending art school in San Francisco, he left sculpture behind and began working as a performance artist. Under the influence of such local Bay Area performance artists as Terry Fox and Howard Fried, he turned to the creation of large-scale spectacles. Although originally designed to be performed outdoors and in unconventional environments, as he and his work became well-known, he adapted his art to oblige the museums, which invited him to stage the pieces within their buildings. The performance work culminated in 1983 with the premiere of *Pixellage*, a piece commissioned by the San Francisco Ballet. Recently, he has concentrated on the production of painted assemblage works, using encaustic techniques and images associated with advertising.

SARGENT, J. MCNEIL (Painter, Printmaker)

12245 Carmel Vista Rd., #193, San Diego, CA 92130

Awards: Outstanding Woman Artist, Pratt Graphics, NYC *Collections:* National Bibliotheque, Paris; Pratt Graphics, NYC *Exhibitions:* Riverside Museum; Prestige Gallery, Boston *Education:* UC-San Diego; Atelier 17, Paris *Dealer:* Tarbox Gallery, San Diego

As a young painter, she was influenced by the Impressionists, Dufy and Monet, and by the Sumi brushstrokes of painter Dae Wei Kwo, with whom she studied for two years. Calligraphy was a paramount interest, and after being invited to work at the San Diego Graphics Center, she turned to printmaking as a natural extension for her fluid lines. Later, she studied with Hayter at Atelier 17 in Paris. Her recent monotypes of florals, figures and Mediterranean landscapes involve viscosity and embossing techniques and show the influence of Matisse' colors, Kirchner's expressionistic strokes and De Stael's bold impasto.

SARMENTO, JULIAO (Painter, Photographer)

Apartado 35, 2766 Estoril, Codex, Portugal

Born: 1948 *Collections:* Moderna Museet, Stockholm; Stadtische Galerie Lemmbachaus, Munich *Exhibitions:* Art L.A. *Education:* Escola Superior de Belas Artes de Lisboa *Dealer:* Comicos, Lisbon

Trained as a painter, he began developing mixed-media pieces in the early 1970s. In these installations he combined photography and text with sound and film. In 1979, he reintroduced painting to his work, gradually discarding the other media. His current pieces are multi-paneled statements with strong references to literature and personal stories. Each panel functions as a word and the panels together form a sentence. In *Sem Titulo*, a three-paneled wood-and-canvas-painting, he mixes the realistic with the abstract.

SASAKI, SUZY BARNARD (Painter)

1435 Allston Way, Berkeley, CA 94702

Born: 1958 *Exhibitions:* Twin Palms Gallery, San Francisco; Lawson Galleries, San Francisco *Education:* San Francisco Art Institute; Bristol Polytechnic, England

Jill Sattler, *Offer of Dust,* 39 x 12 x 3, assemblage. Photograph: WM. B. Dewey

J.L. Searle-Kubby, *Lisé,* 36 x 26 x 20, bronze

After her academic study in England, she came to California in 1981 and focused on self-portraiture. The portraits, painted in oil on rectangular canvases, have increasingly focused on the figure itself until finally the background is eliminated altogether—the pieces becoming cut-outs made of masonite and placed against the wall. The series of paintings make up gatherings of people, the "paintings" painted on both sides and standing free (from 20 to 53 inches in height). Her paint is richly applied and vibrant, recalling the gestures, but not the angst of expressionism. She has recently returned to the rectangular format, now capturing snatches of scenes of people and their surroundings. These triptychs may be grouped in or out of sequence.

SASSONE, MARCO (Painter)
123 Townsend, #450, San Francisco, CA 94103

Born: 1942 *Awards:* Gold Medal, National Academy of Arts, Literature and Science, Italy; Official Knight of the Order to the Merit of the Italian Republic *Collections:* Los Angeles County Museum of Art; Laguna Art Museum *Exhibitions:* Bernheim-Jeune Gallerie, Paris *Dealer:* Diane Nelson Gallery, Laguna Beach

Educated at the Instituto Galileo Galilei and the Academy of Fine Arts, both in Florence, Italy, this landscape painter is known as a colorist. Early canvases recall the Macchiaoli school as well as the post-Impressionists. Subsequent works employ bold colors and an energetic style depicting cityscapes and seascapes, mainly representing San Francisco and Venice, Italy. A recent technique, using backgrounds on canvas to simulate wood, echoes his early method, paint on wood. Full images are created by painting the entire canvas with equal intensity. Recent works have included prints made jointly with the late Guy MacCoy. He has been knighted an Official Knight of the Italian Republic.

SATTLER, JILL (Painter, Sculptor)
P.O. Box 3971, Santa Barbara, CA 93130

Born: 1947 *Collections:* Institute of World Culture, Santa Barbara *Exhibitions:* Art Museum of Santa Cruz; Southern California Assemblage and Contemporary Arts Forum *Education:* Chouinard Art Institute

Divinity, as it operates through man, is her subject. Turkish and Indian miniatures are a major influence. Her art is dedicated to magic and the occult via the sacred symbology of illumination manuscripts. Her paintings achieve the look of ancient regal fabrics. In her assemblages, relics and magical amulets are utilized to create the sacred atmosphere of votive altar pieces. She embosses her sculptural paintings with golds, bronzes and fiery coppers and paints them with large, lavish areas of highly textured, colorful oils. She has done work on African ceremonial symbols, and she recently began working on a series of embossed metallic paintings on the magnetic theme of Sanskrit. Jewelry from antique objects comprises yet another medium for her most transcending, as well as sacred, avenue of expression.

SAULS, FREDERICK (Painter, Printmaker)
1110 N. Hudson Ave., Studio C, Los Angeles, CA 90038

Born: 1934 *Awards:* Harry Lord Ford Prize for Creativity, UC-Berkeley *Collections:* University of California Museum, Berkeley; U. of Minnesota *Ex-hibitions:* R.J. Reynolds Gallery, Lexington, KY; U. of Minnesota Museum *Education:* Stanford U.; UC-Berkeley *Dealer:* Nicolle Mansillon, Los Angeles

He is "willing to let a work find its way to extinction," and he paints with a metallic palette of gold, silver, copper and bronze and a Zen brushstroke that demands complete and immediate success. Influenced by Sidney Gordin and Peter Voulkos, his professors at Berkeley, he is an abstract impressionist whose work sometimes contains traces of figuration. He combines metals to create abstract-impressionist bas reliefs of desert landscapes. With sunni ink on paper, he illustrates poetry and creates landscapes of the female figure.

SAUNDERS, RAYMOND JENNINGS (Painter)
6007 Rock Ridge Blvd., Oakland CA 94618

Born: 1934 *Awards:* Guggenheim Fellowship; NEA Fellowship *Collections:* Museum of Modern Art, NYC; Whitney Museum, NYC *Exhibitions:* San Francisco Museum of Modern Art; Oakland Museum *Education:* Pennsylvania Academy of the Fine Arts; U. of Pennsylvania; Carnegie Institute of Technology; California College of Arts and Crafts *Dealer:* Stephen Wirtz Gallery, San Francisco

In his works, loose brushstrokes and large color fields of abstract expressionism are often combined with pop images such as cartoon characters, with stencilled letters or numbers and with graffiti to create a variety of humorous and enigmatic works reflecting personal experiences and Black history in an urban environment. During the decade of the 1960s, he did not produce art of protest but rather was more interested in the art of genre. His media have also included collage and assemblage, as well as watercolor, as in *Suite of Flowers*.

SAVIO, ALICIA (Painter)
1417 N. Fairview Ct., Burbank, CA 91505

Born: 1956 *Exhibitions:* Sunset Art/Simmonson Gallery, Glendale; Master Gallery, Burbank *Education:* Escuela Nacional de Danzas, Buenos Aires *Dealer:* John Lacey, Burbank

After graduating from art school, she specialized in dry point drawing and developed an interest in capturing the human body in movement. For many years she sketched dancers in theaters and dressing rooms. In 1978, she became a disciple of the master, Vicente Forte, who encouraged her to explore the dancer theme in a watercolor medium. The increased plasticity and freedom of watercolor brought her to a style comparable to that of Degas. She then began using an acrylic gouache technique on rag paper and developed a rich contemporary style which dramatically expressed her Argentine, Italian and Arabic heritage. Her graduate studies in San Francisco have further accentuated her profound and life-long interest in the female anatomy.

SAVO, JOAN (Painter)
1318 Miles Ave., Pacific Grove, CA 93950

Born: 1918 *Awards:* Artist in Residence, American College, Viborg, Denmark *Collections:* Oakland Museum; Santa Barbara Museum *Exhibitions:* The Palace of the Legion of Honor, San Francisco: Crocker Art Museum, Sacramento *Dealer:* Victor Fischer Galleries, San Francisco/Oakland; Site 311 Gallery, Pacific Grove/Santa Monica

Aloah Saxon, *Driftwood,* 16 x 20, oil

Morris Sachs, *Celebration,* 36" high, purpleheart

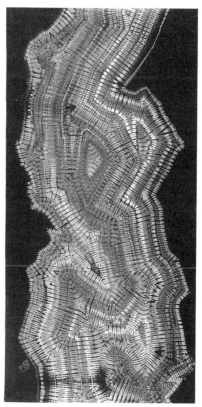

Carter Smith, *Freeform I,* 87 x 46, hand pleated fold dye silk

Her early large oils were alternately figurative and abstract. She integrated a single undetailed figure, not wholly revealed, with a light background. Her abstractions were abstract expressionist in treatment, with highly contrasting values. Recently, color has gained importance, and her figures now waver between representation and semi-abstraction. Recent abstract work is color-field painting, in which she keeps forms to a minimum and her subject is color itself. Though she chooses a predominant color, her painting's significance lies in the interaction she creates by manipulating and arranging color.

SAXON, ALOAH E. (Painter)
1734 Porterfield Pl., El Cajon, CA 92019

Born: 1920 *Awards:* Blue Ribbon, National University Annual Art Festival *Exhibitions:* Southwest Artists Gallery, San Diego; Alpine Frontier Gallery *Education:* Brown College *Dealer:* Southwestern Artists Gallery, San Diego

A painter of seascapes, she received her formal training in Iowa and studied with William De Shazo in California. She paints on masonite board with an oil-based medium that gives her work a luminosity, as if many coats of gloss had been applied. Her inspiration comes from an oceanside life. Serenity and stability are apparent in her expressive, surrealistic work. The viewer is allowed to feel the movement of the water in these paintings of great depth and inner light. Love of the ocean can be felt in her work, which goes beyond photo-realism.

SCANGA, ITALO (Sculptor)
7127 Olivetas, La Jolla, CA 92037

Born: 1932 *Awards:* Cassandra Foundation Grant; NEA Grant *Collections:* Los Angeles County Museum of Art; Oakland Museum *Exhibitions:* Dorothy Goldeen Gallery, Santa Monica; Whitney Museum, NYC *Education:* Michigan State U. *Dealer:* Bette Stoler Gallery, NYC

He was born in Italy, settled in America in 1947 and served in the U.S. Army. After formal study in sculpture, he began to employ mixed media, including found objects, to create installations that present "unresolved cultural value cohabiting the integrated structure." For example, room-sized presentations display religious kitsch resembling icons, sprinkled with red paint, hung near the floor. Urns containing grains or spices such as chili powder are to be smelled or tasted as the viewer kneels to see a painting of Christ or the Madonna. Menacing farm implements often lean against the wall, and dried herbs are hung from the ceiling. Thus he creates a kind of shrine using the imagery of martyrdom typical to poor households in Italy. His complicated iconography points to the disparity between the violent suffering of martyrs and the religious devotional images that glorify the pain, creating a new kind of provocative folklore.

SCHAIRER, MARY (Collage Artist)
11750 Chenault St., Los Angeles, CA 90049

Born: 1919 *Awards:* Purchase Award, Annual California Print and Drawing Exhibition, Chapman College, Orange *Collections:* Chapman College, Orange; Movie Store, Inc., Los Angeles *Exhibitions:* Art Center College of Design; Galeria Ocaso, Los Angeles *Education:* Scripps College; Otis Art Institute *Dealer:* Art Space, Los Angeles

Her original love was drawing. As she became increasingly fascinated by the simultaneous co-existence of the bizarre and the ordinary, she began to make drawings combining images from her imagination with those of the world around her. Eventually, she began to create collages from photocopies of her drawings. Her works are replete with the juxtapositions of visual and thematic opposites: the contemporary with the antique, the man-made with the natural, the feminine with the masculine. In the early 1980s, the passage of time began to interest her, the time in which the ordinary aspects of present experience combine with historical and mythic concerns. She currently combines her own drawings, cut-outs and photocopies of her work with the rich supply of visual materials that are widely available. Her works develop as she comes upon unplanned ideas and relationships. As the collage evolves, it becomes dense and multi-layered, and thus, in itself becomes a metaphor for time.

SCHARF, BARRY W. (Painter, Sculptor)
2034 Oak Glen Pl., Los Angeles, CA 90039

Born: 1946 *Awards:* Hancock Park Art Scholarship *Exhibitions:* L.A.C.E. Gallery; Los Angeles Museum of Science and Industry *Education:* Otis Art Institute; East Carolina U., Greenville, NC

Influenced by Isamu Noguchi, he carves marble abstractions based on ancient cultures. These small pieces look as though they came from ancient tombs. With names such as *Aztec II* and *Artifact,* they are models for commissions in park and building settings. His paintings are serious explorations and have been influenced by Jasper Johns, Stella, Picasso, Ben Shawn and Rothko. He constructs architectural, cross-hatched acryiic pieces by folding and cutting paper into three-dimensional objects. These pieces are bold in design and color. His oils are visions molded into an abstract, lyrical world that reflects his insight and compassion for the human spirit.

SCHEER, ELAINE (Sculptor, Mixed Media Artist)
4333 Holden St., Emeryville, CA 94608

Born: 1958 *Awards:* Arts/Industry Residency, Kohler Co.; Isaac Walters Sculpture Award *Exhibitions:* San Francisco Museum of Modern Art Rental Gallery *Education:* San Francisco Art Institute *Dealer:* Dorothy Weiss Gallery, San Francisco

She was primarily influenced by John Roloff and Robert Rasmussen and created large ceramic and mixed-media sculptures exploring the life and spirit of supposedly inanimate objects. *Mounds,* for example, is a playful display of five mounds made of various materials set on four legs. Other work is of a larger scale, both physically and thematically. *Peace Theater* features a long rectangular ditch with a large globe at one end, surrounded by school-type desks and chairs. This "participatory installation" presents itself to viewers as an opportunity to contribute their expressions of concern for planetary survival actively.

SCHEIR, TOM (Painter)
Contemporary Artist's Services, 9520 Jefferson Blvd., Culver City, CA 90232

Born: 1953 *Collections:* Urban Center, Tampa, FL; Westin Tabor Center Hotel, Denver, CO *Exhibitions:* Los Angeles County Museum of Art; Los Angeles Municipal Gallery *Education:* Yale U.

Betty Riis, *Cocktail Party,* 40 x 50, oil. Courtesy: Knowles Gallery, La Jolla, CA

Cheresé Ross, *Sea Lion Lookout,* 18 x 24, goauche. Courtesy: D.M. Ortiz

Gloria Ross, *Alpha #VIII,* 29 x 41, monoprint. Courtesy: Select Art, Dallas, TX

Ron Russell, *Lumensomnia,* 36 x 48, lacquer. Courtesy: Americana Gallery, Carmel, CA

J. McNeil Sargent, *Les Fleurs,* 22 x 30, monotype.
Courtesy: Tarbox Gallery, San Diego

Julie Lutz Simmons, *Arch Rival II,*
30 x 40, mixed water media

Dorothy Strait, *Wolf Dancers,* 36 x 48, acrylic

A. Secunda, *And God Created the Earth,*
96 x 48, collage, 1981. Courtesy: Eileen Michel,
Owl 57 Galleries, Woodmere, N.Y.

Morris Sachs, *Venus,* 18" high, brazilian marnut

Vincent Suez, *Honey's Dream,* 22 x 12, glazed
and fired clay cone 5 with china paints. Photograph: Hudson Pate

Jill Sattler, *Emanation,* 96 x 48, metallic reflective
mediums, oil on canvas. Photograph: WM. B. Dewey

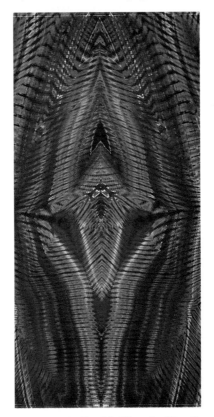

Carter Smith, *Double Phoenix,* 87 x 43,
hand-pleated fold dye silk

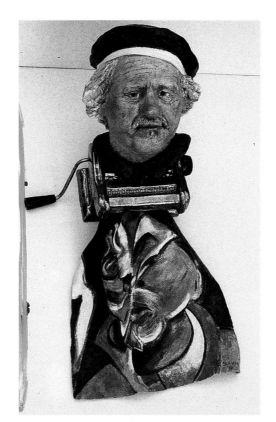

Jean Sillman, *Dynamic Interplay II,* 26 x 16 x 17, ceramic.
Courtesy: Natsoulas/Novelozo Gallery

Jean Swiggett, *Moroccan Rug,* 72 x 48, oil on linen

Aloah Saxon, *The Gulls,* 24 x 48, oil. Courtesy: Robert Stephens

Emilio Soltero, *Classical Stratification,* 48 x 96, oil

Donna Kario Salem, *Overcoming a Corner Bias,*
65 x 34 x 27, bronze

Sylvia Shap, *California Male, 1983,* 74 x 50, oil

Vladimir Sokolov, *Electra,* 72 x 48,
mixed media collage on canvas

Howard Smith, *Labyrinth, 1988,* 20 x 16,
photographic oils on direct positive print

Mikki Staton, *Giant Buddha,* 48 x 48, harra wood.
Courtesy: Edward S. Curtis Gallery, San Anselmo, CA

Ruth Surdez, *Covenant,* 90 x 36, wood.
Courtesy: Sue & Gary Foster, Carmichael, CA

Kumiko Sudo, *Love is Victorious,* 92 x 66, fabric

J.L. Searle-Kubby, *Grace,* 19 x 7 x 6, bronze

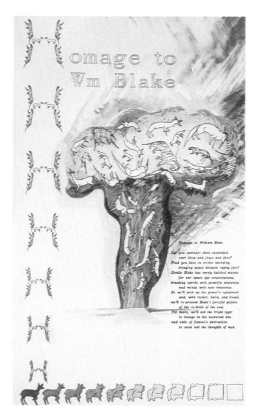

Edith Smith, *Homage to William Blake,*
22 x 15, computer-assisted etching

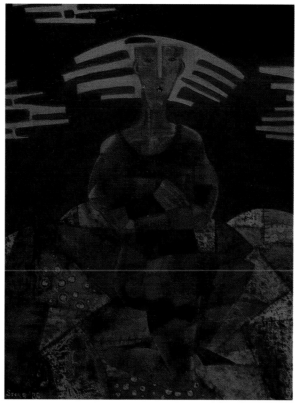

J.L. Sicre, *Portrait of a Western Man,* 12 x 9, oil on canvas
Lee-Lanning Gallery, Sedona, AZ

S. Sylvester, *Kaibab-Mountain Lying on its Side/Synchromy: Red-Orange,* 21 x 29, acrylic emulsion/F.J. head paper

Gary Slater, *Arriba,* 108 x 60 x 24, copper, water.
Courtesy: Elaine Horwitch Galleries

Kristina Simkins, *Far East Romance,* 30 x 22, watercolor.
Courtesy: Desert Moon Gallery, Reno, NV

Emelda Darlene Shirinian, *Once Upon a Time,* (top) 40 x 30, (bottom) 60 x 40,
oil on canvas Photograph: John Mueller, Carmel

Duncan Simcoe, *Song #1,* 79 x 61, oil and
collage on canvas and panel

Rena Small, *Live/Die II,* 20 x 24, Polaroid.
Courtesy: Polaroid Collection, Cambridge, MA

The structure of the sacred in European culture supplies a wealth of distilled, elemental forms through which he constructs an elusive architecture of the imagination. A series based on altarpieces isolates the pointed, parabolic and bisected arches, the narrow ribbons of the frames in favor of detail. The flanking panels that fold over the central image and the predella panels that act as glosses or pictorial footnotes to the main theme serve as components to a vocabulary of form. Since he made a trip to Europe, his paintings have explored the columns, pediments and flattened, punctured facades of northern Italy, and the repetition and schematized plant forms of Moorish design. Brilliant blue, red, green and pink acrylics have rich, textured surfaces rather than their inherent glossy sheen. Sky blues are veiled in milky washes; turquoises shimmer like folded silk. Paint-crayon gives a child-like immediacy to certain sections of canvas. Fragments of gold-leaf are scattered over other parts to evoke ancient mosaics.

SCHINDLER, WILLIAM (Sculptor)
4602 Van Dyke Ave., San Diego, CA 92116

Born: 1946 *Exhibitions:* Artplex Gallery; Circle Gallery, San Diego *Education:* Oberlin College; Stanford U.

Intrigued by the evocative power of broken and fragmented objects, he began to experiment with cracked, polished marble, arranged in shallow boxes filled with sand. Later, patined copper elements, suggesting totems or swords, linked marble pieces in a series entitled "Imagined Relics." Recently, he has begun to include other materials in his work such as brushed aluminum, copper wire and black granite. Wrapped with copper wire, scallop-edged pieces of marble interact with a duller, brushed aluminum surface, creating a sense of increasing energy and vibration. Other pieces include table-top sized sculptures that employ geometric shapes or slightly fluted marble surfaces. The acid-washed copper elements appear to be ambiguously ancient in these arrangements.

SCHLEKER, OTHELL (Painter)
P.O. Box 109, Annona, TX 75550

Born: 1921 *Awards:* 1st Place at Local Shows *Collections:* Chuck Wagon Restaurant, Clarksville, TX; East Texas State Teachers College *Exhibitions:* Bird Nest Gallery, Dallas; Perryton Country Club, TX *Education:* U. of Texas, Arlington *Dealer:* Bird Nest Gallery, Dallas

She studied oil painting with Robert Goen for many years on Long Island, summered in New Jersey, and often traveled to the Delaware Water Gap or Chadds Ford, Pennsylvania to be near the world of Andrew Wyeth. During that period, her admiration for the works of Everett Sloan led her to a more realistic style of rendering. Since returning to her home state of Texas, she has made a career of depicting Texas' old historic buildings. She normally renders many of a single town's historic buildings on a single canvas.

SCHMALTZ, ROY E. (Painter)
1020 Whistler Drive, Suisun, CA 94585

Born: 1936 *Awards:* Fulbright Fellowship; National Art Award, Chautauqua Institute *Collections:* M.H. de Young Memorial Museum, San Francisco; Clemson University *Exhibitions:* M. H. De Young Memorial Museum, San Francisco; UC-Santa Cruz *Education:* San Francisco Art Institute

His work has evolved gradually to figuration using representational elements. Images from dreams have predominated the subject matter in recent years, the pieces worked large in acrylic with oil glazing. Trees are common recurring elements, as in *The Family Tree*, which depicts an animal devouring the tree. Bright colors are applied thickly in a gestural style, leaving a textured surface. Pollock, de Kooning and Guston were important early influences.

SCHMITT, CARL (Ceramist)
145 E. Clinton, Fresno, CA 93704

Born: 1956 *Exhibitions:* Washington Square Gallery, Yountville; Concepts Gallery, San Francisco

He is a ceramist whose primary concerns are rhythm, color and texture. He began his artistic career at the age of eleven, when his father began tutoring him in oil painting. Through his school years, he excelled at brushstrokes, and developed a unique multidisciplinary style. He now scores the surfaces of his ceramic vessels and wall reliefs with complimentary lines or waves that are reminiscent of Southwestern imagery. He then sandblasts the unfired clay to give the surface depth. Finally he low-fires the piece, leaving a porous surface, which he airbrushes or colors with a bisque stain. His clay surface glows and vibrates; the overall effect has been likened to a photograph etched on clay.

SCHOENBERG, BETTY (Painter, Mixed Media Artist)
1753 Sterns Dr., Los Angeles, CA 90035

Awards: 1st Prize, Painting, Westwood Center for the Arts; Traveling Award, Minnesota Museum of Art *Exhibitions:* Forbes Gallery, Santa Monica; Sciana Wachodnia Gallery, Warsaw, Poland *Education:* Cal. State-Dominguez Hills

She works in a variety of media and styles, and has been influenced by an array of artists and movements. Although she most enjoys painting in oil, she is intrigued by the three-dimensional effects she can achieve with modeling compound and encaustic. She also works in acrylics, collage, mixed media, printing and sculpture. Influenced by the boldness of the the German Expressionists and by the sensuality and intellectuality of Kandinsky and Klee, she makes bold images in bright colors. These works are emphatic comments on the world we live in. The strong feminine imagery in the works of contemporary women artists such as Judy Chicago, Gelah Hirsh and Louise Bourgeois has influenced her own "Ancient Goddesses" series. Other motifs and images in her work are derived from African art ancient cave paintings, Oceanic, Greek and Persian art, and by the symbol systems of Native American cultures.

SCHOENFELD, DIANA (Photographer)
P.O. Box 596, Loleta, CA 95551

Born: 1949 *Awards:* NEA Fellowship; Reva and David Logan Grant for New Writing in Photography, Boston U. *Collections:* San Francisco Museum of Modern Art; Graham Nash *Exhibitions:* San Francisco Museum of Modern Art; U. of Michigan Hospital *Education:* U. of New Mexico, Albuquerque

From 1970 to the mid-1980s, she shot large-format (4 by 5 feet and 5 by 7 feet) still lifes. The early pieces were contact-printed in the 19th century style—exposed and developed in sunlight, then toned in gold chloride. In the manner of a collage artist, she created a visual choreography of natural objects, photographs and other imagery. Her last series of this era, "Fractures and Severances: Patient as Artist," dealt with the wave of invisible aftershocks she experienced after receiving a head injury. These photographs met with unexpected response from social, medical and therapy professionals. Recently, she has been photographing in muted color, using square and diamond formats and emphasizing objects in space—usually vast, serene and mythic landscapes. Her recent projects include photographing symbolic sculptural environments in contemporary society and curating an exhibit based upon a soon to be published essay.

SCHONEBAUM, JUDITH (Painter, Mixed Media Artist)
627 N. La Jolla Ave., Los Angeles, CA 90048

Born: 1947 *Exhibitions:* Improvisation, Los Angeles; Zerrien Studios, Venice *Education:* U. of Vermont

With an exuberant use of pale pinks, pale greens and gold and silver highlights, she executes thoroughly contemporary works in oils, mixed media and pastels. A native of Baltimore, she has embraced the artistic environment of the West Coast. The light, color and climate of Southern California are strong influences on her work, as are her historical roots in plein air impressionism. The pieces in her recent series of abstracted quilt patterns on texturized rice paper resemble oriental scrolls and were inspired by her recent pregnancy.

SCHONZEIT, BEN (Painter, Photographer)
109 Mercer St., New York, NY 10012

Born: 1942 *Awards:* Butler Medal *Collections:* Metropolitan Museum of Art, NYC; Guggenheim Museum, NYC *Exhibitions:* Modernism, San Francisco; J.J. Brookings Gallery, San Jose

He studied primarily with abstract expressionists and Bauhaus teachers, and most of his early work shows cubist and surrealist influences. Upon returning from a year in Europe, he began working in photography; this led to paintings in a photo-realist manner in the late 1960s, much of which were larger-than-life still lifes executed with an airbrush. Later, he abandoned the airbrush for a more expressive use of materials. "The Music Room," his series of paintings and works on paper, was based on a single photograph of a baroque music room and marked a departure from a realist approach to a more inventive, dramatic style based on photography. The most recent work contains cubist passages; real objects are now depicted in an environment created by the artist. Although his subjects are still lifes, portraits, figures, interiors and landscapes, the works always maintain a surreal quality and are marked by a synthesis of abstraction, realism and drama.

SCHRANK, SHIRLEY (Painter, Sculptor)
609 Maureen Lane, Pleasant Hill, CA 94523

Born: 1933 *Exhibitions:* Diablo Valley College Art Gallery, Pleasant Hill; Contra Costa Alliance for the Arts, Walnut Creek Civic Arts Gallery

Her studies in drawing, painting, ceramics and figure sculpture led to a strong interest in working in clay, doing figure sculptures and pastel portraits. She is most interested in portraying people as individuals, rather than idealizations of people in pure form. The works of Rodin and Graham have influenced her the most, and she strives to achieve a style somewhere between these two masters. Most of her recent imagery in sculpture revolves around depictions of

women's true selves. Her portraiture is informed by a desire to capture the essence or personality of the subject. She paints from a clear, bright palette of over fifty colors, building up successive layers of color and form.

SCHRUT, SHERRY (Painter, Mixed Media Artist)
911 Honeywood Rd., Los Angeles, CA 90049

Born: 1928 *Awards:* Long Beach Museum of Art; Riverside Museum of Art *Collections:* Skirball Museum, Los Angeles; Hebrew Union College, Los Angeles *Exhibitions:* Los Angeles County Museum of Art; Renwick Gallery, Smithsonian Institution, Washington, D.C. *Education:* Wayne State U.; UCLA *Dealer:* Ruth Bachnofer Gallery, Los Angeles; Eva Cohon Gallery, Chicago

Mixed-media pieces explore the process of archaeology, employing materials such as folded and stained watercolors, handmade, mildewed and antique papers, gold and silver leaf, dyes and ancient calligraphy. She takes license with fraying, cutting, soaking and otherwise processing materials along with watercolor washes and collage techniques, retrieving and assembling these arbitrary shards of various and mysterious origins in order to create a unity from disparity, as well as a holographic sense.

SCHULMAN, KAREN GORDON (Photographer)
4905 Varna Ave., Sherman Oaks, CA 91423

Born: 1946 *Collections:* Agfa Gevaert Photo Collection, Ridgefield Park, NJ; Graham Nash Photo Collection, Los Angeles *Exhibitions:* Sonrisa Gallery, Los Angeles; Otis Art Institute *Education:* Pennsylvania State U.; UCLA

Using photography as a means of self-expression, she is best known for her hand-colored black-and-white photographs in which she takes what is real and superimposes elements of her own imagination. "I love to hand color my favorite images. It gives me the freedom to create a vision of the way I see the world." For technique, oil colors are added and subtracted—areas are highlighted with pencils—until the desired effect is achieved. She recently began working on "Visions of Paradise", a series which consists of hand-colored 16-by-20-inch and 20-by-24-inch black-and-white photographs of above water and underwater scenes which either seem to be "Paradise" or are painted to resemble "Paradise". One photograph in this series, *Red Dawn in Paradise*, is a 20-by-24-inch black-and-white photograph with a painted red, orange and purple sky with rainbow-colored palm fronds in the foreground, a good example of her desire to depict emotional skies and surreal landscapes.

SCHULZE, JOAN (Fiber Artist)
808 Piper Ave., Sunnyvale, CA 94087

Born: 1936 *Awards:* Purchase Award, City of Palo Alto; Visiting Artist, Australia Craft Council *Collections:* Kaiser Permanente, Denver; R. Dakin International, San Francisco *Exhibitions:* Traveling Exhibit, Western Art Museum Association, San Francisco; Pennsylvania State Art Museum, College Station, PA *Education:* U. of Illinois, Urbana

She uses many techniques, including cyanotype, appliquéing, hand- and machine-quilting, dyeing, painting and piecing to create quilts and collages. Materials include silk, nylon and shiny mylar. Her small-sized fabric collages are worked spontaneously in

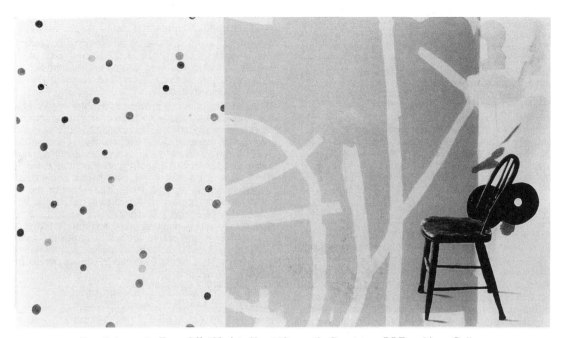

Ben Schonzeit, *Face Off (Chair),* 60 x 118, acrylic Courtresy: J.J.Brookings Gallery

Paul Sershon, *One Great Ride After Another: Tilt-a-whirl,* 36 x 84, acrylic on canvas

an additive and subtractive manner. The large quilts result from drawings and a more conscious methodology. Images are abstract diaries of her thoughts, dreams and impressions. Works include a feminist two-quilt piece entitled *Marriage: Woman/Man*, and *The Bridge*, a depiction of the Statue of Liberty and bridges symbolizing freedom.

SCHULZKE, MARGOT S. (Painter)
P.O. Box 5032, Auburn, CA 95604

Born: 1938 *Awards:* Advisory Board and Past President, Pastel Society of the West Coast *Exhibitions:* Louvre-Insight Gallery, Grass Valley; Artworks Gallery, Fair Oaks *Education:* Brigham Young U. *Dealers:* Artworks Gallery, Fair Oaks; Old Church Gallery, Meadow Vista

While in school, she developed a style which merged elements of cubism with abstract expressionism. She was primarily interested in the visual rhythms she could create with line, texture, color and overlapping and intersecting planes. Working mainly in oils, she achieved rich impasto effects and jewel-like colors. Her current style is more influenced by the works of Degas and Vermeer. It expresses deep space and volume, while continuing the rhythmic patterns of her earlier works. She paints studies of interiors and exteriors, landscapes and figurative subjects, in vibrant pastels applied over gesso and ground pumice, which has been brushed onto museum rag board. Strong linear patterns bring together rich textural effects and vivid, nuanced color fields.

SCHUMACHER, SUZANNE (Painter)
3037 Myrtle St., Oakland, CA 94609

Born: 1951 *Awards:* Menlo Park Arts Festival *Exhibitions:* San Francisco Museum of Modern Art Gallery; Twin Pines Art Center, Belmont *Education:* San Francisco Art Institute

An expressive, non-objective painter, she has been influenced by Jay Defeo, Manuel Neri and Matt Mullican. She combines a personal vocabulary with formal concerns, and joins images of studio installations with observations of natural phenomena. In a recent series, images of circles were used both to delineate form and space, and to signify male and female. She relates aspects of the human condition to natural images, such as her pond series, and recent works denoting the tensions and emotions moving between people.

SCHWARTZMAN, GLENDA (Painter, Multimedia Artist)
2700 Neilson Way, Santa Monica, CA 90405

Born: 1939 *Collections:* Arco, Los Angeles; Colegems, Los Angeles *Exhibitions:* Strasinger Gallery, Venice; Lilia Ivy Gallery, Santa Monica; De Vorson Gallaery *Education:* Chouniard Art Institute

She has always been interested in exploring various aspects of materials. These have included lucite and acrylic, gravel and make-up used as a drawing medium. She has recently begun working with large (48 to 60 inches in diameter), round surfaces and images of planets, stars, moons and other astronomical objects. Executed in mauve, gray, blue, purple and earth tones, these paintings are characterized by layered images over muted backgrounds, emphasizing the space and shape of the painting.

SCHWENNESEN, CAROL (Painter)
606 E. Sixth St., Claremont, CA 91711

Born: 1945 *Exhibitions:* Double Rocking G Gallery, Los Angeles; Cal. Poly U., Pomona *Education:* Western Washington U.; Claremont Graduate School *Dealers:* ToLuca Lake Gallery, Los Angeles; Delilah Staton, Santa Monica

While she includes references to the objective world in her painting, she has always been drawn to the internal expressive perspective, as exemplified in the works of Van Gogh, Jawlensky and Munch. References to the internal and intangible take precedence in her work, as it relates to a specific transformative condition within the human form and mind. She began her current artistic inquiry in the mid-1980s, working with the expressive quality of paint, as it relates to internal human experience. With brightly colored oil paint on large surfaces, an action/reaction process gradually brings to form the environment of a condition with no visual precedence. In addition to many exhibits and showings, she has also had works included in the set design for the film, *Beetlejuice*.

SCOFFONE, CRAIG (Photographer)
1169 Husted Ave., San Jose, CA 95125

Born: 1961 *Exhibitions:* The Vortex, Palo Alto; Museum of Modern Photography, Antwerp, Belgium; Glover-Zaborny Gallery, San Francisco

Working in both color and black and white, he prefers simple forms with an emphasis on strong graphic design and texture. He has experimented with many different films and techniques, and his favorite subjects are figure abstractions, still lifes and urban and natural landscapes. His current projects comprise work in all of these areas, with a concentration on still lifes.

SCOTT, DONNA BEAR (Graphic Artist, Ceramist)
1924 Fearn Ave., Los Osos, CA 93402

Born: 1933 *Exhibitions:* Carpinteria, Santa Barbara; California Polytechnic State U., McPhee Galerie *Education:* Cuesta College

The daughter of painter and curator, Donald Bear, she grew up seeing artistic expression as a way of life. She began drawing and painting at a young age, but it wasn't until 1953 that she began working with enamel on copper. She calls herself an artisan. Over the years, she has worked with many different media. Recently, she has been making color pencil drawings from slides. She begins with an enlargement, and then works intuitively. Her subjects are often well known people, such as a piece which depicts Pavarotti singing. Her present clay work is made on a potter's wheel. She is now exploring the sculptural qualities of clay, applying glazes and stains with airbrush.

SCOTT, JANE W. (Painter)
3178 Dona Marta Dr., Studio City, CA 91604

Born: 1943 *Collections;* White House Collection, Washington, D.C.; American Embassy in Australia *Exhibitions:* Grand Central Gallery, NYC; Peterson Gallery, Beverly Hills

Her images are those of an idyllic turn-of-the-century and early 20th-century America. In bright, uninhibited colors she paints the simplicities of skating on moon-lit ponds, country picnics, bobbing for apples at Halloween, hay rides and quilting bees. For subject matter she consults her memory of an eastern Pennsylvania

Margot S. Schulzke, *Ribbons,* 30 x 38, pastel. Courtesy: Mr. & Mrs. Neil Walker

Kim Shae-Tofaute, *Johnny, San Francisco,* color photo

LOOK AT THEM,

THE POODLE-FAN TREES,

UPRIGHT

AS ANY SELF-RIGHTEOUS

BASTARD

PERPENDICULAR

ONE-WAY ROOFTOP BRUSHES

RUSH NOTHING

TOUCH EPHEMERAL GASSES

Duncan Simcoe, *Poodle-Fan Trees,* 80 x 71,
oil and collage on canvas and panel

Joan Schulze, *Earthquake Country,* 85 x 74, quilt

Harvey Sadberry, *The Cannotos 1,* 56 x 64, acrylic on canvas

Betty Schoenberg, *Cityscape, Skyward II,* 48 x 48, oil on unstitched canvas

upbringing, or travels to New England where she photographs landscapes, buildings and oddities. Few of her paintings, however reflect real, existing scenes. Almost all of her compositions are imaginary, drawn from her own thoughts and emotions. A study of her paintings in chronological order reveals the growth of the youngsters who are her daughter and son.

SCOTT, MORT (Sculptor)
P.O. Box 2823, McKinleyville, CA 95521

Born: 1950 *Exhibitions:* The Crocker Kingsley, Sacramento; City Gallery, Sacramento *Education:* Memphis Academy of Arts

Earlier work on canvas centered on the figure. Later, he incorporated its abstraction into an abstract landscape. This approach became more focused once he was exposed to bronze casting at the Memphis Academy of Arts. Still figurative, his sculptures express a personal interpretation of land forms and humanity's relationship to them. Inherent in the works is the idea that we have interfered in nature, imposing certain structures of our own. He retains an element of humor in his approach. Concrete daily objects may be added to sculptures to render abstractions recognizable.

SEARLE-KUBBY, J.L. (Sculptor)
1738 Wynkoop, Suite 101, Denver, CO 80202

Born: 1938 *Collections:* National Jewish Hospital; Cowboy Hall of Fame *Exhibitions:* TWA European Tour; World's Fair, Knoxville, TN *Dealers:* Simic, Beverly Hills; Eagle Gallery, La Jolla; Mammen II, Scottsdale, AZ; E.H. Lawrence, Aspen

She sculpts in bronze, and her subjects are primarily women in motion. Earlier in her life, she worked as an industrial and engineering illustrator, the head of a newspaper art department and the owner of a national advertising agency. She came upon sculpture almost by accident, but soon found her interest permanent. The culture and rituals of Native Americans were the focus of her earliest work; women dancers, either sculpted or painted in oil or pastel, are the focus of her most recent work. A turning point in her life occurred in 1982, when she was gored by a buffalo and hurled thirteen feet in the air. The incident, reported in the national press, yielded the inspiration for her very next sculpture, *The Buffalo*.

SEBASTIAN, BARBARA (Painter, Ceramist)
1777 Yosemite Ave., #4B-1, San Francisco, CA 94124

Born: 1942 *Exhibitions:* Montalvo Center for the Arts, Saratoga; Civic Arts Gallery, Walnut Creek *Education:* San Jose State U. *Dealer:* Susan Cummins Gallery, Mill Valley

Initially, she was a vessel maker, looking at vessels as containers of energy and atmosphere, but she gradually progressed from three-dimensional vessels to flattened clay slabs as wall hangings. She used symbolic references of doorways to express what she believes is the synchronicity of past and present, painting directly on clay with oil, pastel, pencil and acrylic, using purples, grays, yellow-oranges and reds. Her concern with line, edge and surface, and her three-dimensional, illusionistic painting make her clay forms both two- and three-dimensional.

SECUNDA, ARTURO (Collage Artist, Printmaker)
P.O. Box 6363, Beverly Hills, CA 90212

Born: 1927 *Collections:* Palm Springs Desert Museum; San Francisco Museum of Modern Art *Exhibitions:* Circle Fine Art, San Diego; U. of Judaism, Los Angeles; Galerie Cramer, Geneva, Switzerland; Eileen Michel Gallery, Woodmere, NY *Dealer:* Nahan Gallery, NY

His torn paper collages and limited edition books are internationally recognized for their masterful display of color and composition. He began doing collage work after tearing up some of his watercolor paintings. As he looked at the pieces lying on the floor, he became fascinated by the juxtaposition of color and torn edges. Since then, he has refined his various tearing techniques and prefers silkscreen or handmade lithographs to watercolor. After many years, he still finds tearing paper to be a moment of artistic expression rather than technical calculation. His landscapes exhibit, by turn, Oriental and traditional influences, and his work often refers to the spiritual relation between humanity and nature. He continues to create work with a clean, simple appearance and vast, echoing meaning.

SEEM, OLGA (Painter)
1205 Cleveland Rd., Glendale, CA 91202

Born: 1927 *Awards:* E. D. Foundation Grant *Collections:* Security Pacific Bank, Los Angeles; Hyatt Hotel Corporation *Exhibitions:* Space, Los Angeles; Miller Gallery, Palm Desert *Education:* UCLA *Dealer:* Space Gallery, Los Angeles

Her work always involved biomorphic imagery, but it wasn't until the late 1970s that the artist began infusing her painting with the intensity behind her concerns for the environment. Consequently, the aerial landscapes were abandoned for more intimate, ground-level views, intended to draw the viewer in. Her horizontal format allows room for the multiple view principle of her work. She enhances recognizable natural forms with unexpected colors. Skies can be greenish, or an energetic, hot red; flat, huge leaves stand serenely like heraldic shields. Many of these landscapes hit the viewer on a primal level. Like myth and folk tale, there is something both wondrous and ominous about them. Her use of light creates a tension and sense of expectancy that marks many cityscapes.

SEGEL, DAVID (Sculptor)
2007 Dell Ave., Venice, CA 90291

Born: 1921 *Awards:* 1st Carnegie Prize, Association Artists; Hallmark International Award *Collections:* Chad Everett *Exhibitions:* Galery Maeght, Paris; Ven-Diemen Lilenfeld Gallery, NYC *Education:* Institute of Design, Chicago *Dealer:* William Torphy, Los Angeles

After formal training in drawing and sculpting—training in abstract work at the Institute of Design (Bauhaus)—and several years with Fernand Leger in Paris, he portrayed human figures in abstract, yet recognizable ways. In this work, he used human satire to involve the observer. His recent three-dimensional sculpture combines a thorough knowledge of bronze, wood and clay. He approaches both light and serious subjects in a humorous way. He is able to take the viewer into the depths of design in a comprehensive and interpretive manner. Thus he hopes to create in the viewer an understanding of "modern art."

Olga Seem, *Solemn Mass,* 17 x 46, oil on canvas. Photographer: William Nettles

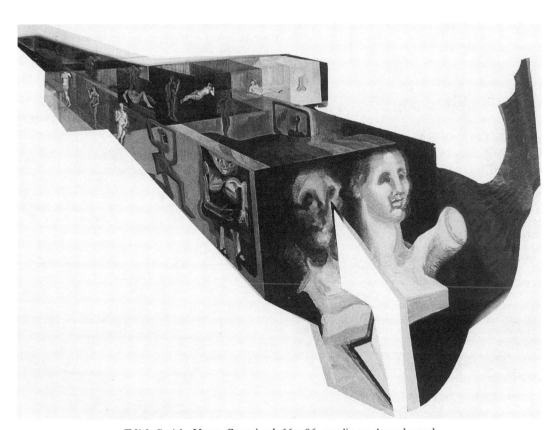

Edith Smith, *Venus Contained,* 66 x 96, acrylic on shaped wood

SEIM, JOHNSCOTT (Painter)
29 Downey, San Francisco, CA 94117

Born: 1954 *Collections:* 26th Floor Partners, Hartford Building, San Francisco *Exhibitions:* Collective exhibition to benefit the homeless, San Francisco; Au Coquelet, San Francisco *Education:* U. of San Francisco; Academy of Art College

The works of de Kooning and Van Gogh have had a profound influence on the development of his visual style and artistic approach. He especially admires Van Gogh's use of color as a structural, compositional element. Found objects inspire his sense of color and texture, and he uses masking, spray painting, sanding, taping, drawing and printing with acrylics to fill out his vision. He often begins by taping the borders of the canvas or by making X's on unprimed, hand-stretched canvas. Oddly shaped canvases, old window frames and personal religious iconography are hallmarks of his recent work.

SELTZER, ADELE (Painter)
1422 Edgewood Dr., Palo Alto, CA 94301

Born: 1941 *Awards:* California State Exposition *Collections:* Atlantic Richfield, Los Angeles; City of Palo Alto *Exhibitions:* De Saisset Museum, Santa Clara; Aldrich Museum of Contemporary Art, Ridgefield, CT *Education:* U. of Pennsylvania; San Jose State U. *Dealer:* Kathy Fimmel, San Mateo

Working with such materials as used metals, paper pulp and transformed fibers with rhoplex, she made constructions of land-oriented visions early in her career. Her recent use of pure canvas and paint has resulted in works of incandescent thought and near ultimate minimalism. These large-scale land images are harsh, yet human and strong. Her emotional use of color imbues the works with sensuality and a spiritual feeling. An admirer of Georgia O'Keeffe's sensual painting and concern with the commonplace, she devotes monumental-scale paintings to small segments of vision.

SELTZER, SELENE (Ceramic Tile Artist)
P.O. Box 4983, Foster City, CA 94404

Collections: Lincoln Plaza Office Building, Sacramento; Hotel Jerome, Aspen, CO *Education:* UC-Berkeley; UC-Davis

She creates tile murals in a variety of styles and colors, both abstract and representational. Much of her work decorates historic homes and businesses (the City of Modesto's McHenry Mansion, for instance), which involves a great deal of accurate replication and design work. Influenced by the art tile of the England's turn-of-the-century arts and crafts movement, her work has a vibrancy reminiscent of stained glass. She takes a unique approach to each project, carefully tailoring it to the location. Her range of techniques is impressive: Sumi-e brushwork on white earthenware, majolica mural work, onglaze, overglaze, lusters and the ancient "cuerda seca" technique, used by the Persians and the Moors. She also does commercial and residential commissions and projects.

SELVIN, NANCY (Mixed Media Artist)
745 Page St., Berkeley, CA 94710

Born: 1943 *Awards:* Skaggs Foundation; NEA Grant *Exhibitions:* Somar Gallery, San Francisco; ProArts Gallery, Oakland *Education:* UC-Berkeley

Her constructions are formal distillations of elements juxtaposing color, form and architectural space to create layered compositions. The works contain subtle relationships that require close observation in order to be consciously noticed. Her small-scale works exhibit a Japanese influence: concentration on muted colors, delicate form and a careful balance of elements. One example is a still life of a ceramic bowl on a tray with two or three rods of glass. The large-scale work often alludes to memories or inner places. The design and construction of a studio led directly to her parallel involvement with large-scale installation work. The installations, often based on photos, are temporary and site-specific and sometimes incorporate sound.

SEMLER, BLESSING (Painter, Printmaker)
12049 Iredell Street, Studio City, CA 91604

Born: 1916 *Awards:* Purchase Prize, Women Painters of the West; National Watercolor Society Award *Collections:* Janco-Dada Museum, EinHod, Israel; National Museum of History, Taipei, Taiwan *Exhibitions:* Mational Museum of History, Taipei; National Museum of Culture, Manila *Education:* UCLA; Otis Art Institute

A former professional harpist, she began making art in the wake of a physical disability. She has been influenced by such "right-brain" artists as Antoni Tapies, Alberto Burri and Antoni Clave, and she makes her own monotypes, monoprints and collographs with an explorer's sense of spontaneity. She paints, collages, tears and cuts, creating with virtually no limitations. Often she integrates pieces of etchings and parts of musical scores into her collages. Her colors are cool blues, greens, aquas and violets; her materials are acrylics, glass, string, nets, burlap, cheesecloth, rhoplex and fabric. She has studied paper-making techniques in Japan and Hawaii.

SERBIN, WALTER (Painter, Illustrator)
1608 Charles Rd., San Leandro, CA 94577

Born: 1914 *Exhibitions:* California State U.-Hayward; San Leandro Art Festival *Education:* Art Academy, Warsaw; Studio of Arts & Craft, Sao Paulo

While he was in Warsaw, his work encompassed posters, graphic art, wood sculpture and caricatures. During the twelve years he spent in Brazil, he continued in these media with the addition of scientific illustration, chronicling the ornithology and botany of the Amazon. He works primarily as an illustrator in a variety of media including oil, tempera, gouache and airbrush. The subject matter is always realistic, ranging in models from landscapes and seascapes to portraits, flowers and animals. His technique involves carefully controlled application of paint, never mixing colors. He also produces paper sculpture portraits of such notables as the Pope, using layered cut sheets of paper.

SERRA, RICHARD (Sculptor)
P.O. Box 645 Canal St. Station, New York, NY 10013

Born: 1939 *Awards:* Skowhegan Medal *Collections:* Museum of Modern Art, NYC; Whitney Museum, NYC *Exhibitions:* University Art Museum, Berkeley; Margo Leavin Gallery, Los Angeles *Education:* UC-Santa Barbara; Yale U. *Dealer:* Pace Gallery, NYC

An interest in process art and the quality of materials produced sculptures utilizing neon tubes, rubber, metal slabs and molten lead. The first of several "Splashpieces" was conducted in 1968, in which molten lead was flung onto the bottom of a wall. The next year, large

Roy Schmaltz, *Family Tree,* 56 x 96, oil and acrylic on canvas

Barbara Sowle, *Simone's Grove,* 36 x 48, acrylic

Blessing Semler, *Freedom,* 40 x 60, acrylic/collage paint-ing. Courtesy: Ruth Bachofner Gallery

metal sheets were leaned against each other, exploring aspects of gravity in the "Prop" series. Site sculptures beginning in the 1970s, such as "Shift," integrated the landscape with sculptural elements like cement or metal sheeting, in order to find "an awareness of physicality in time, space and motion . . . one's relation to the breadth of the land." He has also engaged in graphics work and filmmaking.

SERSHON, PAUL (Painter, Mixed Media Artist)
P.O. Box 634, Lotus, CA 95651

Born: 1952 *Exhibitions:* City Gallery, Sacramento; Jill Youngblood Gallery, Los Angeles *Education:* Sacramento State U. *Dealer:* City Gallery, Sacramento

He has been influenced by the pop art movement and by traditional American realist painters, Estes and Eddy, as is apparent in his large-scale watercolors. The transformation from single-image paintings to multiple-image paintings that are sometimes narrative developed from a series of small studies begun in late 1985. From these small studies grew complicated assemblage paintings utilizing two- and three-dimensional realistic and illusory imagery. To complete these works, he uses whatever materials are appropriate, including oil, acrylic, silkscreen, photographs, photocopies and various found objects.

SEWELL, LEO (Sculptor)
3614 Pearl St., Philadelphia, PA 19104

Born: 1945 *Collections:* NBC, NYC; Ripley's Believe It or Not Museum, St. Augustine, FL *Exhibitions:* J. Noblett, Sonoma; Security Pacific National Bank, Los Angeles *Education:* U. of Delaware

He grew up next to a dump and spent his childhood playing with any object that caught his eye. Today, he creates sculptures by assembling found and kitsch objects with nails, screws and bolts. Essentially self-taught as an artist, he has been influenced by the tenets of naive and grass-roots art.

SEXTON, EDWARD (Painter)
P.O. Box 181, Pt. Reyes Station, CA 94956

Born: 1942 *Exhibitions:* Gallery Route 1, Pt. Reyes Station *Education:* U. of Kansas

His early paintings were influenced structurally by Max Beckmann and Willem de Kooning; the use of color reflects the work of Cezanne, Bonnard and 20th-century American painting. After ten years of painting, he became drawn to sculpture, particularly to the work of Bruce Beasley and others working in plastic. During this period, he worked with fiberglass and cast resin, spraypainting the sculpture with automobile lacquers tinted with dyes. He continued to explore new colors and forms while creating floor lamps, small table lamps and masonite panels. After several years' hiatus from art, he returned to figure drawings and watercolors. His recent work has focused on paintings, monotype prints and sculpture. Paint is applied in a primitive manner in thick layers, using the full dark-to-light range of his early works. Crosses, triangles and prehistoric creatures comprise the dramatic content. Monotypes feature UFO shapes. Sculptural pieces include a fiberglass humanoid skull in a copper-leafed box.

SHACKELFORD, BUD (Painter)
11532 Rolling Hills Dr., El Cajon, CA 92020

Born: 1918 *Exhibitions:* National Academy of Design, NYC; American Watercolor Society, NYC *Education:* Chouinard Art Institute *Dealer:* Knowles Gallery, La Jolla

After working on *Bambi* and *Dumbo* for Disney, he worked in commercial art and advertising. In the 1950s, he decided to concentrate on fine arts work full-time. His earlier pictures depicted highly stylized wildlife, landscapes and seascapes in watercolor and acrylics. He has had three books published on his experimental painting techniques. Recently, he has directed his attention to wildlife preservation. His latest techniques employ pouring of rhythmic lines using liquid acrylic or oils directly on paper or canvas, using experimental methods to render texture and form. These paintings, often 3 by 5 feet in size, are concerned with motion, beauty of line and the depiction of real life.

SHADE, ELLEN KIRBY (Sculptor)
1617 26th St., Sacramento, CA 95816

Born: 1961 *Exhibitions:* 750 Gallery, Sacramento; Accurate Art Gallery, Sacramento *Education:* U. of Colorado, Boulder; Cal. State-Sacramento

While still in school, she was influenced by the art of primitive cultures, the paintings and sculptures of cubism and the works of the German Expressionists. She spent her time exploring three-dimensional form, in terms of the human figure. More recently, she has constructed sculptures from wooden frames, covered with a plaster material. The attainment of strong forms and the body language of human expression have been her main concerns in these pieces. She feels that her work makes use of the human figure to present the temporary, or indefinite, state of being, often found in human experience.

SHAE-TOFAUTE, KIM (Photographer)
5402 W. 36th St., Indianapolis, IN 46224

Born: 1958 *Exhibitions:* Indiana Architectual Society's Bookstore Gallery; Matrix-Bloomington IU School of Education, IN; Zionsville Munce Art Center, IN *Education:* San Francisco Art Institute

The series format intrigues her as a way for an artist to discover new qualities and elements in a subject. While early photographs explored the human form in a formalistic, documentary manner, recent work employs humor and surrealism. The artist turns the typical Midwestern town of Indianapolis into a decidedly weird place, where its enigmatic denizens perform bizarre tasks in their yard at night. Shooting primarily with infrared and color film, she creates cartoonish effects through her wide-angle lens. Her style and approach have been influenced by Walt Disney cartoons and the works of Linda Connor, Richard Misrach and John Pfahl.

SHAFFER, LINDA (Photographer)
1706 S. Genesee Ave., Los Angeles, CA 90019

Born: 1945 *Awards:* Art Quest *Exhibitions:* ARCO Photo Gallery; Los Angeles Municipal Art Gallery *Education:* Cal. State-Northridge *Dealer:* Malinda Wyatt, Beverly Hills

After treating a number of photogravures for Lee Rice and receiving some introduction to photography as a trade, she traveled with the intention of creating a body

Ali B. Shahroudi, *untitled,* 9 x 12, charcoal

Gary Slater, *Corona,* 96 x 48 x 216, stainless steel.
Courtesy: Elaine Horwitch Galleries

of photographic work in the manner of Eugene Smith or Josuf Kudelka. On various excursions between 1978 and 1983, she made fifty images of the acculturation of Tibetan refugees. In Los Angeles, her interest has tended toward what the camera can evoke rather than what it can describe. To this end, she has made a number of composite images and stilllifes involving broken glass over velvet, powders, oils, water, clocks, rocks, fruits, flowers and insects. Her style might be described as romantic surrealism.

SHAHROUDI, ALI B. (Painter)
P.O. Box 4371, Pocatello, ID 83205

Born: 1958 *Exhibitions:* Boise State Art Gallery; Stewart's Gallery *Education:* Idaho State U.

He began his career by studying figurative compositions, mainly concentrating on the human form represented in a semi-realistic manner, primarily in oil. He also experimented with coloration within the framework of traditional portraiture. Later, influenced by such artists as Delacroix, he began making use of bright colors in a loose fashion. The representation of the human form has become more abstract, and he has begun juxtaposing large patches of color that resemble abstract representations of flowers. He has also done abstract treatments of costumes and draperies.

SHANNON, M. K. (Sculptor)
484 Lakepark Ave., Ste. 269., Oakland CA 94610

Born: 1947 *Awards:* Joan Hegerman Spirit Award *Collections:* Shaklee Corporation; Charles Schwab Corporation *Exhibitions:* Cory Gallery, San Francisco; Kirsting Gallery, Sausalito *Education:* U. of New Mexico; Indiana U.

Her work is strongly influenced by her experiences as a child living in Japan, and her style incorporates the use of the abstract in conjunction with the figurative. Starting with harmonious and simple line and form balanced with texture and color, she creates a positive tension. Her association with Bob Bennett encouraged a greater use of motion in her work, and photographer Anne Noggle has influenced her placement of shape, form and contrast created by texture. In recent work, emphasis has been placed on abstract designs as wall reliefs. Her sculptures continue to deepen their exploration of a fluid, graceful form not commonly associated with bronze work. Slender, flowing shapes define negative space and air with a sense of weightlessness and momentum through gestural, calligraphic lines.

SHANNONHOUSE, SANDRA L. (Sculptor)
110 East E St., Benicia, CA 94510

Born: 1947 *Collections:* Utah Museum of Fine Art; Prudential Insurance *Exhibitions:* San Francisco Museum of Modern Art; Renwick Gallery of the Smithsonian Institution, Washigton DC *Education:* UC-Davis *Dealer:* Stephen Wirtz, San Francisco

Her earlier translucent porcelain sculptures of food, glasses, cups and flowers somehow implied a human presence. Stage design was an influence on her work, and she used life-size objects as stage props for real life. In 1976, she began to build the figure from the inside out. She juxtaposed organ forms in space and joined skeletal forms with specific accessories of dress to develop the sense of a unique person. In her recent bronze and clay work, she uses the female figure and symbols resonant with prehistoric, pagan eras (such as

the cross, the triangle, the heart and the vessel) to evoke that which is primordial or spiritually significant.

SHAP, SYLVIA (Painter, Mixed Media Artist)
648 N. Laurel Ave., Los Angeles, CA 90048

Born: 1948 *Collections:* San Antonion Museum of Art; Art Museum of South Texas *Exhibitions:* Art Museum of South Texas; Los Angeles Municipal Art Gallery

The child of holocaust survivors, she was raised in a psychologically intense environment in which she began making self-portraits at the age of six. She approaches each work as a psychological and journalistic treatise and aims both to elicit her subject's personality and to make a statement about individuals and mankind in general. Using recall as her primary source and photography as a supplement, she employs various media in an archival manner to convey textures and to present a heightened realism. Space is used to portray the subject's actual stature as well as other informative subtleties. Likewise, her background colors further enhance these statements.

SHAPIRA, ERIC ZARE (Sculptor)
511 8th St., Montara, CA 94037

Born: 1946 *Awards:* 2nd Place, San Mateo County Fair; Congressional Certificate of Appreciation *Exhibitions:* McEwen Spanish Town Gallery, Half Moon Bay; Peninsula Art Association *Education:* Temple U.; Bethany U.

In 1970, after working with Los Angeles modern artist and sculptor, John Raymond, he began to explore wood, stone and bronze, as media for sculpture. He "discovers" his figures in irregular, fossilized rock. In the two-headed *Moses and Aaron as Promised*, the beards of his figures are natural patterns in the marble. He works regularly in bronze, and often mixes a wood carving with a stone base. Though a few of his works are abstract, most are classically figurative (e.g., his recent marble of a mother and a child).

SHAW, ERIKA CLARK (Ceramist)
15 Seward St., San Francisco, CA 94114

Born: 1954 *Awards:* Honorable Mention, California State Fair *Collections:* Silicon Graphics Corp., Mountain View; Prometheus Corp., Walnut Creek *Exhibitions:* San Francisco Craft and Folk Art Museum; West Coast Clay, Walnut Creek *Education:* California College of Arts And Crafts

A twelve-year involvement with clay and ceramics preceded her work with painted clay wall hangings. These abstract landscapes are influenced by the painterly techniques and textural richness of Helen Frankenthaller and Richard Diebenkorn. She spent years of travelling by plane with her father and living on hilltops. As a result, the juxtaposition of the large aerial view with intimate, emotional visions of objects close to her are widespread in her work. Her landscapes interpret and imitate the way nature uses color and texture to define form and reality. Layering clay slabs of varying textures on wrinkled paper, she uses airbrushed colors to define and enhance form.

SHAW, REESEY (Painter, Sculptor)
7793 Senn Way, La Jolla, CA 92037

Born: 1943 *Collections:* Kaufman and Broad Collections, Los Angeles; La Jolla Museum of Contemporary Art *Exhibitions:* Jeffrey Linden Gallery, Los Angeles; Quint Gallery, San Diego *Education:* Boston U. School of Fine and Applied Arts; Maryland In-

Suzanne Schumacher, *Individuation,* 60 x 72, oil

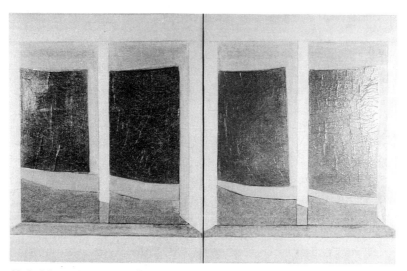

Cleda Marie Simmons, *City Sunrise,* (detail, 2 of 8 panels), 24 x 30, mixed media

stitute College of Art *Dealer:* Jeffrey Linden Gallery, Los Angeles

Her work evolved from paintings of the interiors of elaborate machinery to large color-field paintings that she then cut and re-collaged to create new compositions. Gradually the pieces became heavier and heavier as she built layer upon layer; this necessitated her building wood structures to support the weight. A series of frontal wall forms, made of wood and painted in encaustic (an Egyptian beeswax-based medium) led to the production of free-standing pieces. Her recent work is influenced by Johns and Morandi and by ceramics from the 1930s and 1940s. A recent piece entitled *Morandi Outdoors* is in three parts—a vessel, stand and cube in oxidized, cold-rolled sheet steel: a sculpted version of a Morandi table-top painting.

SHAW, RICHARD (Sculptor)
Dept. of Ceramics, Univ. of California, Berkeley, CA 94720

Born: 1941 *Awards:* NEA Grant; NEA Crafts Grant *Collections:* Oakland Museum; Whitney Museum, NYC *Exhibitions:* Braunstein/Quay Gallery, San Francisco; San Jose Museum of Art *Education:* San Francisco Art Institute; UC-Davis

He is at the forefront of the new movement in ceramic sculpture, advancing the medium from the field of crafts to that of fine art. Employing a sophisticated technique of transfer printing and *trompe l'oeil*, he expands on the earlier American *trompe l'oeil* tradition: while earlier *trompe l'oeil* sculpture sought a perfect illusion in its representation of common objects, he takes that re-creation a step further. His everyday objects made from ceramic—cans, pencils, wood, a book, newspaper clippings—are then assembled in odd, whimsical collections to create a further sculpture, perhaps a human-like figure, as in *Man with Red Arm* and *Melodious Doublestops*. His arrangements of these representations of mundane objects into a new form imbue them with new significance and explore their hidden potential. In *Fifty California Artists*, he says, "Building a figure out of cast and sculptured junk lets me say how I feel about people, recycled trash, movement, humor, clay and so on, all of which I think are beautiful."

SHAWCROFT, BARABARA (Sculptor)
4 Anchor Drive, #243, Emeryville, CA 94608

Awards: NEA Grant *Collections:* Museum of American History and Technology, Smithsonian Institute, Washington DC; Embarcadero Station, Bay Area Rapid Transit, San Francisco *Exhibitions:* National Museum of Modern Art, Tokyo; Lausanne Biennales, Switzerland

Large, organic forms constructed with canvas, plastic and metal meshes, steel wires, threads and newspapers explore wall formations through a variety of engineering techniques. Inspired by the architect Louis Kahn's use of light to create nuances and massing, her recent pieces—solid, compact and employing a variety of mixed media materials—are a development from the knotless, netted-rope sculptures that dominated her work until the 1980s. Colors are combined to enhance the structural and spatial elements of pieces such as *Bricks*, *Boulders* and *Slabs*, so-called for their experiential association with man-made and natural phenomena.

SHEETS, TIMOTHY (Painter)
P.O. Box 775, Pt. Arena, CA 95468

Born: 1962 *Exhibitions:* California Museum of Art at the Luther Burbank Center; Stary-Sheets Art Gallery, Gualala *Education:* Occidental College; Art Students League *Dealer:* Stary-Sheets Art Gallery, Gualala

His watercolor paintings focus on landscapes and still lifes. When painting landscapes, he makes an initial underpainting to capture the essence of the scene and establish the movement of the image. His representational style has been profoundly influenced by his grandfather, Millard Sheets, with whom he studied for over two years. He believes that the two most important qualities for an artist are instinct, which "moves the artist to create;" and intellect, which "makes it possible for the artist to carry out the instinct." Recently, he began paintings of the rugged coastline and dense forests of northern California.

SHEKTER (Painter)
912 Lea Dr., San Rafael, CA 94903

Born: 1925 *Exhibitions:* Marin Arts Guild, Larkspur; Ruth Corwin Gallery, Mendocino

His art education has led him from Switzerland, where he studied impressionism, to Florida and then Scandinavia, where he was exposed to post-impressionism. Studying with Ham Fisher, among others, he learned figure and portrait painting. He has also mastered the skills required for mechanical renditions. His earliest paintings are oils and watercolors. Recent works are primarily in acrylics. While he continues to focus on skyscapes and marine imagery, his style has become more impressionistic, increasingly relying on the palette knife rather than the brush. His watercolors are done on very heavy handmade papers. Paintings are done in a single, intense session after a period of having made a series of very rough sketches.

SHELTON, PETER (Sculptor)
c/o Capp Street Project, 65 Capp St., San Francisco, CA 94103

Born: 1939 *Awards:* Purchase Award, State of Washington; NEA Fellowship *Collections:* State of Washington; Artpark, Lewiston, NY *Exhibitions:* Chapman College, Orange; Center for Contemporary Art, Seattle *Education:* Pomona College; UCLA *Dealer:* Malinda Wyatt Gallery, Venice

His sculptures often involve a literal exploration of architectural space—participatory environments in which viewers crawl and climb through interior passageways—and abstractions of human forms and familiar objects made for human use. Perhaps the most ambitious of such explorations is *floatinghouseDEADMAN*, an installation in which a Japanese-style house floats off the floor of a gallery through the action of massive sculptural counterweights attached to cables—a giant sledgehammer, a life-size metal skeleton, a bed, a chair, letters from the alphabet, a model of the house submerged in water. The largest of these counterweights is the "DEADMAN," a concrete figure that rests outside the gallery building in which the sculpture floats. Participants walk through the house, which wobbles as they move, lending a sense of disturbing instability. This work, like others, is marked by a playful interaction between mass and volume that reveals deeper concerns—the awareness of the physicality that, in this case literally, anchors and allows for our spiritual being.

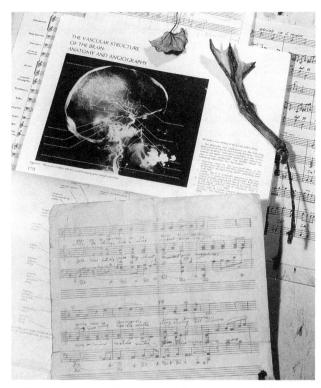

Diana Schoenfeld, *from Fractures and Severances,* 14 x 11, photograph

Barbara Shawcroft, *Legs, 1978,* 600 x 240 x 72, rope.
Photograph: William Hocker

SHERIDAN, AILENE (Sculptor)
1003 G St., Petaluma, CA 94952

Born: 1940 *Exhibitions:* Minx Gallery, San Francisco; Walnut Creek Civic Arts Gallery *Education:* California College of Arts & Crafts; San Francisco State College

Both her painting and sculpture, which has developed since early childhood, continue to focus on the human figure and the human condition. Strongly influenced by the writings of Nikos Kazanzakis, she believes that joy, pain, ecstasy and horror are facades over the face of the divine. Turning to theater, taking impressions from scripts, rehearsals, director's ideas and characters, she gathers material for her work. Thus her art is inspired by an art, which takes as its premise that human emotions are in some sense a mask. Presently, she is building life-sized clay figures from the feet up. Using the potter's method of building with slabs, her figures are hollow. Parking meters and street signs create the scenes for a recent man-and-woman-on-the-street series.

SHERMAN, DAVID J. (Assemblage Artist)
1410 Edgewood Dr., Lodi, CA 95240

Born: 1933 *Awards:* 1st Runner-Up and Best of Show, Modesto *Exhibitions:* Haggin Museum, Stockton; Lodi Art Center

After a twenty-five-year career in agricultural crop marketing, he returned to a childhood fascination with tools and farm implements. Soon after, he began building assemblages using garden spades and shears, army helmets, foxhole shovels, bowling balls, alfalfa mowing machine components, springs, industrial hardware and other assorted items. He donated a realistic rendition of a bird to a municipal fund-raising campaign and thus encouraged, began producing representational sculptures of household pets, barnyard fowl, wild birds and sea creatures.

SHERMAN, ELLY (Mixed Media Artist)
2170 Linnington Ave., Los Angeles, CA 90025

Born: 1925 *Collections:* Musee des Arts Decoratifs, Lausanne, Switzerland *Exhibitions:* Eileen Kremen Gallery, Fullerton; Downey Museum of Art *Dealer:* Kurland-Summers Gallery, Los Angeles

Her poetry and artwork come from her dreams and experiences, featuring images from antiquity and nature. She is interested in the human form, human thought and the interplay of reality and illusion. She creates glass books of original poetry in English, French and German. The books are written in enamel, gold or platinum on kiln-fired colored and etched glass. She uses glass because of an affinity she sees between the medium and the fragility of poetry. Since 1983, she has been at work on a major ongoing project called "Words and Images—A Portrait of Languages." She started with an original eleven-line poem, then called on people to translate the poem. Currently, more than seventy languages, both modern and ancient, are represented. The translations are transcribed on individual glass panels and are accompanied by records and photographs of the translators.

SHERMAN, Z. CHARLOTTE (Painter)
1300 Chautauque Blvd., Pacific Palisades, CA 90272

Born: 1924 *Awards:* Sao Paulo Biennial; Grand Prix de Deauville, Paris *Collections:* Palm Springs Museum; Laguna Museum of Art *Exhibitions:* Heritage Gallery; Pasadena Museum *Education:* Otis Art Institute; UCLA

Influenced by styles ranging from Chinese landscape to American abstract expressionism, she fractures planes in images of mountains, birds, insects and figures. She searches for manifestations of a universal design in nature and enlarges organic forms, focusing on design and color in the microcosm. Magnifying the head of a bee or the shell of a turtle, she conveys the details of natural construction to the viewer. The legacy of action-painting influences her recurring motifs of contour, mass, color, line and texture. Whether in prints, watercolors or painting in oil and acrylic, the artist uses designs established in nature.

SHERRY, WILLIAM GRANT (Painter)
51 Park Terrace, Mill Valley, CA 94941

Born: 1914 *Awards:* 2nd Prize, National Contest, Laguna Beach; Purchase Prize, Springfield Museum of Fine Art, MA *Collections:* Lee Ault Collection; Mary Johnston Collection *Exhibitions:* Le Salon, Paris; National Gallery, London *Dealers:* National Heritage Gallery, Beverly Hills; J.B.M. Gallery, San Francisco

A World War II medical illustrator, his early fine-art work was realistic. Largely self-taught, he studied in Paris after the war and was influenced by the impressionists. In Paris, his work softened and it now hovers between realism and impressionism. His subject matter—ranches, farms, old barns, horses—often come from the scenery of Maine. The simplicity of his realistic subject matter is reflected in his direct but discreet use of earth tones. His brilliantly lit, unpretentious landscapes are worked with a palette knife and brush; his larger works are painted on masonite primed with gesso; and for his smaller works he uses a prepared canvass, which he either stretches or glues on masonite.

SHERWOOD, CAROL (Painter, Mixed Media Artist)
2159 E. Encanto St., Mesa, AZ 85203

Born: 1944 *Awards:* Governor's Art Awards, Arizona Commission on the Arts, Phoenix; Purchase Award, Southwestern Invitational, Yuma, AZ *Collections:* McDonalds Corporate Headquarters, Oakbrook, IL; Picasso Museum, Cannes France *Exhibitions:* Elaine Horwitch Gallery, Santa Fe, NM; Del Mano Gallery, Los Angeles *Education:* Arizona State U.; Mesa Community College, AZ *Dealers:* Elaine Horwitch Gallery, Palm Springs; Del Mano Gallery, Los Angeles

She makes sculptural clay vessels and forms colored and decorated by untraditional methods. Impatient with the repeated firings and attendant delay that made immediate and spontaneous creation impossible but that is required for conventional glazing, and inspired by the ceramic pieces created in the 1950s by Picasso and Miro, she began to paint and draw directly on once-fired clay. An example of this work is the series "Seeding of the Cosmos," in which large, torso-like forms depict in paint the evolution of the human species into a colony in outer space. She has recently been working on a series of sculptures she calls her "car" pieces: humorous vehicles such as might be driven about on her colonies in space. In addition to the oils, acrylics, stains and graphite that she applies to the surface of her clay forms, she also employs woods, metals, modeling paste and metallics.

Pat Sherwood, *Six Long Days,* 44 x 46, oil on canvas

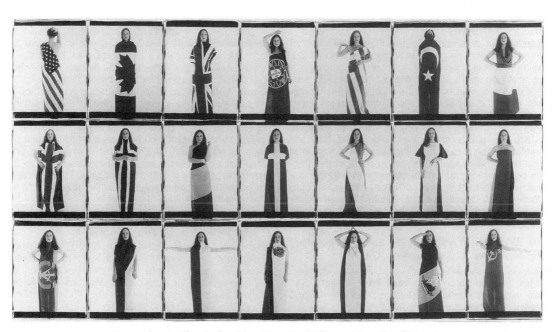

Rena Small, *Flag Series,* 20 x 24 each, 21 Polaroids, 140 x 72 total.
Courtesy: Polaroid Collection, Cambridge, MA

SHERWOOD, PATRICIA W. (Painter, Printmaker)
1500 Arriba Ct., Los Altos, CA 94022

Born: 1933 *Awards:* 1st Place, Lytton Center Exhibit *Collections:* Mills Museum, Oakland; Bank of America, San Francisco *Exhibitions:* Triton Museum, Santa Clara; Pratt Art Institute *Education:* San Jose State U.; Mills College *Dealer:* Gallery One, Denver

Her abstracted landscapes evolved primarily from a childhood spent traveling between Prisoner of War camps with her army officer father in the North American desert. Her sense of space gives the impression of a life in a car with the landscape flying by for hours, and the foreground always blurred. In oil, she is primarily concerned with harmonizing opposing elements. The juxtaposition of smoothly brushed areas against knife textures and weighty forms against fine linear detail creates a stress and direction, through which forces rush together in areas of dramatic confrontation. Thickly painted off-whites may be separated by clusters of irregular forms in clear, glowing colors that are often intensified by elements of black. Landscapes have a clear structure and mobile grace that invoke remembered places. Etchings, monoprints and lithographs experiment with figuration. The ammonium bichromate process allows her to conceive and assemble photo-montages of, often caustic, social comment. Handmade paper has further allowed her to explore the objectification of women and the complexities of sexual bonding through a sculptural interplay of light and spatial depth new to her work.

SHERWOOD, STEPHEN S. (Painter)
35 N. Venice Blvd., #1, Venice, CA 90291

Born: 1954 *Awards:* 3rd Place, Carnegie Art Museum, Oxnard; Honorable Mention, Fall Art Exhibit, Los Angeles *Collections:* Arthur Anderson Corp., Cincinnati *Exhibitions:* Riverside Art Museum; St. Hill Gallery, Pacific Palisades *Education:* Ohio University

Interested in mastering the basic technical skills of painting, he spent two years studying anatomy and dissecting cadavers, training himself in the realistic figurative tradition of Pearlstein and Kamahira. His own work is loosely realistic and of a slightly primitive style. Over time, he has studied many other artists, from Cezanne to Sargent; in any one painting, one finds a variety of influences. Arriving at his own, personal realism, he paints psychological portraits that are revealing of the person as well as the human condition in general. Characteristic, too, are ironic titles that provide both humor and pathos. *Message in a Bottle* is a black and white lithograph portraying a drunken man asleep, next to his empty bottle. The award-winning oil, *Never Without Her*, speaks to the nostalgia that lives in objects.

SHERWOOD, WAYNE A. (Sculptor, Illustrator)
1300 McAllister St., San Francisco, CA 94115

Born: 1953 *Exhibitions:* Sticks and Stones, Skin and Bones, San Francisco; The Bead Store Gallery, San Francisco *Education:* New England School of Art and Design; San Francisco Academy of Art

After leaving art school, he moved back to upstate New York and began working on black-and-white pen-and-ink illustrations of animals. He became interested in the myths of primitive cultures, and began illustrating their mythological creatures. The work had a poin-

tillist bent to it. After studying Native American and pre-Christian shamanistic practices on his own, he returned to school at the San Francisco Academy of Art and studied metal and ceramic sculpture. He now produces three-dimensional jewelry and artifacts for those practicing nature spirituality in California. In these pieces, he combines traditional symbolism with modern sensibilities.

SHIRE, PETER (Sculptor)
1930 Echo Park Ave., Los Angeles, CA 90026

Born: 1947 *Awards:* Award for Contribution to the XXIII Olympiad, Los Angeles *Collections:* Art Institute of Chicago; San Francisco Museum of Modern Art *Exhibitions:* Saxon-Lee Gallery, Los Angeles; Municipal Art Gallery, Barnsdall *Education:* Chouinard Art Institute *Dealer:* Saxon-Lee Gallery, Los Angeles

After a formal training in California ceramics of the late 1950s—pieces that were derivative of early 1950s Swedish and Viennese ceramics—he proceeded to be directly and immediately influenced by the Los Angeles Finish fetish school. In 1972, he began using architectural and mechanical symbols in a broad and unrelenting manner, conveying the terror and alienation of industrialism while keeping in focus the neurosis of the last quarter of the century. He then moved from small ceramics to large, rational works in steel. He uses the strength of the steel to underscore the possibility of the impossible and further stresses his ironic sense by contrasting bright, happy colors with his aircraft-technology-derived materials.

SHIRINIAN, EMELDA (Painter)
P.O. Box 2514, Carmel, CA 93921

Born: 1938 *Exhibitions:* 20th Century Masters Gallery, Carmel; Fresno Art Museum *Education:* Fresno State University; Otis Art Institute *Dealer:* Killingsworth Art International, Monterey

During the 1970s, her work was influenced by the writings of Carl Jung and Erich Neumann. Paintings were large, circular universes depicting the archetypal history of consciousness. The color was brilliant, the mythological images captured the essence of timelessness. The style shows influences of Picasso, Arshile Gorky and Dali, but emerges unique and termed by some, "surrealistic expressionism." In the 1980s, her concepts of the universe were expanded to portray the oneness of all life forms and their peaceful union on earth. Vibrant, strong colors, shapes and forms move in a harmony, a well orchestrated symphony. The result is an inspiring, emotional statement as to our common oneness with the life principal. Her new series of portraits express spiritual qualities that include her Armenian heritage.

SHIRK, HELEN (Metalsmith)
10606 Snyder Rd., La Mesa, CA 92041

Born: 1942 *Awards:* Fulbright Grant; NEA Fellowship *Collections:* National Museum of Modern Art, Kyoto, Japan; Schmuckmuseum, Pforzhem, W. Germany *Exhibitions:* National Museum of Modern Art, Kyoto, Japan; National Ornamental Metal Museum, Memphis *Education:* Skidmore College; Indiana U.

Early work in silver, copper and brass included both jewelry and vessel forms. Her concern in both areas was to convey a feeling of energy both through the projection and penetration of forms, and contrasts of hard edges against fluid surfaces, and space against

Jane Wooster Scott, *The Christening,* 28 x 20, lithograph

Emelda Darlene Shirinian, *Returning Home,* (top) 47" diameter,
(bottom) 71 x 45, oil on canvas

mass. The work had an additive, constructivist feel about it. In 1980, she began a long series of silver/titanium jewelry pieces that were an exploration of space and movement. She worked freely and quickly on these "sketches" and this series has a spontaneity and gestural quality about it that was not present in her previous work. In 1983, she returned to the vessel as her primary form. A series of patinated copper and brass vessels reflected the influence of the desert environment. They explore the alliance of seductive color with aggressive form that is often found in the flora of desert landscapes. A new vessel series, begun in 1986, works within a circular format. More personal than the other series, these pieces are tranquil and intimate.

SHORT, JOHN W. (Photographer)
1681 Amberwood Dr., South Pasadena, CA 91030

Born: 1953 *Awards:* 3rd Place, Redlands Art Association, San Bernardino City Museum *Exhibitions:* Cal. State-San Bernardino; The Corner Gallery, San Bernardino *Education:* U.S. Navy Photo School; Cal. State-San Bernardino

He began his photographic career as a student at the United States Navy Photographic School. After leaving the Navy, he studied with his friend, Scott Ward, at Cal. State-San Bernardino. In the early 1980s, he photographed at night and used multiple flash techniques to bring various amounts of light into the image. By 1986, he had become extremely interested in the history of photography, especially in the work of such masters as Stieglitz and Weston. His work at the time was a series of male/female figure studies in palladium and platinum prints. He recently began photographing downtown Los Angeles.

SHREVES, DON (Painter)
1849 Maltman Ave., Los Angeles, CA 90026

Born: 1918 *Awards:* 1st Prize, California Art Club Show; 3rd Prize, Honorable Mention, Pacific Art Guild Show *Exhibitions:* Women's Club of Hollywood; Laguna Beach Art Festival Pageant of Masters

His post-impressionist style is the result of many years of training, travel and experience. Working in either oil or acrylic on canvas, he varies his subjects from Christian iconography to Western landscapes to portraiture. Darker colors are used to express the moodiness of a remote landscape; a lighter palette is used to highlight the light and shadow of a subject's face. He paints from memory, carefully including what he feels is essential to the viewer's understanding, rather than seeking to depict an exact likeness.

SHUFELT, ROBERT "SHOOFLY"
(Illustration)
16550 Lago Del Oro, Tucson, AZ 85737

Born: 1935 *Collections:* Mera Bank, Phoenix; Southland Corporation *Exhibitions:* Peppertree Ranch, Santa Cruz; Art in the Grand Tradition, Fallbrook *Education:* School of the Art Institute of Chicago *Dealer:* Wadle Galleries, Santa Fe, NM

He has worked as a cowboy since 1976; his previous background included twenty-two years in commercial illustration. While versed in most media, he has chosen pencil as part of the challenge of recognition. He realistically renders the contemporary cowboy and accurately depicts the modern cattle industry based on his own experience. Fusing pencil strokes into a painterly accumulation of planes and textures, he creates dramatic imagery with bold sunlight and shadow. Designs are woven through the compositions to underscore the symbolic. Drawing what he knows to be honest, he captures the spirit of the subject, celebrating its reality and its place in the symbolism of American culture.

SHULER, MIKE (Wood Sculptor)
1735 Rodriguez St., Santa Cruz, CA 95062

Born: 1950 *Awards:* Best of Show, Houston Festival *Exhibitions:* International Turned Wood Objects Show; Del Mano Gallery, Los Angeles

At the age of 14, he first turned wood in his father's basement shop. Since then, he has worked regularly with a variety of materials including all species of wood, plastics, steel and non-ferrous materials. He has had a long career in woodcarving, furniture and cabinetmaking, antique restoration and the architectural crafts and building trades. Most recently, he has returned to the lathe as his primary tool. He now makes numbered segmented wood bowls. To do this, he cuts a board so that it wraps around itself, end meeting end. He has thus produced two vessels of an alternating grain pattern—a large one, twelve inches in diameter and five inches high made of 936 of these segments, and a small one, 5 inches in diameter and 1 1/2 inches high, made of 228 segments.

SIBERELL, ANNE HICKS (Printmaker, Sculptor)
1041 La Cuesta Road, Hillsborough, CA 94010

Collections: Oakland Museum; Oxford University *Exhibitions:* San Francisco State University; Rolando Castellon Contemporary Art *Education:* Chouinard Art Institute *Dealer:* Rolando Castellon Contemporary Art

Her previous work includes woodblocked paper constructions, etchings and handmade books, including *Pierced and Thumbless Hands*. Over the last several years, she has also concentrated on cement sculpture relief, incorporating elements of painting, drawing and writing. Using molds from everyday packages, she forms abstract collages into reliefs with cement, recording the shapes and patterns of the molds. Once formed, the reliefs are painted. She works in earth tones, with images that are uncomplicated and ancient. Often appearing figurative, these abstractions are developed from triggered emotions. Through her incorporation of "artifacts" with artistic intent and medium, the work becomes an archaeology of the present.

SICRE, JORGE L. (Painter)
1966 San Francisco, Long Beach, CA 90806

Born: 1958 *Collections:* Housatonic Museum of Art, Bridgeport, CT; Museum of Modern Art of Latin America, Washington, DC *Exhibitions:* Karin Long Gallery, Long Beach; Fiona Whitney Gallery, Los Angeles *Education:* UC-Santa Barbara *Dealers:* Toluca Lake Gallery, Burbank; Hermila Gallery, Long Beach; Q Gallery, Santa Monica and Los Angeles

He was born into a Cuban family of musicians and artists, but did not decide to become an artist until the age of twenty-one. Working in oil, watercolor and collage, he creates boldly colored fantasy figures in a symbolist style. The mythical and mystical context of his figures makes them metaphors for different aspects of the human condition. Recently, his work has consisted of an eclectic mix of diverse and often contradictory media, figurative images and themes. He has mixed oils and acrylics, as he enjoys the water resistant nature

J.L. Sicre, *Living Like Rats,* 20 x 16, oil on canvas

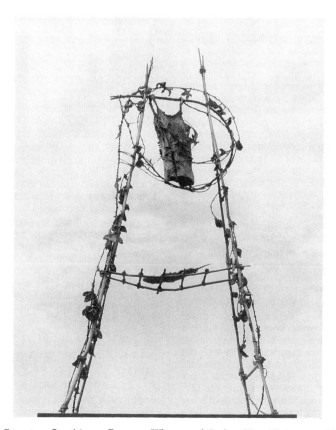

Lynne Streeter, *Sant'Anna, Between Winter and Spring,* 72 x 42, bronze, 1981-83.

of oil-based paints and solvents. He creates surreal figures and sets them in photo-realistic backgrounds. In an attempt to combine classical painterly expression and computer art, he uses a technique he calls "matrix perspective" to make figures appear as if they are floating in space when viewed from the proper distance. For him, art is a way of knowing the self, a way of connecting to cosmic dimensions and forces.

SIDLE, GWENDOLYN (Painter)
P.O. Box 437, Compton, CA 90223

Born: 1960 *Exhibitions:* Artist International Association, San Francisco; West Gallery, Cal. State-Fullerton

Her work is a pastiche of mythology, ancient religious beliefs and modern social trend—all rendered in a classic and neo-expressionist style. In her paintings, she strives to unite the physical and the invisible aspects of human experience.

SIEGEL, KATHLEEN (Painter)
7479 Foothill Ranch Rd., Santa Rosa, CA 95404

Born: 1956 *Exhibitions:* Warehouse Show, San Francisco; Two Dog Gallery

She has been especially influenced by the Expressionists and Fauvists' use of color and content. Matisse, Nolde, and de Kooning are particular favorites. She employs a layered approach to form and color, searching with the media for a sense of "rightness."

SILBERSTEIN, ALEX (Painter)
7831 Claremont Ave., Berkeley, CA 94705

Born: 1949 *Exhibitions:* Studio I, Oakland; Gallery of the Center for Psychological Studies, Albany *Education:* Rhode Island School of Design; Notre Dame

An early interest in surrealism resurfaced in the mid-1970s, as he began using art as a therapeutic tool in work with schizophrenic teenagers. An obsession with black-and-white photography, particularly in manipulating negatives or scenes for unusual effects, led him back to figurative drawing and oil painting of symbolic images from dreams, fantasies and fairy tales. Recently, he began focusing on self-portraits, expressing various aspects of psychological development. Though he may start with a specific idea, he proceeds spontaneously, allowing images and their meanings to change, develop and grow through the interplay of visual ideas, formal qualities of the composition, the character of the medium and the variety of impulses, associations and emotions that emerge.

SILLMAN, JEAN V.K. (Sculptor)
1140 Los Robles St., Davis, CA 95616

Born: 1945 *Awards:* Award of Merit, California St. Fair; Honorable Mention, Northern California Arts 29th Annual Open *Exhibitions:* Natsoulas/Novelozo Gallery, Davis and Sacramento; Slant Gallery, Sacramento *Education:* U. of Rochester; UC-Davis

Though she was initially a painter, her consuming devotion to art did not develop until she had taken a course in ceramic sculpture given by Robert Arneson. She had had some previous experience with clay, but when it was offered as a suitable material for sculpture on any scale, she discovered it was ideally suited to her needs. She is particularly drawn to creating life-size, realistic and distorted figures. She works predominantly in ceramics fired in stoneware ranges, using china paints and traditional glazes for finishing. She is becoming more interested in combining ceramics with other media and techniques such as glass fusing, metalworking and casting. She is also exploring the possibilities of cement sculpture, for occasions when durability requires a sacrifice of the brilliant colors she usually employs. Humor is the main motivation in her work, as she enjoys the idea of multiple meanings. One example, *Dynamic Interplay II,* features a realistic bust of Rembrandt entering a pasta machine and emerging as a cubist portrait.

SIMCOE, DUNCAN (Painter)
524 E. Washington, Orange, CA 92677

Born: 1956 *Exhibitions:* Laguna Beach Museum of Art; Claremont Graduate School of Art *Education:* Cal. State-Long Beach

After a strong initial grounding in figurative art during the mid-1970s, he abandoned traditional modes of arriving at form and began to investigate pure painting. Influenced by Deibenkorn's figurative work, he explored the image's evocative narrative potential, creating "Oblique Narratives" of the Southern Californian suburban environment. He begins pieces without fixed pre-conceptions and relies on the painting's progress to elicit a fluid series of "recognitions." His dense specifics of form are worked out through the process of painting. In his multipanel format, he often opposes his obliquely narrative oil painting with abutting strips of collage overlaid with text.

SIMKINS, KRISTINA (Painter, Graphic Artist)
1908 Chicago Ave., Savanna, IL 61074

Born: 1958 *Awards:* Best of Show & 1st Place in Watercolor, Nevada Artists Association *Collections:* Washoe Medical Center, Reno, NV *Exhibitions:* Desert Moon Gallery, Reno; Tiempo Interiors, San Francisco

She is a self-taught artist who exhibits a natural creative ability in several media. She has had professional experience in forms ranging from scratch board to advertising. Her accomplished watercolors are slightly surreal, highly emotional depictions of still lifes, flowers and animals.

SIMMONS, CLEDA MARIE (Painter)
13655 Woodcock Ave., Sylmar, CA 91342

Born: 1927 *Awards:* Purchase Award, Ateneo De Belles Artes, Madrid, Spain; Pan American Galleries, San Antonio, TX *Collections:* Ateneo De Belles Artes, Madrid, Spain; Continental Waterways *Exhibitions:* Toison Gallery, Madrid, Spain; Johnson Gallery, U. of New Mexico *Education:* U. of New Mexico

Best known for her images of dinghies at rest in calm waters (*Water Babies*), she brings a feeling of space to her views of sprawling cityscapes and creates a sense of tranquility in landscapes of the California hills and Western countryside. Recently working in collage, acrylic overlays and ink or pencil, she displays the strong sense of design that was nurtured by the late Professor Ralph Douglass at the U. of New Mexico. The forms in her work *Elan Vital* appear to be non-objective but are actually distillations of the work of both nature and man. Her subtle colors include roses, peaches, mauve and neutrals.

SIMMONS, JULIE LUTZ (Painter)
P.O. Box 305, Charleston, MO 63834

Born: 1942 *Awards:* Award of Excellence, "An Art Affair," St. Louis; Louisiana Watercolor International *Collections:* Embassy Suites, La Jolla; Coca-Cola, Atlanta *Exhibitions:* Six Artists, Six States Invitational, U.

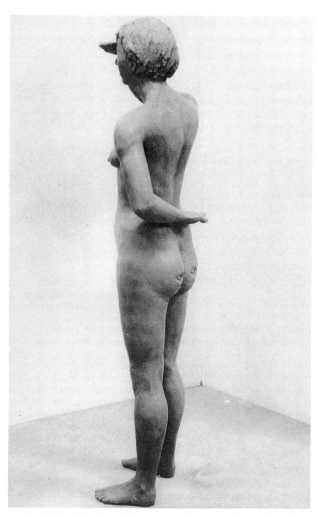

Jean Sillman, *Hindsight,* 60 x 20 x 15, ceramic. Courtesy: Natsoulas/ Novelozo Gallery

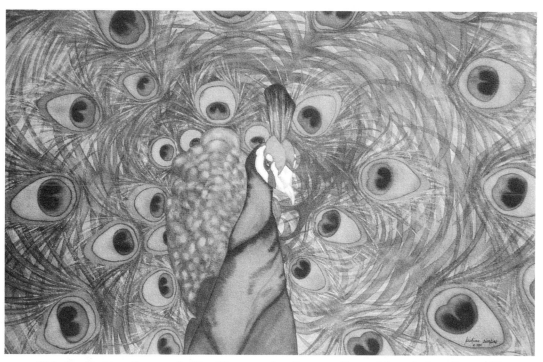

Kristina Simkins, *Promenade,* 22 x 30, watercolor. Courtesy: Desert Moon Gallery, Reno, NV

of Wisconsin; Abstein Gallery, Atlanta *Education:* Murray State U.; Southeast Missouri State U.

Her compositions are close focused. She is fascinated with creating new textures and ways of letting the pigment and water work without manipulation. The coupling of the close focus and the textural planes tends to abstract what are realistic shapes. Her collages are an assemblage of textured papers that she creates and painted realistic elements. Her recent works are watercolor on gessoed masonite finishes with acrylic glazes. Recent experimentation is with metallics. Most involve layering, which suggests a unity of time and space—a means of balancing chaos and order.

SIMNEZ, LINDA (Painter, Ceramist)
19914 7th St. East, Sonoma, CA 95476

Born: 1948 *Exhibitions:* Sonoma Arts Guild; Lee Sclar Gallery, San Francisco *Education:* UC-Berkeley *Dealer:* Elaine Potter, San Francisco

As a painter, she creates expressionistic work that features images captured from the unconscious. Her "House" series— abstract paintings of doors, windows and other house parts executed in bright colors—is an attempt to record with precision the tensions and temptations inside and outside the domestic setting. Her ceramic pieces are quite the opposite of her paintings. Painted in soft pastels, these sturdy, functional porcelain items emphasize a more formal expression of line and color.

SIMON, LENORE (Printmaker, Mixed Media Artist)
3862 Mt. Acadia Blvd., San Diego, CA

Born: 1928 *Awards:* Artist in Residence Grant and Technical Assistance Grant, California Arts Council *Collections:* Data Systems, San Diego; American Tax and Law, San Diego *Exhibitions:* San Diego Museum of Art; San Diego County Law Library *Education:* Cooper Union

She combines spontaneity and control, intuition and intellect, in work that is primarily an interpretation of form and space. Paul Klee, Paul Rand and Pablo Picasso are strong influences; Calder's wire sculptures had an impact on her early, continuous line drawings. Whether working in the intaglio process or experimenting with mixed-media works on paper, she mixes flowing lines with stylized forms. Inspired by chance shadows, doodles or scenes, she chooses media according to her subject matter. Her discipline is in treating the task at hand with total abandon, and then organizing her forms into a working totality.

SIMONE, SARITA (Ceramist)
3500 Meier St., Los Angeles, CA 90066

Born: 1933 *Awards:* 1st Prize, American Ceramic Society, Southern California Chapter *Exhibitions:* Del Mano Gallery; Contemporary Images *Education:* UCLA

After closing an art gallery that she had owned with her husband, she devoted herself to ceramics full time. Her early work was heavily influenced by the materials and motifs of African art. She combined basketry materials such as wood, beads and bone with her clay vessels, and fired them with driftwood, seaweed and other organic materials to achieve earth colors. More recent study with Sana Krusoe has taken her work in a new direction. Extraneous materials are now incorporated more fully into a vessel's cleaner, more simple designs; these "handles" emerge as integrated parts of

the piece. She uses cobalt and copper oxides to color the clay, producing a blue, green or rosy hue. Then she fires the clay with sulfates to give them a matte finish. Her more recent thrown pieces are functional, beautifully displaying their interior and exterior colors and design.

SIMONIAN, JUDITH (Painter)
361 W. 36th St., 12-B, New York, NY 10018

Born: 1945 *Awards:* NEA Fellowship; California Confederation of the Arts *Collections:* Kaufman and Broad, Los Angeles *Exhibitions:* Newport Harbor Art Museum, Newport Beach; Seibu Museum, Japan *Education:* Cal. State- Northridge *Dealer:* Ovsey Gallery, Los Angeles

Influenced by the graffiti-covered walls of her Los Angeles environment, her early work was site-specific, executed in the streets. Growing out of a curiosity concerning the meeting of a work of art with uncontrollable urban forces, her work realized a dialogue between her painted, cut-through, sandblasted walls, and the graffiti writers and gangeros who would cover her work with their marks. Her *Stable Drawing*, for instance, was constructed in the form of a vase in drywall behind a roofless structure in San Diego. When the piece was vandalized, she reconstructed the pieces into an object that had gained a sense of movement and mystery through its unplanned collaboration with an urban form of nature. The duality expressed through architectural, man-made forms trying to integrate with nature has continued into her more recent studio work.

SIMONS, SHERI (Sculptor, Draughtsperson)
4929 Clarke St., Oakland, CA 94623

Born: 1954 *Awards:* NEA Fellowship *Exhibitions:* New Langton Arts, San Francisco; Distinguished Artists Forum, San Francisco State U. *Education:* Cranbrook Academy of Art

She is concerned with the role of technology in modern man's psyche and she focuses on the way humans transfer desires and emotions into machine capabilities. Her drawings and sculptures draw on machinery's anthropomorphic nature, life cycle, futility and obsolescence. In her forms and materials, she combines a machine vocabulary with the fragile and primitive quantities of human anatomy and instinct. She feels that machinery and appliances are the crutches and prostheses with which modern society has fitted itself in hopes of finding heaven on earth.

SINGER, FAY (Painter)
18912 W. Pacific Coast Hwy., Malibu, CA 90265

Born: 1937 *Exhibitions:* Museum of Science and Industry, Los Angeles; Whittier Art Museum *Education:* Mather U.; UC-Berkeley

Moved by the paintings of Beckmann and Kirschner, she creates paintings that continue to show the influence of German expressionism. She recently completed a "Malibu" series of abstract Pacific land and seascapes. Interested in breaking up spatial and tonal relationships, she deliberately juxtaposes warm against cool, weaving color and texture and dark and light in order to lure the viewer deeper into the canvas; at the same time, she attempts to provide compositional motifs that move the viewer across the painting. Her art represents the culmination of her struggle to put to canvas perceptions, feelings and philosophical state-

Betty Saarni, *Evening Light,* 22 x 30, transparent watercolor on paper

Sylvia Shap, *Lady on Opening Night, 1980,*
59 x 42, oil pastel

Donna Scott, *Self Portrait,* 22 x 34, pencil and india ink

ments about the imperfect world she in which she finds herself.

SINNETT, STAN D. (Commercial Illustrator, Painter)
8663 Stewart and Grey Rd., Downey, CA 90241

Born: 1925 *Awards:* Artist of the Year, Downy Art Museum *Collections:* Museum of Plains Indians, Browning, MT; American Realty Advisor, Costa Mesa *Exhibitions:* Museum of Plains Indians, Browning, MT; Death Valley Invitational Western Art Show *Education:* California Institute of the Arts; Cal. State-Fullerton

Influenced by the works of Toulouse-Lautrec, Degas and Monet, he worked as an illustrator for ten years, after he completed his formal training. He continued his education, and during graduate school, he delved into super-realism, painting on a large scale (from 6-by-7-feet to 8-by-30-feet). The child of Blackfeet and French parents, he begins work by putting his ideas down in thumb nail sketches—letting his heritage and love for story have free play. He does research and finds models before executing in paint the best of his sketches. He works in oils, acrylics, watercolor and pencil. He starts his oil or acrylic paintings with an underpainting of very abstract shape and color—usually the compliment of the finished color. As he paints, he is always drawing and redrawing with his brush.

SIPPER, RUTH DOSMAR (Sculptor, Printmaker)
3820 Magee Ave., Oakland, CA 94619

Born: 1922 *Awards:* Best of Show, SFWA Annual; Purchase Award, De Anza College, Cupertino *Collections:* City of Hayward; De Anza College, Cupertino *Exhibitions:* Oakland Museum; Judah L. Magnes Museum *Education:* Aaron Avni School of Art, Tel-Aviv, Israel; California College of Arts and Crafts

Her early training in Israel was primarily in sculpture, largely influenced by Henry Moore's philosophy regarding the intrinsic qualities of materials. Sculptures from that time are mainly concerned with groups of stylized figures. Living in California, she had the opportunity to study some alternate methods of creating sculpture. During this time she produced a series of abstract works, welded or cast in aluminum or bronze. Since 1970 she has concentrated on printmaking. In this, she is mostly self-taught. Her graphics tend toward a sculptural effect, with images embossed in white on a white background, giving play to the effects of light and shade in the raised and recessed portions of the paper. Her diverse themes include Jewish and Biblical material, and next she looks to explore these in cast-paper in which she will incorporate such materials as wire and xerography.

SJODIN, MARGARETA (Painter, Printmaker)
21500 Calle Del Barco, Malibu, CA 90265

Born: 1952 *Exhibitions:* Galleri Eternelle, Stockholm, Sweden; Sollefteå Art Association, Sweden *Education:* Swedish Art Institute, Stockholm *Dealer:* Stella Polaris Gallery, Pacific Palisades

Born in the far north of Sweden, she paints that region's grace, beauty and mystery. She uses watercolor, acrylics and collage to suggest ice and space. Her impressionist landscapes and people are just as often inner landscapes or outerspace-scapes with people and animals hiding in the ice. Her "Marine Suite" was a group of five large etchings of the play of sunlight across an abstract expanse of water. Recently, she has been doing glass casting, finding in glass a three-dimensional medium closer to watercolors than bronze, clay or marble. In Sweden, she also acted in television, films and stage productions such as Ibsen's *Peer Gynt*.

SKIRVIN, WILLIAM D. (Painter, Multimedia Artist)
6593 N. Bungalow, Fresno, CA 93705

Born: 1952 *Exhibitions:* Ward-Nasse Gallery, NYC; Alligator Gallery, San Francisco *Dealer:* Interart Gallery, San Francisco

His style combines photo-realism and surrealism; he works in acrylic and oil on canvas and paper; he is fascinated by classical subjects. After studying the works of Michelangelo, da Vinci, Raphael and Dali, he decided to incorporate a more modern dimension to his paintings. He now works by mounting the canvas on Masonite, then cuts a hole for a television and creates the painting around it. One recent example features a Rubensesque rendering of Jesus on the cross, with a working television in the background. Other subjects include vegetable and fruit still lifes.

SLADKUS, ALLIE (Sculptor)
6432 Camino Del Parque, Carlsbad, CA 92009

Born: 1908 *Awards:* 1st Place, Riverside County National Date Festival; 1st Place, Edward Dean Museum *Collections:* U. of Southern California; Temple Solel, Encinatas *Exhibitions:* Landell Galleries, Carmel; Carlsbad/Oceanside Art League *Education:* Village of Fine Arts Center, Palm Springs *Dealer:* Reflection on Canvas Gallery, Wetfield, NJ

Since studying with Lilia Ryan on the East Coast and Robert Ortlieb and Herb Conrad in California, the artist has been creating sculptures in clay and stone for the past sixteen years. Both abstract and traditional realist styles places emphasis on religious subjects. In a style reminiscent of art deco and the social realists of the 1940s, *Rabbi Blowing a Ram's Horn*, is a relief carved in African wonderstone. Other favored materials include marble, alabaster, onyx and agate. Although pieces were on a larger scale in the past, smaller stones of about sixty to 100 pounds have been featured in the recent pieces.

SLATER, GARY (Sculptor)
638 W. Contessa Circle, Mesa AZ 85201

Born: 1947 *Awards:* Grant, "Art in Schools" *Collections:* Tucson Museum of Art; Bowers Museum, Santa Ana *Exhibitions:* Tucson Sculpture Exhibition; Kimball Art Center, Pale City, UT *Education:* U. of Minnesota; Arizona State U. *Dealer:* Elaine Horwitch Gallery, Palm Springs

Though he painted and worked in figurative wooden sculpture while still a student at the University of Minnesota, his attraction towards welding techniques quickly determined the direction his art would follow. Impressed by the simplicity of Henry Moore's and Clement Meadmore's sculpture and Tony Delap's understated two-dimensional work, he prefers clean, minimal abstract forms. He utilizes the tactile qualities of the physical object by crushing and welding a textural color element to a neutral vehicle element. In one of his first pieces, the corners of a 3-foot stainless steel cube are ripped off, then the spaces are stuffed with copper, which is wrinkled like brown paper. Reduced geometric shapes are usually interrupted in this way by

Jean Swiggett, *Morning Glory,* 18 x 13, colored pencil

Julie Lutz Simmons, *Union Station Window II,* watercolor

textured metal, as though corrosion has exploded from beneath their smooth surfaces. He has recently explored further this textural aspect by combining and perforating metals. Some bronze is used on smaller, 2-to-5-foot sculptures, and steel is painted bright primary colors. Within one piece, these divergent elements take different directions to create an internal tension. This effect is particularly dramatic in his environmental pieces.

SLATER, HELEN (Ceramist)
464 Kilkea Dr., Los Angeles, CA 90048

Born: 1920 *Exhibitions:* Crafts Museum, San Francisco; Wild Blue Gallery, Los Angeles *Education:* USC; Chouinard Art Institute *Dealer:* Free Hand, Los Angeles

She completed a traditional college education in ceramics and now produces both one-of-a-kind commercial and studio pieces. Works from the 1960s and 1970s are of stoneware and porcelain. In the 1980s, she began to work in earthenware. All of her creations are functional, though she continues to experiment with new designs and finishes. She uses a particular firing process—saggar firing—in which the kiln is built brick by brick each time with organic materials—seaweed, leaves and twigs—filling the space between the pots. Through this process, the pots are left with unique colors and textures.

SLAUGHTER, NEILL G. (Painter)
3129 Shipway Ave., Long Beach, CA 90808

Born: 1951 *Awards:* Ford Foundation Fellowship; Faculty Activities Grant, Cal. State U. *Exhibitions:* Minneapolis Art Institute; Riverside Art Museum *Education:* U. of Georgia; Indiana U.

Influenced early by the brushwork on John Singer Sargent, the heightened color of Wayne Thiebaud and the psychological tension of Lucian Freud, he has concentrated for years on painting large figure compositions. Utilizing thick paint and loose brushwork to convey dramatic light and patterns of shadow that describe and distort form, his paintings depict a spontaneous momentary mood, as well as suggest a psychological ambiguity between the figures. Recently, he has been working on a new series inspired by his African travels and entitled "Africa/America Amalgamation." The large diptych oils in this series are more expressionistic than his earlier work and show a concern for cultural and environmental issues. By means of painted images of comparison and contrast, he challenges the notion that what is termed "civilized" is inherently superior to the primitive.

SLAUGHTER, PAUL (Photographer)
771 El Medio Ave., Pacific Palisades, CA 90272

Born: 1938 *Awards:* Gold Award, Art Directions Club, NYC; Steuben Glass Award, Kodak, Rochester, NY *Collections:* George Eastman House, Rochester; Los Angeles Public Library *Exhibitions:* Bridge Gallery, Los Angeles; Los Angeles Center Photographic Studies

He learned the art of lighting as an actor, and this knowledge became extremely useful when he began his photographic career in 1970. He specializes in location work and has traveled in over sixty countries. In 1984 he was the official photographer for the Los Angeles Olympic Organizing Committee. His work has been exhibited in New York, Los Angeles and Hong Kong. Continuing his love for the theater, he has photographed the international companies that appeared in the 1984 Olympic Arts Festival and the 1987 Los Angeles Theater Festival. From time to time, he does special photography in the film industry. "The camera simply works as a medium to express the great admiration I have for the color, design and life we are so fortunate to witness on our small planet," he says.

SLAVIN, NEAL (Photographer)
62 Greene St., New York, NY 10012

Born: 1941 *Awards:* Fulbright Photography Fellowship; NEA Grant *Collections:* Metropolitan Museum of Art, NYC; Museum of Modern Art, NYC *Exhibitions:* Oakland Museum; Galerie Spectrum, Hanover, West Germany *Education:* Cooper Union; Oxford

He has worked on a variety of projects, including group portraiture, book and magazine covers and photo-essays. He works in both large and small formats, black and white and color. An example of his photo-essays is a series of black-and-white prints of social repression under a dictatorship entitled "Portugal". He is probably best known for his group photos, such as the series entitled "When Two or More Are Gathered Together," a series of color portraits of American professional and social organizations.

SLOCUM, CAM (Photographer)
2421 E. 16th St., Los Angeles, 90021

Born: 1957 *Exhibitions:* Pence Gallery, Los Angeles *Education:* U. of California, San Diego

A performance artist for ten years, he turned to painting for a short period but found his true interest was in photography. "Photography is a way for me to start with an image and work my way out, than work my way in through painting," he says. He read an old photography dictionary and rediscovered a 19th-century bichromate non-silver process. Using this process, which involves generating a positive image on a canvas, exposing it in the sun, and developing it with pigmented colors, he produces large images—up to six by six feet. Recently he has been using found photographs in conjunction with linotronic printing, a process which involves the digitalization of the visual information via a computer. With this process, he can distort areas of the image and produce a new 8-by-10-inch negative, which is then used to generate a an 8-by-10-foot photograph. All of his images explore political and social issues.

SMALL, RENA (Multimedia Artist)
727 Navy St., Santa Monica, CA 90403

Born: 1954 *Awards:* "Artists Who Teach," Federal Reserve Board, Washington, D.C. *Collections:* Stuart and Judith-Vida Spence, Pasadena *Exhibitions:* LACE, Los Angeles; Fellows of Contemporary Art, Los Angeles *Education:* Calif. Institute of the Arts, Valencia

She is inspired by the traditions of minimalism, pop, dada and performance art. Her primary medium has been photography, her formats including 20 x 24, 4 x 5, and 8 x 10 Polaroids, sometimes with text. In 1979, she began a series of works combining photographs with American slang. She sets up each photograph like a proscenium with a slang word or phrase and its accompanying definition standing to the left of the picture. For example, in one work she places the definition of "lily-white" next to a partial view of a woman's back and shoulder inclining towards a calla lily that appears to be leaning similarly towards the

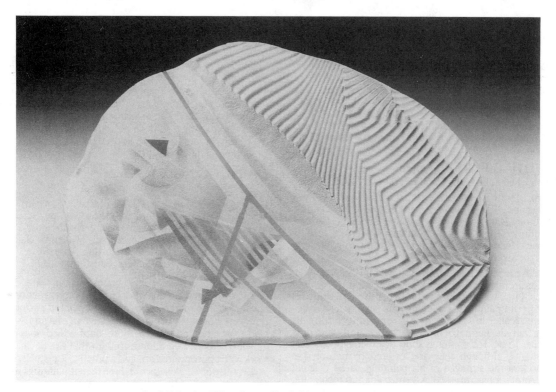

Carl Schmitt, *West Coast Cool,* 24 x 24, clay and acrylic

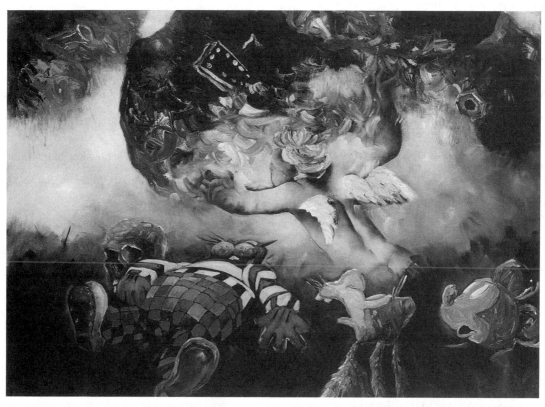

Barbara Bell Smith, *Debris,* 50 x 70, oil on canvas. Courtesy: Dorothy Weiss Gallery. Photograph: Gary Sinick

woman; in another, the definition of "sit-upon" is juxtaposed with a rear view of a nude woman perched on a chair. Her recent work involves a series entitled "The Moon," consisting of black-and-white photos hand-painted with gouache and watercolor in blues, yellows and pinks. The series depicts a draped woman viewed from behind as she gazes at the changing colors of the moon.

SMITH, ALBERT E. (Painter)
1616 El Camino Real, Menlo Park, CA 94025

Born: 1929 *Awards:* Artist of the Year, *Asteion* Magazine, Tokyo *Collections:* UC-Davis *Exhibitions:* Anthony Ralph Gallery, NY; Anne Berthoud Gallery, London; Roger Ramsey Gallery, Chicago; Jeremy Stone Gallery, San Francisco; Marunouchi Gallery, Tokyo; Stremmel Galleries, Reno

A self-educated painter, he has lived in the Bay Area his entire life, and his work is a reflection of the Bay Area. His early work in the 1960s consisted of grid and color-field paintings. Gradually, his paintings have become smaller in scale, and he has taken to mixing his own acrylic paint to produce depth and thickness similar to oil. His paintings show abstract expressionist elements, although they are inspired by nature. He considers the strength of his paintings to be original interpretations expressed in form, color and technique. Unexpectedly powerful composition, carefully built with simple brushstrokes and undiminished pigments, is the trademark of his work.

SMITH, ALONSO (Painter)
232 Club Dr., San Carlos, CA 94070

Born: 1917 *Awards:* 1st Place, Artist's Society International Los Angeles; 1st Place, Political Satire, Supervisors, San Mateo County *Exhibitions:* San Mateo Arts Council; Hatley Martin Gallery, San Francisco *Dealer:* Hatley Martin Gallery, San Francisco

Although influenced by the great Mexican Muralists' social awareness, Bosch's sly, surreal symbolism and the Renaissance Masters' classical techniques, he has developed his own unique, satirical form of surrealism—now called "social surrealism"—to express meaningful concerns in the nuclear age in a variety of arenas: war, politics, psychology, medicine, music, education. Each of his tongue-in-cheek oil paintings, progressing from single to multiple concepts and from a simple to a complex prismatic palette, reveals an exceptionally witty imagination that explores the human condition in vivid color and form. Monsters, people and technology all whirl in and out of incredible backgrounds, creating earthy, poetic fantasies of great variety and depth.

SMITH, ANDREA (Painter)
1590 Lokia St., Lahaina, Maui, HI 96761

Born: 1946 *Awards:* United Nations, University for Peace, Annual World Peace Calendar *Exhibitions:* Lake Art, Palm Desert; Lahaina Gallery, Lahaina, HI *Education:* Wayne State U. *Dealer:* Gary Smith, Lahaina, HI

Her training in realistic painting and drawing eventually gave way to an abstract expressionist style as nontraditional as that of Picasso or Miro. Her bright, mixed-media paintings are filled with human images, flowers and ancient symbols and totems. Her work is the expression of her convictions and is dedicated to the celebration of life and the establishment of world peace. In

Seeing Eye to Eye, two figures share a single eye that gazes out, the lines and colors evoking an emotional as well as an intellectual response. She has participated in numerous international art education programs in association with the U.N. University for Peace and Picture Peace, among other organizations. A permanent collection of her work is housed at the Children's Bibliotheque in Moscow.

SMITH, BARBARA B. (Painter)
4053 Harlan St., #315, Emeryville, CA 94608

Born: 1945 *Awards:* SECA Finalist, Museum of Modern Art, San Francisco *Collections:* de Saisset Museum, University of Santa Clara *Exhibitions:* Pro Arts Gallery, Oakland; de Saisset Museum, Santa Clara *Education:* UC-Berkeley; San Jose State U. *Dealer:* Dorothy Weiss Gallery, San Francisco

She began her career working in abstraction, using oils on canvas. She called this work "gestural construction," because of the method used to build painted surfaces that were both abstract and suggestive of imagery. She also experimented with a more hard-edged style in acrylics. It was as a graduate student that she began to work with appropriated images, a practice for which she is currently quite well known. Her recent paintings use Disney images, particularly Mickey and Minnie Mouse, in very un-Disney-like situations. She uses this juxtaposition to express her feelings about the contradictory and complex nature of the human condition. In paintings such as *Stepping Out, Taking a Swing* and *Homecoming,* the fear and anguish of the characters is very believable, as they are caught in abstract, dark and confusing backgrounds. Some critics have speculated that these works are metaphors for coming of age or for the prolonged adolescence common in contemporary society. Her technique varies from abstract to very representational, as she depicts the inner and outer experiences of life. The paintings are executed in oil on linen and gessoed paper, and the surface varies from smooth to impasto.

SMITH, B.B. (Painter)
241 Trevethan Ave., Santa Cruz, CA 95062

Born: 1947 *Awards:* Honorable Mention, Marin County Fair *Collections:* California State U., Chico *Exhibitions:* Santa Cruz County Art Museum *Education:* UC-Berkeley; Cal. State-Chico

During formal training, she was influenced most by Franz Kline's spontaneity, Matisse's use of color and her teacher David Hockney's flat, stylized landscapes. Subject matter is inspired by wide observation at home and while traveling. Sketchbook drawings in felt-tip brush pens and colored pencil serve as studies for acrylic or oil compositions on paper or gessoed canvas. An intense interaction will develop while painting with the brush and stylus in matching pigment to ground. Years of etching contributed to her sgraffito technique with textures. She strives for flat, shadowless space and loose images, layering colors to maximize brightness. In a recent series of neighborhood scenes, houses and palm trees are silhouetted against various coastal light patterns and textural skies. She also produces underwater fish on floor mats and tropical scenes on shower curtains, in an effort to bring aesthetics into a practical realm.

Nancy Strode, *Poipu II (Skyscape),* photograph

Wally A. Smith, *Churchscene, Transformation of a Myth (4 of 13),*
20 x 24, acrylic and oil on canvas

Ken Steinkamp, *Flesh and Terra II,* 72 x 60, oil on canvas

Karen Gordon Schulman, *Red Dawn. . .Dreamtime,* 20 x 24,
hand-colored black and white photograph

Loran Speck, *Oriental Still Life,* 17 x 14, oil on panel. Courtesy: Loran Speck Gallery

Judy Stabile, *Nine Choirs,* 60 x 52, gold, silver and copper leaf on glass.
Courtesy: Mr. & Mrs. John Bettis

Joan Schulze, *No Sky in Manhattan,* 90 x 79, quilt

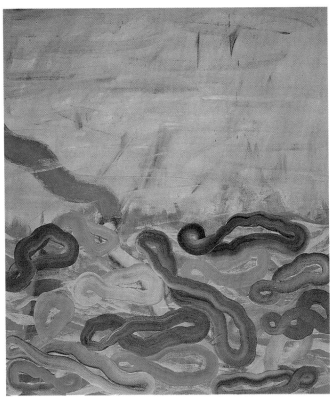

Harvey Sadberry, *Though I Danced in My Chains Like the Sea (D.T.),*
56 x 64, acrylic on canvas

Craig Scoffone, *untitled—from the Painted Abstract Series,*
16 x 20, photograph

Carol Schwennesen, *Watercall,* 65 x 59, oil on canvas

Virginia St. John, *Jeri,* 30 x 44, pastel

Paul Sershon, *Trinity,* 72 x 60, acrylic on canvas

Ian Sutherland, *Parallelogram,* 52 x 48, acrylic

George Stillman, *City Monument,* 36 x 36, oil. Courtesy: Gallery Imago, San Francisco

Betty Schoenberg, *Palace, Knossos,* 48 x 48, oil, masonite, mixed media

Ginny C. Stanford, *Prarie Fire,* 33 x 32, acrylic on canvas. Photographer: Jacques Cressaty

Albert Smith, *untitled, 1988,* 20 x 20, acrylic on paper. Courtesy: Howard and Ingrid Nudelman

Nadinka Szaksz, *Construction II,* 12 x 12, acrylic on canvas and masonite

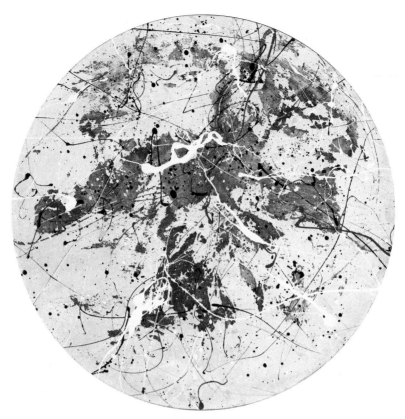

Glenda Schwartzman-Sloan, *World Star,* 41 circle, acrylic and enamel on canvas

Ruth C. Snyder, *King and Queen,* 84 x 84, acrylic on canvas

Pat Sherwood, *Worm Summer Rain,* 43 x 46, oil on canvas.
Courtesy: J.J. Brooking Gallery, San Jose, CA

Lisa Steinbach, *The Universe of Life,* 48 x 56, mixed media paper sculpture.
Courtesy: Mr. and Mrs. Augusto Salvatori, Rome, Italy

Marco Sassone, *House Boats IV,* 64 x 71, oil on canvas. Courtesy: Fiordaliso Gallery

Clyde San Juan, *Don't stand there on the outskirts, this place of sprouting shadows,* 6 x 5, mixed media

Barbara Sowle, *Pushawalla Canyon,* 36 x 30, acrylic

Dorothy Stratton, *Sea Bird,* 38 x 48, acrylic on canvas. Photograph: William A. King

William Grant Sherry, *Spinnaker Run,* 24 x 30, oil

Marjorie Stevens, *House on Steiner,* 30 x 22, watercolor. Photograph: Stone and Steccati

Gregory Sumida, *Trick or Treat,* 24 x 30, oil

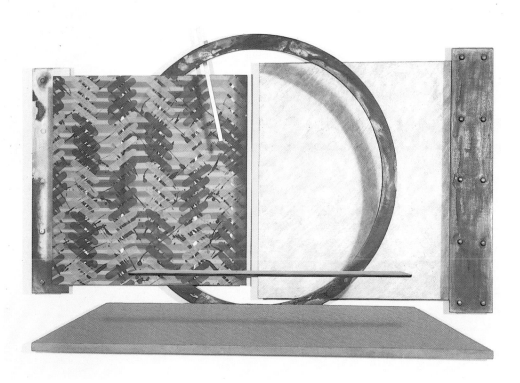

Rufus Snoddy, *Hoop and Stick,* 60 x 40 x 3, acrylic and canvas on wood panel with mixed media.
Courtesy: L.A. Artcore Gallery, Los Angeles

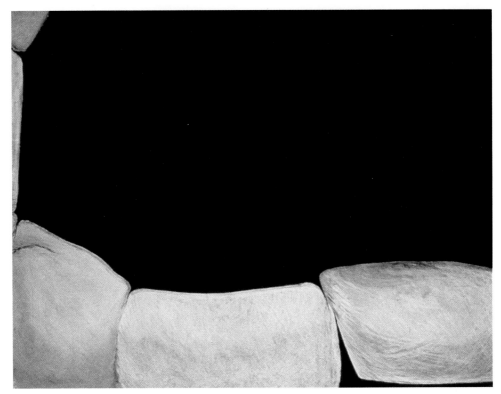

Linda Dodwell Stupski, *Mother's Memory,* 60 x 70, charcoal, chalk

Olga Seem, *Tunnel Vision,* 43 x 54, oil on canvas. Photographer: William Nettles

SMITH, BOB (Painter)
7859 Olive St., Fair Oaks, CA 95628

Born: 1939 *Awards:* Special Award of Excellence, International Art Challenge *Education:* California Polytechnic U., Pomona

Early work explored mood through the cold tones of charcoal and pencil drawing. Experiments with color began with his introduction to oils, which he now uses exclusively. Both his figurative paintings and his landscapes are almost photo-realist in detail. Female nudes are not romanticized or eroticized. A naturally flawed body sits on an orange couch in a room full of detail; the back of a woman looking out a window is hidden from the sun. He renders images touched by light with colors brighter than reality, in order to maximize their contrast with shadow. This play is also seen in his gold country landscapes.

SMITH, CARTER (Fabric Artist)
314 B. Chestnut St., Santa Cruz, CA

Born: 1946 *Exhibitions:* Renwick Gallery, Washington, D.C.; Smithsonian Institution, Washington, D.C. *Education:* UC-Santa Barbara

He creates his intricately patterned fabrics with a new type of hand dyeing. His method is a combination of folding, pleating, injection dyeing, acid and steam setting, discharge, direct vat dyeing, overdyeing and shiburi techniques. In order to create his combination of colors, he uses three different dye types in combination with dye activators and strippers. Because of the range of dyes and fabrics, there is an element of the unexpected in the work. The slightest variations in the dye or fabric can bring about striking changes in the patterns or colors. "The unfolding of each piece is exciting, as only then do you know what to expect."

SMITH, EDITH (Printmaker, Painter)
3732 Laguna Ave., Palo Alto, CA 94306

Born: 1925 *Awards:* Artists' Council Prize, San Francisco Museum of Modern Art *Exhibitions:* Ohio State U. Gallery of Fine Art; Oakland Art Museum *Education:* UC-Berkeley; Atelier Calevaert-Brun, Paris

Trained in painting at Berkeley, she first explored pictorial space in a series of elongated "CONTINUUMS" (influenced by Mark Tobey and Jean-Paul Riopelle). This was followed by diptychs, triptychs and oriental-influenced screens in oil, gouache and mixed media. Further explorations included large, shaped acrylic paintings on plywood. After training in printmaking, concentrating in etching, she used her access to the computer facilities at Stanford University to complete a series of computer-assisted color etchings, combining original poetry and computer transformations of images. Her present work in printmaking continues to incorporate original poetry and etching, using modern desktop computers and photo processes. In painting, she continues her Fauve-influenced, symbolic, cut-out acrylic work, with art-historical references and social and metaphysical themes. In watercolor, she is exploring California landscape, with special emphasis on the interface between nature and human society.

SMITH, ELLEN R. (Painter)
237 N. J St., #A, Lompoc, CA 93436

Born: 1954 *Collections:* Fuller Potter; Richard Jarrette *Exhibitions:* Atelier, Lompoc; Roger Smith Gallery, Boulder Creek *Education:* Middlebury College; University of Rhode Island

After being trained in drawing, painting and sculpture at a number of academies, she credits her apprenticeship with Fuller Potter for teaching her to "see." Painted in oil on unprimed surfaces, her early paintings are heavily influenced by the Abstract Expressionists and governed by the philosophy that "art is a spontaneous expression of energy." During this period, rather than "suffer gallery politics," she ran businesses selling her textiles and porcelains. She sees her formal training as detrimental to the creative process and through disciplined study of Russian, music and engineering she broke from those early influences. Her recent large-scale oils feature an unprimed canvas with areas of thin wash as well as thick resined impasto. The paintings embrace a full palette are and spontaneous in the tradition of Jackson Pollock.

SMITH, GARY DOUGLAS (Printmaker, Draughtsperson)
P.O. Box 244, Inverness, CA 94937

Born: 1948 *Collections:* Achenbach Foundation for Graphic Arts, San Francisco; De Saisset Museum, Santa Clara *Exhibitions:* Vorpal Galleries, San Francisco; Vorpal Galleries, Laguna Beach *Education:* College of Arts and Crafts; Atelier 17, Paris

In his early work, he used sharply pointed colored pencils and layers of cross hatching to create shimmering, illustrative landscapes. Pieces often included architecture, archways and open vistas. In recent work, he draws and silverpoints on large sheets of watercolor paper, which he stretches like canvas over wood frames. The artist mutes his serene Northern California landscapes and simplifies them into a few basic shapes. He achieves a shimmering pointillist effect and his work is more interpretive than photo-realistic. He recently began working in egg tempera and oil painting.

SMITH, HASSEL (Painter)
The Old Rectory, Bradford Rd., Rode Bath, Avon BA3 6PR England

Awards: NEA Award; San Francisco Art Commission Award *Collections:* San Francisco Museum of Modern Art; Los Angeles County Museum of Art *Exhibitions:* Oakland Museum; Iannetti-Lanzone Gallery, San Francisco *Education:* Northwestern U.; California School of Fine Arts

An early period of loose, expressive figure painting which responded to the seen world evolved under the strong influence of Clyfford Still into explosive abstract expressionist works in the 1950s. In the action paintings of this period, paint is applied roughly and violently, masses of volcanic color streaked with flashes of calligraphic intrusions. Yet the introspective collages from the mid-1950s and the increasing concern with shape presaged a transformation in the 1960s to the cool, intellectual, dynamic investigations of geometric forms that have marked his work to the present. The dominant form is the circle, in various manifestations—full, half-circle, crescent, loops—interspersed with squares, rectangles and bands of paint. The forms seem to propel themselves to the edge of the canvas and beyond; he achieves a remarkable diversity of shape and color. He has lived and worked in England since the 1960s, returning to the States to teach on occasion.

SMITH, HOWARD (Photographer, Mixed Media Artist)
824 N. Lafayette Park Place, Los Angeles, CA 90026

Born: 1956 *Awards:* Fulbright Grant *Collections:* Security Pacific Bank, Los Angeles *Exhibitions:* 3rd Annual Photography Exhibit, San Francisco; Rizzoli of Soho, NYC *Education:* U. of Southern Mississippi *Dealer:* LeMieux Galleries, Inc., New Orleans

After an apprenticeship in Paris, primarily in black-and-white photography, he began to experiment with hand-coloring techniques and direct positive printing processes, reminiscent of Talbot and Daguerre. Man Ray and Maholy-Nagy were major influences on his work as well. More recently, he has concentrated on the use of large-format negatives and infrared photography. He creates mixed-media collages that incorporate electronic parts such as diodes, transformers and vacuum tubes taken from old televisions. These "modern hieroglyphs" are unified abstract transformations of what were once machines. Each electrical component is individually colored using a palette of various intensities. He also creates collages from photocopies of found images in technical and historical books, which he combines with organic materials in order to express both the ancient and the modern.

SMITH, JOAN J. (Painter)
2241 Sampson St., Marysville, CA 95901

Born: 1925 *Award:* 1st Place, Watercolor, Yuba Sutter Fair *Collections:* Mathews, Crippen & Boysel *Exhibitions:* Golden Valley Art Center; Yuba-Sutter Chamber of Commerce *Education:* Michigan State U.; U. of California

After formal training in textiles and related arts, she experimented with oil paints, ceramics, printmaking, batik and serigraphy, before settling on watercolors. She has tried to minimize the medium's inherent water, paper and drying time problems, by consistantly using the same paints, paper and studio settings. Her subject is always near at hand and its environment is always her studio/sun-porch. Recently, her primary interests hae been the transparency of glass and its reflection of colors. Her subjects are still lifes of glass dishes, silver serving spoons and glass bowls and fruit. She has been influenced by the work of Barbara Netchis, Janet Fish and Wayne Thiebaud.

SMITH, KIM (Sculptor)
1853 Burnell Dr., Los Angeles, CA 90065

Born: 1951 *Awards:* Honorable Mention, American Drawing Biennale, Muscarelle Museum of Art, Williamsburg, VA; Award, Pacifica, Palo Alto Prints *Collections:* Bibliotheque National, Paris; New Jersey State Museum *Exhibitions:* San Diego Institute of Art; Pacifica Prints, Palo Alto *Education:* Syracuse U. *Dealer:* Green Collections Galery, Tokyo

Growing up in the late, pop-oriented 1960s, she made constructions, usually animals, having a furniture-like aspect. Her sculpture became more formal and less humorous, and began to interact with surrounding planes. Principles of theater began to appear in work as did the influence of dioramas at the Museum of Natural History. She was fascinated by the Museum's stuffed animals standing in a partially three-dimensional environment. To this fascination she added a concern with surface layering and texture that reached back to the highly textured, calligraphic European and Oriental art of the 1950s. Her work explores non-tradi-

tional support and creates the tension of a weighty object floating. In one series, she uses Oriental drapery to suggest bodies that do not actually exist.

SMITH, LINDA K. (Painter, Printer)
29 Winslow Place, Moraga, CA 94556

Collections: Hyatt Regency Hotel, Fort Worth; Visa USA, Inc., San Francisco *Exhibitions:* Ivory/Kimpton Gallery, San Francisco; William Sawyer Gallery, San Francisco *Education:* Stanford U.; California College of Arts & Crafts *Dealer:* Ivory/Kimpton Gallery, San Francisco

Although the images in her works are recognizable forms from nature—grasses, twigs, matted leaves—her concern is not with scientific reporting, nor with celebrating specific beauty. Rather, the pieces reflect a fascination with common structures within species, despite each specimen's singularity and uniqueness. This approach results in often tapestry-like paintings in which the forms lie between natural rendition and abstract pattern. Early work, in pastel on a heavily textured surface, usually features a simple, monolithic form with an obvious figure-ground relationship (perhaps reflecting O'Keeffe and Pearlstein). Later works include monotypes and large acrylic paintings that feature complex compositions of overlapping and interweaving forms.

SMITH, MIRIAM (Painter)
2139 1/2 Laguna Canyon Rd., Laguna Beach, CA 92651

Born: 1949 *Awards:* 1st Place, All Media, Laguna Beach Art Museum; 3rd Place, Pasadena International Art Competition *Collections:* BankAmerica Corp. Art Collection, San Francisco; UC-Irvine *Exhibitions:* Laguna Beach Museum of Art; Paris Green Gallery, La Jolla *Education:* Otis Art Institute; Art Center College of Design

Using layering to provide structure, her early work explored natural botanical forms. Elements supported by a slightly withdrawn approach to perspective combined within this structure to create an element of wonder, to which the nature of the forms themselves is incidental. Her recent exposure to African and Oceanic cultures has brought to her work a more limited vocabulary of black, white and gray, with an airy, sunlit emergence of yellow. These works on scroll-like paper incorporate a sense of form developing in space. Still concentrating on organic shapes, an increasing reality of volume and objectivity creates tangibility within an abstract context. More is revealed about these forms as objects through the shifting of light sources.

SMITH, ROBYNN (Painter, Ceramist)
3430 Main St., Soquel, CA 95073

Born: 1956 *Collections:* Jewish Community Museum, San Francisco; *Exhibitions:* Allegra Gallery, San Jose Braunstien/Quay Gallery, San Francisco *Education:* Rhode Island School of Design; San Jose State U. *Dealer:* Allegra Gallery, San Jose

The sharing of the earth is often the subject of her paintings and sculptures and she is inspired by a love for animals and a deep feeling for nature. Over the last few years, she has evolved a personal mythology based on her relationship with pets. Abstract, shadowy forms of horses, goats, dogs and ducks often appear in her colorful canvases. She paints these large works (up to 5 by 7 feet) with gestural brush strokes and moody

William Grant Sherry, *Emmett Kelly, Sr.,* 22 x 28, oil

Wally A. Smith, *Window, Transformation of a Myth (5 of 13),*
25 x 28, acrylic on canvas

washes. Her whimsical yet subdued ceramic sculptures of goats have a loose painterly quality. Recently, the human figure has become an important element in her ever more ethereal work.

SMITH, WALLY A. (Painter)
3004 Oakbridge Dr., San Jose, CA 95121

Born: 1943 *Exhibitions:* Monterey Peninsula Museum of Art; People's House, Berkeley *Education:* De Anza College

In 1985, he was inspired by painters to work on canvas. He began developing an abstract representational style and was concerned with social themes and the preservation of social reference. The work of Johan Itten then influenced him to use color to enhance and create depth and feeling. He is now painting larger oil and acrylic pieces, seeking an abstract expression through traditional landscape themes and color formats. Paintings such as *Bowtie* are abstracted scenes of California viaducts. The main body of his work has been compiled into a thirteen-piece art exhibition entitled "Transformation of Myth". He is the founder and owner of the Wally A. Smith Studio.

SNODDY, RUFUS (Sculptor, Painter)
2220 S. Beverly Glen Blvd., #206, Los Angeles, CA 90064

Born: 1947 *Awards:* Art In Public Places, Los Angeles *Collections:* Chase Manhattan Bank; American Savings and Loan *Exhibitions:* Exploratorium Gallery, California State U., Los Angeles; L.A. Artcore

Prior to 1974, he painted realistic and photo-realistic oils. Minimalism interested him and he soon began to sculpt and to explore the sculpture of John McCracken, Donald Judd and Robert Morris. In graduate school, he fabricated a series of kinetic works from aluminum, wood, fiberglass, resin and welded stainless steel. In these his interest was in the purity and integrity of form and movement. From sculpture, he proceeded to painting in three dimensions. The textures and colors of nature are now often the subjects of his acrylic "constructions paintings." The works appear as trompe l'oeil, with abstract or geometric shapes floating in space. He fabricates the works from wood, plastics and other materials covered with canvas, which he then paints.

SNOW, CYNTHIA R. (Painter)
13663 Mar Scenic Dr., Del Mar, CA 92014

Born: 1907 *Awards:* 1st Prize, Del Mar Centennial *Collections:* Barnett Endowed; William Beaton Museum of Art, CT *Exhibitions:* Gwyndion Gallery, La Jolla; Quint Gallery, San Diego *Education:* U. of North Carolina, Greensboro; Peabody College

She is a lyrical abstractionist whose abstractions are rooted in nature, particularly in the canyons of the Pacific Coast. Her colors are strong, pure and bright, very much in the French tradition of Matisse. When she paints in oil, it is a direct application with over-painting. When she paints with watercolors, it is a more spontaneous application and she leaves areas of paper showing to emphasize rhythm and the contrast between positive and negative space. She also paints with acrylic and mixed media. Her upbringing and education were in New England and the East Coast. She is a member of the National Society of Women Artists.

SNOW, MARYLY (Painter, Mixed Media Artist)
4053 Harlan, #214, Emeryville, CA 94608

Born: 1944 *Awards:* Honorable Mention, Crown Zellerbach; California State Fair, Sacramento *Collections:* Achenbach Foundation for Graphic Arts, San Francisco *Exhibitions:* Nathan Hart Gallery, San Francisco; Los Medanos College, Martinez *Education:* UC-Berkeley *Dealers:* Hatley-Martin Gallery, San Francisco; Van Straaten Gallery, Chicago

Equally influenced by the Bay Area figurative school and by questions of metaphysics, her early work focused on ceramic sculpture and drawings. The compositional device of a quadrant provided space of varying depths for the central imagery, the "attendant," an abstract shape resembling a knife, an angel or a pillar of fire. The pieces were heavily veiled abstract morality plays and visual meditations. Her oil paintings continue to employ the quadrant, now as a crossroads or boundary between earth's atmosphere and outer space. Her paint-handling combines lyrical abstraction and colorism, with minimal imagery. She is also known for her monotypes and mixed-media assemblages with plexiglas and neon.

SNYDER, FRANCIS (Painter, Multimedia Artist)
302 A Feru Ave., Penngrove, CA 94951

Born: 1949 *Awards:* Best in Show, San Jose Art League *Exhibitions:* California Museum, Santa Rosa; San Francisco Art Institute

She started her artistic career as an abstract expressionist, who created sensuous, non-cerebral paintings. Eventually, she added textural elements to enhance the paintings' physical presence. By the early 1980s, she had adopted a more figurative style. Much of her recent work consists of nearly surreal wall-reliefs in wood and plaster. These masks consist of androgynous faces, with affixed objects, such as fish and toy birds. These intuitive pieces derive directly from the subconscious, and are tangible, waking echoes of dream imagery.

SNYDER, RUTH (Painter, Sculptor)
2200 Main St., Santa Monica, CA 90405

Born: 1928 *Awards:* 1st Prize, International Juried Art Exhibition, NYC; 1st Prize, National Watercolor Society, Los Angeles *Collections:* Smithsonian Institution, Washington DC; Fred S. Wight Gallery, UCLA *Exhibitions:* Bridge Gallery, Los Angeles City Hall; Venice Art Walk *Education:* UCLA; Otis Art Institute *Dealer:* Merging One Gallery, Santa Monica

She is known for both abstract impressionistic paintings and abstract figurative sculpture. The Impressionists, particularly Bonnard and Monet, as well as Goya were the most important early influences on her style and approach. Among her works is the "Malibu" series, featuring environmental studies of light, shapes and colors in space. These arresting, colorful paintings are characterized by a burst of streaked abstract forms against a color field. In *King and Queen*, a large watercolor in bright red, orange and yellow, an abstracted male and female couple are placed against a blaze of color. Goya's treatment of the human figure is recalled in her bronze sculpture entitled *The Wall*, as several figures try to scale a wall. She has also featured three-dimensional figures on large canvases, and she has worked with collage materials including such items as

Ruth C. Snyder, *The Wall,* maquette for monumental piece, bronze

Glenda Schwartzman-Sloan, *Autumn,* 24 x 24, acrylic and resin on lucite

Alonso Smith, *Higher Education II—Pedagogical Chaos,* detail,
48 x 48, oil on panel

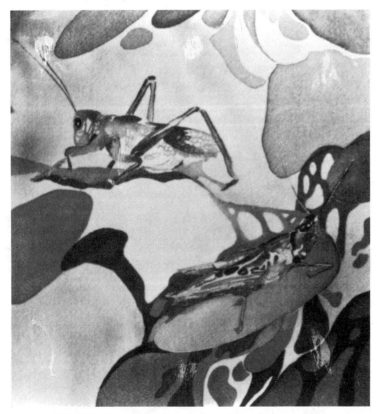

R.H. Schubert, *Hawaiian Hoppers,* 20 x 22, watercolor

Albert Smith, *Untitled, 1987,* 40 x 40, acrylic on paper.
Courtesy: Howard and Ingrid Nudelman

Ian Sutherland, *Four Grey Balls,* 48 x 52, acyrlic

Andrea Smith, *Mother Earth's Prayer #2,* 22 x 30, mixed media

Dorothy Stratton, *Chariot II,* intaglio. Courtesy: William A. King

Vladimir Sokolov, *Veronica,* 48 x 72, mixed media collage on canvas

Synthia Saint James, *Tibetian Women,* 30 x 24, oil on canvas. Courtesy: Collection of Richard Pryor

Howard Smith, *Blood River, 1988,* 14 x 11, silver print. Courtesy: Le Mieux Galleries, New Orleans, LA

blue airmail envelopes, randomly placed numbers, silk, lace, ribbon, buttons, pieces of torn canvas or paper and a variety of other materials.

SNYDER, STEVE (Painter, Mixed Media Artist)
83 Caselli Ave., San Francisco, CA 94114

Born: 1956 *Exhibitions:* Euphrat Gallery, De anza College, Cupertino; Southern Exposure Gallery, San Francisocn *Education:* De Anza College; Southern Oregon State U.

He most enjoys his work when he can use humor to highlight some contemporary political or social issue. Beginning his career as an airbrush illustrator, he moved into computer graphics in the early 1980s, conscious of the strong influence of the contemporary commercial art market. He works from a bright palette, combining at will New Wave, deco and neo-pop images in both his painting and mixed-media pieces. One of these, *Cola Wars*, presents a Pepsi and a Coke can bludgeoning each other on an American flag background. Another assemblage, *Vacation*, features postcards from New York City, toy high-heel shoes and plastic trout, among other objects.

SOBELL, NINA (Video Artist)
190 Eldridge St., New York, NY 10002

Born: 1949 *Awards:* NEA Fellowship; Fellowship, CAPS New York State Council on the Arts *Collections:* Museum of Modern Art, NYC; Manchester Gallery, Manchester, England *Exhibitions:* Contemporary Arts Museum; Long Beach Museum *Education:* Cornell U.

She was the first woman to receive an MFA in sculpture from Cornell U. In her thesis on participation process art, she was influenced by Allan Kaprow's happenings. After leaving school, she began using video to create spatial illusions, which paralleled her sculptural concerns. In her early existential performance video works and brainwave drawing, she showed a close alignment with Chris Burden, Karen Finley and the Kipper Kids. She is presently working on a series of small figurative sculptures, influenced by popular comics like *Transformers* and *Spiderman*. She is also making tapes that incorporate these figures in an animated, surreal style.

SOKOLOV, VLADAMIR (Collagist)
1540 S. Coast Hwy., Laguna Beach, CA 92651

Born: 1932 *Awards:* Purchase Award; City of La Mirada; 1st Place, Painting, Laguna Beach Museum of Art *Collections:* Banco Commerciale Italiana, Chicago *Exhibitions:* Laguna Beach Museum of Art; Newport Harbor Art Museum, Newport Beach *Dealer:* Jerry Petr, Chicago

After training in both commercial and fine art, he developed a precisely unique constructivist style of collage influenced by Ivan Tabakovich and Naum Gabo. At the same time he also experimented with paint surfaces and, influenced by de Kooning, began using his own painted paper (including monoprints) as collage elements. He recently began constructing his abstract collages by mounting long, thin trapezoidal strips of variously colored paper over a color ground. His spiral forms suggest the atmosphere, object and ground. Through layering, he achieves a sculptural effect of objects in space. Most recent work is more concerned with the illusionistic dimensions of color, the radiance of light, and expression of tensions of the era.

SOLDNER, PAUL (Ceramist, Sculptor)
743 W. Baseline Rd., Claremont, CA 91711

Born: 1921 *Awards:* Pris D'Honneur, Biennale Internationale de Ceramique d'Art de Vallauris, Paris *Collections:* Victoria & Albert Museum, London; Los Angeles County Museum of Art *Exhibitions:* El Camino College Art Gallery, Torrance; San Angelo Art Center, TX *Education:* U. of Colorado; Otis Art Institute *Dealer:* Louis Newman Gallery, Los Angeles; Susan Cummins Gallery, Mill Valley

Accepted internationally as a major force in the evolution of contemporary ceramic art, he has punctuated his career with important innovations. In the mid-1950s, while studying with Peter Voulkos, he investigated the idea of extended throwing, creating varied shapes that extended to seven or eight feet in height. These pieces were decorated with expressionistically painted areas. In the 1960s and 1970s, he explored the Buddhist philosophy and worked out a technique that has become known world-wide as American Raku. Then, in the 1970s and 1980s, he pioneered a technique known as low temperature salt firing, which extended his vocabulary and became influential in the ceramics world. New qualities that emerged in his life and work at that time are now being incorporated into his work, which is much larger, layered and sculpturally extended. He is now working on a new bronze casting technique.

SOLTERO, EMILIO (Painter)
1623 24th St., Sacramento, CA 95816

Born: 1965 *Exhibitions:* UC-Davis Art Gallery; Blue Mango Art Exhibition, Davis *Education:* UC-Davis

Strongly influenced by the great Renaissance masters and by classic illustrators, his work in drawing and painting is figurative and naturalistic. He has concentrated on the space surrounding a figure, experimenting with light and shadow. Painting from a full palette, he has recently begun creating murals, working on large pieces of masonite.

SOLWAZI, KEMISOLE (Sculptor)
735 Mayor, Fresno, CA 93706

Born: 1946 *Collections:* Cal. State-Fresno *Exhibitions:* Cal. State-Fresno; Cal. State-Santa Barbara

Influenced by the Cubists, the Harlem Renaissance artists and Elizabeth Catlett's works of the 1960s, she created three-dimensional masks that explored the experience of Black Americans. She processed primary colors to form a turquoise, gold and brown patina, combining this with a broad variety of materials that included bells, bones, leather string and burlap bags filled with dirt that hung from the base of the 2-by-1-1/2- foot masks. A concern with simplicity of form and the use of natural materials prompted recent works, which are very direct and more abstract. Intended to be modern fetishes representing the living aspects of nature, they are splashed with patina, resulting in a thick, corroded surface that symbolizes change and age. Most recently, figuration has been included in a series on material wealth.

SONG, SOONHO (Painter)
4463 Hilltop Rd., Soquel, CA 95073

Born: 1944 *Exhibitions:* Los Angeles Museum of Art; Landell Galleries, Carmel

Long interested in the use of masks in ritual and play, he creates paintings and masks influenced by the styles

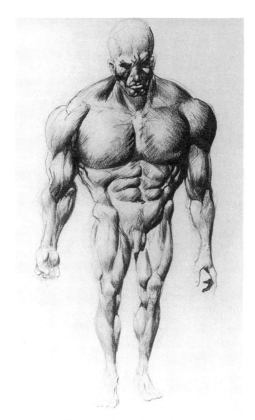

Emilio Soltero, *Stage 2,* 8 x 10, graphite

Andy Stricker, *Evolution of the Noose,* 92 x 144, acrylic on canvas

of Joan Miro and Paul Klee. He works in a variety of media, including pen-and-ink drawing, enamel and watercolor painting, sand, crayons and pastels, as well as paint on rice paper, canvas and—his newest interest—cowhide. As with rice paper, cowhide is a natural material which promises longevity, durability and the permanency that modern chemically treated artist's paper cannot sustain due to acidification. Using oil pastels, shoe dye and a burning engraving tool for line drawing, he continues to explore the combination of these materials in his vision of the abstract.

SONNIER, KEITH (Sculptor)
145 Chambers St., New York, NY 10007

Born: 1941 *Awards:* Guggenheim Fellowship; 1st Prize, Tokyo Prints Biennale *Exhibitions:* Domaine de Kerguehennac, Rennes, France; Nature Morte Gallery, NYC *Education:* U. of Southwestern Louisiana; Rutgers U. *Dealer:* Leo Castelli Gallery, NYC

Early works in cloth were followed by those incorporating neon light and sound. In the 1970s, he began experimenting with video-computer interactions and the "transmissional potential of film." An intensive study of satellites resulted in a work conducted at NASA in which the images of the participants in New York and San Francisco were transmitted to each other. Recent work using native materials are the result of travels to different "outsider" cultures. A Cajun from Big Mamou, he attributes his growing up in the tropical south with influencing his work. The neon works remind him of the cocktail lounges in Louisiana, and having grown up in an "outsider culture" enables him to understand subcultures from around the world.

SOUSA, JAN (Painter, Papermaker)
725 Pine Ridge Ave., Mt. Shasta, CA 96067

Born: 1944 *Awards:* Cover Award, Siskiyou Artists Directory *Collections:* State of Oregon *Exhibitions:* National Miniature Fiber Exhibition; Los Angeles Audubon Society *Education:* Cal. State-San Jose; Southern Oregon State U.; College of Siskiyous

Early studies with Bob Nugent and Dominic DeMare lead her to papermaking and soft sculptural forms. No longer challenged by the Native American-derived masks she was making, she returned to painting in a realistic way and began experimenting with ink abstractions. Since 1986, she has combined the two and now places realistic figures in a semi-abstract environment. She splashes inks onto various colored acid-free boards, spraying them with water or printing on them. She takes the best of these and further works them with ink and watercolor, adding animal or human figures. She has completed series on wolves, birds and fish.

SOWLE, BARBARA (Painter)
P.O. Box 20277, Santa Barbara, CA 93120

Born: 1930 *Awards:* Best of Show, Faulkner Gallery, Santa Barbara *Collections:* Mayor Lodge, Santa Barbara; Santa Barbara Bank & Trust *Exhibitions:* Sojouner Gallery, Santa Barbara; Los Angeles Audubon Society Art Show *Education:* UC-Santa Barbara *Dealer:* CG Productions, Santa Barbara

She studied with Robert Frame, Irma Cavat and Tom Wudl, developing a semi-impressionistic style characterized by the free use of color and uninhibited, straight brushwork. She paints on the diagonal, seeking to create momentum by moving toward the upper right corner. At one time, she worked in acrylic on masonite, but she now prefers the receptivity of canvas. Her California landscapes, inspired by the work of Oskar Kokoschka, glow with layered colors. Her palette includes blues, greens, pinks and ochres.

SPAHR, HERLINDE (Printmaker)
88 Evergreen Dr., Orinda, CA 94563

Born: 1952 *Awards:* Silver Medal, Emerging European Artists; Chancellor Fellowship, UC-Berkeley *Collections:* Morrison Collection, UC-Berkeley; Prenten Kabinet, Antwerp *Exhibitions:* International Center For Graphic Arts, Belgium; Pacific Grove Art Center *Education:* U. of Antwerp; UC-Berkeley

She is a self-taught artist, and her early influences were the drawings and prints of Redon and Knopf. Beneath the well-drafted and seemingly coherent surfaces of her lithographs and drawings are what have been described as disjunct locutions, impossible perspectives and powerful absences. Early works were large-scale black-and-white drawings. In the mid-1980s, she began producing lithographs, and she has recently begun using color. In enigmatic prints and drawings, she tries to "make the blind spot visible," seducing viewers as far as possible, until their perception of the image falls apart. In *The Four Seasons*, a large window displays four panels of the seasons, moving from the innocence of spring to a walled-up view of winter.

SPECK, LORAN (Painter)
P.O. Box 4978, Carmel, CA 93921

Born: 1943 *Awards:* Artists of America Show, Denver; Colorado Historical Society *Collections:* Burt Reynolds; Gavin McLeod *Exhibitions:* Conacher Galleries Show, San Francisco; Colorado History Museum *Education:* Art Conservatory, San Francisco

Strongly influenced by Rembrandt van Rijn, Jan Vermeer, Jean Baptiste Chardin and William Harnet, he paints natural realist still lifes in a Renaissance-like chiaroscuro. His images of fruit, flowers, vases, tables and cracked plaster walls are rich and sensuous. He begins the work by making a series of compositional drawings from life. He then sands a sheet of untempered masonite before blocking in the background with shapes. After painting and repainting the work—he finds that painting over mistakes gives the work character—he adds two coats of varnish. He owns his own studio in Carmel and has studied under Al Froom.

SPERRY, B. (Commercial Illustrator, Painter)
P.O. Box 99424, Pacific Beach, CA 92109

Born: 1931 *Awards:* 1st Place Art Museum, St. Petersberg, FL *Exhibitions:* Hillcrest Art Exhibit, San Diego; San Diego Art Institute *Education:* Louisiana State U.; Sorbonne U.

Growing up in the midst of the Texas-Oklahoma oil boom, she originally used watercolor, ink and soft pastel to paint scenes of oil fields at night. In college, she painted shrimp boats and Gulf Coast scenes in watercolor and soft pastels. After leaving the Sorbonne, she studied under Sid Solomon in New York, Robert Sprague in St. Petersberg, Florida and Joe Sage in New Orleans. Influenced by Corbonio, an instructor in Bird Key, Florida, she moved from her original realism to an impressionistic style. She has recently begun studying silk-screening processes and painting abstracted landscapes, coast scenes, shrimp boats and

Carol Schwennesen, *Nest,* 70 x 58, oil on canvas. Photograph: Christian Mounger

Judy Stabile, *Rita,* 60 x 52, gold, silver and copper leaf on glass

other working boats with enamels on 5-by-6-foot masonite boards and with oils on 3-by-5-foot canvases.

SPILMAN, JULIUS (Painter)
1376 Delaware St., Berkeley, CA 94702

Born: 1941 *Collections:* T. Rusel, Los Angeles; J. & J. Kennedy, Ashland, OR *Exhibitions:* Oakland Museum of Art *Education:* School of the Art Institute of Chicago

Influenced by Picasso, Miro and Chagall, his painting shows the emotion inherent in everything from human life to the objects of nature. Using color and palette knife, the energy of his work relates to the effort it takes to be born, grow and learn about the world. Recently, he has been experimenting with sculpture, using marble, limestone and collage elements. Other recent projects are conceptual, including *Working the Other Side.* This piece explores the shift available in conceptual art not only for the physical environment but the emotional environment as well.

SPIVEK, ILSE (Photographer)
2314 Swarthmore Dr., Sacramento, CA 95825

Education: Institute of Design, Chicago

The Bauhaus influence at Chicago's Institute of Design formed the basis of her photographic vision. The teachings of Paul Stone added to this, and basic compositional forces still remain at the foundation of her art. She works both in black and white and in color; most of her pictures are portraits. Exclusively working on location, her innovative style of lighting and posing gives her pictures an unusual atmosphere of reality. In a recent series called "Details," she captured small details of large structures such as the Golden Gate Bridge. She has recently been working on a series of black-and-white portraits of mothers and children.

SPRING, BARBARA (Sculptor)
Burns Creek, Big Sur, CA 93920

Born: 1917 *Awards:* Home Savings & Loan Purchase Award, Beverly Hills; San Francisco Art Commission Purchase Award *Collections:* Oakland Museum; Los Angeles County Museum *Exhibitions:* William Sawyer Gallery, San Francisco; Richard Nelson Gallery, UC-Davis *Dealer:* William Sawyer Gallery, San Francisco; Asher-Faure, Los Angeles

For ten years she struggled to progress beyond her formal training in England to sculpt with the freedom she now enjoys. Called a "folk sculptor" by some, she works primarily in a wood medium, using any material that might be available; her recent pieces have been in black walnut, Italian cypress, cedar and redwood. She relies on the colors innate to the wood, although she will occasionally stain or paint particular pieces. The rough-hewn treatment recalls the folk tradition, but to this she adds sophistication, insight and wit. Among her works are *Distraught Myrtle*, *Pictures at an Exhibition* (a scene from a cocktail party) and *Mr. and Mrs. Earnest Carving.* The work is gradually becoming two-dimensional, with the same image on each side. For instance, the 1986 display *Horse's Hindquarters With Stable* presented a collection of freestanding horses' backsides with tails on both sides and the "stable" hung on the wall.

STABILE, JUDY (Painter, Sculptor)
1504 W. Washington, Venice, CA 90291

Born: 1948 *Collections:* Atlantic Richfield *Exhibitions:* Molly Barnes Gallery; The Works Gallery *Education:*

California Institute of the Arts; Chouinard Art Institute

While at the Chouinard Art Institute, she experimented with different surfaces and studied the rhythms and illuminating qualities of glass. This resulted in several series of paintings on the reverse side of glass. An early response to nature involved paintings using actual leaves and twigs and free line and color. This work evolved into a full series of overlapping cylinders in the late 1970s. She recently began using gold, silver and copper leaf, to develop a more formal, asymmetric dialogue through repeated illusionary placement of cones and cylinders. She has been influenced by Mark Rothko. Her recent work is a response to the drama of human interdependency.

STALLINGS, SALLY (Draughtsperson)
838 E. University Ave., Fresno, CA 93704

Born: 1941 *Exhibitions:* Fig Tree Gallery, Fresno *Education:* California Polytechnic U.; U. of Minnesota

Originally, her delicate pencil drawings were based on the internally generated, hypnogogic images that she saw before falling asleep. They ranged from landscapes to figuration to rock forms. In all of these instances, she was concerned with the image beneath the surface, such as reading a rock as a face. More recent work has focused on external reality, such as found objects floating in an atmosphere framed by a window. Her technique involves layers of prismacolor pencil that are subtly built up, and areas of strong pressure and defined edges that contrast with the otherwise soft edges and delicate gradations of tone.

STAN, CYNTHIA (Painter, Printmaker)
c/o Hank Baum Gallery, P.O. Box 26689, San Francisco, CA 94126

Born: 1953 *Awards:* Artist Fellowship, Delaware Arts Council; Copeland Fellowship Sabbatical, Wilmington Friends School, Wilmington, DE *Collections:* Security Pacific Bank, Los Angeles; Prudential Life Insurance, Chicago *Exhibitions:* 69th Exhibition, Delaware Art Museum; Miriam Perlman Gallery, Chicago *Education:* Colorado State U.; Penn State U. *Dealer:* Hank Baum Gallery, San Francisco

Acrylic and intaglio techniques have replaced earlier collage, pastel and painting techniques. She combines abstract and figurative elements in an imaginative spatial field of floating geometric shapes, lines and patterns. Motifs derived from Indian, Islamic and African textiles appear throughout her acrylic-on- paper and canvas paintings. Figurative elements include silhouetted animal forms such as cats, fish, birds, flamingos and dogs. These symbols of life contrast with geometric shapes to create whimsical, musical compositions. She has also been influenced by the works of Miro, Kandinsky and Dubuffet.

STANFORD, GINNY C. (Painter)
P.O. Box 2014, Sebastopol, CA 95473

Born: 1950 *Exhibitions:* Hassam & Speicher Fund Exhibition; American Academy of Arts and Letters

Her early paintings of solitary figures in dreamlike, remote settings were executed in thin acrylic washes and subdued colors. Beginning in 1984, she began to focus on the 1912 Joplin, Missouri, farm house she grew up in and on the landscape of the farm surrounding it. She combines realistic rendering with a dramatic use of light, giving her work a radiant yet disconcerting quality. By layering glazes, she achieves a luminosity

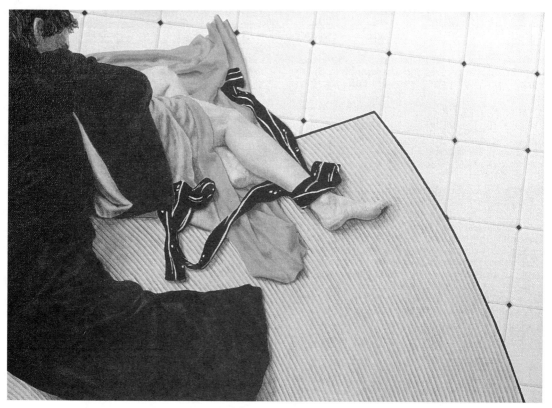

Ginny C. Stanford, *Dreams Leave Their Hindtracks,* 12 x 18, acrylic on canvas

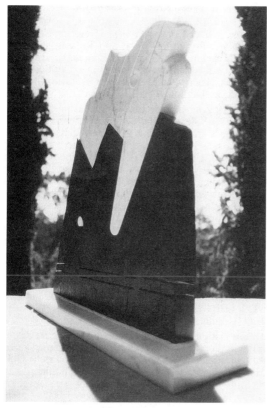

Barry Scharf, *Black and White,* 27 x 26 x 7, marble, slate

Karen Gordon Schulman, *Tree of Life,* 11 x 14, black and white photograph

and brilliance not usually found in acrylic painting. She is continuing to experiment with figuration in a series of men and women in highly decorative, colorful kimonos.

STANTON, BRUCE (Ceramist)
1918 Gillespie, Santa Barbara, CA 93101

Born: 1958 *Awards:* International Art Competition Finalist, NY *Exhibitions:* Elaine Potter Gallery, San Francisco; Del Mano Gallery, Los Angeles *Education:* UC-Santa Barbara

His work has very traditional roots, while he experiments with the foot, body and lip of a vessel. He exaggerates these elements by using hard-edged geometric forms, then distorting them by deviating from the horizontal and vertical. It is not his intention to degrade the functional quality of the vessel, but rather to draw upon its sculptural qualities and to celebrate them. His brightly colored works in earthenware clay are usually 16 to 24 inches tall. He has recently been working on a series of vessels which depict the myriad facets of the ocean and the sport of surfing.

STARBUCK, MARG (Painter)
P.O. Box 3491, 258 Cannery, Terminal Island, CA 90731

Born: 1929 *Exhibitions:* Long Beach Public Corporation for the Arts; L.A. Artcore *Education:* Glassel Museum of Fine Art School; Cal. State-Long Beach *Dealer:* Art Space Gallery, Los Angeles

Her paintings can be characterized by their expressive approach to archetypal images. Conjuring up images from the highly resolved to the elusive, her technique involves the lavish application of paint, often using her hands instead of brushes. Although her subject matter was once exclusively vessels, she has begun exploring the connotations of the human body as a vessel. She also employs water imagery, symbolizing life, and bridges as a means of getting from the conscious to the unconscious. The large-scale works in acrylic ponder images and their making, metaphor, collective meaning and facts.

STARKWEATHER, TERESA (Painter)
1801 Chart Trail, Topanga, CA 90290

Born: 1950 *Awards:* 1st Place, Watercolor, Billy Graham Center, Wheaton College, IL *Exhibitions:* Madison National Watercolor, WI; Ariel Gallery, NYC *Education:* Atlanta College of Art; Art Center School of Design *Dealer:* Ariel Gallery, NYC; Art Trends, San Bernardino

After studying under Lorser Feitelson and Peter Plagens, she became interested in lyrical abstraction. She painted large color fields with an airbrush and experimented with abstract monoprints that resembled landscapes. Her discovery of the watercolors of John Singer Sargent and Joseph Rafael then led her to paint poetic landscapes *en plein air*. She is now doing more studio painting and branching out into figures and still life. Whatever the subject, her concern is with expressing a feeling or mood. She has also worked as a scenic designer for network television and, as a free-lance illustrator, she did a monthly full-page cartoon strip for *Playgirl* magazine.

STARN TWINS (Mixed Media Artists)
155 N. Beacon St., Boston, MA 02135

Born: 1961 *Awards:* NEA Grant *Collections:* Metropolitan Museum of Art, NYC; Ringling Museum of Art, Sarasota, FL *Exhibitions:* Museum of Contemporary Art, Chicago; Museum of Modern Art, San Francisco *Dealer:* Stux Gallery, NYC

These artists are twin brothers who use pieces of photographs in collaborative works that relate closely to sculpture and painting. Photographic conventions are broken by creased and scarred prints, push-pinned or taped into place. The images are often out of focus. Surrounding them are incomplete frames and glass-like fragments serving neither a decorative nor a protective purpose.

STARR, DI (Mixed Media Artist)
P.O. Box 845, El Cerrito, CA 94530

Born: 1953 *Awards:* Board of Directors' Exhibit Award, Berkeley Art Center *Exhibitions:* Post Photo, Hearst Art Gallery, Moraga; Gallery Imago, San Francisco *Education:* U. of Massachusetts; New England School of Art, Boston

During the 1970s, she worked in acrylics and then developed an original expressionistic approach to intaglio printmaking. Exploring themes of materialism and spirituality, she overlaid three plates with soft-ground etching lines and sugarlift painting. After moving to the Bay Area in 1983, she began combining painting and photography. She now enlarges black-and-white gelatin silver prints to 16 by 20 inches, and paints them with a combination of photo oils, photo pencils, pastels and acrylics. She continues to develop a body/spirit color system of symbols—her female and male nudes interact both with each other and the environment in a study of male/female relations.

STARR, PENELOPE C. (Glass Designer)
P.O. Box 2572, San Anselmo, CA 94960

Born: 1935 *Awards:* Pilchuck Scholarship Award *Collections:* Shaklee Corporation; The Berelson Company *Exhibitions:* Projects Gallery, San Rafael; California Crafts Museum, San Francisco *Education:* Radcliffe College; Yale Art School *Dealer:* Dorothy Solomon, The Art Collaborative, NYC; Sara Skersick, The Art Connection, Laguna Niguel

After taking an architecture degree from Radcliffe, she went to Yale and studied under Joseph Albers. In 1959, she started working in stained glass. An early influence was Robert Sowers, but by the early 1970s, she was looking toward the strong line work and abstract designs of the German glass designers Meistermann, Beschulte and Schaffrath. In the early 1980s, she was working "beyond the window." She experimented with contemporary standing lamps, mirrors, hand-carved decorative accessories and slumped glass. She eventually chose slumped glass as her primary medium. The subject of such recent series as "Goddess Robe" and "Flying Shaman" is the empowerment of women. Although her present works are small, she envisions very large scale, walk-through pieces.

STATON, MIKKI (Wood Sculptor)
4337 Allendale, Oakland, CA 94619

Awards: 1st Place, California Carver's Guild; 1st Place, Annual Woodcarver's & Crafters Guild *Exhibitions:* Sargent Johnson Gallery, San Francisco; Prieto Gallery, Mills College, Oakland *Education:* Chouinard Art Institute; Ben Shaw Carving School, Los Angeles *Dealer:* Marian Bowdry, San Francisco

Using only mallets, gouges and chisels, she carves reliefs in natural burl wood. Her subjects concern the African and African-American experience, and the

Marco Sassone, *Alcatraz,* 40 x 50, oil on canvas. Courtesy: Fiordaliso Gallery

Stefen, *Lake Temescal/Kruse Plumbing Co.,* 108 x 144, latex (house paint)

work is powerful, natural and touchable. Her figures are physically true-to-life, with natural expression and muscle tone. In the viewer's mind, her scenes extend beyond the rough borders of the wood. She has had no formal training beyond a six-week course on wood carving tools and a seminar on art appreciation.

STEEL, CLAUDIA (Painter, Printmaker)
5011 Wilson Landing Road, Chico, CA 95926

Born: 1918 *Awards:* Annual Drawing and Print, San Francisco Museum of Art; Memorial Prize in Serigraphy *Collections:* Turner Print Collection *Exhibitions:* Pacific Grove Art Center; 1078 Gallery, Chico *Education:* UC-Berkeley; Mills College

Her range of media—watercolor, oil, linocuts and etchings, serigraphs and photomontage—is equaled by the range of subject matter and treatment. Earlier works include images of small personal objects—an Easter basket figures in one piece—as well as landscapes in which boats float in muddy water. These earlier works have yielded to more symbolic landscapes—for instance, a garbage can lid and tomato box juxtaposed to the negative image of a piece of farm equipment. Although the subjects and techniques continues to evolve, a hierarchical sense of composition characterizes all the work. In many of the pictures a dominant "triangle" functions as the invisible armature upon which the chosen imagery is placed.

STEFEN (Painter, Muralist)
P.O. Box 5191, Berkeley, CA 94705

Born: 1947 *Exhibitions:* Legion of Honor, San Francisco; American Cultural Center, Paris *Education:* U. of Oregon

He is a self-taught painter, whose oil work of the early 1970s was influenced by the Surrealists. By 1974, he had discovered acrylics and was painting large-scale public murals in latex. One large mural was commissioned by the Dutch Boy Paint Company at a prominent Berkeley intersection. He calls himself a "visionary realist"; many of his painted scenes have added surprises, juxtapositions and slight mirage elements. Using illusory, trompe l'oeil images, he attempts to bring nature into the blighted urban environment. He has recently returned to oil painting on canvas, and has completed a series of historical paintings that document the history of Orr Springs in Mendocino County.

STEINBACH, LISA (Multimedia Artist)
1627 Camden Ave., #101, Los Angeles, CA 90025

Born: 1958 *Awards:* Casden Company Purchase Prize; Westwood Art Festival *Collections:* Security Pacific Bank, Los Angeles; Home Savings of America, Los Angeles *Exhibitions:* Masters Gallery, La Jolla; Westwood Art Festival *Education:* UCLA

She is a handmade paper artist whose hieroglyphic and textured canvas backgrounds bespeak a penchant for oceanic influences and ancient ruins. She began her career as a designer of free-form wearable art. When she decided to expand her media, she took formal training in handmade paper techniques. With a previous knowledge of abstract expressionist painting she began creating multidimensional, handmade paper paintings. Oriental papermaking techniques have since become important to her and she now achieves ethereal, mystical, luminescent and transcendent effects by juxtaposing three-dimensional paper sculp-

tures and textured canvases. Her varied media include pastes, found objects, handmade papers and acrylic paints. She is equally at ease with metallics, subtle pearlescents and fluorescent primary colors. Recent paintings reflect cross-cultural images and symbols gathered from extensive travels in Europe and the Middle East.

STEINKAMP, KEN (Painter)
2928-A Santa Monica Blvd., Santa Monica, CA 90404

Born: 1948 *Awards:* ISD Invitational *Collections:* U. of Northern Iowa, Cedar Falls; Trinton Corp., Westwood *Exhibitions:* Francine Ellman Gallery, Los Angeles; James Clark Gallery, Los Angeles *Education:* U. of Northern Iowa; U. of Wisconsin *Dealer:* Michael Conway Gallery, Los Angeles

Influenced by the works of Emile Schumacher, Edvard Munch and the abstract expressionist school, his work encourages viewers to move beyond layered surface images to the subconscious, linear foundations of the paintings. He works primarily in oil, often incorporating textual raw materials, on canvas and on paper to create an organic impression. Using darker maroons, purples, terra-cotta, black, carmine red and Prussian blue, he considers his work abstract impressionist. Recent paintings are quite large, usually 6 by 8 feet.

STEINKE, TERRY M. (Printmaker)
478 25th Ave., San Francisco, CA 94121

Born: 1950 *Exhibitions:* Kings Mountain Art Festival, Woodside; Saratoga Rotary Art Festival

He is a former industrial designer who makes realistic aquatint etchings of untouched landscapes or long-abandoned buildings such as barns. His etchings are moody with their sepia tones and have been compared with the photographs of Ansel Adams and the paintings of Andrew Wyeth. Each piece has a definite sense of time and place about it. He begins the work with photos and drawings from field trips. He then uses acid to etch a copper plate. The work is multitoned and he achieves subtle gradations of color by controlling a stopping out process similar to batik.

STEPHENS, GRETEL GEISER (Painter)
803 Columbia St., South Pasadena, CA 91030

Born: 1935 *Exhibitions:* Richard Evans Gallery, Glendale; Artworks, Los Angeles *Dealer:* Ginger Krueger, Pasadena

After formal studies in figure drawing and painting, she was influenced by the neo-expressionist movement. Seeking through figural painting to reveal psychological aspects of the human condition, she has recently been working on a series of split-screen images in oils and acrylics on canvas. Working in a variety of media, she also assembles experimental bookworks, which focus on domesticity. Recent paintings illustrate areas of personal conflict, particularly the theme of immobility versus action.

STEPHENS, JOANNE (Assemblage Artist)
25251 N. Highway One, Ft. Bragg, CA 95437

Born: 1923 *Exhibitions:* Mendocino Art Center; Phoenix Gallery, San Francisco *Education:* State U. of Iowa; Institute of Design, Chicago

Although trained as a painter at the Chicago Bauhaus in the early 1950s, she found the perfect medium for her artistic expression in found objects. She started doing Schwitters-type collages, using debris found in parks and on streets. With time out to raise her family,

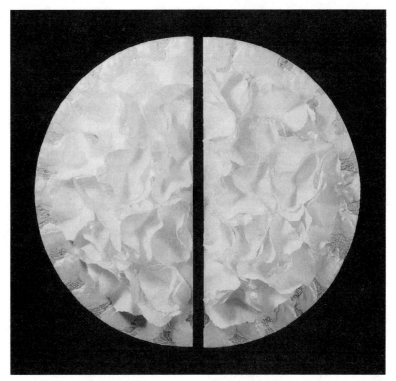

Lisa Steinbach, *The Universe of Life,* 48 x 56, mixed media paper sculpture.
Courtesy: Mr. and Mrs. Augusto Salvatori, Rome, Italy

Joan Salinger, *Space Invaders at the Beach #1,* 21 x 25, type C color print with photogram

she continued doing some collage work, as well as window display, floral design and the buying and decorating of antique shops. Combining her interests in anthropology, kitsch, found objects, medieval religious art, Dada and Max Ernst, her style has recently crystallized into a form that utilizes the mythic qualities in found objects. The process of juxtaposition is the key element in assembling her work: a figurine of a madonna and child placed next to a toy dinosaur inspired a work titled *He Came Too Soon*. By placing knick-knacks in a shrine or a baroque decorative atmosphere, she creates tension between the beautification of the banal and the ironic content of the work's statement. The pieces may be tabletop-sized or larger (floor sculpture or wall piece), self-contained or in a framed shadow box.

STERN, ELLIE (Sculptor, Multimedia Artist)
449 N. Bundy Dr., Los Angeles, CA 90049

Born: 1925 *Awards:* Purchase Prize, Annual National Print Exhibition, Los Angeles Municipal Art Gallery *Exhibitions:* Annual California Sculpture Exhibition, Cal. State-Northridge; Laguna Beach Museum *Education:* Stanford U.; USC Multimedia Studio

After studying and writing on Matisse's Fauve paintings, she enrolled in the California School of Fine Arts, now the San Francisco Art Institute, where she studied drawing with Richard Diebenkorn. Early work in sculpture resulted in the creation of figural abstractions; in the 1970s, she made a body of biomorphic sculpture carved in brown alabaster. The "Rainbow Spaces" of her thesis exhibition at USC were fashioned of clear glass and plexiglas domes patterned on the underside with rainbow-colored geometric shapes. These shapes were made by depositing metal oxides on the domes through masks in a vacuum chamber. The domes were mounted on 30-inch-high plexiglas base and lit by 250-watt quartz beam-shapers mounted in lighting track. An interest in monumental public sculpture led to the creation in 1980 of *Hello Up There*, a 32-foot-tall sculpture of wood poles with steel collars; it was conceived as a dialogue with the huge palm trees growing along the parkway and as a mediator of space between human scale and man made construction. *Sun/Moon*, another large sculpture made of cold-rolled naval brass plate, welded and polished, followed in 1983. She has been working on a large sculpture in stainless steel; other recent work returns to forms in nature, focusing on the richly colored, curling bark of the eucalyptus trees outside her studio.

STERN, LANNING (Painter)
31 Fountain Alley, San Jose, CA 95113

Born: 1943 *Exhibitions:* Allegra Gallery, San Jose; San Jose Institute of Contemporary Art *Education:* Art Center College of Design; Otis Art Institute

For the last twenty years, his graphics and design interiors have been said to occupy a space somewhere between pop culture and fine art. He considers Walt Disney and Andy Warhol, who have influenced his work, to be two contemporary artists who have successfully bridged that distance. His own works feature cartoon images in acrylic on canvas, figurative paintings which are intended for amusement and decoration. Since he believes that all signs are inherently unstable in meaning, he invites viewers to find whatever meanings in his work they can.

STEVENETT, DIANE (Sculptor)
P.O. Box 609, Los Olivos, CA 93441

Born: 1954 *Collections:* Brigham Young University, Springville, UT *Exhibitions:* Zzyzx Fine Art, Los Olivos; Springville Museum of Art, UT *Education:* Brigham Young University, UT *Dealer:* Stevenett Garden Gallery, Los Olivos

After studying traditional form in relief work and figurative carving and modeling, she became influenced by the primitive art of the Cycladic and Egyptian eras. In 1985 she presented a group of seven works carved in black walnut. She has continued working in black walnut, carving some pieces as large as eight feet in height. These recent works represent a combination of her musical sensibilities (she sings opera) and her sculptural vision as she has created lyrical interpretations of the Hermit Songs by Samuel Barber. Her sculpture is "full of grace, crescendos and decrescendos, fortes and pianissimos."

STEVENS, MARJORIE B. (Painter)
1438 Page St., #5, San Francisco, CA 94117

Born: 1902 *Awards:* Society of Western Artists; American Watercolor Society *Collections:* de Saisset Museum, Santa Clara; Michael S. McKenzie, San Francisco *Exhibitions:* American Watercolor Society Traveling Show; De Young Museum, San Francisco

Known for her impressionistic watercolors of Victorian houses, her work has spanned a breadth of media and subjects matter. She makes a personal, unique use of collage. She has painted landscapes and still lifes in both transparent and opaque watercolor. She came her art career late in life. Although she had studied privately under Kingman and George Post and was well grounded in the basics, she did not have her first exhibition until she was fifty. She has earned frequent invitations to sit on juries for various art shows, including the California State Fair Art Exhibition and the Nevada State Fair. She is also a successful chiropractor.

STEVENS, MICHAEL (Sculptor)
3977 Rosemary Circle, Sacramento, CA 95821

Born: 1945 *Awards:* James D. Phelan Award *Collections:* Israel Museum, Jerusalem; University of New Mexico *Exhibitions:* Renwick Gallery, Smithsonian Institution, Washington DC; Crocker Art Museum, Sacramento *Education:* Cal. State-Sacramento; *Dealer:* Braunstein/Quay Gallery, San Francisco; Betsy Rosenfield Gallery, Chicago

His early sculptures were bandaged lumps of wax covered with hair follicles, plastic hair and pimples. The same type of low-brow fascination led him to create a series of painted wood figurines that have been likened to the work of Jim Nutt. As the work progressed, he began to leave evidence of his craft—allowing wood shavings to stay on the pieces and contrasting painted and unpainted areas. At the same time, animal forms began to replace human ones. His recent wood sculptures are elongated creatures made from unpainted sticks and twigs found in the Sierras. The work exudes a formality and mystery that has been likened to ancient Egyptian art.

J. McNeil Sargent, *St. Chapelle,* 22 x 30, monotype.
Courtesy: Tarbox Gallery, San Diego

Ken Steinkamp, *A Friend and I,* 96 x 60, acrylic on canvas

STEWART, BEATRICE (Painter, Mixedmedia Artist)

220 Oceano Ave., #3, Santa Barbara, CA 93104

Born: 1944 *Exhibitions:* Kerkhoff Hall, UCLA; Bropton Gallery, Los Angeles *Education:* International College of Westwood; Pepperdine U.

She began her artistic career by painting realist landscapes with traditional techniques. After attending the International College of Westwood, she began to work in a mixed media of watercolor, cynotype, encaustic, pastels and acrylics. Today, she specializes in landscapes, seascapes and abstracts. Among her commissions is a portrait in oil of a staff member of the University of California. She has exhibited widely and is a member of the Pastel Society of America.

STEWART, KIPP (Painter)

Drawer 6145, Carmel, CA 93921

Born: 1928 *Collections:* St. Francis Hospital *Exhibitions:* Bernstein Gallery, NYC; Source Gallery, San Francisco *Education:* Chouinard Art Institute *Dealer:* Zantman Gallery, Carmel

Early oils were completely abstract. These evolved into abstracted still life forms, and then into near realism. After that, he spent several years doing portraits in acrylic. He continues to work with acrylics, creating entirely imagined landscapes and still lifes. Today, he seldom draws from nature, but composes the surface of his paintings with classical methods. He has studied industrial design, architecture and engineering and has designed restaurants, inns and furniture.

STEWART, VICTORIA C. (Painter)

P.O. Box 4667, Lancaster, CA 93539

Born: 1948 *Awards:* 1st Place Ribbon, Glendale Civic Center, Los Angles; Best of Show, Antelope Valley Fair *Exhibitions:* Glendale Civic Center, Los Angeles; Desert West Juried Art Exhibition, Los Angeles *Education:* Scottsdale Art Institute; Los Angeles Art League *Dealer:* Ashkenazy, Beverly Hills

As a daughter of an Native American, she has had a life-long commitment to American Indian cultures. She has focused on contemporary images of Indian life, painting images of Native Americans in modern settings. For the first eleven years of her career, she painted realistically, but she is now moving toward impressionism; her medium had been oil, but she is now combining oils and pastels, and experimenting with pastel details over oil monoprints on glass or sandpaper. She is co-founder and member of High Desert Women Artists, a signature member of Pastel Society West Coast and a member of the California Federation of Art Associations. She has been influenced by Ramon Kelly, Hal Reed and Harley Brown.

STEWART-METZE, ROBIN (Painter, Sculptor)

P.O. Box 5513, Santa Barbara, CA 93150

Born: 1938 *Exhibitions:* Museum of Science and Industry, Los Angeles; L.A. County Art Museum *Education:* Goddard College; Long Beach State U.

His works reflect a variety of diverse influences: his painting style is derived from Diebenkorn and other Southern California artists; Wendel Castel influenced his work in sculpture and furniture. Abstract paintings are executed in oil or thin washes. He creates heavily sculpted, laminated furniture from logs. In recent work, he uses video to project images for his paintings.

STILES, KRISTINE (Painter)

443 Mississippi St., San Francisco, CA 94107

Born: 1947 *Exhibitions:* Museum of Contemporary Art, New Orleans; San Francisco Museum of Modern Art *Education:* UC-Berkeley *Dealer:* Brody's Gallery, Washington DC

Her paintings are autobiographical projections of past, present and future experiences that symbolically depict her intuitive emotional and psychic life. She is concerned with two primary themes: the relation between power (historically the domain of the male) and "logos and hysteria," or the female intelligence; and the intercourse of gender and race in Western history and culture. Her subject matter and style emerged in the late 1960s, when, working as a fashion model, she identified the objectification of her body with the opacity of surface experience by African-Americans. Works are in oil on canvas, occasionally with elements of collage and language. Her palette includes bright, complementary opposite colors and colors often associated with Mexico and the Caribbean; her style combines expressionistic brushwork with classical portrait painting. She has been influenced by Van Gogh and Carravagio.

STILLMAN, GEORGE (Painter)

1127 Franklin Ave., Ellensburg, WA 98926

Born: 1921 *Awards:* Bender Grant; Scottsdale Jurors Award *Collections:* Metropolitan Museum of Art, NYC; Oakland Museum *Exhibitions:* Metropolitan Museum of Art, NYC; Foster/White Gallery, Seattle *Education:* California School of Fine Arts; Arizona State U. *Dealer:* Foster/White, Seattle

His style has developed from a very early concern with form, and he consistently has maintained an interest in the emotional impact of line, color, form and surface in his paintings. The outward subject matter has been interchangeable, beginning with academic concerns, then with abstract expressionism, and more recently with realism. Working within the realist tradition, he has created landscape paintings that effectively reflect the geography of the Northwest, where he resides. His techniques include oil, egg-oil emulsion, egg tempera, graphite, lithography and etching.

STINTON, NELL (Painter)

1020 Francisco St., San Francisco, CA 94109

Born: 1910 *Collections:* San Francisco Museum of Modern Art; Chase Manhattan Bank, NYC *Exhibitions:* Mills College, Oakland; Fresno Art Center; *Education:* San Francisco Art Institute *Dealer:* Braunstein-Quay Gallery, San Francisco

After studying with Maurice Sterne at the San Francisco Art Institute, she came under the influence of the California Abstract Expressionists and began painting large, colorful, symbolic works. Simultaneously, she made small constructions and playful boxes, which were usually created with a humorous slant. In the late 1960s and early 1970s, she created two long scrolls out of canvas scraps, upon which she created continuous quasi-narrative collages: one was entitled *Under the Table at the Donner Party*, and the other was called *The Social Development of an American Female*. A detail from this latter piece depicts a girl or woman painted in a childish, fingerpaint-like style; beneath her is the caption, "She knew she felt like an artist. She hoped

Marjorie Stevens, *Leland Stanford Home,* 30 x 22, watercolor. Photograph: Stone and Steccati

Othell Jackson Schleker, *Small Town U.S.A.,* 24 x 36, acrylics

that artists would be her new friends and help her in her escape from her family." Recently, she has created a series of paintings dealing with industrial machinery as the contemporary landscape.

STOCK, MARK (Painter)
c/o Tortue Gallery, 2917 Santa Monica Blvd., Santa Monica, CA 90404

Born: 1951 *Collections:* Museum of Modern Art, NYC; National Gallery, Washington, DC *Exhibitions:* Brooklyn Museum; Library of Congress, Washington DC *Education:* U. of South Florida *Dealer:* Tortue Gallery, Los Angeles

He is a self-taught painter who started working seriously in 1978. His first paintings showed the influence of Magritte. In 1981, he became attached to the romantic image of the zeppelin (airship) and did several moody paintings and large-scale pastels on that subject. Since 1984, he has been painting figurative work influenced by Sargent and Manet. The paintings are intensely theatrical, and in his sad works, such as *The Butler's In Love,* he often deals with love lost. He has also designed sets and costumes for the Los Angeles Chamber Ballet's productions of *The Little Prince* (1986) and *Orpheus* (1988).

STOCKMAN, MARIAN W. (Photographer, Printmaker)
3530 Hadley Way, Santa Maria, CA 93455

Born: 1921 *Awards:* 1st Place, Santa Barbara County Fair; 1st Place, Longpoke Annual Show *Collections:* Ambassador, Luxembourg *Exhibitions:* San Luis Fine Arts Center; Gallery 912 1/2, Santa Maria *Education:* Colorado Womans College; Denver University

Over the years , she has worked in a number of media. In high school, she first began to master airbrush; next came silk screening, photo-tinting, engineering drafting and technical illustrating. Her interests also led her beyond two-dimensional work into pottery and sculpture. She has come full circle, returning to serigraphs combining silk screen and airbrush techniques. She is a realistic landscape and nature painter. One recent work features silhouettes of siguaro cactus against a setting Arizona sun, towering rock formations, as well as a close up of delicate berries clustered on a branch.

STOIA, ANDREW (Sculptor)
243 Guante Circle, Santa Barbara, CA 93111

Born: 1956 *Awards:* William Dole Memorial Award *Exhibitions:* Art Museum, UC-Santa Barbara; Dante Exhibition, Ravenna, Italy *Education:* UC-Santa Barbara

Born in Vienna, he spent his childhood near Frankfurt, W. Germany before emigrating to the U.S. in 1970. He studied sculpture with S. Schnittmann and architectural and sculptural restoration in Norway. For him, light is the spirit of art, the material that binds pigment, clay, painting and sculpture. He is interested in manipulating light, not merely reflecting it, with sculpture. He has worked mostly in glass, believing that it offers an aesthetic expressive power that outweighs the considerable technical difficulties of working in this material. Until 1986, his emphasis had been on the female nude, as well as some portraits rendered partially in polished bronze. In recent sculptures, he uses cast glass pieces in sculptures constructed primarily of metal.

STOLL, JEFF (Painter, Performance Artist)
1205 Peralta, Berkeley, CA 94706

Born: 1947 *Awards:* NEA Fellowship; CAC Fellowship *Collections:* Palais du Louvere, France; New York Museum of Art *Exhibitions:* Bienal de Sao Paulo, Brazil; Hotel Project, Multi-Site Bay Area

From a marginal artistic position he addresses questions of synthesis, articulation and contradiction. At the same time, he aspires to express emotions with primitive intensity. His media vary from paintings to solo performances to installations; in all, he artificially and dramatically charges pictorial space. His iconography is personal yet extroverted, and all is pushed together to induce a reflective mood which implies a larger picture. He has been influenced by Robert Rauschenberg, and he has recently been working on a series of mixed-media paintings.

STOLPE, DANIEL O. (Painter, Sculptor)
2539 Mission St., Santa Cruz, CA 95060

Born: 1939 *Awards:* California Arts Council Grant; Santa Cruz Arts Commission *Collections:* New York City Public Library; Portland Art Museum, OR *Exhibitions:* Coos Bay Art Museum, OR; Oregon Art Institute, Portland *Education:* Otis Art Institute; Pasadena City College *Dealer:* Walton-Gilbert Gallery, San Francisco; Native Images Gallery, Santa Cruz

Expressionistic, symbolic works in all disciplines are inspired by Native American legends centering around the theme of the Coyote/Trickster. He has lived, worked, traveled and attended spiritual ceremonies with Indians—specifically the Swinomish Indians of Puget Sound, Washington—for fifteen years. These experiences, combined with the traditions of the European figurative style and German expressionism, influenced his depictions of the coyote and animal/human behavior. The media comprise painting, sculpture and graphics. Using strong line, bold design and intense color, he has sought to develop a highly personal language expressing the magnitude of the coyote's epic nature. He has recently been working on a series of pastel and multimedia drawings and acrylic paintings expressing transformational subjects that erupt with powerful symbolism and mythology. His content is highly personal and reflects the autobiographical dialogue that has imbued his work for more than twenty years.

STONE, CATHY (Mixed Media Artist)
2773 Curtis Way, Sacramento, CA 95818

Born: 1952 *Awards:* Bronze Medal, Sculpture, Olympic Art Festival, International Art Competition *Collections:* Crocker Art Museum, Sacramento *Exhibitions:* Hyatt Hotel, Sacramento; American River College Gallery *Education:* UC-Davis

Although she began her career as an abstract expressionist painter, she quickly began experimenting with spatial relations and the third dimension. Her mixed-media works included horse hair, rocks, Chinese paper and tar as well as paint. By 1979, she had begun using neon. These works concentrated on the concept of unconscious writing as a means of exploring line, balance and color. Currently, her work focuses on the concept of embellishment. A Chinese tenet, embellishment is the effort to resuscitate broken forms by adding red to cracked areas. She constructs wall sculptures built of sheetrock walls arranged in geometric forms. The walls are decorated with conven-

Paul Soldner, *#88-7,* 22 x 33 x 7, clay

Stephen E. Stone, *Rocks #1, Salt Point, Sonoma Co., CA,* 20 x 24, fiberbase photograph

tional painting, clay forms, gold leaf, brass, glass and other materials. Objects such as nails or rocks, used to mar the surface, remain attached to the sculpture as narrative elements, telling the story of the sculpture's "beat-up" appearance. She places red neon in cracks as a form of embellishment.

STONE, JAMES M. (Painter, Printmaker)
P.O. Box 16033, San Francisco, CA 94116

Born: 1947 *Awards:* World of Poetry Golden Poet Award *Exhibitions:* Blue Danube, San Francisco; Hydrohoos, Athens, Greece *Education:* U. of Wisconsin

He is a painter, printmaker and mixed-media artist who is concerned with imagery but not with symbolism. He uses a balanced layout of recognized physical and cultural realities alongside a state of being of the subconscious: a collage of ideas and imagery and materials that draws the viewer closer. Many of his series demonstrate sequences of reproductive changes and evolution of methods and ideas. Also a poet, his *Untitled Poem* was included in *American Poetry Anthology* (1980), published by the American Poetry Association, Santa Cruz.

STONE, STEPHEN E. (Photographer)
2360 Pinecrest Dr., Santa Rosa, CA 95403

Born: 1950 *Awards:* 1st Place, Bodega Bay Fisherman's Festival; 2nd Place, Sonoma County Photography Contest *Exhibitions:* Mill Gallery, Petaluma; Luther Burbank Center for the Arts, Santa Rosa

He has worked as a photographer since the mid-1970s, using the world around him as a source for the expression of his thoughts and feelings, especially his love of nature. Too sensitive to document the world in a photojournalistic style, he prefers more romantic expression with an emphasis on simple, highly organized colors, shapes and forms. He has photographed landscapes from Death Valley, Kansas and Arizona to sites throughout California. He also shoots close-ups of natural subjects, as well as architectural and abstract graphics. Although he still does a great deal of color work and Cibachrome printing, much of his recent work has been in black and white. He works only in the 4-by-5-inch format, and credits mentor Ansel Adams for generously imparting his knowledge to his students while constantly encouraging them to develop an individual style.

STOUT, RON (Painter)
14192 Alder Lane, Sonora, CA 95370

Born: 1932 *Exhibitions:* Kent Lent Gallery, Tiburon; Village Artistry Gallery, Carmel *Dealer:* Miner's Gallery Americana, Carmel

His earliest paintings are characterized by their limited use of color, a result of his color-blindness for red and green. Gradually, however, he overcame his reluctance to use more color. Working in a straightforward representational style, he painted a range of subjects: landscapes, portraits, florals and still lifes. This period was characterized by drawing and painting in oil; eventually, this gave way to painting with acrylics, a fast drying paint for quick layering. At this juncture he spent two years painting in Italy, and one year in Spain. His influences included Bonnard and Monet for color, Louise Nevelson for form, and Joseph Cornell for his poetic and atmospheric qualities. Recent work consists of crisp architectural forms marked by strong color

relationships. The movement is toward more abstract simplicity; the subjects are almost exclusively atmospheric scenes from the Mediterranean area.

STOWE, ONEIDA (Painter)
110 Matheson St., Healdsburg, CA 95448

Born: 1944 *Awards:* Ford Foundation Scholarship; Andrews Portrait Award, Pacific Grove *Collections:* Library, UC-Davis *Exhibitions:* Laguna Beach Museum of Art; Retzlaff Vineyards, Livermore *Education:* California College of Arts and Crafts *Dealer:* Innpressions Gallery, Healdsburg

The influences of American realist illustrators and French impressionist painters are apparent in her watercolor depictions of life in California's beaches and wine country. Her technique has evolved form the loose application of paint on blank canvas, through careful undersketching, to the minimal use of line in a wet-on-wet technique. She has also been exploring the varying color intensities of acrylic on wood in a series of cat studies.

STRAIGHTLINE (Painter)
570 W. 24th St., #3, San Pedro, CA 90731

Born: 1957 *Exhibitions:* Angels Gate Cultural Center, Los Angeles; S.C.R.E.A.M. Festival, U. of California, Los Angeles

His works concern Aktionismus, a school of thought that seeks to envision life without traditional concepts of national culture. He seeks to create art as part of a global religion or culture, drawing heavily on Euro-Catholic iconography and Native American folklore. Such a merging is meant to force a re-analysis of conventional musical and visual forms. Within this school, all work is spontaneous. Using oil and oil pastels, he splashes and spills paint to form provocative designs. Often, he uses a wall or an entire room for his paintings. He cites Hermann Nitsch as the major influence on his style and approach.

STRAIT, DOROTHY MAY (Painter)
P.O. Box 3717, Apache Junction, AZ 85220

Born: 1934 *Awards:* Poster Award, Gallup, NM *Collections:* Red Rock State Park Museum, Gallup, NM; Washington County Museum of Fine Arts, Hagerstown, MO *Exhibitions:* Washington County Museum of Fine Arts, Hagerstown, MO; Wounded Knee Tallery, Santa Monica, CA *Education:* Scottsdale Community College

As a young girl, she was instilled by her parents with the importance of her Cherokee heritage. From her mother, who painted on wood with watercolors, she learned basic watercolor techniques. Later she studied with instructors Mary Willbanks and Budell Moody at Scottsdale Community College. As she advanced, she held to a native American subject matter of dances and ceremonies, but at the same time developed a contemporary style of depiction. She begins by spraying a hand-stretched canvas with watered-down acrylic. She follows this with forms and figures, applying the medium heavily to some areas to accentuate negative space and glazing others so that the dots show through.

STRATTON, DOROTHY (Painter, Printmaker)
4141 N. Henderson Rd., #707, Arlington, VA 22203

Born: 1908 *Awards:* 1st Award, AEA, Washington, D.C.; 1st Prize, San Diego Print Club *Collections:* Long Beach Museum of Art *Exhibitions:* Pasadena Art Museum; La Jolla Museum of Art *Education:*

Daniel O. Stolpe, *Meditation on the Shadow,* 24 x 36, acrylic on canvas

Edward Sexton, *Arrival of the Illuminarian,* 29 x 40, acrylic on canvas

Pratt Institute of Fine Art; Brooklyn Museum School
Dealer: Brighton Press, San Diego

During World War II, she was a special effects artist in Hollywood for Paramount Studios' George Pal Productions. While studying with Rico Lebrun during the 1950s, her vision changed from realism to abstraction, though she still held most consciously to nature. Her 1960s acrylics integrated intuition with plan, monochrome with color. During the 1970s and 1980s, she became more occupied with printmaking. The work is strong, non-sentimental, often mysterious, exploratory and moves toward a narrative approach. An active painter and printmaker her work is exhibited in Washington, D.C. Printmakers Gallery and Intaglio Printmaker, London, England.

STRAUSS, MEREDITH (Mixed Media Artist)
2621 Kennington Dr., Glendale, CA 91206

Born: 1955 *Awards:* Experts' Choice, Artists' Society International, San Francisco *Collections:* Rhode Island School of Design Museum; Hallmark Cards *Exhibitions:* International Textile Fair, Kyoto Japan; Bowers Museum, Santa Ana *Education:* Kansas City Art Institute; UCLA

Influenced by the warp-face pattern weaves of the Andean Highlands, she creates contemporary abstractions by interpreting traditional techniques. During the 1970s, she studied the textiles of Canada, Mexico, Sweden and Finland, but the weaves of the Andes have been the most important to her. She pleats cloth then takes strands of either vinyl tubing or cotton cord and weaves them through holes in a metal grid. Because of the metal's strength she is able to create shaped pieces. By using a double weave, she can create even more complex and complex pieces.

STREETER, GLEN G. (Painter)
137 Kiernan Ave., Modesto, CA 95356

Born: 1935 *Collections:* Bay Meadows Racetrack, San Francisco *Exhibitions:* California Art League, Sacramento; Pastel Society of the West Coast *Education:* Cal. State- Sacramento

He was strongly influenced by George Post; his early years of artistic exploration were spent largely with watercolor. General landscape portrayals were the main subjects of these works, which stressed the rendition of old farm buildings and other structures. The combination of an active sports life and an extensive arts career has resulted in an interest in sports painting—a perfect way for him to express his interest in color, contrast and movement. His recent work in this area has been done in pastels, which, he believes, adds a vibrancy unavailable in other media. He has continued to paint landscapes and seascapes (recently of the San Francisco Bay area), and has also completed several sports posters.

STREETER, LYNNE (Sculptor)
627 Adams St. Albany, CA 94706

Born: 1944 *Awards:* German Academic Exchange Grant; Rotary Club Grant *Collections:* Austin Conkey; Thomas Freudenheim *Exhibitions:* Oakland Museum; U.S. Information Service, Milan, Italy *Education:* San Francisco State; UC-Berkeley

Influenced by Käthe Kollwitz and German Expressionists, she began as a printmaker and fiber artist and advanced to sculpture in cast bronze. She casts flexible materials such as vines, leaves, feathers, thread, bamboo and fabric into bronze. She calls this process the transformation of something fragile and transitory into a permanent and timeless construction. Her experiences living with and filming Mayan Indians in Mexico and Navaho and Hopi Indians in the U.S. show in her "shelter" constructions. She views these pieces as places of refuge in an internal landscape of the psyche. Recently she has incorporated marble into her pieces, and she works in a marble workshop in Pietrasanta, Italy, during the summer.

STRICKER, ANDY (Painting)
14500 Old Condor Bridge Rd., Cloverdale, OR 97112

Born: 1947 *Exhibitions:* Multnomah Art Center; Whitebird Gallery, Cannon Beach, OR *Education:* San Francisco Art Institute *Dealer:* Whitebird Gallery, Cannon Beach, OR

His past work was influenced by Jan Vermeer, Edward Hopper and Wayne Thiebaud. Working primarily in watercolor and pencil sketches, sharp focus realism and the play of strong light were the compelling features of his compositions. As his clarity developed and he continued to pursue greater communication through subject and technique, color became a more important element. He began juxtaposing several images of related and apparently unrelated objects into a cohesive theme, influenced by Leon Golub, Arnold Mesches, Ivan Majdrakoff and Wally Hedrick. Accompanying this transition was a shift in media to acrylic paint on unstretched canvas. Presently, his images deal with controversial issues including war and politics, often drawn from events depicted on the news.

STRICKLAND, MARK W. (Painter)
301 Pleasant St., #6, Pasadena, CA 91101

Born: 1948 *Exhibitions:* Lizardi/Harp Gallery, Pasadena; Pinks Gallery, Brentwood *Dealer:* Lizardi/Harp Gallery, Pasadena

He has been influenced by Diebenkorn, de Kooning, Saunders and Riffino Tomayo. His "Subway Series" was a metaphor for man's tunnel-vision concerning progress. On large canvases (six to nine feet tall), he used drips, spills and smears to coax slightly realistic faces from abstract masks, giving the illusion of high speed travel. His recent "Endangered Series" concerns the possibility of human beings rising to the occasion of the higher self, in recognition of the human plight. These pieces are smaller (ranging from 4 by 4 feet to 4 by 8 feet). He depicts man's higher nature as ascending, abstracted spirits looking upward. His paint application is a scintillating impasto, which gives his figures a phosphorescent effect. Some figures appear to be breaking free of construction elements such as wooden slats or chicken wire

STRODE, NANCY (Photographer)
1487 Hiikala Place, #17, Honolulu, HI 96816

Born: 1925 *Exhibitions:* Artists of Hawaii; Arts of Paradise, Honolulu

She has dedicated her contemplative artform, mandala photography, to human healing. She constructs images which suggest "place" and through which the viewer can be centered in the physical plane. She often chooses air, water, fire, earth and space as her subjects, although a few of her works have to do with the urban landscape. The initial photograph is reversed and rotated, achieving a four quadrant print. The outer edges flow together, an effect achieved through darkroom and computer chromacom techniques. She

Carol Sherwood, *Way Out West,* 22 x 28 x 4, mixed media on ceramic

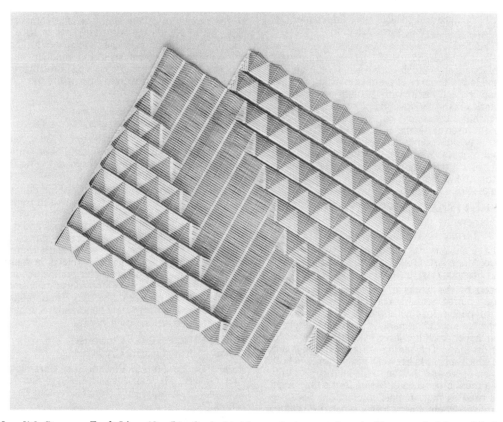

Meredith Strauss, *Fault Line,* 42 x 54 x 3, vinyl tubing and wire metal mesh. Photograph: Myron Moskwa

has been influenced by artist-photographer, Monique Fay.

STUART, VICTOR COHEN (Painter)
5874 Chabot Ct., Oakland, CA 94618

Born: 1946 *Awards:* Eisner Prize, Univ. of California, Berkeley; Young Artist Contemporary Award, Oakland Museum *Collections:* Oakland Museum; Security Pacific Bank, Los Angeles *Exhibitions:* Los Angeles Institute of Contemporary Art; Santa Barbara Contemporary Arts Forum *Education:* UC-Berkeley *Dealer:* Terrain Gallery, San Francisco

On a purely aesthetic level, the artist's mixed-media constructions are possessed of a dramatic, austere beauty. Painted and stretched canvas is rolled or trussed with thick coils, set with wooden stretcher bars, and hung, creating powerful, emotional tensions and rhythms. Undertones of bondage and fetishism are evident in the methodical wrapping of his canvas structures, even in their apparent straining against structural supports. This is cleverly offset by delicate applications of thin, near-natural color. The larger pieces—averaging 6 by 9 feet—exhibit the raw, aggressive stance of primitive shelters and structures. If approached as a metaphor for human skin, bone and sinew, the sculpture might be interpreted as a symbolic representation of the constant struggle for restraint and liberation in man's psyche.

STUBBS, THOMAS (Painter, Printmaker)
902 Cordelia, Glendora, CA 91740

Born: 1956 *Awards:* Chicago Bank and Trust Co. *Collections:* Kemper Group Collection *Exhibitions:* Ariel Gallery, NYC; The Real Thing, Brea *Education:* Cal. State-Fullerton; U. of Wisconsin, Madison

Though his first loves were simply painting and drawing, he has progressed toward baroque-influenced styles of engraving, etching and watercolor and oil painting. He is a believer in the relationship of facility and creativity, and his imagery is often anachronistic and esoteric. In the "Sticks and . . ." series, he depicted the makeshift facades and barriers people construct around themselves, while in the "Playpen" series cherubs, play with bombs and jets that dangle from makeshift mobiles. When printing, he emphasizes the contrasts of extreme lights and darks. He is an art instructor at Mt. San Antonio College in Walnut, California.

STUPSKI, LINDA DODWELL (Painter, Draughtsperson)
4 Presidio Terrace, San Francisco, CA 94118

Born: 1944 *Exhibitions:* Hatley-Martin Gallery, San Francisco; Marin Arts Guild Gallery, Larkspur *Education:* San Francisco Art Institute

Influenced by the works of Cezanne, Matisse and Toulouse-Lautrec, her early work comprised figurative images of people in environments. Since the early 1980s, she has worked primarily in charcoal, pastel and chalk on paper, creating large-scale black-and-white abstract drawings. The sensuous forms, mounds and crevices which appear in her work have sources in both the human figure and the California landscape. Often there is a tension between opposing forms that might be construed as male-female interaction. She uses black extensively, employing forms which are positive and inviting, rather than negative and foreboding. Beginning with a single mark, works evolve through the drawing process, rather than conforming to a preconceived idea, model or subject. The places in her drawings are ones which she would love to visit, somewhere in a primeval or alternate world.

STURMAN, EUGENE (Printmaker, Sculptor)
190 Loma Metisse, Malibu, CA 90265

Born: 1945 *Awards:* NEA Fellowship; New Talent Purchase Award, LACMA *Collections:* Museum of Modern Art, NYC; Los Angeles County Museum of Art *Exhibitions:* Whitney Museum, NYC; Public Sculpture, Los Angeles

His early minimalist work in New York was influenced by British and pop art. In 1969, he moved to Los Angeles and began work at the Tamarind Lithography workshop and studio. There, he manipulated copper foil and chemicals, creating the essence of his "Material Abstraction" wall works. During the late 1970s, he created distressed patinated wall pieces whose opulent surfaces revealed a contemporary sensibility sympathetic with ancient cultures. At the same time he drew geometric, organic and anatomical shapes on copper foil. His 1980 investigation of minimal forms lead to three-dimensional wall objects and eventually to large, free-standing works with historical and mechanical connotations and futuristic overtones.

SUDHAUSEN, AXEL (Painter)
2068 Bordeaux Ln., Half Moon Bay, CA 94019

Born: 1943 *Collections:* Strawberry Ranch, Half Moon Bay *Exhibitions:* McEwen Gallery, Half Moon Bay; Spanishtown Gallery *Education:* Pratt Institute *Dealer:* Marlin Cover Frame Shop, Foster City

His abstract and realist paintings have been influenced by the aesthetics of the Bauhaus, the compositional expertise of Kandinsky and the colors of Klee, Miro and the French Impressionists. He strives for dynamic composition, consistent style and medium integrity. Working in oil on canvas, he is using blues, browns and grays in a series of medium-sized paintings of Princeton Harbor.

SUDO, KUMIKO (Fiber Artist)
500 Grizzly Peak Blvd., Berkeley, CA 94708

Born: 1944 *Awards:* 1st Prize, National Macrame Contest *Exhibitions:* Central Museum, Tokyo; American Museum of Quilts, San Jose *Education:* Ito Mohei Fashion Design Academy, Tokyo

Born in Japan, she was trained in fashion design, and her first work was in millinery. Trained in traditional Japanese crafts, as well as textile arts, patchwork and fiber wall hangings, she taught patchwork and quilting for sixteen years in Tokyo. She recently moved to the U.S., and is now creating works with themes of Japanese culture and religious subjects in figurative and abstract quilted designs. Her techniques include applique, layered pieces, embroidery, macrame, tie-dye and painted material. She uses Kimono Silk, and all of her work is completely handmade. She has published over ten art and craft books.

SUEZ, VINCENT H. (Ceramist)
767 W. 25th St., Upland, CA 91786

Born: 1938 *Exhibitions:* Vincent Suez Ceramics; Fine Arts Gallery, Mt. San Jacinto College, San Jacinto *Education:* Cal. State-Fullerton; Claremont Graduate School

He began as a figurative painter but found that ceramics provided the physical contact he needed. He draws and paints on the majolica type surface of his

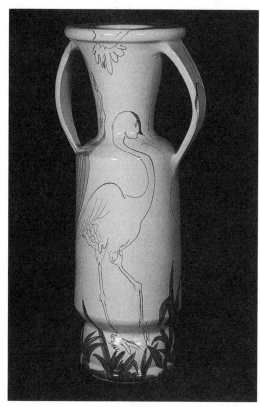

Vincent Suez, *Crane Dance,* 22 x 10, glazed and fired clay cone 5 with china paints.

A. Secunda, *Cypresses,* 14 x 10, collage, 1988.
Courtesy: Eileen Michel, Owl 57 Galleries, Woodmere, N.Y.

vessels using ceramic stains, oxides and china paints. He also uses slips on the surface of wet clay and draws on the fresh clay with a needle, creating a low relief and adding dimensionality to the form. He admires those who have "put themselves on the line for the world's animals" and his subjects have recently been softer colored birds and flowers. In the past he has painted figurative landscapes on his pots.

SUGARMAN, RHODA (Sculptor)
2500 Torrey Pines Rd., La Jolla, CA 92037

Born: 1917 *Awards:* Del Mar Fair; Lake Success Fair *Collections:* Zantman Gallery, Palm Desert *Exhibitions:* San Diego Art Institute; Rougue Gallery, San Diego

She received her art education in New York and has lived in La Jolla since the late 1970s. Most of her sculpture is abstract. She begins the work by seeing the image with her mind's eye. The completed works come in a variety of shapes and styles but in each, she carves a hole to emphasize the continuum of space within and around the piece. A minority of her work is figurative including such subjects as abstracted female torsos. Her materials include Alaskan soapstone, African wonderstone, sandstone, agate, alabaster, malachite, and indian pipestone. She is a member of the International Sculpture Society and the Sculptors Guild of San Diego.

SULLIVAN, CHRISTINE M. (Painter, Multimedia Artist)
1999 S. Coast Highway, #4, Laguna Beach, CA 92651

Born: 1950 *Exhibitions:* "Watercolor West," Riverside; Laguna Beach Festival of the Arts *Education:* UC-Davis

The works of Wayne Thiebaud influenced how she perceived and used color. Painting mostly in watercolor, she explored the effects of contrasting color and halation in landscape, still life and figurative art. After studying the watercolors of Cezanne, and working with many of the California watercolorists, such as Rex Brandt, she became interested in exploring light through using a maximum of white paper and a minimum of paint. She also began exploring the effects of overlapping and tilting planes of space. Since the mid-1980s, she has displayed more interest in combining textured and sculpted surfaces with watercolor. Painting on watercolor paper, she layers the surface with paint, collaged papers, pastels and other media. She sometimes uses dry pastel stick to give a bolder, brighter color. Her imagery is drawn from the landscapes of the Southwest, particularly Yosemite, Big Sur and the trees, rocks and hills of southern California.

SULLIVAN, EVELYN (Sculptor)
P. O. 2654, Castro Valley, CA 94546

Born: 1929 *Collections:* World Airways; Oakland Convention and Visitors Bureau *Exhibitions:* Sun Gallery, Hayward; Interart, San Francisco *Education:* Cal. State- Hayward

After formal training as a jeweler, she turned to large sculpture influenced by the work of Picasso. She experiments continually between media and is presently concentrating on handmade paper pulp and wires. These pieces are large and light and colored by pigment in the paper as well as that applied by airbrush and spray painting. She also works in welded metal sculpture that incorporates found objects. The latest of this series, *Retired from Cooking,* is a construction containing parts of old kitchen appliances; other sculptures use automotive parts. A sense of play is integral to these works—she has likened her process to that of a child playing with blocks, intending to create a sense of wonder and even to cause the viewer to laugh.

SULLIVAN, JOAN V. (Painter)
1455 10th St., Los Osos, CA 93402

Born: 1925 *Awards:* Professional Division Award, Santa Barbara State Fair; Best of Show, Simi Valley Art Association *Exhibitions:* La Galeriea Eclectic, San Luis Obispo; Central Coast Watercolor Society *Education:* U. of Miami; UC-Northridge

Working in an impressionistic style, she paints still lifes and California landscapes. She uses a wet-on-wet technique with contrasting watercolor washes, pen-and-ink renderings and collage to capture the history and atmosphere of locations throughout central California. In particular, she is fond of old, abandoned ranch buildings, missions and other structures dating from the pioneer era. These historical subjects are rendered with a sepia ink wash technique. She also paints large floral arrangements in a cheerful, colorful style. Of late, a greater degree of introspection has emerged in her paintings, with a new emphasis on abstracted forms and a more sophisticated use of color and shading.

SULLIVAN, KAREN (Photographer)
930 Cessna Dr., Crescent City, CA 95531

Born: 1944 *Awards:* Best of Show, Park Forest National Exhibition of Photography *Collections:* Lighthouse Art Center, Crescent City *Exhibitions:* Del Mar Fair International Exhibition of Photography *Education:* College of the Redwoods

Her formal training concentrated on the zone system approach to photography. The main body of her work consists of landscapes and abstracts. Primarily a nature photographer, she works exclusively in black and white, using 25 ASA film in a Pentax 6 x 7 camera. Recently, her work has become more simplified in form and direction, concentrating on the Southwestern landscape, sand dunes, rock formations and old architecture. Although at first she disliked his work, she now cites Edward Weston as a major influence, as well as Miner White and Paul Strand.

SULSKI, VICTORIA (Painter)
525 A Washington St., Santa Cruz, CA

Born: 1952 *Awards:* Popular Award, 14th Annual All Media Exhibition *Exhibitions:* Pacific Grove Museum; Octagon Museum, Santa Cruz *Education:* Cal. State-Long Beach

Influenced by Rico Le Brun, among others, she seeks to capture the humanity of the figure, as exemplified by Rembrandt. Her work expresses an investigative and empathetic response to the figure, as she attempts to capture the inner persona of a subject. She creates her own working surface by fastening handmade paper to cloth, then stretching the cloth onto a pine screen. She applies sand to this surface, creating her own rough sandpaper surface. Working in a non-traditional realistic style, she creates paintings which emphasize strong line and form. Her preferred media are casein paints and pastels.

Ben Schonzeit, *Ginger Jar,* 38 x 46, cibachrome. Courtesy: J.J.Brookings Gallery

Mary Sweet, *Colorado Plateau Series No. 1,* 36 x 48, acrylic on canvas

Synthia Saint James, *Purification,* 36 x 48, oil on canvas. Courtesy: Collection of Richard Pryor

Othell Jackson Schleker, *Texas Sesquicentennial,* 22 x 28, acrylic Courtesy: Jim Cochran, Citizens Bank

Jane Wooster Scott, *The Long Road Home,* 30 x 40, oils

Donna Scott, *Funky Love,* 14 x 18, clay mounted on canvas

Claudia Steel, *Atmospheric Landscape,* 21 x 27, watercolor

Paul Soldner, *#8814,* 29 x 41 x 8, clay

Teresa Starkweather, *Tulip Glass,* 30 x 40, watercolor

Betty Saarni, *The Pier,* 18 x 24, transparent watercolor on paper

Suzanne Schumacher, *Dark Rainbow,* 20 x 40, tempera on paper.

Kim Shae-Tofaute, *Pink Flamingos,* photograph

Margareta Sjödin, *untitled,* mixed media

Joan Salinger, *Magic,* 20 x 25, digitized photograph-cibachrome print

B.W. Scharf, *Circus of Dreams,* 49 x 71, oil on canvas

Carl Schmitt, *Blue Moon,* 24 x 24, clay and acrylic

Sherry Schrut, *Sites 43,* 38 x 50, pastel and collage on paper.
Courtesy: International Business Machine Inc, Atlanta, GA

R.H. Schubert, *Plumeria #42,* 22 x 30, transparent watercolor.
Courtesy: Village Galleries, Lahaina Maui, Hawaii

Magda Santonastasio, *Central American Fragments,* 17 x 24, viscosity.
Courtesy: Tuhuana Press, San Diego, CA

Margot S. Schulzke, *Windsong,* 15 x 30, pastel. Courtesy: Old Church Gallery

Ali B. Shahroudi, *Judgment of Ali,* 30 x 40, oil

Barbara Shawcroft, *Balls, 1987,* largest diameter 3 feet, cloth, paper, steel, wires.
Photograph: Barbara Shawcroft

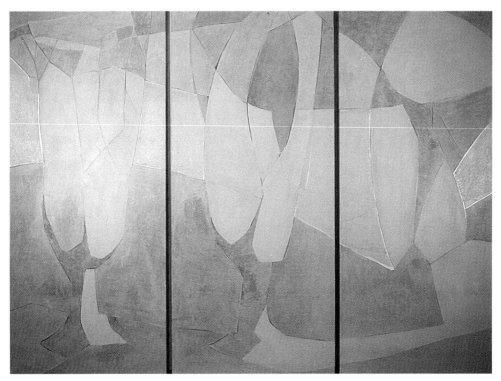

Cleda Marie Simmons, *Elan Vital;* #4, #5, #6 of 6 panels, 36 x 80 each,
acrylic and collage on hardboard

Alonso Smith, *Medical Malpractice,* 36 x 48, oil on canvas

Andrea Smith, *Emotional Wisdom,* 30 x 40, mixed media, watercolor

Stefen, *Dutch Boy Mural,* 300 x 1200, latex (house paint)

Ellie Stern, *Sun/Moon,* 48 x 36 x 24, naval brass plate

Meredith Strauss, *Transformation,* 42 x 96 x 3, cotton cord and wire mesh.
Courtesy: Cubicomp Corporation, Hayward, CA. Photograph: Myron Moskwa

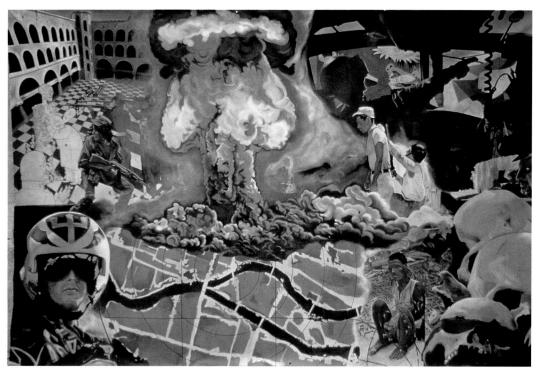

Andy Stricker, *Final Victory: Ground Zero,* 96 x 144, acrylic on canvas

Eugene Sturman, *Homage to Cabrillo—Venetian Quadrant,* 396 x 540 x 720, bronze, copper, stainless.
Photographer: Greg Crawford

Vern Swansen, *Psiana,* 12 x 16, watercolor

Edward Sexton, *Untamed,* 29 x 40, acrylic on canvas

SUMAN, ALVARO A. (Multimedia Artist)
914 Santa Barbara St., Santa Barbara, CA 93101

Born: 1952 *Collections:* Museo de Bellas Artes de San Carlos, Mexico *Exhibitions:* San Francisco Wildlife Refuge; La Casa de la Raza, Santa Barbara *Education:* Instituto Nacional de Bellas Artes *Dealers:* Brooks Adobe Center for the Arts, Santa Barbara

He works in ceramics (including raku with special high-fire glazes), oil paint, etching and sculpture. Inspired by the works of Picasso, Rufinao Tamayo and popular themes and forms in Mexican art, he incorporates traditional Mexican imagery as both literal and metaphorical elements in his work. While somewhat abstract, the birds, fish, endangered animals and human faces and figures are quite expressionistic and colorfully render. To create tension in a painting, he will often render some figures in a more realist style, in contrast with other more surrealistic images. His etchings focus on themes of daily occurrences and are rendered for full optical effect. These works are often accompanied by poetry.

SUMIDA, GREGORY (Painter)
P.O. Box 9210, Stockton, CA 95208

Born: 1948 *Collections:* Andrew Wyeth; Carnegie Museum, Oxnard *Exhibitions:* Maxwell Gallery, San Francisco; Palm Springs Desert Museum *Dealer:* Hunter Gallery, Carmel; Cottago Gallery, Carmel

He made extensive studies of the Old Masters in his youth, teaching himself the skills he applies in his landscape and figure works. Devoting himself to aquamedia, he spent seven years painting the people and landscapes of the San Joaquin delta, the fruits of which produced the basis for a major exhibition. Subsequently becoming interested in American Indian culture and its similarity to spiritual traditions of the Orient, he combines painterly preoccupations with form, color and composition with expressive and emotional visual styles. His works have recently been executed in a variety of media, including hand-made oil pigments and charcoal, and depict variously traditional figurative studies and partly-abstracted landscapes. He has also been designing kimonos to enhance his work. Works are influenced by many cultures and, among other artists, Whistler and Hirochige. "My main concern is emotional honesty," he says.

SUMMERS, CAROL (Printmaker)
133 Prospect Ct., Santa Cruz CA 95065

Born: 1925 *Awards:* Louis C. Tiffany Foundation Fellowship; Guggenheim Fellowship *Collections:* Metropolitan Museum of Art, NYC; Corcoran Gallery of Art, Washington DC *Exhibitions:* Museum of Modern Art, NYC; San Francisco Museum of Modern Art *Education:* Bard College

Early woodcuts featured abstract biomorphic shapes. After 1958, preliminary rough sketches in ink and brayer were applied to paper before the final print was made. During the 1960s, images of domestic life in cubist space, as in *Bon Appetit*, were more recognizable. The artist is known for simplified landscapes and mountainscapes, often each peak a different color. Sometimes color is printed on the back of the paper for the desired color effect. Large and simple landscapes are multicolored, each element saturated with color. Some of these woodcuts are executed in a technique similar to rubbings.

SUNDIN, STEPHEN (Painter)
P.O. Box 41, Jenner, CA 95450

Born: 1942 *Awards:* Juror's Purchase Award, NEA; Honorarium, Kansas City Artists Coalition, Kansas City, MO *Exhibitions:* California Museum of Art, Santa Rosa; Kansas City Arts Coalition Gallery, Kansas City, MO

Self-taught, he has been drawing the human figure for over fifteen years, both from models and his imagination. His travels in Europe brought him in contact with the work of Ensor, Goya, Munch and Redon, all of whom he credits with opening up his artistic vision. Working with oil, acrylics, crayon and chalk, he first applies a layer of wash, and then looks for the imagery inherent in the forms found in the wash. Generally the works are large, with a palette based in dark umber. *Nocturnal Baptism*, an oil on canvas, features two figures in turbulent water. A large woman holds a male figure protectively in her massive arms. She looks over her shoulder expectantly as the male stares out to the viewer. There is a sense of suspended movement: the woman peering into the surrounding dark night; the man looking to the viewer with anticipation.

SURDEZ, RUTH (Sculptor)
19010 North Lower Sacramento Rd., Woodbridge, CA 95258

Born: 1906 *Awards:* 1st Place Purchase Award, California State Fair *Collections:* California State Fair Permanent Collection, Sacramento; St. John's Lutheran Church, Sacramento *Exhibitions:* University of Pacific, Stockton; Crocker Kingsley, Sacramento *Education:* Massachusetts School of Art

Classically trained in Boston, she began her career as a designer of commercial displays. After she moved to California in 1929, her work became more abstract and, since 1960, has reflected an intrigue with found objects. She includes tin can lids, glass plugs, square nails, discarded kitchen utensils, old eyeglass lenses, weathered boards and cores from a foundry fire in her icon-like multimedia assemblages. She draws inspiration from the materials themselves. One piece, a nine-and-a-half-foot rusted steel construction, *Sound Chamber*, echoes voices. Another, a tiny assemblage called *Stop*, incorporates jewels, nails and a small carpenter's level.

SUSSMAN, SANDY (Painter)
12546 Dexter Park Rd., Kagel Canyon, CA 91342

Born: 1946 *Exhibitions:* Urlike Kantor Gallery; UC-Redlands *Education:* Chouinard Art Institute

Picasso's fearless practice of radical evolution has been her greatest influence. The surface of her early figurative paintings implied a deeper psychological depth. Her themes, then as now, were expressive interiors that reflected people's behavior and states of mind, through unconscious symbols. Now concerned with the formal aspects of spatial relationships, her abstract surrealist work has evolved into multicanvas constructions, acrylic collage montages and assemblages.

SUSSMAN, SHARON (Painter)
192 Charles Dr., Santa Cruz, CA 95060

Born: 1951 *Awards:* Grant, Elizabeth Greenshields Foundation *Exhibitions:* Works Gallery, Long Beach *Education:* UC-Santa Cruz

She studied classical oil painting techniques with Miguel Arguello, a Spanish realist, but soon drifted from classical still life to larger, more sculptural installations, in which she combined aluminum mesh, plastic and fabric with classical painting techniques. Her present still lifes were inspired by Diebenkorn's "Ocean Park" series. Like him, she uses sheets of reflective plastic fabric, and plastic cubes and tubes to set up an abstract composition. However, she departs from Diebenkorn's model by painting directly from reality and using layers of oil glazes painted on wood panels. Her results approach the meditative feelings of Ikebana and Japanese reflecting pools.

SUTHERLAND, IAN (Painter)

Born: 1939 *Awards:* Hector Escobosa Award, San Francisco Art Institute *Collections:* Kaiser Permanente, Santa Rosa *Exhibitions:* California State Fair, Sacramento; Alexander Valley Invitational, Sonoma County *Education:* San Francisco Art Institute; Aberdeen Robert Gordon's Technical College

Conscious of the Renaissance painters' use of light and space, he concentrates on the space around a form rather than the form itself. Early work with the figure gave way to a geometric abstraction in which recognizable images may be pursued indirectly. Forms that may emerge through the working process of paintings are rarely conceived in advance. He draws with graphic texture and color in mind, utilizing a combination of acrylics and water-soluble crayons that are often used as washes. The heightened quality of California light has inevitably influenced his broad spectrum of color; Joseph Albers's work with color interaction has further focused his attention on the fact that different colors in different fields take on a variety of hues. Paintings are on paper and average 3 by 4 to 5 by 6 feet in size. Smaller pastel works will often influence larger works. Recent work has shown more curves and organic forms, and a series of human heads has radically departed from his accustomed technique. These were begun with crystallized intent and are representational, through not drawn from nature.

SUYEMATSU, KAZUYE (Ceramist)

1483 San Pablo Ave., Berkeley, CA 94702

Born: 1938 *Collections:* Scripps College, Pomona *Exhibitions:* Aspen Center For Visual Arts, Aspen, CO; Asher/Faure Gallery, Los Angeles *Education:* UC-Berkeley

Geometric shapes and forms from nature are the basis of her ceramic work. She approaches clay as a material to express ideas, exploring the relationship between image-making and object-making. Her clay and glazework has been carefully controlled through recognizable motifs such as flowers, swans and shells. The clay form takes shape by hand, the wheel and casting. She regards the glaze as paint and focuses on intricately tying the glaze image to the clay shape. All pieces are done in porcelain with high-fired glazes. Works include *Sculptured Irises*, a bowl 13 inches in diameter with irises rising from the body to extend beyond the rim. Her tones are soft yellow, brown and violet, both blending and contrasting with the muted white of the iris petals. *Butter Dish* is a gray-white snail shell set on a rectangular, multi-colored plate with folds and ripples.

SUZUKI, DIANE K. (Painter)

118 E. 7th St., Long Beach, CA 90813

Exhibitions: L.A. Artcore, Los Angeles; Alaska State Museum, Juneau *Education:* Cal. State-Long Beach

In her mixed-media wall reliefs, she plays language games with Christian crosses, psychodiagnostic inkblots, primary level children's identification problems, and Buddhist circles and squares (symbolizing spiritual evolution). Through these enigmatic, loaded images she encourage a self-conscious, open-ended reading of her work. Each image is intended to trigger associations; by juxtaposition, she addresses the mechanism of "I." The surfaces of her paintings may be layered, scored, pierced or scraped to reveal their undersurface. Her materials include hair, wood, plaster, dirt, paint, charcoal, graphite or photocopied images.

SVERDLOVE, ZOLITA (Painter)

1445 Indiana Ave., So. Pasadena, CA 91030

Born: 1936 *Awards:* Marymount College; Dallas Museum of Fine Arts *Collections:* Dallas Museum of Fine Arts; Owens-Corning Collection, Toledo Museum, OH *Exhibitions:* Allan Stone Gallery New Talent Show; Valley House Gallery, Dallas *Education:* Cooper Union Art School *Dealer:* Valley House Gallery

Inspired by the California countryside, she paints landscapes of mountains, oceans and sunsets. Colors are intense, reflecting an interest in the use of color and light, and brush strokes comprise the form in abstracted landscapes. In the past five years, she has expanded her vocabulary to include the monotype, which combines her interest in painting and printmaking.

SWANSEN, VERN (Painter)

1140 Montalban St., #8, San Luis Obispo, CA 93401

Born: 1916 *Collections:* Santa Barbara Art Association *Exhibitions:* Gallery of the University Library, California Polytechnic State U., San Luis Obispo *Education:* USC; U. of Strathclyde, Scotland

His interests in architecture and painting date from early childhood, and his subsequent education was dedicated to these areas. For nearly thirty years, his efforts as a painter have been closely integrated with his education curatorship of the Santa Barbara Museum of Art and with his teaching duties at California Polytechnic Sate University, where he is a professor of architectural history and architectural watercolor painting. The full range of general architectural history (Lascaux caves to the present: European, Asiatic, African, American) is reflected in his prolific output—an average of one hundred watercolor paintings per year. Although he has developed an individualistic style, he feels most closely akin to abstractionism, realism and surrealism.

SWANSON, CATHLEEN (Painter)

P.O. Box 16-3102, Sacramento, CA 95816

Born: 1958 *Exhibitions:* Terra Roxa Cafe, Sacramento; Slant Gallery, Davis *Education:* U. of Colorado

She is best known for her line of painted suitcases. Her surrealist style is akin to that of Henry Fuseli, Giorgio de Chirico and Max Ernst. Her functional art finds its way all over the world; she has been known to send suitcases to other artists, who add their own contributions to the "traveling painting." She feels that by creating art on a common object, she can bring art back to the people. Her imagery is often drawn from the native art of Central and South America (where she spent part of her childhood) and from her German and Scandinavian heritage.

Mary Sweet, *Sand Wash, Green River,* 48 x 72, acrylic on canvas

Rufus Snoddy, *Four Planes & Bar of Wood,* 72 x 48, acrylic & canvas on wood panel with mixed media.
Courtesy: L.A. Artcore Gallery, Los Angeles

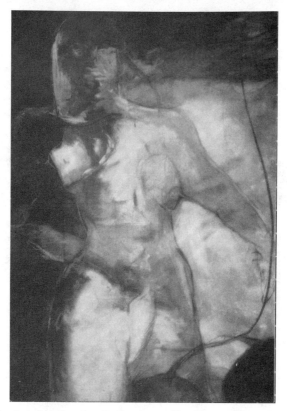

Stephen Sundin, *Atomic Remnants,* 80 x 50, acrylic on canvas

Teresa Starkweather, *Table Light,* 30 x 40, watercolor

Nancy Strode, *Waimea Canyon,* photograph

Loran Speck, *Old Spanish Cabinet,* 26 x 16, oil on panel.
Courtesy: Loran Speck Gallery

Claudia Steel, *Weight of the World,* 24 x 17, embossed intaglio

Ellie Stern, *Bark Series VI,* 24 x 18, pastel drawing

Linda Dodwell Stupski, *Neither From Nor Towards,* 60 x 80 charcoal, chalk on paper

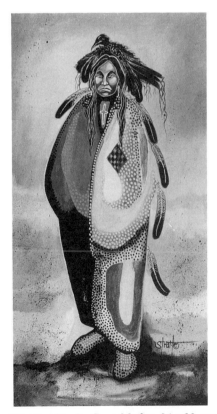

Dorothy Strait, *Crow Mother,* 24 x 30, acrylic

Kumiko Sudo, *Sacred Horse,* 47 x 32, fabric

SWANSON, J.N. (Painter, Sculptor)
Star Rte., Box 120, Carmel Valley, CA 93924

Born: 1927 *Awards:* Atelier Award, Western Artists Show, de Young Museum, San Francisco *Collections:* Cowboy Hall of Fame, Oklahoma City, OK; Cowboy Artists of America Museum, Kerrville, TX *Exhibitions:* Phoenix Art Museum; Mary Hunter Gallery, Carmel *Dealer:* Mary Hunter Gallery, Carmel; Lizbeth Kyle, Los Olivos

He is a working cowboy in Oregon and California whose realistic paintings and lost-wax bronzes are noted for their atmospheric quality and complete accuracy. With a large studio that contains an indoor stall for horse modeling, he works with no reference photos. He begins his paintings of cowboys and horses by making a quick charcoal sketch on gessoed masonite, blocking the whole painting with oils to establish a light source, and then gradually working in the detail. He has been influenced by Remington, Russell and Boren, and he has taught "Drawing the Horse in Action" at the Cowboy Artist Museum in Texas.

SWART-VAN DER STAM, SONJA (Painter, Sculptor)
2121 E. Grand Ave., U84, Escondido, CA 92027

Born: 1931 *Awards:* Russel Award, UC-San Diego *Exhibitions:* UC-San Diego; Palomar College, San Marcos *Education:* UC-San Diego

An active painter since 1971, she began making sculpture after studying with Faith Ringgold and Italo Scanga at the University of California in San Diego. She is known for her innovative and emotional painting and sculpture. In recent sculptural pieces, she used personal experience as a basis for mixed-media representations of the cattle cars used to transport concentration camp victims from Bergen-Belsen to the Nazi gas chambers.

SWEET, JOAN (Painter)
13135 Wolf Rd., Grass Valley, CA 95949

Born: 1937 *Awards:* Best of Show, Roseville Selected Show *Collections:* Caldwell Banker, Grass Valley; Lumatex Corp., Nevada City *Exhibitions:* Foothill Gallery, Grass Valley; AFCH Gallery, Auburn *Education:* Scottsdale Arizona Art School

Her early work, primarily landscapes, featured color as the most important expression of feeling. The influence of John Singer Sargent moved her to begin exploring figurative studies. She switched from oils to watercolor and pastel, and now works on mounted sandpaper. Her layering is such that much of the abstract watercolor underpainting shows through. In recent nudes, drawn from life, the use of color continues to be her most important concern. She uses gentle pastel strokes in a painterly manner, to extend the work beyond the border of the paper. Her own interpretations are subtle, allowing room for the involvement of the viewer.

SWEET, MARY (Painter)
P.O. Box 280, Tijeras, NM 87059

Born: 1937 *Awards:* American Artist Golden Anniversary Award *Collections:* Governor & Mrs. Bruce Babbitt; First National Bank of Albuquerque *Exhibitions:* Kingsley Crocker Museum, Sacramento; Richmond Art Center *Education:* Stanford U.

Influenced by Van Gogh, Monet, Gauguin and Daniel Mendelowitz, her landscapes of California were abstract-expressionist until 1970. Following this, a series of hard-edged renderings protested the destruction of the environment. She subsequently moved to New Mexico and altered her style, though her use of strong, bright colors remained unchanged. The recent works reflect the clear air, the bright sunlight and sharp shadows, and the striking colors of canyon and desert geological formations of the Southwest. Unmodulated colors and flat, hard-edged forms lay next to each other, their combination symbolizing the canyons and mountains. Shapes remain fluid, however, exposing the air in front of them with their clarity and brightness. There is a sense of reality to the direct and specific landscapes, underscored rather than obscured by their symbolic and abstract rendering.

SWIGGETT, JEAN DONALD (Painter, Muralist)
3635 Seventh Ave., Apt. 9E, San Diego, CA 92103

Born: 1910 *Awards:* California-Hawaii Regional Award, San Diego Museum of Art; Award, San Diego Art Institute Annual *Collections:* San Diego Museum of Art; Long Beach Museum of Art *Exhibitions:* Ankrum Gallery, Los Angeles; Brushworks Gallery, San Diego *Education:* Chouinard Institute of Art; USC

In his early career, he worked as an assistant to Norman Chamberlain and Paul Sample on their murals for federal post offices. He continued to paint numerous murals of his own in both public and private buildings throughout Southern California. His paintings were primarily realistic, with a period of experimentation in abstraction. Male and female nudes, flowers, fruit and other natural forms are the dominant elements of his compositions. His large oil paintings are concerned with the use of symbolic imagery to make philosophical statements. Concurrent drawings in colored pencil and acrylic are large and complex, making visual references to art history.

SWILDEN, KARIN (Ceramist, Sculptor)
1916 Pelham Ave., #3, Los Angeles, CA 90025

Born: 1942 *Exhibitions:* Brand Library, Glendale; Gallery Plus One, West Hollywood *Education:* Ecoles de Arts Decoratifs, Paris, France *Dealer:* Collections 85, Los Angeles

Using slabs of clay, she sculpts lovely, expressive faces. This work grew out of extensive sculpting in wood. The pieces are high-fired and finished in hues of gray with occasional splashes of color. Inspired by the writings of Carl Jung, the faces are symbolic and archetypal, and images include the madonna and child, mythological creatures and faces representing types of people, processes or emotions (*Prince, Metamorphosis, Aloof*). Sometimes, two faces are arranged together (*Two in One, Madonna and Child*) or are adorned with jewelry or symbolic artifacts. Although she intends the works to communicate visually, it is important to her that viewers feel invited to touch and caress the sculptures' smooth surfaces.

SWISHER, MARY (Photographer)
640 Lilac Lane, Sacramento, CA 95864

Born: 1937 *Awards:* NEA Organization Grant; Sacramento Metropolitan Arts Commission *Collections:* Crocker Art Museum; California State Library *Exhibitions:* Crocker Art Museum; Lightwork Gallery, Sacramento *Education:* California State U. *Dealer:* Lightwork Gallery, Sacramento

Ruth Surdez, *Bird with Egg in Nest,* 16 x 13, wood & stone. Photograph: Dick Shunk

Eugene Sturman, *Galileo Electro,* 84 x 168 x 120, steel, lead, copper foil. Photographer: Doug Parker

Gregory Sumida, *Flowing Memories,* 24 x 30, oil

Margareta Sjödin, *Floating Ice I,* 30 x 40, mixed media

Nadinka Szaksz, *Curved Straight,* 16 x 120, acrylics

Sherry Schrut, *Shards,* 22 x 30, watercolor collage with handmade papers.
Courtesy: Skirball Museum, Los Angeles, California

1163

After a brief period of painting, she soon devoted her attention to photography. Early photographs are experimental, shot with a large-format (8 x 10) camera to produce black-and-white contact prints on paper negatives, forcing snapshot-like images from the more formal large-format camera. Work has continued in large format as well as with 35mm cameras. The personal images of the early photos have been replaced by landscapes of old pottery or terra cotta found in old churches. Each presents a landscape of light and dark seldom found in conventional exterior scenes, the dark interiors interrupted by striking bursts of light.

SYLVESTER, STEPHEN THOMAS (Painter)
407 N. Ventura Ave., Ventura, CA 93001

Born: 1945 *Awards:* Artist in Residence, Happy Valley Foundation, Ojai *Collections:* Marvin Hamlisch *Exhibitions:* Leo Duvall Associates, Los Angeles; Stanley's, Sherman Oaks *Education:* Banff Fine Art Centre, Alberta, Canada; Brooks Institute *Dealer:* Gilman Gallery, Chicago

A synchromist, his color spectra correspond to musical scales. While studying with James Jarvaise, he began his research into color composition. Later, he composed his first synchromistic paintings while studying under Takeo Tanabe. As an American visionary painter utilizing color expressionistically, he creates visual metaphors. The interior views he created in the twelve paintings of his light key, acrylic emulsion "Santa Cruz Island Series", (begun in 1975) were inspired by the island and its relationship to the mainland. A second "Santa Cruz Island Series" included *Painted Cave,* lit by lichen, and a large canvas *Night Tides.* He recently began work on sixteen 44-by-44-inch synchromist color key compositions titled, "Let It Ring". This series will research synchromism and perceptual psychology.

SZAKSZ, NADINKA (Painter, Designer)
P.O. Box 29434, Los Angeles, CA 90029

Awards: Otis Art Institute Ford Foundation Grant; Scholarship, California Institute of the Arts *Collections:* Richelieu Collection *Exhibitions:* Cosmopolitan Artists Association Art Exhibition, Los Angeles; Otis-Parsons School of Design *Education:* California Institute of the Arts; Otis Art Institute

Raised in Budapest, Hungary during the late 1940s and early 1950s, she was exposed to constructivism and to artists' works, such as those of Lissitzky, Malevich and others whose ideologies were concerned with bridging the gap between art and life as a political gesture. One of her major works, *The Constellation,* is a poetic metaphor consisting of twelve paintings. In it, black represents infinite space without edges. The observer can enter the black space backwards or forwards, up or down without restriction. The viewer can wander in and out without a single fixed view. This series challenges the tunnel vision of the western world because it depicts space and the way we behave in it. These paintings are sometimes exhibited on black walls to emphasize the infinite number of viewpoints. "My paintings are not windows, so the audience is not disconnected from the space by a frame."

SZYMANOWSKI, PATRICIA (Painter)
8038 Briar Ridge Ln., Citrus Heights, CA 95610

Born: 1941 *Awards:* Nominated for Woman of the Year in the Arts *Collections:* Vatican Museum of Modern Art *Exhibitions:* I. Magnin Gallery; Djurovich Gallery

Strongly influenced by the childlike purity of Chagall's work, she has worked for many years in oil, acrylics and watercolors. A trip to Mt. Shasta proved to be a turning point in her artistic career. Swayed by the strong forces she felt, she returned from her trip inspired to try a new way of painting. She began to experiment with drip techniques, allowing the paint to roll around on the paper, making its own images. One of these works, *The Ancient of Days,* features an ethereal likeness some viewers compared to the image of Christ on the Shroud of Turin. On the advice of her family and friends, she donated this painting to the Vatican Museum. More generally speaking, she believes that her paintings invite viewers to look within themselves for meanings, stimulating spiritual growth and understanding.

Bill Viola, *The Theater of Memory,* mixed media. Courtesy: Collection of the Newport Harbor Art Museum.

Di Starr, *Foresight,* 16 x 20, gelatin silver print

N. Tays-Campbell, *Alan Osborne,* life size, bronze. Courtesy: Lee Jones

TACKER, HAL (Painter)
P.O. Box 272, Robbins, CA 95676

Born: 1954 *Exhibitions:* Beale Air Force Base, Heritage Museum; Hotel De Coronado, San Diego *Dealer:* Gallery Americana, Carmel

Son of a crop duster and himself an experienced plane mechanic, he taught himself to depict the machines he at one time worked on. Working in pen and pencil, as well as paint, he renders first generation flying machines with the same meticulous detail and accuracy as his depictions of modern day F-4 navy jets. A serious student of aviation, his years of research and his extensive collection of books, magazines and memorabilia on flight are evident in his almost photographically perfect renderings. His gallery exhibitions have created a wave of interest and positive reaction among art critics, experienced pilots, serious collectors of aviation art and such flying greats as "Pappy" Boyington.

TAETZCH, LYNNE (Painter)
350 Aldwych Rd., El Cajon, CA 92020

Born: 1941 *Exhibitions:* San Diego Art Institute; Friends of Jung, San Diego *Education:* Cooper Union

She paints with acrylics on stretched canvas, in a process of several stages. Two under-coats or pre-painting periods are required to prepare the canvas for the final action painting. One step in the pre-painting is to create something that the final painting must destroy. In many of the canvases, this creation is a strong "frame" within the frame of the canvas, done in bold thick strokes with a palette knife. This frame becomes an obstacle, to be played with and through. The last stage of painting is done with fine lines of paint squeezed directly from the tubes. It is difficult, with these fine lines, to break into the thick frame of the underpainting. Thus, a gradual tension is developed between the two forces.

TAFT, LOUISE D. (Painter)
1257 Ferrelo Rd., Santa Barbara, CA 93103

Born: 1948 *Awards:* Cash Award, Solo Artist for Museum Calendar, Los Angeles County Museum of Art; Invited Participant, White House Easter Egg Festivities, Washington, D.C. *Exhibitions:* Greene Art Gallery, Guilford, CT; Los Angeles County Museum of Art *Education:* Pratt Institute; Rhode Island School of Design

The subject matter and representational nature of her work is categorized as still life, but her work is not "still." In the past, using etched glass, lithography and prismacolor pencils, she has built tension and movement into each work. Specific items are selected for inclusion because they are pieces of a puzzle or a portrait; unusual juxtapositions and arrangements are designed to heighten the sense that personalities and idiosyncrasies are being explored. Though her recent work retains a representational core, she has introduced bolder color, skewed perspectives and intensified texture and pattern in backgrounds of increasing abstraction. This has the effect of forcing the viewer to look past the initial assumptions about subject matter to the inspiration behind the creation of each work. As part of this development, she has moved away from the idea that paintings must be framed, and has begun to paint wooden boxes, tables, floors and other examples of common household furniture. This work is executed in trompe l'oeil style. A recent installation piece consists of a dining room table and chairs. She plans to continue painting art furniture installations.

TAKAHASHI, MASAKO (Painter)
P.O. Box 480277, Los Angeles, CA 90048

Born: 1944 *Awards:* Helen Logan Award, Chautauqua, NY *Collections:* UC-Berkeley *Exhibitions:* Bard College, Annandale-on-Hudson, NY; Kirk De Gooyer Gallery, Los Angeles *Education:* San Francisco Art Institute; UC-Berkeley

Her early abstract expressionist oil paintings were influenced by Wally Hedrick, Neil Williams and Jay Defeo. Intensive travel in India, Asia and the Middle East inspired her to utilize visual iconography, and led to a few years of experimental filmmaking before she returned to painting. After she spent two years in Mexico, her glazed acrylic paintings of floating ladders became more emotional and abstract, exploring the platonic and metaphorical implications of their subjects. Her aim in painting is to make the invisible essentials of life a palpable, visible experience.

TANG, MICHAEL (Painter)
2538 Virginia St., Berkeley, CA 94709

Born: 1958 *Awards:* A.M. Sigourney Award, Newport Art Museum; Escallier Foreign Study Grant, Loyola U., Los Angeles *Collections:* DeSaisset Museum, Loyola U., Chicago; Transco Energy Corp. *Exhibitions:* Eilat Gordin Gallery, Los Angeles; Breckenridge Gallery, San Francisco *Education:* School of the Art Institute of Chicago *Dealers:* Breckenridge Gallery, San Francisco; Eilat Gordin Gallery, Los Angeles

He was influenced by the Fauve painters, Matisse, Derain, Manguin, Bonnard and others, and his early training encouraged a facility with color. Between 1980 and 1983, he painted large, topographical nudes, exploring the surface capabilities afforded by encaustic and oil paint. In his work, he combines his facility with color with an emphasis on gestural, painterly surfaces. Recently he explored the poetry of Gerard Manley Hopkins and the psychological tendencies in the stories of the Brothers Grimm. His current subject matter focuses on the universal significance of myth and ritual.

TANNER, CINDI (Painter)
4605 South Priest #237, Tempe, AR, 85282

Born: 1957 *Awards:* Leslie Levy International Competition; 2nd Prize, Fountain Hills Arts and Crafts Festival *Collections:* Tempe Historical Museum, Tempe AZ; Tanner Southwest, Phoenix *Exhibitions:* Leslie Levy Fine Art Gallery, Scottsdale, AZ; Contemporary Arts Guild, Mesa AZ

Her watercolor paintings and pen-and-ink drawings reflect a meticulous devotion to detail. Influenced by the traditional studies of American naturalist James Audubon, her wildlife and botanical works celebrate the beauty of nature with a self-taught dry brush style. Her subjects are accurate and entirely lifelike: from the poised wing of the hummingbird in flight to the fragility of wildlife root systems. Equally detailed architectural renderings range from pastoral homesteads to the silent shadows of ancient Southwestern Indian ruins. Her credits include design and illustration for greeting cards, cook books and magazines, and work for the Phoenix Symphony Guild and the Phoenix Philatelic Society. She has been lauded by the Arizona Game and Fish Department for her "unique ability to capture the delicate freshness of nature."

Joan Tanner, *Late Drop,* 40 x 46, oil on canvas

Phyllis Thelen, *Na Pali,* 32 x 21, embossed serigraph. Courtesy: Camille Noble

Mary Taylor, *Peregrine Falcon,* 33 x 18 x 11, marble

TANNER, JOAN (Painter)
624 Olive Rd., Santa Barbara, CA 93108

Born: 1935 *Collections:* Atlantic Richfield Corp., Denver; UC-Santa Barbara *Exhibitions:* Santa Barbara Museum of Art; Otis/Parsons Gallery, Los Angeles *Education:* U. of Wisconsin

In earlier work, she was concerned with architectonic form, primarily geometric contradictions of a man-made persistence. The juxtaposition of window grids, braised coils and tubular boundaries were dominating themes. She continues to explore paradoxical themes in reference to human containment, as the embodiment of self in vessel-oriented shapes and in columnar, erect forms, representing the "civilized norm." She works in an abstract tradition in oil paint and oil stick on canvas or linen, and with various assemblage materials on wood panels; she draws on paper.

TARABINI, ROSALIE LYNN (Painter, Draughtsperson)
1584 Partridge Ave., Sunnyvale, CA 94087

Exhibitions: San Francisco Museum of Modern Art; Maxwell's Gallery, San Francisco *Education:* San Jose State U.; West Valley College

Since her first watercolor class, she has been enchanted with the figure. Her interest has continued to this day. Working in crayon, prismacolor and watercolor primarily, her approach is direct. The artist is most satisfied when the essence of the figure is distilled to a single line. Her influences range from the etchings of Yozo Hamaguchi to the paintings of Chagall and Van Gogh. Her palette is at times muted, at times bold. When not focusing on nudes, she draws landscapes, such as a group based on travels to Italy. This "hill work" depicts the old buildings and villages perched on the hills of the Italian countryside.

TARTARSKY, GEOFFREY (Sculptor)
437 Highborn St., Vallejo, CA 94590

Born: 1927 *Awards:* 1st Prize, Taos Art Association Awards Show *Exhibitions:* San Francisco Arts Commission Celebration of Sculpture; The Clocktower, Benicia *Education:* Manchester School of Art, England *Dealer:* Procyon, Vallejo

With an eye for the dramatic, he sculpts groups of tactile objects, which resemble tall plant or tree forms. Eschewing any particular school or movement, he designs these pieces to evoke feeling, rather than intellectual musing. His early work designing theater sets for dance, drama and television has given him the ability to condense large spatial dynamics into sculptures designed for intimate viewing. He works in wood, fiberglass, concrete and fabric, often applying several coats of oils, lacquers and stains to achieve an elegant surface and appearance. His small forests of forms, which stand sixty inches tall, can be arranged in one grouping, or broken into smaller groups. He also sculpts more voluminous forms, which are derivative of the human figure.

TATRO, RON (Sculptor)
210 Highline Trail, El Cajon, CA 92021

Born: 1943 *Collections:* San Jose Museum of Art *Exhibitions:* Art 18, Basel, Switzerland; Harcourts Contemporary, San Francisco *Education:* Southern Illinois U.

Rooted in the general ideas of twentieth-century art, cubism, surrealism, constructivism and abstract expressionism, his sculpture suggests order on the verge of disorder. He contrasts regular geometric shapes with personalized ones and uses surface embellishments to give his pieces a unity which contrasts with their disparate forms. His sculptures are fabricated polychrome steel, hand painted with polyurethane paints. His early works were paintings and he believes that paint "brings to full potential the three dimensional form." One piece stands nearly nine feet high and incorporates geometric blocks with long, slender lines of color.

TAUBOLD, TIM (Painter, Photographer)
179 Jewett St., Fort Bragg, CA 95437

Born: 1950 *Awards:* 1st Prize, Mendocino County Fair *Exhibitions:* Art Attack Gallery, Ft. Bragg; Leonard's Artspace, Modesto *Education:* Academy of Art, San Francisco; California College of Arts and Crafts

Although legally blind, he has adapted to his handicap by using a special magnifying lens and a camera equipped for automatic focus and exposure. Aided by an excellent sense of composition, he paints from the photographs he takes, using oil and watercolor. He constructs his three-dimensional paintings by painting the reverse sides of several 16-by-24-inch photographs. These are then mounted in an accordion-style wooden frame. Viewers receive varying impressions of the paintings and photographs depending on how open or closed the structure is and where they are standing. He has also painted portraits of Linda Ronstadt, John Belushi and John Lennon.

TAVENNER, PATRICIA MAY (Painter, Printmaker)
687 Fairmount Ave., Oakland, CA 94611

Awards: McDowell Fellowship *Collections:* Museum of Modern Art, NYC; San Francisco Museum of Art *Exhibitions:* UC-Berkeley; Hatley Martin Gallery, San Francisco *Education:* Michigan State U.; California College of Arts and Crafts

After school, she continued her explorations of the extension of painting in collage, combining surface elements for depth and texture and later adding photographs. These explorations led to using photographic silkscreens for larger images and light reflecting surfaces to add further depth and mystery to the images. At the same time, she began an artists' newspaper, *Mail Order Art*. This opened up the arena of mail art for fun and the opportunity to communicate with artists. Current media include painting and printmaking silkscreen editions and numbered monoprint sequences. Using a squeegee, she paints landscapes and waterscapes in bright acrylics. She has developed a technique of layering paint in a way which captures the motion and reflectivity of the ocean waters. Rocks and earth formations are the subjects of her monoprints, which she executes in vibrant pastels. She often experiments with monoprints to develop new paintings, a process which gives her work intensity and freshness.

TAYLOR, JACK (Painter)
2394-3A Via Mariposa W., Laguna Hills, CA 92653

Born: 1913 *Exhibitions:* Palace of Fine Arts, Valetta, Malta; Cramm Gallery, Eindhoven, Holland *Education:* Philadephia Museum School of Art; U. of Michigan

A self-described 'renaissance man' whose career has spanned half a century and encompassed a wide

Jack Taylor, *My Past is Always Present,* 30 x 26, acrylic

Alan Thorpe, *Flight of the Ballerina,* 25" high, bronze.
Courtesy: Kersting Galleries, Sausalito, CA

variety of media, he has spent his life executing and teaching art. Past accomplishments include works in ceramics, textiles, glasswork, cloisonne, and photography as well as easel paintings, including a recent series in acrylics. Abstract canvases make use of geometric forms that hold symbolic significance for the artist: squares and cubes representing the masculine; circles and spheres the feminine; and equilateral triangles the spiritual. The artist makes extensive use of black, white and gray in his works, with other colors used primarily to accent the composition. Themes concern the "ultimate struggle that man has created for himself". Influences include world travel and the Greenwich Village bohemia of the Great Depression era. The artist's ceramic works, produced by a self-operated factory, have received wide distribution in the United States as well as Europe.

TAYLOR, JAN (Painter)
120 Center St. #19, Los Angeles, CA 90012

Born: 1953 *Collections:* Epson America; Pacific Mutual Life *Exhibitions:* Marc Richards, West Hollywood *Dealer:* Marc Richards

Her works are based on the belief that painting can be founded in a non-linguistic structure, and toward this end, she has chosen to follow the guidelines established in the works of John McLaughlin, Robert Ryman, and Brice Marden. Her paintings are essentially dichromatic explorations of fundamental and eccentric forms within a figure-ground context. She paints on linen with black or white pieces of lead sheet or foil used as a second design element. These works, which often feature concentric arrangements of geometric forms, are designed to promote a purely visual, completely non-linguistic experience of her personal artistic idiom.

TAYLOR, JANICE (Painter)
499 Alabama, #318, San Francisco, CA 94110

Born: 1947 *Exhibitions:* Hatley-Martin Gallery, San Francisco; Chowning Gallery, San Francisco *Dealer:* Hatley-Martin Gallery, San Francisco

She has been working with oil paints on canvas since the age of eight and long ago fell in love with the medium's color, quality, translucence, texture, permanence, and overall beauty. Although the main body of her work is abstract, she also works with live models on a regular basis. These figurative works, executed with dry materials on rag paper, keep her eye, mind, and hand coordinated. She favors abstract work because when all recognizable objects or reference points are removed from the painting, the viewer must become directly involved and is free to bring his or her own experience to the work. Clyfford Still, Mark Rothko and Frank Lobdell have been influential on her work.

TAYLOR, MARY (Sculptor)
P.O. Box 1456, Healdsburg, CA 95448

Born: 1947 *Awards:* Honorable Mention, Pacific Rim Wildlife Art Show, Tacoma, WA *Exhibitions:* Center Street Gallery, Healdsburg; Santa Rosa City Council

She creates representational, life-size sculptures of birds in steel, stone, bronze and ceramic tile design. Her birds are metaphors for the human spirit, imagination and sense of fantasy. She also intends her pieces as reminders of the fragile quality of nature, and of the many modern threats to the survival of the natural world and its inhabitants.

TAYLOR-BROWN, CAMERON (Fiber Artist)
418 S. Mansfield, Los Angeles, CA 90036

Born: 1953 *Awards:* Ingram Bergman Design Award, Philadelphia College of Textiles and Science *Collections:* Sheraton Hotel, Monterey; William Feldman Associates, Los Angeles *Exhibitions:* Del Mano Gallery, Pasadena; Senior Eye Gallery, Long Beach *Education:* UC-Berkeley; Philadelphia College of Textiles and Science *Dealer:* Del Mano, Pasadena

She was set on a career as a fiber artist after a class with Ed Rossbach. Since then she has produced numerous commercial and fine art pieces characterized by surprising patterns and color combinations. She uses a sixteen harness Macomber handloom, weaving works that could be considered sculptures when finished with an armature, suspended from the ceiling, or set in a display. She also creates woven wall-reliefs. Among her more recent projects is a set of small, mixed-media, wearable, woven pieces executed in collaboration with Lynn Zimmers.

TAYLOR/DANA (Painter)
350 Ward Ave., Suite 106, Honolulu, HI 96814

Born: Taylor, 1942; Dana, 1954 *Awards:* Art Awards, Belleview, WA; Arts in America Program, U.S. State Department Tour *Collections:* Jamaica National Gallery of Art, Kingston; Hyatt Waikoloa, HI *Exhibitions:* Collins Art Gallery, San Francisco; San Francisco Arts Commission

Taylor/Dana is actually two people, the husband and wife team of Gage Taylor and Uriel Dana. They collaborate to created rich, elaborate, highly detailed paintings that have been influenced by Old Master techniques. Their images include the mythological archetypes that reoccur in Western, Eastern, and Middle Eastern culture. Gage Taylor's early works were visionary paintings. Uriel Dana was a sculptor in college and has been painting for several years.

TAY'NAHZA', LINDA (Painter)
Box 1886, Truckee, CA 95734

Born: 1946 *Awards:* Art For the Schools Grant, Lake Tahoe; SITE Council Grant, State of California *Exhibitions:* Jones Center, U. of Nevada, Reno; Micro Gallery, Nevada City *Education:* Calif. College of Arts and Crafts, Oakland *Dealers:* The Hermitage Gallery, Reno, NV; California Capitol Collection, Truckee

She layers acrylic color on canvas in bold, loose abstractions influenced by the work of Fritz Scholder. Recent work focuses on abstractions in metallic acrylics on handmade paper. The figure seen abstractly is a favorite subject. Layering translucent metallics to create luminous variety and visual texture, she plays with color, simple shapes and effective use of space. The wilder colors of earlier paintings have been replaced by a more subdued palette in which muted reds and pinks predominate.

TAYS-CAMPBELL, NETTIE (Painter, Sculptor)
891 Terrace Dr., Los Altos, CA 94022

Awards: National League of American Penwomen; Pacific Art League, Palo Alto *Collections:* Dan Tellep, Saratoga; Nancy and Richard Fouquet, Los Altos *Exhibitions:* Catherine Lorrillard Wolfe Art Club, NYC; Rosicrucian Museum, San Jose

After formal training in the Old Masters' painting techniques and in classical Japanese brushwork, she

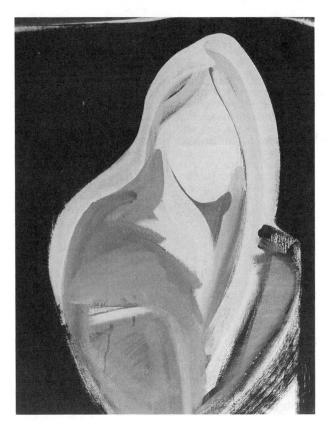

Linda Tay'nahza', *Shidoni,* 26 x 32, acrylic on canvas

Pat Tolle, *You Wanna Blow a Fuse?* 36 x 28, oil

studied all forms of classical sculpture. In 1983, she became interested in Christopher Schinks' abstractions in watercolor and undertook private study with the artist. She is currently working in larger three-paneled surfaces, pre-priming to bring up rough textures in open space. This technique used in conjunction with bolder three-dimensional landscapes forms the basis for a new series, entitled "Open Space and Homestead Structures." Imagery includes floral landscapes, trees and abstract forms of old homesteads and tumble-down sheep sheds. Among her sculptures are bronze portraits of such artists as sculptor Francis Bracken, composer Lou Harrison, poet Consuelo Santos-Killins and painter Jeanne Aurel-Schneider.

TCHAICOVSKY, BENY (Painter)
P.O. Box 793, San Anselmo, CA 94960

Born: 1954 *Awards:* Gold Award, International Connection, Brazil-Japan Exhibition; Best of Show, Natsoulos- Davis Gallery *Collections:* Academy of Art, San Francisco *Exhibitions:* International Connection, Brazil-Japan Exhibition; Natsoulas Novelozo Gallery, Davis *Education:* School of Visual Arts, NYC *Dealer:* Melita Tchaicovsky, San Francisco

Influenced by Magritte and Dali, he makes images that lie at the root of the fantastic. His permanent theme is the departure from the conventional concept of time-space. His paintings are full of "holes" leading to other universes, which open to further universes ad infinitum. His stars resemble brains and his men resemble stars. Planets float in the backgrounds of every day scenes and houses melt like candles burning in the midst of space. The depiction is fantastic but recognizable. Black is an important color, as are the fading purples, greens and oranges of deep space. He was born and raised in Rio de Janeiro in Brazil.

TEACHOUT, DAVID (Painter)
217 1/2 First Ave., Santa Cruz, CA 95062

Born: 1933 *Collections:* UC-Santa Cruz; Occidental College, Los Angeles *Exhibitions:* Corcoran Gallery, Washington, D.C.; Cal. State-Hayward

Color and the color theories of Josef Albers were important in his early abstract expressionist oil paintings. As the paintings grew larger, he progressed from canvases primed with oil to unprimed canvases stained with acrylic paint. In 1971, he became absorbed with the unlimited possibilities of the poured canvas. The results were a series called "Falling" and a group of topographies called "Cold Mountain." In 1980, he returned to drawing and began using nature as a starting point for painting. There was an integration with the earlier work which might be described as color-field landscape painting. The most recent pieces have been geometric abstractions in acrylic.

TEBOR-HONSA, PAT (Painter, Draughtsperson)
4535 Coronado Ave., San Diego, CA 92107

Born: 1929 *Awards:* 1st Place, JCC, San Diego; 3rd Place, San Joaquin Annual *Collections:* Design Planning Interiors, Warren Thompson Architecture, Fresno; Aztec Center, San Diego State U. *Exhibitions:* San Diego Museum of Art; Ankrum Gallery, Los Angeles *Education:* San Diego State U. *Dealer:* A.T. Beasley's Gallery, San Diego

Having studied drawing, etching, lithography and printmaking, she has concentrated on drawing and painting for the last ten years. Her paintings, in particular, reflect her printmaking background, as she works on unprimed canvas with powdered color, linear forms and vast quantities of white paint. In more recent work, she applies plaster to cardboard and canvas and uses pastels, oil pastels and pencils to develop the images. These large paintings, up to 9 by 12 feet, feature abstract imagery. Whatever the medium, she strives to achieve her statement in a spontaneous, direct manner using the medium as a tool or as an end in itself.

TECSON, HERMINIGILDO L. (Painter)
2714 Santa Fe Ave., Long Beach, CA 90810

Born: 1950 *Awards:* 1st Prize, Long Beach Art Association; 1st Prize, Art From the Heart of the Community, Lakewood *Collections:* Philippine Embassy, Saudi Arabia; Children's Museum Library Inc., Republic of the Philippines *Exhibitions:* Potsbach Museum, Tubiguen, Germany; Canadian International Exposition, Toronto *Education:* U. of the East, Manila; Otis Parsons School the Arts, Los Angeles

A love for the art of Paul Gauguin led him to transform Gauguin's strokes of vibrant colors into fine squirts of the airbrush. He searches for new images and forms, creating abstract fragments in a fleeting spiritual puzzle. He tries to reveal the hidden energy of his subject, through color harmony and dissonance. Using an oil base, and acrylic color, he juxtaposes various geometric figures in his recent airbrush work. "My art is feeling, expressed not in words, but in ART."

TELLER, PAULINE (Painter)
290 Harvard Dr., Larkspur, CA 94939

Born: 1914 *Exhibitions:* Museum at Mission San Juan Capistrano; Village Artistry Gallery, Carmel *Education:* Dominican College

Always motivated by color, she has, over the years, moved from realistic landscapes to more abstract renderings. Since 1984, she has spent a good deal of time in the Southwest where she has been inspired by the magnificently colored mountains, the blue sky and the luminous colors of the architectural structures. Her images, such as her painting of the Tesque Pueblo Church in New Mexico, are often simplified views of architecture. They are full of simplicity and mystery. Among those she has studied with are August Madrigal, Connie Smith Siegel and Elizabeth Holland McDaniel. Her biography is included in *Artists in California 1786-1940* by Edan Miltan Hughes (Hughes 1986).

TEMPLE, BROOK (Painter)
590 Las Colindas, San Rafael, CA 94903

Born: 1934 *Awards:* Yale Norfolk Scholarship *Collections:* Chase Manhattan Bank; Oakland Museum *Exhibitions:* Brooklyn Musuem; Palace of the Legion of Honor, San Francisco *Education:* Yale U.; Art Students League *Dealer:* Joanne Chappell Gallery, S.F.

He cites Matisse, Mark Rothko and Josef Albers as enduring influences. Under the tutelage of Albers in the '60s at Yale, he made hard-edge paintings, serigraphs and collages. At that time, his interest in color and color relationship awakened, and that interest has imbued all of his work since. He currently explores color in paper pieces done in oil floated into thinner, the images streaked with enamel oil and pastel; and in abstract figure work on paper and canvas, executed in oil and mixed media. The latter owe their

Louise Dudley Taft, *Apple Aroma,* 44 x 30, colored pencil drawing

Tim Terrell, *Personage,* 48 x 60, ektacolor mural,

Pauline Ivancovich Teller, *Church at Acoma Pueblo, N.M.,* 33 x 23, oil on canvas

inspiration to Francis Bacon, Matisse and the figure painters of the California School and synthesize his abstractions and his figurative drawings.

TEMPLETON, MARK (Painter)
3239 Kempton Ave., Oakland, CA 94611

Born: 1948 *Collections:* City of San Francisco; Mayflower Corporation, Chicago *Exhibitions:* San Jose Museum of Art *Education:* University of Texas *Dealer:* Erickson & Elins Fine Art, San Francisco

He makes paper constructions from watercolors that have been cut and reassembled in abstract patterns, creating an inlaid or woven quality and exploring light, color, texture and design. Incorporating gouache, India ink, pencil, rice paper and gold leaf in addition to watercolor, the work is generated in similar sets as a result of recombining elements from several related compositions. Trained as an architect, he approaches his work from a process orientation, allowing a piece to grow out of a set of structural confines through the union of complementary oppositions. This juxtaposition and inherent structure conceptually imitates patterns of order and beauty in nature.

TERAOKA, MASAMI (Painter, Sculptor)
c/o Space Gallery, 6015 Santa Monica Blvd., Los Angeles, CA 90038

Born: 1936 *Awards:* NEA Fellowship *Collections:* Oakland Museum; Los Angeles County Museum of Art *Exhibitions:* Los Angeles County Museum of Art; Space Gallery, Los Angeles *Education:* Kwansei Gwakuin U., Kobe, Japan; Otis Art Institute

He creates socially concerned art by combining traditional Japanese Ukiyo-e techniques with subject matter that addresses environmental issues, consumerism and the Westernization of Japanese society and culture. In the painting *McDonald's Hamburgers Invading Japan/Tokyo Ginza Shuffle*, he creates a work that had all the flavor and appearance of a 19th-century Ukiyo-e print, but the fast-food hamburger, french fries and napkin lurking in the foreground and corner destroy the gentle, nostalgic image. Non-biodegradable trash, condoms and tampons also invade otherwise traditional scenes, as do sets of American golf clubs and kimono-wearing photographers. Critic Al Morch writes, "Ukiyo-e offers Teraoka a perfect medium for mingling past and present. What grows out of this mix is a is an art that defines the gap between past and present, and maps the dangers in our future . . . We're endlessly bombarded with clean-up-our-act tirades, but Teraoka grabs our attention through a flawless watercolor brush and sense of universal wit. It's painless medicine."

TERRELL, TIM (Sculptor, Photographer)
P. O. Box 5731, Whittier, CA 90607

Born: 1950 *Collections:* GMI Engineering and Management Institute, Flint, MI; Wayland Academy, Beaver Dam, WI *Exhibitions:* Whittier Museum; Los Angeles Center of Photographic Studies *Education:* U. of Michigan; Babson College *Dealers:* Ruth Volid Gallery, Chicago; The 14th Street Gallery, Atlanta; Ward-Nasse, NYC; Pierce St. Gallery, Birmingham, MI

Practicing a form of artistic archaeology, he combs man-made environments, junk yards and industrial landscapes, translating the debris into sculpture and photography. Instead of creating sculpture with the traditional means of constructing and molding, he takes as his prime sculptural acts selecting and naming. Many of his works, such as *Shammon*—a disembodied grill of a 1934 Hudson—are presented in unaltered form, commanding attention by the strength of their visual presence and associative value. In others works, such as *Serpent Spirit*—an assemblage of industrial tubing and an old scale—he recombines objects to achieve specific expressive ends. His photography also brings the viewer to a new confrontation with the texture of the man-made world. Rather than capturing subjects isolated in a surrounding setting, his lens enters his subject, probing its skin for patterns and texture.

TERRY, JAN (Painter, Sculptor)
2578 Rim of the World Dr., Running Springs, CA 92382

Born: 1931 *Awards:* Prize, International Invitational Exhibit *Exhibitions:* Depolio Gallery, Palm Springs; Pickfair, Beverly Hills

She considers herself a colorist, and it was this aspect of impressionist painting that she found most engaging. Working with a knife and with varnish/oil wash, she prefers painting on a large surface, from 48 by 48 inches to wall-size murals. Her palette is radiantly warm, and her favorite subjects are open landscapes and tumultuous seascapes. Her style is mostly representational; her imagery and use of color arise from her emotional response to the subject. Her sculptural technique results from over twenty years of experimentation in marble dust, bronze, concrete sand casting, welded metal and plaster decorated with delicate ink washes. These pieces are figurative and often life-sized.

TERRYVIALE, MARGARET (Painter)
90 El Camino, Sedona, CA 86336

Born: 1949 *Awards:* Pollock-Krasner Foundation Grant *Exhibitions:* Museo Italo Americano, San Francisco; Berkeley Art Center; *Education:* San Francisco Art Institute; UC-Davis *Dealer:* Banaker, Walnut Creek

As a student she explored the figure as subject matter, often being compared to such notables as Manuel Neri and Nathan Oliveira. A recurring theme throughout her work since she completed her training and moved to Los Angeles has been dwelling places, particularly houses. Included in her imagery are images from common experience—rivers, trees, moons, furniture. Uncommon, however, is the treatment. Energized and vibrant, the deep colors, expressive brush and crayon marks give these heavily outlined, almost childlike compositions, a larger significance. The images of an outer world become metaphors from an inner one. The title of one painting, *Inside/Out* speaks of this directly.

TEW, JANICE (Egguery Artist)
P.O. Box 193 Cromberg, CA 96103

Born: 1952 *Awards:* Best of Show, Professional Artists Association, Plumas, CO; 1st Place, California Egg Artistry, Santa Barbara and Anaheim *Exhibitions:* Gumps, San Francisco; Nieman Marcus, San Francisco *Education:* Humboldt State U. *Dealer:* Gumps, San Francisco; Faces West Gallery, Monterey

Trained in stained glass, intaglio printing and textile painting, she was introduced to the ancient Russian art of Pysanky (a wax resist and dye method of egguery)

Margaret TerryViale, *Fenced,* 15 x 11, acrylic on paper

Brook Temple, *Phantom,* 30 x 40, oil on paper.
Courtesy: La Sorda/Ira Gallery

in 1975. She has since developed her own technique and style. Basically self-taught, she learned her art through many years of experimentation. The eggs she now creates employ India inks, aniline dyes, 22k gold and many hours with a steady hand. She draws all her original designs freehand, and dyes her eggs by hand with a toothpick. Each egg is one of a kind, sealed, strengthened and signed.

THACKER, KATE WARD (Painter, Paper Artist)
28130 Langside Ave., Canyon Country, CA 91351

Born: 1955 *Awards:* Fine Art Federation Award, Burbank; 1st Place, Blank Greeting Card Competition, Strathmore Papers *Collections:* Crocker Bank, Los Angeles; The Rowland Association, Indianapolis, IN *Exhibitions:* Brand Library Art Gallery, Glendale; ASI Gallery, San Francisco *Education:* Purdue U. *Dealer:* Art Source, Los Angeles

Through her training and experience as a designer, she was introduced to all types of textiles. Her love and appreciation of quilt designs compelled her to begin creating designs of her own. She soon found, however, that her enjoyment of the design phases provided her with stacks of sketches waiting to be fabricated. She began creating "paper quilts"—torn, painted, pieced and stitched paper constructions—as an alternate method of bringing her designs to life. The painting allows her an infinite range of color, and the torn edges, piecing and stitching, add depth and texture to the pieces. She also enjoys the speed of the process relative to quilt fabrication, which allows her ample opportunity to experiment on successive projects. She considers herself a colorist, involved in constant experimentation with color combinations contained in simple geometric shapes. She uses the properties of color to develop illusions of movement, space, transparency, depth, and "shimmer." Her works vary greatly in size, from six by six inches to 6 by 6 feet.

THAI, YILUN (Painter, Calligrapher)
29 Balboa St. #3, San Francisco, CA 94118

Born: 1965 *Awards:* 1st and 2nd Place, Emerald City Classic *Exhibitions:* Asian Art Museum, Golden Gate Park, San Francisco; Chinese Culture Center, San Francisco *Education:* Academy of Art College

He had experimented with a variety of Western art styles when he became fascinated with Chinese folk art calligraphy. This 200-year-old Chinese art form is based on ancient Chinese calligraphy with some pictorial elements. Wooden applicators are employed to mark paper with Chinese black ink. Each character is created from a single stroke, and it takes from three to five minutes to make each stroke. Since learning this art form, he has experimented with oil and acrylic, developing a new painting style he calls "abstract expressionist calligraphy." These works incorporate complex calligraphic forms with recognizable figures, such as dragons, birds and horses.

THAL, LAURIE (Sculptor)
Star Rte. 352-A, Jackson, WY 83001

Born: 1953 *Exhibitions:* Wyoming State Museum, Cheyenne; Handworks Gallery, Carmel *Education:* School of the Art Institute of Chicago

Known for the rich colors and clarity of her glass, she blows and shapes her graceful vessels freely, without the use of molds. Each one-of-a-kind piece is blown with one or two transparent colors, which she cases

with a layer of clear crystal. Her works include classic, unadorned statements in form and color and other pieces that are decorated with a swirl or wrapped line of color. Recently she has expanded her sculptural work to combine her background in photography and dance with the possibilities that glass presents. Using two processes, one that first sandblasts then airbrushes plate glass and one that transfers photographic images onto glass, she is able to sculpt finely detailed figures. Hand-crafted wood bases create a stage on which the figures then play.

THELEN, PHYLLIS (Printmaker, Collagist)
199 Mountain View Ave., San Rafael, CA 94901

Born: 1926 *Collections:* Independent Indemnity; Butte Oil and Gas *Exhibitions:* Stanford U.; Stephens College Invitational *Education:* Connecticut College *Dealer:* Artesans, Mill Valley

Her classical training in the 1940s included work in such disciplines as etching, oil painting, conte crayon and plastic. After leaving school, this rigid background gave way to a freer use of printing techniques, resulting in experimental applications of etching, screen printing, lino and woodblock. Her interest in Japanese mixed printing techniques led to studies in Japan in 1984. She has since produced a series of large serigraphs with compatible themes and colors and has reconstructed these images using collage and embossments from wood carving. She has additionally extended her medium by introducing pastels as an element.

THIEBAUD, WAYNE (Painter)
1617 7th Ave., Sacramento, CA 95818

Born: 1920 *Awards:* Member, American Academy and Institute of Arts and Letters; Academician, National Academy of Design *Collections:* San Francisco Museum of Modern Art; Metropolitan Museum of Art, NYC *Exhibitions:* San Francisco Museum of Modern Art; Arts Club of Chicago *Education:* Cal. State-Sacramento *Dealer:* Allan Stone, NYC

Before formal art training, he worked as a cartoonist, a designer and an advertising art director—experiences that have influenced his paintings. With thickly applied paint, variations of images of single food items and other products are repeated in bright colors and artificial light. Realistic representations have also included lone figures on white backgrounds executed in a style reminiscent of advertising images. An alliance with the pop movement is evident throughout his work, although his style characteristically incorporates a more realistic approach. He continues to teach art and has received numerous pedagogical awards, including special citations from the College Art Association and the National Association of Schools of Art and Design. He has also been awarded honorary Doctorates of Fine Arts from the California College of Arts and Crafts, Dickenson College and the San Francisco School of Fine Arts.

THIERMANN, ANN ELIZABETH (Painter)
200 Estates Dr. Ben Lomand, CA 95005

Born: 1950 *Awards:* Best of Show, Oxnard Annual Tri-County Juried Show; Award of Excellence, California State Fair *Collections:* City of Santa Monica *Exhibitions:* Carnegie Art Museum, Oxnard; B1 Gallery, Santa Monica *Education:* Art Student's League; Cal. State-Long Beach *Dealer:* B-1 Gallery, Santa Monica; Le Poudre Gallery, Minneapolis

Ann Elizabeth Thiermann, *Lockerroom II,* 40 x 60, pastel. Collection of: Tony Bill

Michael Todd, *Lily Pad Table,* 34 x 96 x 120, steel. Courtesy: Tortue Gallery, Santa Monica, CA

After receiving formal training in portraiture and classical figure painting, she developed a body of graduate work entitled "Reflections." In these pieces, she explored the psychological and physical implications of figures mirrored in space. Mirrors allowed multiple views of the same figure, as well as more compositional abstraction, through a fragmentation of planes. Combining her knowledge of pastels (portraiture) and acrylics (large scale wall murals), she created more direct and dramatic studies by mixing the media. In 1987, she completed a series of large locker room paintings, one of which is set in the famous Gold's Gym. She painted reflections on both canvas and mirrored panels, incorporating different wall planes in the same piece. These multipanel paintings offer viewers multiple perspectives, which directly involve them in the work. She continues to create large figurative and landscape work that includes reflected imagery.

THIGPEN, DANIEL THOMAS (Painter)
6717 W. 88th, Los Angeles, CA 90045

Born: 1950 *Awards:* George Page Fellowship, Los Angeles County Museum *Collections:* Red Cross, Atlanta *Exhibitions:* Atelier Gallery, Santa Monica; ANTI Club, Los Angeles *Education:* USC *Dealer:* Susan Carson Gallery, Denver

His early work employed the same grid technique that such painters as Leonardo da Vinci and contemporary artist, Chuck Close have used. Like Close, he approaches each square as though it were a separate world or separate painting of its own; while the overall effect is a photo-realist image, taken separately each square remains abstract. Eventually he became captivated with these "little paintings," and he started creating large scale versions of them. Works at this time included air brush, oil and inks on canvas, paper and masonite. Recent work emphasizes visual illusion as a metaphor for the world in which we live, and our relationship to it. Subjects as disparate as aerial landscapes, rodeos and piles of firewood make up these pieces. Color is used to evoke moods and mood swings, and in many paintings, layers of underpainting are exposed with their accompanying shadows, as a metaphor for the layers of reality and the accompanying shadow world. This process, too, came about as a result of isolating one element of a landscape (say a tree limb) and discovering the painting therein. While the approach in these later paintings is similar to that of the early work, the brushstroke is wide and gestural, a move he credits to the influence of the "New York school" style of paintings.

THOMA, MARTA (Painter, Commercial Illustrator)
1023 Greenwood, Palo Alto, CA 94301

Born: 1951 *Awards:* Humboldt Arts Council; Best Illustration, San Francisco Art Directors *Exhibitions:* San Francisco Museum of Modern Art; U. of Oregon Museum of Modern Art *Education:* San Francisco State U.; UC-Berkeley

Paintings deal with our relationship to the environment and to each other. Many are populated with humans that have animal heads, representing the conflict between basic drives and the restraints of civilization. She studied abstract expressionism and conceptual art at Berkeley and was affected by the flourishing figurative school there. Very early, she had a personal imaginative style influenced by Magritte and Dali. But only after her study of photo-realism did she develop the technique necessary to enhance the "realness" of her fantasies. The resulting effect lent itself to illustration, and her experience with national publications led to precise, small-scale work. After some time spent experimenting with a looser, larger-scale style, she has returned to focus on segmented, rather than square or rectangular canvas. The space within is now manipulated by the shape of its surface. Thus the work is both illusion and object at once, part painting and part sculpture.

THOMAS, BRUCE & CLONARD (Sculptor)
71-225 Aerie Rd., Palm Desert, CA 92260

Collections: Metromedia, NYC; Dow Chemical *Exhibitions:* The Living Desert Reserve, Palm Desert; Ambienti, Redondo Beach *Education:* U. of Arizona; Otis Art Institute; U. of Arizona-Bruce

Inspired by the natural forms of forests, deserts, riverbeds, and mountains, they create large sculptures from polyester resin, fiberglass, automotive acrylics, bronze and silver. Influenced by the works of Henry Moore, Negoochi, and Rodin, they combine their painting and sculpting talents, using the three-dimensional surface as a canvas. Their recent work as a team is based on mountains, and they work by building forms from the inside out using urethane foam, glass, resin, and paint. Although they often collaborate on projects, they maintain distinct artistic identities. Clonard's recent work has concentrated on three-dimensional sculptures in cast paper. Bruce has been working on sculptural studies of rivers and the flow of water.

THOMAS, JAMES D. (Painter)
6302 Lomitas Dr., Los Angeles, CA 90042

Born: 1957 *Collections:* Kriess Corporation, Atlanta; McKenna, Conner & Cuneo, Los Angeles *Exhibitions:* Design Center of Los Angeles; Los Angeles Artcore Center *Education:* Otis Art Institute/Parsons School of Design *Dealer:* Hunsaker/Schlesinger Gallery, Los Angeles

Utilizing a combination of imagery and more formally direct concerns such as flat, colorful shapes and gold leaf, he creates painted constructions on wood that employ a geometrically classical impulse. The natural surface qualities of wood evoke passages that are at once poignant and subtle. He is concerned with the various manners in which people interact with their environment, and he also focuses on the dialogue between myth and logic as it refers to landscape. These concerns are evident in his recent series, such as "Haiku" and "Euclid's Gift," which chronicle the constant change and transition in nature, paralleling the process the painter undergoes.

THOMAS, LARRY (Draughtsperson, Printmaker,)
601 Chenery St., San Francisco, CA 94131

Born: 1943 *Awards:* NEA Fellowship; S.E.C.A. Art Award, San Francisco Museum of Modern Art *Exhibitions:* U. of the Pacific, Stockton; Fuller/Goldeen Gallery, San Francisco *Education:* Memphis Academy of Arts; San Francisco Art Institute

Native American mythology and religion are the subjects of his often very large, experimental work. His "Fetish Series" of the mid-1970s he depicts wrapped ceremonial bundles. By 1982, he was drawing centralized and vertical vessel-like forms within shallow, pictorial spaces. Other pieces of the era resemble ancient dwellings. In a later series he rubbed several layers of

Henry C. Thompson, *Old Dutch House 'Winter',* 20 x 24, oil

Beny Tchaicovsky, *Arrival,* 42 x 42, acrylic on canvas

medium into large sheets of paper (up to eighty by 176 inches) allowing dusty textures to emerge, echoing an architectural dig. His recent "Pyre" series, uses rich color to illuminate fields around objects which suggest ritualistic activity or relics of ancient societies. He currently teaches at the San Francisco Art Institute.

THOMPSON, CHRISTIAN S. (Photographer)
1237 1/4 N. Fairfax Ave., W. Hollywood, CA 90046

Born: 1960 *Collections:* Rosenthal Collection, Chicago *Exhibitions:* G. Ray Hawkins Gallery, Los Angeles; Diane Nelson Gallery, Laguna Beach *Education:* U. of Nebraska *Dealer:* Richard Green Gallery, Los Angeles

After formal training in commercial advertising, he became a successful print art director. His commercial background has provided a context for his fine art work—most specifically in presentation. He works primarily in Polaroid, and his subject matter is generally grand to the point of pomposity. His lighting is dramatic, and his presentation further accentuates the disparity between the trivial form (Polaroid) and the imposing subject. He is noted for nudes, still lifes and exaggerations that are pulled into perplexing, often funny juxtaposition by the Polaroid.

THOMPSON, DAVID A. (Painter)
1562 62nd St., Emmeryville, CA 94608

Born: 1941 *Collections:* U.S. Information Agency; Delta Airlines *Exhibitions:* Berkeley Art Center *Education:* Wagner College; California College of Arts and Crafts *Dealer:* TM Artworks, San Francisco

An early academic interest in art as a visual puzzle developed into a career in applied art, through experimentation with drawing and watercolor. Later work with acrylic sheet produced shimmering sculptural forms encompassed by color and light. This influenced the figurative bent of his return to painting. The translucent quality of watercolor allows him to continue his play with the interaction of light and color. He continues to refer to his sculptural experience in a search for similarities in shape and line between media, which alternately hide and reveal new images and formal relationships. His portraiture has concentrated on the perfection of form realized by dancers, gymnasts and bodybuilders.

THOMPSON, HENRY C. (Painter)
20720 4th St., #8, Saratoga, CA 95070

Born; 1909 *Awards:* Texas Fine Arts Association *Collections:* Museum of the Battleship Texas *Exhibitions:* 1927 Armory Show; Society of Independent Artists, NYC *Education:* Yale U., New Haven, CT; Metropolitan Museum of Art *Dealer:* Peter Thompson, Saratoga

At home in the use of palette knives, brushes and carving tools, his media include oil, acrylic, watercolor, tempera, pencil, pen and woodblock. His drawing is quick, direct, and skillful. His use of perspective is highly refined and original. Works in progress span a diversity of styles and subjects, including realism and modern American impressionism. His paintings are contemporary, sophisticated and original, and he expresses great sympathy for his fellow man. Unity of thought and the principle of order are expressed through arrangement and presentation of the subject, and all is presented with impasto application of rich color, using a knife, even for intricate shapes.

THOMPSON, M. KATHRYN (Commercial Illustrator)
333 G St., #1, San Rafael, CA 94901

Born: 1957 *Collections:* Caffe Alberto, San Anselmo *Exhibitions:* Bradford Mansion Gallery, San Rafael; Gallery, Seattle Art Institute *Education:* Seattle Art Institute

She creates airbrush illustrations which combine fantasy and reality into ethereal, three-dimensional space. The fluidity of color and imagery suggest a joining of mind and matter.

THOMPSON, RICHARD EARL, SR. (Painter)
80 Maiden Lane, San Francisco, CA 94108

Born: 1914 *Collections:* Naval Art Collection, Pentagon, Washington, D.C.; New Britain Museum of American Art, CT *Exhibitions:* Leigh Yawkey Woodson Art Museum, Wausau, WI; R.W. Norton Gallery, Shreveport, LA *Education:* Chicago Academy of Fine Arts; School of the Art Institute of Chicago

The artist's luminous compositions of light and air vary from high brilliance to subtle mood scenes and tranquil settings. His early canvases included French genre, figurative and landscape subjects textured with gesso. More recent works employ thick paint for a textured look. Subjects for the later works are taken from nature. His intent is to develop the impressionistic technique of his predecessors by capturing the surroundings of the time through light, color and mood. The drama of nature is shown through the interpretation of light and mood that the many phases of nature portray; he has re-introduced earth tones to the impressionist palette. Historian Patricia Jobe Pierce has authored a book on the artist, entitled *Richard Earl Thompson, American Impressionist: A Prophetic Odyssey in Paint.*

THONE, PAULA (Sculptor)
338 Indian Bend Rd., Umpqua, OR 97486

Born: 1947 *Awards:* Honorable Mention, Carrara Annual Exhibit, Italy *Exhibitions:* Dassin Gallery, Los Angeles; James Dannis Gallery, Palm Desert *Education:* U. of California; Whitney Museum *Dealer:* Edwardo Spazzapan, Malibu

Influenced by primitive Mexican themes and by the work of Oliver Andrews, she sculpts figurative pieces in bronze and marble. These human forms are rendered with plasticity, linear tension and a concern for structural integrity. She uses her materials to explore and reveal the spiritual and poetic aspects of her subjects. She has also sculpted monumental works focusing on horses and on bulky, powerful women. Her current work in marble is simplified and sensuous, using more abstract forms. Expanding her artistic vision to include context as well as object, she has begun to design more personal spaces for homes or gardens; these pieces are conducive to meditation and creativity.

THORNTON, JOAN (Painter)
P.O. Box 611, Point Reyes Station, CA 94956

Born: 1932 *Exhibitions:* Artist Paw Gallery, Inverness Park; Gallery Route One, Point Reyes Station *Education:* San Francisco Art Institute *Dealers:* Design Art, La Cienega; Carol Franklin, Los Angeles

Her earlier paintings were pop-surrealist narratives in a landscape setting. For the past several years, the landscapes have included bridges, walls, buildings,

Richard Earl Thompson, *Bridge at Woodstock,* 24 x 36, oil on canvas
Courtesy: Richard Thompson Gallery, San Francisco

Ricardo Tringali, *Metatron,* 29 x 26 x 18, bronze. Photographer: Lee Fatherce

barns and other man-made structures. She works by making on-site prisma drawings. Then, working on a stretched canvas, she does an acrylic underpainting. The main work of the painting is then completed in oil, with an emphasis on strong composition and dramatic color contrasts. Her works have an impressionist appearance, which becomes more abstract on closer inspection. She cites Marsden Hartley, Emily Carr and Philip Guston as major influences.

THORPE, ALAN (Sculptor)
3300 Putter Dr., Soquel, CA 95073

Born: 1948 *Exhibitions:* Center Art Galleries, HI; Zantman Art Galleries, Carmel and Palm Desert *Dealer:* Zantman Art Galleries, Carmel and Palm Desert; Kersting Galleries, Sausalito; Windor's Galleries, Boca Raton, FL

Influenced by Henry Moore, Jacques Lipchitz and Alexander Archipenko, he began creating his "Driftwood Sculptures" from blocks of walnut and redwood in 1974. At the same time, he carved doors on commission. Wanting to give his sculpture a slicker, more contemporary look, he began lacquering and gluing wood mosaics to his pieces. Recently, he became dissatisfied with wood's unstable properties and began using aerospace polyurethane. He glues blocks of the polyurethane together, carves them with chisels and then applies automobile lacquer and wood mosaic to the surface of the completed piece. He uses a combination of hard edge and negative space to give his work a feeling of emotion. His latest floral designs were inspired by Georgia O'Keeffe.

TIBBON, SUSAN (Painter, Sculptor)
1445 Leavenworth St., #4, San Francisco, CA 94109

Born: 1953 *Awards:* Outstanding Alumni Award, San Francisco Art Institute *Collections:* UC-Santa Cruz, *Exhibitions:* Palace of the Legion of Honor, San Francisco; Tiffany and Co., San Francisco *Education:* San Francisco Art Institute; Brown U.

Her painted eggs are visionary worlds full of flora, fauna and inanimate objects. On one egg, *Desert*, she depicts the animals of the desert among cacti, bright colors, and Native American motifs. In 1985, she did a series of eggs on the theme of cafe society. She also makes sculptural jeweled eggs. One is in a carousel design with posts of twisted gold. Another is a Christmas scene with diamond snowflakes. Her first eggs were studies for larger canvas works. When the eggs sold, she expanded to other egg surfaces including ostrich, quail, and rare glazed wooden eggs. The eggs are treated and untreated and she also works on canvas, handmade paper, and silk. She teaches anatomy and drawing at the McAteer School of the Arts in San Francisco.

TIDMUS, MICHAEL (Computer Artist, Mixed-Media Artist)
832 1/4 Mansfield Ave., Los Angeles, CA 90036

Born: 1951 *Collections:* Hill-Pinckert Architects, Irvine *Exhibitions:* Installation Gallery, San Diego; Spare Gallery, Venice

Until 1984, his work was concerned with non-figurative abstraction in traditional painting media and collage. With the advent of the AIDS crisis, work evolved into a more communicative figurative/representational style, with an emphasis on conveying emotion through the use of color, shape and symbol. Work was often finished with deep glazes and layers of graphite, to create a distancing and distressed effect. Current computer-processed photographic images and text is concerned with AIDS, the process of memorialization and personal loss; it also serves to demystify computer art. Pieces are divided into three groups: glazed, gilded photographic images, processed through a computer and collaged onto a canvas ground, covered with pages of text, and fragments of books on psychoanalysis, the holocaust and sexuality; black-and-white computer processed collages, which combine overlapping transparent images; and interactive AIDS related computer software.

TISDALE, DANIEL B. (Painter, Photographer)
1612 McCollum St., Silverlake, CA 90026

Born: 1958 *Awards:* 1st Place Award (2D), 3rd Place Award (3D), 2D and 3D Art Exhibition, Calif. Polytechnic Inst., Pomona; 1st Place, Drawing, Calif. Museum of Science and Industry *Collections:* Calif. Polytechnic Inst., Pomona; White Columns Gallery, NYC *Exhibitions:* Richard Bennett Gallery, Los Angeles; American Museum *Education:* Calif. Polytechnic Inst., Pomona

His work is concerned with the viewer's interpretation of images. Recently, he created a montaged series of polaroid images that he appropriated from the television screen. Through these pieces, he provokes a double dialogue regarding the original state of the image—television—and its reinterpretation outside that context. The irony of grafting television images into a work of art helps to define both the function of media in our culture and the pervasive culture that media itself is. His work removes television images from their manipulated state and asks the viewer to interpret them using his or her own private language.

TODD, MICHAEL (Sculptor)
2817 Clearwater St., Los Angeles, CA 90039

Born: 1935 *Awards:* Fulbright; NEA Fellowship *Collections:* Whitney Museum, NYC; Metropolitan Museum of Art, NYC *Exhibitions:* Hirshhorn Museum; Tortue Gallery, Santa Monica *Education:* Notre Dame U.; UCLA *Dealer:* Tortue Gallery, Santa Monica

Influenced by David Smith's "Drawing in Space" and by the sinuous lines of Oriental art forms, his abstract, non-representational, open-ringed sculpture exhibits a painterly style. He is as concerned with line, surface and plane as he is with traditional sculptural ideas. In all but his most recent work he has made use of found industrial materials and pieces of steel that he welds, lacquers and paints. He has recently begun to use brass and bronze in his work. Though he sees his motif of the circle as representing the cosmos, he nevertheless adds whimsy and playfulness to his works' formalism.

TOKI, JOHN (Sculptor)
642 Spring St., Richmond, CA 94804

Born: 1951 *Collections:* City of Sacramento *Exhibitions:* Civic Arts Gallery, Walnut Creek; Hayward City Center Plaza *Education:* Cal. State-Hayward; California College of Arts and Crafts

The turning point in his career occurred in 1978 at a show of large-scale white plaster sculptures at the Richmond Art Center in Richmond, California. Influenced by minimalism and by Japanese Zen gardens, his work progressed in a new direction to landscape abstractions constructed in clay. A recent series of sculptures, "Earthscapes," fuses the rolling hills and

John Toki, *Earthscape II,* 180 x 32 x 38, ceramic.
Photograph: Scott McCue

Bonese Collins Turner, *Waiting in the Wings,*
40 x 30, watercolor

colorful sky patterns of the San Francisco Bay area with more figurative abstractions. These freestanding columns and wall sculptures are constructed from stoneware, porcelain and stained clay. They are fired at a wide range of temperatures, which affects their color and texture.

TOLLE, PAT (Painter)
10111 Marineview Dr., Everett, WA 98204

Born: 1948 *Awards:* 1st Place, Art Kauai '79; Artists League Traveling Exhibit *Exhibitions:* Santa Barbara Art Museum; Artworks Gallery, Santa Barbara *Education:* Brooks Art Institute

Influenced by Disney cartoons and Wayne Thiebaud's pop art, her work is a deft blend of photo-realism and abstraction. She works from photographs and magazines, humorously exploring the twin obsessions of fast cars and fast women. A sculptor by training, she strives for a complete, three-dimensional illusion. Working in oil on canvas, she uses bright colors and prefers a 40-by-48-inch surface. Her goal is every man's dream combined with a painterly, edible-looking surface.

TOLLIVER, TERESA (Multimedia Artist, Sculptor)
3122 Ewing, Altadema, CA 91001

Born: 1945 *Exhibitions:* Barnsdale Junior Arts College, Hollywood; White's Old Town Gallery, Pasadena

An interest in ethnic arts sparked the emergence of fetish animals, as the main subjects of her multi-media sculptures. She also paints and creates ceremonial masks, all of which are influenced by African, South American and prehistoric art. She constructs the mythical animal figures from wooden frames, covered with leather, batik cloth, feathers, yarn and other materials. These life-sized pieces are fantastic in derivation and expressionistic in style.

TOMKINS, MILLICENT (Painter)
31 Shell Rd., Mill Valley, CA 94941

Born: 1929 *Awards:* 2nd Prize, Society of Washington, D.C. Artists Cash prize, Marin Arts Guild Open Juried Show *Collections:* Brooklyn Museum, NY; Portland Museum, OR *Exhibitions:* UC-Berkeley Hospital; Depot Bookstore, Mill Valley *Education:* UC-Berkeley

Influenced by post-impressionism, among other styles, she has always worked from nature. Her works are generally very realistic, characterized by certain, delicate lines and the use of negative space as another class of form. She prefers pen and ink (as in the "Musical Still Life" series, which has been widely reproduced), watercolors and oil paint. Her most recent works, inspired by Buddhism, consist of gesso-primed canvases with thin underpainting and oil glazes using still-life subject matter and windows with sky. Recent landscapes feature California's rolling brown hills and cloudy skies.

TONTY, CHERYL (Draughtsperson, Mixed Media Artist)
2238 Tomasina Ct., #6, Campbell, CA 95008

Born: 1961 *Awards:* Bay Arts, San Mateo; California Works, San Jose Art League *Exhibitions:* Southern Exposure Gallery, San Francisco; Rutgers National; Rutgers, NJ

The struggle between the frenetic and the serene is the subject of her drawings. She works in black and white, relying on the intensity of form, tone, light, and shadow to convey a surreal world held together by a fluid, fabric-like matter that engulves, threatens to devour, and becomes the primary entity in the drawing. She avoids specific narratives in favor of more open-ended interpretations. There is a dark humor about the work. A psychic tension and nightmarish emotional urgency characterize her figures, anthropomorphized animals, and objects both prosaic and bizarre. Her medium of choice is conte crayon because of its rich black tones and velvety texture.

TORRES, HENRY (Sculptor)
2629 Nevada St., Union City, CA 94587

Born: 1935 *Exhibitions:* San Francisco Art Festival; Union Street Gallery, San Francisco *Education:* Chabolt Sculpture Program

He began making and selling welded pieces in the mid-1960s and has continued doing so since then. He uses primarily bronze and stone castings to make sculptures that create the illusion of movement; occasionally, he uses ceramics to add textural depth to his works. Recently, he has produced realistic works, such as a metal sculpture of a suit of armor. The steel of the suit is soft-welded, creating a soft, round, voluminous image of the historically hard, sharp suit. The artist typically chooses to create images of figures, which, as common ground between artist and audience, serve as vehicles for the artist's expression. He is influenced by the consistency of sculptor David Smith's welded works and has experimented in achieving a fluid, tactile product.

TOWER, CINDY (Painter, Sculptor)
326 Rosemont St., La Jolla, CA 92037

Born: 1958 *Exhibitions:* Petroseno Park, NYC; Brooke Alexander, NYC *Education:* UC-San Diego; Cornell U.

Her multimedia constructions incorporate humor and social commentary. She has painted Titian-like angels on a welded arch of oil drums held up at either end by a giant chainsawed Hermes. Her civic statue, *Diorama*, was a pink, two-headed llama with a rider resembling George Washington. She welded the statue's steel armature, covered it with a fiberglass skin, and then covered its base with specially treated Pink-Panther brand insulation. Among her current themes are transformation and rejuvenation. She recently began a series of plastic Madonnas floating above sculptures of men with their reading interrupted.

TOWERS, JOAN (Painter)
402 Mesa Rd., Salinas, CA 93908

Born: 1929 *Awards:* Ford Foundation Grant *Exhibitions:* Monterey Peninsula Museum of Art; Cuesta College, San Luis Obispo *Education:* Otis Art Institute *Dealer:* Jeremy Stone

Early in her career, she became interested in the ideas of German expressionism, and experimented with a cubist style of flat, hard-edged painting. Later she became fascinated with the work of Willem de Kooning, and by the mid-1980s she was working on a series of figurative paintings called the "Women Paintings." These works, executed in thick oils mixed on the canvas, depict many types of women in a variety of situations. She seeks to present a non-political statement on women's affairs through these works.

TOWGOOD, JEAN (Painter)
652 Moulton Ave., Los Angeles, CA 90031

Di Starr, *Sands Below, Sea Beyond,* 8 x 10, painted photograph

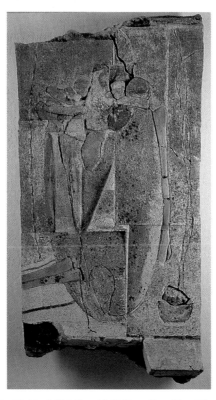

John Toki, *Still Life with Yellow Egg,* 53 x 25 x 7,
ceramic. Courtesy: Toki Studios. Photograph: Scott McCue

Linda Tay'nahza', *Warrior Spirit,* 36 x 48,
acrylic on canvas. Courtesy: Stephanie Erber

Mary Taylor, *Great Horned Owl,* 30 x 13 x 12, marble

Jeff Tritel, *Cycles,* 72 x 72 x 48, bronze

Bonese Collins Turner, *A Tale of the Jaguar King,*
40 x 30, watercolor

Richard Earl Thompson, *Opalascent Autumn,* 30 x 22, oil on canvas.
Courtesy: Richard Thompson Gallery, San Francisco

Janet Turner, *Red Shouldered Hawk Family,* 30 x 22, linocut serigraph

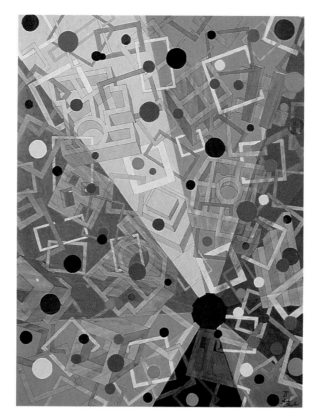

Jack Taylor, *Rock,* 40 x 30, acrylic

Joan Tanner, *Blue Blood,* 72 x 60, oil on canvas

Alan Thorpe, *Mother and Child,* 28 high, lacquer over wood with oak and padouk intarsia. Courtesy: Zantman Art Galleries, Carmel, CA

David Teachout, *Santa Cruz #27,* 76 x 72, acrylic on canvas

1190

Beny Tchaicovsky, *Morphus Prontis,* 40 x 40, acrylic on canvas

Henry C. Thompson, *The Finish,* 20 x 24, oil

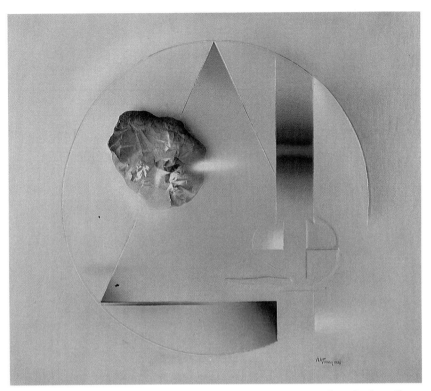

Herminigildo L. Tecson, *Perpendicular to the Star,* 20 x 23, acrylic, mixed media
Courtesy: Hermila Art Gallery. Photograph: Patti Dietrick

Pat Tolle, *KAPAA Postcard,* 40 x 48, oils

Louise Dudley Taft, *Boxes,* 21 x 19 x 19, 19 x 19 x 19, 21 x 19 x 16, painting

Pauline Ivancovich Teller, *Basket Weaver, N.M.,* 22 x 28, oil on canvas

Margaret TerryViale, *Rooted,* 11 x 15, paintstik on paper

Cindi Tanner, *Vermont Winter,* 13 x 21, watercolor

N. Tays-Campbell, *Live Oak,* 36 x 72, oil. Courtesy: Dr. and Mrs. Philip Sunshine

Tim Terrell, *Two Personages,* 16 x 20, cibachrome Courtesy: Ward Nasse Gallerie, NYC

Phyllis Thelen, *Moonlit Shore,* 24 x 36, embossed serigraph collage. Courtesy: Camille Noble

Beverly Trent, *Five Rosebuds,* 22 x 24, watercolor

Kent Twitchell, *Gary Lloyd Monument,* 2 stories, acrylic on concrete. Courtesy: City Seafoods

Ann Elizabeth Thiermann, *Kite Festival,* 42 x 72, acrylic on canvas. Collection of: San Francisco Hilton

Jane Ullman, *Phantasy,* 19 x 8, acrylic paint on stoneware

Marcus Uzilevsky, *Defectors,* 30 x 40, mixed media on canvas

Elda Dixler Unger, *The Family,* 78 x 83, acrylic

Manuel Unzueta, *Mask and Sarape,* 12 x 24, acrylics

Nico Van Den Heuvel, *Venus in Venice,*
15 x 11, mixed media

Carola Von Waldenfels, *Organ Cactus,* 86 x 20,
oil cans, metal, bucket

Exhibitions: Gallery 10, Washington, D.C.; Soho 20 Gallery, NYC *Education:* Cal. State-Fullerton; Golden West College *Dealer:* Overreact Gallery, Long Beach

She cites the abstract expressionist movement as the primary influence on her early paintings, which are, for the most part, large canvases incorporating textured papers in layers of acrylic and gel medium. These early investigations of the unconscious, through abstract drips and layers of paint, began, in 1981, to incorporate Jungian imagery in small implosive paintings and drawings. Falling figures, enigmatic cats, ladders, palm trees and cacti populated dark interiors. In 1984, the move to a large studio and the drive along the ocean through smog-filled sunsets led to her involvement with eco-humanist concerns. Today, with thick mixtures of oil paint and wax medium on large, unstretched canvases, she creates a fluid field, where blood-red skies stretch above the high horizon line. Images of palm trees, withered hands, crosses and isolated figures are enveloped and engulfed in the pulsating energy of the atmosphere. Mutating and interchangeable, they become metaphors for human survival in a world of pollution, nuclear threat, hostility and desolation.

TOYU, BEVERLY (Ceramist)
11431 St. Rte. 1, Box 311, Pt. Reyes, CA 94956

Born: 1944 *Exhibitions:* Blue Cross Headquarters, Oakland; Chinese Cultural Center, San Francisco *Education:* UC-Berkeley; Sonoma State U.

After studying ceramics, she received her master's degree in psychology and spent several years using ceramics as a therapeutic technique. Then in the mid-1970s, she began creating ceramic life masks, sometimes using a high-fire raku process. She treats the subjects face with Vaseline or mineral oil, then applies a plaster of paris mixture. After about five minutes, she removes the material and allows it to dry for a week before making the mask from clay pressed into the plaster of paris mold. Those masks undergo the raku process and are smoked in leaves and straw to produce unpredictable colors, iridescence, and a crackled surface. She uses many different types of glazes and paints to finish the masks. She believes that each mask is an embodiment of the individual's soul, and many of the masks have an archetypal appearance, a concrete manifestation of her universalist spiritual beliefs.

TRAVIS, ROBERT (Painter)
c/o Don Soker Contemporary Art, 871 Folsom St., San Francisco, CA 94107

Born: 1945 *Awards:* Ventura Prize Exhibtions: U. of Santa Clara Art Museum; San Francisco Exploratorium *Education:* U. of Texas-Austin; San Francisco State U. *Dealer:* Don Soker Contemporary Art, San Francisco

Throughout his twenty-five year career in the visual arts, his vision has been influenced by cartoonists and by Tao, Zen and other philosophies. His need for corrective lenses has led him to present perfect and imperfect ways of seeing as alternative interpretive perspectives. He works spontaneously on linen or cotton canvas using a full palette. Emphasizing more textual methods, such as heavy impasto of knifed, sprayed, rollered and thrown acrylics, his recent series of works, *Visual Jazz* challenges the viewer to meet the artist in interpreting his artistic vision.

TRENT, BEVERLY (Painter)
338 E. Hazel St., #7, Inglewood, CA 90302

Exhibitions: Los Angeles City College; Fine Arts Federation of Burbank *Education:* Art Institute of Chicago; UCLA

Her formal training covered all aspects of the fine arts, as well as fashion layout. Along the way, she chose watercolor as her medium. Her current abstract technique consists of fifty to one hundred veils or washes. This work is based on Goethe's theory of color and Steiner's work with watercolor veils. The paintings revolve around primitive images of women—their figures emerging through the layers of blue, violet, rose and golden colors. She employs this technique to render the soul in art.

TREPEL, ELAINE SARA
1416 Del Monte, Modesto, CA 95350

Born: 1950 *Awards:* Blue Ribbon, Riverbank Art Show *Exhibitions:* Phoenix Art Museum; Modest Junion College

Trained in both watercolors and older lithographic techniques, she bases her work on a strong technical background. Colors are fashioned to the moods of her subject matter, influenced by Oriental watercolor styles. Her watercolor technique is clean and crisp, using salt and other crystals to draw off pigment. Space and texture are explored through studies of Chinese scenes, using gold and subdued tones to underscore the traditional themes. Her landscape scenes include figuration, particularly children clothed in bright colors playing at the ocean and in backyards. The work is stylized, and she often employs techniques that give an aged look to the paintings.

TRINGALI, RICARDO (Painter, Sculptor)
4401 San Leandro, #25, Oakland, CA 94601

Born: 1951 *Awards:* Household Finance International Award; Beaux Arts Award *Collections:* Household Finance; Fairmont Hotels *Exhibitions:* Gallery 44, Oakland; Emanuel Walter Gallery *Education:* San Francisco Art Institute; Kendall School of Design

Turning from his earlier field paintings, with their rigid mathematical formalism, he began a series of figurative bronzes and mixed-media pieces. Work invokes a continuum wherein symbols from various hermetic sources are fixed in certain matrices. Figures based on classical history, but fixed in the schism of contemporary myths, are juxtaposed with like or dissimilar systems of thought—bonding or splintering, as they will, in the form of random or fixed events. Events function as a kind of dialogue or oracle, and, though seemingly random, indicate the work of a third hand.

TRITEL, JEFF (Sculptor)
19432 Richmar Lane, Grass Valley, CA 95949

Born: 1949 *Awards:* 1st Place, Sculpture, Old Town Tempe Art Festival, Tempe, AZ *Exhibitions:* Art Expo Cal, Los Angeles; Mini-Sculpture Walk, Los Angeles *Education:* UC-Santa Cruz

His background in mathematics and science strongly influenced his early work and is evident today in his love of pure form and logical progression. He lost interest in pure abstraction quite early on and finds himself drawn to depictions of the human condition. His work tends toward sculptural allegory, and he often uses characters and situations from classical mythology as the subjects of his work. These pieces, as well as other sculptures of human figures, embody opposing concepts such as biological and intellectual creativity, organic and mechanical forms, positive and negative spaces, and humor and seriousness. Currently, he is working in cast bronze and fabricated mixed media. Pieces range from 6 inches to 15 feet in height. His ongoing project is a ten-acre sculpture park in Grass Valley, California.

TRIVERS, JAMES (Painter)
4605 1/2 Ambrose Ave., Los Angeles, CA 90027

Born: 1948 *Exhibitions:* Newspace Gallery, Los Angeles; Barnstall Park, Los Angeles

His current work is also his best known. Drawing from the great works of western art history, he juxtaposes familiar images and renders them three-dimensionally. Viewed through cardboard 3-D glasses, these paintings readily reflect their comic book heritage. This humorous view of the Great Masters points up the standards of Western art criticism; the gray pallor surrounding the images suggests the moribund nature of much of the Western art tradition. He has a penchant for presenting a skewed view of traditionally serious subject matter. An earlier series of Forest Lawn Cemetery paintings, for example, was notable for its weird representation of heaven on earth. Recently, he has used his three-dimensional technique to render current events and the politics of everyday life.

TUNBERG, BILL (Sculptor, Multimedia Artist)
3021 Airport Ave., Santa Monica, CA 90405

Born: 1940 *Awards:* NEA Grant *Exhibitions:* Los Angeles County Museum of Art; Whitney Museum, NYC *Education:* USC

He constructs pieces from wood and a variety of found objects. These sculptures describe abstract experiences in concrete terms. Currently he assembles pieces with Japanese wood joints, and finishes the surfaces various ways, including eccentric methods of intarsia, rubber coating and hot laquers.

TURNER, BONESE COLLINS (Printmaker, Painter)
4808 Larkwood Ave., Woodland Hills, CA 91364

Awards: Purchase Award, Nebraska Libraries; National Watercolor Society *Collections:* Smithsonian Institute, Washington DC; Home Savings and Loan *Exhibitions:* White House, Washington, DC; Olympic Arts Exhibit, Los Angeles *Education:* Cal. State-Northridge *Dealer:* Orlando Gallery, Sherman Oaks

At first, she painted boldly colored abstract expressionist canvases with oils. She gradually developed a personal symbology and an interest in the psychological and mysterious. Through the 1960s, she worked with organic abstraction and experimented with oil and mixed media. As the 1970s dawned, the subtleties of light, color and transparency became important to her, and she experimented in watercolor, acrylic and printmaking media. Her works became less figurative, and she used an airbrush to emphasize veils of light and color. Two recent series involve the troubled Western economy, and personal, mysterious metaphors for the human experience. She has recently begun to make books and and three-dimensional watermedia pieces.

TURNER, JANET (Painter, Printmaker)
567 East Lassen, #701, Chico, CA 95926

Born: 1914 *Awards:* Guggenheim Grant; National Academy of Design Award *Collections:* Philadelphia Museum of Art; Metropolitan Museum of Art, NYC *Exhibitions:* Portland Art Museum; National Academy of Design *Education:* Stanford U.; Columbia U. *Dealer:* Associated American Artists, NYC

She draws her subjects from the wildlife and natural beauty of northern California and the American West, as well as from her extensive travels to wildlife refuges in Alaska and the Canadian Arctic. Studies with Thomas Hart Benton and Millard Sheets in the 1940s influenced her to focus on visual details; she has studied ornithology, botany and natural history in order to depict her subjects more accurately. By including abandoned buildings or other man-made objects, her recent prints and paintings have expressed aspects of a changing society and a concern for the preservation of the environment.

TUTTLE, PAUL (Furniture Artist)
885 Toto Canyon Rd., Santa Barbara, CA 93108

Born: 1918 *Awards:* Design Grant, NEA; International Design Products Award, American Society of Interior Designers *Exhibitions:* Santa Barbara Museum of Art; Design Source

He creates distinctive art furniture for domestic and professional settings. His design sense was shaped by study with Bauhaus disciple Alvin Lustig and by his participation in Frank Lloyd Wright's Taliesin West Fellowship. Later, he worked in Switzerland and Italy, absorbing European modernist design principles. His furniture is characterized by sweeping forms, smooth lines, and an ingenious mix of materials which highlights their intrinsic qualities. He works in wood, steel, glass, leather, textiles, cane and hides, striving to create functional furniture which also presents an artistic vision.

TWITCHELL, KENT (Painter, Muralist)
2160 Sunset Blvd., Los Angeles, CA 90026

Born: 1942 *Awards:* NEA "Art in Public Places;" Calif. Arts Council Grant *Collections:* Valparaiso Museum, IN; Peter and Eileen Norton, Santa Monica *Exhibitions:* Los Angeles Municipal Art Gallery; Loyola Marymount U. *Education:* Otis Art Institute, Los Angeles; Cal. State-Los Angeles

After working during the early '60s as an illustrator in England for the Air Force, he moved to Los Angeles and began doing anonymous "street art" and psychedelic designs. In 1971 he returned to realism, painting a two-story portrait of Steve McQueen on a downtown house and a 45-foot-long mural of Strother Martin on the side of a store in Hollywood. He has since painted over 75 portraits of California movie stars and visual artists for murals from Torrance to San Simeon. Always searching for the ultimate colors and materials to withstand everything from sun, smog and rain to common vandalism, he now uses special, heavily pigmented, hard-resin acrylic paints. At close range, his paintings appear as intricate, hard-edge, abstract designs, but the eye resolves the patterns into soft shapes and textures. His finished murals, studio paintings and drawings typically depict their lone subject or group of subjects standing and looking straight at the viewer.

TYLER, TIMOTHY CARROL (Painter)
P.O. Box 2591, Glendale, AZ 85311

Jeff Tritel, *Violinist II,* 27 inches, bronze

Beverly Trent, *The Hidden Face,* 28 x 22, watercolor

Ron Tatro, *Shape Vision #3,* 34 x 38 x 25, polychrome steel

Kent Twitchell, *Edward Ruscha Monument,* 6 stories, acrylic on concrete. Courtesy: Los Angeles Job Corps

Cindi Tanner, *Candelaria's Roses,* 22 x 17, watercolor,

Janet Turner, *Snowy Owls: Tundra Series* 29 x 22, linocut serigraph

Born: 1958 *Awards:* "Best of Show," 26th Annual Glendale Art Exhibition *Collections:* Western National Warantee Corp., Scottsdale; City of Glendale, Arizona *Exhibitions:* ART-USA Premier Exhibition, Grand Junction, CO *Education:* Vladen, Stiha, Santa Fe, NM; East Central U., OK

His early work was dedicated to the traditional school of painting as distinguished from photo-realism and was influenced by Bierstadt, Church and Homer. Sargent, Fechin and Degas are the major influences on his mature work. In these paintings, primarily portraits, the brushstroke is evident, the paint thick, with a close concern for value, edge, color "temperature," accurate design and drawing. Most of the work is commissioned, including some large, complex murals.

TYSON, BOB (Photographer)
1767 Yorktown Rd., San Mateo, CA 94402

Born: 1945 *Awards:* Artists-in-Schools Grant, California Arts Council; Individual Artist Grant, Peninsula Community Foundation *Collections:* Stanford U.; Ucross Foundation, Ucross, NY *Exhibitions:* 400 Hamilton Gallery, Palo Alto; Arts Council of San Mateo County *Education:* Stanford U. *Dealer:* Betsy Gates, Artfocus, Foster City

During a career in geology, he discovered certain ideas he would be able to express only in visual terms. This prompted him to take up photography. Through his photographs, he strives to elicit the romantic mystery he experiences in the look of the world. Like photographer Garry Winogrand, he is curious about the way things appear, and how they will photograph. Strongly influenced by photographers, including Timothy O'Sullivan, Edward Weston and Robert Frank, and printmakers, from Goya to Nathan Oliveira, he especially enjoys discovering in the photograph the power to celebrate simultaneously the outward appearance of the object and the meaning of its image realized in the print. His works include miniature palladium-platinum contact prints of landscape, portraiture and interiors, and mammoth silver enlargements of the human face. The smaller, introspective photographs explore the transformation of the seen world through the photograph, as a series of hand-made prints. At the other extreme in scale, the enlarged faces reveal shimmering and intimate optical details. In their limited clues to environment, and in the presence of the faces themselves, these photographs are not so much individual portraits as they are images of the human being.

ULLMAN, JANE F. (Sculptor)
800 Woodacres Rd., Santa Monica, CA 90402

Born: 1908 *Awards:* Gertrude Stein Portrait, Culoz, France; Los Angeles County Prize *Collections:* Los Angeles Music Center; Museum of Contemporary Art, Chicago *Exhibitions:* Artcore, Los Angeles; Bowers Museum, Santa Ana *Education:* School of the Art Institute of Chicago; Juliens, Paris, France

Initially a painter, she shifted to sculpture after studying with Alexander Archipenko. Her early sculptures are fired-clay and bronze-cast abstract pieces—portraits and expressions of love, hate and fear. Other, more non-objective work is carved from marble and stone. She has recently been working in painted clay forms, carving carra marble with power tools to rough it out. Most of the work, however, is still carved by hand. Her work is becoming increasingly non-objective, many pieces featuring blocks of various sizes and shapes that appear stacked together, often in gravity-defying arrangements.

ULMAN, ALISON (Sculptor)
136 Alpha St., San Francisco, CA 94134

Born: 1955 *Awards:* Honors in Art, UC-Santa Cruz *Exhibitions:* Bridge Gallery, Santa Cruz; Southern Exposure Gallery, San Francisco *Education:* UC-Santa Cruz

During her formal training, she explored surrealism in a variety of media including wood, plastic, fiberglass, and clay. Although her sculptures of the time were bold and often enormous, her touch was subtle. In her works, she strives to create a lone aesthetic incident that hurtles the viewer from a world of realistic beauty to an engaging matrix of cryptic irony. Her own house is the subject and medium for her recent work. She has turned this normal living situation into an "art ranch" with sculptures and installations at every interior and exterior turn. With carpenter's chalk and agricultural lime, she painted *Chicken Little was Right!*, an enormous puzzle-piece of sky viewable from her bedroom window.

ULTAN, LAWANDA (Painter, Ceramist)
2955 Shasta Rd., Berkeley, CA 94708

Born: 1931 *Awards:* Merit Award, Berkeley Art Center; Merit Award, #1 Market Plaza *Collections:* Union Carbide, San Ramon; Nepenthe Corp., Big Sur *Exhibitions:* Interart, San Francisco; UPB Gallery, Berkeley *Education:* Merritt College, Oakland; UC-Berkeley

She works in clay, as well as painting and printmaking. Using the figure, particularly faces, she creates mood and presence in both realistic and abstracted styles. Presently her work is influenced by the masks, dances and music of Bali, where she recently visited. In her monotypes and paintings, colors are primarily earth tones, inspired by internal visions.

UNDERWOOD, MARIA GARAY (Painter)
4626 Underwood Way, Sacramento CA 95823

Born: 1942 *Awards:* 1st Place, Northern California Artists *Exhibitions:* Crocker-Kingsley Museum; Cosumnes River Gallery *Education:* Sacramento City College

After years of painting with felt pens and watercolors, she studied watercolors with Woody Hansen and developed an expressionistic style, exploring color in more depth. The philosophy and styles of Forney and Picasso influenced her development of feelings and subjects on paper. The wet-on-dry-on-paper paintings combine expressionistic and abstract themes in bold colors, using diverse subject matter that harmonizes with defined shapes and colors. Through these images, painted in *plein air*, she balances the realistic and the abstract. The abstract fantasy of the pieces is exemplified by her painting *Downtown*, showing a man and a woman in a doorway, their faces protruding slightly, yet undistorted; the boldness of her colors creates the abstract effect.

UNGER, ELDA DIXLER (Painter)
6970 Wildlife Rd., Malibu, CA 90265

Born: 1930 *Awards:* Chicago Young Artists Competition; Merit Scholarship, School of the Art Institute of Chicago *Exhibitions:* Fairmont Gallery, Dallas; Museum of Science and Industry, Los Angeles *Education:* Goddard College; School of Art Institute of Chicago; Sorbonne, Paris *Dealer:* Francine Ellman Gallery

Herminigildo L. Tecson, *Stone Composition,* 31 x 31, acrylic, mixed media.
Courtesy: Hermila Art Gallery. Photograph: Patti Dietrick

Manuel Unzueta, *The Call,* 30 x 40, acrylics

Her strongest influences are Picasso and Carl Jung. The work is representation of impressions and other subconscious experiences; she draws material for her major work from her training as an art therapist. Continually delineating and defining the relationship of the finished work and the artist's unconscious, she creates strong-figured images, abstracted and often outlined in black to emphasize the element of design and the sense of spatial structure. Her palette tends towards pinks and reds highlighted by pale greens, whites and yellows. Non-figurative pieces concentrate entirely on form and structure, laying on organic grids within which flower-like areas of bright color float. Her new work, *The Joy of Life*, which depicts a figure holding a child in its arms as they emerge from a flower, externalizes the healing effect of art through lyrically abstract lines and direct symbolism of shared unconscious.

UNZUETA, MANUEL (Painter)
541 Mills Way, Goleta, CA 93117

Born: 1949 *Awards:* Jaycees of America; Outstanding Artist, UC-Santa Barbara Alumni Association *Collections:* Del Parker Collection, Fresno *Exhibitions:* Juarez Museum of Art, Mexico; La Cienega Gallery, Los Angeles *Education:* UC-Santa Barbara; Santa Barbara City College

Study in Europe, while enrolled at Santa Barbara Community College, exposed him to the Renaissance masters, but it was the Orozco murals in Guadalajara that truly solidified his vision as an artist. Since 1970, he has designed and painted more than 20 murals in Mexico, California and the Southwest. His fourth, completed inside the Santa Barbara Chicano community center, La Casa de la Raza, shows five hands, each of a different color, reaching skyward toward the light. He is attracted to muralism's power to express, and by the way in which its very presence encourages collective consciousness. Still, personal elements imbue his socially oriented work. His style reflected Mexican expressionism and American abstraction for a time, during which modern, non-objective imagery was utilized. He has since developed a strong interest in Southwestern iconography and Mexican Indian mysticism. Recent canvases in oil have combined Mexican-American themes with indian facial images. Extreme abstraction highlights emotional aspects, and bright colors invite attention. Recent full color posters extend his audience, further bringing the Chicano identity into public consciousness.

URISTA, ARTURO (Painter)
3756 E. FLoral Dr., Los Angeles, CA 90063

Born: 1961 *Exhibitions:* Galeria Otra Vez, East Los Angeles; Fringe Festival, JACCC, Los Angeles *Education:* Cal. State-Los Angeles

He sees himself as an educator. He is interested in moving viewers of his art to a wider consciousness of the issues that effect individuals and their environment. He is particularly involved in the politics of East Los Angeles, and in the relation between the Chicano art of this area and the art of western Los Angeles. In his most typical paintings, he incorporates lettering as a stylistic element, with imagery drawn from pre-Columbian, Aztec and Mayan art. He is, however, not interested so much in reworking these ancient images as he is driven to keep Mexico's history alive for the Hispanic community, by fusing traditional forms with contemporary art. Recently, he has completed a set of nylon silkscreen banners for the Stock Exchange Exhibition Show. Executed in vibrant colors, these banners tell the ancient story of the four goddesses of the fifth sun.

URTON, ELAINE (Painter, Printmaker)
525 Mira Monte Dr., Santa Barbara, CA 93109

Born: 1914 *Exhibitions:* Esthers Bear Gallery, Santa Barbara; Santa Barbara Art Association *Education:* California College of Arts & Crafts, Santa Barbara *Dealer:* Vallery Art Association, Walnut Creek

For many years watercolor was her medium of choice. In the past six years, however, she has been experimenting with Indian wood blocks—the blocks used in India to decorate fabrics—to create her own designs. Juxtaposing a variety of patterns, building up layers of different designs and colors, she continues to explore the possibilities of this new tool. Today, she remains very interested in the art work of China and India, and still works with the wood blocks, though recently she has gone one step further: working to combine her prints with collage.

UZILEVSKY, MARCUS (Painter, Printmaker)
P.O. Box 166, Woodacre, CA 94973

Born: 1937 *Collections:* Los Angeles County Museum of Art; Portland Art Museum *Exhibitions:* Huntsville (Ala.) Museum of Art; Ryan/Johnson Gallery, Fairfax *Education:* School of Art and Design *Dealer:* Oaksprings Impressions, Forest Knolls

His optimistic career has been characterized by a variety of styles. His "Linearism" of the early 1970s was a series of abstracted landscape drawings inspired by the Marin Hills. He soon moved to a "Soft Focus Linearism" which involved the use of a straight edge to create impressionist/calligraphic landscapes. He went through a pointillist stage but then shifted to his "Silk Road Series" which consisted of large, gestural, watercolor paintings made with a large, Oriental calligraphy brush. His "Musical Series" involved score-like images and colors that were related to sound vibrations. The works he refers to as "Lyrical Expressionism" are abstracted canvases involving dripping of acrylics. More recently he has produced photo-collage, and the highly patterned "Memphis Series." His current "Nuevo Series" involves bold color combinations, in curvilinear and straight-line spatial differentiations.

VACCARINO, ROBIN (Sculptor)
3593 Berry Dr., Studio City, CA 91604

Awards: NEA Fellowship; California Arts Council Grant *Collections:* Los Angeles County Museum of Art; Santa Barbara Museum of Art *Exhibitions:* Cal. State-Long Beach; Security Pacific Plaza, Los Angeles *Education:* Otis Art Institute

His work has been strongly oriented toward classical sculpture in both structure and composition from his earliest exhibitions. But often within this context, and within the composition itself, there are counterpoints in the use of color, shape and space. These evoke questions concerning the formal foundation of classicism and open up the possibility of alternative means of approaching the problem of visual and spatial construction. He usually manages to strike a balance between these opposing elements. Recently as his pieces have grown larger, the classical support of the form has grown less assertive, and he has employed color to undermine any precise view of spatial relations, there-

Elda Dixler Unger, *Close Call,* 24 x 18, oil

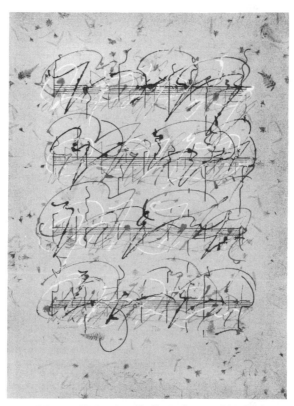

Marcus Uzilevsky, *Shalimar Sonata,* 24 x 30,
watercolor on handmade paper

by creating a constantly changing configuration of forms.

VAIL, ROGER (Photographer)
1148 Fremont Way, Sacramento, CA 95818

Born: 1945 *Collections:* Art Institute of Chicago; San Francisco Museum of Modern Art *Exhibitions:* Rena Bransten Gallery, San Francisco; San Francisco Museum of Modern Art *Education:* School of the Art Institute of Chicago *Dealer:* Rena Bransten Gallery, San Francisco

His work in the 1980s has explored man-made structures that inhabit the natural world. Night photographs with long exposures show light trails of cars, stars and planes juxtaposed against the stillness and mass of ships and buildings, exploring time and the symbolic relationships to the unseen subject of the photograph—man. Said Carol Harmel of Afterimage, "Vail's images reach out towards extending the vocabulary of the known while retaining their grounding in phenomena. The tension results in a sense of exhilaration." The most massive of modern structures, such as oceangoing freighters, become ghostly apparitions or reveal the natural forms from which human beings have extracted a mere suggestion of majesty.

VALA, ROBERT (Painter)
440 Cliff Dr., Aptos, CA 95003

Born: 1930 *Awards:* Prix de Paris, L'Art Moderne, Paris *Collections:* Levi Strauss Co., San Francisco *Exhibitions:* United Nations Building, NYC; Bohman Gallery, Stockholm *Education:* California College of Arts and Crafts; Art Students League, NYC *Dealer:* Will Stone, San Francisco

At the age of 17 he began his career by designing sets for the ballet and opera in association with Eugene Dunkel and Michel Larionov. During the early 1950s he worked for the Ballet Russe. Strongly influenced by the fantasy of the ballet and theater world, he felt a kinship with the romantics. His recent mystic painting rests between romanticism and surrealism. He paints in a mixture of acrylic and oil glazes. The spray of counterpointing color on the surface of his work comes from theater painting technique. In a recent series, he documents the cast, costumes, and sets of a fictional opera company.

VALENTINE, DEWAIN (Sculptor)
69 Market St., Venice, CA 90291

Born: 1936 *Awards:* Guggenheim Fellowship; NEA Grant *Collections:* Los Angeles County Museum of Art; Stanford University Art Museum *Exhibitions:* Los Angeles County Museum of Art; Contemporary Arts Center, Hawaii *Education:* U. of Colorado; Yale-Norfolk Art School

His early sculptures in the mid-1960s were made from cast solid polyester and fiberglass-reinforced polyester. Later that decade he progressed to a single-pour casting technique for large-scale works, exploring geometric forms such as pyramids, wedges, slabs and circles. By the late 1970s, he was working in laminated glass, which allows him to create pieces for outdoor environments. Interior space, light and the inherent qualities of the materials—translucent color, reflectivity—play against the massive scale, creating ethereal works that recall the sea and the sky. The pieces retain their strong geometricity.

VALERIO, DAWN (Painter)
313 Sheffield Ave., Mill Valley, CA 94941

Born: 1935 *Exhibitions:* Tiburon Affair Gallery, Tiburon; American Zephyr Gallery, San Francisco *Education:* Massachusetts School of Art; Boston School of Practical Arts

Early in her career, she worked as a graphic artist and illustrator to support her fine art work. She lived in Paris during the mid- to late-1950s and studied with Andre Lhote and S.I.U. Hayter. Her paintings during this period were cubist. Searching for a freer mode of expression, she began using amorphous shapes inspired by nature and by her own inner emotions. Painting in oil on canvas, her recent works are characterized by muted shapes and slashing, bold colors. Her fascination with nature continues, and she attempts to capture the movement and freshness of nature in her work.

VALLANCE, JEFFREY (Multimedia Artist, Conceptual Artist)
20764 Stephanie Dr., Canoga Park, CA 91306

Born: 1955 *Exhibitions:* Monterey Peninsula Museum of Art; Shoshona Wayne Gallery, Santa Monica *Education:* Cal. State-Northridge; Otis Art Institute *Dealer:* Rosamund Felsen Gallery, Los Angeles

His art, inspired by the highly conceptual work of Chris Burden, has an earnest, childlike quality—indeed, so earnest that political leaders and celebrities, to whom he sends letters, poorly executed drawings and other articles, assume he is a child; their responses, which he uses in his art, are often patronizing and condescending. Other paintings and constructions incorporate autobiographical images from the artist's past, TV images, and kitschy icons. His recent work has been influenced by travels to South Pacific islands; in one series, he recounts his journey in comic-book style. Critic Suzanne Muchinic calls him "an artist who approaches everything with wonder and renders all absurd."

VALLEJO, LINDA (Mixed Media Artist)
2477 Baltic Ave., Long Beach, CA 90810

Born: 1951 *Awards:* Artist-in-Residence, Calif. Arts Council; Brody Arts Fund Individual Fellowship, Calif. Community Foundation *Collections:* Atlantic Richfield Corp.; Self-Help Graphics and Art, Los Angeles *Exhibitions:* U. of Texas, Austin; LA Impressions Gallery, Los Angeles *Education:* Whittier College, Whittier, CA; Cal. State-Long Beach

After receiving formal training in printmaking, she began to tear, fold and pulp old etchings, lithographs and monotypes into handmade paper. Her first series of mixed-media handmade paper sculptures resulted from this process. These works were geometric in formula, influenced in form by the pyramid configurations of Mexico and Egypt and in color by the Impressionists and Fauvists. She began to include found objects such as glass gems, shells, fabric, metal pieces, leather and fiber, along with wood. This led to the use of massive found tree fragments as armatures for heroic, figurative and metamorphic forms in handmade paper. These forms recall archetypes and mythic figures of Mexican/Chicano origin. Several works are dedicated to the elements, animals and aspects of nature.

VAN DEN HEUVEL, NICO (Painter, Mixed Media Artist)
20922 Keller Rd., Topanga, CA 90290

Jane Ullman, *Yin & Yang,* 23 x 18 x 19, bronze

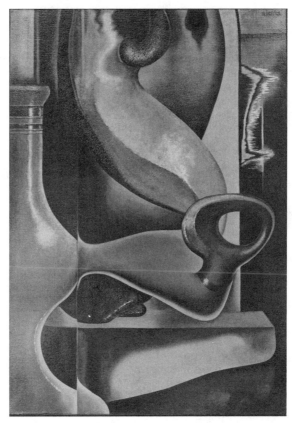

Nico Van Den Heuvel, *Cologne Blue,* 36 x 26, oil and sand
on linen. Photograph: Tom Mitchell

Born: 1929 *Exhibitions:* Duff Gray Gallery, San Pedro; C'est La Vie Gallery, Topanga *Education:* Academy of Fine Arts, Rotterdam

His early training in advertising design left him with a lasting taste for color and form. Inspired by the works of Gris and Braque, he decided to become a cubist painter and collage artist. By the late 1950s, he felt he had exhausted the possibilities of cubism and turned to the 16th- and 17th-century Dutch Masters for a departure in style and subject matter. He incorporated their use of intimate lighting effects into an evolving abstract-surrealist style which defied easy categorization. The work of Abstract Expressionists such as Kline, Appel, Pollock and Vilumsons have influenced his own slash, drip and spatter methods which, when brought into what he calls "controlled isolation," enable him to juxtapose values of tone and texture. He also creates hard-edged geometric paintings which he calls "one-two-three's." The underlying concept of these works is to magnify the insignificant through the stages of production, until the process itself becomes the focus. His other work includes assemblage, junk sculpture and kinetic and robotic sculpture programmed for sound and movement.

VAN FLEET, ELLEN (Mixed Media Artist)
1105 Alamos Ave., Sacramento, CA 95815

Born: 1942 *Awards:* NEA Fellowship; California Arts Council Grant *Collections:* La Jolla Museum of Contemporary Art *Exhibitions:* Whitney Museum of American Art, NYC; California State Capital, Sacramento *Education:* UC-Davis

She received her MFA from UC-Davis during the 1960s, and her fellow graduate students included Steve Kaltenbach and Bruce Naumen, both of whom she credits with having exerted an influence on her work, as did faculty members William Wiley, Wayne Thiebaud and Ralph Johnson. Upon completing her studies, she moved to New York City and began working as an installation artist. She returned to California to teach at the University of California at San Diego and continued to work with multimedia installation pieces. Recently she has visited and painted various pictograph and petroglyph sites in the United States and Mexico.

VANGSGARD, AMY (Sculptor)
517 N. Beachwood Dr., Los Angeles, CA 90004

Born: 1955 *Awards:* Artist's Liaison Award; Society of Illustrators West *Collections:* Ketchum Advertising; Climax Clothing *Exhibitions:* Taylor/Gratzier Gallery, Los Angeles; Gene Sinser Gallery, Los Angeles

After receiving a formal education in commercial illustration, she began making assemblages in the manner of Marisol and Joseph Cornell. In these complete environments, or "contexts of understanding", she used found objects to capture underlying spirits or essences of persons, places, or ideas. These essences form the basis of her narrative style. She now works in bronze and has evolved a figurative imagery based on dreams and expressions of personal growth. In her art she explores a full spectrum of feelings, from fanciful, lighthearted fun, to more serious statements of the sublime.

VAN SANT, TOM (Painter, Sculptor)
146 Entrada Dr., Santa Monica, CA 90402

Born: 1931 *Awards:* Southern Calif. American Institute of Architects Art and Craftsmanship Award

Collections: King Hussein of Jordan; Sir Roland Penrose, London *Exhibitions:* Institute of Contemporary Art, London; Stedelijk Museum, Amsterdam *Education:* Stanford U.; Otis Art Institute, Los Angeles

During the 1970s, he was known for creating large, concrete sculptures from waste molds. He has created more than 70 major sculptures and mural commissions in public places including LAX, the Inglewood Civic Center and Honolulu International Airport. During that period, he also fabricated giant kites of fiberglas and nylon up to 800 feet long. In the '80s, he continues to work on architectural commissions and on kites; he is also interested in remote sensing from satellites. While a fellow at the MIT Center for Advanced Visual Studies, he created the first images on the surface of the earth to be seen from space. The project, entitled *Reflections From Earth*, used mirrors to reflect sunlight back to a Landsat satellite, transmitting the image of a giant eye. The entire construction was 1 1/2 miles across—100,000 times larger than the human eye. Other projects include the use of a scanning electron microscope to etch the image of an eye in a crystal of salt 1/4 micron in size—100,000 times smaller than the human eye.

VAN SCOYOC, LESLIE (Sculptor)
P.O. Box 6863, San Francisco, CA 94101

Born: 1961 *Exhibitions:* New Langton Arts, San Francisco; Richmond Art Center *Education:* San Francisco Art Institute

Her primary image has been the turning magic circle (mandala) traditionally used in situations of psychic confusion and perplexity. She asks the viewer to personally spin the wheel or turn a switch which activates it. The pieces are self lit and they exist in shadowy, magical environments. When in motion they become striking combinations of movement, flashing light, and minimal color. Her smaller pieces are landscapes, unsafe places to explore or escape to. Her larger pieces have become more complex and more machine-like. With hooks and nets she creates the impression of a trap or lure. Her materials include wood, glass, cloth and metal.

VAN YOUNG, OSCAR (Painter)
2293 Panorama Ter., Los Angeles, CA 90039

Born: 1906 *Awards:* Bartels Prize, Art Institute of Chicago; Purchase Award, Chaffey College, Ontario *Collections:* Frye Museum, Seattle; Los Angeles County Museum *Exhibitions:* Corcoran Gallery, Los Angeles; Art Institute of Chicago *Education:* California State U. *Dealer:* Zantman Galleries, Palm Desert, Carmel

He works spontaneously with layers of oil on canvas, creating paintings rich with red and rose overtones. He interprets the inner life of cities. His early Chicago canvases were overcast, gloomy slum scenes. After moving to California, his colors brightened and he created lyrical, jewel-like scenes of the state's underclass. Born in Vienna, he has been influenced by El Greco, Rembrandt, Kokoschka and Soutine. In each of his works there is a strong relationship between color and form. His technique reflects the influence of the Post-Impressionists and the Fauves. He has recently been developing paintings from sketches he made while traveling in Europe.

VARES, KEN (Painter, Sculptor)
208 Goodwin St., Hayward CA 94544

Oscar Van Young, *The Assistant Chef,* 28 x 22, oil on canvas.
Photograph: I. Serisawa

Marlinde Von Ruhs, *The Sun of Guadalajara,* 24 x 20,
oils and goldleaf. Olympic Committee, Mexico City

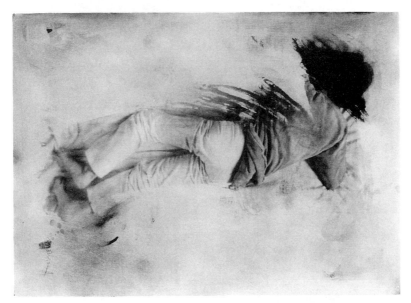

von **Greyerz-Monroe,** *from Positions I,* 30 x 42, hand-applied photo-emulsion and oil on paper

Valerio, *Life is But a Dream,* 40 x 60, oil

Tom Van Sant, *California Migrations,* 156 x 1440, acrylic on canvas. Crocker National Bank, Los Angeles, CA.
Photographer: William Eastbrook

Linda Vidal, *The Rising,* 48 x 96 x 4, acrylic and resin on celotex panel. Photograph: Hedi B. Desuyo

Born: 1917 *Exhibitions:* Artists Co-op, San Francisco; Galerie de Blanche, San Francisco

A former U.S. Air Force artist during World War II, he sculpts in cast bronze, aluminum, welded metal, ceramic and fiberglass. The details he gives to his figurative sculptures such as apron ties or boots, and the postures of the figures themselves, reflect a keen eye for detail. His acrylic paintings are illustrative and cartoonish and explore perspective and scale. In *Nickel Ferry*, an active diorama set in a bathroom, he depicts toy trains, steamships and soldiers surrounding the bathtub and perched on the sink. Two of his paintings have been reproduced as posters.

VAS, SAGI (Painter)
2225 Duxbury Circle, Los Angeles, CA 90034

Born: 1938 *Awards:* 3rd Place, National Competition, British Graphic Design *Collections:* U. of Strathclyde, Glasglow *Exhibitions:* Ickikawa Gallery, Los Angeles; Senior Eye Gallery, San Francisco U. *Education:* Cal. State-Northridge

The sensuality of O'Keeffe's paintings, as well as a surrealistic blend of reality and illusion are apparent influences in her work. Her early drawings and paintings represented her experiences, moods, and observations. Working in strong blues and reds, which symbolize coolness and warmth, with touches of white, which symbolize light, these paintings featured human figures frankly expressing their joys and sorrows. During the following decade, she created a new series of more subtle, dreamlike paintings executed in an expanded palette. Babies and flowers are frequent images in her work. They appear in association with human figures and express the connection between the figures and the forces of nature, rebirth and renewal. She is also concerned with evoking the spiritual through her art, using the nude to represent the naked soul.

VASQUEZ, BRUCE (Painter)
3726 W. Iris Ave., Visalia, CA

Born: 1950 *Awards:* Scholastic Magazine Gold Key Award in Graphics *Exhibitions:* University High School Designers' Showcase House, San Francisco; Cal. State-Fresno *Education:* California College of Arts and Crafts, Oakland; American Conservatory Theater, San Francisco

After formal training in figurative oil painting, he developed an individual, figurative, expressionist style of crowquill penstroke in black ink and colored wash. This style was influenced by the linear work of Matisse and Picasso. In 1978 he met English interior designer, Michael Vincent, whose brilliantly detailed interiors encouraged Vasquez to explore the essence of his style in larger, environmental terms. Progressing from delicate eight-and-a-half-by-eleven-inch drawings of mythological, religious and literary characters, he has recently embraced twenty-two-by-twenty-eight-inch, brushstroked India ink drawings of characters of everyday life brought to life through chiaroscuro reminiscent of the late paintings of Rembrandt. He recently began experiments to bring his "linear" style to ceramic, fabric, and furniture design.

VAPOUR, MEL (Video Artist, Mixed Media Artis)
See Brulc, D.

VELARDE, LYDIA (Painter)
P.O. Box 1147, Poway, CA 92064

Born: 1951 *Awards:* Recognition Award, Chaffey Community Art Association; 2nd Place, Watercolor, Fallbrook Art Association, Fallbrook *Exhibitions:* San Diego Art Institute; Watercolor West XIX

She has recently given up pen and ink and now works only in watercolor. Her paintings are realistic, influenced by Winslow Homer and other realist artists. Landscapes and harbor scenes have gradually taken over from more figurative subjects. She makes detailed watercolor sketches, then applies a layer of color (including white) to the painting. Then she adds shadow and repeats these two steps. Her bright, selective palette includes crimson, ultramarine blue, cadmium orange, burnt sienna and burnt umber. Her paintings are usually rather large (24 by 34 inches). She has recently been working on a painting dedicated to the spirit of the American West. This earth-tone still life features cowboy gear: a saddle and stirrups, a blanket and pillow.

VELARDI, E.J., JR. (Painter)
9513 Jellico Ave., Northridge, CA 91325

Born: 1924 *Awards:* Purchase Award, Henry Ward Ranger Fund; Crescent Cardboard Purchase Award, National Watercolor Society 67th Annual *Collections:* Springfield Art Museum, MO; Crown-Zellerbach, San Francisco *Education:* U. of Illinois *Dealer:* Orlando Gallery, Sherman Oaks

Intuition guides him in his odd juxtaposition of images. At first he painted non-figuratively, but after a number of years, he felt the need for a further use of symbols and desired to extend the expressive content of his work. He then began to paint figuratively. The mood of his current work is somber. One canvas may contain such disparate images as a portion of a house, a giant strawberry and a giant gloved hand, while another contains a fedora in front of a window pane in front of a sky with a cookie in it. He paints with the "forgiving" medium of egg tempera and achieves velvet surfaces and rich, permanent colors. "The unpredictable is done at some risk, but when the gods are kind, magic can result," he says. His work is inspired by de Chirico and Max Klinger.

VELDKAMP, DEBORAH (Painter)
383 Margarita Ave., San Luis Obispo, CA 93401

Born: 1953 *Awards:* 1st Prize, Alameda County Fair; 2nd Prize, Southeast Alaska State Fair *Exhibitions:* Adobe Gallery, Castro Valley; Art Center Gallery, San Luis Obispo *Education:* Art Center College of Design; California College of Arts and Crafts

She concentrates primarily on figurative painting, finding color and humor in portraits of animals and children. Transparent washes and glazes in oil are preferred in conjunction with her à la prima technique, though she also uses watercolor, conte, pastel and charcoal. The member of a family replete with artists, she began studying figure and portraiture with German artist Peter Blos at age fourteen. She studied at the Art Center College of Design in Los Angeles and later worked with Lorser Feitelson and Harry Carmean. She continues to be drawn to the figure as the most challenging subject. Following its unpredicatble lines, she aims for the three-dimensional effect of strong light on a flat surface. Her representations are more impressionistic than realistic, though she always seeks recognizable images. Recent work in oil include a series on chickens in small scale and landscapes painted "on the spot."

E.J. Velardi, Jr., *The Magician's Gift,* 25 x 20, egg tempera

Robert Vala, *The Source,* 16 x 20, mixed media.
Courtesy: Will Stone Gallery, San Francisco

VENABLE, SUSAN (Sculptor)
214 S. Venice Blvd., Venice, CA 90291

Born: 1944 *Awards:* Cash Award, California Crafts XIII; Hortense Fishbaugh Memorial Scholarship, UCLA *Collections:* Los Angeles Institute of Contemporary Art; Sheraton Corporation, Los Angeles *Exhibitions:* Maloney Butler Gallery, Los Angeles; Wichita Art Museum *Education:* UCLA; Cal. State-Dominguez Hills *Dealer:* Maloney Butler Gallery, Los Angeles

Departing from her traditional training in sculpture and drawing, she began to explore non-traditional weaving materials and techniques. After studying in Spain, she became involved with site-specific, ephemeral installations. From there she developed a body of work in which the structure and the surface became the most important factors. Her recent work consists of large-scale wall constructions of painted steel grids and copper wire. The structure its relationship to the surface remain important elements while she investigates illusions of shape through changes in depth and in the colors of the wire. The wire is used for its gestural capacities, hearkening back to her early interest in drawing.

VENDITTI, JERRY (Painter)
8800 Cider Spring Rd., Sebastopol, CA 95442

Born: 1942 *Exhibitions:* Altermann and Morris, Dallas; Zantman Galleries, Palm Desert *Dealer:* Altermann and Morris, Dallas; Zantman Galleries, Palm Desert & Carmel

A master of trompe l'oeil painting, his precise, yet mellow, renditions of people and artifacts show an elegant sense of composition. He has been compared to 19th-century precisionist, William H. Harnett. There is a definite regional character about his depictions of Native Americans, Indian pottery, baskets, beadwork and textiles of the Southwest. Other, more general, topics include fruits or vegetables, musical instruments and old photographs or printed material. He has recently been painting still lifes and portraits. "Art is like life—limitless in form and infinite in expression. I plan to experiment!"

VENTI, ART (Painter)
2401 Santa Fe Ave., #204, Los Angeles, CA 90058

Born: 1949 *Awards:* 1st Prize, Berkeley Art Center *Exhibitions:* Center for the Visual Arts, Oakland; Century Gallery, Sylmar *Education:* School of the Visual Arts, NYC

Influenced by Dali's remote landscapes and dream/nightmare imagery, his style shifted from traditional to surrealistic. He also greatly admired Escher's transformation images, and completed several complex graphite drawings of dreamscapes and changing symbolism. He was involved in the 1960s hallucinogenic art movement, using that form to express his imagination. His later work is more impressionistic and expressionistic, with a looser style and more spontaneity. He uses acrylics when he wants to paint quickly and aggressively, applying paint in bold brushstrokes, using the medium's quick-drying quality to build layers of color and form. His "Endangered Wildlife" series, which includes human, as well as animal, figures, was painted in this manner. He uses oils when spending more time on a painting—often one that has been been worked out in several sketches beforehand.

VEST, DEBORAH (Painter)
744 G St., #107, San Diego, CA 92101

Born: 1954 *Awards:* Public Arts Grant, Grapevine, TX *Exhibitions:* Nouveau Huevo Gallery, San Diego *Education:* North Texas State U. *Dealer:* Nouveau Huevo Gallery, San Diego

After college, she began travelling, spending time in the southwestern U.S. and central Mexico, working with sketches and watercolors. Using the sketches as a visual journal, she was primarily interested in portraying her experiences and observations of people. She has since settled in San Diego and is now operating out of a studio there. She has switched from watercolor to oil or acrylic on canvas. Primarily influenced by Modern-Impressionists, she is very interested in seascapes, where "surf meets turf." She recently embarked upon a triptych of four skateboarders and a roller coaster at Mission Beach, painted in thick impasto with a vibrant full palette.

VICKLAND, SAIBRA (Painter)
6400 Pacific Ave., Playa Del Rey, CA 90293

Born: 1943 *Awards:* Fullbright-Hayes Nominee, Otis Art Institute; Bank of America Woman of the Year *Exhibitions:* Los Angeles Contemporary Exhibitions; Otis Institute of Parsons School of Design, Los Angeles *Education:* UCLA; Otis Art Institute

After formal training in painting, printmaking, and sculpture, she developed an interest in California light and space installations and conceptual outdoor sculpture. A Los Angeles resident since childhood, she has been deeply influenced by the philosophy and work of California artists Robert Irwin, James Turrell, Larry Bell, and New York artist Robert Smithson. She has used such media as tons of earth, glass, sand, wood, plexiglas, and housepaint in her site-specific installations. The drawings which constituted the documentation for this work spurred her interest in painting. Her favorite media are acrylic and oil. She produces large-scale paintings where the pure color auras and ambiguous images of monumental figures are discovered in water, rocks, and landscapes. These paintings show a reverence for the underlying spirituality and power of all forms in the universe, whether they appear inanimate or animate. She continues to incorporate the feeling of light and space in her paintings by the use of luminous metallic oxides and the illusion of great depth.

VIDAL, LINDA (Painter)
P.O. Box 394, Benicia, CA 94510

Born: 1924 *Awards:* Honorable Merit Award in Oil Painting, Walnut Creek Art Exhibit *Exhibitions:* Oakland Art Museum; Art Expo, Benicia *Education:* New York U.; California College of Arts and Crafts *Dealer:* R. Richardson, Mill Valley

After her discharge from the WACs in 1946, she became a bohemian artist in New York's Washington Square. Through the late 1940s and 1950s she worked in various production and art editorial positions in California. Since the late 1970s, she has moved toward expressionism, combining the abstract, non-objective, and figurative styles. She calls her present style "Fusionism." On celotex panels (a polycyranate foam material used in construction), she paints with acrylic colors and casting resins, discovering on each new panel the intrinsic textures inherent to the material. With celotex she is able to achieve the look of

Paul Diego Viramontes, *Boys of Summer,* 32 x 42, watermedia

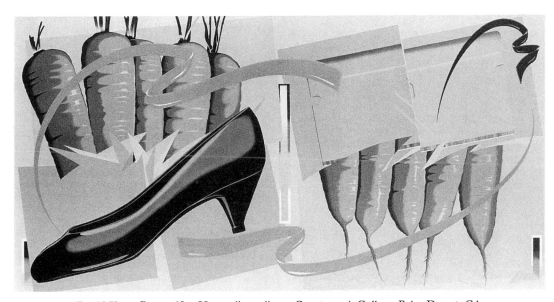

David Vogt, *Pump,* 40 x 80, acrylic on linen. Courtesy: A Gallery, Palm Desert, CA

sculptural stone relief, stoneware, and ceramics. She paints with both fine and broad color strokes.

VILLALOBOS (Painter)
809 W. Duarte Rd., Monrovia, CA 91016

Born: 1949 *Exhibitions:* Jonathan Club, Los Angeles; Carnegie Museum, Ventura *Education:* California Institute of the Arts, Valencia

Once a conventional seascape painter, he was inspired by Russian seascape master, Ivan Constantino Aivasovsky, to create a new form called the "executive seascape." The light and airy sea in the "executive seascape" resembles the sea of clouds one might view when looking out of an airplane window. In each piece he conveys the achievement, success, grandeur, and beauty of the owner along with a pervasive, personal mysticism. The style ranges from abstract impressionist to a slight Turner-influenced mysticism. His medium is oil and his colors are translucent and watercolor-like. He recently began painting a series of realistic, large-scale seascapes.

VIOLA, BILL (Video Artist)
324 Granada Ave., Long Beach, CA 90814

Born: 1951 *Awards:* NEA Fellowship; Guggenheim Fellowship *Collections:* Museum of Modern Art, NYC; Museum of Contemporary Art, Los Angeles *Exhibitions:* San Francisco Museum of Modern Art; Centre George Pompidou, Paris *Education:* Syracuse U. *Dealer:* Electronic Arts Intermix, NYC

He has been working in video and experimental music since 1970, his work beginning as experiments abstracting the purely electronic nature of the medium, but soon, influenced by psychology and philosophy, broadening to highly controlled works exploring the limits of human perception. In experimental music, he was a student of David Tudor, joining Tudor's "Rainforest" group, which later became Composers Inside Electronics. His video works comprise a large body of single-channel videotapes as well as many installations that use three-dimensional space and incorporate projections and multichannel sound. He was an early pioneer in the use of computer video editing, which enabled him to manipulate real images in video space and time, giving his work a poetic and musical quality. His extensive travels and studies, particularly in Eastern cultures, have provided him with a wide range of experience and images to inform his art. Recent installations and video tapes have reflected an interest in medical imagery. In *Anthem*, he skillfully combines images of natural and industrial beauty with medical images of operations and autopsies to create a haunting work on life and death.

VIRAMONTES, PAUL DIEGO (Painter)
21755 Summit Rd., Los Gatos, CA 95030

Born: 1946 *Awards:* Best of Show, Olympiad of the Arts, West Valley College; Best of Show, R.E. Bahia Art Exposition *Exhibitions:* San Jose State U.; San Jose Museum of Art *Education:* San Jose State U.

This former farm-camp laborer made his early "menudo art" out of inexpensive materials he often salvaged from dumpsters or bought at junk shops. Using paper, water-soluble ink and Clorox bleach, he created figurative, expressionistic works of striking power. His recent, boldly colored series of triptychs is also made with water media. These psychologically figurative paintings are saturated with water until transparent. His figures seem to stare at the viewer;

his expressionistic backgrounds are non-objective, removing distraction. When combined, his panels form a piece; when prescinded from each other, they stand on their own.

VIRI, FRANCISO P. (Painter)
904 Beach Park Blvd., #122, Foster City, CA 94404

Born: 1956 *Awards:* Rourke-Eno Paper Co. Design Award *Collections:* Ayala Museum; Makati Metro, Manila *Exhibitions:* Colloquium Gallery, Ogimachi Museum Square, Osaka; Cultural Centre, Manila *Education:* Rhode Island School of Design *Dealer:* Virginia Lynch Gallery, Tiverton, RI; Hatley Martin Gallery, San Francisco

His training included intensive study of the Surrealists, Abstractionists and Russian Constructivists, as well as the reading of structuralist and post-structuralist philosophy. His works began as a series in watercolor and mixed media, then progressed to acrylic as its expression gravitated from pessimism to serenity and tranquillity. His use of color, built up from layer to layer, is highly spontaneous; he also uses line to carry the figure and interact with the abstract configurations in the periphery or central area of the canvas. This use of line serves to intensify or deflate the energy of the space. Elements have simplified in the recent work, which perhaps marks a move toward minimalism. Duality and contradiction play an important role in the works.

VITALE, JAMES (Sculptor, Neon Artist)
2504 W. 7th St., Los Angeles, CA 90057

Born: 1952 *Exhibitions:* Museum of Neon Art; Calif. Institute of the Arts *Education:* Cooper Union, NYC

In college, he studied ceramics, welding, painting and drawing. During graduate school, he incorporated fabric and found objects into his work, producing timed, lighted kinetic installations. In his current work, he combines common household and industrial objects in new contexts, embellishing them with neon light and using both internal illumination and reflective surfaces such as abstract, back-lit mirrors. The toast in his toasters lights up; his plastic and glass assemblages of artificial food double as neon lights. His pieces often express political ideas, humor or wonderment.

VOGEL, JOSEPH (Painter)
508 W. 13th St., Roswell, NM 88201

Born: 1911 *Collections:* Metropolitan Museum of Art, NYC; National Gallery, Washington, DC *Exhibitions:* Whitney Museum, NYC; Metropolitan Museum of Art, NYC *Education:* National Academy of Design *Dealer:* Ryan Gallery, NYC

Early work was abstract expressionist in the idiom of social content. He merged this style with surrealist imagery and conceptual materials, using bold colors and semi-figurative forms. In the 1930's he worked for the W.P.A.'s Graphic Arts Project and there created surreal lithographs that have since been collected. His later work has moved toward formal problems in painting; one major piece was a monochromatic triptych in which he created stylized design elements out of figurative renderings of modern dancers. His current works are oil paintings and mixed-media drawings of marine elements and contemporary symbols.

VOGEL, TYLER S. (Painter, Collage Artist)
2000 Powell St., Suite 1360, Emeryville, CA 94608

Born: 1954 *Awards:* Best of Show, All-Alaska Juried Exhibition; Purchase Award, Anchorage Historical

Kali Weynerowski, *André,* 24 x 36, oil on panel. Photographer: Fran Ortiz

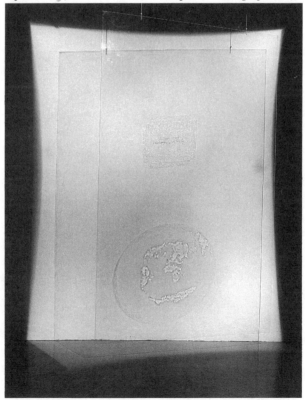

Saibra Vickland, *Memory is a Time Piece,* 60 x 96, installation:
projected light & silk-screened sheets. Courtesy: Otis Art
Institute of Parsons School of Design

Susan Venable, *High Voltage,* 66 x 90, steel, copper construction. Courtesy: E.L.K., Rancho Mirage, CA

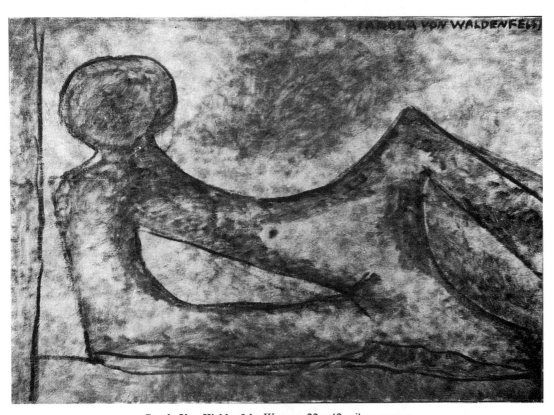

Carola Von Waldenfels, *Woman,* 32 x 43, oil on canvas

Peter Voulkos, *Hall of Justice,* 360 high, bronze.
Photogragh: Roger Gass

Ken Vares, *The Pouring,* 9 x 12, cast bronze

and Fine Arts Museum *Collections:* Anchorage Historical and Fine Arts Museum *Exhibitions:* Elite Fine Art Ltd., Emeryville; Fairbanks Art Association, Alaska *Education:* U. of Illinois *Dealer:* Elite Fine Art Ltd., Emeryville

His compositions contain elements of abstract expressionism and abstract illusionism. His early influences included Rauschenberg, Pollock and Frank Stella. In the early 1980s, he juxtaposed systems of hard-edged geometric shapes with softer, seemingly random strokes, creating tension as the work moved through planes. While the influence of Stella is still present in his painted constructions, his lexicon of marks now shows the influence of African and Native American designs. The planes of his recent two-dimensional work now consist of collage instead of pastel. On canvas, his work breaks the surface in all directions.

VOGT, DAVID (Painter)
102 Linnview Ave., Pittsburgh, PA 15210

Born: 1950 *Exhibitions:* A Gallery, Palm Desert; Artists' Liaison Exhibition, Palm Desert *Education:* Art Institute of Pittsburgh *Dealer:* A Gallery, Palm Desert; Valerie Miller, Los Angeles

His combination of mundane objects and strongly colored geometric abstractions might be termed pop-op art. His iconography is an instantly recognizable group of everyday objects, including paper clips, razor blades and strawberries. To these, he adds geometric forms, creating large-scale montages. His surfaces are large and his images are strongly defined and hard-edged. His earliest works were uniquely shaped wood forms influenced by pop. Through the late 1960s and early 1970s, he painted on shaped canvases. Though the pieces look airbrushed, he paints them with a pencil, a ruler, a paint brush and acrylic paint. His colors range from delicate pastels to deep dark blues and reds.

VON BIESEN, MARGARET (Painter, Photographer)
1307 15th St. #1, Santa Monica, CA 90404

Born: 1945 *Awards:* Purchase Award, Spokane Museum *Exhibitions:* Roark Gallery, Los Angeles; Chasa Club, Los Angeles *Education:* Central Washington State College

She received formal training in abstract expressionism and was influenced by Van Gogh. The technique of her early paintings is similar to Willem de Kooning's. Over time, her work progressed from straight abstraction to figures—nudes and portraits. Her technique is still expressionist, with violent brush gestures accompanied by a subtle palette. In the late 1970s, she began painting on photgraphs using metallic acrylics, chalk and any other materials that would cover high-gloss plastic paper. Her work in oil still reflects her early impulses.

VON GREYERZ-MONROE, DEBORAH (Painter, Printmaker)
1215 Harvard St., #4, Santa Monica, CA 90404

Born: 1947 *Awards:* Atlantis Award, Great Britain; Printmaking Residency, Great Britain *Collections:* Arts Council of Great Britain; Deutsche Leasing A.G. *Exhibitions:* British International Print Biennale; Philadelphia Print Club Annual International *Education:* U. of Rochester; Frankfurt Academy of Art, West Germany *Dealer:* Adrienne Fish, San Francisco

She combines photographic techniques with expressionistic gestures in personal, emotional and referential photo-etchings and photo-paintings. The pieces are incomplete photographic images surrounded by abstract expressionist and Matisse-influenced etching or painting. She has always been concerned with the human condition, and by working in series she is able to expose the ambiguity of human interaction as well as its static nature. Her pieces suggest the isolation of crucial elements, gestures and moods. Both paintings and etchings are typified by subtle grays and a luminosity achieved by oil washes or plate-tone.

VON RUHS, MARLINDE J. (Painter)
P.O. Box 877, Mendocino, CA 95460

Born: 1926 *Collections:* Bridwell Library, Southern Methodist U. *Exhibitions:* Horvath Gallery, San Francisco; Crocker Art Museum, Sacramento *Education:* Academy of Fine Arts, Dusseldorf; Art Students League, NYC

Among her influences were Chagall, Klimt, Hundertwasser, later Bonnard and Vuillard, and finally the archaeological sites in Guatemala, at Tikal and on the Greek Islands. She studied at the summer workshop of Oscar Kokoschka, and this influence may be seen in some of her portraits. However, she works in no one style and in no one medium. In *Games Children Play,* for example, the disembodied heads of children float with a leonine creature in space about a transparent ball and peer at the colorful and varied scene within—the whole evoking the dreamlike quality of Chagall. *El Sol de Guadalajara* depicts a great beast-like head, reminiscent in appearance and intense color of Mexican art. In this work, the more recent influence of poetry and mythology can be seen. Her work of late includes a painting of a jaguar rendered in oil and gold leaf and commissioned by the Mexican government.

VON WALDENFELS, CAROLA (Painter)
P.O. Box 534, Temecula, CA 92390

Born: 1932 *Collections:* Museum of Art, Rosario, Argentina; Museum of Contemporary Art, Buenos Aires *Exhibitions:* Mt. San Jacinto College, Riverside; Robert Freeman Gallery, Rincon *Education:* Munich School of Art

Her art education began in Munich with studies in photography. Soon afterwards, she turned to painting and emigrated to Argentina, where she is considered to be one of that country's finest artists. She now splits her time between Buenos Aires and California. The change of locales is clearly reflected in her work. First, her palette has lightened considerably, her California paintings expressing the discovery of a new sense of space and light. Like many transplanted Europeans, she is fascinated with the forms, colors, plants, and animals of the desert. She has also incorporated some Native American elements into her paintings. Another aspect of American life that sparks her artistic vision is our trash. She collects aluminum cans and other waste, then transforms them into large-scale artworks. Her current paintings are larger and more realistic than her previous works. She cites Rufino Tamayo and Robert Motherwell as major influences.

VOULKOS, PETER (Sculptor)
951 62nd St., Oakland, CA 94608

Born: 1924 *Awards:* Guggenheim Fellowship; Creative Arts Award for Sculpture, Brandeis University *Collec-*

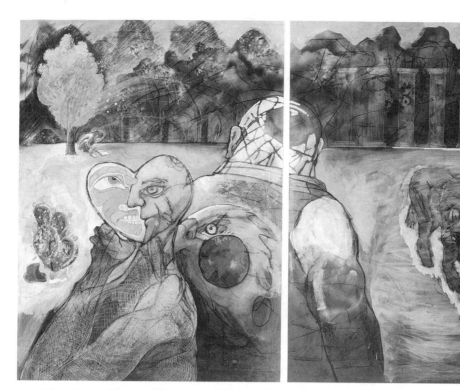

Mark Lewis Wagner, *Homage to the Dog Soldiers (give me reason to hope),* 36 x 60, mixed media

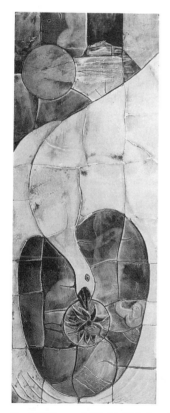

Fred Wilson, *A Night Offering,* 36 x 96, clay mural

Stacey R. Wexler, *Closed for Reconstruction,* 70 x 18 x 14, clay, glass & metal

tions: Museum of Modern Art, NYC; Whitney Museum, NYC *Exhibitions:* Oakland Museum; San Francisco Museum of Modern Art *Education:* Montana State U.; California College of Arts and Crafts *Dealers:* Braunstein Gallery, San Francisco; Exhibit A, Chicago; Charles Cowles Gallery, NYC

He was an abstract expressionist painter in the 1950s, but after studying ceramics he turned to sculpture, helping to revolutionize the use of clay by freeing it from its limits as a craft. An abstract style in naturally colored fired clay suggested innumerable possibilities for the medium and inspired many of his pupils. As an educator, he has wielded a good deal of influence, inspiring the "Funk Art" of Robert Arneson and James Melchert, among others. While a teacher at Berkeley, he made small-scale metal pieces that led to large outdoor sculptures such as the 30-foot-high untitled bronze commissioned by the San Francisco Hall of Justice. The three-year project is an example of the continuous energy in his work, a sturdy tower inhabited by twisting and turning organic bronze forms.

WADDINGHAM, JOHN (Painter)
955 SW Westwood Dr., Portland, OR 97201

Born: 1915 *Awards:* Palme dell Oro, Bhodighera, Italy *Collections:* Bullier & Bullier Collection, Portland, OR; Bank of California, Portland, OR *Exhibitions:* Rental Sales Gallery, Portland Art Museum; U. of Oregon Museum, Eugene

He was born in London and lived in India and Canada before moving to the United States. For 33 years, he was the art director for a metropolitan newspaper and specialized in illustrations. Five years ago, he decided to make his living entirely from fine art. Travels through Asia, the South Pacific and Latin America have provided inspiration both for paintings and for travel stories. His imagery typically consists of landscapes and people at work; his Hawaiian paintings portray marketplaces and vistas of palm trees, mountains and the sea. He works primarily in watercolor and does abstract as well as realistic painting.

WADE, MARC ARTHUR (Painter, Photographer)
940 Los Trancos Woods. Rd., Portola Valley, CA 94025

Born: 1950 *Awards:* 1st Place, Menlo Park Arts Commission Art Show *Exhibitions:* San Mateo County Arts Council; Portola Valley Ranch Associates *Education:* Canada College

His interest in birds, insects, reptiles and fish continues to inspire subjects for his sculpture, paintings and photographs. The sculpture includes pieces in wood, stone, metal and cast jewelry. The paintings are done in acrylic applied in thin washes to produce a transparent effect, with the finishing outlines draw in pen; they often incorporate three-dimensional objects. These are primarily water scenes done in blue, green and yellow with considerable detail. The photographs frequently employ double exposure or are shot from a super-wide-angle lens to create a surrealistic atmosphere.

WAGENER, RICHARD (Printmaker)
8168 Glencrest Dr., Sun Valley, CA 91352

Collections: Purdue U.; Brand Arts Center *Exhibitions:* Mills College, Oakland; Biota Gallery, Los Angeles *Education:* U. of San Diego; Art Center College of Design

In his early paintings, he developed fields of brushstrokes by interweaving various colors into an overall abstract system. When he had woven the system too tightly, he would add random brushstrokes, negating and breaking down his original pattern. The same sensibility is evident in his recent wood engravings. He first creates a field of patterns, lines and marks, then adds a realistic element that contrasts with the underlying abstract structure. Finally, he adds other calligraphic and geometric elements, creating activity within the field.

WAGENET, JOHN MORRISON (Painter, Carver)
P. O. Box 1218, Willits, CA 95490

Born: 1950 *Awards:* Who's Who in California; Jack Whipple Award for Contemporary Art *Collections:* Pioneer Museum, Stockton; Haggin Galleries, Stockton *Exhibitions:* USC; Walnut Creek Civics Arts Gallery *Education:* San Francisco Art Institute

His early influences were Bosch and Dali, but he soon shifted to work depicting direct spiritual influences and visions using positive images. He calls himself a postvisionary California Realist, and his current works show the influence of meditation, California landscape and wildlife, and subtle humor. He works primarily on mainly on masonite with acrylic, but he also stretches silkscreen over masonite as a fine-toothed ground. The paintings direct great attention to situation and to inner light. Landscape images depict imaginary settings, emphasizing sensuous, almost erotic forms suggested by nature and clouds. The recent *Madroñas* shows trees that consist only of trunks, pursuing his use of seminal, almost erotic organic forms with small background compositions. In *Intergalactic Seed*, a crystalline form floats in the vacuum of space with a light trail. Silver cords and other forms emanate from its center.

WAGER, TOVYA (Photographer)
336 Westminster Ave., Los Angeles, CA 90020

Born: 1951 *Exhibitions:* Art Store Gallery, Pasadena; Otis Art Institute, Parsons School of Design

At first, she made Ansel Adams influenced black-and-white photographs. She became interested in the medium for the purpose sharing the beauty and peace of people around the world. Then, for a short time she incorporated drawings into her work. In 1972, she began shooting color slides and disciplining herself to achieve all her effects in camera. There was a rich sense of texture and history in her European images of windows, walls, stairways and mannequins. In 1980, she began her yearly travels to remote areas of China and began documenting the diverse peoples there. Portraits, landscapes and the diversity of ethnic groups in general has since become some of her main topics. Her film is Kodachrome 64, and she shoots portraits primarily with a 24mm lens. She also does abstract-appearing tight shots of repeated patterns such as stacked, slip-cast clay figures and rows of spindles in silk filament factories.

WAGNER, MARK LEWIS (Painter)
4401 San Leandro St. #37, Oakland, CA 94601

Born: 1959 *Awards:* NEA Grant *Exhibitions:* Fobbo Gallery, San Francisco; San Francisco State U.; Ohio State U. *Education:* John F. Kennedy U.

Marc A. Wade, *Beast in the Man that Surfs,* 35mm photography

Ruth J. Waters, *Torso in Brick,* 4 x 8 x 15, red brick.
Photographer: Kathleen M. Podolsky

Patricia Nell Warren, *Hunt of the Autumn Colors,*
23 x 35, acrylic. Courtesy: Victor Burner

His interest in shamanism gives voice to a global awareness which is present in his work. His attraction to the spiritual was initiated when living in New Mexico, where he began to combine images of nature, spirit and the human race in his art. He works in all media, combining a very detailed academic draftsmanship with loose movement of line and space, creating a visual and emotional dynamic balance. He also works as an illustrator and is deeply concerned with social awareness.

WALKER, CHRISTINE (Painter)
171 Lily St., San Francisco, CA 94102

Born: 1948 *Collections:* Bank of America Corporate Art Collection, San Francisco *Exhibitions:* Bank of America Plaza Gallery, San Francisco; San Francisco Open Studio, San Francisco *Education:* San Francisco State U.

She makes colorful paintings in oils on canvas, often in panels of two or three and in large groups pursuing a single theme. "Swimmers" and "Harbors" are the titles of two such series. Studies in various media, such as watercolor and acrylic, support each series, and sculptural elements in wood sometimes accompany her paintings. On either side of her painting *Harbor with Circles,* for example, hang two brightly painted shapes, which echo shapes and reflections found in the painting. A professional designer as well, she occasionally collaborates with Bay Area choreographers to create sets and costumes for dance theater.

WALKER, CLAY (Printmaker)
11660 Turner Hts. Dr., Escondido, CA 92025

Born: 1924 *Awards:* Three Purchase Awards, Library of Congress; M. Boericke Award, Philadelphia *Collections:* Library of Congress, Washington, D.C.; Toledo Museum of Art *Exhibitions:* Gray Gallery, Escondido; Dana Gallery, Rancho Bernardo *Education:* Kent State U. *Dealer:* Lone Oak Press, Escondido

The son of a signpainter, he started making woodcuts at the age of twelve. His artistic approach and style were heavily influenced by the works of Gertrude Stein and Picasso. By 1950, the color woodcut dominated his work, but by the mid-1950s, he had started to search for other complimentary printing processes. During the next several years, he worked with cast plaster and collage materials, labeling these works collographs. His experiments with cast paper were relatively unsuccessful until Conner Everts recommended a book on papermaking. Having since developed allergies to some collography and woodcutting materials, he usually works in cast paper. He often combines several different techniques—plaster molding, as well as direct shaping—and a range of natural colors into organic, abstract shapes.

WALKER, JUDY (Painter)
3650 Deerpass Rd., Glendale, CA 91208

Born: 1956 *Awards:* Purchase Prize, Canyon City Fine Arts Center, CO *Collections:* Art Institute, Gangzhold, China; Canyon City Fine Arts Center, CO *Exhibitions:* Brand Art Library, Glendale; Hightone Records, Alameda

Her painting style has been profoundly influenced by Latin American masters such as Tamayo, Toledo, Matta, Gerzso, and Lam. Working in oils and watercolors, she is interested in expressing both emotional and pictorial depth. She strives to achieve the type of rich surface that leads the eye deeper into the subject of the painting and to the work's psychological foundation. An expressive use of color, and her short, lyrical brushstrokes are ideally suited to her abstract portraits of jazz and blues musicians.

WALKER, MERTI (Sculptor)
64 Sixth Ave., San Francisco, CA 94118

Born: 1943 *Exhibitions:* Suma Gallery; Tiburan Affaire, Tiburan *Education:* Mills College

Influenced by Julio Gonzalez, David Smith and Henri Matisse, her early work was in bronze and wood. Soon, however, she turned to welded metal. She resurrects scraps of steel into abstract welded forms, usually finished in polychrome. Pieces are a flat black with one-color accents, particularly bright primary colors and green and orange. Most of her sculptures stand between 2 feet and 6 feet high and are designed for decks, gardens and other outdoor settings.

WALKER, RONALD C. (Painter)
2822 Mohawk Ave., Ventura, CA 93001

Born: 1958 *Awards:* W & J National Painting Show, Washington, PA *Collections:* Central Missouri State U. *Exhibitions:* Artspace Exhibitions, Sacramento; Germanow Gallery, Rochester, NY

His work is an expression of chaos and tension, made for the contemplation of the viewer. He began as a realistic portrait painter but soon identified with specific symbols and images that he based on apocalyptic themes. His studies of funk and folk art led him to pursue an intense color purity, while at the same time incorporating a humorous, Arneson-like treatment of serious subject matter. He activates his surface through a diversity of styles and techniques ranging from drawing to alma prima to washes and drip splatter. While his techniques vary, he nevertheless pays consistent attention to the organization of subtle geometric values through which he achieves a unity on the canvas.

WALKER, SANDY (Painter, Printmaker)
4141 Gilbert St., Oakland, CA 94611

Born: 1942 *Awards:* MacDowell Colony Fellowship *Collections:* Museum of Modern Art, NYC; Metropolitan Museum of Art, NYC *Exhibitions:* Khiva Gallery, San Francisco; Corcoran Gallery, Washington, DC *Education:* Harvard College; Columbia U.

After receiving her MFA from Columbia University, she worked completely with abstraction for a long period before she turned to painting large-scale works from nature. After traveling through America while painting these pieces, she developed a style that straddles the fence between abstraction and representational landscape painting. Her work is well-grounded in art history and filled with references to a wide variety of artists. She works primarily with oil on canvas, and her brushstrokes tend to be vigorous but used economically, with each stroke bearing weight that well could be distributed over several. She also works with various media on paper and creates prints using the wood-cut technique.

WALKER, SHARYNE E. (Painter)
P.O. Box 120475, Chula Vista, CA 92012

Born: 1949 *Awards:* Best of Show, Grants Pass Museum of Art; Blue Ribbon, Rogue Gallery *Exhibitions:* Images International, HI; EMU Gallery, Eugene, OR

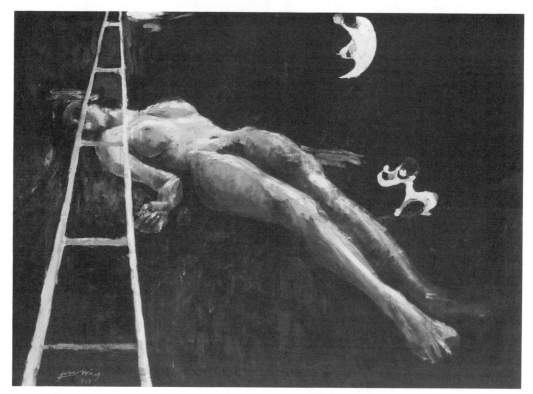

Jian Wang, *Artist's Drame #1,* 36 x 48, oil on canvas

Ronald C. Walker, *We is All Mamels,* 22 x 32, oil on paper

Her narrative mindscapes involve realistically depicted figures and a knowledge of the color spectrum. Some are sophisticated scenes of urban couples, while others show voluptuous females in idyllic, Garden of Eden type settings. In *Follow the Light*, she depicted a young naked child levitating toward the sky with its back to the viewer. Though the figures in many of her paintings are naked, the work is meant to be pure in a religious sense, rather than erotic. Her medium is acrylics and she paints on smooth bristol board and gessoed canvas. She describes her work as surrealistic realism. She is a veterinary specialist in the United States Army.

WALLACE, SHIRLEY (Painter)
1108 W. Prune, Lompoc, CA 93436

Born: 1933 *Awards:* Best of Show, Lompoc Valley Art Association; Best of the Best Art Show, Santa Barbara County Art Commission *Exhibitions:* Lompoc Valley Flower Festival; Art-a-Fair Festival, Laguna Beach

She has had a life-long interest in sketching, but did not practice art during the years she devoted to raising her four children. Since then, she has been working steadily, producing acrylic paintings of the California life using a palette knife technique. The French Impressionists, particularly Renoir, Degas, Cezanne, Monet, and Mary Cassatt, have deeply moved and inspired her from the beginning of her career. Her own style, though, is quite different from theirs. She has been obsessed with the play of light and shadow and tries to capture her thoughts, feelings, and responses to the people and places of central California in her paintings. Recently, she has enjoyed working in large formats.

WALLIN, LAWRENCE (Painter)
895 Toro Canyon Rd., Montecito, CA 93108

Born: 1944 *Collections:* Brand Library; Durango National Bank *Exhibitions:* Peter Nahum, London; Art Angles, Orange, CA *Education:* Otis Art Institute of Los Angeles; UCLA

He paints landscapes of the Pacific seaboard and the American West, on both grand and intimate scales, along with nudes and portraits, prints and monotypes. The landscapes are primarily in acrylic on canvas or paper. Not only the great painters, but photographers such as Weston, Adams and Lartilgue have influenced his work, which he sometimes creates from photographs he makes on his travels. A passionate advocate of ecological and environmental causes, he seeks to communicate through his paintings the idea of nature as a healing agent in the world and to create images that promote peace and order in a violent and chaotic time.

WALLIS, KITTY (Painter)
124 Hunolt St., Santa Cruz, CA 95060

Born: 1938 *Exhibitions:* Harris Gallery, Houston; Dubin's Gallery, Los Angeles *Education:* Cooper Union Art School

A contemporary impressionist, she began her career in New York and spent twenty-five years traveling and painting landscapes and people. In 1980, she moved to Santa Fe and spent four years showing her portraits, landscapes and seascapes. She works with pastel on handmade sandpaper, often underpainting with watercolor or acrylic airbrush. Following the pastoral thread of her development, she delights in the pattern, structure and color of light. She has been influenced by

Monet's respect for light and by Nicholas Carone, her professor at Cooper Union.

WALLIS, LINDA A. (Textile Artist)
3029 Radnor Way, Modesto, CA 95350

Born: 1950 *Awards:* Award of Excellence, Art Metro, NYC *Exhibitions:* Harvest Festival, Los Angeles; American Craft Council, San Francisco *Education:* Modesto Junior College; Columbia College

She has been a journeyman welder and pipe-fitter, plying her trade in Alaska, from Prudhoe Bay to Fairbanks to Nome. She has made her quilts in tiny sleeping cubicles, with the ice thick on the insides of small windows; in the cabs of the huge fuel trucks; and in oil camp laundry rooms and recreation halls. Now she has an apartment in Modesto, where she can work in comparative comfort. Her quilts are enormous, typically involving over nine hundred patches—in velvets, silks, satins, brocades, antique fabrics, painted fabrics, imported fabrics—held together by 1.6 miles of thread, and festooned with twenty-five thousand beads, sequins, rhinestones and such, all sewn by hand.

WALSH, TOM (Painter)
525 A, 23rd Ave., San Francisco, CA 94121

Born: 1945 *Exhibitions:* Sun Gallery, Hayward; Pacific Grove Art Center

Mark Rothko's meditative works inspired his early hard-edged, colorful, abstract style. Line was a prime concern, expressed in full gestures, within the two-dimensional space. By the late 1970s, he had turned to richly colored oil paintings, featuring organic forms. He works by underpainting in acrylics, then building up the surface, to create a three-dimensional appearance. His current paintings are executed in dark oils. Recognizable figures float and fade into expressionistic backgrounds, shimmering with light.

WAMSLEY, HELVI (Painter)
1902 Filbert St., San Francisco, CA 94123

Born: 1918 *Awards:* A.A.A. Gallery *Collections:* Whitney Museum, NYC; Museum of Fine Arts, Santa Fe, NM *Exhibitions:* Art Center, San Francisco; Gibraltar S/C, San Francisco *Education:* San Francisco State College Extension

During the Great Depression she studied at the Art Students League under the tutelage of Charlie Carlson and Hiromu Maehara. Her murals of this era reflected the studied forms of Reubens and the connected forms of Modigliani as well as Scandinavian and Oriental influences. After moving to California, she began studying the unique properties of earthlight. She now combines her own views on earthlight with the old masters' concerns about paint. Her brush creates shadows that emerge into glorious color, and explodes into impasto pockets of captured light. She ranges from realism, to fantasy, to imaged composition.

WANG, JIAN (Painter, Printmaker, Sculptor)
5005 Mevin Dr., Carmichael, CA 95608

Born: 1958 *Collections:* UC-Davis; Marshall Hospital, Placerville *Exhibitions:* Artist Contemporary Gallery, Sacramento; Gump's, San Francisco *Education:* Dalian Railway Institute, China; UC-Davis

As a young man in China, he trained in drawing and painting and took a degree in engineering. In 1986 he came to the United States and began studying under Fred Dalkey and Wayne Thiebaud at the University of California at Davis. Many of his first works were im-

Richard Wilson, *Tebbutts,* 57 x 77, acrylic on canvas

Madge Ward, *Lupine,* 10 x 22, cut paper silhouette

Linda Vallejo, *Jeweled Touch,* 64 x 22 x 15, mixed media with

pressionist-influenced landscapes inspired by California's light and colors. He has since begun incorporating the figure and still life and is now working in several media, including sculpture in clay, etching and a mixed media of pastel and watercolor. He works from photos and attempts to reproduce colors naturally. Before coming to the United States, he was director of the Dalian Calligraphers' Society and a member of the Dalian Young Artists Society.

WARASHINA, PATTI (Ceramist, Sculptor)

120 E. Edgar, Seattle, WA 98102

Born: 1940 *Awards:* NEA Grant; Governor's Award of Special Commendation for Art, Olympia, WA *Collections:* Seattle Opera House; Detroit Art Institute *Exhibitions:* Tucson Art Museum; National Museum of Modern Art, Tokyo *Education:* U. of Washington, Seattle *Dealer:* Foster/White, Seattle

Although formally trained in abstract expressionist painting and ceramics, she was attracted early to the surface work and imagery of the surrealists, particularly Magritte and ceramists Robert Arneson and Ken Price. Her well-known tableaux of low-fire molded figures has developed through a symbiosis of autobiographical iconography and the freedom afforded by working in clay. Delicate, representational imagery barely obscures disturbing details, like crowns of thorns going into the beautiful pink flesh of Northern Renaissance paintings. In one of her early "Altar" pieces, a woman entrapped within a display, evocative of her grandmother's shinto altar, is smiling from a frontal view, but appears to be insane from the side. Most of her work deals in one way or another with women's relationship to their place within male mythology, to their work or to themselves, though she has recently begun to focus on aspects of the human condition in general. She is always absorbing manifestations of the surreal in practical life through the news media and daily experience. Social commentary, distorted through the glass eye of the subconscious, is transformed into narrative ceramic sculpture, and thus appropriated into a slightly bewildered, but less unwieldy personal cosmos.

WARD, MADGE (Fiber Artist, Illustrator)

145 Hillbrook Lane, Auburn, CA 95603

Born: 1908 *Awards:* Auburn Arts, Auburn; Stockton Annual, Stockton *Exhibitions:* Crocker Art Gallery, Sacramento; Auburn ArtCetera Gallery, Auburn *Education:* UCLA; Calif. College of Arts and Crafts, Oakland

She has worked in ink, watercolor and fabric. Following the election of 1972, she created *We Rat-People Hung Ourselves at the Election*, consisting of three stringy fabric rats, each hanging from a wooden gallows. She became inspired to begin highly-detailed botanical studies in pencil and silhouette when her daughter was majoring in botanical drawing, and the many native plants of the Sierra foothills have provided ample subject matter. She also does illustration in a childlike style evident in her large stitcheries and quilts as well. *Insects and Animals*, a quilted wall hanging measuring 42 by 55 inches, is reminiscent of Mexican motifs, with its simple blue and orange color scheme and symmetrically-arranged turtles, rabbits and insects.

WAREHALL, WILLIAM D. (Glass Sculptor, Ceramist)

52 Sepulveda Ave., San Bernardino, CA 92404

Born: 1942 *Collections:* Joan and Walter Mondale; Hubert de Givenchy *Exhibitions:* Jacqueline Anhalt Gallery, Los Angeles; Elaine Potter Gallery, San Francisco *Education:* Wayne St. U.; U. of Wisconsin *Dealers:* Sandy Webster Gallery, Philadelphia; Museum of Contemporary Crafts, NYC

He was influenced early by Don Reitz, and subsequently by Harvey Littleton and Robert Arneson. In the 1970s, he started to deal with traditional, decorative approaches to clay. By the mid-1980s, his clay pieces became more abstract and sculptural. His ceramic pieces looked as if he had painted their surfaces. At the same time, glass became an important part of his work. While on sabbatical at Virginia Commonwealth University, he studied a pate de verre technique, in which tiny crystals of glass are fused together. This casting technique has allowed him to increase scale and develop a sculptural attitude in glass.

WARGO, DANIEL W. (Painter, Audio Collage Artist)

351 Idyllwild Ct., Redwood City, CA 94061

Born: 1950 *Awards:* 1st Prize, Peninsula Art Association *Collections:* Library of Congress, Washington, D.C. *Exhibitions:* KPTA Radio, Berkeley; San Francisco Museum of Modern Art

Executed in oil, acrylic, watercolor and mixed media collage, his paintings show the influences of Jean Dubuffet and aerial photography. He seeks to merge the visual and the tactile to create a more complete artistic experience. He has also worked as an audio collagist, rearranging and electronically altering public domain broadcasts to create a wholly new style of sound and language communication. One work, *The Compendium of Absurdist Essays*, is currently on file at the Library of Congress in Washington, D.C.

WARNER, DORIS A. (Sculptor)

5575 Empire Dr., Santa Cruz, CA 95060

Born: 1925 *Exhibitions:* Jessica Darraby Gallery, Los Angeles; Bank Street Gallery, Palo Alto *Education:* UC-Davis *Dealer:* American Fine Arts Council, Los Angeles

She trained as an abstract expressionist painter, but discovered the world of sculpture in stone and returned to school for instruction as a stone carver. In the 1970s, she explored the world of womanhood—her psyche, sexuality and social roles—in a series of highly abstracted figures, among them *Woman, Mother and Child*, and *Torso*. She usually sculpts in series, reworking the same concept until she has expressed it as powerfully as she can. The grandeur of ancient Rome, as typified by such edifices as the great aqueducts and Hadrian's villa, have inspired a newer series, in which she has taken up the challenge of working in bronze and marble. These materials are worked traditionally as distinct object and base, but she has developed a technique for molding them into a single artistic form using the lost-wax process.

WARNER, LEE (Handmade Paper Artist, Textile Artist)

c/o Hank Baum Gallery, P.O. Box 26689, San Francisco, CA 94126

Susan Venable, *Fire Mirage,* 216 x 144, steel, copper construction.
Courtesy: Pacific Plaza, Walnut Creek, CA

Marlinde Von Ruhs, *Games Children Play,* 36 x 26, oils
and silverleaf. Courtesy: Sara Harkins, Carmel, CA

Oscar Van Young, *Arch, Calle Almudaina Mallorca,*
24 x 20, oil on canvas

Robert Vala, *Opera,* 30 x 40, oil.
Courtesy: Will Stone Gallery, San Francisco

Linda Vallejo, *Tlaloc,* 36 x 25 x 25,
mixed media with handmade paper

Tom Van Sant, *Dreamer,* 30 high, mahogany

E.J. Velardi, Jr., *I Believe Someone is Watching,* 28 x 34, egg tempera

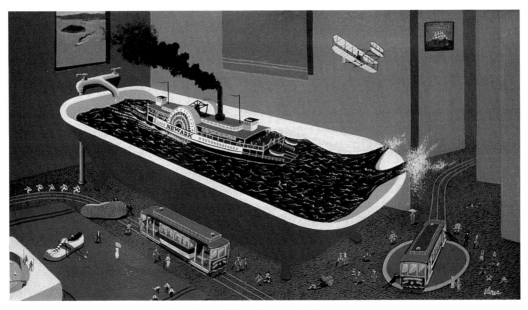

Ken Vares, *Nickel Ferry,* 19 x 34, acrylic

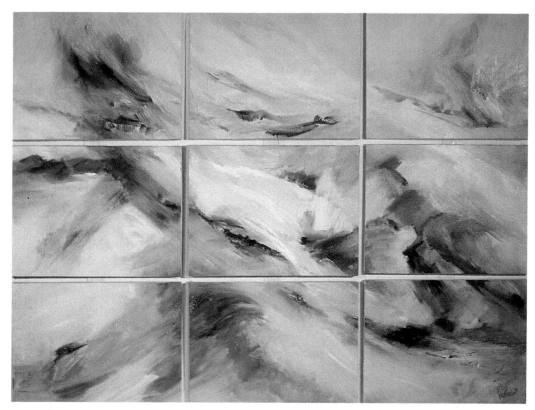

Valerio, *Nine in One,* 75 x 54, oil

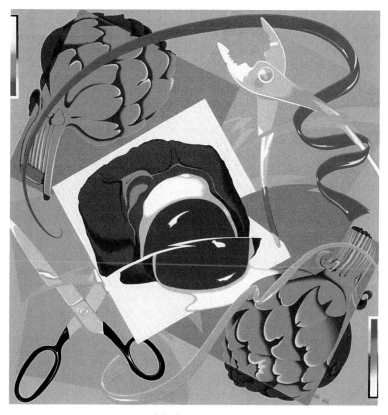

David Vogt, *2 Artichokes,* 58 x 58, acrylic on linen.
Courtesy: A Gallery, Palm Desert, CA

Linda Vidal, *Storm in Nicaragua,* 48 x 96 x 4, acrylic and resin on celotex panel. Photograph: Hedi B. Desuyo

Paul Diego Viramontes, *The Panhandler,* 42 x 32, watermedia

von Greyerz-Monroe, *from Positions II,* 22 x 30, hand-applied
photo-emulsion and oil on paper

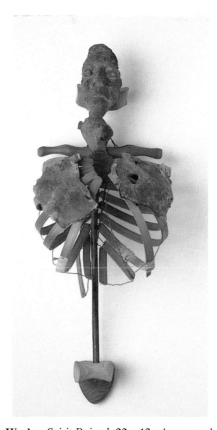

Stacey R. Wexler, *Spirit Ruined,* 22 x 13, glass, wood & copper

Deborah Throop Wilson, *untitled,* 66 x 40, acrylic on canvas.
Courtesy: Oberon Gallery, Napa, CA

Fred Wilson, *Xhosa Woman,* 8 x 10 x 30, clay, brass, & wood.
Photographer: Al Costanzo, Focus Studio

Ruth J. Waters, *Promenade,* 63" high, brass over hardwood

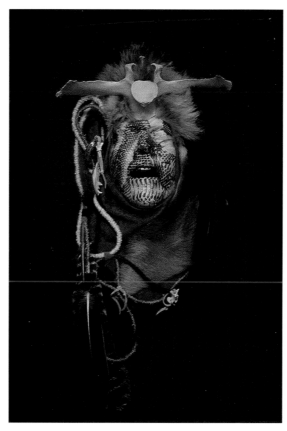

Ellen W. Wolf, *Singer of Songs—Teller of Tales,*
20 x 10 x 4, mixed media

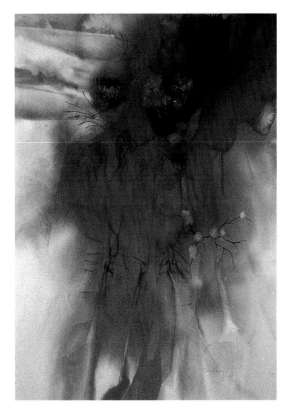

Donna Wright, *Gee-Shas,* 42 x 40, watercolor

Barbara Weldon, *Jazz Dance #26,* 60 x 40, acrylic on canvas

Kitty Wallis, *Morning Mist,* 60 x 40, acrylic
underpainting with pastel on sandpaper

Nelson Williford, *untitled,* 36 x 48, oil on canvas

Ronald C. Walker, *The Big Lick,* 33 x 22, oil on paper

Patricia Nell Warren, *Sweet Medicine,* 18 x 24, acrylic.
Courtesy: Image Maker

Sharyne E. Walker, *Thou Art with Me,* 30 x 24, acrylic on canvas

Kali Weynerowski, *Bonne À Tout Faire,* 26 x 20, oil on panel

M. Ragsdale Wright, *Erotica on Melrose,* 48 x 36, acrylic.
Photograph: Scott Streble

Harry Weisburd, *Inverness,* 32 x 40, acrylic on paper

Helvi O. Wamsley, *Earth-Light Series, Seal,* 48 x 60, oil on linen.
Courtesy: Erick Snyder, Art Center, Bed & Breakfast, San Francisco, CA

Doug Webb, *Lost in the Shuffle—Study #1,* 10 x 8, acrylic

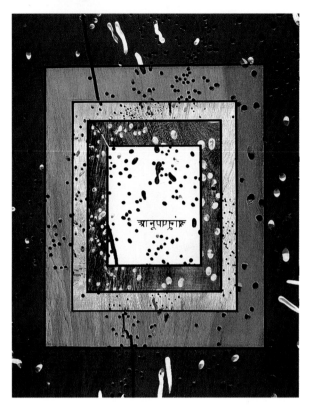

DeWayne Williams, *Interplay,* 18 x 14, photosculpture

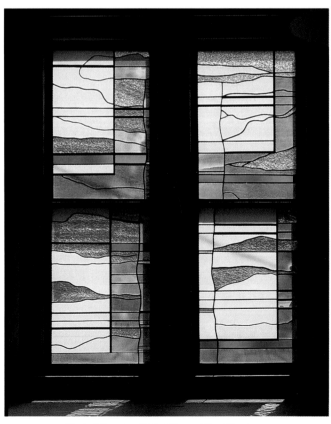

Chris Wrench, *Light Show,* 72 x 60, glass.
Courtesy: Ron Potts and Candace McKinley

Born: 1947 *Awards:* Award of Merit, Redding Museum and Art Center, *Collections:* Cal. State-Chico *Exhibitions:* Redding New Works Gallery, Redding; Reese Bullen Gallery, Cal. State-Humboldt *Education:* Cal. State-Chico *Dealer:* Hank Baum Gallery, San Francisco

Early work with watercolors, concentrating on the relationship between rigid, man-made patterns and soft organic forms, led to an interest in using handmade paper as an element in her compositions. While experimenting with handmade paper, she came across the art of quilting as a celebration of women's traditional folk art and as a vehicle to preserve family history and tradition. The creative process begins with three sheets of handmade paper. Cotton batting is sandwiched between the layers of paper, and the quilt design is drawn and painted on the top sheet using acrylic paints, pastels and prismacolors. The design is then stitched on the sewing machine, and the threads are left untrimmed. While some of the stitching is real, the visible stitches that produce the quilted patterns are drawn. The surface design is worked, scraped and worked again to produce a worn, tattered appearance. The worked surface creates an interplay between reality and illusion, the actual stitching and the drawn, the actual dimensions of the quilt and the illusion of puffiness and texture of the surface. More recently, a family heirloom or photograph gives rise to a work that carries a personal, emotional stamp. Her environment, interests and personal history all merge within her work. Design elements continue to exhibit her interest with organic, natural forms.

WARNER, MARY (Painter)
Dept. of Art, U. of Texas, San Antonio, San Antonio, TX 78285

Born: 1948 *Awards:* NEA Fellowship *Collections:* Crocker Museum of Art, Sacramento; Lannan Foundation, Palm Beach, FL *Exhibitions:* Cal. State U.-Fullerton; Jennifer Pauls Gallery, Sacramento *Education:* Cal. State-Sacramento *Dealers:* Louis Meisel, NYC; Jennifer Pauls, Sacramento

Originally, she created stylized animal figures in watercolor, but she is now best known for hyper-realist depictions of animals, and of animals juxtaposed with people. Using a horse, steer, dog, rabbit or common animal subject, she suffuses the painting with metaphorical and transcendent qualities, thus completely avoiding the sentimentality usually associated with animal subjects. She works in a variety of media, including oil, oil pastel, oil stick and wax. Recently she has chosen a diptych format to contain the works' symbolic meaning and poetic vision. She has also expanded her subject matter to include more overtly political statements, such as one recent painting that portrays the destruction of the rain forest. Another features a sleeping child in the foreground against the aftermath of a bombing.

WARREN, JACQUELINE (Painter, Printmaker)
918 S. Weller, Springfield, MO 65802

Born: 1946 *Awards:* Best of Show, Nelson Atkins Museum, Kansas City, MO *Collections:* IBM; Hallmark *Exhibitions:* Mid America Annual; Francene Ellman Gallery, Los Angeles *Dealer:* Van Stratten Gallery, Chicago

She wishes to ravish the viewer's eye and to excite his sense of touch. Her expressionist canvases are full of bold, inviting interiors, contrasting exterior spaces, evocative distances, and saturated colors. She paints with a freedom of stroke and composition, contrasting flat patterns with deep spaces and pushing and pulling color throughout the picture plane. Her borders heighten the sense of drama about these warmly lit representational scenes. Her recent patterned Mediterranean landscapes possess a slightly disarrayed dream-like luxury. She strives to create paintings for the viewer to "drown in."

WARREN, PATRICIA NELL (Painter, Lithographer)
P. O. Box Nevada City, CA 95959

Born: 1936 *Collections:* Martin Metals Pension Fund, Los Angeles; Carole D. Dunham, Miami Arts Council *Exhibitions:* ArtExpo West, San Francisco; Canossa Park Gallery, San Francisco *Education:* Stephens College, MO

Being a métis (of mixed blood), she fuses the symbols and styles from her European and Native American heritages. To this she adds a deep concern for the lost history of women and a reverence for the Earth's beauty. Her paintings are especially dedicated to images of women in Western history and explore their experiences and achievements. Her canvases are small, usually from 24 by 36 inches to 30 by 40 inches, and identifiable for their brilliant and luminous color, a quality achieved by the multilayering of gloss varnish and paint. The textured brushwork accents this further, simultaneously revealing many layers of color. The technique generates a shifting effect within a fixed image—the play of light down the fold of a robe may suddenly suggest a lightning bolt or a tree.

WARSHAW, MARY (Painter, Printmaker)
157 Rider Rd., Watsonville, CA 95076

Born: 1931 *Exhibitions:* Sesnon Gallery, UC-Santa Cruz; Smith Gallery, UC-Santa Cruz *Education:* Sonoma State U.; UC-Santa Cruz

She received her formal training in the studios of Will Barnett, Vaclav Vytacil and Robert Beverly Hale at the Art Students League in New York. Abstract expressionism strongly influenced her style, which retained some figurative elements, especially the human body. After returning to California, she worked on figurative drawing and painting in oils. She developed an oil technique using thin glazes to retain reflected light, giving an appearance similar to watercolor. In 1980, she studied printmaking with Vida Hackman, Paul Rangell and Kay Metz and began making prints. Her subjects are derived from feminist and ecological concerns, and the themes in her work are political and spiritual. She has been recently working on lithographs, in both small and large formats, as well as monoprints and intaglio work, and she has completed an etched and letter-press edition and an offset edition of a Penobscot tale, *The Baby*, published by Bridge Press.

WASSERMAN, GERALD (Painter, Sculptor)
92 Cuesta Vista Dr., Monterey, CA 93940

Born: 1920 *Awards:* Monterey Peninsula Museum of Art; San Francisco Museum of Modern Art *Collections:* Monterey Peninsula Museum of Art *Exhibitions:* U.S.I.S., Rome; Maxwell Gallery, San Francisco *Education:* School of the Art Institute of Chicago *Dealer:* Carmel Art Association

In the period beginning in 1945, his work was clearly figurative. During this period he painted post-impressionistic landscapes from nature. In 1952, he traveled in Europe and North Africa and subsequently turned to a style based on Romanesque art. By the mid-1960s, his painting had evolved into figurative abstraction, and he had begun producing bronze sculptures in the same style. In the late 1970s, animated by an interest in painters such as Yerones, Pousseu and Claude Lorrain, he returned to a more traditional idiom. He now paints with oil on canvas or paper and has developed a complex technique of monoprinting that involves several printings per image.

WASTMAN, TAKAKO (Painter, Photographer)
129 Beach Park Blvd., Foster City, CA 94404

Born: 1944 *Awards:* Best of Show, Watercolor, San Mateo County Fair *Exhibitions:* Peninsula Art Association; San Mateo Art Council

She was born and educated in Japan, and enjoyed a varied career as a costume designer, illustrator and poet, before emigrating to California in the mid-1970s. Influenced by the German expressionist Emil Nolde, she has worked in watercolor, using the wet-on-wet technique. Her early floral work has gradually given way to landscapes and to more abstract works. She uses color spontaneously, guided by the soft-edged forms which fill out the painting's composition. Patterned after the movement of the sea and the abstract forms of the clouds, her paintings depict an unstable, moving atmosphere. She also works in photography, shooting in black and white with a 4 x 5 Tachihara camera. Her abstract photographs often feature motion and double exposures. She makes and paints ceramic masks, which she photographs in series.

WATANABE, CHISATO (Painter, Mixed Media Artist)
3105 Moon Ave., Stockton, CA 95204

Collections: Cultural Center of the Philippines, Manila *Exhibitions:* Arizona St. U., Tempe; Jennifer Pauls Gallery, Sacramento *Education:* Cal. St.-Sacramento *Dealer:* Jennifer Pauls Gallery, Sacramento

The works of Jackson Pollock, Piet Mondrain and Lucas Samaras greatly influenced her style. Beginning in the mid-1970s, she worked in acrylic on canvas, adding thread, glitter, nets and other collage elements. She was also fascinated by the texture and appearance of Oriental rugs. This interest resulted in the "Rug Series," a set of highly decorative rugs designed with sensual personal images and symbols from her dreams. Gradually, she began to feature images from her everyday life. Works from this period were executed in hot pinks and warm burgundy reds. Her current work is autobiographical with references to her experiences, feelings, and dreams. These paintings are characterized by background movement with flashes of bright yellow, red and green.

WATERS, NAN (Ceramicist, Multimedia Artist)
1963 Grav. Hwy. South, Sebastopol, CA 95472

Born: 1947 *Exhibitions:* California Museum of Art; Luther Burbank Center for the Arts, Santa Rosa

Spending many years testing the plasticity of her medium to the fullest, at first her entire focus was on the effects available through the texture of the clay itself. Her glazing was minimal, with understated, single slashes of color that exhibited a Japanese influence. She recently began using glazes to emphasize the surreal aspects of her sculpture, resulting in a bolder, more outgoing feeling. The influence of American Indian designs has combined with her essentially natural style. Still simple, the whole piece continues to exhibit great concern for texture, now underscored by her glazes, which are often amusing and bright.

WATERS, RUTH (Sculptor)
1870 Ralston Ave., Belmont, CA 94002

Born: 1933 *Awards:* Bay Arts, Belmont; Inaugural Exhibit, Washington Women's Art Center, Washington, DC *Exhibitions:* 1870 Gallery, Belmont; PARTA Gallery, San Mateo *Education:* Stanford U.

Her first love was carving fine hardwoods in the classic subtractive mode using mallet and chisels. Later, she began sculpting marble, and on occasion, has had bronze casts made from hardwood originals. Exploring the human condition has been the main focus of her work for thirty years. She sees infinite possibilities for visual commentary on relationships, in terms of both content and stylistic interpretation, from realism to abstraction. Recently, outdoor sculptures in architectural scale have become a large part of her work. Large works are first carved in wood, then covered in brass or copper. Her newest work involves brick, a material she believes is warm, handsome and durable—ideally suited to public sculpture.

WATERSTREET, KEN (Painter)
3218 Tobari Ct., Sacramento, CA 95801

Born: 1940 *Collections:* San Francisco Museum of Modern Art; Oakland Museum *Exhibitions:* Louis Meisel Gallery, NYC; City Gallery, Sacramento *Education:* Cal. State-Sacramento *Dealer:* Joseph Chowning Gallery, San Francisco

Working in oil paint and color pencil, he was early on influenced by surrealism, and his work betrays a fascination with the real and the unreal, and the difficulty in distinguishing between them. In his early work, he explored the distinction by painting extreme close-ups of very sensual surfaces, such as aluminum foil or soap bubbles. Recently, he has turned to the human figure, creating childlike, almost primitive cartoon characters endowed with poignant, human attributes. These characters are always placed in the most mundane, everyday situations. Despite the cartoonishness of the figures, the draftsmanship is painstaking, and great care is taken in the employment of a rich palette.

WAX, BEA (Sculptor)
P.O. Box 338, Palo Alto, CA 94302

Collections: City of Palo Alto, Permanent Fine Art Collection *Exhibitions:* The Art Corridor, Sacred Heart, Menlo Park; Institute of Contemporary Art, San Jose *Education:* Albright College; San Jose State U. *Dealer:* Vorpal Gallery, San Francisco

Her interests in sculpture and lost civilizations derive from a childhood spent in the Museum of Modern Art and the Museum of Natural History in New York. She works in bronze and porcelain, building pieces as one unit, cutting them up for firing and reassembling them as a finished sculpture. Porcelain's smoothness to the touch and receptive whiteness make this material especially appealing. She applies many layers of oil paint to these surfaces to build depth of color and translucence. The bronze forms a natural complement, and she constructs pieces so that the statement of the por-

Lee Warner, *Around the World,* 12 x 10, mixed media
painting on handmade paper

Kitty Wallis, *May Pole,* 30 x 22, pastel on sandpaper

Helen Winslow, *The Balcony,* 28 x 30, oil

Doris A. Warner, *Arch of Hadrian,* 24 x 22 x 11, marble and bronze. Photographer: Paul Schraub

Mary Warner, *Run,* 72 x 84, oil on linen. Courtesy: Artreach, Dallas, TX

Randa Wells, *Vita,* 54 x 68, acrylic on canvas

celain flows to the bronze, then vice versa, then together into a single aesthetic voice.

WAY, JOSEPH (Painter)
382 Goldenslope Ct., Benicia, CA 94510

Born: 1948 *Collections:* Sharsis, Friese, & Ginsburg, San Francisco; Pacific Telesis, San Francisco *Exhibitions:* Los Angeles International Art Fair; Barclay Simpson Fine Arts, Lafayette *Education:* Pratt Institute *Dealer:* Barclay Simpson Fine Arts, Lafayette

His experience as a designer of custom furniture, often painted with many coats of lacquer, contributed to the development of the layered, fresco-like quality of his abstract watercolors. Salt, sand, water and minute specks of gold are among the materials he uses to pebble and "crater" the surfaces of his paintings. His "landscapes" comprise a wide range of materials, subjects and perspectives: geometric shapes and fragments, lines and thread- like forms, and subtle colors depict subjects from a leaf at one's feet to distant galaxies. Music is also crucial to his creations. A performing musician, he describes his paintings in the vocabulary of music and finds inspiration and guidance in musical structures. His influences include Bach, Scriabin and twentieth-century Western music.

WAYLAND, DREW (Sculptor)
1965 Hornblend, #10, San Diego, CA 92109

Born: 1941 *Education:* American Academy of Art, Chicago

After his formal training in commercial art, he became an ornithological illustrator in Colorado Springs. On moving to San Diego, he worked in ice sculpture for the opening of the Westgate Hotel. Progressing to metal sculpture, he taught himself gas welding and created a realistic life-size copper hippopotamus and a two-thirds life-size humpback whale for a resort in Hawaii. Next he worked in styrofoam, which he used to assemble female robot androids using body-cast parts, tape recorders, mannequin parts, plaster, printed circuit boards and sometimes televisions. Later, he began making wall sculptures to complement these freestanding pieces. These panels are made from plywood, electronic components, tape recorders and found objects. The tape recorders in both types of sculpture are functional; they play monologues recorded by the artist. His figures have been been used as part of the environment for avant-garde dance performances.

WEARE, SALLY (Mixed Media Artist)
6449 Harwood Ave., Oakland, CA 94618

Born: 1942 *Awards:* Artist-in-Residence Fellowship, Briarcombe Foundation; Catherine Morgan Trefethen Fellowship for Painting *Collections:* City of Hayward *Exhibitions:* Camarawork, San Francisco; Herbert F. Johnson Museum of Art, Cornell U. *Education:* Mills College; U. of Chicago *Dealer:* Art in Architecture, San Francisco

In her early photographic images, she manipulated associations to convey meaning. Like a poet, she asked the viewer to "read" her work. In her mixed media pieces of the era she explored the dichotomy between individual and collective perception, questioning the reality that she herself was presenting. She continues to combine contrasting physical surfaces into what she now calls "reactive painting." For these large, two- and three-dimensional objects—from 22 by 30 inches to 8 by 4 feet—she colors paper, wood, glass and metal with paint and pastels to create objects that are seductive to the senses but abstract and opaque in content.

WEAVER, KATHLEEN D. (Painter, Draughtsperson)
c/o Hank Baum Gallery, P.O. Box 26689, San Francisco, CA 94126

Born: 1945 *Awards:* Best of Show, Sacramento Art League Open Competition; Finalist, Shasta County *Collections:* Cal. State-Chico *Exhibitions:* Crocker-Kingsley Annual; Cal Expo, California State Fair *Education:* Cal. State-Chico *Dealer:* Hank Baum Gallery, San Francisco

Her formal education included extensive training in drawing and painting. The Impressionists' use of color and light influenced her early style, as did the works of American artists Mary Cassatt, Winslow Homer, Will Barnet and Edward Hopper. Her combined-technique watercolor drawing produces works resembling collage. These paintings are narrative representations of personalities, events or situations. Objects are presented in a still-life, realist style, using color and light to create impact and emotion. The complexity of her compositions and the close color values she uses sometimes move her work toward the abstract.

WEBB, DOUG (Painter)
21805 Martinez St., Woodland Hills, CA 91364

Born: 1946 *Awards:* 1st Place, Acrylic Painting, International Art Competition, Los Angeles *Collections:* The White House, Washington, DC *Exhibitions:* Easter Egg Exhibit, The White House; Museum of Art Deco, Paris

The artist's technique has developed through self-instruction and membership in a private art guild in the early 1970s. Moving from watercolors to acrylic on canvas, he experimented with surrealism and photographic hyper-realism, finally settling on a hybrid style, hyper-surrealism, which combines the literal clarity of photo-realism with the bizarre juxtapositions of the surreal. Works are based on photographs and models and are given added intensity through exaggerated contrasts, achieved through the manipulation of glazes. The artist bases his work on a belief in the divine origin of his inspiration and on an idealism that places artistic considerations above material ones. He has executed large murals as well as easel paintings and enjoys giving his images wry symbolic twists and punning titles that underscore their moral overtones.

WEBB, PENNY (Printmaker)
2927 Pine St., San Francisco, CA 94115

Born: 1954 *Awards:* Travel Grant, Arizona Commission for the Arts; Travel Grant, Colorado Commission for the Arts *Collections:* Crocker Bank, Los Angeles; Bank of America, Los Angeles *Exhibitions:* Kala Institute, Berkeley; Allport Gallery, San Francisco *Education:* U. of Arizona; San Francisco Art Institute

Following her formal art training, she worked as an animator and art director for film, experiences that influenced the style of her paintings. Her prints and paintings involve the desert landscape and figures. Her large scale monotypes explore brilliant color fields and geometric shapes. Her etchings, consisting of human forms and stark canyon imagery, are visual metaphors for the soul's journey through existence. She works in a variety of sizes and employs collage materials in her print works.

Doug Webb, *Urban Daydream #4,* 24 x 30, acrylic

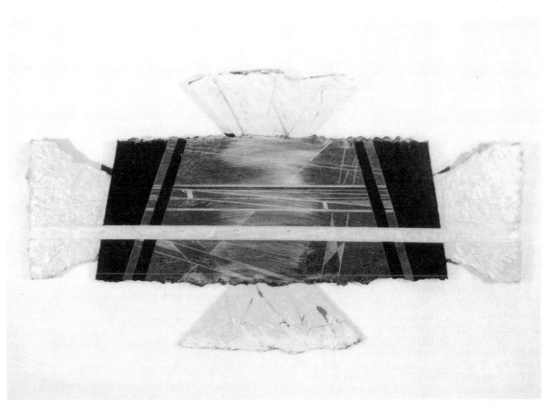

Bill Wheeler, *Broadway Butterfly,* 25 x 36, acrylic on masonite.
Courtesy: Studio Sixteen-Seventeen, Los Angeles

WEBER, ANN (Painter, Sculptor)
P.O. Box 33, Canyon, CA 94516

Born: 1950 *Awards:* George & Dorothy Saxe Award Scholarship *Exhibitions:* Everson Museum of Art, Syracuse, NY; Crocker Art Museum, Sacramento *Education:* Purdue U., IN; California College of Arts & Crafts, Oakland

For fifteen years she maintained a studio in Upstate New York and later in New York City where she designed and produced handmade porcelain tableware. Working to create abstractions of real objects, the original works were thrown on a potter's wheel, the shapes assembled, fired and glazed or painted with acrylics. Finding the processes with clay too cumbersome and too indirect, she switched to plaster, though she still returns to clay on occasion. Whereas she previously turned to objects for inspiration, she now turns to art, translating two-dimensional shapes in Kandinsky paintings into three-dimensional sculptures. After the sculpture is completed, she makes her own painting of it on paper or canvas. The next sculpture derives from the new shapes introduced in that painting, a process that is iterated several times, art creating art.

WEBER, JOAN (Photographer, Mixed Media Artist)
12532 Matteson Ave., Los Angeles, CA 90066

Born: 1933 *Collections:* San Francisco Museum of Modern Art *Exhibitions:* San Francisco Museum of Modern Art; Laguna Art Museum *Education:* UCLA; Cal. State-Northridge

She received her degree in drawing and painting, creating loosely figurative works in which figure and context had equal importance. As time passed, the relationship between subject and ground became an obsession. In the early 1970s, she tried to find ways to extend the context of her paintings and drawings. As a result, she found that by manipulating photographs using reproductive printing processes, photocopying, and other means, she could begin with a painting and end up with a photograph. She uses a combination of photo-silkscreens, black-and-white photographs, paints, pastels, and pencils. These materials undergo size and process manipulations as she photographs and rephotographs the subjects. The resulting prints depict created universes where subjects reflect what their enviroments have done to them, and how they have retaliated.

WEBER, MARSHALL (Mixed Media Artist)
992 Valencia St., San Francisco, CA 94110

Born: 1960 *Collections:* Museum of Modern Art *Exhibitions:* Show 'n' Tell Gallery, San Francisco; Museum of Contemporary Art, Los Angeles *Education:* San Francisco Art Institute *Dealer:* Fred Rinne, San Francisco

His style has been influenced by the radical political artwork of George Jackson, Weather Underground, and the Cuban Poster artists, as well as by other Bay area artists of the conceptual school such as Red Exx and Howard Fried. Starting out with an interest in sculpture, he turned to conceptual video and performance. His work in film, performance, sculpture and installation is infused with specific political, social, and economic themes. He is currently working on a thirteen-part piece called "The Root." It depicts various ideologies in dollar bills.

WEBER, WALTRAUD (Ceramist)
77 Edgecroft Rd., Berkeley, CA 94707

Born: 1933 *Awards:* Purchase Award, San Francisco Art Festival; Best of Show, Mill Valley Art Festival *Collections:* Darmstadter Landesmuseum, Darmstadt; Kunsthandwerk, Munich *Exhibitions:* Elaine Potter Gallery, San Francisco; Diablo Valley College Art Gallery, Pleasant Hill *Education:* U. of Hamburg; Cambridge U., England; Sorbonne, France *Dealer:* Elaine Potter Gallery, San Francisco

Inspired by the glazes of the Orient and with Bauhaus training in design, she produces celadon, copper red, and tenmoku vessels in porcelain, as well as large jars and platters in matt-glazed stoneware. She formulates all her clays and glazes in her own studio and fires in reduction at cone 10 and 11. She also does occasional pit and raku firings. She recently began working on a series of high-fired large platters (up to twenty inches in diameter) on which she paints bold landscape designs on the theme of time using both airbrush and color oxides. She is also expanding into sculptural forms using raku.

WEBERNICK, GARY (Multimedia Artist)
1740 Berry Ave., Santa Fe, NM 87501

Born: 1948 *Awards:* NEA/Rockefeller Grant for Interdisciplinary Artists *Collections:* Washington State Arts Commission, Olympia, WA *Exhibitions:* Smithsonian Institution; SPARC, Venice *Education:* U. of Oklahoma; U. of Texas

After using brushed and sprayed techniques to create non-objective images on canvas, he began incorporating various construction and painting techniques, as well as materials, in his work. In 1972, he abandoned non-objective imagery and began dealing with social, political and personal narratives. At the same time he expanded his media to include wood, metal, plastic, enamel paint, and found objects. In his current installations he shows a concern with of the primitive versus the contemporary and the organic versus the synthetic. His use of light, sound, and movement allows the audience to participate in direct and indirect ways.

WEINER, NORMAN (Painter, Sculptor)
8336 Melrose Ave., Los Angeles, CA 90069

Born: 1922 *Exhibitions:* Arteriors, Los Angeles; City Outdoor Show, Beverly Hills *Education:* Chouinard Art Institute; UCLA *Dealer:* Arteriors, Los Angeles

With a background in industrial design, fine art painting and drawing, he united metals with colored glasses to create a form of luminous, three-dimensional sculpture. He has used this process in both abstract and figurative collections. In search of the ultimate luminosity, he then developed a process of painting with inert materials immersed in lacquer. This material may be applied with a brush, but when allowed it to flow, creates exciting passages and unusual color nuances. His work with this process is semi-abstract and has a relationship with landscape imagery. In his recent series of watercolors, "The Melrose Scene," he depicts the sophisticated boutiques and 1950s-style restaurants of contemporary Los Angeles.

WEISBERG, RUTH (Painter, Printmaker)
2421 3rd St., Santa Monica, CA 90405

Awards: Grant, Ford Foundation; Vesta Award in Visual Arts *Collections:* Art Institute of Chicago; Metropolitan Museum of Art, NYC *Exhibitions:* Associated American Artists, NYC; Seaberg-Isthmus

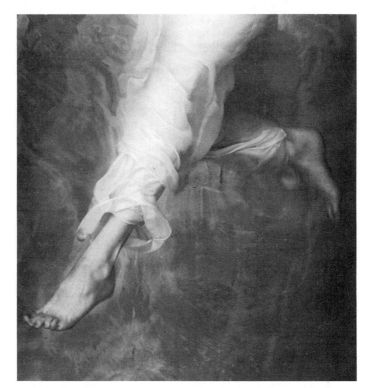

John Wimberly, *Descending Angel,* 16 x 20, photograph

Margaret L. Weiss, *Elephants,* 46 x 37, batik

Gallery, Chicago *Education:* U. of Michigan *Dealer:* Jack Rutberg, Los Angeles

Her work centers around the position of women in the Judaic tradition. Discounting such passages as the books of *Ruth* and *Esther*, which are not in the Torah itself, she believes that the official Judaic tradition has denied the feminine voice any authority on par with the patriarchal voice of the Torah. She also turns her critical gaze on the whole of western culture, which she believes has transformed the woman from a privileged observer and active agent into an object for male perception and action. Her artistic expression acts as a refusal to be so delineated. In both her paintings and in *The Scroll*, a 90-foot ink-and-wash painting meditating on the history of Judaism and the place of the contemporary family in it, she uses a representational style, which both refers to the classical and academic traditions and studiously veers away from any hint of post-modernism.

WEISBURD, HARRY (Painting)
P.O. Box 10036, Oakland, CA 94610

Born: 1938 *Awards:* 1st Prize, Watercolor, Mystic Art Association, Mystic, CT; Purchase Award, North Bay Artists Association, Benecia *Collections:* Bank of America Executive Offices, Santa Clara; Holiday Inn, San Francisco *Exhibitions:* Vorpal Gallery, San Francisco; American Zephyr Gallery, San Francisco *Education:* California College of Arts and Crafts; Parsons School of Design, NYC *Dealers:* Vorpal Gallery, San Francisco; Gallery 30, San Mateo; Art Collector, San Diego; Thrasher Orth Associates, Seattle

While studying art in the bay area during the 1960s, he was influenced by a variety of artists including Diebenkorn, Bonnard, Matisse and Schiele. He was attracted to their use of color and considers himself to be a colorist. Both the colors and images of his work are inspired by the natural beauty and spirituality of the northern California environment. His recent landscape and figurative paintings have evolved from a study of the metaphysical and spiritual aspects of art as influenced by Taoism and as seen in the works and Odilon Redon. He has also been using discrete colors to symbolize certain spiritual states of being. Whether he is paintings figurative works, as in a recent series of erotic art, or landscapes, he tries to reveal the metaphysical nature of his subjects.

WEISMAN, JOSEPH (Painter)
10801 La Grange Ave., #3, Los Angeles, CA 90025

Born: 1907 *Awards:* Scholarship, Chouinard Institute; Laguna Beach Art Association Award *Exhibitions:* San Diego Museum; Los Angeles County Museum of Art *Education:* Chouinard Institute of Art; Art Center College of Design

He is a recognized master of watercolor, oil and acrylic painting. His lengthy and distinguished career includes the art editorship of *Pan* magazine, technical illustration for the Douglas Aircraft Company and various art works for MGM, Warner Brothers, Twentieth Century Fox and other Hollywood movie studios. His portraiture and landscapes are renowned, and he has created murals for churches and restaurants throughout Los Angeles. He works in a realist-impressionist style, and he has exhibited his work in museums throughout the U.S.

WEISS, MARGARET L. (Batik Artist, Ceramist)
1305 Cavalier Ln., San Luis Obispo, CA 93401

Born: 1919 *Exhibitions:* Syracuse Museum of Art, Syracuse, NY; La Galeria Eclectic, San Luis Obispo *Education:* Acton Technical College, London; Free Academy, Nijmegen, Netherlands

She was originally trained as a potter in the tradition of Bernard Leach; a strong Japanese influence continues to be reflected in her work. In the Netherlands she studied the ancient Indonesian art of batik and in her colorful works in that medium she always represents one animal, such as a fish or a bird. In her "Greek" series of batiks, she combined animals with still life Greek scenery. Also a ceramist, she creates garden lanterns out of the large pots, which she cuts out and wires for electricity. She holds the conviction that "each piece should be good to look at, a pleasure to feel, and be functional in some capacity."

WEISS, NANCY PASSMAN (Ceramist)
373 Lombard St., San Francisco, CA 94133

Born: 1938 *Awards:* San Francisco Art Institute, Spring Show; Berkeley Art Center *Exhibitions:* Diego Rivera Gallery, San Francisco Art Institute; Berkeley Art Center Annual Exhibition *Education:* San Francisco Art Institute; California College of Arts & Crafts

After formal training in throwing conventional pots, she quickly moved on to hand-built vessels and nonfunctional sculptural pieces. Her utilitarian vessels are decorated with whimsical, childlike doodles. She has recently been experimenting with non-functional sculptures, as in one recent series, which features a set of giant puzzle pieces covered with coconut and glitter.

WELCH, AUDREY T. (Painter)
1300 Kentucky Dr., Concord, CA 94521

Born: 1958 *Collections:* Zachary Allen Co., San Francisco; Bill Miller, Sausalito *Exhibitions:* Civic Arts Gallery, Walnut Creek; Vallery Art Gallery, Walnut Creek Library *Education:* U. of Delaware *Dealer:* Van Straaten, Chicago

Although the work is abstract, it is inspired by the shapes and gestures found in the natural landscapes around her. She builds up "backgrounds" with layers of closely keyed and toned neutral color. Over these backgrounds, she paints in assertive gestures with a wide brush of bold, often contrasting color. A few of her images suggest the human figure, but most move with the angles, swirls and brush lines of Oriental calligraphy. In either case, the background, with its subtle layers, creates a deep field in which the gestures live and interact structurally. Her recent paintings are exclusively in acrylic on paper or canvas.

WELDEN, LARRY T. (Painter)
7107 West Lane, Loomis, CA 95650

Born: 1922 *Awards:* 1st Prize, Sacramento County Fair; 1st Prize, Kingsley Annual Exhibit *Collections:* Crocker Art Museum, Sacramento; Sacramento City College *Exhibitions:* California Palace Legion of Honor, San Francisco; Jennifer-Pauls Gallery, Sacramento *Education:* California College of Arts and Crafts; Cal. State-Sacramento *Dealer:* Artist's Contemporary Gallery, Sacramento

He deals with the big forms of the Sacramento Valley in structured, expressionistic landscapes that "drip" with color. Watercolor allows him to charge images

Joseph Way, *Masonic Music,* 19 x 33, watercolor. Courtesy: Barclay Simpson Fine Arts

Barbara Weldon, *Jazz Dance #17,* 60 x 84, acrylic on canvas

with transparent veils of color that accentuate the basic geometry of sky, land and water. He also explores its aqueous qualities by running and blending washes into stretched, hot-press paper or soft rag that has been scrubbed to promote absorption and produce textured effects. The white paper supports dynamic contrasts of positive and negative space and creates a sense of luminosity beneath forms. Field sketches are taken to the studio, where abstraction and broad brushwork express mood, presence or time of day, more than location. The images within these sensory landscapes are refinements and reductions of naturalistic forms, not realistic representations. He isolates the energy, the light patterns and the structure beneath the surface of what he sees.

WELDON, BARBARA (Painter)
6131 Romany Dr., San Diego, CA 92120

Born: 1931 *Awards:* National Academy of Design; National Watercolor Society *Collections:* San Diego Museum of Art *Exhibitions:* San Diego Museum of Art; Laguna Art Museum *Education:* San Diego St. U.; UC-San Diego *Dealers:* Ivory/Kimpton, San Francisco; Thomas Babeor, La Jolla; Ruth Bachnofer, Santa Monica

A fascination with architectonic structures motivates her work, along with obsessions with layers, subtle changes and unpredictable combinations of materials. She began her career as both a printmaker and watercolor painter, eventually combining the two media, adding portions of her earlier intaglios and watercolors to paintings. Recently, she has been painting abstract expressionist works in acrylic on paper or on primed, stretched canvas. They are large, free and gestural. She continues to work in a controlled manner, using layers of collage and intense colors. Works since 1985 include the "Tango" series, utilizing a reductive palette of black and raw titanium; the "Soniat" series, named for a restored mansion in New Orleans; and the "Jazz Dance" series, which grew from the "Tango" series but is more heavily painted in black and raw titanium with strong color on paper and large canvas. She has been influenced by Rauschenberg, Diebenkorn, Hoffmann, Kline, Martin and Motherwell.

WELLS, KATHERINE (Mixed Media Artist)
695 W. 10th St., Claremont, CA 91711

Born: 1936 *Awards:* Fulbright Grant *Collections:* Richard/Bennett Gallery, Los Angeles *Exhibitions:* Chaffey College, Rancho Cucamonga; Cal. State-Dominguez Hills *Education:* U. of Wyoming; Otis Art Institute

Her early work focused primarily on the graphic arts, especially the woodcut. The early expressionist achievements of Edvard Munch and Käthe Kollwitz reinforced her intuitive feeling for the stark power inherent in the use of black and white, an aesthetic which still dominates her work. In recent years, O'Keeffe and Magdalena Abakanowicz have been important influences. In addition, a fascination with primal peoples laid the groundwork for her present mixed media sculptures. Her dominant material is bone, mixed with leather, fur, paper and other materials. She uses these materials to add faces and hands to the bones. Her most recent work consists of full productions of sculpture, performance and poetry. Several female figures, all 6 feet, 6 inches tall, made of bone, plaster cast, paper and clothing, stand in front of such settings as waste dumps, Frederick's of Hollywood clothing stores

and military bases; these pieces express the idea that women are taking responsibility for their lives and destinies.

WELLS, LARRY (Painter, Printmaker)
P.O. Box 1004, Redwood City, CA 94064

Born: 1953 *Collections:* Clint Eastwood, Carmel *Exhibitions:* Frame Art Workshop, Mountain View *Education:* Columbus College of Art and Design, OH *Dealer:* Edward Weston Graphics

He is a photo-realist, who builds up layers of oils to produce extremely detailed renderings and clean, but smooth, surfaces. He began his career working with art conservationist Ron Lynn in Columbus, Ohio. He was influenced by the techniques of William Adolphe Bouguereau, and he began concentrating more on form and structure. He also became involved with the way Bouguereau executed his compositions and colors. He now searches for physical perfection— creating paintings without conflict. In his current biblical series, he removes Christ from the cross, and depicts him as healing the sick. He also works with serigraphs, and is beginning a series on nature subjects.

WELLS, RANDA GAEL (Painter)
1427 W. Washington Blvd., Venice, CA 90291

Born: 1945 *Awards:* Gourgaud Fellowship *Collections:* Executive Life Center, Los Angeles *Exhibitions:* Art Rental Gallery, Los Angeles County Museum; New Gallery, Santa Monica *Education:* UCLA

In the mid-1970s, she became immersed in the subtleties of color theory, painting horizontal bands of color on large canvases. In the late 1970s, she began composing works of finely crafted, and exuberantly painted, strips of wood. At first she lined these strips on a single plane, but soon she opened spaces between them creating taut constructivist forms. Her recent return to painting on canvas was prompted by a desire to use the neutral shape of the canvas to dramatize relationships alluded to in the wood constructions. These paintings are composed of loosely geometric and organic shapes—"noun-verbs"— that repeat or mimic one another. The freedom and mystery inherent in abstraction remain her primary challenges.

WELPOTT, JACK WARREN (Photographer)
28 1/2 Precita Ave., San Francisco, CA 94110

Born: 1923 *Awards:* Medal of Arles, France; NEA Fellowship *Collections:* Museum of Modern Art, NYC; San Francisco Museum of Modern Art *Exhibitions:* USC; Metropolitan Museum of Art, NYC *Education:* U. of Indiana

With photographer Judy Dater, he collaborated on a series of photographs primarily of women and often of the same subject, in order to compare the subject's response to a male versus a female photographer. This led to a publication entitled *Women and Other Visions: Photographs by Judy Dater and Jack Welpott.* He studied under and was greatly influenced by Henry Holmes Smith. He also studied painting under Leon Golub and Harry Engle, as well as design under George Rickey.

WESTMAN, RON (Painter)
4001 San Leandro St., Studio 16, Oakland, CA 94601

Born: 1953 *Awards:* Best of Show, Berkeley Art Center; Foster Award, Chautauqua National *Exhibitions:* Ellis/Pilcher Gallery, San Francisco; Lisa Harris Gallery, Seattle *Education:* UC-Berkeley; Central

Kay Whitcomb, *Nest of Robins,* 12 x 8, champlevé enamel on copper

Corrine Whitaker, *Forbidden Dreams,* 24 x 20, matted black and white silver print

Washington University, Ellensburg *Dealer:* Lisa Harris Gallery, Seattle

Nearing the completion of a degree in graphic design, he discovered another world of art: the spirit of Pollock and Guston; the abstraction and movement of de Kooning and Klein; the line of Klee; the color of Corot and Hopper; the light of Rembrandt, Turner and Monet; and the analysis of Cezanne, Motherwell and Held. He returned to school to study painting and develop a body of work based on these influences. He speaks of this early work as "quasi-figurative, planar funk, with an emphasis on value control and implied spatial relationships." His process has remained virtually unchanged over the years. He works primarily in oil, on a variety of flat surfaces, from small to large scale, building up the surface in layers, removing some by wiping, scraping and sanding. Typically, his forms are small, light areas, laden with movement, within a dark surround. Conceptually and symbolically, animal images address the core of human interaction, that of conflict and resolution, and "the quirky form of cooperation arising therefrom."

WETHERBY, SALLY (Photographer)
25 Sycamore Ave., Mill Valley, CA 94941

Born: 1935 *Awards:* Purchase Award, Monterey Peninsula Museum of Art; First Place, Best Portfolio, Maine Photographics Show, NYC *Collections:* Monterey Peninsula Museum of Art; State of Washington *Exhibitions:* San Francisco Arts Commission Gallery; Art Collector Gallery, San Diego *Education:* U. of Wisconsin *Dealer:* C.E. Rynd, Seattle, WA

After exploring many media, including tapestry weaving, assemblage and collage, she learned black-and-white photographic techniques. Early photographs include places where people have been but are no longer: an empty bridge, road, or bench. One also finds rivers, lakes and ocean shots. The pictures are hand-colored in grayed tones, which give them a dreamlike quality. Recent photographs have been still lifes, comprising geometric forms and natural forms such as bones, shells and seed pods; reflective surfaces; and the small, unusual objects one discovers at flea markets and garage sales. Drawing on her collage and assemblage experience, she then combines these images with others—such as old postcards, antique prints and photographs—to create images that are at once nostalgic and surrealistic.

WEXLER, STACEY R. (Sculptor, Mixed Media Artist)
1984 N. Main, #203, Los Angeles, CA 90031

Born: 1961 *Awards:* President's Purchase Award; Aurelias Renzetti Award *Collections:* Provident National Bank, Philadelphia; Philadelphia College of Art *Exhibitions:* GLSC, Hollywood; Chrysallis Gallery, Claremont *Education:* Claremont Graduate School; Philadelphia College of Art

Her early work centered around functional production pottery. She was influenced by Philadelphia's modern architecture, pop art and graffiti. Consequently, her work was hard-edged, geometric and very angular. The pottery's angularity was softened through the use of traditional majolica glazes and bold, fluid colors. Influenced by her studies in Italy, her functional pottery became progressively less functional and funkier, as she portrayed the foibles of humanity. Her current work consists of press-molded body parts and found objects. She uses a combination of materials in these pieces: ceramics, glass, metal and wood, assembled to create life-size figures. These pieces are ghostly, skeletal works in white, bluish-white, earth-tone pigments, and an occasional flash of bright color. The influences of primitive African art and mixed-media artists, Rauschenberg and Kienholz, are apparent in this series.

WEYNEROWSKA, HANKA KALI (Painter)
191 Robinhood Dr., San Francisco, CA 94127

Born: 1918 *Awards:* 1st Prize for Landscape, London Museum, Ontario, Canada *Collections:* Bart Lytton Collection, Los Angeles *Exhibitions:* Palais Des Beaux Arts, Brussels, Belgium; Palace of the Legion of Honor, San Francisco *Education:* Academy of Fine Arts, Warsaw, Poland; Royal Academy of Fine Arts, Brussels, Belgium

She graduated with highest honors from the Academy of Fine Arts in Warsaw, but her art was disrupted by the German invasion of Poland. In the Warsaw uprising of 1944, she was wounded and decorated for bravery. She spent time in a prison-of-war camp in Germany, and at the end of the war she escaped from the Russian zone of occupation and made her way to Belgium, where she could at last resume her career as an artist. Early works are characterized by a somber surrealism. A brighter mood appears in her later pieces—still lifes, figures and whimsical compositions in her own version of Cubism. Her more recent work comprises paintings of Madonnas or Madonna-like figures with an element of unusual stylization and an aristocratic clarity of composition and color. This is further marked by a painting technique in which certain surfaces are slightly raised by a heavier coat of paint, spaces of enamel-like texture alternating with passages of countless raised points.

WHALEY, JO (Painter, Photographer)
6075 A, Manchester, Oakland, CA

Born: 1953 *Awards:* Gyorgy Kepes Grant in Photography, Creators Equity Foundation, Berkeley; Polaroid Corporation's Artist Materials and Equipment Grant, NYC *Collections:* San Francisco Museum of Modern Art; De Saisset Museum, Santa Clara *Exhibitions:* San Francisco Museum of Modern Art; San Francisco Art Commission Gallery *Education:* UC-Berkeley *Dealer:* Scheinbaum & Russek, Santa Fe, NM

She is best known for hand-colored photographs, adorned with oils, gold leaf and collage elements. Her imagery has been influenced by Catholic iconography and by the work of Joseph Cornell. Resembling medieval manuscript illustrations, her evocative photographs investigate human fears and joys, sex, death and religion. "Fig Leafs," a series of black-and-white naturalistic photographs of nude men and women, with collaged photographic fig leaves, uses cerebral sexuality to "cover" corporal reality. Similarly, "Shrines" uses the Catholic means of adoration to celebrate the less elevated human states, such as melancholy, boredom, frivolity and vanity. She constructs the subjects for these photographs with wooden boxes, in which she arranges her chosen materials. The resulting photographs are then hand-colored in an expressive, rather than a representational, manner. Through the blending of photography, painting and sculpture, she tries to communicate the emotional, psychological and social forces which move her to creativity.

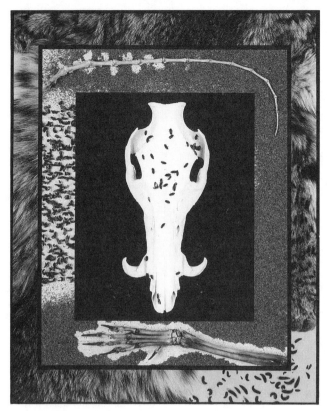

DeWayne Williams, *Transition I,* 10 x 18, photograph

Florence Wong, *Cutting the Birthday Cake,* 18 x 21, graphite

WHEELER, BILL (Painter, Printmaker)
1617 Silver Lake Blvd., Los Angeles, CA 90026

Born: 1948 *Awards:* Elsie De Wolfe Scholarship *Collections:* Bank of America, IBM *Exhibitions:* Rex Wignall Museum/Gallery; Brand Library *Education:* Otis Art Institute, Los Angeles *Dealer:* Studio 1617 Los Angeles

His early representational painting featured strong design elements, but as his sense of abstract composition began to dominate his artistic sensibility, his work became non-representational. Influenced by the Memphis Gallery style and by Post-Modernism in general, he began exploring texture, shape and color. He abandoned the rectangular or framed format and began creating torn, broken and irregularly shaped pieces. Tribal motifs and 20th-century architectural fragments in iridescent pastel colors became his primary images. He makes extensive use of hand coloring in his small-edition intaglio prints, and he paints his large-scale pieces on both masonite and plastic.

WHITAKER, CORINNE (Photographer)
1074 Pine Oak Lane, Pasadena, CA 91105

Born: 1934 *Awards:* Award of Merit, Calif. State Fair; 2nd Prize, *Photo Review* National Photographic Competition *Collections:* Roberts Art Gallery, Santa Monica; Society for Contemporary Photography, Kansas City, MO *Exhibitions:* Los Angeles County Museum of Art, Art Rental and Sales Gallery; Coos Art Museum, Oregon *Education:* Wellesley College

Early work portrayed city images—the underbelly of urban existence as scrawled on windows and walkways. The city art that she depicted blended with its surroundings and resembled the hallucinatory life of dreams. She now works in black and white, combining images and rephotographing to capture already-existing images. Imagery alludes to the chaos of the environment and the way in which we experience it through various media. It also conveys the idea of visual noise as a meaningful unit of communication and relates to the information the viewer actually retains after viewing, as opposed to what he thinks he is seeing at the moment of sensation.

WHITCOMB, KAY (Enameler)
1631 Mimulus Way, La Jolla, CA 92037

Awards: International Shippo Exhibiton, Tokoyo, Japan; Prix du Syndicat d'Initiative, Biennale Internationale Email Limoges, France *Collections:* Thompson Enamel; Parker Collection, Wichita Museum *Exhibitions:* San Diego Museum of Art; Taft Museum, Cincinnati *Education:* Rhode Island School of Design *Dealer:* The Gallery, Bazaar del Mundo, San Diego

Her medium is enameling on copper or steel fired at 1500 degrees Fahrenheit. Inspired by Paul Klee and by pre-Columbian Art, the work often features figuration, geometric patterns and quotations. The enamel gives the pieces a luminous quality, enhanced by the copper behind the transparents. To this, she sometimes adds a contrasting, dull chemical crust. In 1970, she developed a monoprint technique for enamel on steel—unique to this medium—to create mural-sized pieces. In addition to these techniques, she creates *champlevé* enamel and *cloisonné en ronde bosse* beads and objects.

WHITE, CYNTHIA JANET (Painter, Commercial Illustrator)
P.O. Box 351564, Los Angeles, CA 90035

Exhibitions: Museum of African American Art; Daniel Maher Gallery *Education:* Otis Parsons Art Institute; Cal. State-Long Beach

The colors of Palmer Hayden and the graphic lines of John Biggers that give his images an explosive spirituality make up the two major influences in her art. Other influences come from those artists concerned with depicting African American lifestyles. Her own work, done in watercolors, stands in their tradition. Using a full palette, her colors give her figures a passion and determination, pride and confidence. Be it a portrait of a single woman, as in *Annie Marie*, or paintings of people together, as in *Old Friends*—a painting of three women—and *Central Avenue Politicians*—a painting of three men, her paintings speak of cultural pride and identity.

WHITE, DAVID LEE (Painter, Film and Video Artist)
2022 Del Paso Blvd., Sacramento, CA 95815

Born: 1952 *Awards:* Most Popular Painting Award, Calif. State Fair Exhibition; Honorable Mention, Palo Alto Film Festival *Exhibitions:* Beaubourg Art Center, Paris; South of Market Community Center, San Francisco *Education:* San Francisco Art Institute

His training in super-realism was followed by a fascination with the structure of dreams and by a consequent exploration of surrealism. He has been influenced by and employs the early films of Luis Buñuel and Salvador Dali, as well as the writings of the Dadaists and Surrealists and authors such as Thomas Pynchon, William S. Burroughs and Richard Brautigan. He explores visions through use of the written word, the structure of language serving as a clue to the order and chaos of the human mind. Works include subconscious poetry that studies "accidental" wordings, films exploring the apparently chaotic order of dreams, and paintings focusing on the surreal and paradoxical juxtapositions of public images.

WHITE, JOHN (Performance Artist, Painter)
2141 Glencoe, Venice CA 90291

Born: 1937 *Awards:* NEA Fellowship *Collections:* Guggenheim Museum, NYC; Los Angeles County Museum of Art *Exhibitions:* Jan Baum Gallery, Los Angeles; John Doyle Gallery, Chicago *Education:* Otis Art Institute *Dealer:* Contemporary Artists' Services, Los Angeles

He was an early performance artist, having started performing publicly in the late 1960s. His paintings and drawings often are used in his performances in a way similar to a musical score, but they are also exhibited widely on their own. In fact, his two- dimensional work often arises out of his performance concerns and then goes on to function separately. His "Kern Spin" series of paintings, done with paint and oil stick on paper, suggests metropolitan scenes with the bustle and architecture of the city hinted at in an expressionist style which owes a considerable amount to Jackson Pollock. He is the recipient of three National Endowment for the Arts Fellowships.

WHITE, LARRY A. (Sculptor)
1825 Rodriguez, Santa Cruz, CA 95062

Born: 1942 *Awards:* Purchase Award, Crafts National, Mariella, OH *Collections:* California Polytechnic, San Luis Obispo *Exhibitions:* Walter Gallery, Carmel; Contemporary Craft Gallery, Portland *Dealer:* Garrett/White Gallery, Laguna Beach

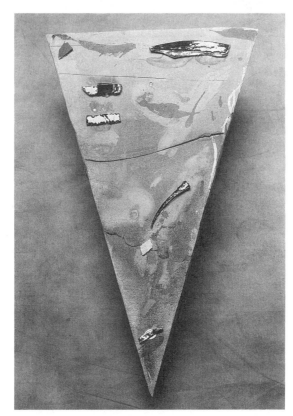

William Warehall, *Triangle,* 32 x 16, ceramic

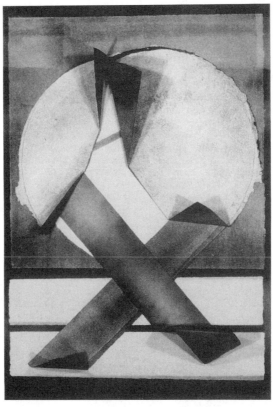

Toby S. Willner, *Energy Series,* 30 x 40, monotype collage, three-dimensional. Courtesy: Davy C's, Toronto, Canada

During a seven year apprenticeship, from 1962-69, with nationally known woodworker, Sam Maloof, he maintained a clay and metal studio producing sculpture in both media. During the 1970s, he focused on developing a design-fabrication studio, producing sculptural furniture and wall pieces made of exotic hardwoods. Recently, he has been producing multimedia, functional and non-functional art, incorporating exotic woods, glass, aluminum, copper, slate and a variety of other materials. His main interests are sculptural tables, lighting and architectural accessories. He uses wood and metal—juxtaposing brushed metal surfaces against the smooth richness of fine finished wood and reflecting glass.

WHITE, SHAWN (Painter, Sculptor)
6640 Abrego Rd., Isla Vista, CA 93117

Born: 1951 *Exhibitions:* Outer Space Gallery, Contemporary Arts Forum, Santa Barbara; Ucen Art Gallery, UC-Santa Barbara *Education:* UC-Santa Barbara

He is best known for his symmetrical, flat-weave abstractions, which are reminiscent of Navaho blankets, tic-tac-toe, West African textiles and other aboriginal arts. This style can be described as "Ticaho," "Afro-Fab" or "Sloppy Geo." He interweaves small, geometric patterns of glowing colors with areas of what appear to be bright stain. The surfaces of these paintings range from very flat to modeled. He uses a variety of materials: the conventional oils and acrylics on canvas, mosquito netting, aluminum cans, PVC tubing and bungie cords. He has also been constructing quite large outdoor sculptures, made from recycled aluminum. Leaving the surfaces unfinished, he permits the sculptures to develop natural patinas, through exposure to the elements. Whether working in painting or in sculpture, he prefers a primitive, natural, aesthetic to any academic artistic school or movement.

WHITE-WOLFF, JUDY (Assemblage Artist, Collage Artist)
3426 Montecito Ave., Santa Rosa, CA 95404

Born: 1947 *Collections:* San Jose Museum of Art *Exhibitions:* Sonoma State U. Art Gallery, Rohnert Park; Smith-Anderson Gallery, Palo Alto

She has worked with many different media, including wood, clay, metal, plastics, paper, paint and photography. In the mid-1970s, she began mixing these elements together, along with found objects to create assemblages and collages. Inez Storer was instrumental to her development in this direction and was a source of inspiration (as were Bruce Conner, George Hermo, and Joseph Cornell). Often using a box format, she manipulates the energies of objects by re-ordering their relationships to time and space. She is intrigued by the outer edge of reality, where meanings are ambiguous and contradictory. Through a process of weaving together moods, symbols and associations, she hopes to touch and give expression to the inner realms of being.

WHITEHEAD, PETER (Sculptor)
455A Valencia, San Francisco, CA 94103

Born: 1952 *Exhibitions:* San Francisco Museum of Modern Art Rental Gallery; Southern Exposure Gallery, San Francisco

With no formal art training, he developed his style and choice of materials from an interest in space and movement. His early steel mobiles have given way to static steel sculptures hung from the ceiling. He works freely, allowing one decision to suggest another. The resulting abstract pieces are constructed of welded steel, with wire to provide support and his desired spatial configurations. He paints many of his pieces, using color to suggest warmth and restfulness. Colors include pastels, rich earth tones and muted blues and yellows. Sometimes he allows a piece to rust, permitting viewers to see the construction process. The sculptures, which measure 3 by 6 feet, are intended to promote contemplation and a sense of repose.

WHITMORE, BILL (Photographer, Painter)
313-J W. Orange, San Gabriel, CA 91776

Born: 1934 *Collections:* Selected for U.S. St. Dept.'s "Art in Embassies" Program *Exhibitions:* Public Library, Rosemead; Public Library, Alhambra *Education:* Pacific U.

Seeking an alternative to color darkroom processing, he tried applying watercolors to black-and-white prints. At first, he had difficulty controlling the water-based medium, but later found its effect more pleasing than what he could achieve with photo oils. He usually uses a Nikon camera, but has tried a pinhole camera as well. He makes large black-and-white prints on Kodak Polycontrast Rapid II RC paper with a matte finish. Using concentrated pigments, brushes and cotton swabs, he applies the paint in realistic, slightly muted tones. He recently completed a three-year project, "In Love with Mexico," and has begun a new series, "Durango." Both series are typical of his work, which concetrates mainly on travel photography.

WIESE, KATRIN (Painter, Sculptor)
P.O. Box 1513, Riverside, CA 92502

Born: 1947 *Awards:* Purchase Prize, All-California Biennial, Riverside Art Museum *Collections:* Los Angeles Museum Council *Exhibitions:* California State Polytechnic University, Pomona; Peppers Gallery, Redlands *Education:* Cal. State-San Bernardino *Dealer:* John Thomas Gallery, Fullerton

Her work falls into two categories. The first consists of three-dimensional, wildly painted, wooden constructions depicting the Smith Family—an organization whose members over a period of time have developed into an extensive multi-racial and interdenominational group of very distinct individuals. The second category consists of two-dimensional, painted, wooden wall pieces. Women are the subject of these pieces—real women who work in bra stores, or generic, mythical women like Zehdra Fiber and her sisters. "You won't find these women in a Pepsodent ad."

WILEY, WILLIAM T. (Painter, Assemblage Artist)
615 Main St., Sausalito, CA 94965

Born: 1937 *Awards:* Purchase Prize, Whitney Museum; William H. Bartels Prize, Art Institute of Chicago *Collections:* Museum of Modern Art, NYC; Los Angeles County Museum of Art *Exhibitions:* Museum of Modern Art, NYC; Art Institute of Chicago *Education:* San Francisco Art Institute *Dealer:* Fuller Gross Gallery, San Francisco; Max Protech, NYC; L.A. Louver, Los Angeles

His early paintings are expressionistic and full of mysterious symbols. He gained recognition in the mid-1960s as a California Funk artist, painting images of minutiae related to surrealism and dada. Verbal puns accompany fragments of letters, logs and notebooks in collages and constructions. Objects such as feathers,

Sharyne E. Walker, *Dream of the Lily,* 14 x 11, a
crylic on bristol board

Nelson Williford, *Untitled,* 16 x 20, oil on canvas

string, rope, and branches—suggesting American Indian artifacts—and children's games of cowboys-and-Indians are incorporated into three-dimensional works that reveal a love for the American West. Imaginative drawings, such as *The Balance is Not So Far Away From the Good Old Daze*, are meticulously drawn and show infinite spatial planes, imaginary charts and metaphysical objects.

WILHELMI, WILLIAM (Ceramist)
1129 Ocean Dr., Corpus Christi, TX 78404

Born: 1939 *Awards:* 1st Place, Corpus Christi Art Foundation; Texas Arts Award in Creativity *Collections:* Long Beach Museum of Art; Everson Museum, Syracuse *Exhibitions:* Cooper-Hewitt Museum; American Craft Museum, NYC *Education:* UCLA; San Diego State U. *Dealer:* Wilhelmi/Holland Gallery, Corpus Christi

Decorative pieces described as "awake fantasies" are highly ornamental. He sees himself as a "potter" and strives to make things that are functional as well as decorative. He is known for works that exploit what he calls "the Texas Mystique", such as *Lidded Texas Boot Box*, the lidded *Texas Oil Well*, and the cowboy boots series. To molded earthenware he often adds carvings, buildups of glazes and oxides, and even beaded fringe. Pieces are glazed in bright colors, using a wax masking with an airbrush method.

WILKINS-NACHT, ELFIE (Photographer, Assemblage Artist)
1114 12th St., Santa Monica, CA 90403

Born: 1937 *Awards:* Woman's Building Commissioned Poster Project; First Place, Black and White Photography, College Category, Focus, NPIA *Collections:* Centre George Pompidou, France; La Jolla Museum of Contemporary Art *Exhibitions:* Los Angeles County Museum of Art, Rental Gallery; The Wight Gallery, UCLA *Education:* UCLA

Originally a painter, she began working with photograms in college. In 1976, she created a triptych *Here and Now*, an assemblage of forty-five 11 x 14 prints, joined in a grid format. Working in the tradition of Schwitters, Cornell and Samaras, she eventually began making multimedia assemblages, combining painting, photography, found images and three-dimensional objects. Her approach concentrates on content, which deals with human relations and its ambivalence, rather than formal or decorative aspects of the work. For more than ten years, she has been working on three distinct portrait series: the intimate, the social and the archetypal. The "Imago" series are intimate self-portrayals; the "Woeman Unpainted" series reveals women as a collective gender from primal time to the present; the "Extended Portraits," a mixture of photography and collage, are the result of collaboration between the artist and subject. Each subject provides a self-portrait and a personal object. These items, together with a photograph of the model by the artist, are constructed into an assemblage. The finished work offers a glimpse of the self and becomes a document of the creative act shared by artist and model.

WILLIAMS, ALLAN (Painter, Sculptor)
21773 B Highway 29, Middletown, CA 95461

Born: 1937 *Exhibitions:* Nathan Gallery, Larkspur; Collins Gallery, San Francisco *Education:* Central Washington State College of Education; Cal. State-Hayward

Working in a variety of media, he has relied on a rich artistic and intellectual heritage for his images—especially on Jung's exploration of cultural archetypes. He painted a series of works on black athletes for the 1984 Summer Olympics in Los Angeles. Working in metal, he continued his interest in sports figures in two sculptures, one of a sprinter and other of a high jumper. He is currently a ceramist, working on a series of busts using his friends' faces as models. One of these pieces, *Persona*, features a delicately curved neck with women's faces, each gazing serenely into space at complimentary angles.

WILLIAMS, DEWAYNE A. (Photographer)
Rt. 4 W. Riverside, Missoula, MT 59802

Born: 1943 *Awards:* Design Contest for Missoula County Seal *Collections:* Center For Creative Photography, Tucson; Bibliotheque National, Paris *Exhibitions:* Idaho State U.; U. of Montana *Education:* Oregon State U.; Florida State U. *Dealer:* Regan/Lane Enterprises, Houston

His early images were straight photographs of the American West. Influenced by Wynn Bullock and Ansel Adams, he began working with a technique called "correlative composite," in which one expands the medium's time frame and integrates subject relationships while maintaining image separation. In 1978 he became interested in Paul Klee's impressionistic expression of biological principles. In his current work he combines the object with its photographic representation. On the object itself, he mounts a large photographic sheet where the object's image is printed in sequential and spatial ways. He often adds graphics, drawings, or paintings to the work. His subjects are related to political and social issues.

WILLIAMS, DON H. (Painter)
377 Church St., Sonoma, CA 95476

Born: 1941 *Collections:* Cargill Inc., Minneapolis; AT&T, NYC *Exhibitions:* M. H. DeYoung Museum of Art, San Francisco; San Jose Museum of Art *Education:* Tulane U. *Dealer:* Allport Gallery, San Francisco

He studied with Reuben Tam and Reuben Kadish at the Brooklyn Museum of Art in the early 1960s. Taking an interest in the familiar and commonplace, specifically as related to America, he gradually progressed from his early figurative style to a realistic one influenced by Homer, Eakins, Sheeler and Hopper. In 1974, he stopped working with oil paints all together, and since then, he has worked exclusively with pastels, which figure well in his work because of their combination in one medium of the graphic qualities of charcoal and the plastic qualities of paint. His pieces usually begin with a photograph from which he works, relying on the photographic images to varying degrees in different works.

WILLIFORD, NELSON (Painter)
785 Idle Hour Ln., Sierra Madre, CA 91024

Born: 1952 *Dealer:* A Tiburon Affair

Influenced by Kandinsky, the Constructivists, Mondrian, Rothko and Newman, he is an architect who uses geometric forms—sometimes complex in their inter-relationships and sometimes severe in their simplicity—to explore the paradox and ambiguity of the two-dimensional canvas. He makes no attempt to

Deborah Throop Wilson, *untitled,* 26 x 36, sumi ink on rice paper. Courtesy: Oberon Gallery, Napa, CA

Diana Wong, *Peng's Journey,* 72 x 144, acrylic enamel

either depict or create an illusion of real space. Figure and ground are usually interconnected. Planes frequently appear to lie both in front of, and behind each other. Sometimes, he uses color as a textural element; other times, he lays out flat gradations of transparent pigment or blocks of flat planes. The intent is to create a doorway to a deeper perception of the work.

WILLIS, NANCY (Painter)
71 Ramona, San Francisco, CA 94103

Born: 1953 *Awards:* Fulbright Grant Finalist; Three Arts Council Scholarship *Collections:* Kaiser Steel, Oakland *Exhibitions:* Cuts Gallery, London; Billboard Cafe, San Francisco *Education:* U. of Cincinnati *Dealers:* Interart, San Francisco; Artline, San Francisco

During her formal training, she was influenced by Mark Rothko and Morris Louis, and she spent the early part of her career painting abstractions. After living in Europe for a year and making no art for five, she returned to San Francisco and painted abstractions of the city, striving to capture its atmosphere. An interest in the German neo-expressionists took her again to Europe, where, greatly impressed by the Berlin Wall, she began to work out the theme that she continues to pursue: Spies and Lovers. These works concentrate on the contrast between the incognito and deception of Cold War espionage, where truth is concealed, and the vulnerablility and exposure of love, where truth is revealed. Mystery and suspense surround both, and at the core is an inquiry into trust and the power of knowledge.

WILLNER, TOBY (Painter, Mixed Media Artist)
6317 Maryland Dr., Los Angeles, CA 90048

Born: 1932 *Awards:* Getty Museum Honorarium; Douthitt Award, Beachwood Museum, Ohio *Collections:* Walt Disney Foundation, Los Angeles; Cal. State Polytechnic U. *Exhibitions:* Sol del Rio Gallery, San Antonio, TX; Loyola Marymount U., Los Angeles *Education:* Cal. State-Northridge *Dealer:* Sol del Rio Gallery, San Antonio, TX

After working as a painter in the realist style and as an enamelist, she studied printmaking and glass. Her works evolved into series of mixed-media collages and monotypes that incorporate such elements as glass, metal and sand in two and three dimensions. Themes include imagined outer-space landscapes, windows into other dimensions, energy-related abstractions and environmental subjects. The more recent paintings have expanded into larger combinations and dimensions in mixed media, using sand, glass, paper, photocopy, silver, acrylic, and oil on canvas and board. She has also produced several videos, including *As I See Myself*, a self-portrait enamel show of 22 California artists.

WILMOT, JUDY A. (Commercial Illustrator)
P.O. Box 999, 1053 Mark Twain Road, Angels Camp, CA 95222

Exhibitions: Angels Art Gallery, Angels Camp; Marina Galleria, Stockton *Education:* U. of Minnesota

A commercial illustrator, she also spends time developing her weaving and macrame skills. She has illustrated books, including *Secret Language of Animals*, a book which took a year to complete and inspired a trip to Africa to study the animals firsthand. She now possesses illustrated cards featuring these

wild animals. Often working from photographs, she uses oils, acrylics, watercolors and pen-and-ink drawings. Her extensive portfolio of commercial art includes maps, brochures, letterheads and business cards. Her next project is compiling her boat sketches. Boats have always been of interest to her and many of her paintings are ocean scenes as well as scenes of the Sierras.

WILSON, DAPHNE T. (Sculptor)
1848 Lombard St., #2, San Francisco, CA 94123

Born: 1937 *Awards:* 1st & 2nd Place, South Carolina State Fair *Exhibitions:* Univ. of South Carolina; The Art Museum of South Columbia, SC *Dealer:* The Bohemian, Columbia, SC

Her hand-built clay sculptures are repositories of human energies; they possess, she says, "spirits of future existential relationships." A self-taught artist, she sees herself as a transmitter of her own and outside energies. Though she still hand-builds her work, over the years her work has become smaller, less functional and more decorative. At times, she minimalizes form and brings in multimedia techniques such as watercolor painting on clay. She uses a full palette and is beginning to emphasize brilliant colors. She is reducing her tendency to combine the functional and the sculptural.

WILSON, DEBORAH THROOP (Painter)
P.O. Box 928, Jackson, WY 83001

Born: 1951 *Collections:* Wyoming State Museum, Cheyenne; Mt. Bell Corporate Collection, Denver *Exhibitions:* Joseph Chowning Gallery, San Francisco; Florida Center for Contemporary Art, Tampa *Education:* UC- Berkeley; Lone Mountain College, San Francisco *Dealers:* Carson-Sapiro Gallery, Denver; Oberon Gallery, Napa

The "Fog" series, a group of paintings from early in her career, show the distinct influences of Chinese landscape painting and of Monet and Rothko. These abstract watercolors, atmospheric in color and sensibility, were folded, then unfolded, melding the geometric with the organic. The next two groups of paintings continued the theme of abstract natural forms. Her watercolor technique has given way to acrylics, thinly applied and layered on paper or canvas. The resulting surface is luminous and colorful. She has more recently been impressed by the work of Diebenkorn, and his geometric style is apparent in her paintings. The organic element remains prominent, and she views her art as an effort to reconcile the organic and the geometric, a metaphor for entrapment and the longing for freedom.

WILSON, DIANA DRAKE (Book Artist, Photographer)
1334 Benton Way, Los Angeles, CA 90026

Born: 1947 *Exhibitions:* Irvine Fine Arts Center; Fresno Arts Center *Education:* UCLA

In the early 1980s, she made two films, *Rose for Red* and *Eclipse Predictions*. These films presented staged objects, photographed frame by frame to create the illusion of the use of optically printed mattes. These two films were extremely ambiguous spatially and had narrative soundtracks. With a growing interest in writing and narrative, she turned to book arts and was soon presenting her narratives in large sculptural books. *Baltimore*, for example, was constructed from ten plywood pages covered with photocollages. The

Stanley C. Wilson, *Installation for South Africa, Altar for South
Africa, altered reality, traditional power confined by sadistic and morally disturbed concerns,*
84 x 96 x 120 wood, clay, African earth, American earth, Negro Hair, Fiber and Cloth

Harry Weisburd, *Beach Panorama,* 40 x 32, acrylic on paper

pages were mounted on vases approximately 6 feet tall, arranged in a semicircle thirteen feet in diameter. Her latest project, *Serpent Mound*, incorporates images of 19th-century photographs with maps of Midwestern archeological sites. A personal narrative accompanies the images, together with eight stereo-photocollages, each with its own viewer made from wood, brass, leaves, wax and dried flowers. Recent work includes the production of a small book version of the eight stereo-photocollages, and additional projects employing photocollage.

WILSON, FRED R. (Ceramist, Sculptor)
4505 4th St., N.W., Albuquerque, NM

Born: 1932 *Awards:* Silver Medal, Bunyol, Spain; Latham Foundation, NYC *Collections:* City of Valencia, Spain; Jewish Museum, NYC *Exhibitions:* Ankrum Gallery, Los Angeles; Simon Rodia, Los Angeles *Education:* Laverne College; Fresno State College *Dealer:* The Wild Strawberry Muddy Wheel Gallery, Albuquerque; Litho Gallery, St. Louis

A sculptor and potter, he is known for his wood and stone carving, and for his prints and fine fabrics. He studied with the cubist, Adoffer Odofer, and the organic artist, Ken Starbird. He describes his work as "organic to cubic, to Oriental [and] a touch of African." In "Chessmen," his series of forlorn, four-foot-tall stoneware pawns, he represented the world of business moguls, politicians and social climbers. In 1968, he founded the Muddy Wheel Gallery, which he later moved to Albuquerque. In the dynamic, clay-wall murals he currently makes for restaurants, corporations and homes, he depicts many varied subjects.

WILSON, JOHN (Sculptor, Designer)
238 B Ave. Cabrillo, San Clemente, CA 92672

Born: 1948 *Exhibitions:* Sherwood Gallery, Laguna Beach; Taylor/Gratzer Gallery, Hollywood *Education:* Pasadena Art Center & School of Design

With fifteen years experience in upholstery, he became interested in soft sculpture in 1981 and developed a product line including trees, people, flowers and animals over the next six years. During that time he also built furniture. Cloud chairs, a bird nest chair, a 1937 Chord car chair and others were produced. A tropical environment he created was used on the "Silver Spoons" television show. He gradually phased out the product line and now focuses on making furniture. Hollywood and the movie industry are his main source of inspiration as at one time he worked for CBS and Paramount. His latest project is a Porsche chair, which is made with a shiny fabric that gives the appear of the reflective surface of a car. He builds his furniture as conventional furniture, with a hardwood frame, springs, cotton and foam. "It's just that my themes are different."

WILSON, LINDA G. (Photographer)
2747 Harrison, San Francisco, CA 94110

Born: 1943 *Awards:* Honorarium Award, Kenyon College, OH *Collections:* San Francisco State Fine Arts Collection *Exhibitions:* Intersection for the Arts, San Francisco; Downstairs Gallery, U. of California *Education:* San Francisco Art Institute; San Francisco State U.

Her interest in women's writings, especially their autobiographies and diaries, led to an exploration in self-portraiture as a means of understanding women's roles in American society. Having first been a painter,

she often subjects her photographs to additional manipulation—some she hand-tints, others she shoots through a series of hand-tinted color photocopies. Her work has recently become less concerned with inner realities, focusing instead on the external world. She is fascinated by "Image-Word-Scapes"—graffiti, billboards, advertising—the images of which she fills her photographs with. The color is carefully composed, and the work is influenced by both formalist and documentary concerns.

WILSON, PEGGY (Painter, Multimedia Artist)
801 Liberty St., Wood, CA 96094

Born: 1953 *Awards:* 3rd Place, Collage, Siskiyou County Competition *Collections:* Historical Lumber Mill Collection of Northern California, Weed-McCloud *Exhibitions:* Yreka Public Theatre's Main Lobby; Mt. Shasta Museum *Education:* UC-Santa Barbara

She studied traditional and modern art. Her major influences are the Impressionists, Twentieth Century and Chinese Art. She has worked extensively preserving past and present in collage pieces using artifacts and natural items exclusively. Her major project of recent years has been documenting the now demolished lumber mill communities in California using a wide variety of materials including drawings, paintings, handmade paper impressions, artifacts, photographs, and interviews of old time lumber mill factory workers. Present work includes oil paintings on stretched canvas using nail polish accents for a special effect.

WILSON, RICHARD BRIAN (Painter)
2175 Waldon St., Redding, CA 96001

Born: 1944 *Awards:* 1st Annual Grand Galleria National Painting Exhibit, Seattle; 15th Painting Annual, Downey Museum, Downey *Collections:* IBM Santa Teresa Laboratory, San Jose; Gulf Oil, Houston *Exhibitions:* San Jose Institute of Contemporary Art; Palm Springs Desert Museum *Education:* Cal. State-San Jose *Dealer:* Victor Fischer Galleries, Oakland/San Francisco

His paintings are part of the minimalist tradition exemplified by such artists as Ad Reinhardt and Mark Rothko. Newer paintings comprise a central rectangle framed by two identical vertical bands and a pair of horizontal bands that extend across the top and bottom. These are not mere studies of form and color, although the simple forms and subtle color modulations account for the works' presence. The pieces are titled after natural phenomena and so become "landscapes" abstracted to their essentials of space and light. In all his work, he continues to explore a narrow range of color and geometric form, not studying the interrelation of color systematically à la Josef Albers, but rather in a series of intuitive responses to life.

WILSON, ROBERT VERNON (Photographer)
2460 Park Blvd., Palo Alto, CA 94306

Born: 1938 *Awards:* 1st Place, Best in Show, Kaiser Permanente Arts Guild; Honorable Mention, Bay Meadows and San Mateo Arts Commission and Recreation Department *Exhibitions:* San Jose Art League; Kaiser Permanente Medical Center

A self-taught photographer, he began his career as a photojournalist for the U.S. Office of Education, documenting its programs to promote literacy. Later, he made editorial and commercial photographs to illustrate textbooks, magazines and advertisements.

M. Ragsdale Wright, *The Wait,* 60 x 48, acrylic. Photograph: Scott Streble

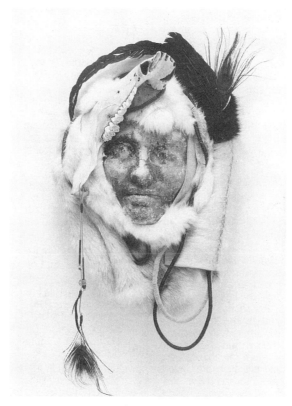

Ellen W. Wolf, *Wanderer,* 20 x 11 x 4, mixed media

After seeing an exhibition of Imogen Cunningham's work, he turned his efforts to fine-art black-and-white photography. Under the influence of her print work in black and white and her treatment of the nude figure, he sought to explore and expand the theme of the human form through the use of wide-angle lenses to create distortion and depth of field. When making prints, he uses Ansel Adams's zone system to create emotional intensity by manipulating light and dark values. His latest work encompasses multi-faceted imagery techniques and non-silver processes.

WILSON, STANLEY C. (Sculptor, Mixed Media Artist)
3407 Verdugo Rd., Los Angeles, CA 90065

Born: 1947 *Awards:* Visual Artist Fellowship, Sculpture, NEA; Artist in Residence, Studio Museum, Harlem, NY *Collections:* Broadway Federal Savings and Loan Association, Los Angeles; Golden State Life Insurance Company, Los Angeles *Exhibitions:* California Afro-American Museum, Los Angeles; Municipal Art Gallery, Los Angeles *Education:* Otis Art Institute *Dealers:* Dorothy Katz, Sol Del Rio Gallery, San Antonio; Alonzo Dale-Davis, Brockman Gallery, Los Angeles

For more than a decade, he has been researching and creating altars and shrines. Referring to a traditional sense of magic, mysticism and religion, his sculpture installations incorporate African traditional forms into the contemporary Afro-American experience. These pieces are based on research conducted in Africa and the Americas and include a variety of materials, such as clay, hair, earth, fiber, wood, bone and ash in metaphorical, rather than literal, presentations. For example, essence bowls may contain bits of natural hair—meant to suggest the power inherent in the African physical and psychological whole—or ashes collected from the burning of a particularly offensive piece of writing. His sculptures are intended to help viewers make contact with ancestral fragments, hidden memories of traditional societies, memories obscured by modern life. Despite his extensive research and traveling, interpretation of his works depends on a semiotic, symbolic understanding rather than anthropological knowledge.

WILSDON BRENNER, JEAN (Painter, Mixed Media Artist)
4105 Arroyo Trail, Carmel, CA 93923

Born: 1935 *Awards:* 1st Prize, Peninsula Museum of Art *Collections:* City of Monterey; Great Western Savings, Monterey *Exhibitions:* Pacific Grove Art Center; State Capitol Building, Sacramento *Education:* Stanford U.

Beginning with the desire to simplify the human face and form, she has developed her own style, referred to as sculptural painting: a clean, hard-edged look where depth is achieved by the physical layering of flat material. She began by cutting her shapes from matte board, painting from a limited palette to highlight lights and darks. In the 1970s, inspired by Matisse's works in which the cut-out left the frame, she began to do large cut-out figures, in which the shapes were set on spacers. In 1981, she and her husband made a two-week rafting trip down the Colorado River. Fascinated by the rock formations and the Grand Canyon, she decided to try and recreate these landscapes in her own style. These pieces were made of foam core, painted in a complex style with acrylics. Reaching five

to ten feet in width, some of her newest pieces are California landscapes presented without a frame on top, adding to the sense of space. These works are layered and constructed of gator foam. She has also experimented with plexiglas reliefs. All of her works, however, are characterized by shapes pushing out from the surface, creating an interplay of light and shadow, the hallmark of her style.

WIMBERLEY, JOHN (Photographer)
2298 Cornell St., Palo Alto, CA 94306

Born: 1945 *Collections:* Chevron U.S.A., Houston; Syntex Corporation, Palo Alto *Exhibitions:* Gallerie Zur Stockereg, Zurich; Museum of Contemporary Arts, Houston *Dealer:* J.J. Brookings & Co., San Jose

His quest to find inner meaning through photography does not allow for a separation of the man and his art. Practically living through his lens, the artist has endured years of harsh elements to obtain his recognizably etheral black-and-white landscapes. Completely self-taught, the artist cites music as the main influence in his print technique. "Printing photographs is like composing visual music," he explains, pointing to the necessity for complete harmony between depth, form, tone and content in both media. The same otherworldly quality that distinguishes his landscapes, infuses his figurative goddess series with an explosive, ecstatic mysticism. Each print is the cumulative end of hours upon hours of meticulous attention to detail. His need for greater control of the process precipitated the development of his own photochemicals.

WING, ANDY (Painter)
1244 Victory Walk, Laguna Beach, CA 92651

Born: 1931 *Awards:* Laguna Beach Art Museum; Downey Museum *Collections:* Xerox; San Diego Gas & Electric *Exhibitions:* Laguna Museum; Vorpal Galleries, Laguna Beach *Education:* Bard College; Cal. State College *Dealer:* Vorpal Gallery, NYC

Working year round in *plein air*, his style is non-representational. His painting technique is primarily nonbrush. He avoids the tricks of illusionistic dimensionality inherent in linear perspective and relies instead on various color mixtures and pigments. He portrays depth of color in ways analogous to nature by focusing paint in sharp delineations and distancing it in washes and broken edges, and by making his own paint from unground pigment in deliberately contrived and unique mixtures. He employs relief, montage, collage, found objects, construction, mosaic, painted glass, and stained and shaped canvas. He works from a state of "unknowing."

WINGO, MICHAEL (Painter)
7051 Figueroa St., Los Angeles, CA 90042

Born: 1941 *Awards:* Purchase Prize, 50th Anniversary Show, Otis Art Institute *Collections:* Santa Barbara Museum of Art; IBM Permanent Collection, Crocker Center, Los Angeles *Exhibitions:* Newport Harbor Art Museum, Newport Beach; Santa Barbara Museum of Art *Education:* Claremont McKenna College; Otis Art Institute, Los Angeles

Influenced early in his career by Lorser Feitelson, John Altoon, Richard Diebenkorn, Franz Kline and others, he painted hard-edged biomorphic forms in acrylic on canvas that appear to be hurtling through space—a comment on the duality of man and nature. More recently, he has produced a series he calls "Black

Chris Wrench, *Celedon,* 24 x 20, glass. Courtesy: Susan Hereford

Ras Wollega, *Inmost Soul,* 24 x 30, oil on canvas

Paintings," in which he simplifies the twisted biomorphic forms, now flattened, and builds up oil paint over a colored gesso ground on a horizontal canvas to produce the appearance of primordial forms floating in space. This current work, done in oil, charcoal and pastel, evolved out of a series of small drawings in graphite on paper and a larger series in charcoal on canvas.

WINSLOW, HELEN (Painter)
9934 West Wanda Dr., Beverly Hills, CA 90210

Born: 1916 *Awards:* Royal Society of Art *Collections:* Vincent Evans Collection *Exhibitions:* Gallery Fair, Mendocino; San Bernadino Museum *Education:* Florida State U.; Art Students League *Dealer:* Fireside Gallery, Carmel

Her early works display the traditional approach and discipline she learned in her formal classical training. Although she experimented for a period with abstraction, her current work is most closely tied to the impressionist tradition in its concern with light and the luminosity of color, but not at the expense of form. Working with the figure, still life and landscape, she composes paintings that are realistic, though not literal. Many paintings find women at ease though deep in thought, sipping tea or enjoying a moment on the patio. In these paintings, form and color are integrated not according to what is actually visual but according to the artist's sensibilities.

WINSLOW, JOYCE (Printmaker)
1984 Riverview St., Euguene, OR 97403

Born: 1942 *Awards:* 11th Annual Willamette Valley Juried Exhibit *Exhibitions:* Gallery L. Saussele, West Germany; Simon Fraser Gallery, British Columbia *Education:* Otis Art Institute

Her works are primarily figurative serigraphs, although she also works in watercolor. Human figures appear in overtly symbolic compositions based on both ancient and modern myths and sometimes inspired by 20th-century poetry as well. Within these reference points, she expresses and emphasizes strong design through an almost Oriental concentration on the interaction of shape and pattern with the figurative elements. Her silkscreening technique is loose and fairly spontaneous, using bright, transparent colors layered in a painterly fashion. *A Dream of Lions* shows a drowsing female figure approached by a curious and apparently tame lion, exemplifying a playful yet deliberate mode of exploration typical of her work.

WINTERS, ROBIN (Performance Artist, Mixed-Media Artist)
591 Broadway, New York, NY 10012

Born: 1950 *Awards:* Englehart Foundation Grant *Collections:* Museum of Modern Art, NYC; Metropolitan Museum of Art, NYC *Exhibitions:* Fuller Goldeen Gallery, San Francisco; University Art Museum, Berkeley *Education:* San Francisco Art Institute *Dealer:* Michael Klein, Inc., NYC

His varied and active artistic career includes performance art events concerned with the public and private character of modern art, and mixed-media paintings featuring crudely rendered, complex images. His paintings elicit complex, often confused reactions from critics and viewers alike. Aggressively non-traditional, these paintings can be read in a variety of ways. Just as children's drawings hold special meanings for them and more universal and complicated meanings for others, the simply drawn figures open themselves to multiple readings, acting as reflectors of the views, prejudices, feelings and knowledge of the viewers. In a recent work, *Circus Ring Filled with Water*, he has created blown-glass figures which float in a moat-like, wooden racetrack eighteen inches long and four feet wide. He believes in keeping the definition of art open, permitting exploration of new media, techniques, and presentations.

WITT, TOM (Conceptual Artist)
2184-7th Ave., Sacramento, CA 95818

Born: 1946 *Awards:* Special Projects Grant, California Arts Council *Collections:* UC-Davis *Exhibitions:* Shackleford and Sears Gallery, Davis; Institute of Design and Experimental Art, Sacramento

Although much of his art is in the form of painting, printmaking, sculpture and video, he calls himself a conceptual artist because it is by way of concepts that the physical forms come to exist. In *Brushstrokes, Bamboo and Artist Seeds*, he intended to make visual an idea that incorporated his own work and that of other artists with the landscape of the Sacramento River Delta. Through symbolic imagery and ritual gesture, he paid spiritual homage to the land in an elaborate process presenting the reciprocal relationship between artistic inspiration and its sources. The piece included an aerial drop of five nylon and bamboo banners representing brushstrokes in the sky; the submergence of a ceramic container holding works by seventy-seven artists as "seeds" of their creativity; and the beneficent gesture of throwing a delta-shaped, steel plate engraved with the words "ART SAFE HERE" into the river. The entire process was documented on film.

WOELFFER, EMERSON (Painter, Sculptor)
475 Dustin Dr., Los Angeles, CA 90065

Born: 1914 *Awards:* NEA Grant; Pollock-Krasner Grant *Collections:* Museum of Modern Art, NYC; La Jolla Museum of Contemporary Art *Exhibitions:* Wenger Gallery, Los Angeles; Gruenebaum Gallery, NYC *Education:* School of the Art Institute of Chicago *Dealer:* Wenger Gallery, Los Angeles

After apprenticing in the W.P.A. and serving in the Army Air Corps in World War II, he taught at the Institute of Design in Chicago and at Black Mountain College in North Carolina. He worked with Moholy Nagy and met Man Ray, Fernand Leger and Matta, as well as Motherwell, Rothko and Aaron Suskind. These experiences and his extensive travel aided in developing an affinity with the art of the modernist period and with its protagonists—Stuart Davis, Alexander Calder, Joan Miro. His art is joyful and communicative, characterized by vibrant colors on dark backgrounds and lyrical, pulsating shapes, beguiling in its sophisticated innocence. Recent works include collages of bold primary colors created through a process of "semi-automatism": tearing shapes without any particular goal in mind. The collages often are used to inspire ideas for paintings. He also works in ceramic sculpture, created with the same direct and automatic approach he takes with paintings and collage.

WOJTYLA, W. HASSE (Painter)
2102 C St., San Diego, CA 92102

Born: 1933 *Awards:* Artist in Residence, KPBS Television; Painting Award, All California Juried Exhibition, Laguna Museum of Art *Collections:* University of Illinois; Bellas Artes, Mexico City *Exhibitions:*

Helvi O. Wamsley, *Whale of a Tail*, 48 x 96, oil on linen. Courtesy: Erick Snyder, Art Center, Bed & Breakfast, San Francisco, CA

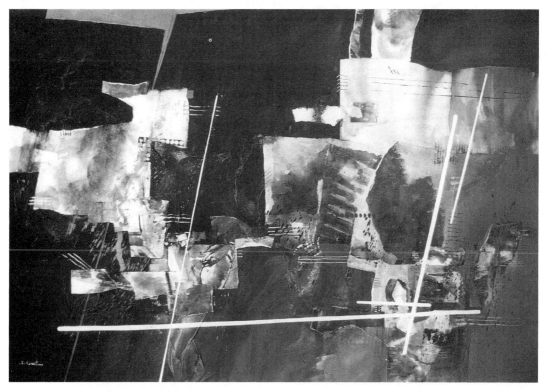

Edwin H. Wordell, NWS, *Summer Event,* 40 x 60, gouache, watercolor & collage

San Diego Art Institute; San Francisco Museum of Modern Art *Education:* School of the Art Institute of Chicago; University of Illinois *Dealer:* San Diego Art Institute

His earliest works were inspired by the surrealism of Dali, but after a move from Chicago to New York in the 1950s, he became influenced by the Abstract Expressionists, and his work turned non-objective. More recent work, though still abstract, has taken up the figure. His recent series of paintings, "Nude in the Shower," were abstracted in a highly individualistic manner, with human forms writhing beneath torrents of flowing water. Other series include "savagist" paintings, which depict abstracted figures engaged in brutal confrontations: each painting is taken from an actual crime incident that has fascinated the artist. Of late, he has also been involved with filmmaking as an art form.

WOLF, ELLEN W. (Painter)
406 E. Cherry Ave., Flagstaff, AZ 86001

Born: 1945 *Awards:* Award of Excellence, Arizona Watercolor Association, Sedona, AZ; 1st Place, National League of American Pen Women, Flagstaff, AZ *Exhibitions:* International Gallery, San Diego; Yuma 20th Southwest Invitational Traveling Exhibition for Arizona Commission on the Arts *Education:* Northern Arizona U. *Dealers:* Elaine Horwitch, Sedona, AZ; Edith Lambert, Santa Fe, NM; Old Town Gallery, Flagstaff, AZ

Her interests are split between watercolor paintings and mixed-media constructions; her recent work is more exclusively mixed-media pieces, and her watercolors also feature mixed-media. Early watercolors primarily depict the patterning of lizards, and the depictions generally follow natural coloring. Mixed-media pieces include early work with large wooden and found-object wall pieces, recalling Louise Nevelson. Human forms cast with plaster gauze material are seldom free-standing but influenced by Segal. From these early works grew a series of masks, in which she continues to work with plaster gauze to cast a face, then covering the pieces with snakeskin and adding found objects such as furs, bones and feathers. In her more recent works, she has begun to incorporate the upper torso as well.

WOLFE, BRUCE (Illustrator)
206 El Cerrito Ave., Piedmont, CA 94611

Born: 1941 *Awards:* Clio, Foster & Kleiser, Zellerbach Award; J. Henniger Best of Show Award *Collections:* Smithsonian; U. of Chicago *Exhibitions:* National Heritage Gallery, Los Angeles; Civic Arts Gallery, Walnut Creek *Education:* San Jose State U.; San Francisco Art Institute

Rembrandt's treatment of light and dimension in his etchings and portraits influenced this illustrator's early work. In addition, the round, sensual bodies of Rodin inspired him to produce sculpture portraits. Kaethe Kollwitz's technique of making black and white look like color lead to explorations in etching and life drawing. Later, he began experimenting in commercial art, in which he was strongly influenced by Arthur Rackman's drawings and forms and N.C. Wyeth's color and dramatic qualities. After working in acrylics, airbrush and charcoal, he has turned to oils in his recent work. These portraits and human forms feature more color and lightness than the bulk of the earlier work.

WOLFE, THOMAS C. (Painter)
P.O. Box 750, Hanalei, HI 96714

Born: 1952 *Collections:* San Anselmo *Exhibitions:* Oakland Museum; Seminar Hall, South San Francisco

He has been influenced by the Pre-Raphaelites and the Old Masters. As a child, he drew from nature; in his twenties, he studied under Maxfield Parrish and painted with oils and canvas. He learned his sense of design from Alphonse Mucha. In the early 1970s, he created a very successful poster series. By 1980, he had founded Renaissance Murals; in 1987, he founded his own publishing company, Arius Collection. He now paints in a very careful and time consuming layered glaze process. His subjects are normally landscapes, though he often brings in mythological references. He continues to be concerned with rendering nature's glorious play of light.

WOLFF, EFRAM (Painter)
14535 Arminta St., Ste. E, Van Nuys, CA 91402

Born: 1950 *Awards:* Kay Neilson Memorial Award; Phelan Award in Printmaking *Collections:* Stedelijk Museum, Amsterdam; Los Angeles County Municipal Art Gallery *Exhibitions:* Davidson Gallery, Seattle; Lang Art Gallery, Claremont *Education:* UC-Santa Barbara; San Francisco Art Institute

He began as a watercolorist and draughtsperson, but by 1971 he had progressed to intaglio and lithographic media. These early pieces studied abstract and figurative concerns. Although his more recent works continue to be figurative, structural elements often now serve as the pivotal points. The images are set in familiar-seeming urban situations, such as a bus station, and involve social issues and observations. One continuing theme is the figure as a foundation for culture and technology; he sets these figures in structures of a flexible nature, and they encompass effects and expressions of personalities as objects and parts of objects. He underscores their relationship with the structural background by a moody use of color shadings and by contrasts of soft and sharp-edged shapes. He has begun to paint in oil and to take a more diverse approach technically. Both Brueghel and Giotto inspired the slightly fantastic yet very human element that pervades the paintings, creating an objectification of life that is stark and moving.

WOLFSON, MURIEL DORIS (Mixed Media Artist)
6419 Colgate Ave., Los Angeles, CA 90048

Born: 1924 *Awards:* 1st Prize, Braithwaite Museum, Cedar City, UT; 1st Prize, Beverly Hills Art League *Exhibitions:* Pacific Design Center, Los Angeles; Los Angeles County Museum of Art *Education:* UCLA; Chouinard Art Institute

She works in a variety of media, including painting, sculpture, lithography, etching and woodcuts. Her work combines painting and sculpture to make intuitive statements with bright colors in a free style. Recently, she has been rendering abstract sculptures in wood as well as paintings, which are assemblages of large, asymmetric canvases. Juxtaposing randomly shaped and cut pieces of 5-ply and 3-ply pine, she moves the forms "like chess players" until the pieces seem to fall into place for her. Then the elements are nailed together and painted with bright stains, which highlight the wood's grain. She prefers to work on a large scale, creating finished pieces from 3 to 8 feet

King Wu, *Paddling Home,* 5 x 7, b/w photograph. Courtesy: Museum of History & Industry, Seattle, WA

Allan Williams, *untitled,* 30 x 24, ceramic

Donna Wright, *Gulls,* 42 x 40, watercolor

long. Recently she made unstretched abstract canvases that were larger than 6 by 12 feet, in order to express a "vigorous introspective originality."

WOLLEGA, RAS (Painter)
P.O. Box 117601, Burlingame, CA 94010

Born: 1956 *Exhibitions:* Contemporary Arts, Berkeley; Art Exposure, Stockton *Dealer:* Brockman Gallery, Los Angeles

Born into an artistic family, he completed his first painting, a landscape in oil on canvas, when he was thirteen years old. He now paints realistic images that are sometimes rendered in an unexpected color scheme. With an emphasis on perspective, his works display an understanding of color-field combinations and composition. He works on large canvases, citing Diego Rivera as a major influence. He paints abstract landscapes as well as additional abstract works that seek to evoke a mystical feeling or highlight the diversity of American ethnic cultures.

WONG, DIANA SHUI-IU (Painter, Printmaker)
1547 1/2 6th St., Santa Monica, CA 90401

Born: 1938 *Awards:* 1st Award, Grubbio, Italy; Jury Award, La Mirada Art Festival *Collections:* First Bank, Los Angeles; Hilton Hotel, Chicago *Exhibitions:* Taipei Fine Arts Museum, Taipei, Taiwan; M.M. Shino Gallery, Los Angeles *Education:* Accademia de Belle Arte, Rome, Italy *Dealer:* Merging One, Santa Monica

Her diverse training, informed by both Oriental and Occidental influences, and her style, which has evolved through several phases, permit her to create paintings charged with light, color, energy and spirituality. Bringing with her a background in calligraphy and brush painting, she studied portraiture and landscape techniques in Rome. Much of her early work, executed in a hard-edged format, featured depictions of a single element rendered in gradations of pastel color. She then began using paint-soaked rags, which she applied to canvas and removed when they were nearly dry. Her recent work is characterized by a much freer style, spontaneous application of paint in wide brushstrokes, various pouring techniques and the combination of acrylic and enamel paints. In manner of execution, these paintings are heavily influenced by her belief in the I-Ching, an ancient Chinese philosophical system founded on revealed destiny and accident. Her "Peng" series, based on a mythological bird, comprises a group of large, acrylic-on-panel paintings with enamel highlights. The bird is represented in the confluence of opposing elements—light and dark, color field and line, poured and rendered compositional elements. She intends her art to be universal, bridging the gap not only between East and West, but between the physical and the spiritual as well.

WONG, FLORENCE (Painter)
835 Elmira Dr., Sunnyvale, CA 94087

Born: 1938 *Awards:* Honorable Mention, Parents Helping Parents Cuisine Art Show, San Jose *Exhibitions:* Triton Museum, Santa Clara; Euphrat Gallery, De Anza College, Cupertino *Education:* UC-Berkeley; Foothill College, Los Altos

Her early works concentrate on floral imagery as an expression and exploration of the self, the treatment of these pastels influenced by the works of Kathe Kollwitz, Georgia O'Keeffe and Judy Chicago. The pieces feature magnified and fragmented shapes, the primary concern being color and its effects. Recent work has moved from floral imagery to the human figure as an exploration of the artist's personal history, in particular memories captured in childhood photographs. She has been expanding this approach to concentrate on the history of Oakland and the impact of Asian immigrants on the city.

WONG, KARLIN (Sculptor)
2911 Acresite St., Los Angeles, CA 90039

Born: 1949 *Awards:* 1st Place, Long Beach Art Association *Exhibitions:* Asian-American Exhibition, California State U., Los Angeles; A Gallery, Palm Desert *Education:* Art Center School of Design; Otis Art Institute

Though his sources are highly eclectic, he has found and continues to find inspiration in nature. His work is human-sized (four to five feet) and consists mostly of rocks and wood. There is a solid, collected zen-like presence about the pieces. He takes the rocks in their natural state and places them carefully into the wood. About the wood there is a crisp dichotomy of textures and shapes ranging from stark black chain-sawed pieces to surfaces that have been painstakingly shaped and polished. He is also experimenting with plastics and bronze. Among his influences are Moore, Noguchi and the classical sculptors.

WONG, STEPHEN K. (Painter)
1212 Masonic Ave., Berkeley, CA 94706

Born: 1941 *Awards:* Artist in Residence, California Arts Council; Prize in Drawing, Berkeley Art Center National Juried Show *Exhibitions:* Crocker Kingsley, Sacramento; Haggin Museum, Stockton *Education:* California College of Arts and Crafts; University of Liverpool, England *Dealer:* Ariel Gallery, NYC; ACCI Gallery, Berkeley

Born in Malaysia, he grew up immersed in Chinese brush painting. Studying in the West, he began to use Western styles, influenced by Francis Bacon. His intensely personal figurative drawings illustrate a mixture of cultures. The "Agony of Change" series explored the conflicts between a seemingly subconscious past and a newly acquired present. He has recently been working on large canvases, using oils for their sensual feeling and fluidity. He tends toward rich browns, and reds with a dark sepia background; his subject matter is a combination of figures and plant life, the latter now symbolizing change. Often in his drawings, he uses barbed wire to suggest loneliness and human conflict.

WONNER, PAUL (Painter)
468 Jersey St., San Francisco, CA 94994

Born: 1920 *Collections:* Guggenheim Museum, NYC; San Francisco Museum of Art *Exhibitions:* John Berggruen Gallery, San Francisco; Los Angeles Municipal Art Gallery *Education:* California College of Arts and Crafts; UC-Berkeley

He originally was involved in the Bay Area Expressionist movement in the 1950s; earliest works were abstract landscapes, which gradually incorporated figures and objects, often eschewing structural principles by placing the objects in the center of the canvas. In the 1960s, he began removing his subjects from their abstract landscapes and placing them in interiors; the objects became more delicately detailed, their environments more stark and geometric. The arrangement of objects and background in his works of the

Helen Winslow, *By the Window,* 28 x 30, oil

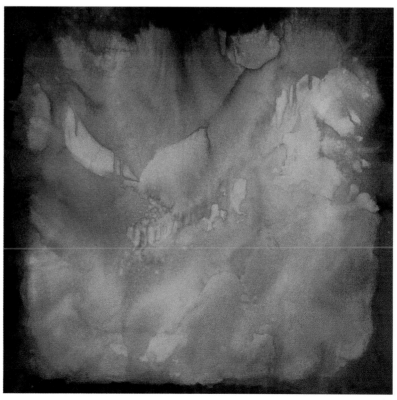

Toby S. Willner, *Windows Thru Space,* 60 x 84, acrylic on canvas.
Courtesy: Westlake Volvo, Thousand Oaks, CA

Ras Wollega, *Little Man and Glen,* 36 x 36, oil on canvas

Jian Wang, *The Spring,* 52 x 78, acrylic and oil pastel on paper

Madge Ward, *Races at Japanese-American Picnic,* 31 x 36, tempera paint

Kay Whitcomb, *Pussycat,* 36 x 40, porcelain enamel on steel. Courtesy: Mark Ratner

Randa Wells, *Walkabout,* 54 x 68, acrylic on canvas

Doris A. Warner, *Colosseum Cells,* 14 x 24 x 12, marble and bronze. Photographer: Paul Schraub

Richard Wilson, *Gull,* 60 x 78, acrylic on canvas

Margaret L. Weiss, *View from a Grecian Grape Arbor,* 72 x 50, batik. Courtesy: Joyce Brown

Lee Warner, *Square and Cross Sampler,* 21 x 30, mixed media painting on handmade paper.
Courtesy: Hank Baum Gallery, San Francisco

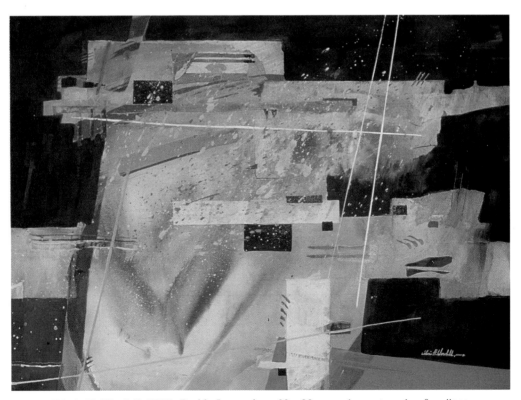

Edwin H. Wordell, NWS, *Pueblo Impressions,* 22 x 30, gouache, watercolor & collage

William Warehall, *Pate de Verre Glass Bowl,* 8 x 10, cast glass (Pate de verre)

Florence Wong, *untitled,* 26 x 20, pastels

Seyburn Zorthian, *No. 1 Big, 1988,* 73 x 42, sumi and oil on linen

Diana Wong, *Day and Night,* 72 x 144, acrylic enamel

Marc A. Wade, *Polynesian Sea,* 20 x 24, acyrlic on canvas

Joseph Way, *Pangaea,* 40 x 61, watercolor. Courtesy: Barclay Simpson Fine Arts

Haeju Andrea Yim, *Cultural Literacy,* 34 x 44, mixed media/oil and
metallic on canvas. Courtesy: Ariel Gallery, Soho, NYC

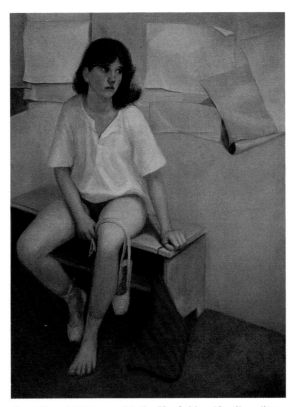

Joan Horsfall Young, *It's So Hard,* 30 x 40, oil on linen

Garcia Lou Young-Willard, *P.J.,* 25 x 21, pastel

Dan Young, *World Class Cyclists,* 23 x 35, hand-painted serigraph

Phyllis Yes, *Outer Self Series #1,* 60 x 84, mixed media

Victor Zane, *Masai Elder,* 24 x 30, oil.
Courtesy: Tucson Creative Group

Stephen Zaima, *untitled,* 30 x 22, oil on canvas, 1987

Douglas Zalud-Mackie, *The Tribulation,* 108 x 132, acrylic on canvas

J. Ronald V. Zaneveld, *Mount Manaia,* 16 x 20, acrylic on canvas

Harriet Zeitlin, *Summer in Minnesota,* 48 x 72, mixed media

Nada Zoric, *The Forms,* 36 x 48, oil. Courtesy: Carnegie Museum, Oxnard, CA

Mary Warner, *Rainforest,* 86 x 120, oil on canvas. Courtesy: Jennifer Pauls Gallery, Sacramento, CA

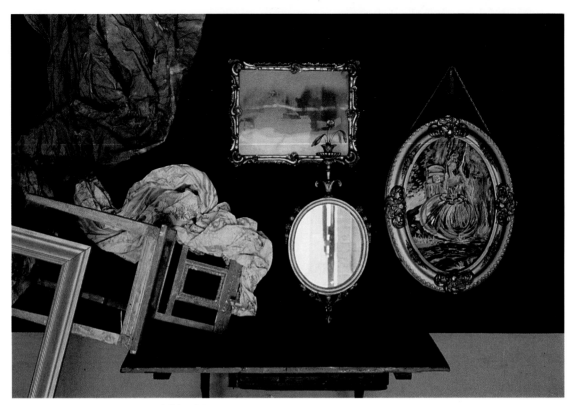

Lisa Zukovsky, *Child Bride (1988),* 48 x 84, oil, wood, latex, fabric & mirror on canvas

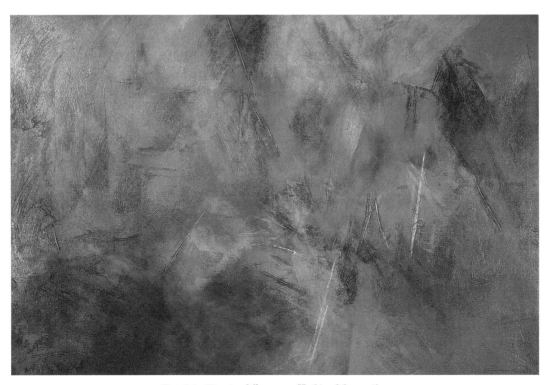

Patricia Zippin, *Minataree II,* 64 x 96, acrylic

1970s often creates crucifix imagery. In his later series of still lifes, objects are arranged individually and somewhat spontaneously, unlike in traditional still lifes, so that each achieves importance and independence. Yet the objects are linked through strong composition—a pen, a fork, a knife or even a shadow will point the eye to some other element in the painting, as if to say, "Now contemplate this other thing." The backgrounds become pure horizons, paintings are divided horizontally, shadows fall directly to the left and the lighting is crisp. The works reveal the strong influence of the 17th- century Dutch Masters.

WOOD, JOAN BERGREN (Painter)
6036 Riverside Blvd. Suite A9, Sacramento, CA 95831

Born: 1941 *Awards:* 1st, 2nd, 3rd Place, Tehema County Fair, Red Bluff, CA *Exhibitions:* Spring International, Alexander's Fine Art, Sutter Creek, CA; Joan & Vincent Wood Studio, Sacramento *Education:* U. of Iowa; Cal. State-Sacramento; Famous Artists School, Westport, CT

As an oil painter, she was influenced by van Gogh for his heavy paint and pure colors and by Thomas Hart Benton and Grant Wood for their patterns, shapes and moods. As a result, the paintings were thick, impressionistic, bright florals and landscapes. For the last fifteen years, however, watercolor has been here preferred medium. The paintings are detailed florals and sky scapes in which she occasionally uses ink line to contrast the softness of the watercolor. The works shows all ranges of tone, with the white paper itself an important color in the painting. She works primarily from photos and sketches on site, presenting an accurate rendering, but the treatment always ranges a bit beyond the real to produce a slightly exaggerated, surrealistic image.

WOODCOCK, MARGARET (Painter, Draughtsperson)
927 26th St., Sacramento, CA 95816

Born: 1951 *Awards:* Juror's Award, Crocker-Kingsley Exhibit *Exhibitions:* Art Gallery, San Francisco State U.; 1078 Gallery, Chico *Education:* Cal. State-Fresno; San Francisco Art Institute

In her early work she concentrated on drawing, formal design, and rendering, a background which is still apparent in her recent paintings. She was influenced by the color, sensuousness, and boldness of the Impressionists and Expressionists. She felt that these styles were especially appropriate for the western landscapes which constitute most of her work. These drawings and paintings convey the heat and stillness associated with the hills and valleys of California. Recent work in oil exhibits traditional glazing techniques and the use of traditional perspective. She has incorporated some surrealist imagery and expressionistic brushwork into her recent painting. The landscapes act as metaphors for the dynamism of life, and she portrays these energies via her combination of intimate, subtle color layers and texturing, and the boldness and stark character of her large brushstrokes and painterly use of color.

WOODCOCK, MICHAEL (Painter, Draughtsman)
P.O. Box 264, Claremont, CA 91711

Born: 1951 *Collections:* Paramount Pictures; Technicolor; Riverside Art Museum *Exhibitions:* Salathe Gallery, Pitzer College; Fine Art Gallery, UC-Irvine

Education: Golden West College; Claremont Graduate School

His early pattern and decorative work showed an intense involvement with materials. The grid patterns of his sewn cloth and paper collages were based on qualities inherent in those media. Ranging from five inches square to over ten feet in length, these pieces were marked and stained with a wide range of media, including paint, blood and handmade dyes and inks. In 1982, he abruptly changed direction. Believing that profound art could be made with simpler materials and familiar subjects, he began using graphite on paper to make small, sensitive, highly realistic drawings of his friends. He has taught at Mount San Antonio College, Scripps College, Claremont Graduate School and the California Prison System.

WOOTEN, MICK (Mixed Media Artist, Photo Collage Artist)
P.O. Box 636, Springville, CA 93265

Born: 1950 *Exhibitions:* Base II Gallery, Los Angeles; Santa Monica College *Education:* El Camino College, Los Angeles

Dissatisfied with his studies in art, he turned to photography, finally leaving school altogether, in order to develop and define his personal style of collage. He has been making collages full- time since 1966; several of them have appeared in limited fine art editions. Using newspapers, magazine photos, advertisements and art reproductions as source materials, he hand-presses the images, gluing them with a non-water base adhesive, to create the illusion that the final image is united in a single plane. Standing squarely in the surrealist tradition, his collages resist interpretation. Fascinated, intrigued and simultaneously frustrated by his suggestive combinations of images, the viewer is lured out of his reality and left in a world of mystery.

WOOTEN, WILLIAM E. (Painter)
7799 Valley View #G103, La Palma, CA 90623

Born: 1954 *Awards:* Honorable Mention, 28th Annual Hillcrest Festival of the Arts *Exhibitions:* "A Night in Fullerton"; Cypress 12th Annual Juried Art Exhibit *Education:* U. of Nebraska

His love of watercolor and his need for control prompted him to learn airbrush techniques. Working in acrylic on canvas, he creates three-dimensional images of folded paper. Golden yellow, red and violet accent gray backgrounds, contrasting with recently added renditions of ropes and knots.

WORDELL, EDWIN H. (Painter, Mixed Media Artist)
6251 Lorca Dr., San Diego, CA 92115

Born: 1927 *Awards:* George Gray Award, U.S. Coast Guard, NYC; 1st Award, Watercolor West, Riverside Art Center *Collections:* NASA, Cape Kennedy, FL; U.S. Coast Guard *Exhibitions:* San Diego Art Institute; The Art Collector Gallery, Old Town, San Diego *Education:* San Diego State U. *Dealer:* The Aesthetics Collection, San Diego

Early influences included Edward Hopper, Fred Hocks (often described as California's first Abstract Expressionist) and Millard Sheets. In the early 1970s, Wordell began painting almost exclusively on rag paper in watercolor and acrylic. He explores the possibilities of water media in both representational and abstract styles. From the mid-1970s to the mid-1980s, he textured paper with white acrylic, then finished the paintings in watercolor. He later began to add water-colored rag paper collage to the textured surfaces, completing them in gouache. This became an on-going series. The representational works are characterized by a highly realistic technique and careful attention to detail, especially to the effects of light, color and shading on various outdoor subjects.

WORTH, DON (Photographer)
38 Morning Sun Ave., Mill Valley, CA 94941

Born: 1924 *Awards:* NEA Photography Fellowship, Guggenheim Fellowship *Education:* Juilliard School of Music, Manhattan School of Music

Originally trained as a musician, he turned to photography as an additional medium of expression following an assistantship with Ansel Adams in the late 1950s. He is widely recognized for his vast collection of photographs of plants. He works in black-and-white and color, and his prints range from photographs of plants taken in extreme close-up to panoramic views of hillsides covered with vegetation. His fascination with flora as a subject has taken him around the world. He has also produced several self- portraits over the years, and shots of urban settings and architecture.

WRENCH, CHRIS (Glazier)
3103 NW Wilson, Portland, OR 97210

Born: 1935 *Awards:* Phi Alpha Theta International Honor Society in History *Exhibitions:* Renwick Gallery, Washington, DC; White Bird Gallery, Cannon Beach, OR *Dealer:* Contemporary Crafts Gallery, Portland, OR

Leaded glass is his medium of expression. He was originally trained in Victorian and art-nouveau glass restoration. Later, he studied with several glass artists and worked under Garth Edwards. He eventually developed a personal and contemporary use of the leaded-glass medium. He is fascinated with how the eye is capable of perceiving movement simultaneously with its perception of resolution, and he is stimulated by the glass idiom's architectural as well as artistic requirements. Currently working on commission, he is creating a set of double doors with geometric designs and earth-toned colors. He has been influenced by Peter Mollica, Garth Edwards, Jochem Poesgen and Paul Marioni.

WRIGHT, BRADFORD (Painter)
629 State St. #240, Santa Barbara, CA 93101

Born: 1944 *Exhibitions:* Jerry Solomon Gallery, Los Angeles; College of Creative Studies, UC-Santa Barbara *Education:* Otis Art Institute, Los Angeles *Dealer:* Yoram Kollerstein

After studying with Peter Krasnow he adopted the California modernist's mystical/constructivist style and made it his own by combining high-key color harmonics with lattice-like superimpositions of shapes, reminiscent of a primitive influence. In 1980 he began to take a more painterly approach which rejected bright colors and defined structures. His forms became dissolute in color and light. Gesture and mark grew in importance. His recent work is in oil on canvas and acrylic on paper. He applies paint in thin layers and scrapes it off building up a translucent, scored surface with visible brushstrokes. He seeks to continue and develop the metaphysical tradition of early modernism, demonstrating that abstraction can serve an inner necessity and express belief and optimism rather than despair and rejection.

WRIGHT, CONNIE (Painter)
651 22 Ave., San Francisco, CA 94121

Born: 1957 *Awards:* Accomplished Oil Pastelist, Oil Pastel Association, New York; American Indian Merit, Berkeley *Collections:* San Francisco Art Institute *Exhibitions:* Foster Goldstrom Gallery, San Francisco; Leopold-Hoesch Museum, Duren, West Germany *Education:* San Francisco Art Institute *Dealer:* Miki Stiles, NYC

Influenced by Milton Avery and Paul Klee, her own work is semi-abstract expressionist. From 1976 to 1985, she painted on unstretched primed canvas with oil pastel and acrylic. Woven with lines of color in oil pastel and solid areas of acrylic, the surface on top is as important as the layer underneath. She considers her pieces diaries, with images of commonplace experiences in the home—for instance, a woman climbing out of bed—or outdoor places she has visited. A sense of movement or activity is characteristic of the work. For the past three years, she has been painting on black paper. The images and colors in these pieces recall American Indian art traditions, in particular the art of the Kachina doll.

WRIGHT, DONNA (Painter)
4551 W. McSwain, Merced, CA 95340

Born: 1943 *Awards:* Best Watercolor Landscape, Southwest Airlines; Merit Award, California State Fair *Collections:* Carl Holvick Co., Inc., San Francisco *Exhibitions:* Landell Gallery, Santa Cruz; Professional Award-Winning Artists Invitational Exhibit, Fresno *Education:* Merced College

Her paintings are a glimpse into the subconscious, a reflection of the image of the soul. Her tools are spontaneity and intuitiveness, and her technique has been referred to as a controlled accident. She begins by pouring surface colors, wet into wet, and then uses various tools to quickly shape the paint in forms. She allows the medium to decide whether she should stop at abstraction, progress to semi-abstraction or develop into full realism. Within an hour, she achieves balance and unity. Colors are used to capture the mood of the moment. Her media are watercolor, acrylic and acrylic collage; all work is executed on 100 percent rag paper. She has been inspired by Barbara Neichis, Maxine Masterfield and Virginia Cobb. Recent subjects include young ladies, geishas, ballet dancers, landscapes and flowers.

WRIGHT, MICHAEL RAGSDALE (Painter, Draughtsperson)
2021 S. Alameda, Los Angeles, CA 90058-1036

Born: 1944 *Exhibitions:* Richard Bennett Gallery, Los Angeles; Cal. State-Los Angeles *Education:* U. of Washington

His interest in art began when he was a senior in college. Since then, he has produced expressionist paintings and drawings. He prefers experimenting with the range of tonal contrasts and the compositional juxtaposition of positive and negative spaces. Many of his figures are placed near open doors or windows, and the streams of light and areas of shadow are a dominant characteristic of his style. He uses acrylics, charcoal, graphite, and pastel grays on large surfaces. His figures exude a brooding or languid air, a state much in contrast to the vigorous handling of the media.

Garcia Lou Young-Willard, *When Old Dreams Find Their Youth Again in the Sunshine,* 40 x 30, pencil

Haeju Andrea Yim, *Easel Painter's Quantative View,* 36 x 36, mixed media collage on canvas

WU, KANG T. (Photographer)
2522 178th St. S.E., Bothell, WA 98012

Born: 1950 *Awards:* Gold Medal & Best of Show, Black and White Division, Photographic Society of America *Exhibitions:* Museum of History and Industry, Seattle; Wyman Park Gallery, La Conner, WA

Born in the People's Republic of China, he escaped the Cultural Revolution by swimming to Hong Kong at age twenty. He came to the United States in the late 1970s and has been an avid photographer since 1980. His first subjects were were watery scenes at Moss Bay in Kirkland, Washington. Today, he photographs in and around Washington State and returns to China annually to photograph its exotic beauty. In an effort to capture the dimensionality of the landscape, he does much of his photographing in the morning or late afternoon. He uses three different cameras: the Nikon FM, the Hasselblad and a 4 x 5 format Linhof Technica. He normally works with a tripod.

XANDERSTAR, EDARE (Painter)
c/o Montecito Fine Arts, 43 E. Montecito Ave., Sierra Madre, CA 91024

Born: 1945 *Awards:* Purchase Prize, Clairmont College *Collections:* Townsend Collection, Pasadena *Exhibitions:* Newport Harbor Museum; Los Angeles Municipal Gallery *Education:* Cal. State-Northridge; California Institute of the Arts, Valencia *Dealer:* Montecito Fine Arts, Sierra Madre

Though he was trained in abstract expressionism and pop art, he was influenced by Chuck Close, D.J. Hall, and Bruce Everett to take up a photo-realistic style. In the early 1970s, he explored the effect of chaotic visual information on visual perception. This led to an investigation of nature and mythology as opposing forces and an imagery based on ideas of life as existing in harmonious balance at the center of a matrix of forces. He works with acrylic on nylon canvas, using structure and grids in combination with areas of free-flowing paint. He employs a non-traditional perspective and often biomorphic forms will emerge from his black backgrounds and fields.

YASAMI, MASOUD (Painter)
14025 Panay Way, Marina del Rey, CA 90292

Born: 1949 *Awards:* Purchase Awards, Arizona Biennal, Tucson Museum of Art *Collections:* Tucson Museum of Art; Utah Museum of Fine Arts *Exhibitions:* Elaine Horwitch Gallery, Palm Springs; Phoenix Art Museum *Education:* Oregon State U.; Arizona State U. *Dealer:* Elaine Horwitch Gallery, Palm Springs

A native of Iran, he came to the U.S. at age 18 to study engineering at Oregon State University. A course in figure drawing persuaded him to take up art, and enamored with the work of Magritte, he sought an art degree. At Arizona, he created a series of "boxes," consisting of unfolding containers, some painted, others wholly constructed. His recent work reveals an interest in optical illusion through the emphasis of contrasting elements: heavy vs. light, bright vs. dark, soft vs. coarse and most importantly, control vs. chaos.

YATES, PAM (Sculptor)
P.O. Box 323, Graton, CA 95444

Born: 1942 *Awards:* Artist of the Year, Santa Rosa *Collections:* Corporate Offices, Steak & Ale Restaurants, Dallas *Exhibitions:* Los Angeles Art Craft and Folk Art Museum; Newport Harbor Art Museum *Education:* Cranbrook Academy; Washington U. *Dealer:* The Works Gallery, Philadelphia

With formal training in the textile and fiber arts, silversmithing, lapidary, printmaking and papermaking, she has pioneered as an entrepreneur in the ancient art of fan making. In the early 1970s, she opted for the fan as a form in her constructions, a form that is "both form and symbol, vital, kinetic, provocative." It is an ornament, a tool of the shaman and priest, as useful in life today as it has been for centuries. She uses several media in traditional and non-traditional techniques: stone, bone, leather and fiber, silver, gold and other metals, lucite and polymers, handmade and hand formed papers, paints and pigments. She sees in her work a celebration, a unifying of the past and present.

YES, PHYLLIS (Mixed Media Artist)
5235 SW View Point Terrace, Portland, OR 97201

Born: 1941 *Awards:* NEA Fellowship; Oregon Arts Commission Grant *Collections:* Security Pacific Bank, Los Angeles; Museum of Art, Univ. of Oregon, Eugene *Exhibitions:* Virginia Breier Gallery, San Francisco; Elizabeth Leach Gallery, Portland *Dealer:* Virginia Breier Gallery, San Francisco; Cathy Carron, NYC

Her mixed media pieces convey an interest in psychological responses to color. The works employ stereotypical visual symbols to result in gender confusion, as in *Por-She*, a lace painted Porsche automobile. Her depictions of ladders, saws, hammers, trowels and other objects are embellished with intricate patterns. She has recently been working on a series of painted, life-size female torsos, entitled "In Honor of Women."

YETT, JANE M. (Photographer, Draughtsperson)
P.O. Box 274, Santa Cruz, CA 95061

Born: 1946 *Exhibitions:* Open Studio, Cultural Council of Santa Cruz County; Santa Cruz Art Center *Education:* Stanford U.; UC-Berkeley

After several years of teaching environmental and political studies at the collegiate level, she turned to the visual dimensions of politics. Inspired by Dorothea Lange and Pedro Luis Raota, she explores new approaches to similar photographic subject matter. Images focus on scenes of everyday life in other countries: for example, the Masa elders of Tanzania and boat crossings in Hong Kong. She also creates pen and ink drawings, which concern awkward, fleeting thoughts of love, and other scenes that display the drama of human emotion.

YIM, HAEJU ANDREA (Painter)
1900 Avenue of the Stars, Ste. 640, Century City, CA 90067

Born: 1951 *Exhibitions:* Hoyer Gallery, Pacific Asia Museum, Pasadena; Theater Gallery, Los Angeles Design Center

After formal training in abstraction, she developed a personal abstract expressionist style which recalls the influences of Arshile Gorky and Vassily Kandinsky. In the mid-1980s, she began to experiment with biomorphic forms, sensuous chromatic visualizations and highlighted patterns, and the ways in which these elements are controlled by conscious artistic creation. Recently her attention has been focused on the works of Jasper Johns, Anselm Kiefer, Helen Frankenthaler and Susan Rothenberg. Also employing acrylics, and

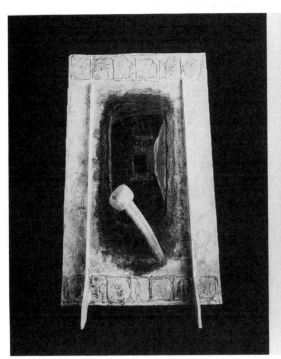

Ronald D. Young, *When the Ball Court Joins the Club,* 27 x 16 x 2, bronze and wood

Dan Young, *The City of Los Angeles Marathon, March 6, 1988,* 24 x 36, hand-painted serigraph

occasionally painting on a mass-media photograph or on a found object, she has been exploring conceptually based art on the subject of consumerism.

YONEMOTO, BRUCE (Video Artist)
20 Brooks Ave., Venice, CA 90291

Born: 1949 *Awards:* NEA Fellowship; Tokyo International Video Festival *Collections:* Museum of Modern Art, NYC; Hara Museum, Tokyo, Japan *Exhibitions:* World-Wide Video Festival, The Hague, Amsterdam *Education:* UC-Berkeley; Otis Art Institute *Dealer:* Electronic Arts Intermix, NYC

His and his brother Norman Yonemoto's investigation of the social impact of narrative information has resulted in a unique body of video artworks which reflexively deconstruct the formulas of popular culture. A variety of sources from television, films, art and advertising are manipulated to extract the conflicting codes that guide their production and through them our concept of living. In *Vault*, the self-parody of television's language is brought to the surface through an appropriation of the narrative and symbolic conventions of soap opera. Production is convincingly accurate, but by distorting slightly the use of flashbacks to illuminate the situation, they are exposed as manufactured motifs rather than honest representations of meaning, and the direct causality between past and present is questioned. Other works, such as *Kappa,* splice actual media footage to effect a chaos in which meaning is sensed but never actually grasped. These works and their current independent feature *Made in Hollywood* seek to create a heightened T.V. reality that reveals the dynamic of our media-propagated cultural myths.

YORK, TINA (Painter, Mixed-Media Artist)
11652 Huston St., N. Hollywood, CA 91601

Born: 1951 *Awards:* Honorable Mention, Beverly Hills Spring Festival; Honorable Mention, Cornell Arts Festival *Collections:* Columbia U., NYC; Hiatt International, Beverly Hills *Exhibitions:* Southern California Art Association, Los Angeles; Alpha Contemporary Exhibits, Los Angeles *Education:* Brandeis U.

A child prodigy on the violin, she was forced to give up music for medical reasons, and turned to the visual arts. One early series was "The Creation," a suite of seven large, realistic oil paintings. Today she primarily does commissions for academic institutions and industry, working in a style she calls "abstract symbolism" or "macrorealism." She is best known for her acrylic, oil and mixed media three-dimensional paintings of science-related subjects, either close-up views of microscopic objects or events, or futuristic visions of human existence. Her style combines vibrant colors and dramatic compositions. A recent undertaking is a book entitled *The Universe Within Us,* which includes more than fifty paintings based on scanning electron micrographs of the human body, with text on scientific subjects. She is also working on the feasibility of translating futuristic scientific imaging into art.

YOSHIMOTO, HIROKO (Painter)
352 Lupine Way, Ventura, CA 93001

Born: 1943 *Exhibitions:* Art Rental Gallery, Los Angeles County Museum of Art; Los Angeles Art Core Center *Education:* UCLA; Santa Raparata Studio, Florence, Italy *Dealer:* Susan Pertle, Chicago

Although her formal art training came in the U.S., she draws from her native Japan for the understanding of a second culture and its art. Her works, such as her "Sengai" and "See No Evil" series, seek a balance between conflicting philosophies and customs. Her teachers include Sam Amato and Nathan Oliveira, and her style is richly textured abstraction in oil. Figures have begun to appear in her recent work. The abstraction has become more expressionistic, although her travels to Japan have influenced her imagery to reflect classical Japanese spatial concepts.

YOUNG, DAN (Painter)
6301 Vista Del Mar, Playa Del Rey, CA 90293

Born: 1950 *Awards:* Pacific Art Guild; Venice Art League Annual Exhibit *Exhibitions:* Beverly Hills Art Guild; The Collection Gallery, La Jolla

A traditional approach to watercolor influenced by the French Impressionists gave way to a freer expressionism with his move to California. He feels no color, style or content restrictions, and enjoys the Southwestern palette suggested by Los Angeles' quality of light. A track runner, he has depicted many sporting events. A unique monoprint process was used on the design selected as the Official Art Poster of the third annual Los Angeles Marathon in 1988. After an image has been blocked on a silkscreen, a water-base textile ink is added with a liberal movement of the brush and squeegee. The result appears hand-painted. His watercolor painting focuses on abstract interpretations of color. He feels that color directly evokes emotional response, and uses high-key colors to inspire excitement without a need for form.

YOUNG, JOAN HORSFALL (Painter)
218 McCarty Dr., Beverly Hills, CA 90212

Born: 1944 *Awards:* Gold Medal Show, California Art Club, Los Angeles; Affair in the Garden, Beverly Hills *Collections:* IBM, Tokyo; Gibraltar Savings, Los Angeles *Exhibitions:* Four Seasons Art Gallery, Glendale; Top of the Mart Gallery, Los Angeles *Education:* Central Art School, Toronto; Cal. State-Northridge *Dealer:* Ojai Art Center

Her influences have always pre-dated this century. Initially, it was the spontaneity and color of the Impressionists; later it was the dark, brooding Barbizon painters. Recently, she has been fascinated with the Dutch and Italian painters of the sixteenth and seventeenth centuries. She speculates that she will find her ultimate mentor in the Neolithic caves of Lascaoux. Her oil on linen paintings address specific states of being, e.g., disciplined, fatigued, relaxed, nervous, or anxious. By combining her landscape experience with her newer love of figurative painting, she places figures—humans and animals—in their own unique settings, allowing the light source and respective shadows to reveal the story. She combines alla prima and glazing techniques to allow more sensitive brushwork to add further interest to the surface of the canvas.

YOUNG, MARION L. (Sculptor)
1120 S. Westgate Ave. #7, Los Angeles, CA

Awards: Best of Show, Affair in the Garden, Beverly Hills; Adolph and Esther Gottlieb Grant *Collections:* Columbia U. School of Medicine; UCLA School of Medicine *Exhibitions:* Upstairs Gallery, Los Angeles; Affaire in the Gardens, Los Angeles

She sculpts figures and heads in bronze, influenced by the realism of Leonardo da Vinci and Houdon, and by their mastery of human anatomy. Her own studies of

Joan Horsfall Young, *A Job Well Done,* 30 x 36, oil on linen

Seyburn Zorthian, *No. 5 Small, 1987,* 48 x 33,
sumi and oil on linen

J. Ronald V. Zaneveld, *The Lightkeeper's House,* 16 x 20, acrylic on canvas

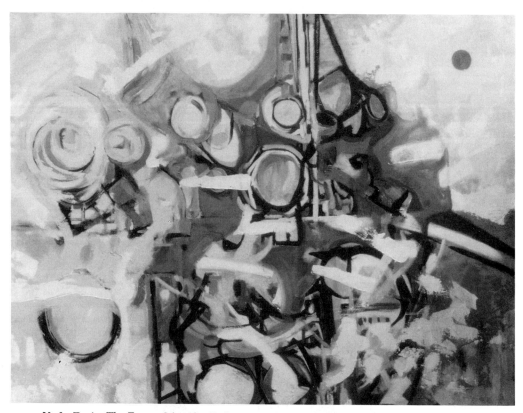

Nada Zoric, *The Forms,* 36 x 48, oil. Courtesy: Cornegy Museum, Oxnard, CA

Lisa Zukovsky, *Rabbit Over Summer on the Beach,* 16 x 20, oil on canvas with frame

Stephen Zaima, *I Am Zaima,* 300 x 720, rhoplex on translucent black scrim, 1985.
Courtesy: The Everson Museum of Art

human anatomy at the University of California Medical School resulted in the bronze sculpture *Essentia,* a half-life-size figure of a skinless woman stepping forward with one arm raised and outstretched. The level of anatomical rendition in this piece compares to Houdon's *Flayed Man.* The more psychologically-oriented work of Rodin has inspired her more recent sculptures, now more impressionistic and influenced by her own studies in psychology. *Archetypes,* a study of the human psyche, is an example of this work. The piece consists of two heads, one male and one female.

YOUNG, RONALD D. (Sculptor)
624 W. 10th Ave., Escondido, CA 92025

Born: 1940 *Awards:* Tiffany Award *Collections:* Johnson and Johnson, New Brunswick, NJ; Downey Museum, Downey *Exhibitions:* North Dakota Museum of Art; Civic Art Gallery, Walnut Creek *Education:* Cal. State-Long Beach; UCLA *Dealer:* Ankrum Gallery, Los Angeles

The artist studied at eight universities between 1959 and 1971, including the Accademia de Belle Art in Rome, where he received a Prie de Rome. He has taught and lectured around the world and recently published one of only two books available in the U.S. on patinas. The artist's works have been of Mayan and pre-Columbian influence, and his most recent pieces encompass the Southwestern theme. Each sculpture consists of one main medium, such as bronze or limestone, to which other materials, often pieces of wood or resin, are introduced. The compositions are organic and richly textured, blending symbols and forms from the past and the present with contrasting materials.

YOUNG-WILLARD, GARCIA LOU (Painter)
8228 N. 19th Ave. #503, Phoenix, AZ 85021

Born: 1944 *Awards:* American Artists' Professional League Award for Pastel; Grumbacher Silver Award for Pastel *Exhibitions:* Salamugundi Club, NYC; Catherine Lorilland Wolfe Art Club *Dealer:* Roger Lee Willard, Phoenix, AZ

Private training in drawing and sculpture, including intensive study of the human form, combined with the influence of Gerrit van Honthurst and John Singer Sargent to produce studies of individuals in their personal environments or engaged activities. Setting and role play an equal part with expression, clothing, and gesture in silverpoint, graphite, and pastel works. A high-contrast style involves the development of abstract areas in chiaroscuro, thereby "establishing important relationships in both the second and third dimensions" with the ultimate end of "exposing the fourth dimension—the visualization of unseen reality". Works are executed in both black and white and full color.

YUMI (Painter)
5700 Baltimore Dr. #40, La Mesa, CA 92042

Born: 1940 *Awards:* 1st Award, International Fine Arts Exhibition *Collections:* La Jolla Fine Arts Gallery; Fuji Bank, Tokyo *Exhibitions:* Johnson Pasadena Art Galleries; Gallery 21, San Diego *Education:* Keio U., Tokyo *Dealer:* Koizumi Art Enterprises, San Francisco

She paints the urban and rural landscapes of France and Holland in a modern impressionist style, accented with an Oriental sensibility. Although she was formally trained in watercolor painting, the strong influence of van Gogh's work prompted her to turn to oils. During the early 1980s, she lived in Holland and worked on refining her technique, which is characterized by bold brushstrokes and brilliant colors. Creating her own palette, she strives to express peace, harmony and emotion through color.

ZAIMA, STEPHEN (Painter, Sculptor)
Studio Arts, Syracuse U., Syracuse, NY 13244

Born: 1947 *Awards:* NEA Fellowship; Ford Foundation Grant *Collections:* Everson Museum of Art, Syracuse, NY; Edward Albee Collection, NYC *Exhibitions:* Stephen Rosenberg Gallery, NYC; Everson Museum of Art, Syracuse, NY *Education:* UC-Davis; San Jose State U. *Dealer:* Stephen Rosenberg, NYC

After studying with William Wiley, Robert Arneson and Wayne Thiebaud, he continued to create sculpture while teaching. Presently an abstract image painter, he applies paint in an eclectic manner, attempting to portray feeling and emotional depth, rather than surface appearance and pictorial depth. Influenced by Beckmann, Morandi and Guston, he paints with oils on canvas, and on wall-hung wood and glass constructions. Throughout his predominantly black, white and red work, he restates images and abstract shapes, searching for new ways to paint the same objects. He is a member of faculty in the department of art at Syracuse University.

ZAJAC, JACK (Painter, Sculptor)
1316 W. Cliff Dr., Santa Cruz, CA 95060

Born: 1929 *Awards:* Guggenheim Fellowship; Rome Fellowship *Collections:* Metropolitan Museum of Art, NYC; Whitney Museum, NYC *Exhibitions:* Orvieto, Italy; Stephen Wirtz Gallery, San Francisco *Education:* American Academy, Rome *Dealer:* Stephen Wirtz Gallery, San Francisco

He began his career as an abstract expressionist painter in Southern California. After going to Rome, he began to sculpt in clay. His first sculptures on the theme of the sacrificial animal, in 1959, were followed by small metamorphic pieces done in direct wax. These led to the cycle of humanistic Judeo-Christian icons, which included the fourteen massive "Ram's Skulls" he completed in the early 1960s. In 1965, he began making the serene stone and bronze images of falling water, streams and swan's wings that have, for the most part, occupied him since. In 1976, he returned to the skull form briefly for a large outdoor show in Orvieto, Italy. These skulls are more abstract and are of a grander scale than those he had previously produced.

ZALUD-MACKIE, DOUGLAS (Painter, Sculptor)
1430 Willamette, #619, Eugene, OR 97401

Born: 1953 *Awards:* Artist In Residence Award, Medford Senior High School *Collections:* Oregon Shakespeare Festival, Ashland *Exhibitions:* Blue Star Gallery, Ashland, OR

He creates figurative and non-figurative sculptures for public places and integral sculptural forms for dance and theatre. He is a dancer himself and many of his large pieces show abstracted figures in athletic positions. His paintings, such as *Woman Prophet* and *Messenger of Light,* have been huge wall-size murals, also dealing with abstracted figures. His recent sculpture reflects his interest in the way light and color effect three-dimensional form. In these pieces, he casts acrylic resin and then applies it in layers to create mirror-like reflective surfaces. He is also placing light

Douglas Zalud-Mackie, *Awakening,* 12 feet high, carved reinforced concrete. Courtesy: Medford High School, Medford, OR

Victor Zane, *Weekend Cowboy,* 24 x 30, oil. Courtesy: California Farmer Magazine

sources within the work. Along with being a sculptor, he is a dancer, choreographer and designer.

ZAMMITT, NORMAN (Painter)
233 N. Wilson Avenue, Pasadena, CA 91106

Born: 1931 *Awards:* Guggenheim Fellowship; Tamarind Fellowship *Collections:* Los Angeles County Museum of Art; San Francisco Museum of Modern Art *Exhibitions:* Ace Contemporary Exhibitions, Los Angeles; Los Angeles County Museum of Art *Education:* Otis Art Institute *Dealer:* Ace Contemporary Exhibitions, Los Angeles

He is influenced by Rembrandt and by the works of the luminist painters of the mid-19th century, as well as the impressionists, abstract expressionists and contemporary painters—these influences leading to his notion that form and content are born in color. His early works explored figurative, landscape and still-life subjects in a range of styles, using oils, mixed media and printmaking. In the '60s, he worked three-dimensionally in acrylic plastics. During this period, he began working entirely in the abstract, letting color dictate and create the form. These "sculptures" led him back to painting, now entirely abstract also. The paintings are large-scale canvases composed of bands of color gradually shifting from light to dark, warm to cool, emanating light seemingly from an internal source of energy. He works on the one hand methodically (adhering to mathematical formulas that calculate mixes and progressions in color), and on the other with great emotion and spirituality, seeking to harness the energy of these conflicting forces resolving themselves in his work.

ZANE, VICTOR (Painter)
20701 Canyon View Drive, Saratoga, CA 95070

Awards: American Painters in Paris Exhibition *Collections:* Baltimore Maritime Museum *Exhibitions:* Landell Gallery, Carmel; Roserock Gallery *Education:* Philadelphia Museum School of Art

His present paintings deal primarily with the people of Africa and the Caribbean; he shows particular interest in the Masai tribes of Kenya and Tanzania. The African series, a departure from his previous concentration on Western images, depicts the nomadic life of the Masai, which is reminiscent of the Plains Indians of the American Old West. His work explores traditional ways of life in their modern context. The paintings are realistic in scope with a strong sense of design and balance running throughout. He attempts to weave a pattern of light and shadow into his paintings to add drama to the subject. His media are oil, watercolor and pen and ink.

ZANEVELD, J. RONALD V. (Painter)
3908 N.W. Walnut Pl., Corvallis, OR 97330

Born: 1944 *Awards:* Artist in Residence, Australia Institute of Marine Science *Collections:* Gauguin Museum, Tahiti; King Tupou IV, Tonga *Exhibitions:* Jean P. Haydon Museum, American Samoa; Northland Art Trust, Whangarei, New Zealand *Education:* Oregon State U.; MIT. *Dealer:* Pegasus Gallery, Corvallis

With formal training in optics and oceanography, he originally combined his scientific knowledge with the techniques of Dutch Renaissance seascape painters. After studying with George Bleich and during his extensive travels, his style became more impressionistic with a major emphasis on the effect of light. In his

brilliantly colored Polynesian paintings, done *en plein air*, he focused on the creation of a luminous object with its own optical validity. In his recent paintings from New Zealand, Australia, and Holland, he has further explored ways of using light, shadow, color, and brushstrokes, to convey his emotional response to a wide variety of subjects. He next plans to carry out a series of paintings from a floating studio on the rivers and canals of Europe. He is a professor at Oregon State University.

ZAREMBA, JAN (Painter)
2000 N. Ivar Ave., Hollywood, CA 90068

Born: 1941 *Exhibitions:* Stella Polaris, Los Angeles; Olympic Arts Festival, Los Angeles *Education:* UCLA

Originally a German expressionist painter, he is better known for his mastery of the Japanese Sumi-e painting technique. After he moved to California from Germany, his use of images and colors changed, a reflection of Southern California's glowing, subtropical light. By the late 1970s, he had begun to seek out a more spiritual approach to art. The culmination of this quest was his four-year apprenticeship to one of "Japan's living national treasures," the Zen master Hisashi Ohta. During this time, he mastered the Sumi-e technique, which involves special inks, inkstone, brushes, rice paper and silk. His current project is a thirty-foot-long scroll painting of Sunset Boulevard in Sumi-e. The scroll rolls sideways, and the viewer is meant to see the painting, section by continuous section, "the way one experiences a journey (along Sunset Boulevard), reads a book or listens to music."

ZEITLIN, HARRIET (Painter)
202 S. Saltair Ave., Los Angeles, CA 90049

Born: 1929 *Awards:* Calif. Arts Council Grant *Collections:* Los Angeles County Museum; Grunwald Foundation, UCLA *Exhibitions:* Santa Barbara Museum; Monterey Museum of Art *Education:* U. of Pennsylvania; Penn. Academy of Fine Arts, Philadelphia

As a student at the Barnes Foundation in Merion, Pennsylvania, she was influenced by French Impressionists, the post-impressionists and the School of Paris. She began her career as a painter, later turning to printmaking and incorporating photography and quiltmaking into her work in the 1980s. This evolved into soft sculpture using a variety of media and found objects. For the past two years, she has been doing large acrylic paintings on canvas, sometimes working on top of printed fabric. Her work is representational, with flattened space and picture plane surfaces. She combines expressive and decorative elements in an exploration of the dualities of life and death, reality and unreality, flesh and stone, and matter and spirit. Her travels in Asia and the Middle East have led to works such as a series depicting dawn, morning, afternoon and evening on the Nile.

ZINGALE, MICHAEL (Ceramist)
c/o Lorel Cornman, 433 Ocean Ave., Santa Monica, CA 90402

Born: 1941 *Exhibitions:* Long Beach Museum of Art Rental Gallery; Museum of Functional Art, Santa Monica *Education:* Yale School of Art and Architecture *Dealers:* Lorel Cornman, Santa Monica

In the late 1960s, he explored new painting techniques, following the examples of Olitski, Noland, and Louis. By pouring and flooding large areas of taped and masked canvas with paint, he generated images show-

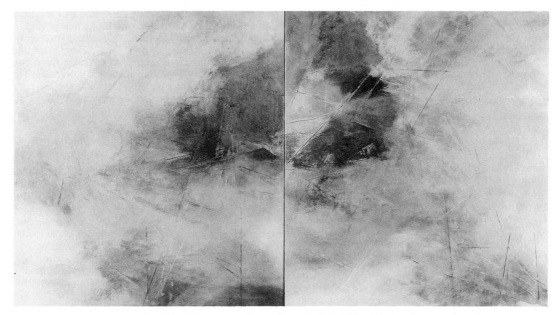

Patricia Zippin, *Raspberry Crystals IV, V,* 52 x 96, acrylic

Harriet Zeitlin, *Nile Night,* 48 x 72, acrylic on canvas

ing how opposites—rigid geometrics versus flowing organic shapes—could be fused together into a whole. In the early 1980s, Japanese ceramics and Sung dynasty stoneware influenced a new direction in his art. He works with high-fire stoneware slabs impressed, "collaged," and painted with oxides, engobes, and glaze. These abstract shapes are a direct response to the materiality of the clay rather than working from a preconceived design or plan.

ZIPPIN, PATRICIA (Painter)
4 Warren Ct., Tiburon, CA 94920

Born: 1930 *Collections:* Zellerbach, San Francisco; Price Waterhouse, San Francisco *Exhibitions:* Interart, San Francisco; Lawrence Salishan, Oregon *Education:* College of Arts and Crafts, Oakland; Academie Julian *Dealer:* Mareety Salishan Gallery, Gleneden Beach OR ; Lawrence Sheridan Gallery, Sheridan OR

After studying in numerous media at a variety of schools—the College of Arts and Crafts in Oakland, Academie Julian in Paris, Fleisher Memorial Graphics, each with its own emphasis and diverse influence—she found that acrylics provided her the freedom and potential to pursue her interest in color and texture. Beginning with an "all-over" plastic texture to establish direction and scale, she lays veils of color to intensify the light and space behind and in front of the established textural definitions. The color is used to define or subdue further the texture, creating a range of spatial qualities.

ZORIC, NADA (Painter, Draughtsperson)
P.O. Box 133, Agoura, CA 91301

Born: 1939 *Exhibitions:* Carnegie Museum, Oxnard; The Art Center, San Luis Obispo

She studied at the Art School of Fine Arts in Sarajevo, Yugoslavia and attended the University of Belgrade, Academy of Fine Art before coming to the U.S. to complete her masters and doctorate. Her paintings reflect her current circumstances in the sunnier climes of California. She now combines classical academic and old master training with poetic use of expressive colors. Her principle subject is the movement of nonobjective forms. Her strokes are free. Her paints penetrate the canvas to create images and yet the movement of her dynamic colors is easily recognizable to the viewer. Her pieces are very contemporary and they continue to grow in completely new directions. Her work is exhibited and collected widely in the U.S. and in Europe.

ZORICK, NANCY NOBLE (Painter)
51-555 Monroe, Sp. 31, Indio, CA 92201

Born: 1946 *Awards:* 1st Place, National Date Festival; 1st Place, Fontana Art Association *Exhibitions:* Coachella Valley Museum *Education:* The Art Institute of Chicago

After studying life drawing in pastels from George Sotos, she progressed to oil painting. In these small

works, she has been influenced, in part, by artists Paul Cezanne and Alphonse Mucha. Her animals appear to have whimsical personalities; her landscapes are either quietly serene or give the promise of a new beginning; and in her portraits of children, she captures the breathless excitement a child feels before a birthday party. She had been an actress in Chicago; she moved to Los Angeles to work in films and television. That career ended when she married a blind athlete and moved to the desert. She paints realistically, with a "joy for reality."

ZORTHIAN, SEYBURN (Painter)
P.O. Box 1007, Solvang, CA 93463

Born: 1948 *Collections:* AT & T, Baltimore, MD; Santa Barbara Arts Council *Exhibitions:* International Sumi-e Exhibition, NYC; Pacific Asia Museum, Pasadena *Education:* California Institute of the Arts

Her paintings are a serene, elegant combination of Japanese philosophy, Chinese calligraphic techniques, and western figuration. In the mid-1970s, she studied in Kyoto, Japan learning "shodou," an abstract form of Chinese calligraphy. She also studied Zen philosophy and developed her own style of sumi-e, or black ink, brushwork. She often uses several different brushes—bamboo and horsehair—on one piece. In her recent work, she has added different colors of oil washes to the swirling black forms, while allowing the surface's linen texture to emerge and remain as a significant design element. She also makes figurative and abstract drawings and straightforward, line-oriented portraits. She will often practice a line or mark up to 200 times before executing the final piece.

ZUKOVSKY, LISA (Painter)
145 Willard, San Francisco, CA 94118

Born: 1959 *Exhibitions:* Headlands Center for the Arts, San Francisco; Art in Various Places, San Francisco *Education:* UC-Berkeley

Her past work was heavily influenced by her admiration and response to the paintings of Vassily Kandinsky, Franz Marc and to the new expressionist school. This breakthrough work was far larger and much bolder in the use of color than later work would be. The focus of that later body of work is the interplay between nature and certain imposed conditions of artifice. In these works, she combines the imagery of nature with elements that refer to a highly structured and stylized environment. The frames are integral to each painting, since they further develop the imposed presence of humanity. The paintings are, for the most part, painted in a heavy, oil impasto with a loose and curvilinear brushstroke. The ground is usually a piece of linen or a mirror. Influences include the horse paintings of George Stubbs, French rococo painters (Fragonard and Boucher) and the salon-style format of hanging, utilized by both the Russian avant-garde and the post-impressionists.

ALAMEDA
ISLAND ALLIANCE OF THE ARTS
2120 Alameda Ave., Alameda, CA 94501
Programs/Activities: Coordinate and strengthen existing arts organizations in the arts; arts directory; workshops.

ALLEGHANY
SIERRA COUNTY ARTS COUNCIL
P.O. Box 951, Alleghany, CA 95910
Programs/Activities: "Artists in the Schools" program; art and dance classes t; traveling juried art show for students and adults; art purchase award.

ALTURAS
MODOC COUNTY ARTS COUNCIL, INC.
212 W. Third St., Alturas, CA 96101
Programs/Activities: Artist-in-Residence program; Arts-in-Action demonstrations; technical assistance and artist training workshops; art reference library; annual spring/summer juried arts and crafts fair; annual fall art exhibition.

AUBURN
ARTCETERA
175 Almond St., Auburn, CA 95603
Programs/Activities: The Auburn Arts Center, which includes a gallery; concerts, performances, theater groups and poetry readings; art exhibitions.

BELMONT
ARTS COUNCIL OF SAN MATEO COUNTY
1219 Ralston Ave., Belmont, CA 94002
Programs/Activities: Two galleries, one in Redwood County and the other in Twin Pines Park, Belmont; yearly open competition for the nine Bay Area counties; artist roundtables; "Meet the Artist" program for ongoing shows; works with the California Arts Council on the Partnership Program.

BENICIA
BENICIA COMMUNITY ARTS
P.O. Box 454 Benicia, CA 94510
Programs/Activities: Gallery exhibitions; art events.

BERKELEY
ASSOCIATION OF CALIFORNIA CERAMIC ARTISTS
1442A Walnut St., Berkeley, CA 94708
Programs/Activities: Lectures, critiques, workshops and semi-annual retreats; two shows a year in San Fransisco.

CIVIC ART COMMISSION
2180 Milvia St., Berkeley, CA 94704
Programs/Activities: Art in Public Places, among many arts programs, lectures and events.

KALA INSTITUTE
1060 Heinz Ave., Berkeley, CA 94710
Programs/Activities: Printmaking workshop, artist-in-residence program, gallery, print archive, annual performance and installation series and classes.

WEST BERKELEY SCULPTURE GARDEN
1102 Fifth St., Berkeley, CA 94710
Programs/Activities: Provides for continuous outdoor placement of monumental sculpture.

CARMEL
CARMEL ART ASSOCIATION
P.O. Box 2271 Carmel, CA 93921
Programs/Activities: Concerts, lectures, film series and demonstrations; scholarship programs for local high school students; gallery.

CHICO
CHICO ART CENTER
814 Glenn St., Chico, CA 95928
Programs/Activities: Art classes for adults and children; ceramics studio; art resources for the community; juried art exhibit every one to two years.

COLOMA
EL DORADO ARTS COUNCIL
P.O.Box 337, Coloma, CA 95613
Programs/Activities: Arts bank and cooperative gallery; arts-in-education program; "Celebrate the Arts Week" county-wide art festival.

CONCORD
CITIARTS – CITY OF CONCORD
1950 Parkside Dr., Concord, CA 94519
Programs/Activities: Four small art exhibit spaces called "Artspots"; exhibitions lasting one month to 6 weeks.

COSTA MESA
COSTA MESA ART LEAGUE
P.O.Box 1727, Costa Mesa, CA 92628
Programs/Activities: Monthly meetings featuring demonstrations by major artists, workshops and critiques; continuous monthly shows at gallery; major show for fine art in September.

CRESCENT CITY
THE DEL NORTE ART ASSOCIATION
200 Marine Way, Crescent City, CA 95548
Programs/Activities: Annual art show; exhibitions in gallery.

DAVIS
THE ARTISTS' COLLECTIVE OF DAVIS
207 G. St. Davis, CA 95616
Programs/Activities: Fine arts and crafts cooperative, featuring over 40 artists; gallery space and retail sales area.

DAVIS CIVIC ARTS COMMISSION
23 Russel Blvd., Davis, CA 95616
Programs/Activities: Local arts contracts; 1% municipal arts fund for Art-in-Public-Places program.

DAVIS SCHOOL ARTS FOUNDATION
P.O. Box 4093, Davis, CA 95617
Programs/Activities: Funding for activities furthering the future of fine arts in the schools; grants to art teachers; a dramatic arts cadre that has written an

articulated drama curriculum for use throughout the district.

EUREKA
HUMBOLDT ARTS COUNCIL
422 First St., Eureka, CA 95501
Programs/Activities: On-going program of monthly exhibits; Humboldt Arts Festival, an annual student art show; workshops, resource library, consultations and distibution of *ARC, the Rural Arts Newsletter* and *RADIUS, The Community Arts Bimonthly.*

THE INK PEOPLE
P.O. Box 1343, Eureka, CA 95502
Programs/Activities: Workspace for printmakers and other artists; classes in art techniques; exhibitions; monthly newsletter and a magazine, *Artmaking.*

FRESNO
INTERNATIONAL REGISTRY FOR RELIGIOUS WOMEN ARTISTS
2530 W. Alamos, #114, Fresno, CA 93705
Programs/Activities: "Loose-Leaf Communicator" shared by sending copies to be collated and mailed out with newsletter; informal get-togethers; tours; art retreats; area art exhibits; workshops; networking by telephone; mailing list.

GRASS VALLEY
NEIGHBORHOOD CENTER OF THE ARTS
212-B Richardson St., Grass Valley, CA 95945
Programs/Activities: Encourages developmentally disabled people in employment-related skills through art; foundation course in visual arts; "Art is Work".

HANFORD
KINGS COUNTY CULTURAL ARTS COUNCIL
1222 W. Lacey Blvd./ P.O.Box 1242, Hanford, CA 93232
Programs/Activities: Annual "Concerts in the Park" series; bi-monthly newsletter; monthly cultural events calendar; Spring Festival in April.

IRVINE
IRVINE CREATIVE ARTS GUILD
Box 4462 Irvine, CA 92716
Programs/Activities: Monthly meetings; art exhibitions.

JACKSON
AMADOR COUNTY ARTS COUNCIL
P.O.Box 666, Jackson, CA 95642
Programs/Activities: Information and referral for artists and organizations; grant application and technical assistance; annual arts directory; liaison to the California Arts Council and local partner in the CAC State-Local Partnership Program; co-sponsor of Chaw'Se Art Show.

LA JOLLA
LANDMARK ART PROJECTS
P.O. Box 3172, La Jolla, CA 92038
Programs/Activities: Promotes the integration of art and the environment; enhances awareness of the role of art in environmental and conservational development; supports, endorses and develops art projects toward those ends.

LA QUINTA
LA QUINTA ARTS FOUNDATION
P.O. Box 777, La Quinta, CA 92253
Programs/Activities: On-going art classes for adults and children; scholarships for college-bound students; three major art festivals annually.,

LOS ANGELES
L.A. ARTCORE
See Listing in Gallery Section.

FOUNDATION FOR ART RESOURCES
4804 Hollywood Blvd., Los Angeles, CA
Programs/Activities: Gallery and theater space; art park; lectures by visiting artists;programs and accepts proposals for a wide range of arts activities.

HIGHLAND ART GUILD
1377 Eagle Vista Dr. Los Angeles, CA 90041
Programs/Activities: Meets ten times a year, twice for a potluck and eight meetings to witness the demonstration of a visiting artist's technique.

LOS ANGELES CENTER FOR PHOTOGRAPHIC STUDIES
Programs/Activities: Promotes photography within the visual arts; exhibitions on historical and contemporary photography; lectures and workshops; critical publications; special projects.

LOS ANGELES CONTEMPORARY EXHIBITS: L.A.C.E.
1804 Industrial St., Los Angeles, CA 90021
Programs/Activities: Programs in static and non-static art forms to enhance the dialog between artists and their audiences.

VISUAL COMMUNICATIONS
263 S. Los Angeles, Los Angeles, CA 90012
Programs/Activities: Visual arts training in photograpy, video and film; photography and video exhibitions; Asian-Pacific media archives; assistance in management and grantsmanship.

WATTS TOWER ARTS CENTER
1727 East 107th St., Los Angeles, CA 90002
Programs/Activities: Program of the Cultural Affairs Department of the City of Los Angeles. Provides changing art exhibits, lectures, classes, performances and extensive assistance to developing and practicing artists; annual Simon Rodia Watts Towers Music & Arts Festival in Late July; annual Day of the Drum Festival in September.

THE WOMEN'S BUILDING, INC.
1727 N. Spring St., Los Angeles, CA 90012
Programs/Activities: Public center for women's culture provides gallery/performance space; women writers series; slide library; typesetting and design service; low-cost studio facilities.

MAMMOTH LAKES
MONO COUNTY ARTS COUNCIL
P.O. Box 1733, Mammoth Lakes, CA 93546
Dues: $15 *Members*: 100
Programs/Activities: educational and multi-cultural workshops and seminars for artists; Sierra Summer Festival in August; Labor Day Arts & Crafts Festival

MARTINEZ
ARTS: CONTRA COSTA
1236 Escobar St., Martinez, CA 94553
Programs/Activities: Workshops, art exhibits and a newsletter, *Spectrum*; technical assistance; exhibitions.

MARYSVILLE
GOLDEN VALLEY ART CENTER
415 10th St., Marysville, CA 95901
Programs/Activities: Art classes, exhibitions, meetings.

YUBA COUNTY-SUTTER COUNTY REGIONAL ARTS COUNCIL
P.O. Box 150, 526 C St., Marysville, CA 95901
Programs/Activities: Television show; Very Special Arts Festival; Artists-in- Residence; Art-in-Public-Places; community planning projects; Arts-in-Education; traveling arts; touring/presenting; video/literary resource library.

NAPA
NAPA COUNTY ARTS COUNCIL
P.O. Box 5604, Napa, CA 94581
Programs/Activities: Arts Registry information, resource and referral service; Cultural Resource Program placing artists in schools as visiting instructors; technical assistance for other nonprofit organizations in Napa county; monthly publication, *Artscan*.

NEVADA CITY
CIRCLES METIS ART, INC.
P.O. Box 1887, Nevada City, CA 95959
Programs/Activities: Non-profit, educational organization providing technical artistic training and opportunities to mixed- blood (metis) artists living in the foothils of the California Sierras; library; resource information on grants, scholarships and competitions; collects, exhibits and preserves Metis works of art.

NEVADA CITY
NEVADA COUNTY ARTS COUNCIL
401 Spring St., Suite 104, Nevada City, CA 95959
Programs/Activities: Microgallery displaying a rotating exhibit of local artists; lease program; monthly publication, *Art Matters*; resources, technical assistance and grants for artists; Sierra Visuals juried art.

NORTH HOLLYWOOD
NATIONAL WATERCOLOR SOCIETY
11850 Hartsook St., North Hollywood, CA 91607
Programs/Activities: Spring Membership Exhibit; National Annual Exhibit; newsletter; annual catalog; grant to children's art program of Los Angeles's Southwest Museum; traveling exhibitions.

OAKLAND

BAY AREA PARTNERSHIP
337 17th St., Oakland, CA 94612
Programs/Activities: Oakland City Assets Committee, a coalition of 40 key leaders from the public, private and nonprofit sectors that serves as a forum for greater communication, collaboration and action in preserving and expanding Oakland's arts, cultural facilities; Bay Area Arts and Humanities Network, with computerized data base; Public Art Network for executives in the public art and cultural planning fields.

OAKLAND FESTIVAL OF THE ARTS
337 17th St., Oakland, CA 94612
Programs/Activities: Year-round organization dedicated to fostering an appreciation for all the arts; annual K-12 Student Art Competition from March through June; Art Explosion annual Labor Day festival.

PRO ARTS
1920 Webster St., Oakland, CA 94612
Programs/Activities: Consultation; service library; seminars and workshops; artists-in-residency program; exhibitions; studio tours.

OXNARD
OXNARD ART ASSOCIATION
424 South "C" St., Oxnard, CA 93030
Programs/Activities: Monthly artists demonstrations; promotion of "public art" in the communities; scholarship for senior in high school.

PACIFIC GROVE
ARTISTS EQUITY – CENTRAL COAST CALIFORNIA
Box HG, Pacific Grove, CA 93950
Programs/Activities: Panel discussions, lectures and workshops on art legislation and judging exhibitions.

PALO ALTO
PACIFIC ART LEAGUE OF PALO ALTO
668 Ramona, Palo Alto, CA 94301
Programs/Activities: Art classes, exhibits, competitions, lectures; open studios; traveling art program for children; biennal juried competition, the Northern California Print Competiton.

PALO ALTO CULTURAL CENTER
1313 Newell Road Palo Alto, CA 94303
Programs/Activities: Exhibition Program ; Studio Program in painting, drawing, papermaking and printmaking; Volunteer Program; Art Education Program; Film and Performing Arts Program; Palo Alto Film Festival.

PARADISE
PARADISE ART CENTER
6686 Brookway, Paradise, CA 95969
Programs/Activities Paradise June Arts Festival, a multi- media presentation of the arts, music, drama, ballet; permanent exhibits at the Paradise Gold Nugget Museum.

PASADENA

PASADENA ARTS COUNCIL
116 Plaza, Pasadena, CA 91101
Programs/Activities: Annual Gold Crown Awards in Pasadena; scholarships to students in high school and college; twice yearly fine arts and crafts fair; monthly calendar of cultural events; monthly gallery exhibitions.

REDDING
SHASTA COUNTY ARTS COUNCIL
1313 Market St., P.O.Box 2595, Redding, CA 96099
Programs/Activities: Monthly gallery exhibits and performing arts in theatre and music; artist referral service; classes for seniors and adults; bi-monthly cultural events calendar; annual juried photography exhibit.

RICHMOND
RICHMOND ART CENTER
Civic Center Plaza, Richmond, CA 94804
Programs/Activities: Classes in arts and crafts, including painting, ceramics, jewelry and textiles; scholarships for needy and gifted students; gallery space; out-reach programs; artists- in-schools program.

RIDGECREST
HIGH DESERT COUNCIL OF THE ARTS
P.O. Box 1689, Ridgecrest, CA 93555
Programs/Activities: On-going community support for the arts; annual arts festival in the spring.

RIVERSIDE
RIVERSIDE ARTS FOUNDATION
3900 Main St., Riverside, CA 92522
Programs/Activities: Annual grants for community outreach projects; artists' registry; seminars, workshops and individual consultancies given to artists and organization; artist directory; arts organization directiory and bi-monthly newsletter; National Date Festival.

ROHNERT PARK
ROHNERT PARK CULTURAL ARTS CORPORATION
6750 Commerce Blvd., Rohnert Park, CA 94928
Programs/Exhibitions: Multicultural International Festival in April; photography show in October.

ROSEVILLE
ROSEVILLE ARTS CENTER
424 Oak St., Roseville, CA 95678
Programs/Activities: Gallery space; crafts boutique; classes and scholarships; Art Docent Program in the schools; shows and exhibitions.

SACRAMENTO
CALIFORNIA ARTS COUNCIL
1901 Broadway, Sacramento, CA 95818
*Programs/Activities:*The California state arts agency. Grants to artists and galleries to pursue their work.

SACRAMENTO METROPOLITAN ARTS COMMISSION
800 10th St., Sacramento, CA 95814
Programs/Activities: Art-in-Public-Places; Artreach employment program; library and referral service; administers awards program.

SAN BERNARDINO
THE ARTS FOUNDATION
157 W. 5th St., P.O. Box 1307, San Bernardino, CA 92402
Programs/Activities: Re-grant program for funds from county; round-table discussions with county artists to discuss art issues and to network; quarterly publication *ArtWorks*; year-round "Arts Express" program of hands-on arts experience for children; "Partners in Art Education" program of two-week residencies in public schools.

SAN DIEGO
BLACK WRITERS & ARTISTS, INC. OF SAN DIEGO
P.O. Box 161136, San Diego, CA 92116
Programs/Activities: Readings; artistic events featuring members' works; yearly conferences and workshops; annual journal, monthly meetings with speakers and critique sessions.

CENTRO CULTURAL DE LA RAZA
2004 Park Boulevard, San Diego, CA 92102
Programs/Activities: Produces and promotes Mexican, Indian and Chicano art and culture through publications, workshops, tours, sponsorship of artists and performing groups, exhibits, community cultural events and exchanges with Mexico; museum of Chicano art and culture.

COMBO (COMBINED ARTS AND EDUCATION COUNCIL OF SAN DIEGO)
701 B Street, P.O. Box 12248, San Diego, CA 92112
Programs/Activities: Funding, consulting, advice and aid to area artists and art organizations; regular meetings of San Diego art organizations; seminars and workshops.

INSTALLATION
930 E St., San Diego, CA 92104
Programs/Activities: Innovative projects by local, regional and national artists working in installation; exhibition space, video room, film screenings, public projects, interdisciplinary activities and artists fees.

SAN FRANCISCO
AMERICAN FEDERATION OF ARTS
270 Sutter St., San Francisco, CA 94108
Programs/Activities: Fine art, film and video exhibitions; fine art insurance; seminars and lectures for museum professionals; educational publications, newsletter, members' bulletin, exhibition catalogs.

ARTCOM
70 12th St., San Francisco, CA 94119
Programs/Activities: Exhibition space; art publishing; video art library.

ARTHOUSE

45 Hyde St., San Fransisco, CA 94102
Programs/Activities Information on affordable artists' housing; information on the legal requirements of live/work space, such as building, zoning, and fire regulations; consultant and ombudsman services. Co-sponsored by the California Lawyers for the Arts and the San Fransisco arts Commission.

BAY AREA VIDEO COUNCIL
1111 17th St., San Francisco, CA 94107
Programs/Activities: Provides low-cost access to production systems and editing facilities; monthly newsletter; resource library; consulting and grant administration; workshops and seminars.

VISUAL ART ACESS (Curatorial Services for American Artists and Groups)
685 McAllister, #212, San Francisco, CA 94102
Programs/Activites: Michael Bell is curator for this professional referral and curatoral services for Califonail artists and groups. As part of his service, he publishes a newsletter entitled Arthrobs. Arthorbs is published approximately every month and is mainly intended for his clients, although anyone may subscribe for a small fee.

CAPP STREET PROJECT
270 14th St., San Francisco, CA 94103
Programs/Activities: Artists' residencies and gallery space to work on projects; lectures, performances and exhibitions by resident and area artists.

CASA HISPANA DE BELLAS ARTES
2702 Folsom St., San Francisco, CA 94110
Programs/Activities: Performing and visual arts program related to the Hispanic experience.

CHINESE CULTURAL FOUNDATION OF SAN FRANCISCO
Programs/Activities: Educational and cultural programs; cultural exchanges; research projects.

GALERIA DE LA RAZA
2851 24th St., San Francisco, CA 94110
Programs/Activities: Exhibition space for Chicano and Latino expression; cross-cultural exhibitions.

NEW LANGTON ARTS
1246 Folsom St., San Francisco, CA 94103
Programs/Activities: Artist-run space for visual art; new music concerts; writers-in-residence.

SAN FRANCISCO CAMERAWORK
70 12th St., San Francisco, CA 94103
Programs/Activities: Exhibitions exclusively on the photographic arts; lectures; quarterly publication; bookstore and reference library; information services.

S.O.M.A.R. (SOUTH OF MARKET CULTURAL CENTER)
934 Brannan St., San Francisco, CA 94103
Programs/Activities: Shows and exhibitions of experimental artists and art.

WORLD PRINT COUNCIL

1700 17th St., San Fransisco, CA 94103
Programs/Activities: Annual membership exhibition; quarterly newsletter on printmaking.

SAN JACINTO
HEMET VALLEY ART ASSOCIATION
24900 San Jacinto, #10, San Jacinto, CA 92383
Programs/Activities: Permanent exhibit art gallery; annual Ramona Pageant Art Festival

SAN JOSE
ARTS COUNCIL OF SAN JOSE
4 N. 2nd St., San Jose, CA 95113
Programs/Activities: Information resources for artists; programs to develop agendas on arts policy and advocacy issues; workshops and seminars; regranting program; fund-raising assistance for arts groups; "Business Volunteers for the Arts"; "Hands on the Arts" festival for children.

SAN JOSE INSTITUTE OF CONTEMPORARY ART
277 S. First ST., San Jose, CA 95113
Programs/Activities: Alternative exhibition space for static and performance art and video; catalogs and publications.

WORKS/SAN JOSE
66 South First St., San Jose
Programs/Activities: Alternative space for dimensional art, performance art, music, film and video.

SAN LUIS OBISPO
SAN LUIS OBISPO ART ASSOCIATION
1010 Broad, San Luis Obispo, CA 93401
Programs/Activities: Workshops/symposiums in printing and crafts; classes in painting & crafts for adults and children; rental and sales gallery; craftmakers exhibition in August, printmakers in December, Watercolor Society in Jan: all juried exhibitions.

SAN RAFAEL
FALKIRK COMMUNITY CULTURAL CENTER
P.O. Box 60, San Rafael, CA 94915
Programs/Activities: Programming in the visual, performing and literary arts.

SANTA BARBARA
SANTA BARBARA ARTS SERVICES
Box 2426, Santa Barbara, CA 93101
Programs/Activities: Technical assistance to artists, cultural organizations and public agancies in the areas of cultural tours; infrastructure and facility development; fundraising and arts promotion; assistance to local governments in planning for cultural development as an element of community development.

SANTA BARBARA CONTEMPORARY ARTS FORUM
7 W. De La Guerra, Santa Barbara, CA 93101
Programs/Activities: Non-profit visual art organization committed to presenting and encouraging contem-

porary art. Two galleries, video viewing room, and a windowspace gallery in downtown Santa Barbara

SANTA CRUZ
CHILDREN'S ART FOUNDATION
P.O. Box 83, 915 Cedar St., Santa Cruz, CA 95063
Programs/Activities: Museum of international children's art with an active exhibition program; after-school art school; *Stone Soup*, a literary magazine written and illustrated by children up to the age of 13.

COUNTY OF SANTA CRUZ ART COMMISSION
701 Ocean St., Room 220, Santa Cruz, CA 95060
Programs/Activities: Publication of *Facilities Inventory*, listing spaces for exhibitions and performances in the county; Arts-in-Public, Arts- in-Education and "Profile Performance," an event honoring local artist as 'Artist of the Year'; funding for trip to Sacramento to participate in "Artsday," sponsored by the Confederacy for the Arts.

SANTA CRUZ ART LEAGUE
526 Broadway, Santa Cruz, CA 95060
Programs/Activities: Resource center for artists; center for working, studying, networking and meetings; low-cost classes by local professionals; juried competitions.

SANTA PAULA
SANTA PAULA SOCIETY OF THE ARTS
963 E. Santa Barbara St., Santa Paula, CA 93060
Programs/Activities: Demonstrations of painting techniques by outstanding artists on second Sunday of each month; outdoor exhibit on third Sunday of each month; scholarships to talented students; two artists featured each month at the local library.

SANTA ROSA
SANTA ROSA ART GUILD
P.O. Box 307 Santa Rosa, CA 95405
Programs/Activities: Demonstrations, slides, critiques; annual show in October featuring over 800 paintings from California residents; judging high school art competitions.

SARATOGA
VILLA MONTALVO CENTER FOR THE ARTS
P.O. Box 158, Saratoga, CA 95071
Programs/Activities: Exhibitions, concerts, theater performances, poetry readings and competitions.

SAUSALITO
HEADLANDS CENTER FOR THE ARTS
944 Fort Barry, Sausalito, CA 94965
Programs/Activities: Non-profit interdisciplinary laboratory for the arts in the Marin Headlands. Artists-in-Residence program with studio space and stipend; commissions to artists and architects for the improvement of building facilities; educational programs and symposia for the public.

LAKE TAHOE

TAHOE TALLAC ASSOCIATION
P.O. Box 1595, So. Lake Tahoe, CA 95705
Programs/Activities: Restoration of existing estates and development of site into a community and cultural center; classical and jazz concerts. Bluegrass festival in August; continuous art exhibits in the summer.

SONOMA
ARTS GUILD OF SONOMA
460 First St. East, Sonoma, CA 95476
Programs/Activities: Co- sponsor of Sonoma Community Art Center, which provides art instruction and workshops in arts and crafts to children, teens and adults; annual Benefit Art Auction where current works by Guild members are auctioned.

STOCKTON
STOCKTON ART LEAGUE
P.O. Box 7243, Stockton, CA 95207
Programs/Activities: Summer visual arts programs for children; annual juried show in April; annual membership show in the Spring; newspaper.

TORRANCE
JOSLYN CENTER OF THE ARTS
3335 Torrance Blvd., Torrance, CA 90503
Programs/Activities: Classes in painting, ceramics, watercolors, crafts; monthly exhibitions

TULARE
TULARE COUNTY REGIONAL ARTS COUNCIL
260 N. "L" St., Tulare, CA 93274
Programs/Activities: Artists-in-the-Schools program; arts referral and resource agency with monthly arts television show; monthly magazine *Horizon*; calendar and newsletter; annual "Very Special Arts Festival"; grants to local arts organizations from the California Arts Council; gallery at the Tulare County Fair annually.

VENICE
SOCIAL AND PUBLIC ARTS RESOURCE CENTER (SPARC)
685 Venice Blvd., Venice, CA 90291
Programs/Activities: Produces, exhibits and preserves public art; Mural Resource Center; exhibitions, workshops and multi-cultural events.

VENTURA
BUENAVENTURA ART ASSOCIATION
576 E. Main St., Ventura, CA 93001
Programs/Activities: Gallery space; scholarships; annual juried competition.

VENTURA ARTS COUNCIL
34 N. Palm, Ventura, CA 93001
Programs/Activities: Re-grant money from city to individuals and art organizations; Young Artists award program; artist residencies in area elementary schools; consultations and lectures; artist studio tours; calendar of events; general information for artists; Momentum Gallery.

Because such a large number of galleries in California show contemporary painting and sculpture, that category has been omitted from this list of specializations; it would be simply too exhaustive. The list which follows represents concentrations of art styles and not necessarily the individual focus of the gallery. Galleries not named below show contemporary American painting and sculpture. This Index to Gallery Specializations has the following listings:

GALLERY SPECIALIZATIONS
Aboriginal, African, Alternate Spaces, Ancient, Animation, Asian, Book/Audio, Craft, Ethnic, Folk, Glass, Historical Periods, Holographic, Latin American, Native American, Photography, Prints, Video and Western/Southwestern.

ABORIGINAL
West Hollywood: CAZ Gallery

AFRICAN
Los Angeles: Baum Gallery **San Diego**: International Gallery **Sherman Oaks**: Orlando Gallery

ALTERNATE SPACES
Los Angeles: L.A. Artcore **Oakland**: Creative Growth Art Center/Gallery **San Francisco**: San Francisco Artspace & Annex; New Langton Arts **San José**: San José Art League

ANCIENT
Los Angeles: NFA Antiquities; David Stuart Galleries **San Francisco**: Wylie Wong Asian Art & Antiquities

ANIMATION
San Francisco: Owl Gallery

ASIAN
Los Angeles: George J. Doizaki Gallery; Baum Gallery **San Francisco**: Wylie Wong Asian Art & Antiquities

BOOK/AUDIO
Los Angeles: Cirrus Gallery; William & Victoria Dailey **San Francisco**: Arion Press; 871 Fine Arts; Limestone Press Gallery

CRAFT
Albany: Adame Ceramics Craft Gallery **Berkeley**: Arts & Crafts Cooperative, Inc. **Carmel**: Water/White Fine Arts Galleries **Hayward**: Adobe Art Center **La Jolla**: Gallery Eight **Los Angeles**: Couturier Gallery; Del Mano Gallery **San Diego**: International Gallery **San Francisco**: Allrich Gallery; Paul-Luster Gallery **San Marcos**: Boehm Gallery **Santa Barbara**: Elizabeth Fortner Gallery **Santa Monica**: DJ'S, the Arts and Crafts Shop

ETHNIC
San Francisco: Eduard Nakhamkin Fine Arts, Inc. (Soviet)

FOLK
Berkeley: Ames Gallery of American Folk Art **Laguna Beach**: Collector's Choice **Los Angeles**: La Luz de Jesus Gallery **San Diego**: International Gallery

GLASS
Cambria: Seekers Collection and Gallery **Los Angeles**: Kurland/Summers Gallery **San Francisco**: Dorothy Weiss Gallery

GALLERIES CROSS-REFERENCED BY SPECIALTIES

HISTORICAL PERIODS
Bellflower: De Ru's Fine Arts **Beverly Hills:** Galerie Michael; Petersen Galleries; **Carmel:** Weston Gallery, Inc. **Huntington Beach:** John and Lynne Bolen Fine Arts **Laguna Beach:** Richard Yeakel Antiques **La Jolla:** Riggs Galleries **Los Angeles:** William & Victoria Dailey; DeVille Galleries; Goldfield Galleries, Ltd.; Tobey C. Moss Gallery; Newspace; Paideia Gallery; Herbert Palmer Gallery **Montecido:** Maureen Murphy Fine Arts **Pacific Grove:** Trotter Galleries **Petaluma:** Madison Street Gallery **San Diego:** Orr's Gallery **San Francisco:** Atelier Dore, Inc.; Frank Born Arts; Carlson Gallery; Jan Holloway Gallery; Harcourts Gallery, Inc.; Robert Koch Gallery; Maxwell Galleries Ltd.; Modernism; Montgomery Gallery; North Point Gallery; Pasquale Iannetti Art Galleries, Inc.; Pence Gallery; St. Albus Fine Arts; Wolf Schulz Gallery **Santa Cruz:** Giltwood Studios, Fine Art; Ted Mills Fine Art

HOLOGRAPHIC
Los Angeles: Holographic Visions **San Francisco:** Holos Gallery

LATIN AMERICAN
Berkeley: Tzin Tzan Tzun Warehouse **Laguna Beach:** Engman Limited **La Jolla:** Tasende Gallery **Palm Springs:** B. Lewin Galleries **San Francisco:** George Belcher Gallery; Frank Born Arts; Gumps Gallery; Harcourts Gallery; Moss Gallery

NATIVE AMERICAN
Palm Springs: Adagio Galleries **San Francisco:** American Indian Contemporary Arts; Images of the North **Westlake Village:** Maurice- Heyman Fine Arts

PHOTOGRAPHY
Carmel: Weston Gallery, Inc. **Costa Mesa:** Susan Spiritus Gallery **La Jolla:** Riggs Galleries **Los Angeles:** G. Ray Hawkins Gallery; Jan Kesner Gallery **San Francisco:** Fraenkel Gallery; Robert Koch Gallery; Mincher/Wilcox Gallery; Vision Gallery; Wirtz Gallery **Santa Monica:** Roy Boyd Gallery

PRINTS
Carmel: First Impressions/Barbara Linhard Gallery **Los Angeles:** Cirrus Gallery; Gemini G.E.L.; Heritage Gallery; Lasorda/Iri Gallery; Earl McGrath Gallery; Mixografia Gallery; Tobey C. Moss Gallery; Marilyn Pink Fine Arts, Ltd. **Palo Alto:** Smith Anderson Gallery **San Francisco:** Allport Gallery; Hank Baum/Graphics Gallery; Crown Point Press; Graystone; Harcourts Gallery; Miller/Brown Gallery **Santa Monica:** Merging One Gallery; Schwartz Cierlak Gallery

VIDEO
La Jolla: Mandeville Gallery, University of California-San Diego **San Francisco:** San Francisco Museum of Modern Art Rental Gallery; New Langton Arts

WESTERN/SOUTHWESTERN
Beverly Hills: Petersen Galleries **Calistoga:** Donlee Gallery **Los Angeles:** Goldfield Galleries, Ltd. **Palm Springs:** Adagio Galleries; Elaine Horwitch Galleries

APTOS
CABRILLO ART GALLERY
Director: Jane Gregorius
Visual Arts Chairman: Howard Ikemoto
Director: Jane Gregorius

BAKERSFIELD
KERN COUNTY MUSEUM
Director: Carola G. Rupert

BERKELEY
BERKELEY ART CENTER
Chairman of the Board: Ann B. Gilbert
Director: Michael Brown
Gallery Assistant: Jenifer Bloomfield

KALA INSTITUTE
Executive Director: Archana Horsting
Artistic Director: Yuzo Nakano
Programs Administrator: Patricia Thomas
International Exhibitions Co-ordinator: Margaret Herscher
Workshop Managers: Chad Buck, Patty Scott

LOWIE MUSEUM OF ANTHROPOLOGY
Director: Dr. Burton Benedict
Collections: Head of Collections: Dr. Frank A Norick
Curators: Dave D. Herod; Barbara E. Busch; Larry E. Dawson
Registration: Head: Joan Knudsen
Assistant: Patricia Podzorski
Conservator: Geoffrey I. Brown
Exhibitions Curator: Renee Ross

JUDAH L. MAGNES MUSEUM
Chairman: Stanley R. Harris
Director: Seymour Fromer
Special Projects Curator: Ruth Eis
Prints and Drawings Curator: Florence Helzel
Painting and Sculpture Assistant Curato: Sheila Draufman
Judaica Library Curator: Jane Levi
Western Jewish History Center Archivist: Ruth Rafel
Institute for the Righteous Acts Director: Samuel P. Olinar
Jewish American Hall of Fame Director: Mel Wacks

UNIVERSITY ART MUSEUM, UNIVERSITY OF CALIFORNIA, BERKELEY
President of the Board: John Bransten
Director: Jacquelynn Bass
Curatorial Senior Curator: Sidra Stich
Curator of Exhibitions and Programs: Susan Teicholz
Curator of Film: Edith Kramer
Assistant Curator: Micheal Floss
MATRIX Curator: Lawrence Rinder

CHERRY VALLEY
EDWARD-DEAN MUSEUM
Chairman of the Board: Margaret hanson
Vice Chairman: Pat Moorten
Director: Jan Holmlund
Curator: Cathy Gilbert

CLAREMONT
GALLERIES OF THE CLAREMONT COLLEGES
Director: Marjorie Harth Beebe
Curator of Collections: Kay Koeninger
Curator of Exhibitions: Mary MacNaughton
Registrar: Steve Comba
Galleries Manager: Gary Keith

CUPERTINO
EUPHRAT GALLERY
Chairman of the Board: Joan Barram
Director: Jan Rindfleisch

DOWNEY
DOWNEY MUSEUM OF ART
Chairman of the Board: Helen Boggs
Director: Scott Ward
Public Relations: Barbara Carson

FRESNO
FRESNO ART MUSEUM
Chairman of the Board: Susan McCline
Director: Robert Barret
Registrar: Marian Graham

FRESNO METROPOLITAN MUSEUM
President, Board of Trustees: William M. Lyles
Director: Ross McGuire
Director of Programs/Curator of Art: Ric Ambrose
Registrar Curator of Ethnography: Linda Dick
Elizabeth Olson: Director of Development
Andrea Ambrose: Director of Education

FULLERTON
FULLERTON MUSEUM CENTER
President: Janet Buzan
Director: Joseph Felz
Exhibitions Administrator: Lynn Labate

MUCKENTHALER CULTURAL CENTER
Chairman of the Board: Beverly Gunter
Director: Judy Peterson
Curator: Norman Lloyd
Education Director: Karen Bonfigli
Administrator: Tim Campbell

HALF MOON BAY
COASTAL ARTS LEAGUE MUSEUM
President: Helen Bedeson
Director/Curator: A.M. Decker

IRVINE
SEVERIN WUNDERMAN MUSEUM
President: Severin Wunderman
Director: Tony Clark
Curatorial Curatorial Admistrator: John Ahr
Museum Assistant: Jeanne Perry
Volunteer Curator, Josef Nassy Collection: Dr. Monica Rothchilds-Boros
Research Research Director: Dr. William Emboden
Research Assistant: Alison Jane Guest Griffith

LAGUNA BEACH
LAGUNA ART MUSEUM
Director: Charles Desmarais
Curatorial Curator of Education: Diane Sherman
Curator of Collections/Registrar: Bolton Colburn
Assistant Curator: Susan M. Anderson
Exhibitions Designer/Preparator: Stephen Clugston
Director of Development: Lynn Kirst

LA JOLLA
LA JOLLA MUSEUM OF CONTEMPORARY ART
President: Mrs. Lela Axline
Director: Hugh M. Davies
Director of Development: Anne Farrell
Associate Director for Finance and Administration: Norman J. Hannay
Bookstore Manager: Lima Heftmann
Head Curator: Linda Fosha

LODI
SAN JOAQUIN COUNTY HISTORICAL MUSEUM
President: Thomas J. Shephard, Sr.
Director: Michael W. Bennett
Curator: Sarah LeCompte
Registrar: Deborah Mastel

LONG BEACH
LONG BEACH MUSEUM OF ART
Chairman of the Board: Linda McCullough
Director: Harold B. Nelson
Curatorial Senior Curator: Josine Ianco-Starres
Media Arts Curator: Micheal Nash
Head Preparator: Martin Betts
Director of Communication: Jon C. Moynes

QUEEN MARY/SPRUCE GOOSE ENTERTAINMENT CENTER
Vice President/General Manager: Keith Kambak
Attractions/Operations Manager: Larry Nunez
Exhibits/Archives Supervisor: William Winberg
Assistant Archivist: Ellene Mahoney

UNIVERSITY ART MUSEUM, CALIFORNIA STATE UNIVERSITY, LONG BEACH
Director: Constance W. Glenn
Curator of Exhibitions: Lucinda Barnes
Director of Education: Sally Steiner
Registrar: Noreen Becker
Public Relations Officer: Wendell Eckholm
Administrator: Ilee Kaplan
Preparators Chairman: Marie Laibinis-Craft

LOS ANGELES
THE AMERICAN FILM INSTITUTE
Chairman of the Board: Gene F. Jankowski
Director: Jean Firstenberg
Deputy Director: James Hindman

GENE AUTRY WESTERN HERITAGE MUSEUM
Chairman of the Board: Gene Autry
President: Jackie Autry
Director: Joanne D. Hale
Administrator: Deborah Brown
Marketing: Robert P. Coontz
Curatorial Chairman: James H. Nottage
Collections Management Chairman: Mary Ellen Hennessey Nottage
Conservation Chairman: Robert F. McGiffin
Research and Publication Chairman: John P. Langellier, PhD.
Education Chairman: Cynthia Harnish

CALIFORNIA AFRO-AMERICAN MUSEUM
President: Charlene Meeks
Interim Director: Bridget Lambert-Cullerton
Assistant Director: Jackie Dewalt
Visual Arts Curator: Lizzetta LeFalle-Collins
Director of Education: Bridget Lambert Cullerton
Associate Editor: Nancy McKinney

CRAFT AND FOLK ART MUSEUM
President: Frank S. Wyle
Director: Patrick Ela
Curator: Lourie Beth Kalb
Registrar: Marcia Page
Development: Judith Teitelman
Education: Janet Marcus
Shop Manager: John Browse

JOSE DRUDIS-BIADA ART GALLERY
Director: Olga Seem

FISHER GALLERY, UNIVERSITY OF SOUTHERN CALIFORNIA
Chairman of the Advisory Committee: Leo Braudie
Director: Sclama Holo
Exhibition Coordinator/Collections Manager: Georgia Freedman-Harvey
Preparator: Philo Northrop

FOWLER MUSEUM OF CULTURAL HISTORY
Director: Dr. Christopher B. Donnan
Conservator: Robin Chamberlin
Registrar: Sarah Kennington
Assistant Registrar: Paulette Parker
Collections Manager: Owen Moore
Publications Director: Danny Brauer
Editor: Henrietta Cosentino
Photographer: Richard Todd
Gift Shop Manager: Polly Svenson

HEBREW UNION COLLEGE SKIRBALL MUSEUM
President, Hebrew Union College: Dr. Alfred Gottschalk
Chairman, Hebrew Union College Board of Governors: Richard J. Scheuer
Museum Director: Nancy M. Berman
Curatorial Curator: Grace Cohen Grossman
Curator: Dr. Barbara Gilbert
Registrar: Karen Goddy

JUNIOR ARTS CENTER

Director: Harriet S. Miller
Curator: Gilbert Steel
Friends of the Junior Arts Center President: Elizabeth Eastman

LOS ANGELES CHILDRENS MUSEUM
Chairman of the Board: Bruce Corwin
President: Richard G. Reinis
Director: Dr. James G. Leaf
Director of Marketing and Communications: Deborah Buckelew
Director of Development: Susan Krinsky
Director of Finance: Zoe Miller
Director of Exhibits and Programs: Mary Worthington

LOS ANGELES COUNTY MUSEUM OF ART
Director: Dr. Earl A Powell, III
Deputy Director: Ronald Bratton
Exhibitions: Elizabeth Algermissen
Publications: Mitch Tuchman
Membership & Development: Julie Johnston
Registrar: Pieter Meyers
Conservation: Pieter Meyers
Education: William Lillys
Film: Ronald Haver
Music: Dorrance Stalvey
European Paintings & Sculpture: Philip Conisbee
20th Century Art: Maurice Tuchman
American Art: Michael Quick
Indian Art: Pratapaditwa Pal
Far Eastern Art: George Kuwayama
Ancient & Islamic Art: Thomas Lentz
Decorative Arts: Leslie Green Bowman
Photography: Kathleen Gauss
Costumes & Textiles: Edward Maeder
Prints & Drawings: Victor Carlson

LOS ANGELES MUNICIPLE ART GALLERY
Director: Edward Leffingweel
Curator: Marie de Alcuaz Kish
Sattelite Galleries Curator: Scott Cantry
Education Coordinator: Carla Fantozzi

LOS ANGELES MUNICIPAL ART GALLERY
President of the Board: Judy Weinstein
Director: Edward Leffingweel
Curator: Marie de Alcuaz
Education: Carla Fantozzi

MUSEUM OF CONTEMPORARY ART
Director: Richard Koshalek
Exhibition Production Manager: John Bowsher
Facilities and Operation Manager: Brick Chapman
Director of Development: Erica Clark
Associate Director: Sherri Gelden
Bookstore Manager: Pam Richei
Registrar: Mo Shannon
Curator: Mary Jane Jacob
Director of Education: Vas Prahbu

MUSEUM OF NEON ART
Chairman of the Board: Catherine Stribling
Director: Lili Lakich

Curator: Mary Carter
Timothy Benson

OTIS PARSONS GALLERY
Director: Anne Ayres

PLAZA DE LA RAZA CULTURAL CENTER FOR THE ARTS AND EDUCATION
Chairman of the Board: Eddie Albert
Director: Gema Sandoval
School of Visual and Performing Arts Chairman: Denise Nelson Nash

SOUTHWEST MUSEUM
President of the Board of Trustees: James F. Dickason
Director: Jerome R. Selmer
Curatorial Durator of Anthropology: Jonathan Batkin
Curator of Education: Barbara Arvi
Curator of Folklore: Dr. Michael Heisley
Curator of Exhibits: Jeannette L. O'Malley
Registrar/Collections Manager: Cheri Falkenstien-Doyle
Head Librarian: (on leave of absence through June 1990) Daniela Moneta
Acting Head Librarian: Craig Klyver
Store Manager: Jan Posson

WIGHT ART GALLERY, U.C.L.A.
Vice Chancellor: Andrea L. Rich
Director: Dr. Edith A Tonelli
Curatorial: Chairman, Painting, Sculpture, and Architectural Drawings: Elizabeth Shepherd
Chairman, Works on Paper: Cynthia Burlingham
Conservator: Susan Melton
Grunwald Center for the Graphic Arts
Chairman: Dr. James Cuno
Education and Community Development
Chairman: Cindi Dale

THE WOMAN'S BUILDING
President: Carolyn A. Dye
Director: Pauli DeWitt
Gallery Coordinator: Ruth Ann Anderson
Programs Coordinator: Deborah F. Lawrence
Slide Librarian: Jennifer Lockwood
Building Manager: Cheri Gaulke

LOS GATOS
LOS GATOS MUSEUM ASSOCIATION
President: John Barns
Volunteer Curator: Lyn Pickens-Packard
Historical and Arts Curator: Madelyn Crawford

MONTEREY
MONTEREY PENINSULA MUSEUM OF ART
President of the Board of Directors: Mrs. John Potten
Director: Jo Farb Hernandez
Assistant Curator and Preparator of Photography: Richard Gadd
Art Director: Marc D'Estout
Registrar: Ann Petersen
Director of Development: Donna Kneeland

MORAGA
HEARST ART GALLERY
Director: Ann Harlow
Curator: Marvin Schenck

NEVADA CITY
MUSEUM OF ANCIENT AND MODERN ART
President: Dr. Claude W. Needham
Curatorial Curator of Ancient Art: Jeff Spencer
Curator of Modern Art: Linda Coriveau
Librarian Morgan Fox

NEWPORT
NEWPORT HARBOR ART MUSEUM
Director: Kevin E. Consey
Curator: Paul Schimmel
Registrar: Betsy Severance

OAKLAND
MILLS COLLEGE ART GALLERY
Director: Philip E. Linnares
Assistant Director: Suzann Brent Dunaway

THE OAKLAND MUSEUM
Director: Kay Winer
Art Acting Chief Curator: Harvey Jones
Curators: Therese Heyman, Keneth Trapp
History Chief Curator: L. Thomas Frye
Natural Sciences Chief Curator: Donald Linsdale

OXNARD
CARNEGIE ART MUSEUM
Chairman of the Cultural and Fine Arts Commission: Mona Broyles
Director: Andrew C. Voth
Curator: Szanne Bellah
Gallery Manager: Kasuko Knowles

PALM SPRINGS
PALM SPRINGS DESERT MUSEUM
President: Marshall Gelfand
Director: Morton Golden
Natural Sciences Curator: James Conett
Fine Art Curator: Katherine Hough
Performing Art: Morton Golden
Registrar: Kathy Clewell

PALO ALTO
PALO ALTO CULTURAL CENTER
President, Cultural Center Guild: J. Casey McGlynn
Director: Georgianna Lagoria
Exhibitions Curator: Dyana Chadwick
Studio Art Supervisor: Gary Clarien
Education Director Project LOOK!: Jamey Kugler
Facilities Manager: Jean Dickson

STANFORD UNIVERSITY MUSEUM OF ART
Director: Lorenz Eitner
Painting and Sculpture Curator: Carol M. Osborne
Prints and Drawings Curator: Betsy G. Fryberger
Photographs Curator: Joel Leivick

Asian Art Curator: Patrick J. Maveety

PASADENA
NORTON SIMON MUSEUM
President and Executive Director: Mrs. Jennifer Jones Simon
Executive Vice President: Walter Primoshur
Curatorial Chief Curator: Sara Campbell
Curator: Lanier Graham
Curator: Gloria Williams
Registrar: Andrea Clark
Marketing: Philip Juwig

PACIFIC ASIA MUSEUM
Chairman of the Board: George A. Brumder
President: Bruce S. Ross
Director: David Kamansky
Administration Chairman: Sherrill Livingston
Communications Chairman: Philip Pang
Development Chairman: Mary Pechanec
Education Chairman: Trina Duke
Registrar: Debra Bailey
Curator: Kent Tobey

PASADENA HISTORICAL SOCIETY
President of the Board of Trustees: Peg Stewart
Executive Director: Bradley Williams
Curator: Theresa Heinaman
Archivist: Susan Coffman
Museum Educator: Kimberly Haas
Store Manager: Barbara Waddell

RANCHO PALSO VERDES
PALOS VERDES ARTS CENTER
Exhibitions Coordinator: Dee Dee Rechtin
Education: Registrar: Nancy Black
Administrative Assistant: Joyce Schrello

REDDING
REDDING MUSEUM AND ART CENTER
Chairman: Bill Evanhoe
Director: Kieth Foster
Art Curator: Rob Wilson
Conservator: Alice Hoveman
Registrar: Sherill Ferrara
Preparator: Rick Ray, Richard Bower, David Pitz

RICHMOND
RICHMOND ART CENTER
President of the Board: Katherine Church Holland
Director: Kathryn Reasoner
Exhibitions Curator: Michael Schwager
Curatorial Assistant: Zlata Baum
Education Chairman: Mary Law
Outreach Chairman: Tobey Kaplan

THE RICHMOND MUSEUM
President: Lois Boyle
Director: Kathleen Rupley

RIDGECREST
MATURANGO MUSEUM OF THE INDIAN WELLS VALLEY

President, Board of Directors: Carroll Evans
Director: Patricia Brown-Berry, Ph.D.
Art Curator: Mary Lundstrom
Curator: Elva Younkin
Natural History Curator: Anna Martyn

RIVERSIDE
CALIFORNIA MUSEUM OF PHOTOGRAPHY
Chancellor, University of California at Riverside: Rosemary S.J. Schraer
Acting Director: Concha Rivera
Assistant Director: Cathleen Walling
Collections Manager: Roy McJunkin
Exhibitions: Designer: Kevin Jon Boyle
Curatorial Acting Associate Director: Edward W. Earle
Curator of Education: Deborah Klochko

THE RIVERSIDE ART MUSEUM
Chairman of the Board: Paul Sundeen
Curator: Jim Reed
Education Coordinator: Emmie Lou Chandler

UNIVERSITY ART GALLERY, UNIVERSITY OF CALIFORNIA, RIVERSIDE
Director: Katherine Warren
Assistant Director: Deborah Dozier
Preparator: John Dingler

ROHNERT PARK
UNIVERSITY ART GALLERY, SONOMA STATE UNIVERSITY
Director: Dr. Richard Kubiak
Curator: Beth Goldberg Martin
Assistant to the Director: Jill Bacon Davey
Administrative Assistant: Patricia Gingell

SACRAMENTO
CROCKER ART MUSEUM
President: Susan Willoughby
Director: Barbara Gibbs
Curator: Janice T. Driesbach
Education Curator: KD Kurvitz
Registrar: Paulette Hennun
Marketing and Public Affairs: Jill Estroff
Finance and Administration Officer: Todd Petty

SAN BERNARDINO
SAN BERNARDINO COUNTY MUSEUM
Director: Allan D. Griesemer
Curatorial Natural Sciences: Robert Reynolds
Biological Sciences: Eugene Cardiff
Anthropology: Carol Rector
History: Ann Bethel
Education: Margaret Foss
Art: Noela Benvenuti

SAN DIEGO
MINGEI INTERNATIONAL MUSEUM OF WORLD FOLK ART
President: Dorothy D. Stewart
Director: Martha W. Longenecker

Assistant Director: Ann Weaver
Registrar: Julia Brashares

MUSEUM OF PHOTOGRAPHIC ARTS
President: Murray Galinson
Executive Director: Arthur Ollman
Exhibition Designer/Registrar: Joseph Bellows
Museum Store Manager: David Kinney

SAN DIEGO MUSEUM OF MAN
President: Richard D. Huffman
Director: Dr. Douglas Sharon
Curatorial: Chief Curator: Ken Hedges
Curator of Physical Anthropology: Rose Tyson
Curator of Latin American Collections: Dr. Alana Cordy-Collins
Curator of Folk Art: Grace Johnson
Curator of Southwest American Indians Collections: Stefani Salkeld
Curator of California Collections: Ken Hedges
Registrar: Linda Fisk

SAN DIEGO HISTORICAL SOCIETY
President of the Board: Frederick K. Kunzel
Director: James M. Vaughan
Photography Curator: Larry Booth
Library and Manuscripts Collection Curator: Rick Crawford
Curatorial Collection Curator: Bruce Kamerling
Junipero Serra Museum Curator: Eleanor Nealy
Villa Montezuma Museum Curator: Lucinda Eddy

Museum of San Diego History
Curator: Debra Casho

TIMKEN ART GALLERY
President: Robert Ames
Director: Nancy A. Peterson

SAN DIEGO STATE UNIVERSITY ART GALLERY
Director/Curator: Tina Yappeli

SAN FRANCISCO
ASIAN ART MUSEUM OF SAN FRANCISCO, THE AVERY BRUNDAGE COLLECTION
Chairman of the Board: Mrs. Alice Lowe
Director: Rand Castile
Curatorial Chief Curator: Clarence Shangraw
Chinese Art Curator: Patricia Berger
Indian and Himalayan Art Curator: Terese Tse Bartholomew
Southeast Asian Art Curator: Nancy Hock
Japanese Art Curator: Yoshiko Kakudo
Curator: Yoko Woodson
Conservator: Linda Scheifler
Director Public Relations and Marketing: Lilia Villanueva

CALIFORNIA ACADEMY OF SCIENCES
Chairman of the Board: Jeffery W. Meyer
President: Dr. James C.Kelley
Director: Roy Eisenhardt

CALIFORNIA HISTORICAL SOCIETY

President: Mrs. Bernard R. Maushaidt
Director: D. Nathan Sumner
Art and Exhibitions Curator: Barbara Doscher

THE FINE ARTS MUSEUMS OF SAN FRANCISCO

M. H. DE YOUNG MEMORIAL MUSEUM

CALIFORNIA PALACE OF THE LEGION OF HONOR
Chairman of the Board: Mrs. W. Robert Phillips
Director: Harry S. Parker III
American Painting
Chairman: Marc Simpson
Curator: Sally Mills
Conservator: James Wright
European Painting
Chairman: Dr. Lynn Orr
Curator: Marian Stewart
Conservator: Kristin Hoermann
American Sculpture and Decorative Arts
Chairman: Donald Stover
Curator: Lee Hunt Miller
Conservator: Gene Munsch
European Sculpture and Decorative Arts Chairman: Laura Camins
Conservator: Elisabeth Cornu
Achenbach Foundation for Graphic Arts (Prints & Drawings)
Chairman: Robert F. Johnson
Curator: Karin Breuer
Conservator: Robert Futernick
Textiles Chairman: Cathryn Cootner
Curator: Melissa Leventon
Conservator: Leslie Smith
Art of Africa, Oceania, and the Americas
Chairman: Kathleen Berrin
Curator: Kathe Hodgson
Conservator: Lesley Bone

THE EXPLORATORIUM
Chairman of the Board: F. Van Kasper
Director: Robert L. White
Curator Artist-in-Residence Program: Peter Richards
Curator Performing-Artist-in-Residence Program: Pamela Winfrey

FRIENDS OF PHOTOGRAPHY
Chairman of the Board: Peter C. Bunnell
President: Phyllis K. Dryden
Director: Ronald S. Egherman

THE MEXICAN MUSEUM
Director: Marie Azosda-Colón
Curator of Education: Nora E. Wagner
Assistant Curator of Education: Beatrice Hocker
Registrar: Gloria Jaramillo

MUSEO ITALOAMERICANO
Chairman of the Board: Modesto Lanzone
Executive Director and Curator: Robert A. Whyte

MUSEUM OF MODERN MYTHOLOGY
Director: Ellen Havre Weis

Director of Programming: Robyn Talman
Director of Development and Corporate/Business Membersips: Patty Nasey

SAN FRANCISCO ART INSTITUTE
Director of Exhibitions and Public Programs: Jean-Edith Weiffenbach

SAN FRANCISCO CAMERAWORK
President: Thomas Meyer
Director: Marnie Gillett

SAN FRANCISCO CRAFT & FOLK ART MUSEUM
Chaiman of the Board: Gertrud Parker
President: Ann C. Stephens
Executive Director: J. Weldon Smith
Curator: Carole Austin
Museum Administrator: Mary Ann McNicholas

SAN FRANCISCO MUSEUM OF MODERN ART
Chairman of the Board: Brooks Walker
President of the Board: Sandra S. Hobson
Director: Dr. John R. Lane
Painter, Sculpture, and Works on Paper Curator: John Caldwell
Architecture and Design Curator: Paolo Polledri
Photography Curator: Sandra L. Phillips
Assistant Curator: Diana Dupont
Media Arts Curator: Robert Riley
Conservation Chief Conservator: Inge-Lise Eckman
Education Curator: Rozanne Stringer

TATTOO ART MUSEUM
Chairman of the Board: Lyle Tuttle
Director: Judith Tuttle

SAN JOSE

AMERICAN MUSEUM OF QUILTS AND TEXTILES
Chairman of the Board: Mary Lou Breithaupt
Exhibits Chairman: Beryl Self
Collections Chairman: Lois Johnson
Educational Outreach Chairman: Marlene Grove

ROSICRUCIAN EGYPTIAN MUSEUM AND PLANETARIUM
Executive Director: Burnham Shaa
Egyptian Museum Administrative Director and Curator: Dale Jordan
Planetarium Administrative Director: Dale Jordan

SAN JOSE HISTORICAL MUSEUM
Director: Mignon Gibson
Archivist: Leslie Masunaga
Collections: Curators: Milita rios-Samaniego, Sarah H. Nunes, Nancy Valby
Education Curator: Virginia Kay Beck
Events Curator: Monte Duran

SAN JOSE INSTITUTE OF CONTEMPORARY ART
President of the Board: Rand Schiltz
Director: Katheryn Funk

Assistant Director: Stacie Rehbein

SAN JOSE MUSEUM OF ART
President of the Board of Trustees: James Compton
Director: I. Michael Danoff
Curator: Colleen Vojvodich
Registrar: Deborah Norberg
Curator for Education: Diane Levinson

SAN MARCOS
BOEHM GALLERY
Director: Louise Kirtland

SAN MARINO
HUNTINGTON LIBRARY, ART COLLECTIONS AND BOTANICAL GARDENS
Chairman of the Board: R. Stanton Avery
Director: Robert Allen Skotheim
Art Division Curator: Robert R. Wark
Associate Curator, British and Continental Art: Shelly M. Bennett
Associate Curator, American Art: Amy Meyers
Research Head of Research: Martin Ridge
Library Librarian: Daniel H. Woodward
Curator (Rare Books): Alan Jutzi
Curator (Manuscripts): Mary Robertson
Botanical Director: James P. Folsom
Curator of Desert Gardens: Joe Clements
Curator, Japanese Gardens: Kayoko Hamada
Curator, Palm and Jungle Gardens: Ronald Harris
Curator, Rose Garden: Clair Martin II
Curator, Camellia Garden: Ann Richardson
Curator, Desert Collections: John Trager

SAN RAFAEL
FALKIRK CULTURAL CENTER
Director: Carol Adney
Curator: Linda Samuels
Marketing Facilities Coordinator: Karla Dakin

SANTA ANA
CHARLES W. BOWERS MEMORIAL MUSEUM
President: Harriet Harris
Director: Paul M. Piazza
Director of Development: David G. Tucker
Facilities Director: Timothy Culbert
Director of Public Relations and Marketing: Ria Marie Carlson
Director of Accounting: Judith Berzins
Curatorial Chief Curator: Armand J. Labbé
Curator of Folk Art: Paul Apodaca
Registrar: Margaret Key
Programs Program Director: Josie DeFalla
Curator of Education: Barney Malesky

ORANGE COUNTY CENTER FOR CONTEMPORARY ART
Director: Bardene Allen
Exhibitions Chairman: David Reager
Receptions Chairman: Eric Strauss
New Membership Chairman: Ann Duran

OCCA at Hutton Center Chairman: Steven Osborne
Educational Outreach: Theresa Fernald
Special Exhibitions Co-Chairperson: Elizabeth Jennings
Co-Chairperson: Joan Mueller
Co-Chairperson: R. Lee Willmore

SANTA BARBARA
SANTA BARBARA CONTEMPORARY ARTS FORUM
Chairman of the Board: Shan O'Brien
Director: Betty Klausner
Assistant Director: Rita Ferri
Registrar: Bob Debris

SANTA BARBARA MUSEUM OF ART
President: Arthur S. Schultz
Director: Richard V. West
Curatorial Chief Curator: Robert Henning, Jr.
20th Century Art: Nancy Poll
Asian Art: Susan Tai
Collections: Barry Heisler
Exhibitions: Merrily Peebles
Designer: Terry Atkinson
Administration Assistant Director: Thomas R Mathews, Jr.
Education Curator: Deborah Tufts
Registrar: Cherie Summers
Director of Development: Barbara B. Luton
Programs and Publications Assistant Director: Shelley S. Ruston

SANTA BARBARA MUSEUM OF NATURAL HISTORY
Chairman of the Board: Jack Hundley
Director: Dr. Dennis Power
Exhibits Chairman: Norman Ikeda
Gallery Coordinator: Teri Paul Mann
Education Chairman: Kay Woolsey
Curator: Mary Gosslin
Library Chairman: Susan Dixon
Curator: Terri Sheridan
Anthropology Chairman: John Johnson Ph.D.
Curator: Jan Timbrook
Vertebrate Zoology Chairman: Chuck Woodhouse
Curator: Paul Collins
Invertebrate Zoology Chairman: Eric Hochberg Ph.D.
Curator: Paul Scott
Development Chairman: Charles Sclosser

UNIVERSITY ART MUSEUM, SANTA BARBARA
Chairman of the Board: Julia Emerson
Director: J. David Farmer
Curatorial Chairman: Phyllis Plous
Museum Design and Preperation Chairman: Paul Prince
Registration Chairman: Rober Schroeder
Education Chairman: Corinne Horowitz
Public Relations Officer: May Lynn Soini

SANTA CLARA

DE SAISSET MUSEUM
Chairman of the Advisory Board: Marilyn Dorsa
Director: Robert McDonald
Assistant Director: Rebecca Schapp
Chief Preparator: Fred Shepard
Public Relations Coordinator: Anna Koster

TRITON MUSEUM OF ART
President: Judith Bambury
Director: Bill Atkins
Curator of Art: George Rivera
Curator of Education: Karen Shellhammer

SANTA CRUZ
THE ART MUSEUM OF SANTA CRUZ COUNTY
Chairman of the Board: Earleen Overend
Director: Charles Hilger
Program Director: Tobin Keller
Administrative Coordinator: Dorothy Rose
Development Coordinator: Nada Velimirovi

SANTA MONICA
ELI BROAD FAMILY FOUNDATION
Director: Eli Broad
Curator: Michele D. De Angelus
Registrars: Lee Armstrong, Kristin West
Assistant Curator: Barbara Steffen
Curatorial Assistant: Kirsten Y. Biller

SANTA MONICA MUSEUM OF ART
Chairman of the Board: Richard Hirsh
Director: Thomas Rhoads
Exhibition Coordinator: Adam Reav Finkel
Museum Assistant: Scott Coberg

SARATOGA
MONTALVO CEANTER FOR THE ARTS
President: Lionel M. Allan

Acting Executive Director: Elisbeth J. Challener

STOCKTON
THE HAGGIN MUSEUM
President of the Board: Brigadeer General: Alfred L. Sanderson
Director: Tod Ruhstaller
Chief Administrator/Comptroler: Setsuko Ryuto
Curatorial Curator of History: Tod Rustaller
Curator of Exhibits and Designs: Dave Denney
Registrar: Joanne Avant

THOUSAND OAKS
CONEJO VALLEY ART MUSEUM
President of the Board: Maria Dessornes
Director: Ginger Worthley

UKIAH
HELD POAGE RESEARCH LIBRARY
Director: Lila J. Lee

UPAND
MUSEUM OF HISTORY AND ART, ONTARIO
Director: Lou Ann Svenson

WALNUT CREEK
CIVIC ARTS GALLERY
Director of Civic Arts, Town of Walnut Creek: Gary Schaub
Curator: Carl Worth
Education Specialist: Marti Klinkner
Curatorial Assistant: Warren Dreher

WILMINGTON
THE GENERAL PHINEAS BANNING RESIDENCE MUSEUM
Director: Zoë Bergquist

MEDIA COVERING THE ARTS

Listed below are newspapers and periodicals in California that cover the arts. The name provided is that of the principle art critic or writer or, for papers with no principle writer, the features editor.

ANAHEIM

Anaheim Bulletin
Tim Sosbe
1771 S. Lewis St.
Anaheim, CA 92805

ANTIOCH

Antioch Daily Ledger
Clay Kallam
1700 Cavallo Rd.
Antioch, CA 94509

BAKERSFIELD

Bakersfield Californian
Rick Heredia
1707 Eye St.
Bakersfield, CA 93301

BERKELEY

East Bay Express
John Rayside
P.O. Box 3198
Berkeley, CA 94703

CHICO

Chico Enterprise-Record
Gary Kupp
400 E. Park Ave.
Chico, CA 95926

COSTA MESA

Orange Coast Daily Pilot
Roger Bloom
330 W. Bay St.
Costa Mesa, CA 92627

DUBLIN

The Herald
Joan Boer
6207 Sierra Ct.
Dublin, CA 94568

EL CAJON

Daily Californian
Karen Barnett
1000 Pioneer Way
El Cajon, CA 92022

ESCONDIDO

Escondido Times-Advocate
E'Louise Omdash
207 E. Pennsylvania
Escondido, CA 92025

EUREKA

Eureka Times Standard
Kathy Dillon
930 6th St.
Eureka, CA 95501

FAIRFIELD

Fairfield Daily Republic
Ted Hoffman
1250 Texas St., BB 47
Fairfield, CA 94533

FREMONT

The Argus
Cheryl Greger
37427 Centralmont Pl.
Fremont, CA 94536

FRESNO

Fresno Bee
David Hale
1626 E. St.
Fresno, CA 93786

FULLERTON

Fullerton News Tribune
Kelly Anderson
701 W. Commonwealth Ave.
Fullerton, CA 92632

GLENDALE

Glendale News-Press
David Perry
111 N. Isabel, P.O. Box 991,
Glendale, CA 91209

HAYWARD

Daily Review
Sharon Betz
116 W. Winton Avenuw
Hayward, CA 94544

LA HABRA

La Habra-Brea Daily Star Progress
Barbara Giasone
600 S. Palm St.
La Habra, CA 90632

LONG BEACH

Long Beach Press-Telegram
Todd Cunningham
604 Pire Ave.
Long Beach, CA 90844

LOS ANGELES

Art Issues
Gary Kornblau
8721 Santa Monica Blvd.
#535
Los Angeles, CA 90069

Los Angeles Herald Examiner
Christopher Knight
1111 S. Broadway
Los Angeles, CA 90015

Los Angeles Opinion
Juan Rodriguez
1436 S. Main St.
Los Angeles, CA 90015

Los Angeles Reader
Lynn Woods
5550 Wilshire Blvd., Ste. 301
Los Angeles, CA 90036

Los Angeles Times
William Wilson
Times Mirror Square
Los Angeles, CA 90053

Los Angeles Weekly
Peter Frank
P.O. Box 29905
Los Angeles, CA 90029

New Art Examiner
Richard Smith
600 Moulton Ave., Ste. 304
Los Angeles, CA 90031

MARTINEZ

Martinez News Gazette
Harriet Burt
615 Estudillo St.
Martinez, CA 94553

MARYSVILLE

Yuba-Sutter Appeal-Democrat
Julie Watson
1530 Ellis Lake Dr.
Marysville, CA 95901
(916)741-2345

MERCED

Merced Sun-Star
Colleen Bondy
3133 N. G St.
Merced, CA 95340

MODESTO

Modesto Bee
Leo Stutzin
1325 H St.
Modesto, CA 95354

MONTEREY

Herald
Rick Dergon
Pacific at Jefferson
Monterery, CA 93940

NAPA

Napa Register
Pierce Carson
1615 2nd St.
Napa, CA 94558

NOVATO

Marin County Independent Journal
Phyllis Bragdon
Alameda Del Prado 150
Novato, CA 94947

OAKLAND

ArtWeek
Cecile McCann
1628 Telegraph Ave.
Oakland, CA 94612

Oakland Tribune
Harriet Swift
409 13th St.
Oakland, CA 94623

OCEANSIDE

North City Blade Tribune
Ramona Hattendorf
1722 S. Hill St.
Oceanside, CA 92054

ONTARIO

Ontario Daily Report
Jerry Rice
2041 E. Fourth St.
Ontario, CA 91764

ORCUTT

Santa Maria Times
Karen White
3200 Skyway Dr.
Orcutt, CA 93455

OXNARD

Oxnard Press Courier
Lisa McKinnon
300 W. 9th St.
Oxnard, CA 93939

PALM SPRINGS

The Desert Sun
Bruce Tessier
611 S. Palm Canyon Dr.
Palm Springs, CA 92262

PALMDALE

Antelope Valley Press
Steve Hendrickson
37414 N. Sierra Hwy.
Palmdale, CA 93550

PALO ALTO

Times Tribune
Jane Ayres
245 Lytton Ave.
Palo Alto, CA 94301

PASADENA

Star News
Kathy Register
525 E. Colorado Blvd.
Pasadena, CA 91109

POMONA

Pomona Progress Bulletin
Jerry Rice
300 S. Thomas St.
Pomona, CA 91766

REDDING

Redding Record Searchlight
Laura Christman
1101 Twin View Blvd.
Redding, CA 96099

RIVERSIDE

Morning Press Enterprise
Loretta Scott
3512 Fourteenth St.
Riverside, CA 92501

SACRAMENTO

Sacramento Bee
Scott Lebar
21st & Q Streets
Sacramento, CA 95813

Sacramento Union
Holly Johnson
311 Captiol Mall
Sacramento, CA 95814

SALINAS

Salinas Californian
Tom Leyde
123 W. Alisa St.
Salinas, CA 93901

SAN DIEGO

San Diego Union
Robert Pincus
350 Camino de la Reina
San Diego, CA 92108

San Diego Tribune
Susan Freudenheim
P.O. Box 191
San Diego, CA 92112

SAN FRANCISCO

San Francisco Bay Guardian

Harry Roche
2700 19th St.
San Francisco, CA 94110

San Francisco Chronicle
Kenneth Baker
901 Mission St.
San Francisco, CA 94103

San Francisco Examiner
David Bonetti
110 5th St.
San Francisco, CA 94103

San Francisco Weekly
Art Silverman
230 Ritch St.
San Francisco, CA 94107

SAN JOSE

San Jose Mercury News
Dorothy Burkhart
750 Ridder Park Dr.
San Jose, CA 95190

SAN MATEO

San Mateo Times
Mary Helen McAllister
1080 S. Amphlett Blvd., P.O. Box 5
San Mateo, CA 94402

SAN PEDRO

San Pedro News Pilot
[See Torrance Daily Breeze]
362 W. Seventh St.
San Pedro, CA 90731

SANTA ANA

Orange County Register
Barbara O'Dair
625 N. Grand Ave.
Santa Ana, CA 92701

SANTA BARBARA

Santa Barbara News Press
Gary Robb
De la Guerra Plaza
Santa Barbara, CA 93101

SANTA CRUZ

Santa Cruz Sentinel
Rick Chatenever
207 Church St.
Santa Cruz, CA 95060

SANTA ROSA

Santa Rosa Press Democrat
Dan Taylor
427 Mendocino Ave.
Santa Rosa, CA 95404

SAN BERNARDINO

San Bernardino Sun
Owen Sheeran
399 "D" St.
San Bernardino, CA 92401

SAN LUUS OBISPO

San Luis Obispo Telegram Tribune
Tony Hazarian
1321 Johnson Ave.
San Luis Obispo, CA 93406

STOCKTON

Stockton Record
Janet Krietemeyer
530 E. Market St.
Stockton, CA 95202

TORRANCE

Daily Breeze

Jim Brooks
5215 Torrance Blvd,
Torrance, CA 90509

VALLEJO

Vallejo Times Herald
Zilleh Bahar; Deborah Wandel
800 Curtola Pkwy.
Vallejo, CA 94590

VENTURA

Ventura City Star-Free Press
Rita Moran
5250 Ralson St.
Ventura, Ca 93003

VICTORVILLE

Victor Valley Daily Press

Rae Dawn Olbert
13891 Park Ave.
Victorville, CA 92392

WALNUT CREEK

Contra Costa Times
Carol Fowler
2640 Shadelands Dr.
Walnut Creek, CA 94598

WEST COVINA

San Gabriel Valley Daily Tribune
Johnny Bender
1210 Azusa Canyon Rd.
West Covina, CA 91790

WOODLAND

Daily Democrat
Mary Goetz
702 Court St.
Woodland, CA 95695

INDEX

How to use this index: Museums, galleries and artists are listed below alphabetically. In the gallery section of the book, galleries are listed alphabetically with corresponding gallery numbers (in numerical order) next to their titles. Artists affiliated with or showing at a gallery are also indexed by gallery number, followed by the gallery's page number. For example, Robert Arneson, indexed G# 38, 71, is found by locating gallery number 38 in the gallery section, which the Richard L. Nelson Gallery on page 71.

INDEX

INDEX

INDEX

INDEX

INDEX

INDEX

INDEX

INDEX

INDEX

INDEX

INDEX

INDEX

INDEX

INDEX

INDEX

INDEX

INDEX

INDEX